Parent and Teacher
Internet Resources

Go Online

Log on to glencoe.com for...
- Online Student Edition access
- Curricula correlations
- Teacher Resources

Go to Glencoe's *Online Learning Center* where students can:
- Complete Student Web Activities.
- Use the Interactive Health Tutor to play health vocabulary games, including crossword puzzles, concentration, and eFlashcards.
- Listen to downloadable podcasts.
- Download Study-to-Go activities to their PDA.

Students can use Glencoe's *Fitness Zone* information to
- Learn how to incorporate fitness into their lives.
- Complete Fitness Zone workbook activities.
- Learn nutrition, physical activity, and injury prevention tips.

Have students watch Glencoe's Health eSpotlight chapter launcher videos where they can:
- Watch Health eSpotlight videos that introduce each chapter.
- View interactive Study Guides.
- Take Online Self-Check Quizzes.

Teacher Wraparound Edition

Glencoe
Health

In Partnership With
TIME HEALTH
&
BusinessWeek

Mary H. Bronson, Ph.D.

TIME

McGraw Hill Glencoe

About the Author

Mary H. Bronson, Ph.D., has taught health education in grades K–12, as well as health education methods classes at the undergraduate and graduate levels. As health education specialist for the Dallas School District, Dr. Bronson developed and implemented a district-wide health education program, *Skills for Living*, which was used as a model by the state education agency. She has assisted school districts throughout the country in developing local health education programs. She is also the author of Glencoe's *Teen Health* textbook series.

TIME

TIME is the nation's leading news and information magazine. With more than 80 years of experience, TIME provides an authoritative voice in the analysis of the issues of the day, from politics to pop culture, from history-making decisions to healthy living. TIME Learning Ventures brings the strength of TIME and TIME For Kids editorial and photographic excellence to education resources for school and home.

The McGraw-Hill Companies

Printed in the United States of America.

Send inquiries to:
Glencoe/McGraw-Hill
21600 Oxnard Street, Suite 500
Woodland Hills, California 91367

ISBN: 978-0-07-875876-8 (Student Edition)
MHID: 0-07-875876-9 (Student Edition)
ISBN: 978-0-07-875877-5 (Teacher Edition)
MHID: 0-07-875877-7 (Teacher Edition)

1 2 3 4 5 6 7 8 9   071   12 11 10 09 08 07

Health and Educational Consultants

Unit 1: A Healthy Foundation

Lisa M. Carlson, M.P.H, C.H.E.S.
Academic Program Director
Emory Transplant Center
Atlanta, Georgia

Betty M. Hubbard, Ed.D., C.H.E.S.
Professor of Health Education
Department of Health Sciences
University of Central Arkansas
Conway, Arkansas

Unit 2: Mental and Emotional Health

Rani Desai, Ph.D., M.D.
Associate Professor
Yale University
New Haven, Connecticut

Unit 3: Healthy and Safe Relationships

Jill English
Health Education and Evaluation Consultant
Orange, California

Unit 4: Nutrition and Physical Activity

Roberta Duyff, R.D., C.F.C.S.
Food and Nutrition Education Consultant
St. Louis, Missouri

Don L. Rainey
Lecturer and Director
Physical Fitness and Wellness Program
Texas State University
San Marcos, Texas

Unit 5: Personal Care and Body Systems

Dyan Campbell, R.N., M.P.H.
Campbell Consulting L.L.C.
Parksville, New York

Ismael Nuño, M.D.
Chief, Cardiac Surgery
LAC+USC Medical Center
Los Angeles, California

Unit 6: Growth and Development

Susan Giarratano Russell, Ed.D., M.S.P.H., C.H.E.S.
Health Education and Evaluation Consultant
Valencia, California

Unit 7: Drugs

Donna Breitenstein
Health Educator
Boone, North Carolina

Jeanne Title
Coordinator, Prevention Education
Napa County Office of Education and
Napa Valley Unified School District
Napa, California

Unit 8: Diseases and Disorders

Donna Breitenstein
Health Educator
Boone, North Carolina

Ismael Nuño, M.D.
Chief, Cardiac Surgery
LAC+USC Medical Center
Los Angeles, California

Unit 9: Safety and Environmental Health

Kelly Cartwright
College of Lake County
Department of Biological and Health Sciences
Grayslake, Illinois

Ismael Nuño, M.D.
Chief, Cardiac Surgery
LAC+USC Medical Center
Los Angeles, California

Greg Stockton
American Red Cross
Washington, D.C.

Teacher Reviewers

Mark Anderson
Supervisor of Health and Physical Education
Cobb County Schools
Marietta, Georgia

Nita Auer
Health Educator
North Side High School
Ft. Wayne, Indiana

Theresa Despino
Health and Physical Education Teacher
Alexandria Senior High School
Alexandria, Louisiana

Colette Dux
Health Educator
El Camino Real High School
Woodland Hills, California

Cindy Henderson
Health Teacher
Putnam City North High School
Oklahoma City, Oklahoma

Mimi Herald
K–12 Health Education Coordinator
Bethel Public Schools
Bethel, Connecticut

Jia Oliver Jordan
Health Educator
Booker T. Washington Magnet High School
Montgomery, Alabama

Kathy Marlowe
Healthful Living Educator
A. C. Reynolds High School
Asheville, North Carolina

Randall Nitchie
Department Chair and Health Educator
Osseo Area Schools
Maple Grove, Minnesota

Phyllis Simpson
Consultant
DeSoto, Texas

Tammy Smith
Assistant Athletic Director
Tulsa Public Schools
Tulsa, Oklahoma

Cindy Williams
Health Educator
Russellville Junior High
Russellville, Arkansas

Tom Williams
Health Educator
Fayetteville High School
Fayetteville, Arkansas

Table of Contents

Glencoe and Macmillan/McGraw-Hill Your Solution for K–12 Health and Fitness

McGraw-Hill, the leader in health education, offers a comprehensive and sequential K-12 health education program designed to assist schools in developing and implementing a coordinated school health education curriculum.

Start with a Healthy Foundation with *Health & Wellness*

Macmillan/McGraw-Hill presents *Health & Wellness* for grades K-5. This easy-to-manage program provides integrated curriculum strategies tailored for the elementary classroom. The program is packed with quick-and-easy student-guided activities structured for success, laying the foundation for building lifelong health skills.

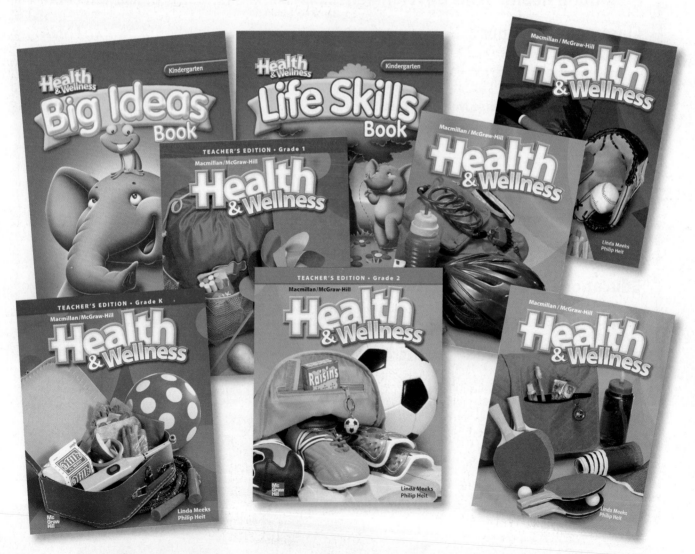

"No knowledge is more crucial than knowledge about health, for without it no other life goal can be successfully achieved..."

—*The Carnegie Foundation*

Promote Healthy Behaviors with *Teen Health*

Teen Health, the three-book series offered by Glencoe/McGraw-Hill, is designed specifically for students in grades 6-8. The inviting style, easy-to-read format, and motivating activities engage middle school learners. *Teen Health* combines scientifically accurate, age-appropriate health content with extensive practice and application of skills. Colorful and informative photos, visuals, charts, and diagrams engage student interest and facilitate learning.

Foster Lifelong Health and Wellness Behaviors

A comprehensive approach to health and fitness is essential in motivating teens to stay safe and healthy, reduce health risks, and practice high-level wellness. *Glencoe Health, Health & Wellness,* and *Foundations of Personal Fitness* provide flexible formats to improve health and wellness among high school students. Real-life application of health skills helps students apply what they learn in health class toward practicing healthy behaviors for a lifetime. Hands-on features are integrated with technology, embedded assessments, and up-to-date health content.

Glencoe's Online Learning Center: Offering Technology Solutions

At glencoe.com you and your students will find a variety of interactive features and study tools to enhance the print programs.

Glencoe Health—
A Model of Excellence for the 21st Century

Glencoe/McGraw-Hill's health and fitness program provides a comprehensive health and physical education curriculum for students in grades K–12.

- *Glencoe Health* combines scientifically accurate, age-appropriate health content with extensive instruction, practice, and application of the skills necessary to achieve optimal health and wellness.
- *Health & Wellness* introduces K-5 students to beginning skills that promote physical activity and health literacy.
- *Teen Health*, a three-book series for students in grades 6 through 8, builds upon the K-5 program, and *Glencoe Health* continues building upon what students know to foster lifelong healthful behaviors.
- *Foundations of Personal Fitness* expands upon the physical activity and fitness content presented in the health program.

Educating the Whole Child— Support for No Child Left Behind

The evidence is in—academic achievement is enhanced by focusing on the whole child in a comprehensive approach that includes adequate nutrition, regular physical activity, mental and emotional support, and building skills for a lifetime of health and wellness. In accordance with the 2001 *No Child Left Behind* Act, the *Glencoe Health* program provides all the elements necessary to support these goals:

- Strong accountability for student success
- Increased flexibility and local control for schools
- Expanded options for parents to participate in education
- An emphasis on proven or scientifically based teaching methods

Provides Differentiated Learning for All Learning Ability Levels

Glencoe Health offers engaging, relevant, and appropriate content for the widest range of learners. The content is supported with differentiated instruction strategies and presented in a visually dynamic style that will engage and motivate your students.

Meets the National Health Education Standards

Throughout the program, *Glencoe Health* is correlated to the revised National Health Education Standards, which emphasize knowledge of concepts and skills that influence health promotion and disease prevention. The comprehensive chart on each Planning Guide shows how each lesson meets those standards.

"Health is directly linked to educational achievement, quality of life, and economic productivity."

—*World Health Organization*

Delivers Research-Based Content

Glencoe Health has achieved the highest degree of accuracy through rigorous, scientifically based research. This edition contains the results of the most recent research studies and teacher feedback, as well as detailed editorial development.

Promotes Health Skills and Provides Authentic Assessment

Glencoe Health is loaded with classroom activities that provide application, reinforcement, and enrichment with a variety of embedded assessments.

Health Skills Activity offers realistic scenarios for students to practice skills in communication, decision making, refusal, conflict resolution, and goal setting.

Real World Connection, Math Practice, and Reading/Writing Practice activities give students experience in analyzing information, evaluating facts, and forming conclusions about health using primary source materials.

Hands-On Health presents engaging activities to strengthen your students' understanding of health content.

Provides Dynamic Instruction to Motivate Students

Glencoe Health is designed to enhance students' health literacy while providing tools to improve reading comprehension.
- Engaging lesson introductions include Guide to Reading, Big Idea, Before You Read, and New Vocabulary.
- Health eSpotlight Videos, *BusinessWeek* Health News Online, Hands-On Health, Real Life Issues, Real World Connection, and TIME® Health News provide real-life application to the study of health concepts and behaviors.
- Chapter Summary and Reading Review offers a concise summary of chapter topics and can be used to preview, review, or summarize chapter content.

- Project-Based Assessment offers alternative assessment options.
- Standardized Test Practice gives students the opportunity to practice for state and national exams.

Promotes Healthful Behaviors for Healthy Living

Glencoe Health informs, guides, and encourages teens to practice behaviors that enhance their well-being and safety by:
- Emphasizing the importance of supportive parents, dedicated teachers, positive peer relationships, and role models.
- Fostering critical thinking and encouraging responsible decision making.
- Delivering a strong and consistent abstinence message to promote positive health behaviors and character development.
- Highlighting positive and negative influences of peer pressure and the media.
- Encouraging a positive attitude about health information and related issues.

Offers a Wealth of Resources

The program provides outstanding resources that give teachers unlimited choices. These comprehensive resources include:
- New Online Student Edition. Complete student text available for convenient access to lessons and chapter reviews, features, and activities.
- Complete Teacher Support. Teacher planning, resources, calendar, and correlations with the exclusive TeacherWorks Plus™ DVD. The Teacher Wraparound Edition (TWE) offers print, audio, and technology resources. The Teacher Classroom Resources (TCR) box contains more than 9 blackline master booklets, including transparencies.
- Integrated Technology Options. Directly correlated to points of use in the text, videos, DVDs, computerized testbanks, and the Internet are integrated into the program for maximum utility and ease of use.

Glencoe Health Promotes Healthful Living and Risk Reduction

Health education in today's school environment is charged with improving students' understanding of basic health concepts and promotion of the skills needed to take action in health promotion and disease prevention. Evidence that students can apply these skills to improve their own health and the health of others is necessary in a successful health program.

Glencoe Health's comprehensive content follows the revised National Health Education Standards (NHES), which provide the framework for fostering health literacy. The following table outlines the four characteristics of a health-literate individual. The Centers for Disease Control and Prevention identifies six adolescent health-risk behaviors that contribute to the leading causes of morbidity and mortality. *Glencoe Health* addresses these risk behaviors within the context of the ten core curriculum areas identified for comprehensive health education programs. By using the *Glencoe Health* program, students will be able to assess their own health status and understand the relationships between healthful living and their quality of life.

Characteristics of a Health-Literate Individual	CDC Adolescent Risk Behaviors	Comprehensive Health Education Content Areas
• Critical Thinker and Problem Solver • Responsible, Productive Citizen • Self-Directed Learner • Effective Communicator	• Tobacco use • Dietary patterns that contribute to disease • Sedentary lifestyle/physical inactivity • Sexual behaviors that result in HIV infection, other STDs, and pregnancy • Alcohol and other drug use behaviors • Behaviors that contribute to unintentional injuries and violence	• Community Health • Consumer Health • Environmental Health • Family Life • Mental and Emotional Health • Injury Prevention and Safety • Nutrition • Personal Health • Prevention and Control of Disease • Substance Use and Abuse

Glencoe Health Supports Research-Based Instructional Strategies

Research shows that skills-based health education and interactive teaching methods promote healthy lifestyles and reduce risk behaviors. *Glencoe Health* integrates specific research-based strategies, outlined below, into the student text, activities, and teaching materials. These strategies provide a variety of proven methods to engage students, enhance learning, and encourage the development of health-literate individuals. Throughout the program, students have opportunities to work individually or in group settings, and teachers are provided with comprehensive, interactive instructional opportunities designed to build health skills and promote lifelong healthy behaviors in every student.

Instructional Strategies Used in *Glencoe Health*	
1. Practicing Important Tasks and Skills	**5.** Authentic Instruction and Achievement
2. Using Prior Knowledge	**6.** Developing Reading Comprehension and Writing Skills
3. Using Visuals to Communicate, Organize, and Reinforce	**7.** Learning by Using Study Strategies
4. Balancing Explicit and Implicit Instruction	**8.** Cooperative Learning Opportunities

Evidence of the Effectiveness of Glencoe Health

Several authentic, independent evaluation studies have been conducted by independent research firms to determine how the use of the *Glencoe Health* program helps students achieve mastery of the National Health Education Standards.

The results indicate that *Glencoe Health* contributes positively to high school students' mastery of the National Health Education Standards, improving students' understanding of health concepts and their ability to apply health-enhancing skills in their lives. Overall, these studies provide persuasive evidence that *Glencoe Health* can help students achieve excellence in health education.

To read the details of these evaluations, see the *Glencoe Health* White Paper, Research-Based Strategies Used to Develop *Glencoe Health* available at **glencoe.com**. In this document you will find specific examples from the Student Edition, Teacher Wraparound Edition, ancillary program, and technology resources, highlighting extensive use of these research-based, educationally sound strategies that help students learn health concepts.

Be Healthy and Active with *Glencoe Health*

Help students take control of their personal, physical, and emotional well-being. *Glencoe Health* focuses on personal fitness information, practical skills, and real-world applications that encourage students to become responsible for their own fitness and well-being throughout life.

Get Energized with Glencoe's Online *Fitness Zone*

Fitness Zone Online is a multimedia resource that helps students find ways to be physically active each day.

The Nutrition and Physical Activity Resources include:
- Clipboard Energizer Activities
- Fitness Zone Videos
- Polar Heart Rate Monitor Activities
- Nutrition, Physical Activity, and Injury Prevention Tips
- Links to Nutrition and Physical Activity Resources
- And More!

Strengthen Student Reading and Writing...

Glencoe Health is designed to enhance students' health literacy while providing tools to improve reading comprehension.

In the Student Edition

- **Guide to Reading** at the beginning of each lesson provides an overview of the big idea, new vocabulary, and Before You Read strategies.

- **Reading Checks** within the lesson content, at the end of every main section, stimulate quick recall and keep students focused on the main ideas.

READING CHECK

Describe Identify and describe three types of friendships.

LESSON 1

 **GUIDE TO READING**

BIG Idea Mutual respect and honesty are important characteristics of healthy friendships.

Before You Read

Create a Cluster Chart. Draw a circle and label it "Friendship." Use surrounding circles to define and describe this term. As you read, continue filling in the chart with more details.

Friendship

New Vocabulary
- platonic friendship (p. 194)
- clique (p. 195)

Review Vocabulary
- peers (Ch.1, L.2)
- friendship (Ch.6, L.1)
- prejudice (Ch.6, L.2)
- stereotypes (Ch.6, L.2)

Safe and Healthy Friendships

Real Life Issues ....

Maintaining Friendships. Tom and Jarod have been friends since the sixth grade. They promised to join the same clubs and sports teams in high school to stay close friends. Now that they're sophomores, Tom is meeting new friends, and his interests have changed. He wants to try new things but wants to remain friends with Jarod, too.

Writing *If you were Tom, how might you express your concerns? Write a brief letter to Jarod explaining your thoughts and feelings.*

Peer Relationships

Main Idea We will all have many types of friends.

During adolescence, you continue to develop and strengthen your personal identity. The development of your identity will be influenced by many factors, including your peers. Peers are people of similar age who share similar interests. Peer relationships can play an important role in your health and well-being. Your friends and peers may influence you to try new activities, such as joining the debate club or learning to play tennis. These activities, in turn, can promote all aspects of your health.

As you get older, your social groups expand. You may also get a part-time job where you'll meet new people. These opportunities to meet people from different age groups, cultures, races, and religions contribute to your social development. Some of the people you meet during your high school years may become lifelong friends.

■ **Figure 8.2** Friendships can contribute positively to your well-being and enrich your life. *Identify some qualities of strong and healthy friendships.*

Recognizing Problems in Friendships

Main Idea It's important that you know how to recognize problems in a friendship and how to resolve those problems.

Friendships can have a positive or negative effect on you.

- **Caption Questions** for every photo and infographic offer a visual approach to learning. Students are asked to apply what they have read by interpreting the visual.

with Active Reading and Study Skills

- **Main Ideas** appear throughout each lesson and identify the main points to help the students navigate the text.

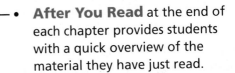

Resisting Negative Peer Pressure

Main Idea Practicing refusal skills will help you deal with negative peer pressure.

Peer pressure does not stop at the end of your teen years. Throughout your life, you will experience instances in which peers, including friends and co-workers, try to influence you

LESSON 1 **ASSESSMENT**

After You Read

Reviewing Facts and Vocabulary
1. Define the word *peers*.
2. Define *friendship*. Identify four traits of healthy friendships.
3. List two problems that may affect friendships.

Thinking Critically
4. **Evaluate.** What actions can you take to promote safe and healthy friendships?
5. **Describe.** Name two possible outcomes of lying to a friend. How might this affect the friendship?

Applying Health Skills
6. **Communication Skills.** With a classmate, role-play a scenario in which close friends communicate needs, wants, and emotions in healthful ways.

Writing Critically
7. **Expository.** Write a dialogue in which peers express disagreement about an issue while still showing respect for self and others.

Go Online
Visit glencoe.com and complete the Interactive Study Guide for this lesson.

- **After You Read** at the end of each chapter provides students with a quick overview of the material they have just read.

In the Teacher Edition

- **Academic Integration** features throughout each chapter include additional effective reading and writing techniques.

- **Reading Strategy** at point-of-use provides activities to help teach reading within the health content.

- **Writing Support** throughout the Teacher Wraparound Edition offers writing opportunities to aid comprehension while developing writing skills.

- **Academic Vocabulary** provides added information for teachers to explain common words used in textbooks that every successful student should know. It also includes a description of each word and an exercise to help students grasp the meaning.

Reading Support Materials

Available in the Unit *Fast Files*
- Reading Strategies
- Vocabulary Practice

FAST FILE

Student Activity Workbook
- **Note-Taking** activities based on Cornell Note-Taking model.
- **Academic Integration** activities reinforce lesson content.

Online Learning Center
- eFlashcards
- Vocabulary Puzzlemaker
- Online Audio Summaries available in English and Spanish

How Can I Help My Students Learn Academic Vocabulary?

by Robin Scarcella, Ph.D.

What Is Academic English?

Academic English is the language used by the educated and by leaders in business, academic, and other professional disciplines. It is the type of English used in professional books, including textbooks, and it contains specific linguistic features that are associated with academic disciplines like social studies. Proficiency in reading and using academic English are especially related to long-term success in all parts of life.

Academic vocabulary is the basis for academic English. By reinforcing academic vocabulary and academic English, teachers can help learners to access authentic, academic texts—not simplified texts that dumb down the content. In this way, they can provide information that will help build their students' background knowledge rapidly.

What Is Academic Vocabulary?

By the time children have completed elementary school, they must have acquired the knowledge needed to understand academic vocabulary. How many words should they acquire to be able to access their textbooks? A basic 2,000-word vocabulary of high-frequency words makes up 87 percent of the vocabulary of academic texts. Eight hundred other academic words comprise an additional eight percent of the words. Three percent of the remaining words are technical words. The remaining two percent are low-frequency words. There may be as many as 123,000 low-frequency words in academic texts.

Why Should Students Learn Academic Vocabulary?

English learners who have mastered a basic 2,000-word vocabulary are ready to acquire the majority of general words found in their academic texts.

Knowledge of academic words combined with continued acquisition of general words can significantly boost an English learner's comprehension level of academic texts. English learners who learn and practice these words before they graduate from high school are likely to master academic material with more confidence and speed. They waste less time and effort in guessing words or consulting dictionaries than those who only know the basic 2,000 words that characterize general conversation.

Also, consider academic success in terms of measurement and assessment—state standards-based assessments, the SAT, the ACT, and the GRE—with regards to word mastery. All demand an understanding of academic vocabulary.

How Do I Include Academic Vocabulary and Academic English in My Teaching?

Teachers can provide their students with rich samples of academic vocabulary and help students understand and attend to the academic English of their text. To develop academic English, learners must have already acquired a large amount of basic proficiency in the grammar of everyday English.

Academic English should not be taught overtly but rather within the contexts that make sense. In terms of instruction, teaching academic English includes providing students with access to core curriculum—in this case health.

Academic English arises not only from knowledge of a linguistic code and cognition but also from social practices in which academic English is used to accomplish communicative goals. The acquisition of academic vocabulary and grammar is necessary to advance the development of academic English.

Tips for Teaching Academic Vocabulary:

- *Expose Students to Academic Vocabulary* Do not teach it. You do not need to call attention to words students are learning because they will acquire them subconsciously.
- *Do Not Correct Students' Mistakes When Using the Vocabulary Words* All vocabulary understanding and spelling errors are developmental and will disappear once the student reads more.
- *Help Students Decode the Words Themselves* Once they learn the alphabet, they should be able to decode words. Decoding each word they don't recognize will help them more than trying to focus on sentence structure. Once they can recognize the words, they can read "authentic" texts.
- *Do Not Ignore the English Learner in This Process* They can learn academic vocabulary before they are completely fluent in English.
- *Helping Students Build Academic Vocabulary Leads to Broader Learning* Students who have mastered the basic academic vocabulary are ready to continue acquiring words from the rest of the groups. To help determine which words are in the 2,000-word basic group, refer to West's General Service List of English Words (1953). The list is designed to serve as a guide for teachers and as a checklist and goal list for students. For additional information about the list, visit: http://www.vuw.ac.nz/lals/research/awl/info.html or you can check http://www.uni-trier.de/uni/fb2/anglistik/projekte/stubbs/awl.htm

Guidelines for Teaching Academic English and Vocabulary:

1. Direct and planned instruction
2. Models (that have increasingly difficult language)
3. Attention to form (pointing out linguistic features of words)
4. Practice
5. Motivation
6. Instructional feedback
7. Assessment (on a regular basis)

Robin Scarcella is professor and Director of Academic English/ESL, at the University of California at Irvine, Irvine, CA.

Academic Skills

Academic skills are crucial for success both inside and outside the classroom. In addition to traditional academic skills, your students will need communication skills, interpersonal skills, and strong technology skills in order to enhance their quality of life. Basic skills will support your students in completing the tasks that their jobs and lives will demand.

The No Child Left Behind Act

The No Child Left Behind Act of 2001 emphasizes student achievement in basic academic subjects. It introduces strict accountability measures for schools in the form of standardized testing. Traditionally, core academic subjects have been defined as language arts, science, and mathematics. No Child Left Behind names the following academic subjects:

- English
- Reading/Language Arts
- Mathematics
- Science
- World Languages
- Civics and Government
- Economics
- Art
- History
- Geography

Integrate academic skills into the classroom as a regular part of your classroom activities. For example, by having students read assignments and texts, write letters and reports, give presentations, and perform math exercises, you are helping them improve their academic skills. *Glencoe Health* integrates academic skills in the following ways:

- **Real World Connection**—provides a mathematics or writing activity.

- **Real Life Issues**—allows students to practice their writing skills.

Real World CONNECTION

Sexual Content on TV

Media messages can play an important role in a teen's decisions regarding sexual activity. Studies have shown that adolescents with higher exposure to sexual content on TV are more likely to engage in sexual activity. Consider these statistics:

▶ 64 percent of all television programs contain sexual content.

▶ Of programs with sexual content, 15 percent show abstinence or risk of sexual activity.

Analyzing media messages and comparing to real-life situations is an important develop. It will help you resist external es and stay committed to abstinence.

Activity Mathematics

Assume that 1,500 TV programs were surveyed.

1. How many programs had sexual content?
2. How many programs depicted abstinence or risk of sexual activity?
3. **Writing** Write a short essay describing how the higher rate of sexual content on TV influences teen behavior.

Concept Number and Operations: Percents A percent is a ratio comparing a number to 100. It can also be represented as a fraction with 100 as the denominator. To find a decimal equivalent, divide the percent by 100. To convert a decimal to a percent, multiply it by 100.

Real Life Issues

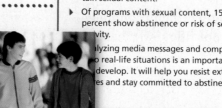

Maintaining Friendships. Tom and Jarod have been friends since the sixth grade. They promised to join the same clubs and sports teams in high school to stay close friends. Now that they're sophomores, Tom is meeting new friends, and his interests have changed. He wants to try new things but wants to remain friends with Jarod, too.

Writing *If you were Tom, how might you express your concerns? Write a brief letter to Jarod explaining your thoughts and feelings.*

- **Standardized Test Practice**— gives students the opportunity to improve testing skills.

Standardized Test Practice

Math Practice

Interpret Graphs. The table below shows 12-year trends related to sexual activity among teens in the ninth through twelfth grades. Use the graph to answer the questions.

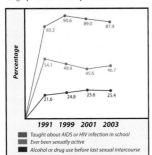

Percentage

90.6 89.0 87.9
83.3

54.1 49.9 45.6 46.7

21.6 24.8 25.6 25.4

1991 1999 2001 2003

■ Taught about AIDS or HIV infection in school
■ Ever been sexually active
■ Alcohol or drug use before last sexual intercourse

Adapted from the Youth Risk Behavior Survey: 1991–2003, Centers for Disease Control and Prevention.

1. By what percentage has sexual activity among teens decreased between 1991 and 2003?
   A. 10.2　　C. 4.3
   B. 7.4　　　D. 12.6

2. Which year shows the highest rate of teens reporting alcohol use before engaging in sexual activity?
   A. 2001　　C. 1991
   B. 1999　　D. 2003

3. Identify the years with the lowest and highest percentage of AIDS/HIV education. What is the difference in percentage between the two years?
   A. 3.2　　　C. 7.3
   B. 6.0　　　D. 4.5

G⊙ Online

For more test practice, visit glencoe.com and complete the Online Quizzes for Chapter 8.

Reading/Writing Practice

Understand and Apply. Read the passage below, and then answer the questions.

> I have been best friends with Tamara since the first grade. Tamara is nice to me and to other people.
> Tamara's kindness shows in many ways. Once she gave her circus tickets to some kids who had never been to the circus. Tamara visits a nearby nursing home at least once a month. She worries about some of the people she has met there because they have no family.
> Tamara was a good friend to me when my parents divorced. She listened to me for hours as I talked about how upset I was. She also let me cry and never told me that I was overreacting. I knew that she couldn't do anything to change the situation, but she always made me feel better.

1. How does the author show that Tamara is good friend?
   A. By comparing Tamara's actions to those of her other friends
   B. By pointing out that Tamara once helped with a canned-food drive
   C. By citing examples of Tamara's kindn
   D. By saying that Tamara does not gossi

2. When Tamara listened to her friend talk about divorce, what characteristics of frie ship did she show?
   A. Mutual respect　　C. Support
   B. Caring　　　　　　D. All of the abov

3. Describe the qualities that you think m someone a good friend. Give examples details to support your opinions.

National Education Standards

Math: Number and Operations, Problem Solving
Language Arts: NCTE 1, NCTE 3, NCTE 4

Chapter 8 Standardized Test Prac

- **Academic Integration**—gives more opportunities for students to strengthen their academic skills.

Academic Integration: Math

Chapter 7 Family Relationships

Lesson 1 Healthy Family Relationships

Directions: The following graph contains data from the U.S. census about the composition of American families in 2005. Review the graph carefully, then answer the following questions.

Families by Composition

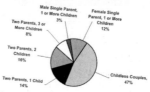

Male Single Parent, 1 or More Children 3%
Female Single Parent, 1 or More Children 12%
Two Parents, 3 or More Children 8%
Two Parents, 2 Children 16%
Two Parents, 1 Child 14%
Childless Couples, 47%

Source: U.S. Census Bureau, 2005

1. According to the pie chart, what is the combined percentage of all single-parent families?
   A. 3 percent
   B. 12 percent
   C. 15 percent
   D. None of the above

2. Which slice of the pie represents the smallest percentage of all households with two parents?
   A. The slice labeled "Two Parents, 3 or More Children"
   B. The slice labeled "Two Parents, 2 Children"
   C. The slice labeled "Two Parents, 1 Child"
   D. The slice labeled "Childless Couples"

3. Based on the pie chart, which of the following statements is true?
   A. The number of single-parent families has decreased in recent years.
   B. There are twice as many two-parent families with two children than two-parent families with three children or more.
   C. More than half of all families have no children.
   D. More single-parent households are headed by a male parent.

Chapter 7 Chapter 7 *Student Activity Workbook* **89**

- **Academic Integration**—teacher activities in the Teacher Wraparound Edition provide another academic skill for teachers to give students.

Academic Integration

Math　Refusal skills can make it possible to not give in to peer pressure when it comes to drinking alcohol. According to the 2005 Youth Risk Behavior Survey, approximately 13,917 students completed the questionnaire. It was found that 56 percent of high school students did not take a drink of alcohol in the month before the survey.

Pair students, and ask them to calculate the number of students who did not drink alcohol more than once in the 30 days before the survey. (Answer: 7,794 students)

Complete Support for the Health Teacher

The Teacher Wraparound Edition provides comprehensive lesson plans, teaching suggestions, supplemental information, cross-references, and more—all conveniently "wrapped" around every page of the reduced student text. The format of concise and easy-to-follow lesson plans gives a wide variety of teaching strategies to motivate students and to introduce, teach, assess, and reinforce concepts. Alternative teaching strategies that allow teachers to customize the program to accommodate a broad range of different teaching and learning styles are a key aspect of the Teacher Wraparound Edition's design.

National Health Education Standards   **Resources**   **Technology Resources**

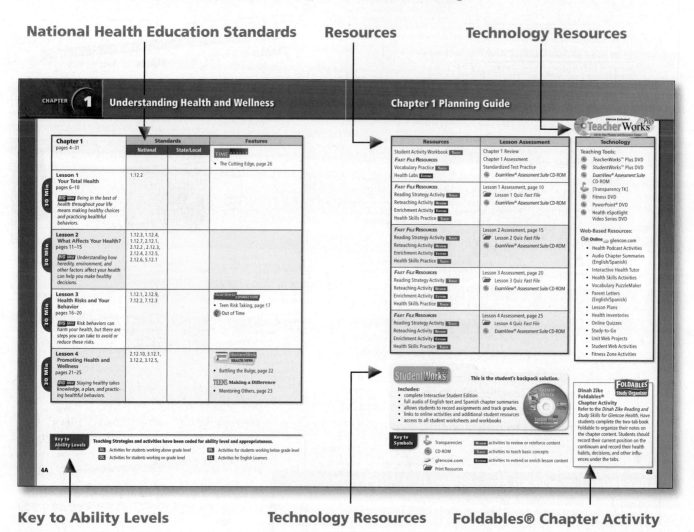

Key to Ability Levels   **Technology Resources**   **Foldables® Chapter Activity**

Understanding the Letter Icons

The letter icons on the reduced Student Edition pages identify the type of strategy or activity. They are placed at point-of-use to show you where and when to teach each concept. See the key below to learn about the various types of strategies and activities.

Key for Using the Teacher Wraparound Edition

Use this key to help you identify the different types of prompts found in the Teacher Wraparound Edition.

R **Reading Strategy** activities help you teach reading skills and vocabulary.

C **Critical Thinking** strategies help students apply and extend what they have learned.

U **Universal Access** activities provide differentiated instruction for students learning to speak English, along with suggestions for teaching various types of learners.

HS **Health Skills Practice** activities reinforce health skills concepts and help students apply these skills in their everyday lives.

W **Writing Support** activities provide writing opportunities to help students comprehend the text.

CA **Cultural Awareness** activities help you teach sensitivity and understanding of other cultures.

AL **Active Learning** strategies provide a variety of activities for presenting lesson content, including engaging classroom projects that get students actively involved.

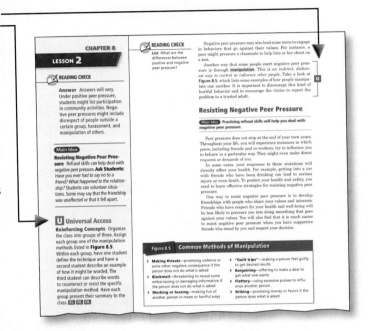

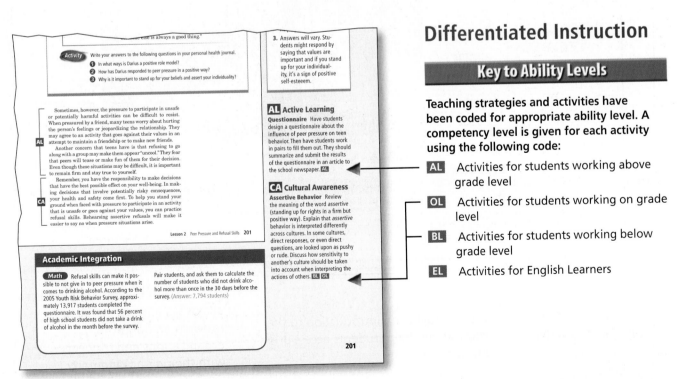

Differentiated Instruction

Key to Ability Levels

Teaching strategies and activities have been coded for appropriate ability level. A competency level is given for each activity using the following code:

AL Activities for students working above grade level

OL Activities for students working on grade level

BL Activities for students working below grade level

EL Activities for English Learners

Teaching the Unit

Units begin with a technology course manager preceding each unit of the student edition. This guide shows how to use available technology for each section of the chapter.

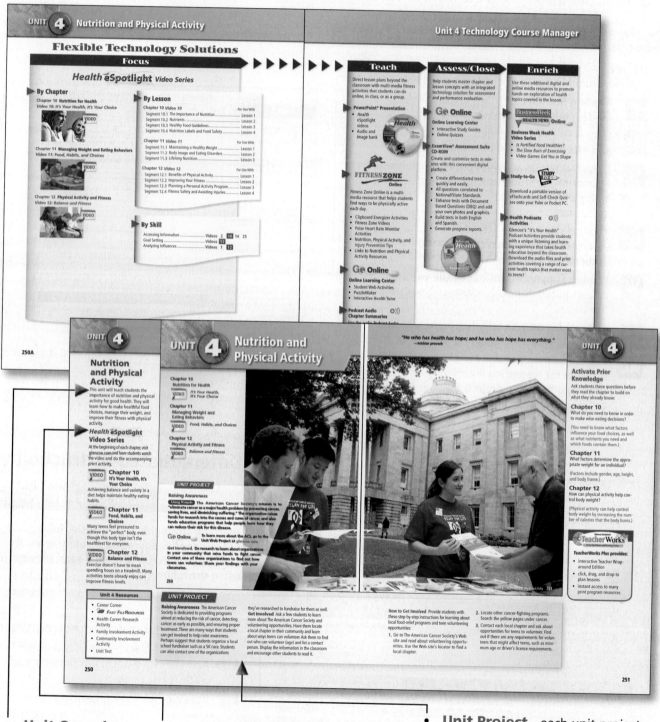

- **Unit Overview**— introduces the unit with an overview.

- **Health eSpotlight Video Series**— videos provide an introduction to the content and help students access prior knowledge.

- **Unit Project**—each unit project allows students to conduct research on nonprofit organizations and connect with their own community.

Units end with a Real-World Health feature.

- **Teens Speak Out**—offers differing views on contemporary health topics relevant to teens. This feature promotes critical thinking by challenging students to define and express their own views.

- **Unit Thematic Project**—Each unit ends with a Beyond the Classroom project.

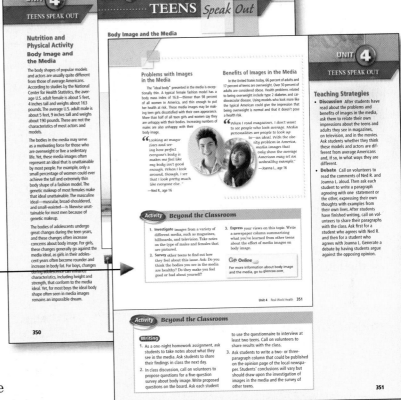

Teaching the Chapter

Introduce chapter content and the Big Idea at the beginning of each chapter.

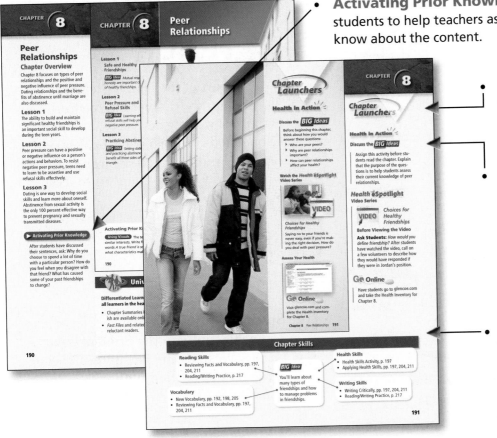

- **Activating Prior Knowledge**—questions for students to help teachers assess what students know about the content.

- **Chapter Launchers**—activities and videos for students before they begin reading the chapter.

- **BIG Idea**—activities help students understand the conceptual structure of the chapter—starting with the Big Idea overarching the chapter to the Main Ideas that are the focus of each section.

- **Chapter Skills**—graphic organizer shows where reading, vocabulary, writing, and health skills can be found in each chapter.

Teaching the Lesson

Lesson Plans

The teaching material follows a consistent, easy-to-use pattern. The complete lesson cycle—Focus, Teach, Assess/Close—makes it easy to plan a lesson. The lesson plan includes:

❶ FOCUS

- **Guide to Reading**—prompts students with the Big Idea to help them understand the main idea of the chapter.

- **Main Idea**—offers students key concepts of the lesson and allows for class discussion.

- **Real Life Issues**—activity encourages students to relate content to their lives.

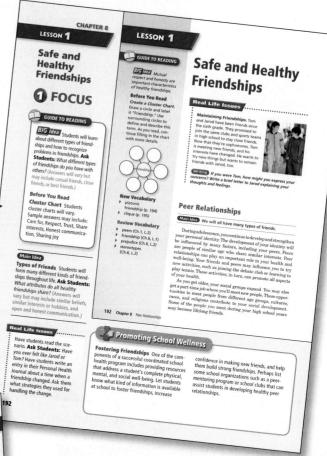

❷ TEACH

This part of the lesson provides suggestions for discussion, reading activities, writing activities, answers to questions on each page, health skills practice, and resource suggestions.

- **Reading Check**—answers to recall questions
- **Bottom Column Boxes**—provide supplemental information related to the lesson.
- **Health education features**
- **More teaching strategies**

Special Features Boxes

Each activity in the Student Text has a corresponding box in the Teacher Wraparound Edition that offers additional health skills practice.

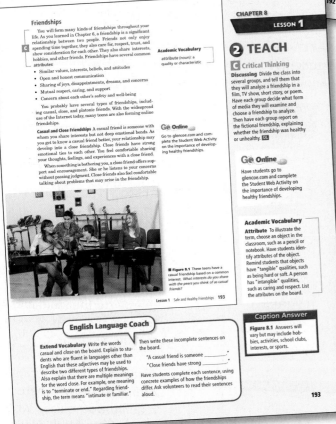

③ ASSESS/CLOSE

Assessment techniques help determine the level of mastery and include strategies for reteaching students who might have difficulty with important lesson concepts. Enrichment activities are designed for students who are motivated to explore the content on deeper and more enriched levels.

Chapter Review and Standardized Test Practice

- **Answers** to Chapter Assessment questions are found here.

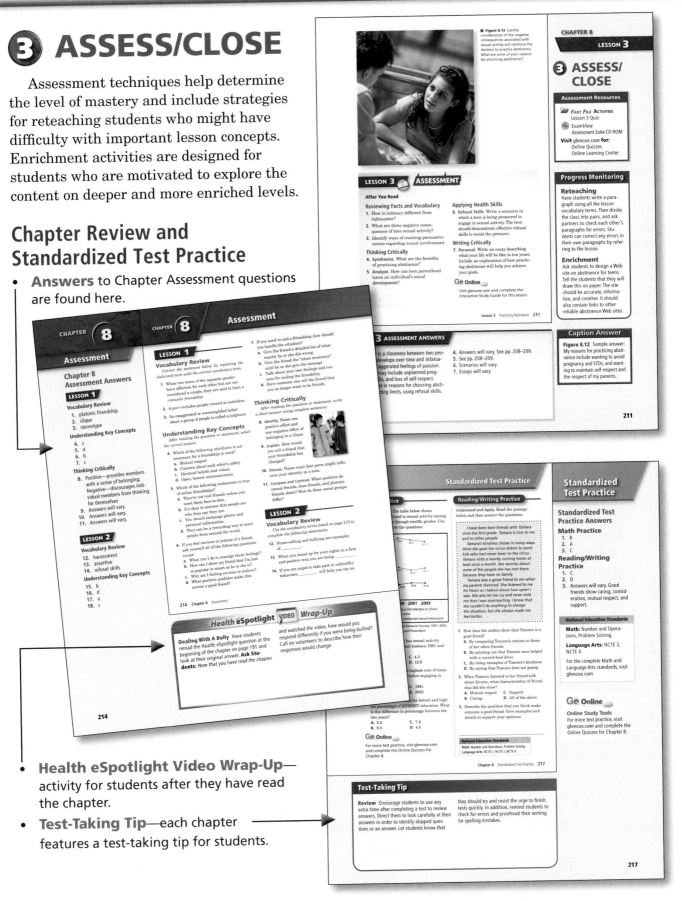

- **Health eSpotlight Video Wrap-Up**— activity for students after they have read the chapter.

- **Test-Taking Tip**—each chapter features a test-taking tip for students.

Teaching Skills to Help Students Make Health-Enhancing Choices

The following health skills are identified by health educators across the nation as essential for students to promote health and contribute to overall wellness. They are included in the National Standards for Health Education to provide professionals with a framework to help determine the content of health education curricula. These skills can be developed and practiced by your students. *Glencoe Health* presents Health Skills Activities that guide students through real-life scenarios and step-by-step instructions to **practice** the skill. Finally, students **apply** the skill to their own lives. They can then use these skills to promote their own health and the health of others.

Accessing Information This skill addresses the important steps to take to get valid health information and appropriate health services.	**Self-Management and Practicing Healthful Behaviors** This skill is the actual practice of healthful behavior. It includes the steps and procedures used to promote wellness.
Stress Management This skill involves the use of techniques that reduce and manage stress.	**Refusal Skills** This skill involves strategies to refuse behaviors that may put one's health at risk.
Conflict Resolution This skill involves specific strategies to resolve conflicts peacefully.	**Decision Making** This skill requires speculation into the future based on a particular action.
Analyzing Influences This skill involves analysis of the dynamic factors of families, media, peers, personal interests, and pressures that affect health decisions.	**Goal Setting** This skill is an interactive process for individuals. It requires planning and revision throughout the application of the process.
Communication This skill is an interactive process between and among individuals to clarify ideas, thoughts, needs, and feelings.	**Advocacy** This skill calls for the use of persuasion to promote positive health choices personally and for others.

Health Skills Scoring Rubrics

The following health skills are skills that we develop and practice throughout life. Research has shown that the cultivation of these skills helps teens and adults promote health and contribute to overall wellness. To evaluate students' understanding of each skill, key components are provided.

Advocacy—This skill calls for the use of persuasion to promote positive health choices personally and for others. Key components of this skill are:
—clear, health-enhancing stand
—support for the position with relevant information
—awareness of the audience
—encouragement of others to make healthful choices
—passion/conviction

Goal Setting—This skill is an interactive process for individuals. It requires planning and revision throughout the application of the process. Key components of this skill are:
—clear progression through a goal-setting process
—inclusion of a clear goal statement
—identification of a realistic goal
—plan for reaching the goal
—evaluation or reflection on the action

Communication—This skill is an interactive process between and among individuals to clarify ideas, thoughts, needs, and feelings. Key components for this skill are:
—interactions among individuals
—clear, organized message
—listening skills
—use of "I" messages
—respectful tone
—appropriate body language
—reason(s) for their request

Decision Making—This skill requires speculation into the future based on a particular action. Students speculate if *this* action is taken then *that* result can be expected. The evaluation of potential results in a decision. Key components of this skill are:
—clear description of the situation
—several options with possible outcomes of each
—influence of values on possible decisions
—health-enhancing decision and an evaluation of it

Analyzing Influences—This skill involves analysis of the dynamic factors of families, media, peers, personal interests, and pressures that affect health decisions. Key components of this skill are:
—identification and analysis of external/internal factors
—attention to interrelationships and complexity of influences
—variety of influences as appropriate

Accessing Information—This skill addresses the important steps to take to get valid health information and appropriate health services. Key components of this skill are:
—citation of specific sources
—evaluation of the validity of the source
—rationale for the appropriateness of the source
—ability to access appropriate community resources to meet specific needs
—type of help available from the sources

Refusal Skills—This skill involves specific strategies to refuse involvement in behaviors which may risk health. Key components of this skill are:
—inclusion of the word no in their response
—an explanation of why they were refusing
—alternatives to the proposed activity
—body language they use to back up their words
—a description of walking away from the situation

Self-Management Skills—This skill is the actual practice of healthful behavior. Key components of this skill are:
—demonstration of healthful behaviors, habits, and/or techniques
—identification of protective behaviors (e.g., first aid techniques, safety steps, strategies) to avoid/manage unhealthy or dangerous situations
—listing steps in correct order

Conflict Resolution—This skill involves specific strategies to resolve conflicts peacefully. Key components of this skill are:
—take turns explaining each side of the conflict
—use "I" messages
—listen carefully and ask appropriate questions
—brainstorm solutions
—agree on a solution that benefits both sides

Stress Management—This skill involves the use of specific techniques that reduce and manage stress. The key components of this skill are:
—ability to identify situations that cause stress
—demonstration of techniques that help manage and reduce stress (e.g., deep breathing, exercise, relaxation strategies)

Making Real-Life Connections

Connecting Skills to Real Life

Great care has been taken to make the connections among standards, curriculum instruction, and assessment. Therefore, you will see that the standards addressed are linked to the features in the text. The teaching strategies in the Teacher Wraparound Edition provide appropriate practice as a part of the instruction. Finally, the assessment is a natural extension of the instruction and the criteria point directly back to the standard.

- **Situation**—Students are presented with a scenario that challenges them to use a health skill to reduce risk and enhance health. In this case, the necessary skill is communication.

- **Skills Described**—Students are provided with direction to apply the skill to this situation. In this case, students are reminded of the five guidelines to better communication.

- **Skills Practice and Application**—The activity and student written response provide critical practice in the use of the skill, resulting in a student product that can be used for assessment purposes.

- **Teaching Strategies**—Teachers are given the methodology for effectively using the feature with strategies that specifically link the standards, objectives, process, and assessment.

- **Skills Assessed**—Student products are used as evidence of skill development. Scoring criteria directly relate to the Health Standards. They are used to judge the quality of student work on this performance task.

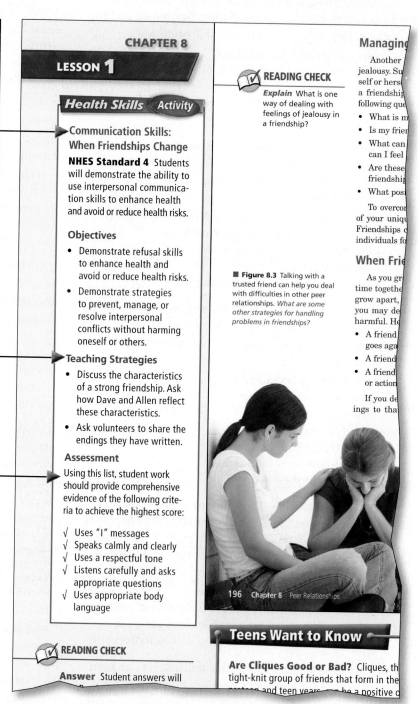

CHAPTER 8

LESSON 1

Health Skills   Activity

Communication Skills: When Friendships Change

NHES Standard 4 Students will demonstrate the ability to use interpersonal communication skills to enhance health and avoid or reduce health risks.

Objectives

- Demonstrate refusal skills to enhance health and avoid or reduce health risks.
- Demonstrate strategies to prevent, manage, or resolve interpersonal conflicts without harming oneself or others.

Teaching Strategies

- Discuss the characteristics of a strong friendship. Ask how Dave and Allen reflect these characteristics.
- Ask volunteers to share the endings they have written.

Assessment

Using this list, student work should provide comprehensive evidence of the following criteria to achieve the highest score:

√ Uses "I" messages
√ Speaks calmly and clearly
√ Uses a respectful tone
√ Listens carefully and asks appropriate questions
√ Uses appropriate body language

READING CHECK

Answer Student answers will

READING CHECK

Explain What is one way of dealing with feelings of jealousy in a friendship?

■ **Figure 8.3** Talking with a trusted friend can help you deal with difficulties in other peer relationships. *What are some other strategies for handling problems in friendships?*

196   Chapter 8   Peer Relationships

Teens Want to Know

Are Cliques Good or Bad? Cliques, th tight-knit group of friends that form in the

Managin

Another
jealousy. Su
self or hers
a friendship
following que
- What is m
- Is my frien
- What can
  can I feel
- Are these
  friendship
- What posi

To overco
of your uniq
Friendships
individuals fo

When Frie

As you gr
time togethe
grow apart,
you may de
harmful. He
- A friend
  goes aga
- A friend
- A friend
  or action

If you de
ings to that

Teens Making a Difference

TEENS Making a Difference

"Don't let people get you down."

Standing Up for What You Believe

Darius B. of North Carolina joined his high school S.A.V.E. (Students Against Violence Everywhere) Step team to teach others that there are alternatives to violence. Through dancing and storytelling, the team teaches elementary children to be respectful, get good grades, and avoid violence.

Darius is sometimes teased about being the only male on the team. Despite the teasing, he thinks S.A.V.E. is well worth the effort. "We have a lot of fun and the children like to dance. It gets our message across that there are other things to do than fight and other ways to act than being disrespectful and rude."

If you dare to be different, Darius says: "Keep your head up and don't let people get you down. Helping someone else is always a good thing."

Activity Write your answers to the following questions in your personal health journal.

1. In what ways is Darius a positive role model?
2. How has Darius responded to peer pressure in a positive way?
3. Why is it important to stand up for your beliefs and assert your individuality?

Real Life Issues

Real Life Issues

Facing Peer Pressure. Karen and Ann met at tryouts for the school gymnastics team. The coach gave each girl a list of fitness tips to prepare for the tryouts. The tips included eating a low-fat diet, getting enough sleep, stretching before each workout, and avoiding tobacco and alcohol use. On the way home, Ann pulled a pack of cigarettes out of her bag and offered one to Karen. Karen doesn't like smoking and really wants to make the team.

Writing *If you were Karen, what would you say to Ann? Write your response in a brief paragraph.*

Teens Speak Out →

UNIT 4 Real-World Health
TEENS *Speak Out*

Body Image and the Media

It's no secret that the average person you see on the street doesn't look like a model in a magazine. The average fashion model is 7 inches taller than the average American woman, yet weighs 23 pounds less. Men in the media also have a typical look: broad-shouldered, narrow-waisted, muscle-clad, and free of body hair. That's far from the look of the average American male.

Some people think the bodies we see in the media are unrealistic and ...think they represent a healthful ideal. Take a look at what ...to say, and then decide how you feel.

Real World Connection

Real World CONNECTION

Sexual Content on TV

Media messages can play an important role in a teen's decisions regarding sexual activity. Studies have shown that adolescents with higher exposure to sexual content on TV are more likely to engage in sexual activity. Consider these statistics:

▸ 64 percent of all television programs contain sexual content.

▸ Of programs with sexual content, 15 percent show abstinence or risk of sexual activity.

Analyzing media messages and comparing them to real-life situations is an important skill to develop. It will help you resist external pressures and stay committed to abstinence.

Activity Mathematics

Assume that 1,500 TV programs were surveyed.

1. How many programs had sexual content?
2. How many programs depicted abstinence or risk of sexual activity?
3. **Writing** Write a short essay describing how the higher rate of sexual content on TV influences teen behavior.

Concept Number and Operations: Percents A percent is a ratio comparing a number to 100. It can also be represented as a fraction with 100 as the denominator. To find a decimal equivalent, divide the percent by 100. To convert a decimal to a percent, multiply it by 100.

350 Unit 4 Real-World Health

Teacher Manual TM25

Backward Mapping

How can my instruction help students succeed in a standards-based system?

by Emily M. Schell, Ed.D.

Content standards articulate what students should know and be able to do in every health classroom. Effective instructional planning based in the standards and maximizing available resources are essential for meaningful teaching and learning of health knowledge and skills. Planning instruction with educational goals in mind makes for the most effective teaching.

How do I map my curriculum?

Mapping the curriculum from beginning to end, and from the end to the beginning—backward mapping—makes for solid instruction.

Mapping out the curriculum allows teachers to achieve several goals. These goals include a better understanding of the standards and content-specific objectives, organization and pacing of the curriculum, and focused assessment related to specific goals and objectives.

- *Analyze the Health Education Content Standards* To begin, teachers analyze the body of content standards for health. Then they compare and contrast these standards to additional sources of information that support effective teaching and learning in the health curriculum. This process works best with colleagues, fellow health educators who bring varying perspectives and expertise to teaching the subject. As a result of this collaboration, strengths and weaknesses of the standards become apparent. Teachers will have a better understanding of the standards and identify concerns and questions for follow-up while mapping.
- *Analyze the Organization of the Standards-Based Content* Most health teachers agree that health is best taught in a skills-based, hands-on environment that is relevant to students' lives. Presenting health in the context of skills development helps students translate knowledge into action. The new health education standards focus on skill-building to help students use information to achieve or maintain good health for themselves, their families, and their communities.
- *Identify the Content and Order of Teaching* A plan is developed to present content in a certain order. Incorporating content that is either missing from the standards or is essential in building background knowledge with students enters the curriculum map as well. Outside resources brought into the classroom are good supplements.
- *Separate Overlapping Units* Identify areas of instruction related to the Health content areas, Big Ideas, or Main Ideas. It is at this stage that backward planning is introduced for the development of instructional units, which will support the grade-level curriculum map. The instruction must support the planned assessment.
- *Map Curriculum at Each Grade Level* Curriculum planning should be shared among all subject-area teachers. Teachers will have a better understanding of what knowledge and skills students bring to their coursework if they take into consideration what has been learned previously.

How do I use backward mapping?

After a semester or year-long course of study is mapped out, further develop each unit through backward mapping. Start with the end in mind—know your curricular goals and objectives at the outset, which are often found in the content standards and articulated in the curriculum maps.

Once goals have been determined, teachers develop assessments that will show progress toward those goals and objectives. In the final step of this backward mapping process, teachers determine meaningful teaching and learning strategies and identify useful resources that support the assessment.

To use backward mapping in developing your units of instruction, consider the following steps:

Step One: Know Your Targets

First, identify exactly what students must know and do in this unit. Analyze content standards and any other resources that support curricular goals and objectives for this unit. As you plan, ask yourself:

- What do I want my students to know as a result of this unit?
- What health and life skills will students develop during the course of this unit?
- How do I describe these goals clearly and concisely to my students so they understand where we should be at the end of this unit?
- What essential knowledge will students need to access to make sense of this information?
- Do my instructional goals align with strategies identified in the curriculum map?

Step Two: Identify and Develop Assessments

Second, consider the multiple forms of formal and informal assessments that will help you determine to what degree each student has achieved the stated goals and objectives seen in Step One. Some assessments are embedded throughout the instructional unit, while others come at the end of the unit. Some assessments are performance-based, while others are not. Ask yourself:

- What do I want to know and see from each student?
- What are the best methods for students to demonstrate what they know and can do based on the goals and objectives?
- How many assessments do I need to determine what students know and can do?
- How will I balance informal and formal assessments?
- How will I assess students with diverse learning styles, skills, and abilities?
- How will these assessments promote student progress in health?
- At what time(s) during the unit will I administer these assessments?

Step Three: Develop Meaningful Instruction

After the assessments for the unit have been determined, consider the meaningful and effective teaching strategies that will support learning and student achievement on assessments. While developing lesson plans for instruction, ask yourself:

- How will students learn what they are expected to know?
- How will I engage students in the concepts of this unit?
- In what ways might students relate or connect to this information?
- How will I differentiate my instruction to meet the diverse needs of my students?
- How will I scaffold or provide access to the curriculum for my English learners?
- What vocabulary requires attention in this unit?
- How much time will I have to effectively teach this unit?
- How will I use the textbook and other resources to support the goals and objectives for this unit?
- What lessons will I develop?
- In what sequence will I teach these lessons during this unit?
- How will these lessons support the assessments from Step Two?

Step Four: Locate and Manage Resources

Effective teaching and learning of health requires varied resources. Consider what you have available in your classroom, including your textbook, and identify resources you will add in order to teach this unit successfully. Ask yourself:

- What parts of the textbook are required for the lessons determined in Step Three?
- What ancillary materials are needed for the lessons in this unit?
- What Web sites will I recommend to students to support these lessons?
- Do I need to contact guest speakers or obtain outside resources?

Emily M. Schell is a visiting professor at San Diego State University and social studies education director at SDSU City Heights Educational Collaborative, San Diego, CA.

Meeting the Diverse Needs of Your Students

by Douglas Fisher, Ph.D.

Today's classroom contains students from a variety of backgrounds with a variety of learning styles, strengths, and challenges. As teachers, we are facing the challenge of helping each student reach his or her educational potential. With careful planning, you can address the needs of all students in the health classroom. The basis for this planning is universal access. When classrooms are planned with universal access in mind, fewer students require specific accommodations.

What is universal design?

Universal design was first conceived in architectural studies when businesspeople, engineers, and architects began making considerations for physical access to buildings. The idea was to plan the environment in advance to ensure that everyone had access. As a result, the environment would not have to be changed later for people with physical disabilities, people pushing strollers, workers who had injuries, or others for whom the environment would be difficult to negotiate. The Center for Universal Design, **www.design.ncsu.edu/cud**, defines universal design as: *The design of products and environments to be usable by all people, to the greatest extent possible, without the need for adaptation or specialized design.*

Universal Design and Access in Education

Researchers, teachers, and parents in education have expanded the development of built-in adaptations and inclusive accommodations from architectural space to the educational experience, especially in the area of curriculum.

In 1998, the National Center to Improve the Tools of Educators (NCITE), in partnership with the Center for Applied Special Technology (CAST), proposed an expanded definition of universal design focused on education: *In terms of learning, universal design means the design of instructional materials and activities that allow the learning goals to be achievable by individuals with wide differences in their abilities to see, hear, speak, move, read, write, understand English, attend, organize, engage, and remember.*

How does universal design work in education?

Universal design and access, as they apply to education and schooling, suggest the following:

- *Inclusive Classroom Participation* Curriculum should be designed with all students and their needs in mind. Glencoe Health was designed for a wide range of students. For example, because English learners and students who struggle with reading will use this textbook, new vocabulary, academic vocabulary, and review vocabulary are specifically taught and reinforced. Similarly, the teacher-support materials provide multiple instructional points to be used depending on the needs of the students in each class. Further, the main ideas are identified for all learners. Throughout the text, there are multiple opportunities to activate students' prior knowledge. Connections between what students know and think about are made throughout the text.

- *Maximum Text Readability* In universally designed classrooms that provide access for all students, texts use direct language, clear noun-verb agreements, and clear construct-based wording. In addition to these factors, the Glencoe Health text uses embedded definitions for difficult terms, provides for specific instruction in reading skills, uses a number of visual representations, and includes note-taking strategies at the lesson level.

- *Adaptable and Accommodating* The content in this textbook can be easily translated, read aloud, or otherwise changed to meet the needs of students in the classroom. The section and end-of-chapter assessments provide students with multiple ways of demonstrating their content knowledge while also ensuring that they have practice with thinking in terms of multiple-choice questions. Critical thinking and analysis skills also are practiced.

How is differentiated instruction the key to universal access?

To differentiate instruction, teachers must acknowledge student differences in background knowledge and current reading, writing, and English language skills. They also must consider student learning styles and preferences, interests, and needs, and react accordingly. There are a number of general guidelines for differentiating instruction in the classroom to reach all students, including:

- *Link Assessment With Instruction* Assessments should occur before, during, and after instruction to ensure that the curriculum is aligned with what students do and do not know. Using assessments in this way allows you to plan instruction for whole groups, small groups, and individual students. Backward mapping, in which you establish the assessment before you begin instruction, is also important.

- *Clarify Key Concepts and Generalizations* Students need to know what is essential and how this information can be used in their future learning. In addition, students need to develop a sense of the Big Ideas—ideas that transcend time and place.

- *Emphasize Critical and Creative Thinking* The content, process, and products used or assigned in the classroom should require that students think about what they are learning. While some students may require support, additional motivation, varied tasks, materials, or equipment, the overall focus on critical and creative thinking allows for all students to participate in the lesson.

- *Include Teacher- and Student-Selected Tasks* A differentiated classroom includes both teacher- and student-selected activities and tasks. At some points in the lesson or day, the teacher must provide instruction and assign learning activities. In other parts of the lesson, students should be provided choices in how they engage with the content. This balance increases motivation, engagement, and learning.

Below is an example of a classroom activity for teaching the benefits of regular physical activity. It is followed by an example of the methods this text provides teachers for differentiating instruction to meet all students' needs.

Classroom Activity

Display transparencies, computer slides, or charts that illustrate results of studies by the CDC about the decrease in physical activity among youth. Next show data that showcase the increase in obesity in the United States. Discuss with students what they have learned about the health benefits of physical activity, nutrition, and weight management.

Strategies for Differentiating This Activity:

- Ask students to imagine that they are reporters assigned to inform people about the importance of physical activity for health. Have them write a newspaper article informing the general public about the obesity epidemic and the health benefits of being physically active.
- Have students create a concept map tracing the relationship between obesity, nutrition, and physical activity levels. Have them identify a minimum of five benefits of fitness and how it can help reduce the risk of obesity.
- Have students conduct research using the Internet and other reliable sources of information to find out more about the obesity rates and trends in the United States over the last 10 years. Ask them to write a two-page report on the facts they find at the CDC Web site and the President's Council on Physical Activity.
- Assign students to work in groups of three or four. Have them work together to develop a radio script or PSA informing listeners about the benefits of physical activity and fitness. Allow time for students to practice performing their script, and then let them present it to classmates in a role-play or present their recordings.

How do I support individual students?

The majority of students will thrive in a classroom based on universal access and differentiated instruction. However, wise teachers recognize that no single option will work for all students and there might be students who require unique systems of support to be successful.

Tips for Instruction

The following tips for instruction can support your efforts to help all students reach their maximum potential.

- Survey students to discover their individual differences. Use interest inventories of their unique talents so you can encourage contributions in the classroom.
- Be a model for respecting others. Adolescents crave social acceptance. The student with learning differences is especially sensitive to correction and criticism, particularly when it comes from a teacher. Your behavior will set the tone for how students treat one another.

- Expand opportunities for success. Provide a variety of instructional activities that reinforce skills and concepts.
- Establish measurable objectives and decide how you can best help students meet them.
- Celebrate successes and make note of and praise "work in progress."
- Keep it simple. Point out problem areas if doing so can help a student affect change. Avoid overwhelming students with too many goals at one time.
- Assign cooperative group projects that challenge all students to contribute to solving a problem or creating a product.

How do I reach students who have learning disabilities?

- Provide support and structure. Clearly specify rules, assignments, and responsibilities.
- Practice skills frequently. Use games and drills to help maintain student interest.
- Incorporate many modalities into the learning process. Provide opportunities to say, hear, write, read, and act out important concepts and information.
- Link new skills and concepts to those already mastered.
- If possible, allow students to record answers on audiotape.
- Allow extra time to complete assessments and assignments.
- Let students demonstrate proficiency with alternative presentations, including oral reports, role-plays, and art or musical projects.
- Provide outlines, notes, or tape recordings of lecture material.
- Pair students with peer helpers, and provide class time for pair interaction.

How do I reach students who have behavioral challenges?

- Provide a structured environment with simple and clearly defined schedules, rules, seat assignments, and safety procedures.
- Reinforce appropriate behavior and model it for students.
- Cue distracted students back to the task through verbal and nonverbal signals and teacher proximity.
- Set small goals that can be achieved in the short term. Work for long-term improvement in the big areas.

How do I reach students who have physical challenges?

- Openly discuss with the student any uncertainties you have about when to offer aid.
- Ask parents or therapists and students what special devices or procedures are needed and whether any special safety precautions need to be taken.
- Welcome students with physical challenges into all class activities, including field trips, special events, and classroom and community projects.
- Provide information to assist class members and parents in their understanding of support needed.

How do I reach students who have visual impairments?

- Facilitate independence. Modify assignments as needed.
- Teach classmates how and when to serve as visual guides.
- Limit unnecessary noise in the classroom if it distracts the student with visual impairments.

- Provide tactile models whenever possible.
- Foster a spirit of inclusion. Describe people and events as they occur in the classroom. Remind classmates that the student with visual impairments cannot interpret gestures and other forms of nonverbal communication.
- Provide taped lectures and reading assignments for use outside the classroom.
- Team the student with a sighted peer for written assignments.

How do I reach students who have hearing impairments?

- Seat students where they can see your lip movements easily and where they can avoid any visual distractions.
- Avoid standing with your back to the window or other light source.
- Use an overhead projector so you can maintain eye contact while writing information for students.
- Make sure students sit where they can see all speakers.
- Post all assignments on the board, or hand out written instructions.
- If the student has a manual interpreter, allow both student and interpreter to select the most favorable seating arrangements.
- Teach students to look directly at each other when they speak.

How do I reach English learners?

- Remember, students' abilities to speak English do not reflect their academic abilities.
- Try to incorporate students' cultural experience into your instruction. The help of a bilingual aide may be effective.
- Avoid any references in your instruction that could be construed as cultural stereotypes.
- Preteach important vocabulary and concepts.

- Encourage students to preview text before they begin reading, noting headings.
- Remind students not to ignore graphic organizers, photographs, charts, graphs, and tables, since there is much information in these visuals.
- Use demonstrations and specimens whenever possible to build background knowledge and understanding. For example, you can display different types of leaves in order to facilitate an understanding of classification.

How do I reach students who are working above level?

- Make arrangements for students to take selected subjects early and to work on independent projects.
- Ask "what if" questions to develop high-level thinking skills. Establish an environment safe for risk taking in your classroom.
- Emphasize concepts, theories, ideas, relationships, and generalizations about the content.
- Promote interest in health by inviting students to make connections to other disciplines that interest them.
- Let students express themselves in alternative ways, such as creative writing, acting, debates, simulations, drawing, or music.
- Provide students with a catalog of helpful resources, including agencies that provide free and inexpensive materials, appropriate community services and programs, and community experts who might be called upon to speak to your students.
- Assign extension projects that allow students to solve real-life problems related to their communities.

Douglas Fisher is a professor at San Diego State University, San Diego, CA.

English Language Learners (ELL)

How can I reach English language learners in the health classroom?

American classrooms reflect the rich and diverse cultural heritage of the American people. Students come from different ethnic backgrounds and different cultural experiences into a common classroom that must assist all of them in learning. Multicultural and/or bilingual students often speak English as a second language or not at all. In providing for ELL students, the focus needs to be on overcoming the language barrier. It is important not to confuse ability in speaking and reading English with academic ability or intelligence. In general, the best method to assist ELL students is to provide them with a variety of ways to learn, apply, and be assessed on the concepts. *Glencoe Health* has risen to this challenge with a full complement of ancillaries and technology for English learners.

Help Students Master Concepts

ELL strategies, worksheets, and technology components in the *Glencoe Health* program provide practical tools and suggest modifications that can help students master health concepts while developing their English language skills. The book focuses on methods for successful inclusion of ELL students in the health classroom. These strategies rely not only on teacher intervention but also on student intervention to create ownership of the learning process.

The Spanish Student Edition of *Glencoe Health* facilitates the learning of health concepts for students whose first language is Spanish.

The StudentWorks Plus CD-ROM includes Spanish audio summaries of each chapter to aid the reading comprehension of English learners in the health classroom.

The English/Spanish Glossary/Glosario in both the English and Spanish versions of

Glencoe Health's Student Edition helps native Spanish speakers learn health vocabulary.

Reading Strategies (Before You Read, Reading Checks, and *After You Read)* are supported by ancillary worksheet activities and technology components designed to help students use recognized reading strategies to improve their reading-for-information skills. The supporting activities help students practice basic writing skills, find main ideas, review vocabulary terms, and more.

Within the *Fast Files,* the Note Taking activities provide a guide designed to help students succeed in learning health content. It contains note-taking tools based on the Cornell Note-Taking System.

ELL strategies in the Teacher Wraparound Edition provide teachers with additional support for ELL students in the health classroom. The proportion of ELL-supported teaching strategies in each chapter is consistent with the national statistics for ELL learners in the U.S. population.

Alternative Assessment Strategies

How can I go beyond tests to assess students' understanding of health skills, knowledge, and concepts?

In response to the growing demand for accountability in the classroom, educators must use multiple assessment measures to accurately gauge student performance. In addition to quizzes, tests, essay exams, and standardized tests, assessment today uses a variety of performance-based measures and portfolio opportunities.

What are some typical performance-based assessments?

There are many kinds of performance-based assessments. They all share one common characteristic: they challenge students to create written or oral reports that demonstrate what they know. One good way to present a performance assessment is in the form of an open-ended question. Many of the Health Skills Activities presented in *Glencoe Health* are effective as performance-based assessments to measure health skills development.

Writing

Performance-based writing assessments challenge students to apply their knowledge of health concepts and skills in various ways. Writing activities are most often completed by one student, rather than by a group.

- *Journals* Students write regular entries to develop personal health goals and track their own progress.
- *Letters* Students compose a letter to a family member or other audience.
- *Position Paper or Editorial* Students explain a controversial issue and present their own opinion and recommendations, supported with strong evidence and convincing reasons.

- *Newspaper* Students write a variety of stories from the perspective of a reporter.
- *Biographies and Autobiographies* Students write about health either from the third-person point of view (interview) or from the first person (autobiography).
- *Creative Stories* Students integrate health concepts into a piece of fiction.
- *Poems and Songs* Students follow the conventions of a particular type of song or poem as they demonstrate a specific health skill or tell about an experience or scenario.
- *Research Reports* Students synthesize information from a variety of sources into a well-developed report.

Oral Presentations

Oral presentations allow students to demonstrate their health literacy before an audience. Oral presentations are often group efforts, although this need not to be the case.

- *Simulations* Students hold simulations or role-plays demonstrating health skills such as decision making or refusal skills.
- *Debates* Students debate two or more sides to a health-related issue. Students can debate from a contemporary perspective or through role-playing, from the viewpoint of a fictional character or contemporary real-life personality.
- *Interview* Students conduct a mock interview of a health expert.
- *Oral Reports* Students present the results of research efforts in an oral report.
- *Skits and Plays* Students use demonstrations or health scenarios as the basis for a play or skit.

Visual Presentations

Visual presentations allow students to demonstrate their understanding of health concepts in a variety of visual formats. Visual presentations can be either group or individual projects.

- **Model** Students make a model to demonstrate or represent a body system or fitness concept.
- **Museum Exhibit** Students create a rich display of materials around a topic. Typical displays might include models, illustrations, photographs, videos, writings, and audio-taped presentations.
- **Graph or Chart** Students analyze and represent authentic health data in a line graph, bar graph, table, or other chart format.
- **Drawing** Students represent or interpret a health concept or process through illustration, including political cartoons.
- **Posters and Murals** Posters and murals might include graphs, charts, tables, maps, time lines, diagrams, illustrations, photographs, and text that reflect students' understanding of health information.
- **Quilt** Students sew or draw a design for a patchwork quilt that shows a variety of perspectives, events, or issues related to a key topic.
- **Videotapes or DVDs** Students film a video or DVD to demonstrate a healthy behavior, health concept, or skill. Students can also film plays they have written that incorporate health in some way.
- **Multimedia Presentation or Slideshow** Students create a computer-generated multimedia presentation to illustrate a health topic.

How are performance assessments scored?

There are a variety of means available to evaluate performance tasks. Some or all of the following methods can be used.

- **Scoring Rubrics** A scoring rubric is a set of guidelines for assessing the quality of a process and/or product. It sets out criteria used to distinguish acceptable responses from unacceptable ones, generally along a scale from excellent to poor.
- **Models of Excellent Work** Teacher-selected models of excellent work give a concrete illustration of what is expected and help students set goals for their own projects.
- **Student Self-Assessment** Common methods of self-assessment include ranking work in relation to the model, using a scoring rubric, and writing their own goals and then evaluating how well they have met these goals. Regardless of the method or methods students use, they should be encouraged to evaluate their behaviors, processes, and the finished product.
- **Peer or Audience Assessment** Many of the performance tasks target an audience other than the classroom teacher. If possible, an audience of peers should give the students feedback. Have the class work together to create rubrics for specific projects.
- **Observation** As students carry out their performance tasks, you might want to formally observe students at work. Start by developing a checklist, identifying the specific behaviors and knowledge you expect students to demonstrate. Then observe students as they carry out performance tasks and check off these items on your checklist as you observe them.
- **Interviews** As a form of ongoing assessment, you might want to conduct interviews with students, asking them to analyze, explain, and assess their participation in performance tasks. When projects take place over an extended period of time, you can hold periodic interviews as well as exit interviews. In this way, you can gauge the status of the project and guide students' efforts along the way.

Print Ancillaries

Glencoe Health comes with an extensive variety of easy-to-use resources and support materials designed for your convenience.

Unit Resources masters contain all the materials you need for the unit and chapter, together in one convenient booklet, with answer keys.

Reproducible Student Resources include:

- **Reading Strategies**—show students how to employ a variety of techniques to organize and understand what they read. These activities utilize the reading strategies developed in Project CRISS.

- **Reteaching Activities**—provide students with a review of the major concepts presented in each lesson, which can be especially helpful for students who are having difficulty mastering the lesson content.

- **Enrichment Activities**—extend the concepts introduced in the lesson and challenge the students to apply their knowledge, critical thinking skills, and creativity by completing projects and debating current health-related issues.

- **Health Skills Practice Activities**—reinforce lesson content and provide an opportunity for students to practice health skills based on those identified in the National Health Education Standards.

- **Vocabulary Practice**—provides students with an aid to learning and understanding both the key health terms from each chapter and the terms that are included in the Academic Word List, a compilation of the 570 most common words found in academic texts.

- **Health Labs**—give students experience in making observations, formulating hypotheses, collecting and recording data, and reaching conclusions based on the analysis and interpretation of experimental results.

- **Health Behavior Contracts**—help students discuss their own behaviors, identify those behaviors that are dangerous to their health, and determine ways to change those dangerous behaviors into healthful ones.

- **Family Involvement Activities**—guide students in communicating effectively with family members about health, helping them to apply their knowledge and skills to real life.

- **Community Involvement Activities**—enable students to involve community members in their health education and advocate for health causes in their communities.

- **Health Career Research Activities**—encourage students to consider the various careers in the health care industry and to think critically about choosing a career, regardless of the field.

- **Lesson Quizzes, Chapter Tests, and Unit Tests**—provide a tool for assessing students' understanding of the major concepts and key vocabulary terms presented in each lesson, chapter, and unit.

Student Activity Workbook

- **Test Taking activities**—provide students with study and preparation tips, as well as chapter-review questions presented in a standardized test format.
- **Real World Connection activities**—enable students to see the relevance of what they are learning by giving them the opportunity to relate health content from the chapter to situations in their own lives.
- **Note Taking activities**—help students to master lesson content and improve their note-taking skills by guiding them through the note-taking process. These activities follow the Cornell Note-Taking model.
- **Academic Integration activities**—reinforce lesson content while emphasizing skills utilized in core academic subjects.

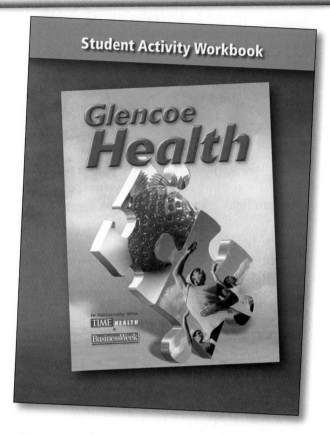

Teaching Transparencies

- **Teaching Transparencies**—includes 108 transparencies plus an activity booklet complete with teaching strategies for each transparency.

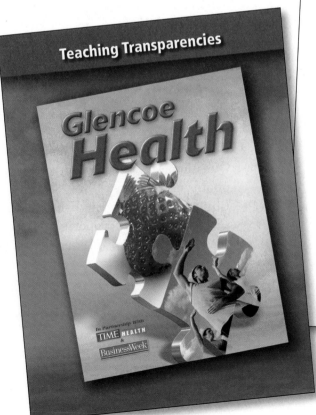

Technology

TeacherWorks™ Plus
All-In-One Planner and Resource Center

Use your all-in-one teacher resource center to personalize lesson plans, access resources, connect to the Internet, or create a to-do list.

Includes:
- Interactive Teacher Wraparound Edition
- Click, drag, and drop to plan lessons
- Editable worksheets
- Access electronic versions of all print materials with the click of your mouse
- Standards and correlations listed section-by-section

PowerPoint® Presentations

Lesson planning is simple with editable Microsoft® PowerPoint® presentations. Use this tool to teach key concepts from each section or customize your own presentations. The *Glencoe Health* PowerPoint® program comes with an overview of content from each chapter and lesson, discussion notes, and review questions.

Includes:
- Health eSpotlight videos
- Audio and animations
- Image bank
- Hotlinks to transparencies and online content
- This product can be used with TurningPoint® response-pad technology.

StudentWorks Plus

This is the student's backpack solution, bringing together a complete collection of resources in one, convenient digital platform.

Includes:
- Complete electronic Student Edition
- Health eSpotlight videos
- Full audio of English and Spanish chapter summaries
- Allows students to record assignments and keep track of activity grades
- Links to online activities and additional student resources
- Access to all student worksheets

ExamView® Assessment Suite

- Create differentiated tests quickly and easily.
- All questions correlated to National Standards.
- Enhance tests with Document Based Questions (DBQ) and add your own photos or graphics.
- Build tests in both English and Spanish.
- Generate progress reports and disaggregate data with Test Manager.
- Analyze reports to make sure assessment aligns with instruction.
- All questions can be used with TurningPoint® response-pad technology.

Glencoe Health Video Series

The *Glencoe Health* program provides teachers with engaging videos to help students make real-world connections between classroom learning and their own lives.

Health eSpotlight Video Series

At the beginning of each chapter, students can watch the video and do the accompanying print activity. The Teacher Wraparound Edition offers additional activities for each video, too!

Health eSpotlight videos give you the flexibility to customize your health course by:

- Topic
- Chapter
- Lesson
- Skill

From the Student Edition ⟶

Watch the *Health eSpotlight* Video Series

Choices for Healthy Friendships

Saying no to your friends is never easy, even if you're making the right decision. How do you deal with peer pressure?

From the Teacher Wraparound Edition ↓

Health eSpotlight VIDEO *Wrap-Up*

Dealing With A Bully Have students reread the Health eSpotlight question at the beginning of the chapter on page 191 and look at their original answer. **Ask Students:** *Now that you have read the chapter* *and watched the video, how would you respond differently if you were being bullied?* Call on volunteers to describe how their responses would change.

Health eSpotlight Video Series

VIDEO *Choices for Healthy Friendships*

Before Viewing the Video

Ask Students: *How would you define friendship?* After students have watched the video, call on a few volunteers to describe how they would have responded if they were in Jordan's position.

VIDEO **BusinessWeek** HEALTH NEWS

BusinessWeek Health News videos provide real-world health content. Students can be directed to **glencoe.com** to watch the video and do the accompanying print activity. The Teacher Wraparound Edition contains additional teaching strategies.

VIDEO **BusinessWeek** HEALTH NEWS

After students have watched the video, *The Slow Burn of Exercising*, lead a class discussion on which elements of fitness might be improved by doing slow motion exercises. Some students may contend that these exercises could improve all five elements, while other students might contend that these exercises would probably not improve cardiorespiratory endurance.

From the Teacher Wraparound Edition ⟵

Visit *Glencoe Health* Online at glencoe.com

Glencoe Health Online provides up-to-date resources and activities that are fully integrated with Glencoe's comprehensive health program.

For Students

Student Center

At glencoe.com click on Online Student Edition to access the entire text of *Glencoe Health*:

- Student Web Activities
- Building Health Skills
- Interactive Study Guides
- Health Inventories
- Health Podcast Activities
- Online Quizzes
- Interactive Health Tutor
- Podcast Audio Chapter Summaries (English/Spanish)
- eFlashcards
- Fitness Zone Activities
- Career Corner

For Teachers

Teacher Center

At glencoe.com click any of the features below to access both student and teacher-specific resources:

- Health eSpotlight Video Series
- Correlations and National and State Standards
- Lesson Plans
- Professional Development Articles
- Conference/Grant Links
- National Organizations
- Teaching Today
- Inclusion Strategies
- Health Podcast Activities
- Fitness Zone Activities
- PuzzleMaker
- Parent Letters (English/Spanish)
- *ExamView Assessment Suite* Instructions
- Scope and Sequence

Fitness Zone Online is a multimedia resource that helps students find ways to be physically active each day.

The Nutrition and Physical Activity Resources include:

- Clipboard Energizer Activities
- Fitness Zone Videos
- Polar Heart Rate Monitor Activities
- Nutrition, Physical Activity, and Injury Prevention Tips
- Links to Nutrition and Physical Activity Resources
- And More!

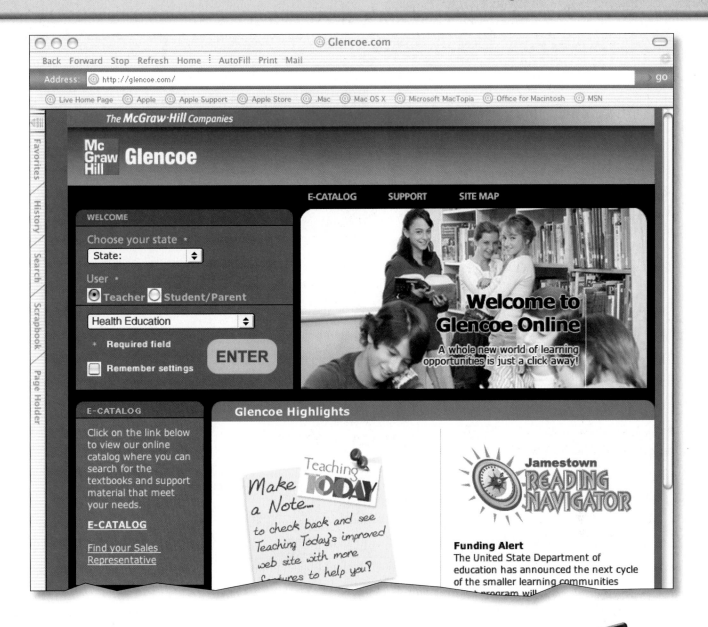

PuzzleMaker Online

Build vocabulary skills with custom-designed puzzles. Create word searches and crossword puzzles using vocabulary words from each lesson. Includes puzzles in English and Spanish.

Study-to-Go

Study-to-Go lets students download free content to their PDA and gain instant mobile access to Online Quizzes and eFlashcards directly from the *Glencoe Health* Web site at glencoe.com. Students can study anytime and anywhere—between classes, during work breaks, or while waiting for the bus.

Education Partners

TIME®

TIME Health features are fun, educational articles developed for high school students by TIME magazine. Each feature is tailored to fit the content of a particular chapter and contains a TIME to Think activity that allows students to apply what they have learned.

TIME HEALTH
SCIENCE & TECHNOLOGY

GETTING BURNED BY A TREND

Effects of too much tanning aren't as far off as you might think—skin cancer is striking more young people.

Kylie-Ayn Kennedy, 16, of Easton, PA, is one of the estimated 2.3 million teens who pop into a tanning parlor at least once a year. She's helping make indoor tanning a $5 billion-a-year business. Many of these teens go only in the spring ... or the prom. More and more, ... seeking year-round "bronzitude," ... ermatologists. And these experts ... y the risks of so much exposure to ...) radiation.

...anning Too Far
... o tanning salons, doctors say, ... uting to a spike in skin-cancer ... ... young. The incidence of mela- ... ... deadly form of skin cancer, has ... .S. since 1975 among women ... ... 2008, about 2,050 women in ... ... re expected to be diagnosed

"Skin cancer used to be something old people got," says Dr. James Spencer, a professor of dermatology at New York City's Mount Sinai School of Medicine. "But now, not a month goes by that I don't see somebody in their 20s. That was unheard of 10 years ago." Doctors worry about the long-term consequences of adolescent tanning. The World Health Organization estimates that up to 60,000 deaths worldwide are caused each year by excessive UV exposure and urges youths under 18 to steer clear of indoor tanning and to always use sunblock or sunscreen if they spend a lot of time outdoors in strong sunlight.

But Kylie-Ayn—and many other teens—shrugs off the downsides. "It may make my skin wrinkle a little bit earlier," she says, "but I'm going to look good while I can." But doctors agree that when it comes to tanning, looking good may come at an extremely high price—your life. ■

TIME to THINK... | About Tanning

Is there a relationship between the depletion of Earth's ozone layer and increased rates of skin cancer? Using the Internet and your library's media center, research any connections that may exist between the two and make a list of what evidence you do—or don't—find.

Physical Benefits

Being active on a regular basis improves your **physical fitness**, *the ability to carry out daily tasks easily and have enough reserve energy to respond to unexpected demands.* Teens should try for at least 60 minutes of physical activity every day. Depending on what kind of activity you do, it can strengthen your muscles and bones, boost your energy level, or improve your posture. You might feel that committing 60 minutes every day to physical activity will be difficult. Try dividing the time into smaller segments to get your 60 minutes throughout the day.

You can achieve specific fitness goals through **exercise**, *purposeful physical activity that is planned, structured, and repetitive, and that improves or maintains physical fitness.* All kinds of physical activity—not just exercise—will improve your health. Being physically active can help you maintain a healthy weight and may reduce your risk of many serious diseases. **Figure 12.1** shows the ways in which physical activity can benefit several different body systems and maintain your overall health.

| Figure 12.1 | The Active Body |

This illustration shows just a few of the ways physical activity makes your body stronger. *Which systems in your body benefit from regular physical activity?*

Cardiovascular System
Regular physical activity strengthens the heart muscle so that it pumps blood more efficiently. It reduces blood pressure and lowers the levels of artery-clogging cholesterol.

Respiratory System
As your activity level increases, your lungs begin to work more efficiently, pulling in larger amounts of air and increasing the amount of oxygen delivered to your body. As a result, you can do many activities more easily — for example, running a greater distance without becoming short of breath.

Musculoskeletal System
Physical activity strengthens muscles and bones, reducing your risk of developing fragile bones as you age. Strengthening your bones and muscles can also improve your balance and coordination.

Lesson 1 Benefits of Physical Activity **319**

ELL Support

Similar Phrases, Different Meanings Write vocabulary terms on the board: *physical activity* and *physical fitness*. Read aloud the definition of each term. Point out that the term *physical activity* is used to describe a type of movement or recreation. By contrast, the term *physical fitness* is used to describe a personal characteristic.

Beginning Use sentences such as "Juan improves his physical fitness by playing soccer." Ask students to repeat the sentence. Use the other term in a sentence, and ask students to repeat.

Intermediate Ask students for sentence examples for each term.

Advanced Have students write a paragraph in which both terms are used.

Business Week HEALTH NEWS | VIDEO

Slow Burn of Exercising
Analyze. Go to glencoe.com and watch the video *The Slow Burn of Exercising*. As a class, discuss slow motion exercises and decide if it is a fitness routine worth trying. Recall what you already know about getting in shape and share your ideas.

CHAPTER 12
LESSON 1

❷ TEACH

AL Active Learning
Physical Activities Have pairs brainstorm a list of every physical activity the two have participated in during the last three days. This list might include everything from playing sports to doing household chores. Have pairs share their lists with the class. Discuss how even common, everyday activities can have benefits for your health. BL

VIDEO Business Week HEALTH NEWS

After students have watched the video, *The Slow Burn of Exercising*, lead a class discussion on which elements of fitness might be improved by doing slow motion exercises. Some students may contend that these exercises could improve all five elements, while other students might contend that these exercises would probably not improve cardiorespiratory endurance.

U Universal Access
Gifted Students There is evidence that regular physical activity benefits another important system of the body, the immune system. Encourage students to investigate this concept using library and online resources. Have students present their findings in a written report, including citations for their sources. AL

Caption Answer
Figure 12.1 Cardiovascular system, respiratory system, and musculoskeletal system

319

Business Week

BusinessWeek is the leading global resource for ground-breaking business news and analysis that offer essential insight into the real world of business. *BusinessWeek* Health News videos provide real-world health content. Students can watch the video at **glencoe.com** and then do the accompanying print activity.

The *Glencoe Health* program meets the National Health Education Standards

The National Health Education Standard 1

Students will comprehend concepts related to health promotion and disease prevention to enhance health.

1.12.1 Predict how healthy behaviors can impact health status.

1.12.2 Describe the interrelationships of emotional, intellectual, physical, and social health.

1.12.3 Analyze how environment and personal health are interrelated.

1.12.4 Analyze how genetics and family history can impact personal health.

1.12.5 Propose ways to reduce or prevent injuries and health problems.

1.12.6 Analyze the relationship between access to health care and health status.

1.12.7 Compare and contrast the benefits of and barriers to practicing a variety of healthy behaviors.

1.12.8 Analyze personal susceptibility to injury, illness, or death if engaging in unhealthy behaviors.

1.12.9 Analyze the potential severity of injury or illness if engaging in unhealthy behaviors.

The National Health Education Standard 2

Students will analyze the influence of family, peers, culture, media, technology, and other factors on health behaviors.

2.12.1 Analyze how family influences the health of individuals.

2.12.2 Analyze how culture supports and challenges health beliefs, practices, and behaviors.

2.12.3 Analyze how peers influence healthy and unhealthy behaviors.

2.12.4 Evaluate how the school and community can impact personal health practice and behaviors.

2.12.5 Evaluate the effect of media on personal and family health.

2.12.6 Evaluate the impact of technology on personal, family, and community health.

2.12.7 Analyze how the perceptions of norms influence healthy and unhealthy behaviors.

2.12.8 Analyze the influence of personal values and beliefs on individual health practices and behaviors.

2.12.9 Analyze how some health risk behaviors can influence the likelihood of engaging in unhealthy behaviors.

2.12.10 Analyze how public health policies and government regulations can influence health promotion and disease prevention.

The National Health Education Standard 3

Students will demonstrate the ability to access valid information and products and services to enhance health.

3.12.1 Evaluate the validity of health information, products, and services.

3.12.2 Utilize resources from home, school, and community that provide valid health information.

3.12.3 Determine the accessibility of products and services that enhance health.

3.12.4 Determine when professional health services may be required.

3.12.5 Access valid and reliable health products and services.

The National Health Education Standard 4

Students will demonstrate the ability to use interpersonal communication skills to enhance health and avoid or reduce health risks.

4.12.1 Utilize skills for communicating effectively with family, peers, and others to enhance health.

4.12.2 Demonstrate refusal, negotiation, and collaboration skills to enhance health and avoid or reduce health risks.

4.12.3 Demonstrate strategies to prevent, manage, or resolve interpersonal conflicts without harming self or others.

4.12.4 Demonstrate how to ask for and offer assistance to enhance the health of self and others.

The National Health Education Standard 5

Students will demonstrate the ability to use decision-making skills to enhance health.

5.12.1 Examine barriers that can hinder healthy decision making.

5.12.2 Determine the value of applying a thoughtful decision-making process in health-related situations.

5.12.3 Justify when individual or collaborative decision making is appropriate.

5.12.4 Generate alternatives to health-related issues or problems.

5.12.5 Predict the potential short- and long-term impact of each alternative on self and others.

5.12.6 Defend the healthy choice when making decisions.

5.12.7 Evaluate the effectiveness of health-related decisions.

The National Health Education Standard 6

Students will demonstrate the ability to use goal-setting skills to enhance health.

6.12.1 Assess personal health practices and overall health status.

6.12.2 Develop a plan to attain a personal health goal that addresses strengths, needs, and risks.

6.12.3 Implement strategies and monitor progress in achieving a personal health goal.

6.12.4 Formulate an effective long-term personal health plan.

The National Health Education Standard 7

Students will demonstrate the ability to practice health-enhancing behaviors and avoid or reduce risks.

7.12.1 Analyze the role of individual responsibility for enhancing health.

7.12.2 Demonstrate a variety of healthy practices and behaviors that will maintain or improve the health of self and others.

7.12.3 Demonstrate a variety of behaviors to avoid or reduce health risks to self and others.

The National Health Education Standard 8

Students will demonstrate the ability to advocate for personal, family, and community health.

8.12.1 Utilize accurate peer and societal norms to formulate a health-enhancing message.

8.12.2 Demonstrate how to influence and support others to make positive health choices.

8.12.3 Work cooperatively as an advocate for improving personal, family, and community health.

8.12.4 Adapt health messages and communication techniques to a specific target audience.

Contents

Table of Contents

v

UNIT 2 Mental and Emotional Health

UNIT 3 Healthy and Safe Relationships

UNIT 4 Nutrition and Physical Activity

UNIT 5 Personal Care and Body Systems

UNIT 6 Growth and Development

UNIT **7** Drugs

UNIT 8 Diseases and Disorders

UNIT 9 Safety and Environmental Health

Health Skills Activity

Real World CONNECTION

TEENS Making a Difference

Hands-On HEALTH

TIME HEALTH

Reading Skills Handbook

▶ Reading: What's in It for You?

What role does reading play in your life? The possibilities are countless. Are you on a sports team? Perhaps you like to read about the latest news and statistics in your sports or find out about new training techniques. Are you looking for a part-time job? You might be looking for advice about résumé writing, interview techniques, or information about a company. Are you enrolled in an English class, an algebra class, or a business class? Then your assignments require a lot of reading.

Improving or Fine-Tuning Your Reading Skills Will:

- ◆ Improve your grades.
- ◆ Allow you to read faster and more efficiently.
- ◆ Improve your study skills.
- ◆ Help you remember more information accurately.
- ◆ Improve your writing.

▶ The Reading Process

Good reading skills build on one another, overlap, and spiral around in much the same way that a winding staircase goes around and around while leading you to a higher place. This handbook is designed to help you find and use the tools you'll need **before, during,** and **after** reading.

Strategies You Can Use

- ◆ Identify, understand, and learn new words.
- ◆ Understand why you read.
- ◆ Take a quick look at the whole text.
- ◆ Try to predict what you are about to read.
- ◆ Take breaks while you read and ask yourself questions about the text.
- ◆ Take notes.
- ◆ Keep thinking about what will come next.
- ◆ Summarize.

▶ Vocabulary Development

Word identification and vocabulary skills are the building blocks of the reading and the writing process. By learning to use a variety of strategies to build your word skills and vocabulary, you will become a stronger reader.

Use Context to Determine Meaning

The best way to expand and extend your vocabulary is to read widely, listen carefully, and participate in a rich variety of discussions. When reading on your own, though, you can often figure out the meanings of new words by looking at their **context,** the other words and sentences that surround them.

Tips for Using Context

Look for clues like these:

◆ A synonym or an explanation of the unknown word in the sentence:
Elise's shop specialized in millinery, or hats for women.

◆ A reference to what the word is or is not like:
An archaeologist, like a historian, deals with the past.

◆ A general topic associated with the word:
The cooking teacher discussed the best way to braise meat.

◆ A description or action associated with the word:
He used the shovel to dig up the garden.

Predict a Possible Meaning

Another way to determine the meaning of a word is to take the word apart. If you understand the meaning of the **base,** or **root,** part of a word, and also know the meanings of key syllables added either to the beginning or end of the base word, you can usually figure out what the word means.

Word Origins Since Latin, Greek, and Anglo-Saxon roots are the basis for much of our English vocabulary, having some background in languages can be a useful vocabulary tool. For example, *astronomy* comes from the Greek root *astro,* which means "relating to the stars." *Stellar* also has a meaning referring to stars, but its origin is Latin. Knowing root words in other languages can help you determine meanings, derivations, and spellings in English.

Prefixes and Suffixes A prefix is a word part that can be added to the beginning of a word. For example, the prefix *semi* means "half" or "partial," so *semicircle* means "half a circle." A suffix is a word part that can be added to the end of a word. Adding a suffix often changes a word from one part of speech to another.

Using Dictionaries A dictionary provides the meaning or meanings of a word. Look at the sample dictionary entry on the next page to see what other information it provides.

Thesauruses and Specialized Reference Books A thesaurus provides synonyms and often antonyms. It is a useful tool to expand your vocabulary. Remember to check the exact definition of the listed words in a dictionary before you use a thesaurus. Specialized dictionaries such as *Barron's Dictionary of Business Terms* or *Black's Law Dictionary* list terms and expressions that are not commonly included in a general dictionary. You can also use online dictionaries.

Glossaries Many textbooks and technical works contain condensed dictionaries that provide an alphabetical listing of words used in the text and their specific definitions.

Dictionary Entry

Forms of
the word

Part of
speech

Numbered
definitions

Example
of use

Usage label

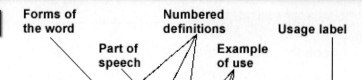

help (help) **helped** or *(archaic)* **holp**, **helped** or *(archaic)* **hol-pen**, **help-ing**. *v.t.* **1.** to provide with support, as in the performance of a task; be of service to: *He helped his brother paint the room.* ▲ also used elliptically with a preposition or adverb: *He helped the old woman up the stairs.* **2.** to enable (someone or something) to accomplish a goal or achieve a desired effect: *The coach's advice helped the team to win.* **3.** to provide with sustenance or relief, as in time of need or distress; succor: *The Red Cross helped the flood victims.* **4.** to promote or contribute to; further. *The medication helped his recovery.* **5.** to be useful or profitable to; be of advantage to: *It might help you if you read the book.* **6.** to improve or remedy: *Nothing really helped his sinus condition.* **7.** to prevent; stop: *I can't help his rudeness.* **8.** to refrain from; avoid: *I couldn't help smiling when I heard the story.* **9.** to wait on or serve (often with to): *The clerk helped us. The hostess helped him to the dessert.* **10.** **cannot help but.** *Informal* cannot but. **11. so help me (God).** oath of affirmation. **12. to help oneself to.** to take or appropriate: *The thief helped himself to all the jewels.*—*v.i.* to provide support, as in the performance of a task; be of service. —*n.* **1.** act of providing support, service, or sustenance. **2.** source of support, service, or sustenance. **3.** person or group of persons hired to work for another or others. **4.** means of improving, remedying, or preventing. [Old English *helpan* to aid, succor, benefit.] **Syn.** *v.t.* **1. Help, aid, assist** mean to support in a useful way. Help is the most common word and means to give support in response to a known or expressed need or for a definite purpose: *Everyone helped to make the school fair a success.* **Aid** means to give relief in times of distress or difficulty: *It is the duty of rich nations to aid the poor.* **Assist** means to serve another person in the performance of his task in a secondary capacity: *The secetary assists the officer by taking care of his corresponding.*

Idioms

Origin
(etymology)

Synonyms

Recognize Word Meanings Across Subjects Have you learned a new word in one class and then noticed it in your reading for other subjects? The word might not mean exactly the same thing in each class, but you can use the meaning you already know to help you understand what it means in another subject area. For example:

Math Each digit represents a different place **value**.

Health Your **values** can guide you in making healthful decisions.

Economics The **value** of a product is measured in its cost.

▶ Understanding What You Read

Reading comprehension means understanding—deriving meaning from—what you have read. Using a variety of strategies can help you improve your comprehension and make reading more interesting and more fun.

Read for a Reason

To get the greatest benefit from your reading, **establish a purpose for reading.** In school, you have many reasons for reading, such as

- to learn and understand new information.
- to find specific information.
- to review before a test.
- to complete an assignment.
- to prepare (research) before you write.

As your reading skills improve, you will notice that you apply different strategies to fit the different purposes for reading. For example, if you are reading for entertainment, you might read quickly, but if you read to gather information or follow directions, you might read more slowly, take notes, construct a graphic organizer, or reread sections of text.

Draw on Personal Background

Drawing on personal background may also be called activating prior knowledge. Before you start reading a text, ask yourself questions like these:

- What have I heard or read about this topic?
- Do I have any personal experience relating to this topic?

Using a K-W-L Chart A K-W-L chart is a good device for organizing information you gather before, during, and after reading. In the first column, list what you already **know,** then list what you **want** to know in the middle column. Use the third column when you review and assess what you **learned.** You can also add more columns to record places where you found information and places where you can look for more information.

K (What I already know)	W (What I want to know)	L (What I have learned)

Adjust Your Reading Speed Your reading speed is a key factor in how well you understand what you are reading. You will need to adjust your speed depending on your reading purpose.

Scanning means running your eyes quickly over the material to look for words or phrases. Scan when you need a specific piece of information.

Skimming means reading a passage quickly to find its main idea or to get an overview. Skim a text when you preview to determine what the material is about.

Reading for detail involves careful reading while paying attention to text structure and monitoring your understanding. Read for detail when you are learning concepts, following complicated directions, or preparing to analyze a text.

▶ Techniques to Understand and Remember What You Read

Preview

Before beginning a selection, it is helpful to **preview** what you are about to read.

> ### Previewing Strategies
>
> ◆ Read the title, headings, and subheadings of the selection.
> ◆ Look at the illustrations and notice how the text is organized.
> ◆ Skim the selection: Take a glance at the whole thing.
> ◆ Decide what the main idea might be.
> ◆ Predict what a selection will be about.

Predict

Have you ever read a mystery, decided who committed the crime, and then changed your mind as more clues were revealed? You were adjusting your predictions. Did you smile when you found out you guessed the murderer? You were verifying your predictions.

As you read, take educated guesses about story events and outcomes; that is, **make predictions** before and during reading. This will help you focus your attention on the text and it will improve your understanding.

Determine the Main Idea

When you look for the **main idea**, you are looking for the most important statement in a text. Depending on what kind of text you are reading, the main idea can be located at the very beginning (news stories in newspaper or a magazine) or at the end (scientific research document). Ask yourself the following questions:

• What is each sentence about?
• Is there one sentence that is more important than all the others?
• What idea do details support or point out?

Taking Notes

Cornell Note-Taking System: There are many methods for note taking. The **Cornell Note-Taking System** is a well-known method that can help you organize what you read. To the right is a note-taking activity based on the Cornell Note-Taking System.

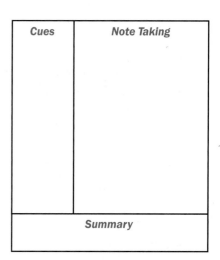

Graphic organizers: Using a graphic organizer to retell content in a visual representation will help you remember and retain content. You might make a **chart** or **diagram,** organizing what you have read. Here are some examples of graphic organizers:

Venn diagrams When mapping out a compare-and-contrast text structure, you can use a Venn diagram. The outer portions of the circles will show how two characters, ideas, or items contrast, or are different, and the overlapping part will compare two things, or show how they are similar.

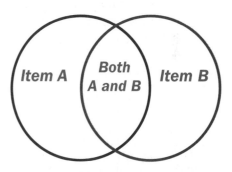

Flow charts To help you track the sequence of events, or cause and effect, use a flow chart. Arrange ideas or events in their logical, sequential order. Then draw arrows between your ideas to indicate how one idea or event flows into another.

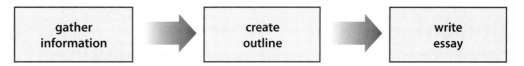

Visualize

Try to form a mental picture of scenes, characters, and events as you read. Use the details and descriptions the author gives you. If you can **visualize** what you read, it will be more interesting and you will remember it better.

Question

Ask yourself questions about the text while you read. Ask yourself about the importance of the sentences, how they relate to one another, if you understand what you just read, and what you think is going to come next.

Clarify

If you feel you do not understand meaning (through questioning), try these techniques:

> **What to Do When You Do Not Understand**
>
> ◆ Reread confusing parts of the text.
> ◆ Diagram (chart) relationships between chunks of text, ideas, and sentences.
> ◆ Look up unfamiliar words.
> ◆ Talk out the text to yourself.
> ◆ Read the passage once more.

Review

Take time to stop and review what you have read. Use your note-taking tools (graphic organizers or Cornell notes charts). Also, review and consider your K-W-L chart.

Monitor Your Comprehension

Continue to check your understanding by using the following two strategies:

Summarize Pause and tell yourself the main ideas of the text and the key supporting details. Try to answer the following questions: Who? What? When? Where? Why? How?

Paraphrase Pause, close the book, and try to retell what you have just read in your own words. It might help to pretend you are explaining the text to someone who has not read it and does not know the material.

▶ Understanding Text Structure

Good writers do not just put together sentences and paragraphs, they organize their writing with a specific purpose in mind. That organization is called text structure. When you understand and follow the structure of a text, it is easier to remember the information you are reading. There are many ways text may be structured. Watch for **signal words**. They will help you follow the text's organization (also, remember to use these techniques when you write).

Compare and Contrast

This structure shows similarities and differences between people, things, and ideas. This is often used to demonstrate that things that seem alike are really different, or vice versa.

Signal words: similarly, more, less, on the one hand / on the other hand, in contrast, but, however

Cause and Effect

Writers use the cause-and-effect structure to explore the reasons for something happening and to examine the results or consequences of events.

Signal words: so, because, as a result, therefore, for the following reasons

Problem and Solution

When they organize text around the question "how?" writers state a problem and suggest solutions.

Signal words: how, help, problem, obstruction, overcome, difficulty, need, attempt, have to, must

Sequence

Sequencing tells you in which order to consider thoughts or facts. Examples of sequencing are:

Chronological order refers to the order in which events take place.

Signal words: first, next, then, finally

Spatial order describes the organization of things in space (to describe a room, for example).

Signal words: above, below, behind, next to

Order of importance lists things or thoughts from the most important to the least important (or the other way around).

Signal words: principal, central, main, important, fundamental

▶ Reading for Meaning

It is important to think about what you are reading to get the most infor–mation out of a text, to understand the consequences of what the text says, to remember the content, and to form your own opinion about what the content means.

Interpret

Interpreting is asking yourself, "What is the writer really saying?" and then using what you already know to answer that question.

Infer

Writers do not always state exactly everything they want you to understand. By providing clues and details, they sometimes imply certain information. An **inference** involves using your reason and experience to develop the idea on your own, based on what an author implies or suggests. What is most important when drawing inferences is to be sure that you have accurately based your guesses on supporting details from the text. If you cannot point to a place in the selection to help back up your inference, you may need to rethink your guess.

Draw Conclusions

A conclusion is a general statement you can make and explain with reasoning, or with supporting details from a text. If you read a story describing a sport where five players bounce a ball and throw it through a high hoop, you may conclude that the sport is basketball.

Analyze

To understand persuasive nonfiction (a text that discusses facts and opinions to arrive at a conclusion), you need to analyze statements and examples to see if they support the main idea. To understand an informational text (a text, such as a textbook, that gives you information, not opinions), you need to keep track of how the ideas are organized to find the main points.

Hint: Use your graphic organizers and notes charts.

Distinguish Facts and Opinions

This is one of the most important reading skills you can learn. A fact is a statement that can be proven. An opinion is what the writer believes. A writer may support opinions with facts, but an opinion cannot be proven. For example:

Fact: California produces fruit and other agricultural products.

Opinion: California produces the best fruit and other agricultural products.

Evaluate

Would you take seriously an article on nuclear fission if you knew it was written by a comedic actor? If you need to rely on accurate information, you need to find out who wrote what you are reading and why. Where did the writer get information? Is the information one-sided? Can you verify the information?

▶ Reading for Research

You will need to **read actively** in order to research a topic. You might also need to generate an interesting, relevant, and researchable **question** on your own and locate appropriate print and nonprint information from a wide variety of sources. Then you will need to **categorize** that information, evaluate it, and **organize** it in a new way in order to produce a research project for a specific audience. Finally, **draw conclusions** about your original research question. These conclusions may lead you to other areas for further inquiry.

Locate Appropriate Print and Nonprint Information

In your research, try to use a variety of sources. Because different sources present information in different ways, your research project will be more interesting and balanced when you read a variety of sources.

Literature and Textbooks These texts include any book used as a basis for instruction or a source of information.

Book Indices A book index, or a bibliography, is an alphabetical listing of books. Some book indices list books on specific subjects; others are more general. Other indices list a variety of topics or resources.

Periodicals Magazines and journals are issued at regular intervals, such as weekly or monthly. One way to locate information in magazines is to use the *Readers' Guide to Periodical Literature.* This guide is available in print form in most libraries.

Technical Manuals A manual is a guide or handbook intended to give instruction on how to perform a task or operate something. A vehicle owner's manual might give information on how to operate and service a car.

Reference Books Reference books include encyclopedias and almanacs, and are used to locate specific pieces of information.

Electronic Encyclopedias, Databases, and the Internet There are many ways to locate extensive information using your computer. Infotrac, for instance, acts as an online readers guide. CD encyclopedias can provide easy access to all subjects.

Organize and Convert Information

As you gather information from different sources, taking careful notes, you will need to think about how to **synthesize** the information, that is, convert it into a unified whole, as well as how to change it into a form your audience will easily understand and that will meet your assignment guidelines.

1. First, ask yourself what you want your audience to know.
2. Then, think about a pattern of organization, a structure that will best show your main ideas. You might ask yourself the following questions:
   - When comparing items or ideas, what graphic aids can I use?
   - When showing the reasons something happened and the effects of certain actions, what text structure would be best?
   - How can I briefly and clearly show important information to my audience?
   - Would an illustration or even a cartoon help to make a certain point?

Flexible Technology Solutions

Focus

Health eSpotlight *Video Series*

By Chapter

Chapter 1 Understanding Health and Wellness
Video 1: Taking Care of You

Chapter 2 Taking Charge of Your Health
Video 2: Making Decisions About Your Personal Health

By Lesson

By Skill

Analyzing Influences.......................... Videos **1** 12
Accessing Information .... Videos **2** 10 14 25

■ Indicates videos featured in the unit that teach the corresponding skill. Other videos listed can also be used to teach that skill.

Teach

Direct lesson plans beyond the classroom with multi-media fitness activities that students can do online, in class, or as a group.

PowerPoint® Presentation

- *Health* eSpotlight videos
- Audio and image bank

FITNESS ZONE
Online

Fitness Zone Online is a multimedia resource that helps students find ways to be physically active each day.

- Clipboard Energizer Activities
- Fitness Zone Videos
- Polar Heart Rate Monitor Activities
- Nutrition, Physical Activity, and Injury Prevention Tips
- Links to Nutrition and Physical Activity Resources

Go Online

Online Learning Center

- Student Web Activities
- PuzzleMaker
- Interactive Health Tutor

Podcast Audio Chapter Summaries

Use the audio Podcast Audio Chapter Summaries to teach and review key concepts, and engage students with health content that they can download to a computer or portable MP3 player.

Assess/Close

Help students master chapter and lesson concepts with an integrated technology solution for assessment and performance evaluation.

Go Online

Online Learning Center

- Interactive Study Guides
- Online Quizzes

ExamView® Assessment Suite CD-ROM

Create and customize tests in minutes with this convenient digital platform.

- Create differentiated tests quickly and easily.
- All questions correlated to National/State Standards.
- Enhance tests with Document Based Questions (DBQ) and add your own photos and graphics.
- Build tests in both English and Spanish.
- Generate progress reports.

Enrich

Use these additional digital and online media resources to promote hands-on exploration of health topics covered in the lesson.

Business Week Health Video Series

- *Battling the Bulge*

Study-to-Go

Download a portable version of eFlashcards and Self-Check Quizzes onto your Palm or Pocket PC.

Health Podcasts Activities

Glencoe's "It's Your Health" Podcast Activities provide students with a unique listening and learning experience that takes health education beyond the classroom. Download the audio files and print activities covering a range of current health topics that matter most to teens!

A Healthy Foundation

This unit identifies the relationship between health and wellness and describes strategies that teens can use to take charge of their health.

Health eSpotlight Video Series

At the beginning of each chapter, visit **glencoe.com** and have students watch the video and do the accompanying print activity.

 Chapter 1
Taking Care of You

Activities such as spending time with friends and family, playing sports, and enjoying a nutritious meal can help teens achieve a balanced life.

 Chapter 2
Making Decisions About Your Personal Health

The media can portray activities that promote an unhealthy lifestyle. It is possible to set and achieve health goals in spite of unhealthful messages.

Unit 1 Resources

- Career Corner
- 📁 **FAST FILE RESOURCES**
- Health Career Research Activity
- Family Involvement Activity
- Community Involvement Activity
- Unit Test

Chapter 1
Understanding Health and Wellness

 Taking Care of You

Chapter 2
Taking Charge of Your Health

 Making Decisions About Your Personal Health

UNIT PROJECT

Building Healthy Communities

Using Visuals America on the Move Foundation is a national nonprofit organization dedicated to promoting healthful eating and active living among individuals, families, and communities. Every year during the month of September, America on the Move sponsors *Step*tember, a campaign promoting physical activity and good nutrition.

 To learn more about America on the Move, go to the Unit Web Project at glencoe.com.

Get Involved. Conduct research to identify nonprofit organizations that work to promote healthy living in your community. Contact one organization and find out how teens can volunteer to help.

2

UNIT PROJECT

Building Healthy Communities America on the Move Foundation provides information about healthful eating and physical activity to individuals, groups, and health care providers. The organization's Web site includes a personalized home page feature that guides individuals through the process of setting and achieving personal health goals related to fitness and healthful eating. Information for teachers and school groups is also available.

Get Involved Direct students to work in small groups to indentify voluntary health organizations that promote healthy living in your community. Students may need to use phone directories, the Internet, or talk to the school nurse to identify these organizations. Remind students to obtain contact information for the organization they have identified.

"Health is a state of complete physical, mental and social well-being, and not merely the absence of disease or infirmity."
— from the constitution of the World Health Organization

Activate Prior Knowledge

Ask students these questions before they read the chapter to build on what they already know.

Chapter 1
What are some aspects of your life that are impacted by your overall health?

(Sample answers: Ability to do well in school, activities with friends, relationships with others)

Chapter 2
What are some actions individuals can take that have a positive effect on health?

(Sample answers: Healthful eating, getting enough physical activity, getting plenty of rest)

TeacherWorks Plus provides:

- interactive Teacher Wrap-around edition
- click, drag, and drop to plan lessons
- instant access to many print program resources

Unit 1   A Healthy Foundation   **3**

How to Get Involved Provide students with these step-by-step instructions on how they can assemble information about volunteer opportunities.

1. Each group should contact the organization it has identified to find out more about volunteer opportunities.
2. Remind students to inquire about any requirements for volunteering for the

organization, such as a minimum age.

3. Have students ask about one-time events, such as fund-raisers or health fairs, as well as ongoing volunteer opportunities.
4. Have each group of students share the information it has learned with the remainder of the class in a short oral report.

3

Understanding Health and Wellness

Chapter 1 pages 4–31	Standards		Features
	National	**State/Local**	
	1.12.1–1.12.3, 1.12.7, 2.12.2– 2.12.6, 2.12.9, 2.12.10, 3.12.2, 3.12.5, 5.12.1, 7.12.2–7.12.3		**TIME** HEALTH • The Cutting Edge, page 26
30 Min **Lesson 1** **Your Total Health** pages 6–10 **BIG Idea** *Being in the best of health throughout your life means making healthy choices and practicing healthful behaviors.*	1.12.1, 1.12.2, 5.12.6, 6.12.1, 6.12.4, 7.12.1, 7.12.3, 8.12.1, 8.12.2, 8.12.3		
30 Min **Lesson 2** **What Affects Your Health?** pages 11–15 **BIG Idea** *Understanding how heredity, environment, and other factors affect your health can help you make healthy decisions.*	1.12.3, 1.12.4, 1.12.7, 2.12.1, 2.12.2, 2.12.3, 2.12.4, 2.12.5, 2.12.6, 2.12.8, 5.12.1, 6.12.1, 6.12.3, 6.12.4, 7.12.1, 7.12.2, 7.12.3		
30 Min **Lesson 3** **Health Risks and Your Behavior** pages 16–20 **BIG Idea** *Risk behaviors can harm your health, but there are steps you can take to avoid or reduce these risks.*	1.12.1, 1.12.5, 1.12.8, 1.12.9, 2.12.7, 2.12.8, 2.12.9, 6.12.1, 7.12.2, 7.12.3		**Real World CONNECTION** • Teen Risk Taking, page 17 • Out of Time
30 Min **Lesson 4** **Promoting Health and Wellness** pages 21–25 **BIG Idea** *Staying healthy takes knowledge, a plan, and practicing healthful behaviors.*	1.12.6, 1.12.7, 2.12.4, 2.12.7, 2.12.10, 3.12.1, 3.12.2, 3.12.5, 5.12.1, 5.12.2, 5.12.4, 6.12.3, 6.12.4, 7.12.1		**VIDEO BusinessWeek HEALTH NEWS** • Battling the Bulge, page 22 **TEENS Making a Difference** • Mentoring Others, page 23

Key to Ability Levels

Teaching Strategies and activities have been coded for ability level and appropriateness.

AL Activities for students working above grade level

OL Activities for students working on grade level

BL Activities for students working below grade level

EL Activities for English Learners

Chapter 1 Planning Guide

Glencoe Exclusive!
TeacherWorks *Plus*™
All-In-One Planner and Resource Center

Resources	Lesson Assessment	Technology
Student Activity Workbook **TEACH** *FAST FILE* **RESOURCES** Vocabulary Practice **TEACH** Health Labs **EXTEND**	Chapter 1 Review Chapter 1 Assessment Standardized Test Practice ⊙ *ExamView® Assessment Suite* CD-ROM	**Teaching Tools:** ⊙ *TeacherWorks*™ Plus DVD ⊙ *StudentWorks*™ Plus DVD ⊙ *ExamView® Assessment Suite* CD-ROM 🕹 Transparencies ⊙ Fitness DVD ⊙ PowerPoint® DVD ⊙ Health eSpotlight Video Series DVD
FAST FILE **RESOURCES** Reading Strategy Activity **TEACH** Reteaching Activity **REVIEW** Enrichment Activity **EXTEND** Health Skills Practice **TEACH**	Lesson 1 Assessment, page 10 📁 Lesson 1 Quiz *Fast File* ⊙ *ExamView® Assessment Suite* CD-ROM	**Web-Based Resources:** **Go Online** glencoe.com • Health Podcast Activities • Audio Chapter Summaries (English/Spanish) • Interactive Health Tutor • Health Skills Activities • Vocabulary PuzzleMaker • Parent Letters (English/Spanish) • Lesson Plans • Health Inventories • Online Quizzes • Study-to-Go • Unit Web Projects • Student Web Activities • Fitness Zone Activities
FAST FILE **RESOURCES** Reading Strategy Activity **TEACH** Reteaching Activity **REVIEW** Enrichment Activity **EXTEND** Health Skills Practice **TEACH**	Lesson 2 Assessment, page 15 📁 Lesson 2 Quiz *Fast File* ⊙ *ExamView® Assessment Suite* CD-ROM	
FAST FILE **RESOURCES** Reading Strategy Activity **TEACH** Reteaching Activity **REVIEW** Enrichment Activity **EXTEND** Health Skills Practice **TEACH**	Lesson 3 Assessment, page 20 📁 Lesson 3 Quiz *Fast File* ⊙ *ExamView® Assessment Suite* CD-ROM	
FAST FILE **RESOURCES** Reading Strategy Activity **TEACH** Reteaching Activity **REVIEW** Enrichment Activity **EXTEND** Health Skills Practice **TEACH**	Lesson 4 Assessment, page 25 📁 Lesson 4 Quiz *Fast File* ⊙ *ExamView® Assessment Suite* CD-ROM	

StudentWorks *Plus*

This is the student's backpack solution.

Includes:
• complete Interactive Student Edition
• full audio of English text and Spanish chapter summaries
• allows students to record assignments and track grades.
• links to online activities and additional student resources
• access to all student worksheets and workbooks

FOLDABLES® Study Organizer

Dinah Zike Foldables®
Chapter Activity
Refer to the *Dinah Zike Reading and Study Skills for Glencoe Health.* Have students complete the two-tab book Foldable to organize their notes on the chapter content. Students should record their current position on the continuum and record their health habits, decisions, and other influences under the tabs.

Key to Symbols		
🕹 Transparencies	**REVIEW**	activities to review or reinforce content
⊙ CD-ROM	**TEACH**	activities to teach basic concepts
🖱 glencoe.com	**EXTEND**	activities to extend or enrich lesson content
📁 Print Resources		

Understanding Health and Wellness

Chapter Overview

Chapter 1 focuses on factors that influence health and ways that healthful behaviors and decisions can promote wellness.

Lesson 1

Individuals can take charge of their physical, mental/emotional, and social health by making healthy choices and practicing healthful behaviors.

Lesson 2

Understanding the factors that impact health can lead to healthful decision making.

Lesson 3

The ability to identify risk behaviors and their consequences can help teens reduce or avoid these risks.

Lesson 4

Health education is the key to improving health literacy, reducing heath disparities, and promoting health to individuals and the nation as a whole.

▶ **Activating Prior Knowledge**

Have students complete their sentences. **Ask Students:** *What are some characteristics of healthy people? Do you know people who you consider healthy? Why?*

CHAPTER 1

Understanding Health and Wellness

Lesson 1
Your Total Health

BIG Idea *Being in the best of health throughout your life means making healthy choices and practicing healthful behaviors.*

Lesson 2
What Affects Your Health?

BIG Idea *Understanding how heredity, environment, and other factors affect your health can help you make healthy decisions.*

Lesson 3
Health Risks and Your Behavior

BIG Idea *Risk behaviors can harm your health, but there are steps you can take to avoid or reduce these risks.*

Lesson 4
Promoting Health and Wellness

BIG Idea *Staying healthy takes knowledge, a plan, and practicing healthful behaviors.*

Activating Prior Knowledge

Using Visuals Look at the picture on this page. Write three sentences beginning with the words *These people appear healthy because . . .* Discuss your ideas about what makes someone healthy.

4

Universal Access

Differentiated Learning Glencoe provides teacher support and student materials for all learners in the health classroom.

- Chapter Summaries in English and Spanish are available online at **glencoe.com**.

- *Fast Files* and related worksheets support reluctant readers.

- Universal Access strategies throughout the Teacher Wraparound Edition and *Fast Files* help you present materials for gifted students, at-risk students, physically impaired students, and those with behavior disorders or learning disabilities.

Health in Action

Discuss the **BIG** Ideas

Before beginning this chapter, think about how you would answer these questions:
- ▶ What is *health*?
- ▶ Why would you want to be healthy?
- ▶ Who is most responsible for your health?

Watch the *Health* eSpotlight Video Series

Taking Care of You

What do you consider "healthy" activities? How could you promote healthy living in your school or community?

Assess Your Health

Go Online

Visit **glencoe.com** and complete the Health Inventory for Chapter 1.

Chapter 1   Understanding Health and Wellness   **5**

Chapter Launchers

Health in Action

Discuss the **BIG** Ideas

Assign this activity before students read the chapter. Explain that the purpose of the questions is to help students assess their current knowledge of health.

Health eSpotlight
Video Series

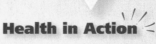

Taking Care of You

Before Viewing the Video

Ask Students: *What kinds of healthful activities do you do to take care of yourself?* These activities might include physical fitness or something as simple as brushing your teeth twice a day. After students have watched the video, ask whether they might incorporate some of the same healthful behaviors they saw in the video.

Go Online

Have students go to **glencoe.com** and take the Health Inventory for Chapter 1.

Chapter Skills

Reading Skills
- Reviewing Facts and Vocabulary, pp. 10, 15, 20, 25
- Reading/Writing Practice, p. 31

Vocabulary
- New Vocabulary, pp. 6, 11, 16, 21
- Reviewing Facts and Vocabulary, pp. 10, 15, 20, 25

BIG Idea

Personal choices and behaviors can affect health throughout an individual's life.

Health Skills
- Applying Health Skills, pp. 10, 15, 20, 25

Writing Skills
- Real World Connection, p. 17
- Writing Critically, pp. 10, 15, 20, 25
- Reading/Writing Practice, p. 31

LESSON 1

Your Total Health

1 FOCUS

 GUIDE TO READING

BIG Idea Being in good health means making healthy choices and practicing healthful behaviors. **Ask Students:** *What are some everyday decisions teens face that can affect their health?* (Sample answers: Deciding whether or not to use tobacco products, drugs, or alcohol; deciding what foods to eat)

Before You Read

Cluster Chart Students' cluster charts will vary, but should include social, physical, mental/emotional, and spiritual.

Main Idea

Take Charge of Your Health
Students will learn that they are responsible for their own health. **Ask Students:** *What are some ways that people can take charge of their health?* (Sample answers: Getting regular check-ups, eating nutritious foods, getting regular physical activity)

Real Life Issues . . . .

Before students write Keisha's journal entry, have them work in small groups to discuss the role of good health in achieving goals. **Ask Students:** *How do the health-related choices you make today impact your future?*

6

 # LESSON 1

 **GUIDE TO READING**

BIG Idea *Being in the best of health throughout your life means making healthy choices and practicing healthful behaviors.*

Before You Read

Create a Cluster Chart. Draw a circle and label it "Health." Use surrounding circles to define and describe this term. As you read, continue filling in the chart with more details.

(Health)

New Vocabulary

▸ health (p. 6)
▸ spiritual health (p. 8)
▸ wellness (p. 9)
▸ chronic disease (p. 10)

Your Total Health

Real Life Issues . . . .

Being Healthy. On the first day of spring semester, Keisha comes home thinking about the challenge her health teacher had presented during class: What does *health* mean to you and your future? Keisha opens her journal and pauses. There are so many things to write about. She starts thinking about what she wants to accomplish in life, and the role that good health will play in helping her achieve her goals.

Writing *Write Keisha's journal entry for this day.*

Take Charge of Your Health

Main Idea You are responsible for your own health.

You probably have several ideas about what makes somebody healthy. Do you picture a healthy person as someone who is physically active and involved in sports? Do you think that a healthy individual gets along well with others and generally feels good about himself or herself? These images are all part of the "big picture" of **health,** *the combination of physical, mental/emotional, and social well-being.* Every day, you make decisions that shape your health. That's what this book is all about: giving you the knowledge and skills you need to take charge of your health for a lifetime.

Your Health Triangle

Main Idea It's important to balance your physical, mental/emotional, and social health.

When you are in good health, you have the energy to enjoy life and pursue your dreams. So, what can you do to stay healthy? Start by understanding the three areas of health.

6 **Chapter 1** Understanding Health and Wellness

◆ Promoting School Wellness

The Health Triangle A coordinated school health program provides services that enhance all three sides of the health triangle. For example, physical education classes, health classes, and nutrition services enhance students' physical health. Counseling, psy-

chological services, and family and community involvement programs enhance students' mental/emotional and social health. These services allow students to improve their total health in the short term and to develop skills that enhance health throughout their lives.

These include your physical health, mental/emotional health, and social health. It's important to pay attention to all three areas of your health triangle. If you concentrate too much or too little on one area, the triangle can become unbalanced.

Physical Health

Physical health is all about how well your body functions. Having a high level of physical health means having enough energy to perform your daily activities, deal with everyday stresses, and avoid injury.

What does it take to get and keep a healthy body? Here are five important actions you can take:

- Get eight to ten hours of sleep each night.
- Eat nutritious meals and drink eight cups of water each day.
- Engage in 30 to 60 minutes of physical activity every day.
- Avoid the use of tobacco, alcohol, and other drugs.
- Bathe daily, and floss and brush your teeth every day.

Mental/Emotional Health

Mental/emotional health is about your feelings and thoughts. It's a reflection of how you feel about yourself, how you meet the demands of your daily life, and how you cope with the problems that occur in your life.

FITNESS ZONE

I keep hearing that we should try to walk 10,000 steps every day. So my best friend and I wear pedometers and walk as much as possible. Instead of taking a bus, we walk. We also use the stairs rather than an escalator or elevator. We've been doing this for three months now, and we feel great! For more physical activity ideas, visit the Online Fitness Zone at **glencoe.com**.

■ **Figure 1.1** Your health triangle is made up of three equally important areas. *What do you do to stay in good health?*

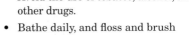

Lesson 1 Your Total Health **7**

② TEACH

R Reading Strategy

Analyzing a Graphic Have students examine **Figure 1.1**, which shows the three sides of health. Have students name other activities that could improve one or more of the three sides of health. **OL**

Caption Answer

Figure 1.1 Sample answer: I ride my bike with friends and play basketball at the park.

U Universal Access

English Language Learners Ask English language learners to review the terms *physical health*, *mental/emotional health*, and *social health* with students who are fluent in English. Have students work in pairs to practice using each of the terms in spoken sentences. Ask volunteers to share their sentences with the class. **EL**

Writing Strategy

Health Journal Explain to students that a journal is an effective way to monitor their health-related actions, behaviors, and decisions. Ask students to review the bulleted lists of behaviors and actions that enhance each side of the health triangle. Tell students that for the next two weeks, they should write a daily journal entry in which they evaluate how their daily decisions and actions impact their total health. Remind students that they can keep their journal entries confidential.

■ **Figure 1.2** Each person strives to keep his or her health triangle in balance throughout life. *How might the health triangles of these two individuals be alike or different?*

U **Universal Access**

Demonstration Use a balance with a pan or platform on either side to help students visualize and understand the concept of balance as it applies to total health. Place several pennies or paperclips in one pan of the balance to represent a person who works to achieve physical health but does not work on mental/emotional or social health. Add items until balance is achieved. Tell students that this is similar to a person who works to improve all areas of health. BL EL OL

Academic Vocabulary

Appropriate Write the term *appropriate* on the board. Have a volunteer define the term aloud for the class. Ask students to identify appropriate ways to express emotions. Then ask a volunteer to explain why appropriate expression of emotions is a sign of good mental and emotional health.

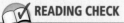 **READING CHECK**

Answer Physical, mental/emotional, and social health

Academic Vocabulary

appropriate *(adjective):* proper or fitting

People who are mentally and emotionally healthy

- enjoy challenges that help them grow.
- accept responsibility for their actions.
- have a sense of control over their lives.
- can express their emotions in **appropriate** ways.
- usually can deal with life's stresses and frustrations.
- generally have a positive outlook.
- make thoughtful and responsible decisions.

Spiritual Health Mental/emotional health also includes **spiritual health**, *a deep-seated sense of meaning and purpose in life*. Being spiritually healthy does not necessarily mean that you belong to a religious group, although it could include being a member of a spiritual community. Spiritual health involves having a feeling of purpose and a sense of values.

Social Health

Getting along with others, also known as *social health*, is as important to your overall health and wellness as having a fit body and mind. Your social network includes your family, friends, teachers, and other members of your community. You don't need to have lots of friends to have good social health. Sometimes just having a few special people with whom you can share your thoughts and feelings is enough. Maintaining healthy relationships is one way of caring for your social health. This involves

- seeking and lending support when needed.
- communicating clearly and listening to others.
- showing respect and care for yourself and others.

 READING CHECK

Identify List the three components of health.

Home and Community

Community Resources Have students work in small groups to identify and research community facilities and programs that enhance one or more sides of the health triangle. For example, a group of students might learn more about an exercise program offered at the community center or a card club at the local senior citizens' center. Have each group share its information with the rest of the class, clearly explaining which side or sides of the health triangle are promoted by the facility or program they researched.

Keeping a Balance

When your health triangle is balanced, you have a high degree of **wellness**, *an overall state of well-being or total health*. Wellness comes from making decisions and practicing behaviors that are based on sound health knowledge and healthful attitudes. Maintaining wellness means keeping a balance among the three components of health.

Think about someone whose friends are the most important part of her life. She enjoys spending a lot of time with them, but she doesn't always get the rest she needs. Her social health is fine, but her physical and mental/emotional health are suffering.

What about a teen who spends all his time working out? He may be physically fit, but he doesn't have many friends, so he sometimes feels lonely and depressed. This teen pays too much attention to his physical health at the expense of his mental/emotional and social health.

Ignoring any area of your health triangle affects your total health. To keep a balance, you need to pay equal attention to all three areas of your health. Throughout this book, you will learn how to make responsible decisions and practice healthful behaviors that will help you keep a balance and maintain your wellness.

The Health Continuum

Main Idea Healthful behaviors will promote your wellness.

W Your health and wellness are always changing. For instance, you may feel great one day and catch a cold the next. Your health at any moment can be seen as a point along a *continuum,* or sliding scale, such as the one in **Figure 1.4** on page 10. The continuum spans the complete range of health, from a loss of health and wellness at one end to high-level wellness at the other.

■ **Figure 1.3** When you feel your best, you perform at your best. *Which areas of this teen's health triangle are receiving attention?*

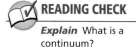

READING CHECK

Explain What is a continuum?

Lesson 1 Your Total Health **9**

Main Idea

The Health Continuum Healthful behaviors will promote wellness. **Ask Students:** *What are some events or actions that could positively or negatively change a person's health?* (Sample answer: Illness and injury have negative effects on total health; taking part in physical activity and choosing healthful foods have positive effects on total health.)

W Writing Support

Descriptive Writing Have each student write a short story about an individual whose place on the health continuum changes due to a decision that the individual has made. The movement on the health continuum described in the story can be toward a higher level of health or lower level of health. The story should include interesting characters, a plot, and a clearly described setting. Have each student proofread and correct his or her work before turning it in. **OL** **AL**

READING CHECK

Answer If you adopt health-promoting behaviors, you are likely to maintain a place toward the higher end of the continuum with good health and a positive quality of life. If you do not practice health-promoting behaviors, you are likely to end up on the lower end of the continuum.

Caption Answer

Figure 1.3 Physical, mental/emotional

Teacher to Teacher

Colette Dux • El Camino Real High School, Woodland Hills, CA

Practicing Concepts To help students learn about the elements of health, I have them get into groups with three note cards. Students write behaviors that primarily promote each component of their social, physical, and mental/emotional health. For example, starting an exercise program, washing hands more often, or volunteering. On the opposite side, students draw flow charts of how the actions interconnect with other areas. Groups present their cards to the class by placing each on one area of the triangle (drawn on the board), and asking if the class agrees. Then, groups move their cards to other areas while discussing relationships.

9

3 ASSESS/ CLOSE

Assessment Resources

📁 *FAST FILE* **ACTIVITIES**
Lesson 1 Quiz

💿 *ExamView*
Assessment Suite CD-ROM

Visit glencoe.com for:
Online Quizzes
Online Learning Center

Progress Monitoring

Reteaching
Have students make lists of actions they can take to improve their own health. Ask volunteers to share some of the actions on their lists with the class.

Enrichment
Have students write a paragraph that explains why social health and mental/emotional health are just as important as physical health when determining an individual's level of overall wellness.

G⊙ Online
Have students visit **glencoe.com** and complete the Interactive Study Guide for this lesson.

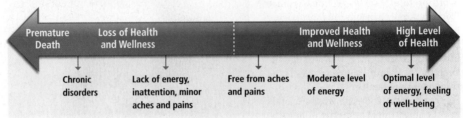

Figure 1.4 **The Health Continuum**

Your health can be measured on a sliding scale. *Where would you place your health along the continuum right now?*

Premature Death — Loss of Health and Wellness — Improved Health and Wellness — High Level of Health

| Chronic disorders | Lack of energy, inattention, minor aches and pains | Free from aches and pains | Moderate level of energy | Optimal level of energy, feeling of well-being |

As you mature, your position on the continuum continues to change. Many Americans, unfortunately, start moving toward the lower end of the continuum. One-half of all American adults live with a **chronic disease**, *an ongoing condition or illness* such as heart disease, obesity, and cancer. The leading risk factors for many chronic diseases are smoking, lack of physical activity, poor nutrition, being overweight, and lack of health screenings. However, by making a lifelong commitment now to practice healthful behaviors, you will be more likely to maintain a high level of wellness and stay at the higher end of the continuum.

LESSON 1 **ASSESSMENT**

After You Read

Reviewing Facts and Vocabulary
1. Define the word *health*.
2. List important steps you can take to promote your physical health.
3. What is the health continuum? Describe the continuum's endpoints.

Thinking Critically
4. **Relate.** How can poor mental/emotional health affect physical health?
5. **Predict.** How might your behaviors today affect your health now? How might they affect your health in the future?

Applying Health Skills
6. **Communication Skills.** Create a poster that explains the three areas of health to fourth or fifth graders.

Writing Critically
7. **Persuasive.** Write an editorial for the school newspaper about why each person is responsible for his own health, and why this is important.

G⊙ Online

Visit **glencoe.com** and complete the Interactive Study Guide for this lesson.

10 **Chapter 1** Understanding Health and Wellness

LESSON **1** ASSESSMENT ANSWERS

1. *Health* is the combination of physical, mental/emotional, and social health.
2. Sample answers: Get enough sleep; eat nutritious foods and drink plenty of water.
3. The health continuum is a sliding scale that allows you to assess your health status.
4. Sample answer: Someone who is depressed might not have the energy to exercise and might not participate in group activities.
5. Sample answer: Eating healthful foods and exercising regularly will prevent weight gain; avoiding tobacco and alcohol use will prevent chronic disease.
6. Posters will vary, but should clearly communicate the three areas of health at a fourth–fifth grade level.
7. Editorials will vary, but should clearly relate personal responsibility to health.

What Affects Your Health?

What Affects Your Health?

Real Life Issues

Too Much Sun. Jason enjoys being outdoors, and he spends a lot of time in the sun as a member of the cross-country team. He always uses sunscreen. During the summer months, he and his friends enjoy swimming and boating at the lake. He has invited his cousin Sean to come to the lake for a week. The first day, when Jason offers Sean some sunscreen, Sean says no. He tells Jason he doesn't like the sticky feeling it leaves on his skin.

Writing *Write a brief dialogue between Jason and Sean. Have Jason try to convince Sean to protect his health by using sunscreen.*

Influences on Your Health

Main Idea Heredity, environment, attitude, behavior, media, and technology can all influence your health.

It is your responsibility to make healthy decisions and take actions to ensure your well-being. Factors such as heredity, environment, attitude, behavior, media, and technology can influence how you live. Understanding these influences will help you make informed decisions about your health.

Heredity

Your **heredity** refers to *all the traits that were biologically passed on to you from your parents.* LaToya inherited her brown eyes, black hair, and tall body type from her parents. LaToya also inherited genes that put her at risk for diabetes, a serious disorder that prevents the body from converting food into energy. Both of LaToya's parents have diabetes.

Reading Strategy

Summarize Tell students that they should evaluate their understanding of each section of text as they read. As students reach the end of the lesson, have them look back at the main headings in the lesson. For each main heading, call on a volunteer to share a one-sentence summary of the information in that section of text in his or her own words. Explain that effective readers stop often while reading to check their understanding of small sections of text.

GUIDE TO READING

BIG **Idea** *Understanding how heredity, environment, and other factors affect your health can help you make healthy decisions.*

Before You Read

Create a K-W-L Chart. Make a three-column chart. In the first column, list what you **k**now about influences on your health. In the second column, list what you **w**ant to know about this topic. As you read, use the third column to summarize what you **l**earned.

K	W	L

New Vocabulary

▶ heredity (p. 11)
▶ environment (p. 12)
▶ peers (p. 13)
▶ culture (p. 13)
▶ media (p. 14)
▶ technology (p. 14)

1 FOCUS

GUIDE TO READING

BIG **Idea** Understanding factors that affect a person's health can contribute to making healthy decisions. **Ask Students:** *What are some ways that a person's surroundings can influence his or her health?* (Sample answer: Being outdoors encourages physical activity, which has a positive influence on health.)

Before You Read

K-W-L Chart Students' K-W-L charts will vary, but should include an accurate summary of the lesson content in the third column.

Main Idea

Influences on Your Health Factors that influence health include heredity, environment, and lifestyle factors. **Ask Students:** *What are some factors you have control over that influence your health?* (Sample answer: Food choices and participation in physical activity are factors that affect my health over which I have control.)

Real Life Issues

Have students read the scenario. **Ask Students:** *Have you ever encouraged a friend or family member to take part in a healthful behavior?*

2 TEACH

HS Health Skills Practice

Analyzing Influences Have students brainstorm ways that heredity can affect health. Have each student write a paragraph identifying at least three specific ways heredity influences health. Students may need to do additional research using the library or the Internet. **OL**

AL Active Learning

Design a Postcard Bring in examples of postcards to show students. Explain that postcards use pictures to show the characteristics of a physical environment. Postcards also have space on the back for a written description of a location. Distribute blank pieces of paper that have been cut to postcard size. Ask students to draw a picture on the front showing a physical environment that could have a positive impact on health. On the back, have students add a short written description of the environment and an explanation of how it could positively influence health. **OL**

Caption Answer

Figure 1.5 Answers will vary, but should show students' awareness of both positive and negative influences in their environment, as well as ways they maintain their health in their environment.

They have taken steps to control their diet and started an after-dinner walking program to keep their condition from getting worse. By watching her parents, LaToya has learned to eat healthfully, maintain a normal weight, get adequate rest, and stay active. She's learned from her parents' example that these healthful behaviors may help her avoid getting diabetes herself.

It's important to understand the influences heredity has on your health. Ask your parent or grandparent questions about what health conditions and diseases run in your family. Knowing this information can help you take actions to stay well and healthy. **HS**

Environment

Your **environment** is *the sum of your surroundings,* including the physical places in which you live and the people who make up your world. The culture you live in is part of your environment as well.

Physical Environment You may not have much control over your physical environment at this time in your life. However, it's still important to recognize how your physical environment can impact all aspects of your health. Some environmental factors that can affect your health include **AL**

- neighborhood and school safety.
- air and water quality.
- availability of parks, recreational facilities, and libraries.
- access to medical care.

There are some things in your environment over which you *do* have control. For instance, you can keep your room clean and help reduce litter at your school. How else can you improve your physical environment?

■ **Figure 1.5** Your physical environment influences your health in several ways. *Identify some positive and negative influences in your physical environment. How do you use the positive influences to protect your health? How can you overcome the negative influences?*

12 Chapter 1 Understanding Health and Wellness

More About...

Caring for the Physical Environment Pollution has a negative impact on the physical environment. Different types of pollution, such as smog or acid rain, are prevalent in different parts of the country. Have students work in small groups to research how different types of pollution affect health. Ask students to consider not only physical health, but mental/emotional and social health as well. Have each small group share its findings with the class.

■ **Figure 1.6** These teens are being influenced by their physical and social environments. *What are some environmental influences that affect you physically? What are some that affect you socially?*

Social Environment Your social environment is made up of all the people around you, including your family and peers. Your **peers**, *people of the same age who share similar interests*, also include your friends. All these people can be positive role models who support your healthful decisions, or they can increase your health risks. For example, Brandon promised his dad that he wouldn't drink. Hanging out with peers who drink, though, made it hard to keep that promise. Ultimately, Brandon decided to honor his commitment to his dad and found a new group of friends. Peers can have a positive influence on you, too. If your friends are involved in community service, chances are good that you'll join them in such activities.

Culture **Culture** refers to *the collective beliefs, customs, and behaviors of a group*. This group may be an ethnic group, a community, a nation, or a specific part of the world. Culture may include the language you speak, the foods you eat, your spiritual beliefs, and the traditions you practice. These **factors** can be a big influence on your health. For instance, some cultures enjoy a diet based on vegetables, fruits, grains, and very little meat. People from these backgrounds may be less likely to develop high cholesterol and may be better able to maintain their weight than those who eat a higher-fat diet.

Attitude

Your attitude, or the way you view situations, can have a big effect on your health. If you believe that adopting health-ful habits will influence your health in positive ways, then you're more likely to make the decision to practice them.

Academic Vocabulary

factor *(noun):* an element that contributes to a particular result

---

U Universal Access

Visual Learners Ask students to identify factors in their social environment that can have a positive influence on health. Record their responses in a list on the board. Then have each student select one of the factors on the list to illustrate on a poster. Ask students to share their completed posters with the class. **BL**

CA Cultural Awareness

Cultural Impact on Health
Divide the class into small groups. Have each group discuss the following questions: *Why is it important to understand the culture or cultures of your own family? Why is it important to understand the cultures of other families in your community? How does an understanding of your own and other cultures help you stay healthy?* Have each group share responses with the class. **OL**

Academic Vocabulary

Factor Ask students to read the definition of the word *factor* provided in the text. Then have them work in pairs to develop a list of five factors that influence health. Call on each pair to share entries from their list.

Caption Answer

Figure 1.6 Sample answers: The weather is a factor that affects me physically; my friends are a factor that affect me socially.

ELL Support

Spanish Cognates **Explain that many of the terms used in this lesson have very similar Spanish counterparts.**

Beginning Write the following terms on the board: *community-comunidad; culture-cultura.* Point out the similarities between these English terms and their Spanish counterparts.

Intermediate Build on the Beginning activity by asking students to write sentences in English describing how culture, and community can influence health.

Advanced After pointing out the Spanish counterparts for the terms *culture* and *community*, ask students to write a brief paragraph that uses these terms.

 **READING CHECK**

Answer It allows you to make decisions that are based on valid, reliable information.

W **Writing Support**

Persuasive Writing Have a class discussion on the ways celebrities and media personalities can influence the behaviors of others, both positively and negatively. Then have each student write a paragraph that examines how the actions of one specific media personality could influence the decisions and behaviors of teens. Remind students to edit their work before turning it in.
OL

G⊙ Online

Have students visit **glencoe.com** and complete the Student Web Activity on how media influences health and wellness.

U **Universal Access**

Reviewing Lesson Vocabulary Pair English language learners with students who are strong readers of English. Have each pair of students review the paragraph about Internet influence. Have each pair list two Web sites that are valid sources of information. Circulate among the students to monitor their work. **BL**
EL

Caption Answer

Figure 1.7 It is important to know which media messages are reliable, because using unreliable information can harm your health.

 **READING CHECK**

Analyze Why is it important to understand the influences on your health?

G⊙ Online

Visit **glencoe.com** and complete the Student Web Activity on how the media influences your health and wellness.

■ **Figure 1.7** The HONcode seal tells you that a Web site's information is of high quality. *Why is it important to know whether media messages are trustworthy?*

In addition, optimists—people who "see the glass as half full"—are usually in better health than pessimists, who "see the glass as half empty." Even if you have a natural tendency toward pessimism, you can remind yourself to look at challenging situations positively.

Behavior

Although you can't choose your heredity and may have only limited control over your environment, you have total control over your own behaviors. You can choose to avoid high-risk behaviors in favor of healthful behaviors, like choosing low-fat, nutritious foods and participating in daily physical activity.

Media and Technology

Every day you encounter one of the most powerful influences on your health—the media. **Media** are the *various methods for communicating information.* This content is delivered via **technology,** such as *radio, television, and the Internet,* and through print media, like newspapers and magazines. The constant presence of media messages has a significant influence on your decisions.

Media personalities and celebrities might be seen as role models because they get a lot of attention. Sometimes this attention is related to positive achievements, such as excelling in athletics or contributing time and money to help others in need. Sometimes the attention is related to negative behaviors. For example, some actors or models may practice unsafe eating habits in an attempt to maintain an extremely thin appearance. You also know about athletes who take drugs to help them perform better. Characters in movies or TV programs may drive dangerously, use alcohol, smoke, or engage in sexual activity. They never seem to face any consequences associated with these behaviors. When you see these behaviors in the media, you may get the false impression that everyone is doing it. **W**

More powerful and far reaching than radio, television, newspapers, and magazines is the Internet, which surpasses all other forms of media as an information source. Thousands of pages of health information from all over the world are available at the click of a mouse. Unfortunately, not all health messages and sources are valid. Some Web sites are sponsored by advertisers who only want you to buy their products. For valid health information, stick to Web sites that have *.gov* and *.edu* in their addresses, or sites maintained by professional health organizations, such as the American Medical Association and the Centers for Disease Control and Prevention (CDC). **U**

14 **Chapter 1** Understanding Health and Wellness

Teens Want to Know

How Do I Know What Advertisements to Believe? Advertisements are found in many forms of media, including television, radio, print materials, and the Internet. Students may wonder how they can determine whether health information in advertisements is valid. Share the following tips:

- Understand that the primary goal of advertisers is to sell a product.
- Many advertisements use techniques, such as testimonials, to promote a product that might not be right for everyone.
- Advertisements for prescription drugs do not take the place of a medical professional's advice.

One way to tell whether a Web site has reliable information is to look for the HONcode. HONcode is run by the Health On the Net Foundation, which is dedicated to improving the quality of online health information. Web sites accredited by the HONcode must follow a strict code of conduct.

Understanding Your Influences

Main Idea You can take control of your health by understanding the factors that influence it.

Think about all the factors that influence your health, including your heredity, your physical and social environments, your culture, your attitudes, your behaviors, and the media. Understanding these influences and committing to a healthy lifestyle are the first steps toward taking charge of your health.

In the pages that follow, you will learn more about risks and behaviors that are harmful to your health. You will gain the knowledge and skills you need to take responsibility for promoting your own health by avoiding these risks. You will also learn ways to promote the health of others. Learning these health skills and knowledge will help you achieve and maintain wellness.

 READING CHECK

Explain How would understanding the influence of media and technology make a difference in your health?

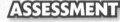 **LESSON 2 ASSESSMENT**

After You Read

Reviewing Facts and Vocabulary

1. What does *heredity* mean?
2. Define *environment*. Identify three types of environment.
3. List two ways that media and technology may influence your health.

Thinking Critically

4. **Evaluate.** How does the environment in which you live affect your health?
5. **Synthesize.** Oliver's family has a history of heart disease. What steps might he take to protect his health?

Applying Health Skills

6. **Communication Skills.** With a classmate, role-play a scenario in which a teen tries to persuade a friend to adopt a positive health behavior.

Writing Critically

7. **Narrative.** Write a short story about Jesse, who just moved from a small town to a large city. Choose one of the possible influences on his health and describe how his well-being might be affected by this influence.

Go Online

Visit **glencoe.com** and complete the Interactive Study Guide for this lesson.

❸ ASSESS/ CLOSE

Assessment Resources

 FAST FILE ACTIVITIES
Lesson 2 Quiz

 ExamView
Assessment Suite CD-ROM

Visit glencoe.com for:
Online Quizzes
Online Learning Center

Progress Monitoring

Reteaching
Each of the vocabulary terms in Lesson 2 identifies a factor that impacts health. Ask students to write a sentence for each of the terms explaining how that factor affects their health.

Enrichment
Have students work in small groups to develop a motivational lesson to share with other students of the same grade level.

Go Online

Have students visit **glencoe.com** and complete the Interactive Study Guide for this lesson.

LESSON **2** ASSESSMENT ANSWERS

1. *Heredity* is all the traits biologically passed on to you by your parents.
2. *Environment* is all the things that surround you. It includes the physical and social environments. Culture is also a part of the social environment.
3. Sample answers: Celebrities or other media figures may be role models that you want to emulate; media creates a set of norms for how people behave; the Internet may provide incorrect health information.
4. Answers will vary, but should include mention of factors listed on page 12.
5. Sample answers: Avoid tobacco, get plenty of physical activity, eat healthfully, get regular check-ups
6. Role-plays will vary, but should demonstrate communication skills and should correctly identify a positive health behavior.
7. Stories will vary.

15

LESSON 3

Health Risks and Your Behavior

① FOCUS

GUIDE TO READING

BIG Idea There are steps a person can take to avoid or reduce risk behaviors. **Ask Students:** *What are some behaviors that put health at risk?* (Sample answers: Using alcohol, not using seat belts, inadequate physical activity)

Before You Read

Cluster Chart Students' charts should include risks mentioned in the lesson.

Main Idea

Identifying Health Risks Risk behaviors can damage health. **Ask Students:** *Why is it important to know what behaviors put your health at risk?* (Sample answer: Knowing what behaviors put your health at risk can help you avoid those behaviors.)

Real Life Issues

Have students read the scenario. **Ask Students:** *What are some situations in which you would speak up to help a friend avoid a risk behavior?* (Sample answer: I would speak up if a friend did not put on his or her safety belt in the car.) Have volunteers share their completed dialogues with the class.

LESSON 3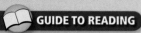

GUIDE TO READING

BIG Idea *Risk behaviors can harm your health, but there are steps you can take to avoid or reduce these risks.*

Before You Read

Create a Cluster Chart. Draw a circle and label it "Health Risks." Use surrounding circles to define and describe this term. As you read, continue filling in the chart with ways to reduce these risks.

New Vocabulary

▸ risk behaviors (p. 16)
▸ cumulative risks (p. 18)
▸ prevention (p. 18)
▸ abstinence (p. 19)
▸ lifestyle factors (p. 20)

Health Risks and Your Behavior

Real Life Issues ....

Worrying About a Friend. Jenna and her best friend, Madison, are discussing their plans for the weekend. Jenna is excited because Jackson, a classmate, has invited her to a party on Saturday night. The party is at the home of a classmate whose parents will be away. Madison suspects there will be alcohol at the party and no adult supervision. Jackson has a reputation for being wild, and Madison is worried for Jenna.

Writing *Write a dialogue in which Madison discusses with Jenna the potential dangers of going to the party.*

Identifying Health Risks

Main Idea Engaging in risk behaviors can harm your health.

Every day you are faced with some degree of risk. Simple events, such as crossing a street or using electrical appliances, carry a degree of risk. Being aware of certain risks to your health is part of becoming an adult.

Risk behaviors are *actions that can potentially threaten your health or the health of others*. It's important to recognize that you can control most risk behaviors. By understanding the risks associated with certain behaviors, you can make safe and responsible decisions about which risks to avoid. In this way, you actively protect and promote your health.

Recognizing Risk Behaviors

The Centers for Disease Control and Prevention (CDC) has identified six risk behaviors that account for most of the deaths and disability among young people under age 24.

Myths & Reality

Risk Behavior

Myth: Bicycle helmets are just for young children.

Fact: Not wearing a bicycle helmet is a major cause of unintentional injury in children and teens. Bicycle helmets should be worn by riders of all ages. Bicycle helmet use results in a 74 percent–85 percent reduction in serious brain injuries.

Myth: Consuming beer or wine does not pose the same risk as consuming hard liquor.

Fact: Consumption of any alcoholic beverage is a risk behavior. The alcohol in beer and wine impairs judgment and coordination in the same way that the alcohol in hard liquor does.

R These risk behaviors can lead to heart disease, cancer, and other serious illnesses later in life:

AL
- Tobacco use
- Unhealthy dietary behaviors
- Inadequate physical activity
- Alcohol and other drug use
- Sexual behaviors that may result in HIV infection, other sexually transmitted diseases, and unintended pregnancies
- Behaviors that contribute to unintentional injuries and violence

Real World CONNECTION

Teen Risk Taking

To track patterns of risk taking among teens, the CDC developed the Youth Risk Behavior Survey (YRBS). It is administered every two years to a sample of high school students across the country. The information gathered in this survey is used in a variety of ways to influence change and improve the health and well-being of teens. Some of the major risk behaviors, with key findings in each category, appear in the graph below. When you analyze the data, you may be surprised. Despite the headlines, most teens are not drinking or using drugs. Most wear automobile safety belts, and two-thirds are physically active.

Activity — Mathematics

Use the graph to answer these questions.

1. Approximately what percent of teens did *not* participate in vigorous physical activity three or more days per week?
2. Which risk behaviors did 90 percent of teens avoid?
3. **Writing** Write a paragraph explaining how you think these statistics can be used to promote teens' health and well-being.

Concept Data Analysis: Interpreting Graphs A bar graph represents data using shaded bars to show each value. The legend explains what each shade represents.

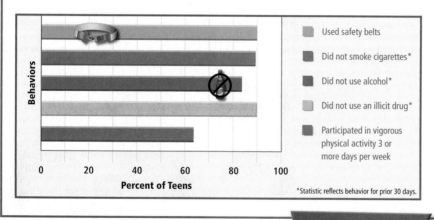

Used safety belts
Did not smoke cigarettes*
Did not use alcohol*
Did not use an illicit drug*
Participated in vigorous physical activity 3 or more days per week

*Statistic reflects behavior for prior 30 days.

Behaviors / Percent of Teens

2 TEACH

R Reading Strategy

Organizing Information Model for students how to outline the lesson by writing the first heading in the lesson, *Identifying Health Risks*, on the board. Under it, write the headings *Recognizing Risk Behaviors* and *Risks and Consequences*. Ask students to state some serious illnesses that can arise as a result of risk behaviors. **EL** **BL** **OL**

AL Active Learning

Comic Strip Have students work in pairs to create a comic strip that focuses on strategies for avoiding one of the six risk behaviors listed in the student text. Remind students that their comic strip should use both words and images to show ways that the risk behavior can be avoided. Have students share their completed comic strips with the class. **OL** **AL**

Real World CONNECTION

Answers to Activity Questions

1. 36 percent
2. Using illicit drugs, riding in a car without a safety belt
3. Students' paragraphs will vary. Students may note that understanding that most teens avoid risk behaviors can encourage other teens to make healthful choices and avoid risks.

English Language Coach

Initialisms and Acronyms Point out the terms *CDC* and *YRBS*. Explain that these are initialisms, which are formed using the first initial of a series of words with each initial pronounced separately. Contrast initialisms with acronyms such as *AIDS* (acquired immune deficiency syndrome), which are pronounced as a single word. Make a T-chart on the board. Label one side "Initialisms" and the other side "Acronyms." Have students find examples to add to each side of the T-chart. (Hint: Students can find examples in the index of the student edition. Sample initialisms: *AED (automated external defibrillator), BBB (Better Business Bureau);* Sample acronym: *WHO (World Health Organization)*)

Critical Thinking

Identifying Cause and Effect
Have students make charts that list common risk behaviors and possible short- and long-term consequences of each risk behavior. Point out that risks and consequences have a cause and effect relationship.
BL **OL**

Main Idea

How to Avoid or Reduce Risks
Teens can take action to reduce exposure to health risks. **Ask Students:** *What are some strategies for avoiding health risks?* (Sample answer: Avoiding peers who take part in risk behaviors.)

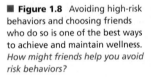 **READING CHECK**

Answer Risk behaviors are harmful to your short-term and long-term health.

Caption Answer

Figure 1.8 Sample answers: Friends who avoid risk behaviors can exert positive peer pressure that can help me avoid risks.

Risks and Consequences

Risk behaviors can have a serious impact on your health. In other words, these behaviors carry significant consequences. Both the short-term and long-term consequences can harm your health and well-being. Some risk behaviors can even be fatal. Before you engage in risk behaviors, it's important to evaluate the consequences. For example, smoking can have immediate health consequences, such as bad breath, yellow teeth, and headaches. If a person continues to smoke, the long-term consequences can include lung cancer, emphysema, and heart disease.

Risks can also add up over time. **Cumulative risks** are *related risks that increase in effect with each added risk*. Eating an occasional high-fat meal at a fast-food restaurant probably won't permanently affect your overall health. If you regularly eat high-fat meals, though, the negative effects accumulate over time and may lead to serious health problems.

Cumulative risks also increase when several risk factors are combined. For example, using a cell phone while driving carries risks. So does speeding. If an individual engages in both of these risk behaviors, the chances of getting into a car accident becomes even greater. The more risk behaviors you participate in, the more likely you are to experience negative consequences.

C

READING CHECK

Evaluate Why is it important to understand risk behaviors?

How to Avoid or Reduce Risks

Main Idea You can take action to reduce your exposure to health risks.

You can protect your health and minimize the possibility of risk by practicing positive health behaviors. Many of your automatic safety checks—wearing a safety belt when you get into a car, checking the depth of water before diving, or wearing a helmet when riding a bike—are positive health behaviors. Another way to reduce health risks is through **prevention**.

■ **Figure 1.8** Avoiding high-risk behaviors and choosing friends who do so is one of the best ways to achieve and maintain wellness. *How might friends help you avoid risk behaviors?*

Health Literacy

Brain Development and Risk Behavior
Research shows that patterns of brain development during adolescence are a cause of the prevalence of risk behavior among teens. Researchers have found differences in the way teens' brains generate impulses, react to impulses, and measure risks and rewards as compared to adults' brains. This research highlights the importance of finding positive risks for teens to take, such as learning a new skill, taking part in sports competitions, or performing in music or drama. Have students work as a class to generate a list of positive risks for teens.

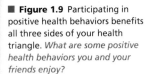

Figure 1.9 Participating in positive health behaviors benefits all three sides of your health triangle. *What are some positive health behaviors you and your friends enjoy?*

This means *taking steps to keep something from happening or getting worse.* Prevention includes getting regular medical and dental checkups. Checkups can detect health problems early, thus preventing them from getting worse.

Abstaining from High-Risk Behaviors

AL

One of the most effective strategies for protecting your health is practicing abstinence. **Abstinence** is *a deliberate decision to avoid high-risk behaviors, including sexual activity and the use of tobacco, alcohol, and other drugs.*

All areas of your health triangle benefit when you choose to abstain from high-risk behaviors. For example, when you avoid tobacco, alcohol, and other drugs, you protect yourself from the chronic diseases associated with using these substances. You also feel good about yourself, which strengthens your mental/emotional health and your social relationships.

When you abstain from high-risk behaviors, you show that you value your well-being. You demonstrate maturity by taking responsibility for your health and playing an active role in maintaining your wellness.

Promoting Your Health

Main Idea Regularly participating in health-promoting behaviors will help you reach a high level of wellness.

HS

Every day you make decisions, large and small, that **affect** your health. For example, if you choose to play a sport after school, you are likely to have fun and feel energized. If you choose to play video games instead, you may end up feeling sluggish because you didn't get enough physical activity. Understanding how your decisions impact your health will inspire you to adopt healthful behaviors that can promote wellness and prevent the development of disease.

Academic Vocabulary

affect *(verb):* to produce an effect upon

Lesson 3 Health Risks and Your Behavior **19**

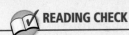

 READING CHECK

Answer Sample answers: Practice abstinence; choose friends wisely; stay connected to family, school, and community

 ASSESS/ CLOSE

Assessment Resources

📁 **FAST FILE ACTIVITIES**
Lesson 3 Quiz

💿 *ExamView*
Assessment Suite CD-ROM

Visit glencoe.com for:
Online Quizzes
Online Learning Center

Progress Monitoring

Reteaching

Have students work in pairs to discuss specific strategies individuals can use to reduce risks and enhance health. Ask each pair of students to share one of the strategies it has identified.

Enrichment

Have students write a letter to the editor of the school or local newspaper encouraging teens to practice a particular habit or behavior that reduces health risks. Provide students with model letters before they begin writing.

Go Online

Have students visit **glencoe.com** and complete the Interactive Study Guide for this lesson.

 READING CHECK

Identify List three lifestyle factors that can promote your health.

Lifestyle Factors

Lifestyle factors are *the personal habits or behaviors related to the way a person lives.* Scientists have found that these habits make a difference in people's overall health, happiness, and longevity. In other words, people who practice positive health habits regularly tend to be healthier and live longer. Lifestyle factors that can improve a person's level of health include

- getting eight hours of sleep each night.
- starting each day with a healthy breakfast.
- eating a variety of nutritious foods each day.
- being physically active for 30 to 60 minutes most days of the week.
- maintaining a healthy weight.
- abstaining from smoking or using other tobacco products.
- abstaining from the use of alcohol and other drugs.

Think about your daily habits. Do you regularly practice the lifestyle factors listed above? Can you think of ways to incorporate more of these behaviors into your daily routine? Remember, you have control over your lifestyle. By making the best possible decisions for yourself, you can achieve a high level of wellness now and into adulthood.

LESSON 3 ASSESSMENT

After You Read

Reviewing Facts and Vocabulary

1. Define the term *risk behavior*.
2. Why is cumulative risk a serious concern?
3. How might changes in lifestyle factors influence your health in positive ways?

Thinking Critically

4. **Explain.** How might monitoring risk behaviors affect the well-being of teens?
5. **Synthesize.** Consider a risk behavior teens are exposed to, and predict how lifestyle factors can positively influence teens to avoid that risk.

Applying Health Skills

6. **Accessing Information.** Research organizations that offer after-school programs to help teens avoid risk behaviors. Write a short description of one such organization in your community.

Writing Critically

7. **Expository.** Using the data shown on page 17, write an article about the results of recent research on how many teens avoid risk behaviors.

Go Online

Visit **glencoe.com** and complete the Interactive Study Guide for this lesson.

LESSON 3 ASSESSMENT ANSWERS

1. *Risk behavior* is any action that can potentially threaten your health or the health of others.
2. The likelihood of negative outcomes increases as the number of risk factors increases.
3. Adopting positive lifestyle factors influences your health positively, leading to good health now and in the future.
4. Monitoring of risk behaviors provides information about ways that teens can improve their health and can be used to evaluate the effectiveness of health-promoting programs that are currently in place.
5. Sample answer: Teens may be exposed to opportunities to use drugs or alcohol, but knowing ways to avoid these substances will protect their health.
6. Descriptions will vary.
7. Articles will vary.

Promoting Health and Wellness

 GUIDE TO READING

BIG **Idea** *Staying healthy takes knowledge, a plan, and practicing healthful behaviors.*

Before You Read

Create Vocabulary Cards. Write each new vocabulary term on a separate note card. For each term, write a definition based on your current knowledge. As you read, fill in additional information related to each term.

Health Education

New Vocabulary
▸ health education (p. 22)
▸ *Healthy People* (p. 22)
▸ health disparities (p. 23)
▸ health literacy (p. 25)

1 FOCUS

 GUIDE TO READING

BIG **Idea** Knowledge, planning, and careful decision making can help people stay healthy. **Ask Students:** *What is one way that taking this health class will help you make more healthful decisions?* (Sample answer: I'll learn how to make better food choices.)

Before You Read

Vocabulary Cards Students' vocabulary cards should reflect their current knowledge of the lesson.

Main Idea

The Importance of Health Education Planning and responsible behavior are important to individual, family, community, and national health. **Ask Students:** *What is one way that society would change if people took better care of their health?* (Answers will vary.)

Real Life Issues

Learning from Experience. Taylor is taking an elective class called Intergenerations. Students in this class are paired with older adults. Taylor's "classmate" is an active 89-year-old man named Harry. Harry remembers riding in a horse-drawn cart from his family farm to church on Sunday mornings. He also remembers there was no television while he was growing up, and that his family ate what they grew on the farm. Taylor's assignment is to interview Harry about his secrets to a long, healthy, and happy life.

Writing *Write a short questionnaire listing what Taylor might ask Harry. Cover all the factors you think might contribute to a long, healthy life.*

The Importance of Health Education

Main Idea Individual, family, community, and national health require planning and responsible behavior on everyone's part.

Achieving a high level of wellness means a higher quality of life for each individual. It means more time in which to feel physically and mentally healthy, to enjoy family and friends, and to achieve your personal goals.

Keeping people healthy is also a good investment. Today, America spends $1.9 trillion each year on health care, or $6,280 per person. Much of that expense could be avoided if people made healthier decisions about the way they live, adopted health-promoting habits, and took responsibility for maintaining their wellness.

Lesson 4   Promoting Health and Wellness   **21**

Academic Integration

Math Point out the sentence in the student text that states: America spends $1.9 trillion on health care each year, or $6,280 per person. Use this information to review different forms in which numbers can be written. On the board, write 1.9 trillion; 1,900,000,000; and 1.9×10^9. Explain that these are all ways to express the same number. Challenge students to write the number 6,280 in at least one other form. (Sample answers: six thousand, two hundred and eighty; 6.280×10^3)

Real Life Issues

Have students read the scenario. **Ask Students:** *Harry told Taylor that there was no television when he was a child. How would having no television influence health?*

② TEACH

C Critical Thinking

Extending Concepts Students may think of health education as something that takes place only in school classrooms. Ask students where else they think health education takes place. Do they ever provide health education to others? Have students explain their responses. **BL** **OL**

VIDEO BusinessWeek
HEALTH NEWS

After students have watched the video, *Battling the Bulge,* lead them in a class discussion on weight management options. Ask students to identify the options they feel are most beneficial to total health. Then have them write a paragraph supporting their choices. Students should support their opinions with information from the video.

AL Active Learning

Multimedia Presentation Have students work in small groups and use library or Internet resources to learn more about *Healthy People 2010.* Ask each group to choose a different aspect of *Healthy People 2010* on which to focus their research. Then, have each group prepare a multimedia presentation to share what group members learned. **OL** **AL**

Caption Answer

Figure 1.10 Sample answer: Because it influences quality of life and is a major expense for individuals.

VIDEO BusinessWeek
HEALTH NEWS

Battling the Bulge

Analyze. Go to glencoe.com and watch the video ***Battling the Bulge.*** As a group, discuss the different kinds of weight management options that are available and decide which are the most beneficial to your overall health. Write a paragraph supporting your choice or choices.

Educating the public is the key to creating a healthier nation. **Health education** includes *providing accurate health information and teaching health skills to help people make healthy decisions.* Understanding health information and learning health skills empower people to live healthfully and improve their quality of life. **C**

The Nation's Health Goals

Good health is such an important goal that the federal government has established national health goals and objectives. ***Healthy People*** is *a nationwide health promotion and disease prevention plan designed to serve as a guide for improving the health of all people in the United States.* The plan is revised every ten years. Its title changes according to the year to which the plan's goals apply: *Healthy People 2010* has objectives for the year 2010. As you can see in **Figure 1.10**, one of the goals of *Healthy People 2010* is to reduce the overweight and obesity rates in America. **AL**

By developing programs to promote health and prevent disease, *Healthy People* provides a common plan for everyone to follow. National, state, and local health agencies across the country carry out programs based on the plan's goals. The government tracks health behaviors and outcomes to measure their progress in achieving the national objectives.

Figure 1.10 Overweight and Obesity Rates

This table shows that 18.8% of children and 17.4% of adolescents in the United States were overweight or obese in 2003–04. The nation has set a goal of reducing these percentages to 5% of children and adolescents. *Why do you think health is important enough to set national health goals?* **R**

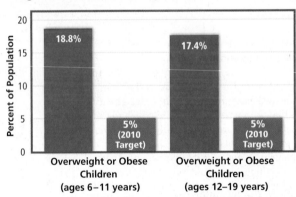

Source: Centers for Disease Control and Prevention, *National Health and Nutrition Examination Survey (NHANES) 2003–04.*

22 Chapter 1 Understanding Health and Wellness

Skills for the 21st Century

Promoting Personal and Social Responsibility Write the following question on the board: How does personal responsibility for health benefit society as a whole? After students have discussed this question, ask them to consider whether the government should provide incentives, such as tax breaks, for positive health decisions or disincentives, such as fines, for those who participate in risk behaviors. Have students work in small groups to develop a plan to promote personal and social responsibility for one specific health behavior. Have each group share its plan with the class.

TEENS — Making a Difference

"I'm helping to make things happen."

Mentoring Others

Matt M. from Georgia has found a way to save teens from boredom. "I heard about the Youth Council of Fayette County (YCFC) and their mission . . . to change the lives of teens in our county."

YCFC schedules all kinds of events, including the Battle of the Bands competition, holiday caroling at a nursing home, monthly trivia nights at a local pizzeria, and volunteering at the local thrift store.

Since joining YCFC three years ago, Matt has had little time to be bored. "Our long-term goal is to build a teen center where middle school students can go after school to get help with homework and play games. High school students would be mentors," says Matt. "Instead of complaining about my town, I'm helping to make things happen."

Activity Write your answers to the following questions in your personal health journal.

1. What is the purpose of the Youth Council of Fayette County?
2. How will the teen center help teens become leaders?
3. What steps would you take to create a Youth Council in your community?

Goals of *Healthy People*. *Healthy People 2010* established two general goals for the future: increase the quality and length of a healthy life for all Americans, and remove differences in health outcomes that result from factors such as gender, race, education, disability, and location. These *differences in health outcomes among groups* are called **health disparities**. Working toward these two goals will ensure that more people can enjoy the benefits of a healthy life.

Planning is under way for *Healthy People 2020,* the blueprint that will shape the nation's health priorities for the next ten years. The health goals that are guiding early development of *Healthy People 2020* include the following:

1. Promote the best possible health in order to end preventable death, illness, injury, and disability.
2. Eliminate health disparities.
3. Make wellness a way of life and enhance quality of life for individuals and communities.
4. Promote healthy places and environments.

READING CHECK

List What are some of the goals for *Healthy People 2020*?

Lesson 4 Promoting Health and Wellness **23**

TEENS — Making a Difference

Answers to Activity Questions

1. The purpose of the Youth Council of Fayette County is to change the lives of teens in their county.
2. The teen center will help teens become leaders by asking them to serve as mentors to middle school students.
3. I would first ask several adults to serve as leaders. I would then ask teens to join the group. With these other teens, I would set goals and plan activities for the group.

R Reading Strategy

Interpreting a Graphic Explain that a percentage is used to express "parts per hundred." You can help students remember this by pointing out the word part *cent* in the word *percentage,* and relating it to 100 cents equaling a dollar. **Ask Students:** *If the national health goals are met, how many adolescents out of every one hundred would be overweight or obese?* (5) **EL** **OL**

U Universal Access

Reluctant Readers Pair English proficient students with English language learners and have each pair of students review the *Healthy People 2020* goals. Each pair should pick one and make a poster representing that goal. **EL** **BL**

Cooperative Learning

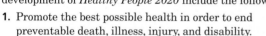

Promoting the Nation's Health Goals
Have students work in small groups to develop projects that will enhance health literacy among students at their school. Project ideas might include, but are not limited to, a presentation explaining how to interpret the instructions on a prescription bottle, a poster showing how to find reliable health information on the Internet, or a skit that shows how to ask a doctor questions at a check-up. Have each group share its completed project with other students in the school.

HS Health Skills Practice

Accessing Information Have students work in small groups to find an example of a reliable source of health information. (Remind students that this source may be an Internet site, a medical journal, a medical professional, or a health organization.) Have each group share information about its source with the class, providing several reasons why the source is reliable. OL

Main Idea

Becoming Health Literate
Health literacy involves locating and understanding health information. **Ask Students:** *What are some specific situations in which understanding health information is important?* (Sample answers: When you read the instructions on a prescription bottle, when a doctor gives you verbal instructions, when you find health information on the Internet)

Caption Answer

Figure 1.11 Sample answers: Health professionals, the Internet, advertisements

Becoming Health Literate

Main Idea A health-literate person knows how to find and use reliable health information.

Go Online

Explore glencoe.com and complete the Student Web Activity on what health literacy is and how it can affect your health.

Every day people all across the country have to make important decisions that affect their health. To become an informed individual who can make sound health decisions, one must

- know where to find health information.
- decide if the information is correct.
- assess the risks and benefits of treatment.
- figure out how much medicine to take.
- understand test results.

HS

What You Can Do

In order to increase your knowledge and take steps to improve your wellness, you need to develop health literacy.

■ **Figure 1.11** People who are informed know how to interpret the information they need to make good health decisions. *Where do you find information to make your daily health decisions?*

Home and Community

Nonprofit Health Organizations
Explain that there are a wide variety of nonprofit health organizations that promote good health, provide informational and educational materials, and raise funds to support health research. Some examples include the American Heart Association, the American Cancer Society, and the American Diabetes Association. Ask students to work in small groups to investigate what these organizations do and ways that these organizations are active in their community. Have each group share what it learned with the class.

Health literacy refers to *a person's capacity to learn about and understand basic health information and services, and to use these resources to promote one's health and wellness.* Experts believe that poor health literacy influences a person's health more than age, income, and education.

Qualities of a health-literate individual include being

- **a critical thinker and problem solver**—a person who can develop evaluation criteria for health information before making decisions. This person knows how to apply these criteria to make responsible, healthy choices.

- **a responsible, productive citizen**—someone who acts in a way that promotes the health of the community. This person chooses safe, healthful, and legal behaviors that are **consistent** with family guidelines and that show respect for the individual and others.

- **a self-directed learner**—someone who searches for health information to make health-related decisions. This person knows how to evaluate health information to determine if it is reliable, accurate, and current. Such information is available on television and radio, on the Internet, and from health care professionals.

- **an effective communicator**—a person who is able to express health knowledge in a variety of ways.

 **READING CHECK**

Explain What are the attributes of a health-literate person?

Academic Vocabulary

consistent *(adjective):* free from variation or contradiction

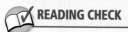 **READING CHECK**

Answer A critical thinker and problem solver; a responsible, productive citizen; a self-directed learner; an effective communicator

3 ASSESS/ CLOSE

Assessment Resources

📁 *FAST FILE* **ACTIVITIES**
Lesson 4 Quiz

💿 *ExamView Assessment Suite* CD-ROM

Visit glencoe.com **for:**
Online Quizzes
Online Learning Center

Progress Monitoring

Reteaching
Ask students to review the text to find each of the main ideas of the lesson. Then, have each student write a sentence or two that summarizes the main ideas using his or her own words.

Enrichment
Ask students to work in pairs to prepare a script for a television commercial that describes and promotes the goals of *Healthy People 2010.* Have each pair of students share its completed commercial with the class.

Gǒ Online

Have students visit **glencoe.com** and complete the Interactive Study Guide for this lesson.

LESSON 4 ASSESSMENT

After You Read

Reviewing Facts and Vocabulary

1. Why is health education important?
2. What are *health disparities*?
3. List three criteria that are needed for an individual to make sound health decisions.

Thinking Critically

4. **Analyze.** How does *Healthy People* hope to help the United States become a healthier country?
5. **Synthesize.** What are some steps you can take to become a health-literate individual?

Applying Health Skills

6. **Accessing Information.** Work with classmates to compile a list of resources in your community that support healthy lifestyle behaviors. Examples might include parks, libraries, and health organizations.

Writing Critically

7. **Expository.** Write an essay explaining what individuals, families, and communities can do to promote wellness.

Gǒ Online

Visit **glencoe.com** and complete the Interactive Study Guide for this lesson.

LESSON 4 ASSESSMENT ANSWERS

1. Health education provides information about health so people can make responsible health-related decisions. It helps people maintain a high quality of life and can reduce national health-care costs.
2. *Health disparities* are differences in health outcomes between groups.
3. Know where to find health information, decide if information is correct, figure out the risks and benefits of treatment, figure out when and how to take medications safely, understand test results
4. *Healthy People* provides a common set of goals and objectives and tracks progress toward those goals.
5. Be a critical thinker and problem-solver; responsible, productive citizen; self-directed learner; effective communicator
6. Lists will vary.
7. Reports will vary.

The Cutting Edge

Focus

Motivator
Ask students, "What do you think of when you hear the word surgery?" Write their response on the board for later use.

Teach

Outpatient Care According to this article, gallbladder surgery is now an outpatient operation when it used to require a hospital stay. Ask, "How might an outpatient procedure provide health advantages over a hospital stay?" Have students refer to their Motivator responses and consider concepts such as patient stress, expense, recovery time, impact on family, etc. Ask, "Are there potential risks for sending a patient home after surgery?" (complications may go undetected) "How do doctors minimize those risks? Do you think the benefits outweigh the risks?"

About Telerobotics Tell students that telerobotics is the latest in a long line of technological breakthroughs that have changed medicine. Divide students into small groups. Direct each group to research a medical/technological breakthrough that has taken place in the last 50 years. (Examples may include pacemakers, artificial hearts, laser surgery, ultrasound, magnetic resonance imaging, etc.) Students should answer the following questions:

• What is this new technology?
• What condition is the technology used to treat?
• What are the benefits of this technology and why?
• What are the potential risks?

Ask students to present their work to the class.

TIME HEALTH
SCIENCE & TECHNOLOGY

The Cutting EDGE

HIGH-TECH DOCTORS GIVE NEW MEANING TO LONG-DISTANCE RELATIONSHIPS.

Doctor Mehran Anvari is a specialist in laparoscopy. In this medical procedure, a doctor inserts long-handled instruments and a special camera through tiny incisions in a patient's body. That way, a surgeon can perform an operation while viewing the inside of the body on a video screen. Laparoscopy reduces recovery time from many different types of operations. "For example, gallbladder surgery is now an outpatient operation," Anvari says. "It used to mean three or four days in the hospital."

Telerobotic Surgery

In recent years, Anvari has also used live, long-distance videoconferencing with surgeons while they perform operations. The "telementoring" allows the expert to see what's going on and advise the surgeon through the procedure. Anvari is taking that process a giant step further with a "telerobotics" program. It lets faraway experts physically assist in operations, using a three-armed robotic device. "The goal is not to replace local surgeons but enhance care by increasing the level of support for them," Anvari says.

Telerobotic surgery uses electronic impulses to transmit the movements of a surgeon's hand, wrist, and fingers across space. High-tech robots mirror the surgeon's movements, thus allowing the robot to perform the same operations across the room—or much farther away.

Robotic surgery is common in more than one hundred hospitals around the globe, but only recently has the world's first long-distance operation taken place. Surgeons at a New York City lab successfully removed the gallbladder of a 68-year-old woman in Strasbourg, France.

Anvari's work has caught the attention of NASA, which is looking for ways to deal with any astronaut who needs emergency surgery in space. "Improving in-flight medical capabilities is more important with astronauts flying ever-longer missions," says one NASA researcher. Even the sky may not be Anvari's limit. ∎

TIME to THINK... About Telerobotics

Astronauts are just one group of people who might benefit from the growing technology of telerobotics. Brainstorm at least five other types of workers who might also benefit. List one specific way that each type of worker might find telerobotics useful on the job.

More About...

Short Story Fifty years ago, telerobotics might have sounded like science fiction. Have students imagine how surprised a patient in a hospital 50 years ago would have been to hear about this treatment. Tell students to imagine a new medical technology. Ask them to write a short story in which the technology is used to treat a real medical condition. Ask them to consider whether or not they think this technology is likely to become a reality within the next 50 years. Why or why not?

To download quizzes and eFlashcards to your PDA, go to **glencoe.com** and click on the Study to Go icon.

LESSON 1

Your Total Health

Key Concepts

▶ Health is the combination of physical, mental/emotional, and social well-being.

▶ It is important to balance the three components of health.

▶ Making a lifetime commitment to practice healthful behaviors can improve your long-term well-being.

Vocabulary

▶ health (p. 6)
▶ spiritual health (p. 8)
▶ wellness (p. 9)
▶ chronic disease (p. 10)

LESSON 2

What Affects Your Health?

Key Concepts

▶ Your heredity plays a role in your health and wellness.

▶ You cannot always control your physical environment, but you can look for ways to overcome its negative influences.

▶ A positive attitude and healthful behaviors promote wellness.

Vocabulary

▶ heredity (p. 11)
▶ environment (p. 12)
▶ peers (p. 13)
▶ culture (p. 13)
▶ media (p. 14)
▶ technology (p. 14)

LESSON 3

Health Risks and Your Behavior

Key Concepts

▶ Risk behaviors can harm your health and the health of others.

▶ Risk behaviors that contribute to illness and disability include tobacco use, unhealthy dietary behaviors, inadequate physical activity, and alcohol and other drug use.

▶ Abstaining from high-risk behaviors will protect your health.

Vocabulary

▶ risk behaviors (p. 16)
▶ cumulative risks (p. 18)
▶ prevention (p. 18)
▶ abstinence (p. 19)
▶ lifestyle factors (p. 20)

LESSON 4

Promoting Health and Wellness

Key Concepts

▶ Health education is the key to creating a healthier nation.

▶ The national health goals of *Healthy People* provide guidelines for promoting health and preventing disease.

▶ A health-literate person has the necessary skills to function in today's health promotion and disease prevention environment.

Vocabulary

▶ health education (p. 22)
▶ *Healthy People* (p. 22)
▶ health disparities (p. 23)
▶ health literacy (p. 25)

Go Online

Students can visit **glencoe.com** to

• review content online with the Online Student Edition.

• test their knowledge of chapter content with Online Quizzes.

• access Interactive Health Tutor for more practice with vocabulary.

Assessment Resources

FAST FILE ACTIVITIES
Chapter 1 Test

ExamView
Assessment Suite CD-ROM

Visit glencoe.com for:
Audio Chapter Summaries
Online Quizzes

Tell students to visit **glencoe.com** where they can download quizzes and eFlashcards.

Chapter 1 Review **27**

Study Tips

Study Out Loud Suggest that students review by speaking out loud. Explain that this method improves retention and helps identify confusing concepts. Model this for students in the following way: Turn to the beginning of Lesson 1. State out loud: "This lesson describes total health. I know that total health includes physical health, mental/emotional health, and social health." Continue to state main ideas and definitions of vocabulary terms from Lesson 1. Then ask students to work with a partner to review aloud the material in Lessons 2, 3, and 4.

Chapter 1 Assessment Answers

LESSON 1

Vocabulary Review

1. Health
2. Spirituality
3. wellness

Understanding Key Concepts

4. b
5. d
6. c
7. a

Thinking Critically

8. Sample answers: Enjoys challenges that help him or her grow, accepts responsibility for actions, has a sense of control over life, can identify emotions and express them in appropriate ways, can usually deal with life's stresses and frustrations without feeling overwhelmed, can change negative thoughts to have a more positive outlook, makes thoughtful and responsible decisions

9. Your health triangle becomes unbalanced when you concentrate too much on one area over the others. When an imbalance in the three areas occurs, your overall health suffers.

10. Sample answers: Eat healthfully; drink water; get enough sleep and rest; stay physically active; practice good hygiene; avoid tobacco, alcohol, and drugs

11. Sample answers: Positive health behaviors will place you at a high level of health on the health continuum.

LESSON 1

Vocabulary Review

Use the vocabulary terms listed on page 27 to complete the following statements.

1. _____ is the combination of physical, mental/emotional, and social well-being.

2. _____ provides people with a deep-seated sense of meaning and purpose in life.

3. A person with a balanced health triangle is said to have a high degree of _____.

Understanding Key Concepts

After reading the question or statement, select the correct answer.

4. Which of the following is *not* an aspect of physical health?
   a. Eating well and drinking water
   b. Making and keeping friends
   c. Being physically active
   d. Getting enough sleep

5. Which statement is true about a person who is in good social health?
   a. She spends a lot of time alone.
   b. She has few friends at school.
   c. She may not be in good physical health.
   d. She gets along with others.

6. You are likely to move in a negative direction on the health continuum if
   a. you engage in physical activity daily.
   b. you accept responsibility for your health.
   c. you fail to practice healthful behaviors.
   d. you regularly eat a healthful diet.

7. Which of the following is *not* true of someone with good mental/emotional health?
   a. He dwells on negative thoughts.
   b. He is not overwhelmed by life's frustrations.
   c. He likes to try new challenges.
   d. He can stand up for his beliefs when necessary.

Thinking Critically

After reading the question or statement, write a short answer using complete sentences.

8. **Describe.** What are some characteristics of a person with good mental/emotional health?

9. **Explain.** How can your health triangle become unbalanced, and how can this imbalance affect your health?

10. **Identify.** List specific actions that teens can take to improve their wellness.

11. **Explain.** How do your health behaviors affect your position on the health continuum?

LESSON 2

Vocabulary Review

Correct the sentences below by replacing the italicized term with the correct vocabulary term.

12. Your *environment* consists of traits that are biologically passed on to you by your parents.

13. A person's ethnicity, religion, and language are part of her *peers*.

14. *Technology* personalities may become our role models for how to behave.

Understanding Key Concepts

After reading the question or statement, select the correct answer.

15. What technique can you use to locate valid health information on the Internet?
   a. Find sites that are the most popular.
   b. Use only sites belonging to manufacturers of health care products.
   c. Locate sites that use *.gov* or *.edu* in their addresses.
   d. All of the above

Health eSpotlight Wrap-Up

Taking Care of You Have students reread the Health eSpotlight question at the beginning of the chapter (page 5) and look at their original answer. **Ask Students**: *Now that you have read the chapter and watched* the video, what other activities would you add to your list of healthy activities? Call on volunteers to describe how their responses would change.

16. Cultural influences on your health include
    a. biologically inherited traits.
    b. beliefs, customs, and behaviors.
    c. the health continuum and triangle.
    d. all of the above.

17. The media is a powerful influence because it
    a. encourages teens to live healthy lives.
    b. is constantly present.
    c. provides healthy role models.
    d. warns the audience of risk behaviors.

Thinking Critically

After reading the question or statement, write a short answer using complete sentences.

18. **Describe.** What are some ways that peers can influence your health both positively and negatively?

19. **Analyze.** Think about your own culture, including your ethnic background, spirituality, language, and community. What are some practices within your culture that influence your health?

20. **Describe.** What are some ways that your attitudes influence your health?

LESSON 3

Vocabulary Review

Choose the correct term in the sentences below.

21. *Risk behaviors / Prevention* means taking steps to keep something from happening or getting worse.

22. *Resiliency / Abstinence* is a deliberate decision to avoid high-risk behaviors.

23. *Cumulative / Serious* risks are risks that add up over time.

Understanding Key Concepts

After reading the question or statement, select the correct answer.

24. Which of the following statements is true?
    a. Risk behaviors are illegal for everyone.
    b. Risk behaviors can harm your health.
    c. Most teens engage in risk behaviors.
    d. There is no way to avoid risk behaviors.

25. A person who practices multiple risk behaviors at the same time is likely to
    a. be unaware of what he is doing.
    b. be a role model for his friends.
    c. face more negative consequences.
    d. show sound judgment.

26. Personal habits and behaviors that relate to the way a person lives are called
    a. negative consequences.
    b. risk participation.
    c. health promotion.
    d. lifestyle factors.

Thinking Critically

After reading the question or statement, write a short answer using complete sentences.

27. **Identify.** What are two risk behaviors that pose a threat to the health of teens today?

28. **Discuss.** How are teens' perceptions of risk behaviors influenced by what they believe others are doing?

29. **Synthesize.** What is abstinence, and what are the effects of practicing abstinence?

LESSON 4

Vocabulary Review

Use the vocabulary terms listed on page 27 to complete the following statements.

30. _____ empowers people to live healthfully and improve their quality of life.

Chapter 1 Assessment **29**

LESSON 2

Vocabulary Review

12. heredity
13. culture
14. Media

Understanding Key Concepts

15. c
16. b
17. b

Thinking Critically

18. Sample answer: Peers can encourage you to participate in healthful activities, such as joining an athletic team or going for a daily walk together. Peers can also pressure you to engage in high risk or unhealthful behaviors, such as smoking or drinking.

19. Sample answers: Food choices, religious practices/spirituality, beliefs about illness

20. Having a positive attitude will help you adopt behaviors that will influence your health in positive ways.

LESSON 3

Vocabulary Review

21. Prevention
22. Abstinence
23. Cumulative

Understanding Key Concepts

24. b
25. c
26. d

Create and customize tests in minutes with this convenient digital platform.

- Create differentiated tests quickly and easily.
- All questions correlated to National/State Standards.
- Enhance tests with Document Based Questions (DBQ) and add your own photos or graphics.
- Build tests in both English and Spanish.
- Generate progress reports.

To order, go to **glencoe.com** and search for ISBN 0-07-888173-0.

29

Assessment

Thinking Critically

27. Sample answers: Using tobacco, alcohol, or other drugs; engaging in sexual activity; engaging in violence; driving recklessly

28. Answers will vary, but students should address the fact that if teens believe others are participating in risk behaviors they may be influenced to do the same.

29. Abstinence is the deliberate decision to avoid high-risk behaviors. By practicing abstinence you will be protecting your health and you will feel good about yourself because you value your well-being and take responsibility for your own health and wellness.

LESSON 4

Vocabulary Review

30. Health education
31. *Healthy People*
32. health literacy

Understanding Key Concepts

33. b
34. d

Thinking Critically

35. Sample answer: Almost $2 trillion spent on health care could be reduced considerably if people made healthier choices and decisions.

36. Individuals can set health goals and adopt health behaviors that are supportive of overall *Healthy People* goals.

37. Health education provides individuals with the knowledge and skills they need to stay healthy.

38. A self-directed learner takes action to positively affect his or her own health literacy.

---

31. Health goals for the United States may be found in _____.

32. A person who lacks _____ finds it difficult to obtain, understand, and use valid health information.

Understanding Key Concepts

After reading the question or statement, select the correct answer.

33. Health education provides
    a. medical health coverage.
    b. accurate health information.
    c. a wellness guarantee.
    d. none of the above.

34. Experts think that poor health literacy influences a person's health more than
    a. critical thinking and problem solving.
    b. attitude, environment, and income.
    c. education, income, and attitude.
    d. age, income, and education.

Thinking Critically

After reading the question or statement, write a short answer using complete sentences.

35. **Explain.** Why is it a good investment for the United States to keep its citizens healthy?

36. **Evaluate.** What role does the individual play in helping the nation achieve the goals of *Healthy People*?

37. **Describe.** How can health education help the nation achieve the *Healthy People* goals?

38. **Analyze.** How does being a self-directed learner affect a person's health literacy?

Project-Based ASSESSMENT

A Health Initiative

Background
Healthy People is an initiative set forth by the Department of Health and Human Services. The initiative establishes specific guidelines and goals that various people, states, communities, and professional organizations can use to improve the health of all Americans.

Task
Research the goals and guidelines of the initiative, and prepare an oral presentation that applies the guidelines to your school.

Audience
Students at your school

Purpose
Create a set of specific recommendations that can help the students in your school be healthier.

Procedure

1. Review the information in Chapter 1 regarding general health and wellness.
2. With a small group of three to four students, develop a policy for improving school health and a script for an oral presentation.
3. Divide the main task into smaller tasks, including research, writing, and delivering the presentation.
4. After the research is complete, meet as a group to discuss the possible applications for your school of *Healthy People*.
5. Meet with an administrator to discuss what role the school can play in the initiative.
6. Create a formal policy and a presentation, sharing the policy with your school.

30   Chapter 1   Assessment

Project-Based ASSESSMENT

Step 1 Brainstorm Have students decide first who will research, who will write, and who will deliver the presentation. Students assigned to researching should review the *Healthy People* initiative to get ideas for improving school health.

Step 2 Write Presentation Students should meet as a group and decide on which information to include and how they will present their findings. Students should also set up a meeting with a school administrator.

Step 3 Evaluate Students' presentations should reflect the research completed and realistic ideas that their school can implement.

Visit **glencoe.com** for Project-Based Assessment rubrics.

Math Practice

Analyze Geometric Properties. Read the passage, and use the equilateral triangle ABC to answer the questions.

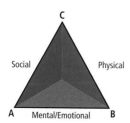

Natalie is doing a report on the health triangle. She sketched a model, but now she needs to make a larger version on poster board so that everyone in the classroom can see it. In her sketch, side AC is 9.5 cm long. Natalie decides to make the triangle on the poster board 3.25 times larger than her scale model.

1. When Natalie finishes drawing the large triangle on the poster board, what will be the approximate measure of side BC? Round to the nearest centimeter.

2. Side AB of the health triangle measures $5x$. Side BC measures $x + 20$. Which of the following statements explains why the equation $5x = x + 20$ can be used to solve for x?
   A. The angle measures of an equilateral triangle are never equal.
   B. Equilateral triangle have unequal sides.
   C. All sides of an equilateral triangle are always equal.
   D. Only two sides of an equilateral triangle are equal.

3. How might Natalie visually represent the health triangle of someone who neglects one or more aspects of health?

Go Online

For more test practice, visit glencoe.com and complete the Online Quizzes for Chapter 1.

Reading/Writing Practice

Understand and Apply. Read the passage below, and then answer the questions.

> (1) Veronica was late for her soccer game. (2) On her way to the field, she realized she had forgotten to pack her water bottle. (3) She did not think to get a drink from a nearby water fountain.
>
> (4) Near the end of the first half, Veronica's leg cramped up. (5) After resting and drinking a bottle of water, she began to feel better. (6) But her coach told her that she had become dehydrated and refused to let her back into the game. (7) Veronica hadn't even felt thirsty before she got the cramp.
>
> (8) Veronica didn't recognize you cannot count on thirst for knowing when you need water. (9) People can become dehydrated without feeling thirsty. (10) Before playing any sport, make sure you drink plenty of noncarbonated fluids.

1. Which sentence includes details that support the author's point of view?
   A. Sentence 2   C. Sentence 9
   B. Sentence 7   D. Sentence 10

2. How does the writer show that the purpose of this essay is to persuade?
   A. The writer emphasizes the use of proper-fitting protective gear.
   B. The writer contrasts the different types of soccer gear people use.
   C. The writer explains that soccer's increasing popularity has led to more injuries.
   D. The writer describes what happened to someone who did not drink enough water.

3. Write a paragraph explaining the importance of drinking plenty of water before, during, and after sports activities.

National Education Standards

Math: Number and Operations, Geometry
Language Arts: NCTE 1, NCTE 3, NCTE 4

Standardized Test Practice Answers

Math Practice
1. 31 centimeters
2. C
3. Answers should show one or more sides shorter, making the triangle unbalanced.

Reading/Writing Practice
1. C
2. D
3. Answers will vary, but should identify reasons for staying hydrated.

National Education Standards

Math: Number and Operations, Geometry

Language Arts: NCTE 1, NCTE 3, NCTE 4

For the complete Math and Language Arts standards, visit glencoe.com.

Go Online

Online Study Tools
For more test practice, visit glencoe.com and complete the Online Quizzes for Chapter 1.

Test-Taking Tip

Writing an Extended Response Point out to students that some questions, such as question 3 on this page, require an extended written response. In this case, students are required to write a paragraph. Review the components of a paragraph with students: a topic sentence that clearly states the main idea of the paragraph, several sentences that give details that support the topic sentence, and a concluding sentence that restates the main idea. Have students review their completed paragraphs to be sure they have included all of the requested information. In this case, they should be certain they have included the importance of drinking water before, during, and after sport activities.

Chapter 2 pages 32–59	Standards		Features
	National	**State/Local**	*Hands-On* **HEALTH**
	1.12.1, 1.12.5, 1.12.7, 2.12.1, 2.12.2, 2.12.4, 2.12.5, 2.12.8, 3.12.1, 3.12.5, 4.12.1, 4.12.3, 5.12.1, 5.12.2, 5.12.3, 5.12.7, 6.12.2, 8.12.3		• All About You *(Goal Setting)*, page 54
Lesson 1 **Building Health Skills** pages 34–39 **BIG Idea** *You can develop skills that will help you manage your health throughout your life.*	1.12.7, 2.12.1, 2.12.2, 2.12.3, 2.12.4, 2.12.5, 2.12.6, 2.12.7, 2.12.8, 4.12.1, 4.12.2, 4.12.3, 5.12.1, 6.12.1, 8.12.3		
Lesson 2 **Making Responsible Decisions and Setting Goals** pages 40–45 **BIG Idea** *You can actively promote your well-being by making healthful choices and setting positive goals.*	2.12.8, 5.12.1, 5.12.2, 5.12.3, 5.12.5, 5.12.6, 5.12.7, 6.12.1, 6.12.2, 7.12.1, 7.12.2, 7.12.3		**Health Skills Activity** • Making New Friends *(Decision Making)*, page 45 Out of Time
Lesson 3 **Being a Health Literate Consumer** pages 46–49 **BIG Idea** *A health literate consumer carefully evaluates health products and services.*	1.12.7, 2.12.2, 2.12.5, 2.12.6, 2.12.7, 3.12.1, 3.12.5, 5.12.1, 7.12.1, 7.12.2		**Real World CONNECTION** • Comparing Products, page 49 Out of Time
Lesson 4 **Managing Consumer Problems** pages 50–53 **BIG Idea** *Knowing how to handle consumer problems is an important skill to learn.*	1.12.5, 1.12.7, 2.12.4, 2.12.10, 3.12.1, 3.12.2, 3.12.3, 3.12.5, 4.12.4, 5.12.1, 5.12.4		

Key to Ability Levels

Teaching Strategies and activities have been coded for ability level and appropriateness.

AL Activities for students working above grade level   **BL** Activities for students working below grade level

OL Activities for students working on grade level   **EL** Activities for English Learners

Chapter 2 Planning Guide

Glencoe Exclusive!
TeacherWorks *Plus*
All-In-One Planner and Resource Center

Resources	Lesson Assessment	Technology
Student Activity Workbook TEACH *FAST FILE* RESOURCES Vocabulary Practice TEACH Health Labs EXTEND	Chapter 2 Review Chapter 2 Assessment Standardized Test Practice ExamView® Assessment Suite CD-ROM	**Teaching Tools:** TeacherWorks™ Plus DVD StudentWorks™ Plus DVD ExamView® Assessment Suite CD-ROM Transparency Fitness DVD PowerPoint® DVD Health eSpotlight Video Series DVD
FAST FILE RESOURCES Reading Strategies Activity TEACH Reteaching Activity REVIEW Enrichment Activity EXTEND Health Skills Practice TEACH	Lesson 1 Assessment, page 39 Lesson 1 Quiz *Fast File* ExamView® Assessment Suite CD-ROM	**Web-Based Resources:** Go Online glencoe.com • Health Podcast Activities • Audio Chapter Summaries (English/Spanish) • Interactive Health Tutor
FAST FILE RESOURCES Reading Strategies Activity TEACH Reteaching Activity REVIEW Enrichment Activity EXTEND Health Skills Practice TEACH	Lesson 2 Assessment, page 45 Lesson 2 Quiz *Fast File* ExamView® Assessment Suite CD-ROM	• Health Skills Activities • Vocabulary PuzzleMaker • Parent Letters (English/Spanish) • Lesson Plans • Health Inventories
FAST FILE RESOURCES Reading Strategies Activity TEACH Reteaching Activity REVIEW Enrichment Activity EXTEND Health Skills Practice TEACH	Lesson 3 Assessment, page 49 Lesson 3 Quiz *Fast File* ExamView® Assessment Suite CD-ROM	• Online Quizzes • Study-to-Go • Unit Web Projects • Student Web Activities • Fitness Zone Activities
FAST FILE RESOURCES Reading Strategies Activity TEACH Reteaching Activity REVIEW Enrichment Activity EXTEND Health Skills Practice TEACH	Lesson 4 Assessment, page 53 Lesson 4 Quiz *Fast File* ExamView® Assessment Suite CD-ROM	

StudentWorks *Plus*

This is the student's backpack solution.

Includes:
- complete Interactive Student Edition
- full audio of English text and Spanish chapter summaries
- allows students to record assignments and track grades.
- links to online activities and additional student resources
- access to all student worksheets and workbooks

FOLDABLES®
Study Organizer

Dinah Zike Foldables®
Chapter Activity
Refer to the *Dinah Zike Reading and Study Skills for Glencoe Health*. Have students complete the six-tab Foldable to organize their notes on health skills. As students read the lessons, have them add details about the six health skills under the appropriate tabs.

Taking Charge of Your Health

Chapter Overview

Chapter 2 focuses on skills individuals can use to promote their health. Making responsible decisions, setting goals, being a health-literate consumer, and knowing how to handle consumer problems are also discussed.

Lesson 1

Learning health skills can help a person stay healthy throughout his or her life.

Lesson 2

Actively promote well-being by making healthful choices and setting positive goals.

Lesson 3

Health-literate consumers, who carefully evaluate health products and services, are able to make choices that enhance health.

Lesson 4

People who know how to handle consumer problems can avoid fraud and malpractice.

▶ **Activating Prior Knowledge**

After students have completed their paragraphs, **Ask Students:** *What skills are these teens using to help them make healthful choices?* (They are making a comparison.)

CHAPTER **2**

Taking Charge of Your Health

Lesson 1
Building Health Skills

BIG Idea *You can develop skills that will help you manage your health throughout your life.*

Lesson 2
Making Responsible Decisions and Setting Goals

BIG Idea *You can actively promote your well-being by making healthful choices and setting positive goals.*

Lesson 3
Being a Health-Literate Consumer

BIG Idea *A health-literate consumer carefully evaluates health products and services.*

Lesson 4
Managing Consumer Problems

BIG Idea *Knowing how to handle consumer problems is an important skill to learn.*

Activating Prior Knowledge

Using Visuals Look at what is happening in this photo. Why is it important to comparison shop when buying health-related products? Explain your thoughts in a short paragraph.

Universal Access

Differentiated Learning Glencoe provides teacher support and student materials for all learners in the health classroom.

- Chapter Summaries in English and Spanish are available online at **glencoe.com**.

- *Fast Files* and related worksheets support reluctant readers.

- Universal Access strategies throughout the Teacher Wraparound Edition and *Fast Files* help you present materials for gifted students, at-risk students, physically impaired students, and those with behavior disorders or learning disabilities.

Chapter Launchers

Health in Action

Discuss the BIG Ideas

Before beginning this chapter, think about how you would answer these questions:

▶ What is a health skill?
▶ How can health skills help you achieve wellness?
▶ Why should you be a health-literate consumer?

Watch the *Health eSpotlight* Video Series

Making Decisions About Your Personal Health

How might messages in the media influence people's lifestyle decisions and behaviors?

Assess Your Health

 Online

Visit glencoe.com and complete the Health Inventory for Chapter 2.

Chapter 2   Taking Charge of Your Health   **33**

Chapter Launchers

Health in Action

Discuss the BIG Ideas

Assign this activity before students read the chapter. Explain that the purpose of the questions is to help students assess their current knowledge of health skills.

Health eSpotlight
Video Series

Making Decisions About Your Personal Health

Before Viewing the Video

Ask Students: *What are some media messages you've read, heard, or seen that promote a healthy lifestyle?* (Answers will vary.)

Online

Have students go to **glencoe.com** and take the Health Inventory for Chapter 2.

Chapter Skills

Reading Skills
- Reviewing Facts and Vocabulary, pp. 39, 45, 49, 53
- Reading/Writing Practice, p. 59

BIG Idea

Individuals who develop health skills can take charge of their health.

Health Skills
- Health Skills Activity, p. 45
- Applying Health Skills, pp. 39, 45, 49, 53

Writing Skills
- Real World Connection, p. 49
- Writing Critically, pp. 39, 45, 49, 53
- Reading/Writing Practice, p. 59

Vocabulary
- New Vocabulary, pp. 34, 40, 46, 50
- Reviewing Facts and Vocabulary, pp. 39, 45, 49, 53

Building Health Skills

① FOCUS

BIG Idea Developing skills will help a person manage their health throughout life. **Ask Students:** *What are some skills you use to maintain your health?* (Sample answers: Decision-making skills, refusal skills)

Before You Read

Vocabulary Cards Students' vocabulary cards should provide definitions for each of the lesson vocabulary terms.

Main Idea

Learning Health Skills Health skills are tools that people can use to manage their health. **Ask Students:** *How can teens use skills, such as decision-making and communication skills, to enhance their health?* (Sample answer: Decision-making skills can be used to avoid behaviors that harm your health, such as using tobacco or alcohol.)

Real Life Issues

Have students brainstorm a list of physical activities for Alejandro, such as walking, bike riding, and swimming. Tell students they can refer to the list as they write their dialogues. **Ask Students:** *What are some ways that you are physically active?* (Sample answers: Walking to work, weekend basketball games)

GUIDE TO READING

BIG Idea *You can develop skills that will help you manage your health throughout your life.*

Before You Read

Create Vocabulary Cards. Write each new vocabulary term on a separate note card. For each term, write a definition based on your current knowledge. As you read, fill in additional information related to each term.

Health Skills

New Vocabulary

▶ health skills (p. 34)
▶ interpersonal communication (p. 35)
▶ refusal skills (p. 36)
▶ conflict resolution (p. 36)
▶ stress (p. 38)
▶ stress management skills (p. 38)
▶ advocacy (p. 39)

Building Health Skills

Real Life Issues

Fitting in Fitness. Alejandro is carrying a full schedule of advanced courses this semester. He also plays an instrument in the school jazz band and has a part-time job at the grocery store. Alejandro wants to add some physical activity to his schedule, but can't figure out how to fit it in. He asks his good friend Phil for suggestions.

Writing *Write a conversation in which Alejandro explains his situation to Phil. Phil should be supportive and offer possible strategies that can help Alejandro add physical activity into his schedule.*

Learning Health Skills

Main Idea Health skills help you manage your health.

Health skills are *specific tools and strategies to maintain, protect, and improve all aspects of your health.* Health skills are also called *life skills*, because once you've developed these skills, you can use them throughout your life to stay healthy. **Figure 2.1** lists the health skills you will learn in this chapter. You will have opportunities to practice them throughout the rest of the book.

Communication Skills

Main Idea Good communication is a vital health skill.

Three health skills—interpersonal communication, refusal skills, and conflict resolution—deal with how you give and receive information. Communication is more than just talking.

Skills for the **21st** Century

Communication and Collaboration
The ability to communicate and collaborate with others is vital to success in many areas. These skills are also used within families on a daily basis. Ask students to make a list of three specific ways that they use communication or collaboration skills with their families or friends. Then have students identify specific ways they could improve their communication and collaboration skills. Ask volunteers to share some of their responses with the class.

Figure 2.1   The Health Skills

Health skills are tools that help you take responsibility for your health.

Health Skill	Benefit to Your Health
Communication	You share your ideas and feelings, and listen carefully when others express theirs.
Refusal	You say no to unhealthy behaviors.
Conflict Resolution	You resolve problems with others in healthy ways.
Accessing Information	You locate valid sources of health information, products, and services.
Analyzing Influences	You understand the many influences on your health, including peers, family, culture, media, and technology.
Practicing Healthful Behaviors	You act to reduce risks and protect yourself against illness and injury.
Stress Management	You use healthy ways to reduce and manage stress in your life.
Advocacy	You work to improve your own health and the health of your family and your community.
Decision Making	You use a step-by-step process to evaluate your options and make healthy choices.
Goal Setting	You set goals and develop a plan to achieve those goals.

It involves carefully choosing your words and expressions to clearly say what you really mean. It also involves listening closely to others. **Interpersonal communication**—*the exchange of thoughts, feelings, and beliefs between two or more people*—helps you build strong relationships with others.

You can strengthen your interpersonal communication skills by doing the following:

- **Use "I" messages to express your feelings.** Saying "I feel upset when I'm left out of our plans" focuses on your emotions rather than placing blame.
- **Communicate with respect and caring.** Keep your voice calm and use a respectful tone when talking to another person.
- **Be an active listener.** Pay attention to what the other person is saying. Let him say what he has to say without interrupting. Try to understand the other person's point of view.

You will learn more about interpersonal communication in Chapter 6.

Go Online

Go to glencoe.com and complete the Student Web Activity on building better communication skills with friends and family.

---

2 TEACH

R Reading Strategy

Analyzing a Chart Have students examine the chart that identifies health skills and the benefits to health. For each identified health skill, have a volunteer read the entry in the "Benefit to Your Health" column. Then have students brainstorm specific situations in which teens might apply that particular skill. For example, communication skills might be applied when a teen discusses a failing grade with a teacher. Refusal skills might be applied when a teen tells some friends that he will not smoke with them. BL OL

AL Active Learning

Demonstration Have students work in small groups to plan a method for demonstrating interpersonal communication skills to students in fourth through sixth grades. Remind students to use "I" messages. Have each group share its demonstration with the class, and if possible, with younger students. OL AL

Go Online

Have students go to glencoe.com and complete the Student Web Activity on building better communication skills with friends and family.

Cooperative Learning

Using Body Language Explain that body language is an essential part of effective communication. Divide the class into small groups. Have students work within their groups to write role-plays about a teen whose friend has borrowed and accidentally damaged a valuable item. The role-play should show how body language can be used to effectively convey emotions as part of respectful communication. Have each group share its role-play with the class. Ask students to evaluate the body language in the role-plays of other groups.

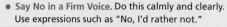

Figure 2.2 Refusal Strategies

These refusal strategies can help you say no to potentially harmful activities.

- **Say No in a Firm Voice.** Do this calmly and clearly. Use expressions such as "No, I'd rather not."
- **Explain Why.** State your feelings. Tell the other person that the suggested activity or behavior goes against your values or beliefs.
- **Offer Alternatives.** Suggest a safe, healthful activity to do instead of the one offered.
- **Stand Your Ground.** Make it clear that you don't intend to back down from your position.
- **Leave if Necessary.** If the other person continues to pressure you, or won't take no for an answer, simply walk away.

W Writing Support

Persuasive Writing Have students write a dialogue in which one teen uses refusal skills to avoid a harmful activity. Remind students to edit and correct their work before turning it in. OL

CA Cultural Awareness

Cultural Impact on Conflict Resolution Explain that cultural background influences the way that individuals manage conflict. In some cultures, maintaining harmony within a group is considered more important than the feelings of individuals. In other cultures, individuals' feelings are considered more important than group harmony. Ask students to discuss ways that these differing views would impact the way people deal with conflict. OL

READING CHECK

Answer Interpersonal communication, conflict resolution, refusal skills

Refusal Skills

Refusal skills are *communication strategies that can help you say no when you are urged to take part in behaviors that are unsafe or unhealthful, or that go against your values.* Someone may ask you to ride in a car with a driver who has been drinking. Or, someone may offer you a cigarette even though you don't smoke. Developing strong refusal skills helps you say no firmly, respectfully, and effectively.

Figure 2.2 lists important refusal strategies that will help you the next time a person tries to influence you to engage in an activity that you don't want to do. You may use one or several of these strategies in your refusal. Chapter 8 provides additional information on refusal strategies.

READING CHECK

Identify Name three communication skills that help protect your health.

Conflict-Resolution Skills

Think of a recent argument you had. How was it resolved? Were all the people involved satisfied with the outcome? If so, you probably used the skill of **conflict resolution**, *the process of ending a conflict through cooperation and problem solving.* This health skill can help people resolve problems in ways that are agreeable to everyone involved.

Conflict-resolution skills include stepping away from an argument, allowing the conflict to subside, using good interpersonal communication skills, and maintaining an attitude of respect for yourself as well as for the other person. Sometimes, individuals must make a compromise in order to resolve the conflict. In a compromise, both parties give up something but still gain a desired result. You will learn more about conflict resolution in Chapter 9.

CA

36 **Chapter 2** Taking Charge of Your Health

Promoting School Wellness

Health Skills A comprehensive health education curriculum is a component of a coordinated school health program in which students learn health skills. Health skills, which include communication, conflict resolution, accessing information, stress management, goal-setting, and decision-making, can be used throughout students' lives to help them enhance health. Have students practice these health skills throughout the year.

Accessing Information

Main Idea Use reliable sources of health information.

Knowing how to find and evaluate health information will help you make decisions that benefit your well-being. To decide whether health information is valid, you need to determine the reliability of the group or individual sharing the information. Some valid sources include

- health care providers and professionals.
- valid Internet sites, such as those of government agencies and professional health organizations.
- parents, guardians, and other trusted adults.
- recently published material written by respected, well-known science and health professionals.

Analyzing Influences

Main Idea Understanding what influences you helps you to make more healthful choices.

Do you ever stop and think about *why* you do the things you do? Many factors can influence our decisions and actions. **Figure 2.3** identifies some examples of influences on our behaviors. The more aware you are of the various influences in your life and how they affect *you*, the better able you are to make informed choices about your health.

 READING CHECK

Explain Why is the ability to find valid health information an important tool for protecting your health?

Figure 2.3 Influences on Your Health

Many factors influence your health. *Which sources have the most influence on you?*

Personal Values • Things I think are important • Likes and dislikes • Skills and talents	Your Family and Culture • Beliefs, behaviors, and habits • Family traditions • Food served at home
Personal Beliefs • Plans for the future • Goals • Hopes and dreams	Media and Technology • TV and movies • Magazines • Internet
Perceptions • Behaviors that I think are common or accepted	Friends and Peers • Behaviors and opinions of my friends and classmates
Curiosity/Fears • Things I wonder about • Things that scare or frighten me • Things I want to try • Things I never want to try	School and Community • Place where I live • School I attend • Air quality • Sources of recreation

R

Lesson 1 Building Health Skills **37**

Main Idea

Accessing Information It's important to use reliable sources of health information. **Ask Students:** *Why is it important to be sure that your sources of health information are trusted and reliable?* (Sample answer: Information that is not reliable can lead you to take actions or make decisions that could jeopardize your health.)

Main Idea

Analyzing Influences People make better decisions when they understand the influences that affect their decisions. **Ask Students:** *What are some of the factors that influence your decisions?* (Sample answer: Television, my parents, my friends)

R Reading Strategy

Applying Information Write the following question on the board: What affects your health? Ask volunteers to provide answers to the question, and record their responses on the board. Explain that all of the responses are influences on health. OL

READING CHECK

Answer Accurate health information gives you the foundation to make healthful decisions.

Caption Answer

Figure 2.3 Sample answers: Family, peers, culture, values, environment, technology

Writing Strategy

Poetry Tell students the topics that are frequently used as the subject of poems—dreams and hopes, family and friends, the physical environment—are also factors that influence health. Have students research a poem that deals with one of these topics. Alternatively, have students write their own poems about one of these topics. Have each student share the poem he or she has researched or created with the class. Follow up by having students work as a class to make a list of the factors that influence health that were used as poetry topics in this project.

LESSON 1

Main Idea

Self-Management Skills
Healthful habits can play a role in protecting health. **Ask Students:** *What are some healthful habits that you try to make a part of your life?* (Sample answers: Getting plenty of physical activity, avoiding alcohol)

U Universal Access

English Language Learners
Read aloud for students the factors that influence health listed in **Figure 2.4**. Have students locate pictures in magazines or draw pictures to represent as many of the influences as possible. Have students work together to use the pictures to make a collage of factors that influence health. **BL EL**

HS Health Skills Practice

Goal Setting Have students review the list of health behaviors in **Figure 2.4** and choose the one that they feel they most need to improve. Ask each student to develop a personal health goal related to the behavior he or she has selected. Remind students that they may keep their goal confidential. Tell students that they should write down their goal, steps they will take to achieve the goal, and people who can help them. Remind students to periodically evaluate their progress toward their goal and to reward themselves when they reach their goal. **OL**

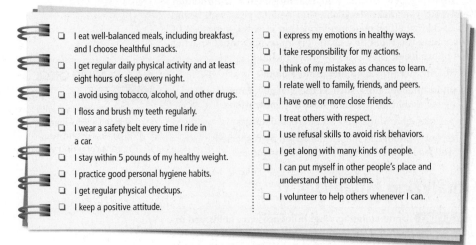

Figure 2.4 **Health Behaviors Checklist**

Developing good health habits is important to maintaining your health. *Which of these health habits do you practice every day?*

- ❏ I eat well-balanced meals, including breakfast, and I choose healthful snacks.
- ❏ I get regular daily physical activity and at least eight hours of sleep every night.
- ❏ I avoid using tobacco, alcohol, and other drugs.
- ❏ I floss and brush my teeth regularly.
- ❏ I wear a safety belt every time I ride in a car.
- ❏ I stay within 5 pounds of my healthy weight.
- ❏ I practice good personal hygiene habits.
- ❏ I get regular physical checkups.
- ❏ I keep a positive attitude.

- ❏ I express my emotions in healthy ways.
- ❏ I take responsibility for my actions.
- ❏ I think of my mistakes as chances to learn.
- ❏ I relate well to family, friends, and peers.
- ❏ I have one or more close friends.
- ❏ I treat others with respect.
- ❏ I use refusal skills to avoid risk behaviors.
- ❏ I get along with many kinds of people.
- ❏ I can put myself in other people's place and understand their problems.
- ❏ I volunteer to help others whenever I can.

U

Self-Management Skills

Main Idea Practicing healthy habits will protect your health.

Academic Vocabulary

promote *(verb):* to contribute to the growth of

Self-management means taking charge of your own health. When you manage your behaviors, you act in ways that protect your health and **promote** your own well-being. There are two self-management skills:

- **Practicing healthful behaviors.** You practice healthful behaviors when you make good health habits part of your everyday life. Take a look at the checklist shown in **Figure 2.4**. These positive behaviors can contribute to all aspects of your health.

- **Managing Stress.** Do you get nervous just before a test? Do you get stage fright? These are signs of **stress**, *the reaction of the body and mind to everyday challenges and demands*. Stress is a normal part of life, but too much unrelieved stress can lead to illnesses. That's why it's important to learn **stress management skills**, *skills that help you reduce and manage stress in your life*. Exercising, relaxation, and managing time efficiently are some effective ways to manage stress. You will learn more about stress management in Chapter 4.

HS

38 Chapter 2 Taking Charge of Your Health

Myths & Reality

Managing Health

Myth: Health is not something individuals have control over.

Fact: Individuals can practice behaviors that promote well-being and enhance health. The choices and decisions people make can have positive or negative impacts on their health.

Myth: I'm young; I don't need to worry about my health until I'm older.

Fact: Practicing healthful behaviors during the teen years can have a lifelong, positive impact on health.

Advocacy

Main Idea Advocacy lets you share your health knowledge.

At the beginning of this unit, on pages 2–3, you saw a picture of teens participating in a community event. This is an example of **advocacy**, *taking action to influence others to address a health-related concern or to support a health-related belief.* Participating in such activities allows you to encourage others to practice healthful behaviors. You can also advocate for better health by obeying laws that protect community health, sharing health information with family and friends, and developing and sending out health messages.

LESSON 1 — ASSESSMENT

After You Read

Reviewing Facts and Vocabulary

1. Define the term *health skills*.
2. What are two interpersonal communication skills that can reduce your health risk?
3. What is *advocacy*?

Thinking Critically

4. **Synthesize.** Why is it important to recognize and analyze the various influences on your behavior?
5. **Analyze.** How can advocacy help you with health issues that are important to you?

Applying Health Skills

6. **Stress Management.** List all the healthful strategies you used in the past week to relieve stress. Which ones were most helpful?

Writing Critically

7. **Narrative.** Marcos and Sarah disagree about which movie to see. Write a dialogue in which they resolve their disagreement using effective interpersonal communication strategies.

 Online

Visit **glencoe.com** and complete the Interactive Study Guide for this lesson.

Main Idea

Advocacy Advocacy allows you to share health knowledge. **Ask Students:** *What are some ways you could advocate good health to members of your own family?* (Sample answer: I could remind my little sister to brush her teeth.)

③ ASSESS/CLOSE

Assessment Resources

📁 **FAST FILE ACTIVITIES**
Lesson 1 Quiz

💿 *ExamView*
Assessment Suite CD-ROM

Visit glencoe.com for:
Online Quizzes
Online Learning Center

Progress Monitoring

Reteaching
Have students work in pairs to review **Figure 2.1**. Have each pair develop and share with the class one fictional scenario in which a teen uses a specific health skill.

Enrichment
Have students write a persuasive paragraph that encourages other teens to practice a specific health skill. Students should explain the benefits of practicing the health skill.

 Online

Have students visit **glencoe.com** and complete the Interactive Study Guide for this lesson.

39

LESSON 1 ASSESSMENT ANSWERS

1. *Health skills* are tools and strategies used to maintain, protect, and improve all aspects of your health.
2. Conflict resolution and refusal skills
3. *Advocacy* is any action that influences others to address a health-related concern or support a health-related belief.
4. Sample answer: There are many sources of health information, but they are not all reliable or valid. Finding reliable information allows you to make decisions and choices that enhance health.
5. Sample answer: If you can advocate for an issue, it shows you understand the significance of an issue and it shows you care about other people.
6. Students' lists will vary, but should include some of the strategies for stress management that were mentioned in the lesson.
7. Dialogues will vary.

LESSON 2

Making Responsible Decisions and Setting Goals

1 FOCUS

GUIDE TO READING

BIG Idea People can take charge of their health by making healthful choices and setting positive goals. **Ask Students:** *What are some health-related decisions that teens face on a daily basis?* (Sample answer: Food and physical activity choices, choosing friendships)

Before You Read

K-W-L Chart Students' K-W-L charts will vary.

Main Idea

Decisions, Goals, and Your Health Responsible decisions are the first step toward good health. **Ask Students:** *How can health-related decisions impact each side of your health triangle?* (Sample answer: Food choices affect physical health, choices about friends impact social health, and choices about the future affect mental/emotional health.)

Real Life Issues

Discuss possible positive and negative consequences for Tara if she tries out for soccer and if she doesn't try out. After students have written their conversations, have volunteers share with the class.

 GUIDE TO READING

BIG Idea *You can actively promote your well-being by making healthful choices and setting positive goals.*

Before You Read

Create a K-W-L Chart. Make a three-column chart. In the first column, list what you **k**now about decision making and goal setting. In the second column, list what you **w**ant to know about this topic. As you read, use the third column to summarize what you **l**earned.

K	W	L

New Vocabulary

▶ values (p. 41)
▶ decision-making skills (p. 41)
▶ goals (p. 42)
▶ short-term goal (p. 43)
▶ long-term goal (p. 43)
▶ action plan (p. 44)

Making Responsible Decisions and Setting Goals

Real Life Issues ·······························

Making Decisions. Tara has been playing soccer since elementary school. Tryouts for the varsity soccer team are coming up, and she's having trouble deciding whether to try out. Tara loves soccer, but she's not sure she's good enough to make the team. If she *does* make the team, she might not have enough time to study and do well in school.

Writing *Write a conversation in which Tara explains her situation to her school counselor. The counselor should help Tara figure out what the potential outcomes of her choices might be.*

Decisions, Goals, and Your Health

Main Idea Achieving good health begins with making responsible decisions.

Now that you're in high school, do you have more freedom than you did when you were younger? Maybe you're allowed to stay out later on weekends and have more control over your schedule and activities. You may have a wider circle of friends than you did in middle school. Having more freedom is an exciting benefit of growing up.

As you're probably finding out, the freedom you gain as you grow older comes with more responsibility. For example, you may have to make tough decisions. You'll also have to set goals for yourself and plan how to reach them. Making decisions and setting goals means you're taking responsibility in determining your life's purpose and direction.

 **Teens Want to Know**

Why Is It so Hard to Make Decisions? Point out that teens often become frustrated with the increasingly complex decisions they are required to make as they approach adulthood. There are many reasons why teens struggle with decision making. First, teens often fail to see a wide spectrum of possibilities for a decision, but instead, see an either/or type of situation. Teens also tend to focus more on social consequences of decisions, rather than seeing potential physical or mental/emotional consequences. Teens also lack the life experiences adults call on when making decisions. Reassure teens that decision making is a skill that continues to develop into adulthood.

Decision Making

Main Idea Decision-making skills help you make successful, responsible choices.

Life is filled with decisions. You make plenty of them every day. Some decisions are small, like what to wear to school or what to eat for breakfast. Other choices may be life changing, like deciding which college to attend or which career to pursue. Developing good decision-making skills will help you make responsible choices that contribute to your health and quality of life.

Your Values

The decisions you make reflect your personal values and the values of your family. **Values** are *the ideas, beliefs, and attitudes about what is important that help guide the way you live.* For example, you may value a strong, healthy body. The decisions you make about how to take care of your body will reflect this value. If you value your relationships with family and friends, you will make choices that show your caring and respect.

Because you first learned your values from your family, it's often a good idea to talk with family members about a decision that is troubling you. You share important values with them, so they can provide you with helpful feedback.

The Decision-Making Process

Have you ever thought about what actually goes into making a decision? **Decision-making skills** are *steps that enable you to make a healthful decision.* **Figure 2.7** on page 42 illustrates the six steps in making good decisions. Notice that one of the steps involves the HELP strategy. This strategy includes asking yourself the following questions:

- **H** *(Healthful)* Does this choice present any health risks?
- **E** *(Ethical)* Does this choice reflect what you value?
- **L** *(Legal)* Does this option violate any local, state, or federal laws?
- **P** *(Parent Approval)* Would your parents or guardians approve of this choice?

READING CHECK

Analyze Why is it important to develop good decision-making skills?

■ **Figure 2.6** Family members often know you better than anyone else knows you. *Why is it a good idea to talk over important decisions with family members?*

41

② TEACH

Main Idea

Decision Making Decision-making skills can lead to responsible choices. **Ask Students:** *How do the decisions you make as a teen differ from the decisions you made as a young child?* (Sample answer: The decisions I make now are more difficult and have a greater impact on my future than the decisions I made when I was a child.)

C Critical Thinking

Predicting Lead a class discussion on ways that values can differ between individuals. Ask students to identify factors, such as age or culture, which can cause individuals to have differing values. Then ask students to predict some positive and some negative consequences that might occur when individuals with different values interact. **OL**

READING CHECK

Answer Good decision-making skills can help a person make responsible choices that contribute to health and quality of life.

U Universal Access

English Language Learners Explain that decisions are a part of everyone's life. Give students an opportunity to practice their speaking skills in a discussion of everyday decisions teens face. To generate discussion, pose questions such as: What decisions do you make in the school cafeteria? Have volunteers respond verbally. **EL**

ELL Support

Name and Repeat Write the word *value* on the board. Tell students that the word *value* is an example of a word with more than one meaning.

Beginning Ask students to locate the word *values* in the text. Explain that, in this lesson, the word *value* means "ideas, beliefs, and attitudes about what is important."

Intermediate Build on the Beginning activity by asking students to find the word *value* in an English dictionary. Point out that

value can also refer to the monetary worth of an object.

Advanced After reviewing the meanings of the word *value*, ask students to write two sentences, one using the word to refer to their attitudes, ideas, and beliefs and one using the word to refer to monetary worth.

Main Idea

Goal Setting Setting and meeting goals is a way that individuals can have the future they desire. **Ask Students:** *What are some health-related goals a teen might set?* (Sample answers: To get more physical activity, to eat lower-fat foods)

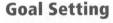 **Writing Support**

Narrative Writing Have students write a narrative that tells about a teen who has to make an important decision. Give them some scenarios as a starter. Remind students to use the decision-making process. Also remind them that the narrative should include a setting, plot, and characters, and should be told in a logical order. Remind students to proofread and correct their work before turning in a final product. **OL AL**

U Universal Access

Behavior Disorders For students with behavior disorders, even short-term goals can prove overwhelming. Discuss with students the idea of breaking down short-term goals into very small, manageable steps. For example, a student may have a short-term goal of reading a chapter of a book in one week. Breaking this down into a number of pages to read each day can prove to be much more manageable. Explain that the small steps for reaching a short-term goal can be listed on a piece of paper and checked off as they are achieved. **BL OL**

Figure 2.7 **Steps of the Decision-Making Process**

STEP 1 **State the Situation.**
Clearly identify the situation. Ask yourself: What decision do I need to make? Who is involved? Am I feeling pressure to make a decision? How much time do I have to decide?

STEP 2 **List the Options.**
What are all the possible choices you could make? Remember that sometimes it is appropriate *not* to take action. Share your options with parents or guardians, siblings, teachers, or friends. Ask for their advice.

STEP 3 **Weigh the Possible Outcomes.**
Weigh the consequences of each option. Use the HELP strategy to guide your choice.

STEP 4 **Consider Values.**
A responsible decision will reflect your values.

STEP 5 **Make a Decision and Act on It.**
Use everything you know at this point to make a responsible decision. You can feel good that you have carefully thought about the situation and your options.

STEP 6 **Evaluate the Decision.**
After you have made the decision and taken action, reflect on what happened. What was the outcome? How did your decision affect your health and the health of those around you? What did you learn? Would you take the same action again? If not, how would your choice differ?

Goal Setting

Main Idea Working toward goals helps you achieve your hopes and dreams.

How do you see yourself in the future? What would you like to accomplish? What are your hopes and dreams? The answers to these questions form your **goals**, *those things you aim for that take planning and work*. Whether you reach your goals—and how successfully you reach them—depends on the plans you make now. Suppose your goal is to go to college. To reach that goal, you'll plan what courses to take in high school so that you meet the entrance requirements of the college you choose. You'll also work hard to earn the grades that will get you in.

Just as you set life goals because you have dreams for the future, you also set goals for your health in order to stay well. For instance, you may set a goal to drink more water and

42 **Chapter 2** Taking Charge of Your Health

 Home and Community

The HELP Strategy Point out to students the last step in the HELP strategy is to consider whether your parents or guardians would approve of the choice. Have students work in groups to write role-plays in which a teen facing a decision receives valuable input from a parent, guardian, or trusted adult in their community. Follow up with a discussion of why an adult's input is valuable, even for more independent teens. Then ask teens to make a list of adults in their family or community who could help them with difficult choices. Remind students that they may keep their lists confidential.

fewer soft drinks. To reach this goal, you need to plan how to make water available instead of soda when you're thirsty. You might plan to carry a refillable water bottle in your backpack, and to order water instead of soda when you're eating out with friends.

Types of Goals

AL Time is a consideration when you're setting goals. How long do you think it will take to reach your goal? A **short-term goal**, like finishing a term paper by Friday, is *a goal that you can reach in a short period of time.* A **long-term goal** is *a goal that you plan to reach over an extended period of time.*

Sometimes short-term goals become stepping stones to long-term goals. For example, making a high school sports team can be a stepping stone to your goal of becoming a professional athlete.

Short-Term Goals You can accomplish a short-term goal fairly quickly. Let's say your goal is to find and read three articles on an assigned topic over the weekend. On Saturday you search the Internet, locate, and print out your articles. On Sunday you read the articles so you're ready to discuss them in class on Monday.

Long-Term Goals Long-term goals call for more time as well as more planning. If you want to run a 10K (6.2-mile) race, you know you need to train for several months to build up your endurance and speed. A series of short-term goals can help you achieve this. You can practice running shorter distances until you are able to run a mile in a reasonable time.

Figure 2.8 Many teens set health-related goals based on personal assessments of their health. *What steps can you take to improve your health? What strategies could you use?*

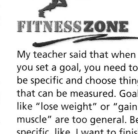

My teacher said that when you set a goal, you need to be specific and choose things that can be measured. Goals like "lose weight" or "gain muscle" are too general. Be specific, like, I want to finish a 5K race, or I want to eat at least five servings of fruits and vegetables a day. That way you can track your success. For more ideas on fitness goals, visit the Online Fitness Zone at glencoe.com.

 **READING CHECK**

Describe Identify and describe two types of goals.

AL Active Learning

Interviews Lead a class discussion that emphasizes the importance of goals to people of all ages. Then, have students interview a family member who is at a different stage of life to learn more about their goals. After students have completed their interviews, have them compare their goals with those of the family member. **OL**

This activity is similar to Simon Says:

- Have students get into groups of 6–8.
- A leader will name an exercise and then say "please."
- Everyone in the group will perform the exercise until a new exercise is given.
- If leader does not say "please," the exercise should not be performed.

READING CHECK

Answer Short-term goal: Eating healthful foods on a particular day. Long-term goal: Wanting to become more healthful overall.

Academic Integration

English Divide the class into small groups. Ask students in each group to talk about the decisions made by characters in novels or short stories they are currently reading or have recently read. Write the following questions on the board. Call on each group to summarize their responses to the questions.

- What character did you discuss?
- What decision did this character make?
- Did the character follow the steps of the decision-making process?
- What was the outcome of the character's decision?
- What decision would you have made if you were in the character's situation?

Caption Answer

Figure 2.8 Sample answer: I could walk 20 minutes each day. A strategy I would use is to set a time to walk each day with a friend, so we can encourage each other.

■ **Figure 2.9** This teen trained hard to reach the State Finals. *What other types of long-term goals might you set that can be reached by setting short-term goals?*

Health Skills · Activity

**Decision-Making Skills:
Making New Friends**

NHES Standard 5 Students will demonstrate the ability to use decision-making skills to enhance health.

Objectives

- Identify the potential consequences of health-related decisions.
- Apply decision-making skills to make a health-promoting decision.

Teaching Strategies

- Have students review the steps of the decision-making process.
- Ask students to explain the role that Justine's values play in her decisions.

Assessment

Using this list, student work should provide comprehensive evidence of the following criteria to achieve the highest score:

√ Clearly describes the situation
√ Lists several options with possible outcomes of each
√ Weighs possible outcomes
√ Considers values
√ Makes a health-enhancing decision and includes an evaluation of that decision

Then, you work up to running 5K (3.1 miles). Working short-term goals into the planning of your long-term goal helps you feel good each week as you run faster and farther.

Reaching Your Goals

To reach your goal, you need an action plan. An **action plan** is *a multistep strategy to identify and achieve your goals.* You can turn your dreams into reality by following the steps in **Figure 2.10**.

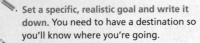

Figure 2.10   **Developing an Action Plan**

- Set a specific, realistic goal and write it down. You need to have a destination so you'll know where you're going.

- List the steps you will take to reach your goal. Think of short-term goals as the steps that lead you to the long-term goal.

- Identify sources of help and support. Who are your team members? They might include friends, family members, teachers, or community leaders.

- Set a reasonable time frame for achieving your goal. Write down your time frame next to your goal statement.

- Evaluate your progress by establishing checkpoints. Your checkpoints could be particular dates within your time frame, or they could be short-term goals that you plan to accomplish.

- Reward yourself for achieving your goal. Celebrate with family and friends when you reach your goal. Plan smaller rewards along the way as you accomplish each short-term goal. This will help keep you motivated.

44   Chapter 2   Taking Charge of Your Health

Caption Answer

Figure 2.9 Attending college is a long-term goal that starts by setting short-term goals of getting good grades.

Cooperative Learning

Decision Making and Healthy Behaviors Teens' decision-making skills can have a direct impact on their avoidance of risk behaviors. Have volunteers identify several risk behaviors other than smoking. Record their responses on the board. Have students work in small groups, and ask each group to select one of the risk behaviors from the list. The group members should develop a written explanation of how decision making could be applied by teens in order to avoid the selected risk. Have each group share its work with the class.

Health Skills Activity

Decision-Making Skills

Making New Friends

Justine made a new friend, Michelle, in biology class. Justine really likes Michelle, and the two girls have a lot in common. However, Justine knows that Michelle hangs out with a group of friends who smoke.

During class this morning, Michelle asked if Justine wanted to go to the mall with her and some friends on Saturday. Justine wants to go, but she doesn't want to be pressured about her choice not to smoke. She also doesn't want to lose Michelle as a friend. Justine wonders how she should handle the situation.

Writing Write the decision-making process that Justine should work through to figure out a way to keep her new friend, not feel pressured to smoke, and still protect her health. Be sure to include each of these steps:

1. State the situation.
2. List the options.
3. Weigh possible outcomes.
4. Consider values.
5. Make a decision and act.
6. Evaluate the decision.

LESSON 2 ASSESSMENT

After You Read

Reviewing Facts and Vocabulary

1. How can decision-making skills improve your health?
2. Why would you set a health goal?
3. Give an example of one short-term and one long-term goal related to improving physical fitness.

Thinking Critically

4. **Evaluate.** What might happen if a teen made a decision that went against her personal values?
5. **Analyze.** How can responsible decision making help you achieve your health goals?

Applying Health Skills

6. **Goal Setting.** Choose a short-term goal that you personally would like to achieve. Write an action plan to accomplish your goal.

Writing Critically

7. **Descriptive.** Recall a time when you had to make a health-related decision. Describe how you made the decision, what happened as a result, and how you might change your decision-making process based on what you learned in this lesson.

Go Online

Visit **glencoe.com** and complete the Interactive Study Guide for this lesson.

LESSON 2 ASSESSMENT ANSWERS

1. Decision-making skills let you make responsible health decisions to protect you from harmful or unhealthful behaviors.
2. Health goals provide a direction for improving or maintaining your health.
3. Sample answers: Short-term goals may include walking 20 minutes per day this week or running a mile by one week from now; long-term goals may be to enter a 10k walk/race.
4. Sample answer: The decision could negatively affect her mental/emotional health by increasing stress levels. It could also affect social health if family or friends disagree with the decision.
5. Sample answers: Responsible decision making will lead you to make choices that help you achieve health goals.
6. Goals will vary. Action plans should include each of the steps listed in the text.
7. Descriptions will vary.

③ ASSESS/CLOSE

Assessment Resources

📁 **FAST FILE ACTIVITIES**
Lesson 2 Quiz

💿 *ExamView Assessment Suite* CD-ROM

Visit glencoe.com for:
Online Quizzes
Online Learning Center

Progress Monitoring

Reteaching

Have students write a short paragraph explaining how the HELP strategy can be used to evaluate choices.

Enrichment

Ask students to write a ten-question quiz that could be used to assess another student's understanding of the material in this lesson. Have students trade quizzes. Ask each student to take the quiz he or she receives, then trade back for grading.

Go Online

Have students visit **glencoe.com** and complete the Interactive Study Guide for this lesson.

45

Being a Health-Literate Consumer

① FOCUS

GUIDE TO READING

BIG Idea Health literacy involves the careful evaluation of products and services. **Ask Students:** *What are some types of products and services people use to maintain or improve their health?* (Sample answers: Over-the-counter medication, sunscreen, soaps, and shampoos)

Before You Read

Cluster Chart Students' charts should include words and phrases that describe a health-literate consumer.

Main Idea

Making Informed Choices Individuals can learn to make good consumer choices. **Ask Students:** *What are some strategies for being a smart shopper?* (Sample answers: Checking prices, reading product labels)

Real Life Issues ⋯⋯⋯⋯⋯

Have students write their paragraphs as directed. Ask volunteers to share their completed work with the class. **Ask Students:** *If you are buying shampoo, what kinds of factors do you consider when deciding between different kinds?* (Answers will vary.)

46

GUIDE TO READING

BIG Idea *A health-literate consumer carefully evaluates health products and services.*

Before You Read

Create a Cluster Chart. Draw a circle and label it "Health-Literate Consumer." Use surrounding circles to define and describe this term. As you read, continue filling in the chart with more details.

New Vocabulary

▸ health consumer (p. 46)
▸ advertising (p. 46)
▸ comparison shopping (p. 47)
▸ warranty (p. 48)

Being a Health-Literate Consumer

Real Life Issues ⋯⋯⋯⋯⋯⋯⋯⋯⋯⋯⋯⋯⋯

Analyzing Product Labels. Brad's skin is starting to break out, and he decides to buy an acne cream. In the skin care section at the drugstore, he finds 20 different products. Brad starts to read the package labels. After the fifth label, he feels overwhelmed and doesn't know how to sort out all the information.

Writing *If you were Brad, how would you respond to this situation? Write a paragraph explaining which criteria you use to select health products.*

Making Informed Choices

Main Idea You can learn to make good consumer choices.

Are you a smart buyer? Do you try to get a good-quality product at a reasonable price when you shop? Being a smart shopper is especially important when it comes to making choices about health products and services. It's up to you, as a **health consumer**—*someone who purchases or uses health products or services*—to make informed buying decisions.

Probably the most important influence you need to be aware of as a consumer is advertising. **Advertising** is *a written or spoken media message designed to interest consumers in purchasing a product or service.* Although advertising can provide useful information, its primary purpose is to get you to buy the product.

Advertisers use various techniques and hidden messages to promote their products and services. **Figure 2.11** shows some of these common techniques. Being a health-literate consumer means being aware of these messages and knowing how to evaluate them.

Health Literacy

Advertising and Health Media and advertising can influence consumer choices in a number of ways. For example, advertising for fast food restaurants typically encourages the consumption of high-fat, high-calorie foods. These advertisements are often directed at young people. Advertising can also have positive effects on consumer choices and health. An advertising campaign that uses celebrity endorsements to encourage milk consumption is one example. Ask students to work in small groups to brainstorm strategies that advertisers could use to promote healthy choices among teens.

Figure 2.11 **Hidden Messages in Advertising**

Recognizing advertising techniques will help you make informed purchasing decisions.

Technique	Example	Hidden Message
Bandwagon	Group of people using a product or service	Everyone is using it, and you should too.
Rich and famous	Product displayed in expensive home	It will make you feel rich and famous.
Free gifts	Redeemable coupons for merchandise	It's too good a deal to pass up.
Great outdoors	Scenes of nature	If it's associated with nature, it must be healthy.
Good times	People smiling and laughing	The product will add fun to your life.
Testimonial	People for whom a product has worked	It worked for them, so it will work for you, too.

Evaluating Products

There are two effective ways to sharpen your consumer skills when buying health products: read product labels, and do some comparison shopping before you buy.

Product Labels Labels give you important information about what a product contains. Product labels carry the product's name, its intended use, directions, warnings, manufacturer's information, and the amount in the container. You will usually find the product's ingredients listed by weight in descending order. The active ingredients are the most important: they're the ones that make the product effective. By comparing the amount of active ingredients in different acne medications, for example, you can figure out which one contains more of the active ingredient, or whether a less expensive product contains the same active ingredient as a brand-name product.

Comparison Shopping A second great tool for smart health consumers is **comparison shopping**, or *judging the benefits of different products by comparing several factors, such as quality, features, and cost.* Here are some criteria you can use to judge health products and services:

• **Cost and quality.** Generic products may work the same as brand-name products. Compare the quality of lower-cost items, and look for products that meet your needs but cost less.

Go Online

Explore glencoe.com and complete the Student Web Activity on the impact of advertising targeted at teens.

READING CHECK

Describe How does advertising influence your decision to purchase a health-related product?

Lesson 3 Being a Health-Literate Consumer **47**

TEACH

Active Learning

Make a Poster Provide poster paper, glue, markers, and discarded magazines to students. Have each student find examples of advertisements that use the advertising techniques described in **Figure 2.11**. Ask students to label the pictures according to the advertising technique used and create a poster that shows some of the best examples. **EL BL OL**

Go Online

Have students visit **glencoe.com** and complete the Student Web Activity on the impact of advertising targeted at teens.

Reading Strategy

Applying Information Have students review the bulleted list of tips for comparison shopping. Then demonstrate the process of comparison shopping for students. Show students pictures of two similar products. In a step-by-step fashion, describe how you would compare the products based on the instructions for comparison shopping in the text. **BL**

READING CHECK

Answer Advertisements use specific techniques to convey a hidden message that may not be entirely true.

Teacher to Teacher

Theresa Despino • Alexandria Sr. High School, Alexandria, LA

Being a Conscious Consumer Set up a trip to the local grocery store. Each student is assigned three different products (example: milk, cereal, and detergent) to check out. When comparing, they must choose three different brands of each item and compare size, contents, and price. They then record their findings and make a comparison chart to be presented to the class. This can also be done in groups and/or as an assignment.

HS Health Skills Practice

Accessing Information Have students work in pairs to use the Internet or library resources to practice accessing valid health information. Ask each pair of students to find one site or resource that is a source of reliable health information for antibiotic ointment. Then have students share their findings with the class. **OL** **AL**

U Universal Access

English Language Learners Have English language learners work with students who are proficient in English to develop a list of reliable health information sources. Encourage students to use both words and pictures on their lists. Ask students to name some of the sources on their lists. **EL** **OL**

■ **Figure 2.12** Product labels contain useful health-related information. *How can you tell if a product has been safety tested?*

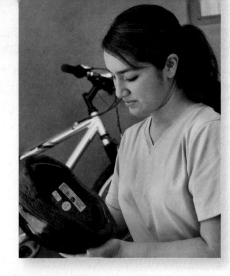

- **Features.** Figure out which product features are most important to you so that you don't waste money on features you don't want.
- **Warranty.** Many products come with a **warranty**, *a company's or a store's written agreement to repair a product or refund your money if the product doesn't function properly.* Ask about warranties before buying expensive products, and read them carefully to make sure you understand what they cover.
- **Safety.** When you are evaluating sports, recreation, and home-safety products, look for logos from well-known, reputable organizations that show the product has been tested for safety. For example, the **Underwriters Laboratories (UL)** tests and certifies products such as electrical appliances and fire extinguishers. **Snell,** a nonprofit foundation, and the **American National Standards Institute (ANSI)** monitor safety standards for helmets and other protective equipment.
- **Recommendations.** Listen to the opinions of people you trust who have used the product or service that you are considering. Also, check the consumer product ratings from organizations such as Consumers Union.

Academic Vocabulary

valid *(adjective):* well-grounded or justifiable

Evaluating Information and Services To evaluate health information or services, ask yourself these questions:

- Does this information come from a **valid** source? Does the service come from a respected provider?
- If the source is a Web site, who pays for the site? Is it a reputable organization? What is the purpose of the site?

HS

Keep in mind that your doctor, nurse, and pharmacist are also great sources for reliable health care information.

More About...

The FDA The Food and Drug Administration is a part of the Department of Health and Human Services. The FDA regulates many of the health-related products consumers use. Among the products regulated by the FDA are over-the-counter and prescription drugs, cosmetics, health devices, bottled water and most foods, and veterinary medicines. Products not regulated by the FDA include alcohol, illegal drugs, meat and poultry, health insurance, pesticides, and municipal water supplies. The FDA also provides targeted information for children, teens, and adults on its Web site.

Real World CONNECTION

Comparing Products

Teens spend $155 billion each year on clothing, music, personal care items, and other products. As a result, retailers pay close attention to teens' consumer behaviors and promote products directly to them.

It's important to look past the glossy advertising and fancy packaging to evaluate a product carefully. One feature to consider is cost and how to get the most for your money. Compare the following products.

Product	Size	Price
A. Celebrity-brand purifying gel	5.5 oz.	$25.99
B. Foaming acne cleanser	6 oz.	$6.99
C. Generic-brand acne cleanser	6 oz.	$4.99

Activity Mathematics

Use the chart to answer these questions.

1. What is the unit price of each cleanser?
2. If you use one bottle of product B every four months, how much will you pay for this product in a year?
3. **Writing** Write a paragraph describing two or more features you would compare when shopping for a facial cleanser.

Concept Number and Operations: Unit Price To calculate unit price, divide the cost of the product by the volume, or total ounces. This will yield the cost per ounce.

LESSON 3 ASSESSMENT

After You Read

Reviewing Facts and Vocabulary

1. Who is a *health consumer*?
2. How does comparison shopping make you a smart consumer?
3. Define *warranty*.

Thinking Critically

4. **Synthesize.** Susie wants to buy an expensive suntan lotion after seeing her favorite actress use it in an ad. The ad says the product uses only natural ingredients. What hidden messages in the ad is Susie responding to?
5. **Analyze.** How does a warranty help you become a smarter consumer?

Applying Health Skills

6. **Accessing Information.** Your friend takes a multivitamin, and you're wondering if you should too. You check a few Web sites to learn more about multivitamins before you ask your parents for permission to use them. How would you evaluate the validity of the information you find?

Writing Critically

7. **Expository.** Find three ads in a teen magazine. Write a short essay explaining the advertising techniques used in each ad. Refer to Figure 2.11.

Go Online

Visit **glencoe.com** and complete the Interactive Study Guide for this lesson.

Lesson 3   Being a Health-Literate Consumer   **49**

Real World CONNECTION

Answers to Activity

1. Celebrity-brand gel: $4.73, Foaming acne cleanser: $1.17, Generic-brand acne cleanser: $0.83
2. Three bottles; the cost would be $20.97.
3. Students' paragraphs will vary.

③ ASSESS/ CLOSE

Assessment Resources

 FAST FILE ACTIVITIES
Lesson 3 Quiz

 ExamView Assessment Suite CD-ROM

Visit glencoe.com for:
Online Quizzes
Online Learning Center

Progress Monitoring

Reteaching
Have students work in pairs to review the vocabulary terms from the lesson. Circulate among the students to monitor their work.

Enrichment
Have students think about a recent purchase they have made. Then have each student write a paragraph that analyzes the factors that influenced his or her decision to buy that particular product.

LESSON 3 ASSESSMENT ANSWERS

1. A *health consumer* is anyone who buys a health-related product or service.
2. Sample answer: It allows you to get a good-quality product at a reasonable price; it allows you to identify and obtain the features in a product or service that you most want; it ensures that you are buying safe products.
3. A *warranty* is a written agreement to repair a product or refund your money if the product doesn't function properly.
4. It must be healthy if it's natural, and a celebrity says it works for her.
5. A warranty increases your consumer power because it helps you understand what is covered if the product is defective and you need to return it.
6. Identify the source and its credibility—is the site run by a company that is selling vitamins?
7. Essays will vary.

Managing Consumer Problems

GUIDE TO READING

BIG Idea Knowing how to handle consumer problems is an essential skill for health consumers. **Ask Students:** *What are some reasons a consumer might have problems with a product?* (Sample answers: It is defective or does not work as advertised.)

Before You Read

Vocabulary Cards Students' vocabulary cards should reflect their current knowledge of the lesson vocabulary terms as well as information they learn while reading the lesson.

Main Idea

Resolving Consumer Problems
Consumers can take action to resolve problems with products and services. **Ask Students:** *What are some steps you could take if a product you buy doesn't work?* (Sample answer: I could take it back to the store and ask for a refund.)

Real Life Issues ....

Before students write their answers, **Ask Students:** *What do you think would happen in one month if he did not buy the product but did 100 sit-ups a day?* (Sample answer: He would probably get the same result)

50

LESSON 4

GUIDE TO READING

BIG Idea Knowing how to handle consumer problems is an important skill to learn.

Before You Read

Create Vocabulary Cards. Write each new vocabulary term on a separate note card. For each term, write a definition based on your current knowledge. As you read, fill in additional information related to each term.

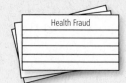

Health Fraud

New Vocabulary

▶ consumer advocates (p. 51)
▶ malpractice (p. 52)
▶ health fraud (p. 52)

Review Vocabulary

▶ warranty (Ch.2, L.3)

Managing Consumer Problems

Real Life Issues ....

Believing Claims. Stefano is watching an infomercial on TV late at night. The spokesperson on the program says that if you do 100 sit-ups a day and apply his "clinically proven" cream, you'll have "six-pack" abs in just one month. Stefano is tempted. Should he send in $19.95 for a chance to improve his physique?

Writing *Consider infomercials or commercials you have seen on TV or the Internet. Based on what you know about these types of media messages, write a convincing answer to Stefano's question.*

Resolving Consumer Problems

Main Idea Take action to correct consumer problems.

Have you ever bought a product and been dissatisfied with it after you used it? Maybe the product didn't work the way it should, didn't work at all, or a part was missing or broken. What can you do when this happens?

When you shop for a product, find out what the store's return policy is *before* you make a purchase. If the product has a warranty, check that it's in the package or that the salesperson gives it to you. Scan the warranty and read the store's return instructions. After you get home and open the product, save the packaging, along with your receipt and warranty.

If the product comes with instructions, read them carefully. Pay particular attention to the directions for skin and hair care products. Follow all the steps for the product's use or assembly. Make sure you use the product exactly the way it was designed and made to be used.

Myths & Reality

Consumer Problems

Myth: Because of government regulations, all advertising must be accurate.

Fact: Advertisements often use phrases, such as "world's best," that cannot be proven right or wrong. Advertisements also use statistics that may be misleading. For example, a an advertisement that includes the phrase "2 out of 3 doctors surveyed" does not give you enough information to determine if this is a valid, scientific result.

Myth: Internet advertising is not regulated; don't believe any ads you see on the Web.

Fact: Advertising on the Internet is regulated by the Federal Trade Commission. Ads must be truthful and not misleading, and any claims made must be substantiated.

■ **Figure 2.13** Most products have instructions that tell you how to use them correctly. *What are some products you use that have specific directions to follow?*

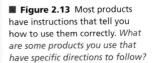
② TEACH

Caption Answer

Figure 2.13 Sample answer: I have recently used acne cream that had specific directions for use.

C Critical Thinking

Applying Concepts After students have read the information in the text about resolving consumer problems, ask them to make lists of the steps they would take if they purchased a product that broke the first time it was used. Ask volunteers to share their lists with the class. **BL OL**

W Writing Support

Persuasive Writing Have students write a persuasive letter encouraging consumers to report fraudulent products and services to the Better Business Bureau or other consumer advocacy organizations. Explain that persuasive writing states an opinion and offers supporting reasons why the opinion is valid. Remind students to proofread and correct their letters. **OL AL**

If you are using the product correctly and it isn't working the way you expected, read the warranty to learn how the manufacturer requires you to return it. You may be able to return it to the store where you bought it. However, some manufacturers want the product returned directly to them. Put the product back in its original packaging, and follow the manufacturer's return instructions. You may be asked to write a letter describing the problem and requesting a replacement or your money back. Date your letter and keep a copy for your files, along with a shipping receipt to prove you returned the product.

If you are not satisfied with the response to your efforts, ask for help from one of the following organizations:

- The **Better Business Bureau** handles complaints about local merchants. Its basic services are dispute resolution and truth-in-advertising complaints.

- **Consumer advocates** are *people or groups whose sole purpose is to take on regional, national, and even international consumer issues.* Some, like Consumers Union, test products and inform the public about potential problems. Others keep an eye out for consumer concerns about products and services.

- **Local, state, and federal government agencies** work to protect consumers' rights. The federal agencies most concerned with consumer health issues are the FDA, which is responsible for ensuring that medicines are safe, effective, and properly labeled, and the Consumer Product Safety Commission, which recalls dangerous products.

 READING CHECK

Describe What would you do if you purchased a product that didn't work?

READING CHECK

Answer Read the store's return policy and product warranty, return the product to the store or manufacturer, ask for a replacement or refund.

Lesson 4   Managing Consumer Problems   **51**

Reading Strategy

Identifying Problems and Solutions
As students read the lesson, have them use a two-column table to organize the information. Students should label the left column of the table "Problems" and the right column of the table "Solutions." For each consumer problem they read about in the text, have them summarize the problem in the left column and a possible solution in the right column. After students have read the entire lesson, ask volunteers to share entries from their tables with the class.

R Reading Strategy

Vocabulary Write the vocabulary term *malpractice* on the board. Underline the word part *mal-*. Tell students that this word part means "bad." Ask students to brainstorm other words that use the word part *mal-* (*malnutrition, malady, malice, malicious*). Point out that the word part *mal-* has the same meaning in Spanish words, as well as being used alone in Spanish to mean "bad." EL OL

Academic Vocabulary

Approach Have students provide examples of how they have *approached* studying for a test. Students should write down their examples and have volunteers read theirs to the class.

Main Idea

Health Fraud Learning to avoid health fraud is a way that individuals can protect their health. **Ask Students:** *What are some signs that a health-related product might be fraudulent?* (Sample answers: Claims that a product will provide miraculous results; claims that a product is made from a secret formula)

AL Active Learning

Bulletin Board Have students collect examples of labels and advertisements that contain claims that may be fraudulent. Students may make their own full-page, magazine-style ads including red flags that indicate health fraud. Have students circle the words, phrases, or other aspects of the ad that indicate a product may be fraudulent. Display results on the bulletin board. EL BL OL

Academic Vocabulary

approach *(noun):* a particular manner of taking steps

Sometimes people run into problems with their health care providers, such as difficulty in scheduling appointments, or their health insurance won't cover nontraditional **approaches** such as acupuncture or herbal treatments. Often, people can avoid more serious problems by changing health care professionals or insurance companies. To make sure they are getting the best care possible, many people get a second opinion from another doctor for any major health concern, especially if it involves surgery or other serious treatment.

Occasionally, health care professionals may fail to provide adequate treatment and may be guilty of **malpractice**, *failure by a health professional to meet accepted standards*. If you experience a serious problem with a health care professional, you can contact organizations such as the American Medical Association or a state licensing board for help. **R**

Health Fraud

Main Idea Protect yourself from health fraud.

Have you ever seen an ad on TV or in a magazine that promises an instant cure for a health problem? Did you think that sounded too good to be true? You were probably right. Such ads are a kind of **health fraud**, *the sale of worthless products or services that claim to prevent disease or cure other health problems*. Health fraud is often called *quackery*. **AL**

Weight-loss and beauty products are two areas particularly susceptible to health fraud. Read ads for these products very carefully before deciding to buy. Look out for claims like the following:

- "Secret formula"
- "Miracle cure"
- "Overnight results"
- "All natural"
- "Hurry, this offer expires soon"

■ **Figure 2.14** You can consult a registered pharmacist if you have questions about a product's health claims. *What other reliable sources can you go to for medical advice?*

Skills for the 21st Century

Information and Media Literacy The ability to distinguish reliable, valid claims and information from misleading or fraudulent information is a valuable skill for all health consumers. Make a T-chart on the board. Label one side "Reliable Information" and the other side "Fraudulent Information."

Ask students to volunteer words and phrases for each side of the T-chart. After the T-chart has been completed, ask a volunteer to summarize the importance of being able to distinguish reliable information from fraudulent information.

Health clinics that provide "miracle" cures for ailments or questionable treatments, such as "microwaving" cancer cells, are also guilty of health fraud. Some fraudulent clinics have been shut down after it was discovered that the people running them were not the doctors they claimed to be; some even had criminal records. These clinics often take advantage of people who are very ill and desperate for a cure.

To protect yourself from health fraud, you can do the following:

- Check out the product's or service's claim with a doctor or other health professional.
- Talk to family and friends to get their opinion.
- Check with the Better Business Bureau to see if there have been complaints about the product or service.
- Check with a professional health organization about the claim. The American Heart Association, for example, will be familiar with health frauds related to heart disease treatment.

Remember, you have the power and the responsibility to protect your health and well-being!

 READING CHECK

Describe How can you protect yourself from health fraud when buying a health-related product?

LESSON 4 ASSESSMENT

After You Read

Reviewing Facts and Vocabulary

1. How do consumer advocates help you to be a better health consumer?
2. What is *malpractice*?
3. Define *health fraud*.

Thinking Critically

4. **Analyze.** Why is it important for health consumers to take an active role if they are dissatisfied with a product or service?
5. **Evaluate.** Review the list of claims that are often associated with health fraud. What do these claims have in common?

Applying Health Skills

6. **Advocacy.** Two of your friends are thinking about purchasing products that promise immediate weight loss. You know these claims are unrealistic and that the products may be unsafe. Create a text message that warns your friends about unrealistic claims in weight-loss products.

Writing Critically

7. **Narrative.** Write a story about a teen who encounters a consumer problem. Your story should describe the problem and demonstrate how the teen handles it.

G Online

Visit glencoe.com and complete the Interactive Study Guide for this lesson.

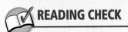 **READING CHECK**

Answer Check out the product's claims with credible sources.

❸ ASSESS/ CLOSE

Assessment Resources

📁 *FAST FILE* **ACTIVITIES**
Lesson 4 Quiz

💿 *ExamView Assessment Suite* CD-ROM

Visit glencoe.com for:
Online Quizzes
Online Learning Center

Progress Monitoring

Reteaching
Have students work in pairs to make a list of claims that indicate health fraud.

Enrichment
Ask students to research a state or local agency that protects consumers' rights. Have students summarize their findings in a short, written report.

G Online

Have students visit glencoe.com and complete the Interactive Study Guide for this lesson.

LESSON **4** ASSESSMENT ANSWERS

1. Consumer advocates test products for safety and keep an eye out for health fraud.
2. *Malpractice is* the failure of a health professional to meet accepted standards.
3. *Health fraud* is the sale of worthless products or services that claim to prevent disease or cure other health problems.
4. Taking an active role resolves problems and helps protect you and other consumers.
5. These claims promise instant results and/or strive to create pressure to buy.
6. Text messages will vary, but should convey the message that products with unrealistic claims are usually fraudulent.
7. Stories will vary, but should accurately describe the problem and include information from the lesson on handling consumer problems.

All About You

NHES Standard 6 Students will demonstrate the ability to use goal-setting skills to enhance health.

Teaching Objectives

- Identify external and internal influences that have an impact on health goals.
- Develop and implement a plan for a personal health goal.

Teaching Strategies

- Give each student a sheet of white paper, 8½ × 11 inches, and a business envelope, which they will address to themselves.
- Optional: Have students place a postage stamp on their envelope, if possible.
- Instruct students to complete steps 1–3 of the activity.
- Collect student letters, and return them in one week for a personal reflection regarding their action plan.
- Keep student letters and have students revisit their goal during the course of the year. Distribute or mail the letters to students before the end of their health course as a reminder of their personal health goal.

Assessment

Using a rubric, student work should provide comprehensive evidence of the following criteria to achieve the highest score.

- ✓ Identifies and analyzes external and internal factors
- ✓ Includes a clear goal statement
- ✓ Presents a realistic goal
- ✓ Includes a plan for reaching the goal
- ✓ Evaluates or reflects on the action

Hands-On
HEALTH

Activity All About You

This activity is all about you! You will write a letter describing yourself and assessing your health habits. In the letter, you will set a health goal and develop a plan to reach that goal.

What You'll Need

- paper
- pen or pencil

What You'll Do

Step 1

Review Chapter 2. Then write a letter to yourself describing your personality, your likes and dislikes, and your values. In your letter, identify a health habit or skill you want to improve.

Step 2

Develop a health-related goal statement and an action plan for reaching that goal. Identify people who can provide help and support.

Step 3

Share your letter with a peer and ask for feedback. Revise your goal and action plan if necessary.

Apply and Conclude

At the end of one week, reread your letter. Write a reflection, and identify influences that affected your progress. These might include family, peers, culture, media, and personal values. Continue challenging yourself to reach your goal.

Checklist: Goal Setting

- ✓ Identification of realistic goal
- ✓ Clear goal statement
- ✓ Plan for reaching the goal
- ✓ List of people who can provide help and support
- ✓ Evaluation or reflection on the plan

🏔️👥 Home and Community

In the Community Community service becomes a part of the school curriculum in service-learning programs. These programs, which tie in academic content with volunteer activities, have been shown to increase test scores and student motivation. Service learning can be implemented at any grade level, and many sources of information about service learning are available online. Have a class discussion of a community need that could be met. Have students brainstorm ways that meeting this need could tie in with a topic being studied at school.

To download quizzes and eFlashcards to your PDA, go to glencoe.com and click on the Study to Go icon.

LESSON 1

Building Health Skills

Key Concepts

▶ Health skills are tools that help you manage your health.
▶ Good interpersonal communication helps you build strong relationships with others.
▶ When you are aware of how influences such as family, peers, culture, media, and personal values affect you, you are better able to make informed choices about your health.

Vocabulary

▶ health skills (p. 34)
▶ interpersonal communication (p. 35)
▶ refusal skills (p. 36)
▶ conflict resolution (p. 36)
▶ stress (p. 38)
▶ stress management skills (p. 38)
▶ advocacy (p. 39)

LESSON 2

Making Responsible Decisions and Setting Goals

Key Concepts

▶ Use the steps in the decision-making process to make safe and responsible decisions.
▶ Short-term goals can help you reach long-term goals.
▶ To accomplish your goals, create an action plan.

Vocabulary

▶ values (p. 41)
▶ decision-making skills (p. 41)
▶ goals (p. 42)
▶ short-term goal (p. 43)
▶ long-term goal (p. 43)
▶ action plan (p. 44)

LESSON 3

Being a Health-Literate Consumer

Key Concepts

▶ To be a smart consumer, read labels, comparison shop, and evaluate advertisements for hidden messages.
▶ Evaluate health information and services carefully to make sure they come from valid sources or respected providers.

Vocabulary

▶ health consumer (p. 46)
▶ advertising (p. 46)
▶ comparison shopping (p. 47)
▶ warranty (p. 48)

LESSON 4

Managing Consumer Problems

Key Concepts

▶ Always read and follow the instructions for products you buy.
▶ Consumer and health organizations help fight health fraud.

Vocabulary

▶ consumer advocates (p. 51)
▶ malpractice (p. 52)
▶ health fraud (p. 52)

Chapter 2 Review **55**

Go Online

Students can visit **glencoe.com** to

• review content online with the Online Student Edition.
• test their knowledge of chapter content with Online Quizzes.
• access Interactive Health Tutor for more practice with vocabulary.

Assessment Resources

 FAST FILE ACTIVITIES
Chapter 2 Test

ExamView Assessment Suite CD-ROM

Visit glencoe.com for:
Audio Chapter Summaries
Online Quizzes

 Tell students to visit glencoe.com where they can download quizzes and eFlashcards.

Study Tips

Work with a Partner Suggest that students choose a partner with whom to review the chapter content. Explain that studying with a partner allows them to share information and help each other identify areas that need more study. Suggest that students use a question-and-answer format to study with a partner, with each student alternating between asking and answering questions. Students may wish to use the After You Read questions from each lesson as a starting point.

Assessment

Chapter 2 Assessment Answers

LESSON 1

Vocabulary Review
1. Health skills
2. advocacy
3. stress management

Understanding Key Concepts
4. a
5. b
6. c

Thinking Critically
7. Sample answer: Both of these skills involve respectful exchanges of information. Conflict resolution typically is needed during a disagreement to prevent it from escalating, whereas interpersonal communication skills are used in all exchanges between people.
8. Sample answers: Name of the organization and whether it is reputable and well known; date of information and whether it is current and accurate; HONcode reflecting adherence to high standards on the Internet
9. The Internet may provide inaccurate health information. Media such as television and Internet provide external influences through advertising.
10. A commitment to health, knowledge of a health issue, good communication skills, caring about other people and their health.

Vocabulary Review
11. T
12. F
13. T

LESSON 1

Vocabulary Review
Use the vocabulary terms listed on page 55 to complete the following statements.

1. _____ are tools that you can use to maintain all aspects of your health.

2. If you influence another person to adopt a healthful behavior, that's called _____.

3. A person who goes for a brisk walk when feeling overwhelmed by a busy schedule is practicing a health skill called _____.

Understanding Key Concepts
After reading the question or statement, select the correct answer.

4. Sofia is angry that Alisa interrupts her. If Sofia says, "I'm upset because my ideas are not being heard," she is
   a. using an "I" statement to express her feelings.
   b. blaming Alisa for interrupting her.
   c. practicing poor interpersonal communication skills.
   d. all of the above.

5. Joe and Tony are having a heated argument. Tony decides to cool off before continuing the discussion. Tony is practicing a health skill called
   a. advocacy.
   b. conflict resolution.
   c. stress management.
   d. accessing information.

6. Which of the following best describes stress management?
   a. Avoiding the most difficult tasks
   b. Taking advantage of the situation
   c. Using healthy ways to reduce and manage stress in your life
   d. Managing your peer group to avoid confrontations

Thinking Critically
After reading the question or statement, write a short answer using complete sentences.

7. **Compare and Contrast.** How are interpersonal communication and conflict-resolution skills similar? How are they different?

8. **Evaluate.** What types of information could you use to evaluate the validity of health information?

9. **Explain.** How does technology influence your health choices?

10. **Analyze.** What does it take to advocate for health?

LESSON 2

Vocabulary Review
Mark the following sentences as True (T) or False (F).

11. The decisions you make about your health should reflect your values.

12. Decision making is a random process, depending on your mood.

13. Breaking a long-term goal into several short-term goals can make the long-term goal easier to achieve.

Understanding Key Concepts
After reading the question or statement, select the correct answer.

14. It's a good idea to talk over major decisions with your family because
   a. they always know what is best for you.
   b. they have a right to know everything you do.
   c. they share your values, the basis for making decisions.
   d. they will tell you what you should do.

Health eSpotlight Wrap-Up

Making Decisions About Your Personal Health Have students reread the Health eSpotlight question at the beginning of the chapter on page 33 and look at their original answer. **Ask Students:** *Now that you have read the chapter and watched the video, how would you respond differently to* media messages that promote an unhealthy lifestyle? Call on volunteers to describe how their responses would change. Remind students about the video they watched and encourage them to be aware of what kind of healthful choices they make on a day-to-day basis.

15. Setting health-related goals
    a. ensures that you will obtain your goals.
    b. helps you plan and safeguard your well-being.
    c. takes a lot of time and creates stress.
    d. is a one-time event when you set healthy goals.

16. An action plan should include
    a. a written statement of your goal.
    b. the steps you will take to accomplish it.
    c. neither a nor b.
    d. both a and b.

Thinking Critically

After reading the question or statement, write a short answer using complete sentences.

17. **Analyze.** Why is decision making a key health skill? How can this skill contribute to your safety and well-being?

18. **Evaluate.** What criteria are important in weighing the possible consequences of your choices?

19. **Analyze.** Why is it important to set health-related goals?

Vocabulary Review

Use the vocabulary terms listed on page 55 to complete the following statements.

20. Each of us is a(n) _____ because we all buy health products and services.

21. Evaluating the features of two similar products is called _____.

22. _____ techniques include bandwagon, rich and famous, free gifts, great outdoors, good times, and testimonial.

Understanding Key Concepts

After reading the question or statement, select the correct answer.

23. To be a critical thinker about advertising,
    a. note how often you see the same ad.
    b. remember product names.
    c. look for hidden messages in ads.
    d. compare ads for similar products.

24. Smart health consumers
    a. read product labels.
    b. listen to infomercials.
    c. write to product manufacturers.
    d. try out different products.

Thinking Critically

After reading the question or statement, write a short answer using complete sentences.

25. **Explain.** What strategies do smart consumers use to protect their health when purchasing health products?

26. **Discuss.** How does an understanding of advertising help you become a smarter consumer?

27. **Evaluate.** What are some effective strategies for evaluating health information and services?

LESSON 4

Vocabulary Review

Choose the correct term in the sentences below.

28. Someone who tests products and informs the public about potential problems is a *product expert / consumer advocate*.

29. Selling a worthless weight loss product is an example of *health fraud / trickery*.

30. When a doctor fails to live up to professional standards in medicine, he may be accused of *arrogance / malpractice*.

Understanding Key Concepts

14. c
15. b
16. d

Thinking Critically

17. Knowing how to make decisions helps you to make responsible health choices and protects you from risky behaviors.
18. Whether your choice is healthful, ethical, legal, and likely to be approved by your parents or guardian
19. Setting health-related goals allows you to decide what aspects of your health need improvement and to focus on taking actions to make improvements.

LESSON 3

Vocabulary Review

20. health consumer
21. comparison shopping
22. Advertising

Understanding Key Concepts

23. c
24. a

Thinking Critically

25. Read the product label and comparison shop.
26. It helps you understand the hidden message that the advertiser is using to persuade you to buy its product.
27. You will need to ask yourself questions about the validity of the source or provider of the information and services. You should research Web sites to find out who pays for the information, and what is its purpose.

Assessment

LESSON 4

Vocabulary Review

28. consumer advocate
29. health fraud
30. malpractice

Understanding Key Concepts

31. a
32. d

Thinking Critically

33. Consumers can return defective or harmful products; consumers can complain about a merchant to the Better Business Bureau or other consumer advocate organizations; knowledgeable consumers can protect themselves against health fraud.

34. Read the store's return policy and product warranty; return the item to the store or to the manufacturer; document what is wrong with the product and ask for a replacement or refund.

35. People are looking for a quick cure that does not require a serious behavior change.

36. Answers will vary, but should include getting recommendations from trusted individuals and evaluating the validity of the source.

Understanding Key Concepts

After reading the question or statement, select the correct answer.

31. If you buy a product and are not satisfied with it, you should
    a. read the warranty to find out how to return it.
    b. throw it away.
    c. immediately buy a replacement.
    d. all of the above.

32. Which of the following is *not* a good way to protect yourself from health fraud?
    a. Checking out claims with a health care professional
    b. Trying the product or service for yourself
    c. Talking to others who have used the product or service
    d. Consulting with the Better Business Bureau

Thinking Critically

After reading the question or statement, write a short answer using complete sentences.

33. **Synthesize.** How are consumers empowered to protect their health and well-being?

34. **Explain.** What are the best steps to take if you are dissatisfied with the health-related product that you have purchased?

35. **Analyze.** Why are some people attracted to products that make fraudulent claims?

36. **Discuss.** What criteria would you use to evaluate health services?

Project-Based ASSESSMENT

Volun-teen

Background
There are many ways teens can advocate for healthy living on the local, national, and international level. You can help make a difference by getting involved in this effort too!

Task
Research volunteer opportunities that promote healthy living and are available to teens in your community. Write a newspaper article that describes the volunteer opportunities and encourages teens to get involved.

Audience
Students in your class and teens in your community

Purpose
Inform teens of health-related volunteer opportunities, and encourage their involvement.

Procedure

1. Research volunteer opportunities with several health organizations. Examples include hospitals, the Red Cross, and the American Cancer Society.

2. Gather details about the volunteer opportunities. Find out the type of work involved, the minimum age requirement, the length of the assignment, and any necessary contact information.

3. Review several newspaper articles to familiarize yourself with their writing style.

4. Write a newspaper article that describes the volunteer opportunities you researched.

5. Make sure the article encourages teens to pursue volunteer opportunities.

58 Chapter 2 Assessment

Project-Based ASSESSMENT

Step 1 Choose a topic. Have each student choose an organization that helps promote healthy living to research and write about. An example might be their local American Red Cross chapter. Students should first find out if their organization provides ways for teens to get involved.

Step 2 Write a newspaper article. Provide examples of newspaper articles for students to use as models. Have each student write a newspaper article about the volunteer opportunity he or she has researched.

Step 3 Evaluate each article and its accompanying research notes. Submit excellent examples of articles to the school or local newspaper.

Visit **glencoe.com** for Project-Based Assessment rubrics.

Math Practice

Interpret Graphs. The graph below shows the percentages of young adults who volunteer each year. Use the graph to answer Questions 1–3.

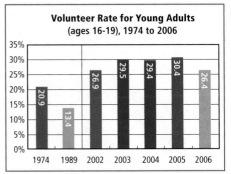

Volunteer Rate for Young Adults (ages 16-19), 1974 to 2006

Year	Rate
1974	20.9
1989	13.4
2002	26.9
2003	29.5
2004	29.4
2005	30.4
2006	26.4

Adapted from "Volunteering in America: 2007 State Trends and Rankings in Civic Life," Corporation for National and Community Service, April 2007.

1. Which years show an increase from the previous year in the volunteering rate among young adults?
   - **A.** 1974 and 2002
   - **B.** 1989 and 2006
   - **C.** 2003 and 2005
   - **D.** 2004 and 2006

2. Between which two years is there a change of only one-tenth of a percent?
   - **A.** 2002 and 2003
   - **B.** 2003 and 2004
   - **C.** 2004 and 2005
   - **D.** 2005 and 2006

3. According to the graph, how do volunteering rates in the 2000s compare to rates in the late 1900s?
   - **A.** Fewer young adults volunteer in this century.
   - **B.** More young adults volunteer in this century.
   - **C.** There is no change in the number of young adults who volunteer.
   - **D.** More adults volunteer than young adults during both centuries.

Go Online

For more test practice, visit glencoe.com and complete the Online Quizzes for Chapter 2.

Reading/Writing Practice

Understand and Apply. Read the passage below, and then answer the questions.

> Good communication is a skill you can use every day. One way you can demonstrate effective communication skills is to be a good listener. The speaker may think that you are not listening if your eyes wander around the room. Closed body language, such as crossing your arms, conveys that you may not be open to hearing what others have to say.
>
> To show that you are listening attentively, make eye contact and let the other person finish what he or she is saying before you speak. Use body language such as nodding your head to show that you are interested in what the person is saying. A good listener makes statements that encourage the speaker to explain his or her views, such as "What do you mean by that?" It can also be helpful to restate what the person tells you to make sure that you understand what is being said.

1. Which of the following is a behavior that characterizes good listening skills?
   - **A.** Crossed arms
   - **B.** Making eye contact
   - **C.** Wandering eyes
   - **D.** Interrupting

2. Which statement best summarizes the main point of the article?
   - **A.** Closed body language is negative.
   - **B.** You can demonstrate effective communication by being a good listener.
   - **C.** Always ask speakers to explain their views.
   - **D.** Never restate what you hear.

3. Describe the effects of attentive listening and poor listening on communication.

National Education Standards

Math: Number and Operations, Data Analysis
Language Arts: NCTE 1, NCTE 3, NCTE 4

Standardized Test Practice

Standardized Test Practice Answers

Math Practice
1. C
2. B
3. B

Reading/Writing Practice
1. B
2. B
3. Answers will vary but should include examples from the article.

National Education Standards

Math: Number and Operations, and Data Analysis

Language Arts: NCTE 1, NCTE 3, NCTE 4

For the complete Math and Language Arts standards, visit glencoe.com.

Online Study Tools
For more test practice, visit glencoe.com and complete the Online Quizzes for Chapter 2.

Test-Taking Tip

Use the Entire Allotted Time Period
Tell students that they should use the entire time period they are allotted for their test, even if they complete the test before time runs out. Help students plan a strategy for using the remaining time wisely. Tell them that proofreading essay and short-answer questions for spelling, grammar, and sentence structure is a good way to use time. If a question has multiple parts, have students check to be sure that they answered each component. Remind students not to change an answer unless they are absolutely sure their first response is incorrect.

CAREER CORNER Health Careers

Health Careers
Group Activity

- Divide the class into three groups.
- Assign a career to each group.
- Have students research to find more information about their group's assigned career. Suggest that students find out more about the educational requirements of the career as well as potential places of employment.
- Have each group make a poster that uses words and images to inform others about its assigned career.
- Have groups share their posters with the class. Tell students to be prepared to answer questions about their assigned career.

Health Teacher

Health teachers help students understand how to maintain good health. These teachers provide information on nutrition, fitness, and social issues. They can also give basic information on how the human body functions. Health teachers may need to spend time organizing lesson plans, as well as group and individual activities.

A health teacher must have a four-year teaching degree. Public school health teachers must be licensed, but this is not a requirement for private school health teachers. High school classes that can help prepare a student to become a health teacher include biology, science, fitness, and communications.

Medical Writer

If you like to write and are interested in health care, becoming a medical or health writer might be a good career for you. These professionals organize and write complex medical information for the public in lay-person's terms. Medical writers may work for publishing companies, hospitals, radio and TV stations, universities, government agencies, and pharmaceutical companies.

Medical writers need a bachelor's degree, with courses in science and English or journalism. To prepare for this career, high school students should take classes in biology, chemistry, math, and English.

Health Information Technician

If you think of yourself as well organized and detail oriented, you might enjoy a career as a health information technician. These technicians assemble patients' health information and assign codes to medical diagnoses and procedures. Some use computer programs to tabulate and analyze data for research.

Health information technicians are employed at hospitals, clinics, doctors' offices, and insurance companies. You need a two-year degree in health informatics to become a health information technician. To get into a qualified program, take biology, chemistry, health, and computer science courses in high school.

Home and Community

Home Health Aide Home health aides provide a vital service for people who need assistance to be able to live in their own homes. This service allows elderly and disabled individuals to remain in their homes and communities for as long as possible. Have students research organizations that employ home health aides in their community. If possible, have students interview a home health aide to learn more about this career and ways that home health aides contribute to the health of individuals and the health of the community.

CAREER SPOTLIGHT

Health Promoter

Elizabeth Pedroza became a health promoter with the Hispanic Health Projects before she knew anything about diabetes or women's health. Today, she spends her days teaching community members about diabetes and other health issues, developing diabetes education materials, and translating medical information for Spanish-speakers.

Q. How can you teach others when you are not a health expert?

A. *I work with experts who teach me what I need to know. The experts know the content and I know the culture. You don't need a college degree for my job. It's more about asking questions, listening, and sharing important information.*

Q. What specific training have you received?

A. *I'm a skilled interviewer with good communications skills, and I am comfortable talking to people with different backgrounds.*

I've also been trained on how to get better information out of people, how to present myself in a respectful way, and how to foster trust. These are important talents to have when you are trying to improve someone's health.

Q. What attracted you to this job?

A. *It provides the opportunity to go into the community and help people. It isn't about what I would gain from it, but what I could give.*

Activity — Beyond the Classroom

Writing Health Education Careers. Identify organizations in your community where health educators work. Don't forget to include your school! Interview three or four health educators to find out more about what they do and what they find challenging about their jobs.

Based on what you learn, write a newspaper recruitment ad for a health educator's job.

Go Online
For more information, go to the Career Corner link at glencoe.com.

CAREER SPOTLIGHT

Health Promoter

Have students discuss ways that health promoters can impact community and individual health.

- Have students work in small groups to discuss the importance of translating medical information into languages spoken in the community. Have each group of students generate a list of three ways, other than language translation, that health information could be made more accessible to those in the community.

- Ask each group to develop a list of characteristics, skills, and talents that would make a person well-suited to a career as a health promoter. Have each group share its list with the class.

Encourage interested students to visit **glencoe.com** for more information on this career.

Activity — Beyond the Classroom

Writing Students may work in groups to share the task of interviewing. Encourage students to develop a list of questions before they begin their interviews. After students have gathered their information, provide several newspaper articles for students to use as models. Remind students that newspaper articles are factual and informative. Have students proofread and correct their work before turning it in.

61

Flexible Technology Solutions
Focus

Health eSpotlight *Video Series*

▶ **By Chapter**

Chapter 3 Achieving Mental and Emotional Health
Video 3: The Strength to Stand Out

Chapter 4 Managing Stress and Coping with Loss
Video 4: Managing Strong Emotions

Chapter 5 Mental and Emotional Problems
Video 5: Signs of Trouble

▶ **By Lesson**

Chapter 3 *Video 3*   For Use With

Segment 3.1   Developing Your Self-Esteem .... Lesson 1
Segment 3.2   Developing Your Personal Identity and
              Character.. Lesson 2
Segment 3.3   Expressing Emotions in Healthy Ways .... Lesson 3

Chapter 4 *Video 4*   For Use With

Segment 4.1   Understanding Stress .... Lesson 1
Segment 4.2   Managing Stress .... Lesson 2
Segment 4.3   Coping with Grief and Loss........................ Lesson 3

Chapter 5 *Video 5*   For Use With

Segment 5.1   Dealing with Anxiety and Depression .... Lesson 1
Segment 5.2   Mental Disorders....................................... Lesson 2
Segment 5.3   Suicide Prevention .... Lesson 3
Segment 5.4   Getting Help .... Lesson 4

▶ **By Skill**

Practicing Healthful Behaviors .... Videos **3** 13 17 19 23
Stress Management .... Videos **4** 7
Communication Skills .... Videos **5** 6 27

■ Indicates videos featured in the unit that teach the
corresponding skill. Other videos listed can also be used
to teach that skill.

Teach

Direct lesson plans beyond the classroom with multi-media fitness activities that students can do online, in class, or as a group.

PowerPoint® Presentation

- *Health* eSpotlight videos
- Audio and image bank

FITNESS ZONE Online

Fitness Zone Online is a multimedia resource that helps students find ways to be physically active each day.

- Clipboard Energizer Activities
- Fitness Zone Videos
- Polar Heart Rate Monitor Activities
- Nutrition, Physical Activity, and Injury Prevention Tips
- Links to Nutrition and Physical Activity Resources

Go Online

Online Learning Center

- Student Web Activities
- PuzzleMaker
- Interactive Health Tutor

Podcast Audio Chapter Summaries

Use the audio Podcast Audio Chapter Summaries to teach and review key concepts, and engage students with health content that they can download to a computer or portable MP3 player.

Assess/Close

Help students master chapter and lesson concepts with an integrated technology solution for assessment and performance evaluation.

Go Online

Online Learning Center

- Interactive Study Guides
- Online Quizzes

ExamView® Assessment Suite CD-ROM

Create and customize tests in minutes with this convenient digital platform.

- Create differentiated tests quickly and easily.
- All questions correlated to National/State Standards.
- Enhance tests with Document Based Questions (DBQ) and add your own photos and graphics.
- Build tests in both English and Spanish.
- Generate progress reports.

Enrich

Use these additional digital and online media resources to promote hands-on exploration of health topics covered in the lesson.

Go Online

Online Learning Center

- Interactive Health Tutor
- Vocabulary PuzzleMaker

Study-to-Go

Download a portable version of eFlashcards and Self-Check Quizzes onto your Palm or Pocket PC.

Health Podcasts Activities

Glencoe's "It's Your Health" Podcast Activities provide students with a unique listening and learning experience that takes health education beyond the classroom. Download the audio files and print activities covering a range of current health topics that matter most to teens!

Mental and Emotional Health

This unit identifies and describes factors that impact mental and emotional health. Students will also learn strategies that promote positive mental and emotional health.

Health eSpotlight Video Series

At the beginning of each chapter, visit glencoe.com and have students watch the video and do the accompanying print activity.

Chapter 3
The Strength to Stand Out

Determining values and goals is an important step in developing health self-esteem.

Chapter 4
Managing Strong Emotions

Stress can affect physical and mental health. It's important to learn how to manage emotions.

Chapter 5
Signs of Trouble

Constant feelings of worry and hopelessness indicate a serious mental illness.

Unit 2 Resources

- Career Corner
- 📁 FAST FILE RESOURCES
- Health Career Research Activity
- Family Involvement Activity
- Community Involvement Activity
- Unit Test

Chapter 3
Achieving Mental and Emotional Health

 The Strength to Stand Out

Chapter 4
Managing Stress and Coping with Loss

 Managing Strong Emotions

Chapter 5
Mental and Emotional Problems

 Signs of Trouble

UNIT PROJECT

Mental and Emotional Support

Using Visuals Big Brothers Big Sisters of America is the oldest and largest mentoring program in the United States. The program matches children with teen and young adult volunteers from the community. The one-to-one relationships that form have a long-lasting, positive effect on both the mentors and the children.

 To learn more about Big Brothers Big Sisters of America, go to the Unit Web Project at glencoe.com.

Get Involved. Which organizations in your community provide mentoring for children and teens? Research community resources to find out how you can contribute or participate. Based on your findings, create a brochure advertising these mentoring programs.

UNIT PROJECT

Mental and Emotional Support The Big Brothers and Big Sisters organizations were formed separately more than 100 years ago and merged in 1977. Research has shown that children who are mentored through Big Brothers Big Sisters have stronger family relationships, are less likely to use illegal drugs and alcohol, and are more likely to have good school attendance than peers from similar backgrounds who are not matched with a mentor.

Get Involved Ask students to assemble information about volunteer opportunities in their community that offer mentoring programs for children and teens. Have students prepare a brochure describing these services. Use a bulletin board to display students' completed brochures.

> **"Learn from yesterday, live for today, hope for tomorrow.
> The important thing is not to stop questioning."**
> — Albert Einstein, 20th-century physicist

Unit 2   Mental and Emotional Health   **63**

Activate Prior Knowledge

Ask students these questions before they read the chapter to build on what they already know.

Chapter 3
What are some characteristics of a person who demonstrates good mental and emotional health?

(Sample answers: Positive self-esteem, resiliency, sense of belonging, sense of purpose, ability to enjoy life)

Chapter 4
What are some factors that commonly cause stress for teens?

(Sample answers: Schoolwork, peer relationships, family relationships)

Chapter 5
What are some warning signs that could indicate an individual may have a serious mental or emotional problem?

(Sample answers: High-risk behaviors, extreme mood changes, frequent physical complaints, dramatic changes in eating or sleeping patterns)

TeacherWorks Plus provides:

- interactive Teacher Wrap-around Edition
- click, drag, and drop to plan lessons
- instant access to many print program resources

How to Get Involved Provide students with these step-by-step instructions on how they can assemble information about volunteer opportunities.

1. Choose an organization, such as Big Brothers Big Sisters.
2. Call the organization and find out if they are looking for volunteers or if there are other ways to participate or donate.
3. Are there any requirements to be a volunteer? Find out if the organization has any guidelines that volunteers must follow. Is there an age requirement?
4. Have students obtain information about Bowl for Kids' Sake events, fundraising and awareness events that raise money annually for Big Brothers Big Sisters.

Chapter 3 pages 64–89	Standards		Features
	National	**State/Local**	
	1.12.1, 1.12.2, 2.12.8, 4.12.1, 4.12.3, 5.12.1, 6.12.1, 7.12.2, 8.12.1–8.12.4		TIME HEALTH • Five Ways to Boost Your Self-Confidence, page 84
Lesson 1 **Developing Your Self-Esteem** pages 66–71 **BIG Idea** *Good mental and emotional health helps you develop healthy self-esteem.*	1.12.1, 1.12.2, 2.12.7, 2.12.8, 6.12.2, 6.12.4, 7.12.4		
Lesson 2 **Developing Personal Identity and Character** pages 72–77 **BIG Idea** *Healthy identity is based on being a person of good character.*	1.12.1, 1.12.5, 2.12.8, 4.12.1, 6.12.4, 7.12.1, 7.12.2		*Real World* CONNECTION • Your Sources of Support, page 77 🕐 Out of Time
Lesson 3 **Expressing Emotions in Healthful Ways** pages 78–83 **BIG Idea** *Managing your emotions allows you to express them in healthful ways.*	1.12.1, 1.12.2, 4.12.1, 4.12.2, 4.12.3, 7.12.2		*Health Skills* Activity • Managing Your Anger *(Practicing Healthful Behaviors)*, page 83 🕐 Out of Time

(30 Min markers appear beside Lesson 1, Lesson 2, and Lesson 3)

Key to Ability Levels

Teaching Strategies and activities have been coded for ability level and appropriateness.

AL Activities for students working above grade level

OL Activities for students working on grade level

BL Activities for students working below grade level

EL Activities for English Learners

Chapter 3 Planning Guide

Resources	Lesson Assessment	Technology
Student Activity Workbook **TEACH** **FAST FILE RESOURCES** Vocabulary Practice **TEACH** Health Labs **EXTEND**	Chapter 3 Review Chapter 3 Assessment Standardized Test Practice ◉ *ExamView® Assessment Suite* CD-ROM	**Teaching Tools:** ◉ *TeacherWorks*™ Plus DVD ◉ *StudentWorks*™ Plus DVD ◉ *ExamView® Assessment Suite* CD-ROM 🕹 Transparency ◉ Fitness DVD ◉ PowerPoint® DVD ◉ Health eSpotlight Video Series DVD
FAST FILE RESOURCES Reading Strategies Activity **TEACH** Reteaching Activity **REVIEW** Enrichment Activity **EXTEND** Health Skills Practice **TEACH**	Lesson 1 Assessment, page 71 📁 Lesson 1 Quiz *Fast File* ◉ *ExamView® Assessment Suite* CD-ROM	**Web-Based Resources:** Go **Online** glencoe.com • Health Podcast Activities • Audio Chapter Summaries (English/Spanish) • Interactive Health Tutor • Health Skills Activities • Vocabulary PuzzleMaker • Parent Letters (English/Spanish) • Lesson Plans • Health Inventories • Online Quizzes • Study-to-Go • Unit Web Projects • Student Web Activities • Fitness Zone Activities
FAST FILE RESOURCES Reading Strategies Activity **TEACH** Reteaching Activity **REVIEW** Enrichment Activity **EXTEND** Health Skills Practice **TEACH**	Lesson 2 Assessment, page 77 📁 Lesson 2 Quiz *Fast File* ◉ *ExamView® Assessment Suite* CD-ROM	
FAST FILE RESOURCES Reading Strategies Activity **TEACH** Reteaching Activity **REVIEW** Enrichment Activity **EXTEND** Health Skills Practice **TEACH**	Lesson 3 Assessment, page 83 📁 Lesson 3 Quiz *Fast File* ◉ *ExamView® Assessment Suite* CD-ROM	

This is the student's backpack solution.

Includes:
- complete Interactive Student Edition
- full audio of English text and Spanish chapter summaries
- allows students to record assignments and track grades.
- links to online activities and additional student resources
- access to all student worksheets and workbooks

FOLDABLES Study Organizer

Dinah Zike Foldables® Chapter Activity
Refer to the *Dinah Zike Reading and Study Skills for Glencoe Health*. Have students make a layered-look book/pyramid Foldable for the levels of Maslow's hierarchy of needs. As students read and discuss the chapter, have them record facts under the appropriate tabs.

Key to Symbols

 Transparencies   **REVIEW** activities to review or reinforce content

 CD-ROM   **TEACH** activities to teach basic concepts

 glencoe.com   **EXTEND** activities to extend or enrich lesson content

 Print Resources

64B

Achieving Mental and Emotional Health

Chapter Overview

Chapter 3 focuses on ways to develop self-esteem, the relationship between a healthy identity and good character, and healthful ways to express emotions.

Lesson 1

Good mental and emotional health are directly related to healthy self-esteem.

Lesson 2

Being a person of good character can build a healthy personal identity.

Lesson 3

Learning to manage emotions in healthful ways contributes to good mental and emotional health.

▶ **Activating Prior Knowledge**

After students have completed their lists, ask volunteers to share their responses with the class. Ask students what factors may have influenced the teen's identity. (Sample answers: Role models, personal likes and dislikes, character traits)

Achieving Mental and Emotional Health

Lesson 1

Developing Your Self-Esteem

BIG Idea *Good mental and emotional health helps you develop healthy self-esteem.*

Lesson 2

Developing Personal Identity and Character

BIG Idea *Healthy identity is based on being a person of good character.*

Lesson 3

Expressing Emotions in Healthful Ways

BIG Idea *Managing your emotions allows you to express them in healthful ways.*

Activating Prior Knowledge

Using Visuals Look at the picture on this page. How is this teen expressing his identity? List three characteristics that help define who we are.

Universal Access

Differentiated Learning Glencoe provides teacher support and student materials for all learners in the health classroom.

- Chapter Summaries in English and Spanish are available online at **glencoe.com**.

- *Fast Files* and related worksheets support reluctant readers.

- Universal Access strategies throughout the Teacher Wraparound Edition and *Fast Files* help you present materials for gifted students, at-risk students, physically impaired students, and those with behavior disorders or learning disabilities.

Chapter Launchers

Health in Action

Discuss the **BIG Ideas**

Before beginning this chapter, think about how you would answer these questions:

▸ How would you describe your level of self-esteem?

▸ How is your self-esteem related to your identity?

▸ How does the way you express emotions reflect your mental health?

Watch the *Health eSpotlight* Video Series

VIDEO

The Strength to Stand Out

What values are important to you? How can you express these values through your goals?

Assess Your Health

Go Online

Visit glencoe.com and complete the Health Inventory for Chapter 3.

Chapter Launchers

Health in Action

Discuss the **BIG Ideas**

Assign this activity before students read the chapter. Tell students that they may keep their responses confidential. Explain that the purpose of the questions is to help students assess their current knowledge of mental and emotional health. Remind students to keep these questions in mind as they read the chapter.

Health eSpotlight
Video Series

VIDEO

The Strength to Stand Out

Before Viewing the Video

Ask Students: *What activities do you currently do that help build your self-esteem?* (Answers will vary.)

Go Online

Have students go to glencoe.com and take the Health Inventory for Chapter 3.

Chapter Skills

Reading Skills
- Reviewing Facts and Vocabulary, pp. 71, 77, 83
- Reading/Writing Practice, p. 89

BIG Idea

Self-esteem, good character, and managing emotions in healthful ways are all related to mental and emotional health.

Vocabulary
- New Vocabulary, pp. 66, 72, 78
- Reviewing Facts and Vocabulary, pp. 71, 77, 83

Health Skills
- Health Skills Activity, p. 82
- Applying Health Skills, pp. 71, 77, 83

Writing Skills
- Real World Connection, p. 77
- Writing Critically, pp. 71, 77, 83
- Reading/Writing Practice, p. 89

65

LESSON 1

Developing Your Self-Esteem

① FOCUS

📖 GUIDE TO READING

BIG Idea Students will learn that good mental and emotional health contributes to healthy self-esteem. **Ask Students:** *What are some factors that impact teens' self-esteem?* (Sample answers: Relationships with peers, relationships with family members, ability to achieve goals)

Before You Read

Outline Students' outlines should include all of the heading and subheadings found in the lesson. Details included in the outlines will vary.

Main Idea

Mental and Emotional Health Good mental and emotional health can have a positive impact on everyday life. **Ask Students:** *What are some aspects of everyday life that affect an individual's mental and emotional health?* (Sample answer: Family relationships)

Real Life Issues ....

Have students read the scenario. **Ask Students:** *How could Josh's response to his difficult situation impact his self-esteem?* (Being able to bounce back from a setback contributes to positive self-esteem.)

66

LESSON 1

📖 GUIDE TO READING

BIG Idea *Good mental and emotional health helps you develop healthy self-esteem.*

Before You Read

Create an Outline. Preview this lesson by scanning the pages. Then organize the headings and subheadings into an outline. As you read, fill in your outline with important details.

```
I.
   A.
      1.
      2.
   B.
II.
```

New Vocabulary

▸ mental/emotional health (p. 66)
▸ resilient (p. 67)
▸ self-esteem (p. 68)
▸ competence (p. 68)
▸ hierarchy of needs (p. 70)
▸ self-actualization (p. 70)

Developing Your Self-Esteem

Real Life Issues ....

Staying Positive. Josh has just lost the election for class president. He thought he was more popular and had better ideas than Annie, who won. He worked long and hard during the campaign, and thought most of the people in his class agreed with his platform. He feels bad about losing, and he's not sure how he can face all his classmates.

Writing *Imagine you are Josh's close friend. Write a dialogue between yourself and Josh discussing how he might handle his defeat.*

What Is Mental and Emotional Health?

Main Idea Mental and emotional health helps you function effectively each day.

Do you see yourself in a positive way? Are you able to handle challenges and setbacks well? The ability to answer "yes" to these questions is one sign of mental and emotional health. **Mental/emotional health** is *the ability to accept yourself and others, express and manage emotions, and deal with the demands and challenges you meet in your life.* Having good mental/emotional health is an important part of your total health.

Most people have ups and downs throughout their lives. For example, you may have felt proud because you performed well during a school play, but were disappointed when you didn't make the varsity team at school. Such ups and downs are normal, especially during the teen years when you are adapting to many changes in your life.

Promoting School Wellness

Supporting Mental and Emotional Health Services that promote mental and emotional health are important components of a successful coordinated school health program. As students learn more about mental and emotional health as they read the chapter, be certain to share with them the services that are available at school. These might be the school nurse, guidance counselor, trusted teachers, etc. Provide students with detailed information about how these services can be accessed. Perhaps ask your school counselor to come and give a talk to the class.

The Importance of Mental and Emotional Health

Mentally healthy people are, in general, happy and enjoy their lives. They feel confident and comfortable spending time alone or with others. They're also flexible and can cope with a wide variety of feelings and situations.

Good **mental** and emotional health influences your physical and social health too. For example, if you're worried, you might eat an unhealthful diet, not get enough sleep, or stop exercising regularly. If you're worried and become irritable, your relationships with friends and others may suffer.

Characteristics of Good Mental and Emotional Health

How do you know if you have good mental and emotional health? Here are some general characteristics.

- **Sense of belonging.** Feeling close to family members, friends, teachers, and others provides you with support.
- **Sense of purpose.** Recognizing that you have value and importance as a person lets you set and reach goals.
- **Positive outlook.** Seeing the bright side of life reduces stress and increases your chances of success.
- **Self-sufficiency.** Having the confidence to make responsible decisions promotes your sense of independence and self-assurance.
- **Healthy self-esteem.** Having healthy self-esteem helps you accept and recover from difficulties and failures.

Everyone has to manage difficult and stressful situations. Mentally and emotionally healthy people handle stresses in positive ways. These people are **resilient**—they have *the ability to adapt effectively and recover from disappointment, difficulty, or crisis.*

Academic Vocabulary

mental *(adjective):* of or relating to the mind

 READING CHECK

Name What are the characteristics of good mental/emotional health?

■ **Figure 3.1** Close friends encourage one another. *How might this kind of encouragement affect a person's mental health?*

② TEACH

AL Active Learning

Report Ask students to find out more about how mental and emotional health affects physical health. Encourage students to find reliable sources of information that show how poor mental and emotional health can contribute to illness. Have students prepare an oral report to share their finding with the class. **AL**

C Critical Thinking

Discussing Have students brainstorm ways in which the mental and emotional health of teens is impacted by their peers. Ask students which of the five characteristics of good mental and emotional health do they feel is most affected by peers. (Sample answer: I think peers are most likely to affect a teen's sense of belonging.) **OL**

READING CHECK

Answer Sense of belonging; sense of purpose; positive outlook; self-sufficiency; healthy self-esteem

Caption Answer

Figure 3.1 Sample answers: Increases sense of belonging and self-esteem, instills confidence, encourages self-sufficiency

Academic Integration

English **Character Analysis** Write the five characteristics of good mental and emotional health on the board (sense of belonging, sense of purpose, positive outlook, autonomy, healthy self-esteem). Ask students to select a character from a book they have read. Have students write a paragraph that analyzes the character's mental and emotional health using the five characteristics listed on the board. Ask students to provide specific examples of situations in the book in which the character does (or does not) display each of the characteristics of good mental and emotional health.

Main Idea

Self-Esteem Healthy self-esteem is a key component of good mental and emotional health. **Ask Students:** *What factors influence an individual's self-esteem?* (Sample answers: Interactions with peers, interactions with family, feelings about yourself)

FITNESS ZONE

Have students break into groups of three or four.

- Groups should stand in a circle facing each other.

- One person leads group in an exercise of his or her choice for 32 counts.

- Continue around the circle with each person being a leader.

☑ **READING CHECK**

Answer Feeling good about yourself; taking pride in your abilities, skills, and accomplishments.

Writing Support

Write a Dialogue Have students read the "How You Develop Self-Esteem" section and then write a dialogue between two teens. One teen is trying to lend support to the other teen to help him or her improve self-esteem. **OL**

FITNESS ZONE

My team lost the last game of the season, and I thought about quitting the sport. Then my dad told me that Michael Jordan was cut from the varsity basketball team when he was in 10th grade. Imagine if he had quit! He wouldn't have become one of the greatest NBA basketball players in history. I decided to be like Mike and not to give up on exercise or sports. For more physical activity ideas, visit the Online Fitness Zone at **glencoe.com**.

☑ **READING CHECK**

Describe Identify several benefits of healthy self-esteem.

Self-Esteem

Main Idea Healthy self-esteem is necessary for good mental/emotional health.

Developing **self-esteem**, or *how much you value, respect, and feel confident about yourself,* influences the other characteristics of good mental health. If you feel valued, loved, and accepted by others, and you value, love, and accept yourself your overall attitude and outlook will be good. Having good self-esteem will also affect your overall attitude and the health choices you make. Taking healthful risks can raise your self-esteem. Trying new challenges can also raise your sense of **competence**, or *having enough skills to do something.*

How You Develop Self-Esteem

You probably remember a time when your family praised you for doing something well, or reassured you and gave you advice on tasks you hadn't yet mastered. When you are praised for mastering a task or reassured when you do not, your self-esteem increases. Self-esteem also increases when you believe that you can succeed, or when you master new challenges.

No one succeeds at new tasks and activities all the time. If you don't succeed at a new task or activity, think about the reasons why you may not have succeeded. How did you prepare? Was it realistic to expect to succeed on your first try? Also, everyone has unique abilities. You may have to work harder at a new task or activity if you do not have the unique abilities to master that task or activity easily.

How you react emotionally to situations also affects your self-esteem. *Self-talk,* the encouragement or criticism that you give yourself, can affect your self-esteem. Using positive self-talk will strengthen your self-esteem. Try to replace negative thoughts by using positive self-talk.

W

Benefits of Healthy Self-Esteem

Healthy self-esteem helps you feel proud of yourself and your abilities, skills, and accomplishments. You believe that setbacks are temporary. You have the confidence to confront challenges and overcome them.

Healthy self-esteem also gives you the confidence to try new things. You're not afraid to try a new sport, or join a club at school, or even get a job and learn new tasks. People with healthy self-esteem know that they may not be as good at some tasks as they are with others. They don't see themselves as a failure if they don't succeed at something.

Myths & Reality

Self-Esteem

Myth: Teens with healthy self-esteem are stuck-up, arrogant, or feel that that they are better than everyone else.

Fact: Teens who act arrogant or superior to others are often masking low self-esteem. Individuals with healthy self-esteem do not feel they need to treat others badly to bolster their own image.

Myth: If you have poor self-esteem, it's a problem you'll have for your entire life.

Fact: Individuals can control their level of self-esteem. Self-esteem changes throughout life, and there are numerous ways to improve your self-esteem.

■ **Figure 3.2** Important people in your life play a role in shaping your self-esteem. *How has someone important to you affected your self-esteem?*

Main Idea

Improving Self-Esteem There are many ways that individuals can improve their self-esteem and mental and emotional health. **Ask Students:** *How could improving your self-esteem have a positive effect on your relationships with others?* (Sample answer: Improved self-esteem would help me form more positive relationships with others.)

Improving Your Self-Esteem

Main Idea You can improve your self-esteem and your overall mental and emotional health.

U

You can control many things that affect your self-esteem. Avoid criticizing yourself, or spending time with people who criticize you. Set realistic expectations, and don't expect everything to be "perfect." Expecting perfection can prevent you from enjoying your successes. You may judge a success as a failure if it doesn't meet your critera for perfection. These additional suggestions can help you improve your self-esteem.

HS

- Choose friends who value and respect you.
- Focus on positive aspects about yourself.
- Replace negative self-talk with supportive self-talk.
- Work toward accomplishments rather than perfection.
- Consider your mistakes learning opportunities.
- Try new activities to discover your talents.
- Write down your goals and the steps you will take to achieve them.
- Exercise regularly to feel more energized.
- Volunteer your time to help someone.
- Accept the things you can't change, and focus your energy on changing the things you can.

Go Online

Go to **glencoe.com** and complete the Student Web Activity on avoiding negative self-talk.

Caption Answer

Figure 3.2 Sample answers: My mother encourages me to do well in school. My sister helps me improve my basketball skills.

U **Universal Access**

Reluctant Readers Reluctant readers and students learning English may be discouraged when faced with reading the great number of suggestions for improving self-esteem offered in the student text. Ask students to each select one bulleted suggestion and choose a creative way to illustrate it. For example, students may choose to make a poster, a comic strip, or a photo collage. Have students share their work with the class. **BL** **EL**

HS **Health Skills Practice**

Practicing Healthful Behaviors Have each student choose one of the bulleted suggestions in the text for improving self-esteem. Have each student make a written plan describing how he or she could incorporate the chosen suggestion into everyday life. Encourage students to follow up after one week to evaluate the suggestion's impact on their self-esteem. **OL**

Writing Strategy

Letter to the Editor Provide students with examples of appropriate letters to the editor from a local newspaper. Point out that letters to the editor provide an opportunity for individuals to share their point-of-view with others. Have students write a letter to the editor encouraging teens to take steps to improve their self-esteem. Remind students that their letters should provide a persuasive reason for why teens should work to improve self-esteem, and specific activities teens can participate in that would help. Ask students to share their completed letters with the class. If possible, submit some or all of the letters for publication in a school or local newspaper.

Main Idea

Developing Self-Awareness
Understanding and meeting needs in healthy ways can help individuals achieve their full potential. **Ask Students:** *What are some needs that all individuals have?* (Sample answers: food, sleep, love)

C Critical Thinking

Applying Information Ask students to recall a time when they were too hungry, thirsty, or tired to pay attention in class. Have one or two volunteers share their experiences. **Ask Students:** *How does Maslow's hierarchy of needs apply to the examples just heard?* (Sample answer: If someone has not met his or her physical needs, which are the bottom of Maslow's hierarchy, he or she cannot focus on achieving in school, which is part of the fourth level of Maslow's hierarchy.) **AL**

R Reading Strategy

Analyzing an Infographic
Discuss each level of Maslow's hierarchy in the following way: Ask students to locate the level on the infographic. Have a volunteer read aloud the text associated with each level. Ask another student to state ways that teens can meet the described need. **OL**

Developing Self-Awareness

Main Idea Understanding your needs and meeting them in healthy ways will help you reach your highest potential.

As infants, we rely on others to meet our basic needs. Those needs include food, clothing, and physical safety and comfort. As we grow, our needs become more complex. The psychologist Abraham Maslow created a theory that explains human development and motivation (see **Figure 3.3**). The **hierarchy of needs** is *a ranked list of those needs essential to human*

Figure 3.3

Maslow's Hierarchy of Needs

Maslow's model helps us understand our needs. Meeting these needs in healthy ways strengthens our mental/emotional health.

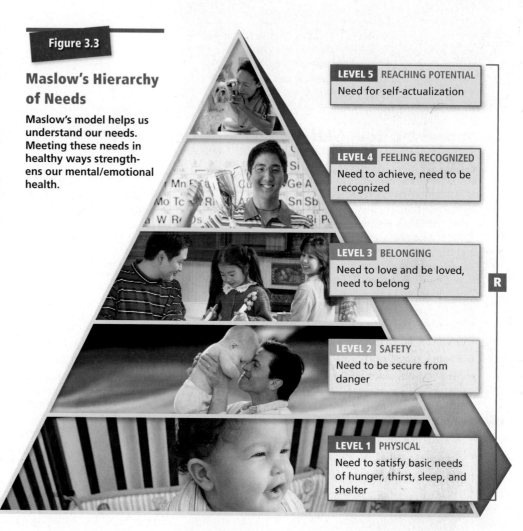

LEVEL 5 REACHING POTENTIAL
Need for self-actualization

LEVEL 4 FEELING RECOGNIZED
Need to achieve, need to be recognized

LEVEL 3 BELONGING
Need to love and be loved, need to belong

LEVEL 2 SAFETY
Need to be secure from danger

LEVEL 1 PHYSICAL
Need to satisfy basic needs of hunger, thirst, sleep, and shelter

70 **Chapter 3** Achieving Mental and Emotional Health

🏠👪 Home and Community

Staying Safe Point out that safety needs are the second level of Maslow's hierarchy. Remind students that individuals cannot reach their potential if they do not feel safe. Ask students to find out more about programs that are designed to keep students safe at home, at school, and in the community. Suggest that students contact local law enforcement, school officials, or community leaders to learn about laws and other initiatives that focus on safety. Have students share their findings with the class.

growth and development, presented in ascending order, starting with basic needs and building toward the need to reach your highest potential.

Maslow's hierarchy shows that our earliest motivations are to satisfy our physical needs. Once these basic needs are met, we become interested in meeting the need to belong and be loved, the need to be valued and recognized, and the need to reach our potential or to acheive **self actualization** or *to strive to be the best you can.*

As well as understanding needs, you need to learn how to meet them in healthy ways. Meeting a need in a high-risk way will not lead to healthful development. For example, some teens may join gangs in order to belong to a group. Joining a gang is a high-risk behavior that affects all sides of the health triangle.

Try using Maslow's model to evaluate your personal development. What needs are you focused on right now? How are you meeting those needs? As your self-awareness grows, you can begin to take more control of your personal growth. Reaching out to others can help you develop deeper relationships and a stronger support group.

■ **Figure 3.4** These teens have found a way to contribute to their community. *Why do you think taking time to attend to the needs of others is beneficial to self-esteem?*

 READING CHECK

Explain Why is joining a gang an unhealthy way to meet the need to be valued?

LESSON 1 ASSESSMENT

After You Read

Reviewing Facts and Vocabulary

1. List the characteristics of good mental/emotional health.
2. Define the term *self-esteem*.
3. Identify the five levels of Maslow's hierarchy of needs.

Thinking Critically

4. **Analyze.** Explain how being mentally and emotionally healthy contributes to the quality of your life.
5. **Identify.** What are three ways that you can demonstrate healthy self-esteem and good mental/emotional health?

Applying Health Skills

6. **Practicing Healthful Behaviors.** Keiko just found out that she didn't make the track team. Write a script showing how she can use positive self-talk to deal with this disappointment.

Writing Critically

7. **Descriptive.** Imagine a teen whose suggestions are ignored during a group project. With healthy self-esteem, how might the teen respond?

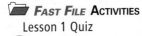

Visit **glencoe.com** and complete the Interactive Study Guide for this lesson.

Lesson 1 Developing Your Self-Esteem **71**

---

1. Sense of belonging, sense of purpose, positive outlook, self-sufficiency, healthy self-esteem
2. *Self-esteem* is how much you value, respect, and feel confident about yourself.
3. Physical needs, safety needs, need to belong, esteem needs, need to reach potential
4. Sample answer: Mentally healthy people enjoy themselves and their lives.
5. See page 69.
6. Scripts will vary, but should demonstrate the use of positive self-talk.
7. Responses will vary, but should reflect that a teen with healthy self-esteem might bounce back from this setback using strategies such as positive self-talk.

Caption Answer

Figure 3.4 Sample answer: Helping others gives you a chance to gain perspective on your own life.

③ ASSESS/ CLOSE

Assessment Resources

📁 *FAST FILE* ACTIVITIES
Lesson 1 Quiz

💿 *ExamView Assessment Suite* CD-ROM

Visit glencoe.com **for:**
Online Quizzes
Online Learning Center

Progress Monitoring

Reteaching

Have students review the lesson vocabulary terms with a partner using flashcards. Call on each pair of students to share a definition of one of the terms.

Enrichment

Have students write a paragraph that summarizes the reasons why positive self-esteem is important for teens. Ask volunteers to share their completed paragraphs with the class.

G⊙ Online

Have students visit **glencoe.com** and complete the Interactive Study Guide for this lesson.

Developing Personal Identity and Character

1 FOCUS

GUIDE TO READING

BIG Idea A healthy identity can be achieved by being a person of good character. **Ask Students:** *What are some positive characteristics that make you unique?* (Sample answers: Athletic talent, ability to write stories)

Before You Read

Cluster Chart Students' cluster charts will vary, but should include words and phrases that define and describe character.

Main Idea

Personal Identity Personal identity describes who a person is. **Ask Students:** *Do you think your personal identity will stay the same throughout your life, or do you think it will change?* (Sample answer: My interests and activities will change throughout my life, so my personal identity will probably change, too.)

Real Life Issues ....

After students have completed their paragraphs, have them develop a list of careers based on their interests and talents.

GUIDE TO READING

BIG Idea *Healthy identity is based on being a person of good character.*

Before You Read

Create a Cluster Chart. Draw a center circle and label it "Character." Draw circles around it and use these to define and describe this term. As you read, continue filling in the chart with more details.

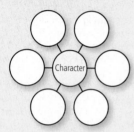
Character

New Vocabulary

▶ personal identity (p. 72)
▶ role model (p. 73)
▶ personality (p. 73)
▶ character (p. 73)
▶ integrity (p. 74)
▶ constructive criticism (p. 76)

Review Vocabulary

▶ values (Ch.2, L.2)

Developing Personal Identity and Character

Real Life Issues ....

Choosing a Path. Casey is in the process of deciding what to do after he graduates next year. He visits the school guidance counselor to discuss his options. The counselor begins by asking, "What are you interested in? What are your talents?"

Writing *What are your interests and talents? Write an essay describing how these interests and talents might play a role in your future.*

Your Personal Identity

Main Idea Your personal identity describes who you are.

When you first meet someone, you tell that person your name. As you get to know the person better, you may share more information. These attributes are your **personal identity**, *your sense of yourself as a unique individual.*

Your personal identity depends a lot on your age and circumstances. Other parts of your personal identity are unique to you. Identity development is one of the most important tasks you will accomplish during your teen years.

How Identity Forms

Identity is partly formed by recognizing your likes and dislikes. Your relationships and experiences with family and friends also influence your personal identity. As you mature, you'll meet a greater number and variety of people, and will develop your own opinions. As your experiences broaden, you develop likes and dislikes based on how your experiences fit with your values and beliefs.

Teens Want to Know

Will I Ever Establish My Identity?
Discussions on personal identity can be frustrating for teens who are experiencing rapidly changing interests, emotions, and goals. Remind students that identity development is an ongoing process and that even adults continue developing their personal identities throughout their lives. Have students focus on the progress they have made since childhood in establishing a personal identity.

You may identify a **role model**, *someone whose success or behavior serves as an example for you*. Your identity will change throughout your life as your interests change. You will struggle at times with alternatives and choices, but eventually you will develop a clear sense of your own values, interests, beliefs, occupational goals, and relationship expectations.

Aspects of Identity

One aspect of your identity is your **personality**, *a complex set of characteristics that makes you unique*. Your personality sets you apart from other people and determines how you will react in certain situations. Although it plays a big role in defining your identity, it isn't the only thing. Other relationships, such as those with your family, your ethnic group, and even your close friends, also define who you are. These shared characteristics and your unique qualities form your identity.

The Importance of Good Character

Main Idea   Character plays a significant role in your decisions, actions, and behavior.

An important aspect of your identity is your **character**, *the distinctive qualities that describe how a person thinks, feels, and behaves*. Good character is an outward expression of inner values and is a vital part of healthy identity. A person of good character demonstrates *core ethical values,* such as responsibility, honesty, and respect. Such values are held in high regard across all cultures and age groups.

READING CHECK

List What are some aspects of personal identity?

■ **Figure 3.5** Friends share similar values. *What values do you share with your friends?*

Lesson 2   Developing Personal Identity and Character   **73**

C Critical Thinking

Discussing Have students brainstorm a list of sports stars, actors, and musicians whom teens look up to as role models. **Ask students:** *If these individuals know that many teens look up to them, should they feel obligated to behave as positive role models?* In leading the discussion, explain that there is no right or wrong answer to this question, but ask students to justify their opinion.
OL **EL**

READING CHECK

Answers Some aspects of personal identity are personality, relationships and shared characteristics with family and friends, character, and one's own unique qualities.

Main Idea

The Importance of Good Character Character guides a person's decisions, actions, and behaviors. **Ask Students:** *What are some specific ways that teens can demonstrate good character?* (Sample answer: Helping a friend with homework)

Caption Answer

Figure 3.5 Sample answer: My friends and I share the values of responsibility and caring.

ELL Support

Related Terms Write the vocabulary terms *personality* and *personal identity* on the board. Ask volunteers to point out any similarities they see in these terms.

Beginning Underline *person* in each of the terms on the board. Pronounce the word aloud and have students repeat. Explain that *person* is a word that refers to one individual.

Intermediate Point out that the terms *personal identity* and *personality* are based on the word *person*. Review the definition of these terms with students. Have students use the terms *personality* and *personal identity* in spoken sentences.

Advanced Ask students to use the terms *personal identity* and *personality* in written sentences. Call on volunteers to read their sentences aloud.

FITNESS ZONE

CA Cultural Awareness

Traits of Good Character
Explain that the traits of good character described in the text are valued in all cultures. However, the ways that these traits are demonstrated may differ among cultures. For example, bowing is used to show respect in some cultures. Have students work in small groups to find out the similarities and differences in two different cultures with regards to the trait of responsibility. Have each group share its findings with the class. **EL** **OL**

FITNESS ZONE

Handshakes have been a cultural form of greeting for centuries. Have students try this:

- In pairs, they should make up a handshake.
- Each handshake should have four different parts and at least one body movement.
- Put two pairs together to exchange handshakes.

 **READING CHECK**

Answer Trustworthiness, respect, responsibility, fairness, caring, citizenship

Caption Answer

Figure 3.6 Sample answer: I show respect by taking good care of items I have borrowed from friends.

FITNESS ZONE

I've noticed that there's definitely a connection between having a positive outlook on life and feeling healthy. One day last week, no one could go skateboarding with me. I was bored and started to feel sad. Then I remembered that a family with a girl about my age moved in down the street. I stopped by and introduced myself. She and I went for a walk. We got some fresh air and exercise and I had a chance to make a new friend—it felt great! For more physical activity ideas, visit the Online Fitness Zone at **glencoe.com.**

 READING CHECK

Identify What are the six traits of good character?

■ **Figure 3.6** Courtesy is a sign of respect. *How do you show respect for others?*

Traits of Good Character

Six traits are commonly used to describe good character. By demonstrating these traits consistently in your actions and behaviors, you show others that you have **integrity**, or *a firm observance of core ethical values.*

- **Trustworthiness.** You are honest, loyal, and reliable—you do what you say you'll do. For example, if you tell a friend that you'll meet at a certain time, you try your best to be on time. You have the courage to do the right thing, and you don't lie, cheat, or steal.

- **Respect.** You are considerate of others and accept their differences. You make decisions that show you respect your health and the health of others. Even if you disagree with another person's point of view, you use good manners in your dealings with people. You treat them and their property with care and respect.

- **Responsibility.** You use self-control—you think before you act and consider the consequences. You are accountable for your choices and decisions, and don't blame others for your actions. You try your best and complete projects you start, even when things don't go as planned.

- **Fairness.** You play by the rules, take turns, and share. You are open minded, and you listen to others. You don't take advantage of others, and you don't blame others.

- **Caring.** A caring person is kind and compassionate. You express gratitude, are forgiving toward others, and want to help people in need.

- **Citizenship.** Demonstrating good citizenship means you advocate for a safe and healthy environment at school and in your community. You take an interest in the world around you. You obey rules and laws, and show respect for authority.

CA

Skills for the 21st Century

Media Literacy Explain that, in addition to family and peers, the media (television, radio, print materials, and the Internet) also play a role in the development of character. Ask students to evaluate the impact of popular media on character development. For example, ask students to debate the impact of music videos on the amount of respect that teens show to individuals of the opposite gender. Have students discuss the impact of media on the development of each of the six traits listed in the text.

Working Toward a Positive Identity

Main Idea You can develop a healthy identity.

You may think that your family and your circumstances form your identity. This is partly true, but *you* control who you *become*. As you mature, you will make more personal choices and decisions. For example, you will choose a career. The list in **Figure 3.7** can help you develop a positive identity.

Recognize Your Strengths and Weaknesses

To begin to understand your identity, analyze your strengths and weaknesses. Be honest and realistic. If you are a trustworthy friend or a talented singer, be proud of yourself. At the same time, evaluate your weaknesses without being too critical, and set realistic goals to improve. For instance, if you tend to put things off, such as homework, set a goal to develop new habits. With planning and commitment, you can improve habits.

Demonstrate Positive Values

Practicing good character is not always easy, but it helps you build a positive identity. For instance, if you are an honors student who feels pressured to cheat on an exam, that action could harm your self-esteem, your reputation, or both.

READING CHECK

Explain How is developing a purpose for your life helpful?

Develop a Purpose in Your Life

HS

A sense of purpose helps you set goals and work to achieve them. It also provides you with a framework to build a healthy identity. Some of your goals will be short term, like studying for and passing an exam. Others will be long term, such as planning for higher education and acquiring job skills.

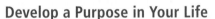

Figure 3.7 Tips for Promoting a Healthy Identity

- **List your skills and strengths.** Include physical, mental/emotional, and social strengths. Read the list when you're feeling down.
- **Surround yourself with positive, supportive people.** Choose friends who support and respect your rights and needs.
- **Find something that you love to do, and do it frequently.** If you're always too busy to do the things you enjoy, you're not taking care of yourself.
- **Stop making life a contest.** Recognize that there will always be people more and less able than you in areas of life. Be content with doing the best you can in all areas that matter to you.
- **Help someone else.** One way to feel good about yourself is to see the positive effects of your own words or actions on someone else's life.

Main Idea

A Positive Identity Individuals can actively shape a positive identity. **Ask Students:** *How has your ability to make choices and decisions about your life changed since you were a young child?* (Sample answer: I have more choices now that I am older, and I am able to make better decisions.)

HS Health Skills Practice

Goal Setting Point out to students that short-term and long-term goals are tools that can be used to promote a sense of purpose in one's life. Direct students to brainstorm one short-term goal and one long-term goal and record the goals in writing. Then have them list steps that will help them achieve each goal. They can make a note of any individuals who can offer support and encourage them to evaluate their progress toward their goals at appropriate time intervals. Remind them to reward themselves for achieving or making progress toward a goal. OL

READING CHECK

Answer A purpose in life provides a framework for your mental and emotional health and helps build a healthy identity.

Cooperative Learning

Role-Plays Have students work in pairs to develop role-plays that demonstrate the use of constructive criticism. Ask each pair of students to practice its role-play, and then perform it for the class. After all of the student pairs have performed, have a class discussion on effective (and ineffective) strategies for constructive criticism. Make a T-chart on the board. Label one side "Effective" and the other side "Not Effective." Have students identify characteristics that make constructive criticism effective or ineffective. Add their responses to the chart.

Academic Vocabulary

crucial *(adjective):*
important or essential

Form Meaningful Relationships

Meaningful relationships, such as those with family, friends, and others, are **crucial** to the development of your identity. Relationships provide a support system that can help you build confidence and develop a sense of security and belonging. Within a meaningful relationship, family, frends or others may give you **constructive criticism**, or *nonhostile comments that point out problems and encourage improvement.* For example, when a friend doesn't do well at a task, you might make helpful suggestions without judging the way your friend performed.

C

Avoid Unhealthful High-Risk Behaviors

Risk taking is part of life. Playing sports, taking part in artistic or creative activities, public speaking, and making friends all involve some risk. These risks are healthful. They challenge you to develop skills and to mature in new ways. However, high-risk behaviors, such as using tobacco, alcohol, or other drugs, reckless driving, or joining a gang, are dangerous and harmful.

Contribute to the Community

Your community is your extended support system. It provides services and resources to meet many of your needs. For a community to remain strong, however, all of its members must participate in making it work. Giving back to the community in the form of volunteering is part of being a good citizen. Volunteering within your community improves the quality of people's lives, gives you a sense of accomplishment and belonging, and increases your self-esteem.

W

Explore glencoe.com and complete the Student Web Activity on demonstrating good character.

Academic Vocabulary

Crucial Help students understand the meaning of *crucial* by posing the following questions: What equipment is crucial when playing football? What supplies are crucial for school? Brainstorm additional questions based on students' interests.

C Critical Thinking

Promoting a Healthy Identity Pair English language learners with students who are fluent in English. Have students work in pairs to review the information on meaningful relationships. **Ask Students:** *Who is your support system?* (Sample answers: mom, dad, friends) **EL** **OL**

W Writing Support

Listing Assets and Strengths After students have read the tips for promoting a healthy identity listed in **Figure 3.7**, ask them to make a list of their own assets and strengths. Explain to students that they may keep their list confidential. **Ask Students:** *What are some situations in which you contribute to the community?* (Sample answer: I help out in the library after school.) **BL** **OL**

■ **Figure 3.8** This player relies on his coach for honest feedback. *Whom else might a teen rely on for honest feedback?*

Caption Answer

Figure 3.8 Sample answers: teachers, parents, peers

Home and Community

Hobbies Remind students that finding something they love to do is one way to promote the development of a healthy identity. Explain that a hobby is a pastime people take part in for enjoyment. Tell students that there are many kinds of hobbies, such as reading, gardening, bike riding, and painting. Have students ask family members and trusted adult members of their community about the hobbies they enjoy. Then have students make a personal health goal to explore an interest that could become a hobby.

Real World CONNECTION

Your Sources of Support

People around you regularly provide support. Some offer material needs, others offer comfort and honest opinions, and others provide information. One thing that all of these people have in common is a genuine concern for you. Together they form your support system.

▸ Identify your support system. Make a chart with the following categories: **Material support** (providers of money, transportation, physical help), **Emotional support** (providers of comfort, sympathy, encouragement), **Information support** (providers of knowledge, referrals), and **Appraisal support** (providers of feedback, praise, suggestions).

▸ Under each category, identify who you count on and why. List those people whose names appear often. These individuals make up your core support group.

Activity Reading / Writing

Pick one person from your core support group.

1. Write that person a letter expressing your appreciation for his or her support and encouragement.
2. Identify ways that the person has supported you.
3. Describe how the support helped build your identity.
4. Tell that person how his or her support has shaped your goals for the future.
5. Describe to the person how his or her support has influenced you to support others throughout your life.

3 ASSESS/CLOSE

Assessment Resources

 FAST FILE ACTIVITIES
Lesson 2 Quiz

 ExamView
Assessment Suite CD-ROM

Visit glencoe.com for:
Online Quizzes
Online Learning Center

Progress Monitoring

Reteaching
Direct students to list the six traits of good character. Call on several volunteers. Have each volunteer share one of the traits on his or her list and provide a description of that trait.

Enrichment
Helping others and contributing to the school community can contribute to the development of a positive identity. Have students investigate an opportunity in the school for teens to help others, take care of school property, or raise funds for school activities. Ask students to share what they learned with the class.

LESSON 2 ASSESSMENT

After You Read

Reviewing Facts and Vocabulary
1. Define the term *personal identity*.
2. Identify the six traits of good character.
3. Explain the benefit of constructive criticism.

Thinking Critically
4. **Analyze.** Describe how role models help in forming identity.
5. **Describe.** Explain how healthful risk taking can help you mature in new ways.

Applying Health Skills
6. **Communication Skills.** With a classmate, role-play situations where constructive criticism is given.

Writing Critically
7. **Expository.** If you were to choose a role model, who would it be? Write a short essay explaining your choice.

Go Online
Visit **glencoe.com** and complete the Interactive Study Guide for this lesson.

Lesson 2 Developing Personal Identity and Character **77**

Go Online
Have students visit **glencoe.com** and complete the Interactive Study Guide for this lesson.

LESSON 2 ASSESSMENT ANSWERS

1. *Personal identity* is your sense of self as a unique individual.
2. Trustworthiness, respect, responsibility, fairness, caring, citizenship
3. Constructive criticism helps you see things objectively when emotions or your perspective could cloud your thinking.
4. A role model can influence a person to assume certain desirable characteristics or set a goal to have a similar career.
5. Sample answer: Healthful risk-taking can provide the opportunity to develop new skills and gain confidence.
6. Role-plays will vary, but should demonstrate the positive impact of constructive criticism.
7. Choice of role-models will vary; students' paragraphs should justify their choices.

LESSON 3

Expressing Emotions in Healthful Ways

① FOCUS

BIG Idea Acknowledging and managing emotions allows a person to express them in healthful ways. **Ask Students:** *What are some common emotions experienced by teens?* (Sample answers: Happiness, disappointment, love, anger)

Before You Read

K-W-L Chart Students' charts will vary.

Main Idea

Understanding Emotions
Mental and emotional health are enhanced when emotions are recognized and acknowledged in healthful ways. **Ask Students:** *What is an example of an emotion that can be challenging to express in a positive way?* (Sample answers: anger, sadness)

Real Life Issues

Have students complete dialogues. **Ask Students:** *Have you ever felt like Valerie?* (Sample answer: Yes, I was sad when my best friend did not come to my party.)

 GUIDE TO READING

BIG Idea *Managing your emotions allows you to express them in healthful ways.*

Before You Read
Create a K-W-L Chart. Make a three-column chart. In the first column, list what you **k**now about emotions and ways to express them. In the second column, list what you **w**ant to know about this topic. As you read, use the third column to summarize what you **l**earned about the topic.

K	W	L

New Vocabulary
▶ emotions (p. 78)
▶ hormones (p. 78)
▶ hostility (p.79)
▶ empathy (p. 80)
▶ defense mechanisms (p. 81)

Expressing Emotions in Healthful Ways

Real Life Issues ....

Expressing Feelings. Valerie feels a little angry and hurt when she sees her friend Sue. The last time Sue agreed to go to a movie with Valerie, Sue didn't show up. Valerie was hurt that Sue didn't seem to care enough about their friendship to call and let her know she wasn't coming.

Writing *Write a dialogue between Valerie and Sue in which Valerie is honest about her feelings in a way that doesn't hurt their friendship.*

Understanding Your Emotions

Main Idea Recognizing and acknowledging your emotions is a sign of good mental and emotional health.

Have you ever seen a movie that made you feel happy, sad, or even scared? These feelings are examples of **emotions**, *signals that tell your mind and body how to react.* The emotions you experience when watching a movie may feel exhausting, but they have no real consequences. Many times, the most intense emotions you feel will be related to an event in your life. How you respond to your emotions can affect your mental/emotional, physical, and social health.

Changes during puberty are caused by **hormones**—*chemicals produced by your glands that regulate the activities of different body cells.* These hormones can make you feel as if your emotions are swinging from one extreme to another. You may have recognized that your emotions seem to feel more intense as you go through puberty. It's normal for teens to feel overcome by emotions during this time of life.

78 **Chapter 3** Achieving Mental and Emotional Health

More About...

Mood Swings Mood swings are a part of teenage life. Researchers attribute the mood swings associated with the teen years to several causes. Studies have shown that teen brains process certain hormones differently than adult brains do. Teens are also less experienced in dealing with emotions. Many teens lack the coping mechanisms that adults have. These factors combine to make teens experience faster and more dramatic mood shifts than those experienced by most adults.

U Learning to recognize your emotions and to understand their effects on you will help you learn to manage them in healthful ways. Below are some common emotions.

- **Happiness.** Being satisfied and feeling positive are good descriptions of happiness. When you are happy, you usually feel energetic, creative, and sociable.

- **Sadness.** Feeling sad is a normal, healthy reaction to difficult life events. These feelings may be mild, like being disappointed because you didn't do well on a test, or they may be deep and long lasting, such as the grief you feel when a pet or family member dies.

- **Love.** Strong affection, deep concern, and respect are expressions of love. Loving someone means that you support the needs and growth of that person and respect the person's feelings and values.

- **Fear.** When you are startled by someone or something, you may feel fear. Feelings of fear can increase your alertness and help you escape from possibly harmful situations. Some people let fear of imagined threats prevent them from taking healthful risks.

- **Guilt.** Guilt is the feeling of shame and regret that occurs when you act against your values. Sometimes people feel guilt about situations that they have no control over. For instance, some children and teens may blame themselves if their parents divorce.

- **Anger.** Anger is a normal reaction to being emotionally hurt or physically harmed. Anger that is not handled in a constructive way can lead to violence. Another form of anger is **hostility**, *the intentional use of unfriendly or offensive behavior.* Hostility can hurt others, as well as the hostile person. Often, anger is complicated because it can hide another emotion, such as hurt or guilt.

 READING CHECK

Explain How do hormones affect emotions?

■ **Figure 3.9** Actors portray strong emotions by using body language and changing their tone of voice. *How might an actor use body language to convey each of the emotions described above?*

---

②TEACH

U Universal Access

Visual and Kinesthetic Learners Ask volunteers to express specific emotions without using words. Encourage students to use actions, facial expressions, movements, and body posture to convey an emotion described in the text. Have the other students identify the emotion being demonstrated. EL BL OL

READING CHECK

Answer Hormones cause emotions to swing from one extreme to another.

AL Active Learning

Emoticons Have students describe common emoticons used to convey emotions in e-mails, text messages, instant messages, and on the Internet. For example, the characters :) are often used to represent happiness. Have each student choose an emotion that is mentioned in the lesson. Then ask students to make a poster of the emoticon that could be used to express that emotion. Encourage students to be creative and to develop new, original emoticons. OL

Caption Answer

Figure 3.9 Sample answers: An actor may jump or recoil in order to convey fear. An actor might slump his or her shoulders and frown to show sadness.

Teacher to Teacher

Mark Anderson • Cobb County School District, Marietta, GA

Relaxation Techniques Just as I encourage students to plan proper nutrition and physical activity, I also ask them to try and incorporate stress-relieving strategies into their daily life. Deep breathing is a great way to relax the body and mind. Another strategy for relaxation involves releasing muscular tension. Students can sit in a comfortable position. For the first few minutes, they should concentrate on the breaths going in and out of their body. They can begin by tensing the toes/feet for 10 seconds, then relax. Progressively move this tension/relaxation to the knees, hips, torso, shoulders, neck, and face. They can finish this with a focus on breathing.

Main Idea

Managing Emotions Emotions can be managed in healthful ways.
Ask Students: *What are some specific ways that you manage your emotions?* (Answers will vary.)

W Writing Support

Short Story Write the following on the board: *Chris couldn't believe it. The soccer team list was finally posted, and his name was not on the list.* Have students complete this story, describing how Chris handled his emotions in this situation in a positive way. Encourage students to self-edit and illustrate their stories. Ask volunteers to share their stories with the class. OL

U Universal Access

English Language Learners
Pair English language learners with students who are proficient in English. Have students work with their partners to review the bulleted questions in the text that describe dealing with emotions in positive ways. Direct each pair of students to rephrase one of the questions in their own words. Call on pairs of students to share one of the questions with the class. EL

Caption Answer

Figure 3.10 Sample answers: Cheering to encourage your team is a healthful way to express happiness.

Managing Your Emotions

Main Idea Knowing how to recognize your emotions can help you manage them in healthful ways.

Emotions are neither good nor bad. The way you express your emotions, however, can produce good or bad consequences. Learning to express emotions in a healthful way will not only help you cope with emotional upsets, but also helps those around you to better handle their emotions.

Dealing with Emotions in Positive Ways

As a young child, you learned from parents, teachers, and friends how to express your emotions. Some emotions, such as happiness and love, are expressed through facial expressions like smiles and glances, and through behaviors like laughing and hugging. **Empathy**, or *the ability to imagine and understand how someone else feels*, is expressed by supporting a friend who is going through a difficult time. You may also have learned that emotions are private if you know people who are uncomfortable expressing their feelings.

No doubt you also learned that people sometimes deal with their feelings in harmful ways. They may exaggerate their emotions, pretend they have no feelings, or even hurt another person deliberately while expressing emotions.

To help you recognize your emotions and express them in positive ways, ask yourself these questions:

W

- Why do I feel the way I do about this event?
- Will this event matter later on in my life?
- Why should I wait before responding?
- What can I do to feel better?
- Who can I ask to help me deal with my negative feelings?

U

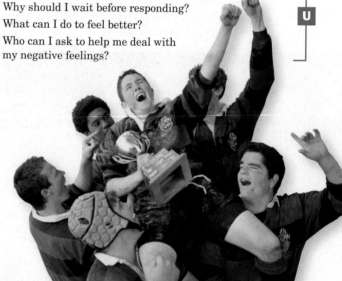

■ **Figure 3.10** Healthful expression of feelings lets you enjoy life more. *What are some positive ways to express emotions?*

Myths & Reality

The Truth About Emotions

Myth: Some emotions are positive, and others are negative.

Fact: Emotions are not good or bad. Some emotions may be more difficult to deal with than others, but emotions in and of themselves are not positive or negative. An individual's response to an emotion may be positive or negative.

Myth: Using defense mechanisms is always an unhealthful way to manage emotions.

Fact: Although defense mechanisms are not healthful when they are used as long-term solutions to problems or as a way to deal with daily problems, they can be helpful in coping with difficult emotions on a short-term basis.

Figure 3.11 Common Defense Mechanisms

- ▶ **Repression.** Involuntarily pushing unpleasant feelings out of one's mind.

- ▶ **Regression.** Returning to behaviors characteristic of a younger age, rather than dealing with problems in a mature manner.

- ▶ **Denial.** Unconscious lack of recognition of something that is obvious to others.

- ▶ **Projection.** Attributing your own feelings or faults to another person or group.

- ▶ **Suppression.** Consciously and intentionally pushing unpleasant feelings out of one's mind.

- ▶ **Rationalization.** Making excuses to explain a situation or behavior, rather than taking responsibility for it.

- ▶ **Compensation.** Making up for weaknesses and mistakes through gift giving, hard work, or extreme efforts.

AL

Responding to Difficult Emotions

W Feeling bad, or emotional, when things happen in your life is normal. These feelings, however, can be managed. Some techniques to reduce the intensity of your emotions include taking several deep breaths, relaxing your muscles, getting away from the situation until you calm down, analyzing your emotions by writing about them in a private journal, or talking to someone you trust about the way you feel.

Some people choose to manage difficult emotions by avoiding situations that make them uncomfortable. **Defense mechanisms** are *mental processes that protect individuals from strong or stressful emotions and situations*. **Figure 3.11** lists some common defense mechanisms used to respond to difficult emotions.

Sometimes you may use defense mechanisms unconsciously as a way to protect yourself from intense emotional pain. You may not even be aware you are using them. Although defense mechanisms can help you deal with emotions for a short time, eventually you will need to work through the problem. Relying on defense mechanisms too long can keep you from facing—and solving—what's upsetting you.

Some emotions, such as fear, guilt, and anger, can be very damaging. People may respond to these emotions without thinking about the consequences. By analyzing the cause of these feelings, you can learn to manage them.

Handling Fear Most people are afraid of something. You can overcome some fears by recognizing that you're afraid and figuring out what is causing this fear. For example, you may be afraid to speak in front of a group, but need to give a presentation as part of a group assignment. For this type of fear, try talking to a friend or an adult who can suggest ways to organize your material and prepare for the presentation.

FITNESS ZONE

Some days I just don't feel like exercising. On those days, I use positive self-talk to remind myself how good I feel after a workout. Now, I congratulate myself every time I take a step toward one of my goals. After I finish a workout, I think, "Awesome! I did it!" For more physical activity ideas, visit the Online Fitness Zone at glencoe.com.

Lesson 3 Expressing Emotions in Healthful Ways **81**

Reading Strategy

Health Skills Activity

Practicing Healthful Behaviors: Managing Your Anger

NHES Standard 4 Students will demonstrate the ability to use interpersonal communication skills to enhance health and avoid or reduce health risks.

Objectives

- Identify healthful strategies for managing anger.
- Demonstrate communication skills in expressing emotions in healthy ways.

Teaching Strategies

- Ask students to brainstorm a list of healthful ways that Tina could manage her anger.
- Ask volunteers to share their rewritten scenarios with the class.

Assessment

Using this list, student work should provide comprehensive evidence of the following criteria to achieve the highest score:

√ Identifies at least one healthful strategy for managing anger
√ Uses "I" statements
√ Presents a clear, organized message

Caption Answer

Figure 3.12 Sample answer: If I were experiencing anger, I would talk with my aunt to get advice about how to handle the problem.

Academic Vocabulary

resource *(noun):* a source of supply or support

READING CHECK

Explain How do people use defense mechanisms?

■ **Figure 3.12** Physical activity is a healthy way to use the energy that can build up with anger. *Which strategy for dealing with anger would you most likely use?*

Other fears, such as the fear of going to college or learning to drive a car, may require the help of **resources** within your community. If you're unable to control your fears, consider seeking the help of a mental health professional.

Dealing with Guilt Guilt is another very destructive emotion. If it is not managed, it can harm your self-esteem. If you feel guilty about something, think about the cause. Have you hurt someone? Admitting a mistake, apologizing, and promising to be more thoughtful in the future can help manage feelings of guilt. Keep in mind that you may not be able to control some situations. Look at the circumstances realistically and honestly. Some situations are out of your control. For instance, if your parents are divorcing, it may upset you, but it's not your fault.

Managing Anger Anger is one of the most difficult emotions to handle. As with guilt, it is best to figure out what is causing your anger, and then deal with it in a healthy way. When you first feel anger building up inside you, take time to calm down. You might try deep breathing or slowly repeating a calming word or phrase. If this doesn't work, physically remove yourself from the situation. Then try one of these strategies:

- **Do something to relax.** Listen to soothing music, read a book, or imagine sitting on a beach or walking through the woods.

- **Channel your energy in a different direction.** Use the energy generated by your anger to do something postive. Take a walk, go for a bike ride, play the piano or guitar, or write your feelings down in a private journal.

- **Talk with someone you trust.** Sharing your thoughts and feelings with a trusted friend or family member may help you see the situation from the viewpoint of another person. Not only will you feel better, but the listener also may be able to give you some tips on how to deal with the situation.

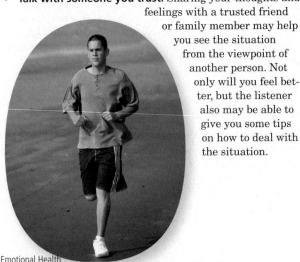

More About...

Fear Although fear is a normal and healthful reaction in some situations, individuals can also experience irrational and uncontrollable fears, called phobias. A fear is classified as a phobia if it is in response to something that poses little or no actual risk and interferes with everyday life. Some common phobias are altophobia (the fear of heights), or agoraphobia (the fear of open spaces or being out in public). Phobias are a type of anxiety disorder that can be treated by medical professionals. Some individuals who experience phobias can be treated with behavioral therapy, others are treated with medication. Encourage interested students to learn more about phobias and their treatment and share what they learn with the class.

Health Skills Activity
Practicing Healthful Behaviors

Managing Your Anger

When Tina took out her favorite sweater to wear to a party, she saw a big stain on the sleeve. Furious, she marched into her sister Judy's room. "I never said you could borrow my sweater! Look what you did to it! It's ruined!"

"It was clean when I put it back in your closet!" Judy shot back.

"I don't believe you," Tina said. "Now I don't have anything to wear tonight. Don't ever touch my things again!"

"But when I put it back, it was clean," said Judy.

Tina stormed back to her room and slammed the door.

Writing How might Tina have better dealt with her immediate feelings of anger? Rewrite this scene having Tina deal with her anger using the following steps:

1. Use strategies to reduce anger such as taking deep breaths or relaxing your muscles.
2. Analyze your feelings to recognize your emotions.
3. Talk to a parent about your feelings.
4. Write a letter to Judy expressing your feelings to her.

LESSON 3 ASSESSMENT

After You Read

Reviewing Facts and Vocabulary

1. What are *emotions*? How can emotions affect your behavior?
2. What are five common defense mechanisms?
3. List three strategies for handling anger in a healthful way.

Thinking Critically

4. **Analyze.** What role do hormones play in affecting a teen's emotions?
5. **Explain.** Describe what can happen when you take time to think before you respond to a strong emotion. How can this help you stay healthy?

Applying Health Skills

6. **Communication Skills.** Write a one-page script describing how a teen helps a friend manage an emotion, such as fear or excitement.

Writing Critically

7. **Descriptive.** Write a poem describing a situation that was emotional for you. Tell how you managed your emotions in a healthful way.

G⊙ Online

Visit glencoe.com and complete the Interactive Study Guide for this lesson.

---

❸ ASSESS/ CLOSE

Assessment Resources

📁 *FAST FILE* **ACTIVITIES**
Lesson 3 Quiz

◉ *ExamView* *Assessment Suite* CD-ROM

Visit glencoe.com for:
Online Quizzes
Online Learning Center

Progress Monitoring

Reteaching
Ask students to review the Main Ideas in the lesson. Call on students to restate one of the main ideas in their own words.

Enrichment
Have students do further research using Internet or library resources to find out more about hormones that affect emotions. Ask students to write a short report summarizing their findings.

G⊙ Online

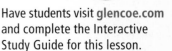

Have students visit glencoe.com and complete the Interactive Study Guide for this lesson.

LESSON ❸ ASSESSMENT ANSWERS

1. *Emotions* are signals that tell your mind and body how to react.
2. *Any five:* Repression, suppression, rationalization, regression, denial, compensation, projection
3. See page 82.
4. Hormones can cause emotions to change rapidly from one extreme to another.
5. Sample answer: Reflecting before responding to a strong emotion would prevent acting out in an inappropriate or harmful manner. It would also allow you to understand the emotion and the situation that caused it. Reflecting before responding can also give you time to think through a strategy to resolve the situation.
6. Scripts will vary.
7. Poems will vary.

Five Ways to Boost Your Self-Confidence

Focus

Motivator

Ask students, Do the teens in this photo look self-confident? Can you always tell by looking at someone if he or she has a strong self-esteem? Why or why not?

Teach

Language Arts/Compare and Contrast Write the following words on the board:

- Self-confidence
- Personal identify
- Self-awareness
- Self-actualization
- Self-esteem
- Self-respect
- Self-efficacy

Ask students to write a definition of each term and then share their work. Are some of these words based on accomplishment and others on personal qualities? Is it possible for someone to have self-respect without strong self-esteem? Is it possible to be self-aware but not self-confident?

Add these terms to the board:

- Egotism
- Arrogance
- Narcissism

About Self-Esteem As students work on their pamphlets encourage them to incorporate goal-setting and decision-making skills. For instance, under "Reach Out" have students write a goal statement such as "When I'm anxious about a test, I will ask my sister for help studying." Under "Give Yourself a Push" ask students to identify options and possible consequences of each.

Five Ways TO BOOST YOUR SELF-CONFIDENCE

1. ACCENTUATE THE POSITIVE

Remind yourself what you're good at—whether it's a talent like drawing or a personality trait such as being outgoing. This is a great way to ward off that nagging voice of negativity in your head, says Michael Riera, Ph.D., a psychologist in Berkeley, California. Make a list of your strengths and read it aloud every day until you really believe it.

2. REACH OUT
When you feel overwhelmed by school, family, or social pressures, don't ride it out alone: Call a friend to calm your nerves. Don't make the mistake of thinking that asking for support is a sign of weakness. Checking in with someone who cares will make you feel less alone and better able to understand what's making you feel bad about yourself.

3. GIVE YOURSELF A PUSH

Challenging yourself to tackle uncomfortable situations can boost your self-esteem, no matter what the outcome. If you want to talk to your teacher about an extension on an assignment, don't imagine the 12,000 ways that it could go wrong. Instead, says Riera, "see yourself getting through it. Then, even if the teacher says no, acknowledge that by giving it a try you succeeded."

4. HAVE A CHEERLEADING SQUAD
Find a "support network who believes in you," advises Riera, whether that includes friends, family, or a school guidance counselor, and lean on them when you're feeling insecure. They'll be able to see you—and your problems—more clearly than you can see yourself.

5. TRY, TRY AGAIN
You may not reach all your goals the first time you go out for them, but by being realistic about your ambitions, you can pace yourself—and be proud of your improvements along the way.

TIME to THINK... About Self-Esteem

Create a personal "to do" pamphlet. On each page, write one of the above tips. Write two ways that you can use each tip in your daily life. Draw an empty box next to each example, and add a check mark as you accomplish each one.

Health Literacy

Self-Esteem Tell students that in recent years controversy has grown about teaching self-esteem in the classroom. Proponents argue that helping students feel good about themselves leads to success in school and in life. Detractors claim that there is little or no evidence linking self-esteem to life success.

They argue that a "feel good" approach to self-esteem, unrelated to one's actual achievements, can lead to disappointment and frustration in the real world. What do your students think? Ask several interested students to research the self-esteem controversy and present their findings to the class.

 To download quizzes and eFlashcards to your PDA, go to glencoe.com and click on the Study to Go icon.

LESSON **1**

Developing Your Self-Esteem

Key Concepts

▶ Mentally healthy people sometimes have mental and emotional problems, but can cope with their emotions as well as know when to seek help.

▶ Healthy self-esteem involves having a sense of personal worth and a sense of competence.

▶ You can improve your self-esteem.

Vocabulary

▶ mental/emotional health (p. 66)
▶ resilient (p. 67)
▶ self-esteem (p. 68)
▶ competence (p. 68)
▶ hierarchy of needs (p. 70)
▶ self-actualization (p. 71)

LESSON **2**

Developing Personal Identity and Character

Key Concepts

▶ You develop your personal identity by developing a clear sense of your values, beliefs, skills, and interests.

▶ A person of good character demonstrates core ethical values.

▶ You can build a healthy identity from both the good and bad influences in your life.

Vocabulary

▶ personal identity (p. 72)
▶ role model (p. 73)
▶ personality (p. 73)
▶ character (p. 73)
▶ integrity (p. 74)
▶ constructive criticism (p. 76)

LESSON **3**

Expressing Emotions in Healthful Ways

Key Concepts

▶ Recognizing and understanding your emotions will provide you with ways to maintain your emotional health.

▶ Learning to manage your feelings is an important part of being mentally and emotionally healthy.

▶ When you deal with difficult emotions, such as fear, guilt, and anger, you may need to carefully consider the situation and use specific strategies to handle your feelings.

Vocabulary

▶ emotions (p. 78)
▶ hormones (p. 78)
▶ hostility (p. 79)
▶ empathy (p. 80)
▶ defense mechanisms (p. 81)

Chapter 3 Review **85**

Go Online

Students can visit glencoe.com to

• review content online with the Online Student Edition.

• test their knowledge of chapter content with Online Quizzes.

• access Interactive Health Tutor for more practice with vocabulary.

Assessment Resources

📁 *Fast File* Activities
Chapter 3 Test

💿 *ExamView*
Assessment Suite CD-ROM

Visit glencoe.com **for:**
Audio Chapter Summaries
Online Quizzes

STUDY TO GO Tell students to visit glencoe.com where they can download quizzes and eFlashcards.

Study Tips

Use the Figures Suggest that students review each of the photos, illustrations, charts, and graphs found in the chapter. For each figure, have students discuss with a partner the idea that the figure conveys.

Remind students that they should be able to answer all caption questions associated with the figures. If students cannot answer a particular caption question, have them review the associated material in the text.

Chapter 3 Assessment Answers

LESSON 1

Vocabulary Review

1. competence
2. self-esteem
3. resilient

Understanding Key Concepts

4. b
5. a
6. c
7. d

Thinking Critically

8. Everyone experiences minor mental and emotional problems in everyday life. However, some people are better able to handle these problems than others.

9. Experiencing poor mental and emotional health can wear the body down and lead to physical illness.

10. Answers will vary, but should relate to any one of the suggestions listed on p. 69.

11. Sample answer: The person with healthy self-esteem will have more confidence and probably a better result. The person with poor self-esteem will likely feel stressed and fearful because of the challenge.

12. Sample answer: Positive self-esteem gives you a sense of self-worth and encourages you to strive to reach your potential.

LESSON 2

Vocabulary Review

13. role model
14. Integrity
15. Constructive criticism
16. personality

LESSON 1

Vocabulary Review

Use the vocabulary terms listed on page 85 to complete the following statements.

1. Having enough skills to do something is called _____.

2. Valuing, respecting, and feeling confident about yourself describes _____.

3. Having the ability to adapt successfully and recover from disappointment, difficulty, or crisis is called being _____.

Understanding Key Concepts

After reading the question or statement, select the correct answer.

4. Which of the following is *not* a characteristic of good mental and emotional health?
   a. Sense of purpose
   b. Pessimistic outlook
   c. Autonomy
   d. Healthy self-esteem

5. Which statement about self-esteem is *not* true?
   a. Self-esteem is always the same.
   b. Self-esteem develops over time.
   c. Self-talk affects self-esteem.
   d. Feedback from others affects self-esteem.

6. When you don't have healthy self-esteem, you
   a. take pride in your abilities.
   b. feel confident and satisfied.
   c. enjoy positive events for only a short time.
   d. tend to be more outgoing.

7. Which need within Maslow's hierarchy is the highest-level need?
   a. A safety need
   b. An esteem need
   c. A physical need
   d. The need to reach your potential

Thinking Critically

After reading the question or statement, write a short answer using complete sentences.

8. **Explain.** Why do you think one person can be considered mentally healthier than another when neither has a serious mental problem?

9. **Describe.** How can poor mental health affect your physical health?

10. **Synthesize.** Select one of the suggestions for improving self-esteem. Explain a practical way to make the action or behavior part of your life.

11. **Compare and Contrast.** How might a person with healthy self-esteem respond to a difficult challenge differently than a person with poor self-esteem?

12. **Explain.** Describe how self-esteem can affect your ability to reach your potential.

LESSON 2

Vocabulary Review

Correct the sentences below by replacing the italicized term with the correct vocabulary term.

13. A *friend* is someone whose success or behavior serves as an example for you.

14. *Trustworthiness* is a firm observance of core ethical values.

15. *Judgment* involves positive comments that point out problems and encourage improvement.

16. Your *personal identity* is the complex set of characteristics that make you unique.

Health eSpotlight VIDEO *Wrap-Up*

The Strength to Stand Out Have students reread the Health eSpotlight question at the beginning of the chapter on page 65 and look at their original answer. **Ask Students:** *Now that you have read the* chapter and watched the video, can you identify some additional ways that your values influence your goals? Call on volunteers to describe how their responses would change.

Assessment

Understanding Key Concepts

After reading the question or statement, select the correct answer.

17. A person's unique characteristics and group affiliations are known as
    a. features of character.
    b. strengths and weaknesses.
    c. features of identity.
    d. examples of core ethical values.

18. Which quality of good character reflects the importance of community concerns, such as obeying laws and voting?
    a. Responsibility
    b. Trustworthiness
    c. Caring
    d. Citizenship

19. Choosing not to cheat is an example of
    a. recognizing your strengths and weaknesses.
    b. demonstrating positive values.
    c. developing a purpose in your life.
    d. forming meaningful relationships.

20. The groups you belong to help you define
    a. characteristics that you share with other people.
    b. ways to get along with other people.
    c. how people are different.
    d. none of the above.

Thinking Critically

After reading the question or statement, write a short answer using complete sentences.

21. **Discuss.** Name some values that parents likely pass on to their children.

22. **Synthesize.** Why do you think responsibility, honesty, and respect are values that exist across cultures?

23. **Explain.** How might unhealthful risk behaviors affect your health and identity?

24. **Identify.** What are some examples of healthful risk behaviors?

25. **Describe.** What are some ways that good character is related to healthy identity?

LESSON 3

Vocabulary Review

Use the vocabulary terms listed on page 85 to complete the following statements.

26. A chemical produced by your glands that regulates the activities of different body cells is a(n) _____.

27. The intentional use of unfriendly or offensive behavior is called _____.

28. The ability to imagine and understand how someone else feels is called _____.

29. Mental processes that you use to protect yourself from strong or stressful emotions or situations are called _____.

Understanding Key Concepts

After reading the question or statement, select the correct answer.

30. Which of the following is *not* true about anger?
    a. It can result in violence.
    b. Often another emotion is involved.
    c. You become angry as you think about a situation.
    d. It causes little emotional harm.

31. A cause of guilt is
    a. acting against your values.
    b. doing a good deed.
    c. repressing an unpleasant feeling.
    d. recognizing you are not the cause of a negative situation.

Understanding Key Concepts

17. c
18. d
19. b
20. a

Thinking Critically

21. Trustworthiness, responsibility
22. Sample answer: Honesty, responsibility, and respect exist across all cultures because they are core ethical values.
23. Sample answer: Unhealthful risk behaviors can be dangerous to your health and can cause you to form habits and adopt values that work against maintaining a healthy identity.
24. Sample answers: Engaging in athletic, artistic, or creative activities; public speaking; traveling; making new friends
25. Sample answer: Being of good character enables you to have stronger relationships and a consistency in your behaviors. This is helpful during times when you must make tough choices that could affect your identity.

LESSON 3

Vocabulary Review

26. hormone
27. hostility
28. empathy
29. defense mechanisms

Understanding Key Concepts

30. d
31. a

Assessment

Understanding Key Concepts

32. c

33. b

Thinking Critically

34. As these people demonstrate ways of expressing and managing emotions, you learn both positive and negative ways of dealing with emotions.

35. Teens have fluctuations in hormone levels that affect emotions, therefore teens can expect to experience changing and possibly confusing emotions.

36. Emotions are just signals. It's how you deal with them that leads to good or bad outcomes. For example, handling emotions healthfully can strengthen physical, mental/emotional, and social health. In contrast, handling emotions in a negative way can harm both the individual and others.

37. Tolerance, compassion, and empathy are three characteristics that are developed when you learn to acknowledge and express emotions in healthful ways. These characteristics will help make relationships deeper and stronger and will ensure that you influence others in a positive way.

38. A violent response can result in punishment at home and at school and can even result in criminal charges. Violence can affect all aspects of individual health, leading to feelings of guilt, damaged relationships, and personal injury.

32. Which is *not* a positive way to express an emotion?
a. Hugging
b. Smiling
c. Yelling
d. Laughing

33. Which of the following defense mechanisms uses excuse-making to explain a situation?
a. Repression
b. Rationalization
c. Denial
d. Compensation

Thinking Critically

After reading the question or statement, write a short answer using complete sentences.

34. **Analyze.** How do peers, family, and friends influence the way you express and manage emotions?

35. **Evaluate.** What might the effects of changing hormone levels during the teen years have on emotions?

36. **Explain.** Why are emotions neither good nor bad?

37. **Identify.** Name one positive characteristic that can be developed when you learn to recognize and express emotions in healthful ways. Discuss how acquiring this characteristic might affect your relationships.

38. **Evaluate.** What are possible consequences to everyone involved when a person responds violently to anger?

Project-Based ASSESSMENT

Watching for Signs of Mental Illness

Background

Good mental health is important to the well-being of everyone. The signs of mental illness, however, are sometimes easy to miss. Recognizing the early signs can help address and treat these problems.

Task

Research and create a poster to illustrate the early warning signs of one or two mental illnesses.

Audience

Students at your school

Purpose

Help students recognize the warning signs of mental illness in themselves and others, and to encourage them to seek help for themselves and others.

Procedure

1 Work in groups to review the information in Chapter 3 regarding mental health. Assign tasks and responsibilities to each group member.

2 Interview the school nurse or school counselor to learn what type of information, including early warning signs, should be presented in your poster.

3 Organize the information that will be on the poster. Sketch the illustrations you will use to show clear examples of warning signs.

4 On the poster, add text to explain how mental illness affects teens, and list sources of help.

5 Ask the school nurse, a counselor, or the principal to review the poster.

6 Present the poster in the cafeteria during lunch.

88 Chapter 3 Assessment

Project-Based ASSESSMENT

Step 1 Brainstorm Have students brainstorm or review the chapter for how to recognize warning signs of mental illness.

Step 2 Research Students can research online or at the library. Each member should have a specific task. One member should be responsible for interviewing the school nurse or school psychologist.

Step 3 Make a Poster Have students gather materials to make their poster. They should be sure to include visuals. They should also include reliable sources of information on where to get help for mental illness.

Visit **glencoe.com** for Project-Based Assessment rubrics.

Math Practice

Interpret Graphs. A survey of 500 U.S. teens ages 14 to 17 shows that participating in afterschool activitites can improve grades. Use the graph to answer Questions 1–3.

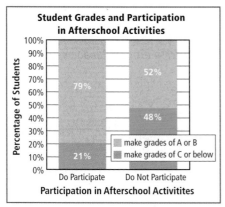

Student Grades and Participation in Afterschool Activities

- make grades of A or B
- make grades of C or below

Adapted from "The YMCA's Teen Action Agenda" by Nels Ericson, *Office of Juvenile Justice and Delinquency Prevention Fact Sheet,* May 2001.

1. Among 1,000 teens who do not participate in afterschool activities, how many receive grades of A or B?
   - A. 210
   - B. 480
   - C. 520
   - D. 790

2. Choose the percentage of teens who participate in afterschool activities and receive grades of A or B.
   - A. 1/8
   - B. 1/7
   - C. 1/4
   - D. 3/4

3. Using the information in the chart, what could you conclude about teens between the ages of 14 and 17?
   - A. Most make grades of A or B.
   - B. Most make grades of C or below.
   - C. Most are in afterschool activities.
   - D. Most are not in afterschool activites.

For more test practice, visit glencoe.com and complete the Online Quizzes for Chapter 3.

Reading/Writing Practice

Understand and Apply. Read the passage below, and then answer the questions.

> Rob had a social studies project due on Monday. "I've got plenty of time," he decided on Thursday. On Friday, he waited for a brilliant idea before giving up. Saturday he went to a baseball game. Rob finally sat down Sunday and worked late into the night. His grade reflected the lack of time and planning he spent on the project.
>
> Rob experienced two common reasons why people procrastinate, or put things off: waiting for inspiration to strike and lack of planning. There are several ways to overcome procrastination. Break large tasks into smaller, more manageable parts. Make a list of everything that needs to be done. Work on each item separately. Tell friends and family your deadlines to help reduce distractions.

1. Which statement best sums up the main point? Procrastination
   - A. can be overcome by approaching a task in a variety of ways.
   - B. prevents you from starting projects.
   - C. creates negative consequences.
   - D. causes delays starting for fear of not doing a good enough job.

2. Which of the following does not summarize a suggestion for overcoming procrastination?
   - A. Break down the task into smaller, more manageable parts.
   - B. Make a list of everything you need to do.
   - C. Just sit down and do the work.
   - D. Set a deadline for completing.

3. Write a brief essay describing three ways you can avoid Rob's dilemma.

National Education Standards
Math: Number and Operations, Data Analysis
Language Arts: NCTE 3

Standardized Test Practice Answers

Math Practice
1. C
2. D
3. A

Reading/Writing Practice
1. A
2. C
3. Essays will vary, but should state that the article presents a variety of suggestions for overcoming procrastination.

National Education Standards

Math: Number and Operations, Data Analysis

Language Arts: NCTE 3

For the complete Math and Language Arts standards, visit glencoe.com.

Online Study Tools
For more test practice, visit glencoe.com and complete the Online Quizzes for Chapter 3.

Test-Taking Tip

Use Time Wisely Discuss with students various strategies for time management during standardized tests. For example, point out that it is important not to spend a disproportionate amount of time on a single question.

Tell students that if a question seems difficult and time-consuming, they should complete other questions first and go back to the difficult question only if they have time.

Chapter 4 pages 90–111	Standards		Features
	National	**State/Local**	*Hands-On* **HEALTH**
	1.12.1, 1.12.2, 4.12.4, 5.12.1, 6.12.2, 6.12.3, 7.12.1, 8.12.1– 8.12.4		• Juggling Stress *(Stress Management)*, page 106
Lesson 1 **Understanding Stress** pages 92–96 **BIG Idea** *Stress can affect you in both positive and negative ways.*	1.12.2, 1.12.7, 2.12.1, 2.12.3, 2.12.4, 2.12.5, 2.12.9, 5.12.1, 7.12.1, 7.12.2		*Real World* **CONNECTION** • How Stressed Out Are You?, page 96 🕐 Out of Time
Lesson 2 **Managing Stress** pages 97–101 **BIG Idea** *You can manage stress by learning skills to reduce the amount and impact of stress in your life.*	1.12.1, 1.12.2, 1.12.7, 4.12.2, 5.12.1, 6.12.1, 6.12.2, 6.12.3, 7.12.1, 7.12.2, 7.12.3		*Health Skills* **Activity** • When Demands Are Too High *(Stress Management)*, page 100 🕐 Out of Time
Lesson 3 **Coping with Loss and Grief** pages 102–105 **BIG Idea** *Understanding the grieving process helps you cope with loss and manage your feelings in healthy ways.*	1.12.2, 1.12.7, 2.12.2, 2.12.3, 3.12.2, 4.12.2, 4.12.4, 5.12.1, 6.12.1, 7.12.1, 7.12.2		

*(Margin labels for Lessons 1, 2, and 3: **30 Min**)*

Key to Ability Levels

Teaching Strategies and activities have been coded for ability level and appropriateness.

AL	Activities for students working above grade level	**BL**	Activities for students working below grade level
OL	Activities for students working on grade level	**EL**	Activities for English Learners

Chapter 4 Planning Guide

Glencoe Exclusive!
TeacherWorks *Plus*
All-In-One Planner and Resource Center

Resources	Lesson Assessment	Technology
Student Activity Workbook `TEACH` **FAST FILE RESOURCES** Vocabulary Practice `TEACH` Health Labs `EXTEND`	Chapter 4 Review Chapter 4 Assessment Standardized Test Practice *ExamView® Assessment Suite* CD-ROM	**Teaching Tools:** • *TeacherWorks*™ Plus DVD • *StudentWorks*™ Plus DVD • *ExamView® Assessment Suite* CD-ROM • Transparency • Fitness DVD • PowerPoint® DVD • Health eSpotlight Video Series DVD
FAST FILE RESOURCES Reading Strategies Activity `TEACH` Reteaching Activity `REVIEW` Enrichment Activity `EXTEND` Health Skills Practice `TEACH`	Lesson 1 Assessment, page 96 📁 Lesson 1 Quiz *Fast File* 💿 *ExamView® Assessment Suite* CD-ROM	**Web-Based Resources:** **Go Online** glencoe.com • Health Podcast Activities • Audio Chapter Summaries (English/Spanish) • Interactive Health Tutor • Health Skills Activities • Vocabulary PuzzleMaker • Parent Letters (English/Spanish) • Lesson Plans • Health Inventories • Online Quizzes • Study-to-Go • Unit Web Projects • Student Web Activities • Fitness Zone Activities
FAST FILE RESOURCES Reading Strategies Activity `TEACH` Reteaching Activity `REVIEW` Enrichment Activity `EXTEND` Health Skills Practice `TEACH`	Lesson 2 Assessment, page 101 📁 Lesson 2 Quiz *Fast File* 💿 *ExamView® Assessment Suite* CD-ROM	
FAST FILE RESOURCES Reading Strategies Activity `TEACH` Reteaching Activity `REVIEW` Enrichment Activity `EXTEND` Health Skills Practice `TEACH`	Lesson 3 Assessment, page 105 📁 Lesson 3 Quiz *Fast File* 💿 *ExamView® Assessment Suite* CD-ROM	

StudentWorks *Plus*

This is the student's backpack solution.

Includes:
• complete Interactive Student Edition
• full audio of English text and Spanish chapter summaries
• allows students to record assignments and track grades.
• links to online activities and additional student resources
• access to all student worksheets and workbooks

FOLDABLES
Study Organizer

Dinah Zike Foldables®
Chapter Activity
Refer to the *Dinah Zike Reading and Study Skills for Glencoe Health.* Ask students to make a tri-fold book Foldable to organize what they learn about stress. Have students add definitions and other important details to the appropriate columns as they read the chapter.

Managing Stress and Coping with Loss

Chapter Overview

Chapter 4 describes effective strategies for managing stress and healthful ways to cope with loss.

Lesson 1

Stress affects people in both positive and negative ways. There are many potential causes of stress, but the body responds the same way regardless of the cause.

Lesson 2

Stress-management techniques include strategies to help people avoid stress and to reduce the effects of unavoidable stress. Staying healthy and building resiliency also help people cope with stress.

Lesson 3

Grieving is a common and natural reaction to any loss. People typically go through several stages of grief.

▶ **Activating Prior Knowledge**

Call on volunteers to share their paragraphs with the class. Discuss how not dealing with stress might affect a teen's performance in this or a similar situation.

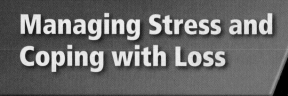

CHAPTER 4

Managing Stress and Coping with Loss

Lesson 1

Understanding Stress

BIG Idea *Stress can affect you in both positive and negative ways.*

Lesson 2

Managing Stress

BIG Idea *You can manage stress by learning skills to reduce the amount and impact of stress in your life.*

Lesson 3

Coping with Loss and Grief

BIG Idea *Understanding the grieving process helps you cope with loss and manage your feelings in healthy ways.*

Activating Prior Knowledge

Using Visuals Look at the picture on this page. How is this teen managing her stress? What other types of activities can help you manage stress? How do you deal with the stressors in your life? Explain your thoughts in a paragraph.

90

Universal Access

Differentiated Learning Glencoe provides teacher support and student materials for all learners in the health classroom.

- Chapter Summaries in English and Spanish are available online at glencoe.com.

- *Fast Files* and related worksheets support reluctant readers.

- Universal Access strategies throughout the Teacher Wraparound Edition and *Fast Files* help you present materials for gifted students, at-risk students, physically impaired students, and those with behavior disorders or learning disabilities.

Chapter Launchers

Health in Action

Discuss the **BIG** Ideas

Before beginning this chapter, think about how you would answer these questions:

▶ What is stress?
▶ Can you avoid stress?
▶ In what ways can other people help you deal with stress?

Watch the *Health* eSpotlight Video Series

VIDEO

Managing Strong Emotions
Stress can affect your physical and mental health. How do you manage stress?

Assess Your Health

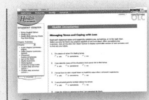

G⊙ Online

Visit **glencoe.com** and complete the Health Inventory for Chapter 4.

Chapter 4   Managing Stress and Coping with Loss   **91**

Chapter Launchers

Health in Action

Discuss the **BIG** Ideas

Assign this activity before students read the chapter. Explain that the purpose of the questions is to help students assess their current knowledge of stress and loss.

Health eSpotlight
Video Series

VIDEO

Managing Strong Emotions

Before Viewing the Video

Ask Students: *What are some things you do that help you relieve stress?* After students have watched the video, discuss how stress not only affects the mind, but can have serious consequences on the body.

G⊙ Online

Have students go to **glencoe.com** and take the Health Inventory for Chapter 4.

Chapter Skills

Reading Skills

BIG Idea

Stress-management techniques can help people deal with stress, and knowledge of the grieving process can help them manage feelings of loss.

Health Skills

Writing Skills

Vocabulary

91

LESSON 1

Understanding Stress

① FOCUS

GUIDE TO READING

BIG Idea The effects of stress can be positive or negative. **Ask Students:** *What is stress?* (Sample answers: tension, pressure)

Before You Read

K-W-L Chart Students' K-W-L charts will vary. Sample answer: Know—Stress can be bad for your health. Want to know—How does stress affect me? Learned—Stress is a natural part of life.

Main Idea

What Is Stress? How you think about a challenge determines whether you will experience positive or negative stress. **Ask Students:** *Which is more stressful, an upcoming test that you think will be difficult or one that you think will be easy?* (The test you think will be difficult)

Real Life Issues ·············

Have students read the scenario. **Ask Students:** *How do you feel when you have to speak in front of a group?* (Sample answers: tense, worried) After students write their paragraphs, call on a few volunteers to share what they wrote with the class. Discuss which responses are likely to be most effective.

92

LESSON 1

GUIDE TO READING

BIG Idea *Stress can affect you in both positive and negative ways.*

Before You Read

Create a K-W-L Chart. Make a three-column chart. In the first column, list what you **k**now about stress. In the second column, list what you **w**ant to know about this topic. As you read, use the third column to summarize what you **l**earned.

K	W	L

New Vocabulary

▸ perception (p. 92)
▸ stressor (p. 93)
▸ psychosomatic response (p. 95)

Review Vocabulary

▸ stress (Ch.2, L.1)

Understanding Stress

Real Life Issues ·····················

Stage Fright. Cari woke up this morning with a vague sense of dread. Now, sitting at her desk at school, she has butterflies in her stomach and her palms are sweaty. Today is oral report day, and Cari is next. She is nervous about speaking in front of her classmates.

Writing *Why do you think Cari is experiencing these symptoms? How might she try to calm herself for the presentation? Explain your thoughts in a paragraph.*

What Is Stress?

Main Idea How you think about a challenge determines whether you will experience positive or negative stress.

Feeling stress is a natural part of life. Stress is the reaction of the body and mind to everyday challenges and demands. It might appear quickly, like when you are late and running to catch the bus. Stress can also slowly build for days, like when you feel the pressure to perform well in your next basketball game or on a final exam.

Often, situations associated with stress are unavoidable. How much the stress of an event affects you, however, depends in part on your perception of it. **Perception** is *the act of becoming aware through the senses*. For example, based on your perception, you might believe that a disagreement with a friend has ruined your relationship. Your friend, on the other hand, might believe that you'll eventually work out the issue. Because of your perception of the event, you are more likely to experience a higher level of stress about the situation than your friend is.

More About...

Perception and Stress Our perceptions not only help define our problems, but also limit the solutions we think are possible. For example, most teens perceive a strict curfew as their parents' attempt to control their child's social life. This negative perception limits the teen's possible solutions to submission, defiance, or persuading the parents to change curfew and only results in a stressful feeling of being powerless to change the negative situation. However, if the situation was perceived as positive and simply the parents' attempt to protect their child, then the teen would only need to demonstrate maturity so the parents would feel less need to protect. This solution gives the teen a sense of control over the situation and is likely to be less stressful.

Your reaction to stressful events depends on your previous experiences. If you enjoy playing in a band, performing a solo may not make you nervous. However, if you've made a mistake during a band performance, you might worry about how well you'll play during a solo.

Reacting to Stress

Some people believe that stress is always unhealthy. Stress can have both a positive and a negative effect. Positive stress can motivate you. For example, this type of stress can inspire you to work harder if you have a deadline approaching.

Stress has a negative effect, however, when it interferes with your ability to perform. It might cause you to feel distracted, overwhelmed, impatient, frustrated, or even angry. Negative stress can harm your health. Understanding the causes of stress and how you respond to it will help you develop effective stress-management skills.

Causes of Stress

Main Idea Stressors vary among individuals and groups.

A **stressor** is *anything that causes stress*. Stressors can be real or imagined, **anticipated** or unexpected. People, objects, places, events, and situations are all potential stressors. Certain stressors, like sirens, affect most people the same way—causing heightened alertness.

As you've learned, the specific effects of most stressors will depend on your experiences and perceptions. What causes stress for you may not cause stress for someone else. **Figure 4.2** on page 94 identifies some common teen stressors.

READING CHECK

Explain How can your perception of an event affect the amount of stress you feel?

Academic Vocabulary

anticipate *(verb):* to expect

■ **Figure 4.1**
Meeting the demands of an active schedule can be stressful. *How do you deal with the stresses of a regular school day?*

Lesson 1 Understanding Stress **93**

Writing Strategy

Descriptive Writing Ask students to write two paragraphs about one of the teen stressors listed in **Figure 4.1**. In the first paragraph, a teen should respond negatively to the stressor. In the second paragraph, the teen should respond to the same stressor in a positive way. In each case, students should describe how the teen perceives the stressor and how that perception influences the teen's reaction to the stressor. For example, changing schools might be perceived as a serious loss and cause feelings of sadness, or it might be perceived as a new beginning and cause feelings of excitement.

❷ TEACH

ⓤ Universal Access

Explaining Concepts Write this sentence on the board: "You are stressing me out." Point out that this is how the word *stress* is commonly used. Explain that this usage implies that stress is something that other people or events do to us, suggesting that stress is beyond our control. Explain that stress is how we react to people or events, so it is at least partly under our control. Ask a volunteer to rewrite the sentence to reflect the correct meaning of stress (e.g., "I am reacting to you with stress"). **BL** **OL**

✓ READING CHECK

Answer Your perception of an event determines how you view it and feel about it.

ⒶⓁ Active Learning

Role-Play Ask small groups of students to select a common teen stressor and create a role play to show why it is stressful. For example, show how waking up late for school could have a negative effect on the day. Give groups a chance to present their role plays to the class. After the role plays, encourage students to discuss the relative influence of different stressors in teens' lives. **OL**

Main Idea

Causes of Stress Stressors vary among individuals and groups. **Ask Students:** *What are some typical causes of stress for teens?* (Sample answer: homework, dating, peer pressure)

93

Main Idea

Your Body's Response to Stressors Stressors activate the nervous system and specific hormones. **Ask Students:** *When something suddenly startles you, how does your body respond?* (Sample answer: My heart races, my breathing speeds up, and I start to sweat.)

C Critical Thinking

Explaining Challenge students to think of examples that help explain why different groups of people may have different stressors. (Sample answers: Fear of crime might be a greater stressor for people who live in cities than in rural areas. Worry about money might be a greater stressor for unskilled workers than for professionals.) **OL** **AL**

U Universal Access

Giving Examples Pair English language learners with English proficient students, and have each pair choose one of the teen stressors listed in **Figure 4.2**. Ask students to think of a specific example that shows why the stressor might cause a teen stress. Then have partners list thoughts and feelings they might have if they were the teen in the example. **EL** **OL**

Go Online

Have students visit **glencoe.com** and complete the Student Web Activity on the effects of stress.

Go Online

Visit glencoe.com and complete the Student Web Activity on the effects of stress.

READING CHECK

List What are the three stages of the body's stress response?

Your Body's Response to Stressors

Main Idea Stressors activate the nervous system and specific hormones.

When you perceive something to be dangerous, difficult, or painful, your body automatically begins a stress response. For example, if you walk by your neighbors' house and their dog barks, you would likely feel startled and your heart might start racing. The sudden, loud barking is a stressor that affects you automatically, without any thought.

Both your nervous system and endocrine system are active during your body's response to stress. This physical response is largely involuntary, or automatic. The stress response, which occurs regardless of the type of stressor, involves three stages:

- **Alarm.** Your mind and body go on high alert. This reaction, illustrated in **Figure 4.3**, is sometimes referred to as the "fight-or-flight" response because it prepares your body either to defend itself or to flee from a threat.

- **Resistance.** If exposure to a stressor continues, your body adapts and reacts to the stressor. You may perform at a higher level and with more endurance for a brief period.

- **Fatigue.** If exposure to stress is prolonged, your body loses its ability to adapt. You begin to tire and lose the ability to manage other stressors effectively.

Figure 4.2	**Stressors for Teens**			
Life Situations	**Environmental**	**Biological**	**Cognitive (Thinking)**	**Personal Behavior**
• School demands	• Unsafe neighborhood	• Changes in body	• Poor self-esteem	• Taking on a busy schedule
• Problems with friends, bullying	• Media (TV, magazines, newspapers, Internet)	• Illness	• Personal appearance	• Relationship issues
• Peer pressure		• Injury	• Not fitting in	• Smoking
• Family problems, abuse	• Natural disasters	• Disability		• Using alcohol or other drugs
• Moving or changing schools	• Threat of terrorist attacks			
• Breaking up with a girlfriend or boyfriend	• War			
	• Global warming			

FUTURE   DRUGS
LOVE   POLLUTION
PRESSURE   VIOLENCE
RACISM   HATE
FAMILY   GRADES
DANGER   WAR

94 **Chapter 4** Managing Stress and Coping with Loss

Teens Want to Know

How Can I Tell If I Have Stress Overload? People who are exposed to severe or long-term stressors—such as physical abuse or undiagnosed learning disorders—may show signs of stress overload. Signs include:

- panic or anxiety attacks.
- constant feelings of being pressured.
- allergic reactions such as asthma or eczema.

- frequent sadness or feelings of hopelessness.

Anxiety disorders may also cause people to experience signs of stress overload, even without severe or long-term stressors. Anxiety disorders are serious conditions that can be treated with medications, so it is a good idea to get a professional evaluation if you have an unreasonable amount of stress.

Figure 4.3 The Alarm Response

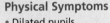

 Alarm begins when the *hypothalamus,* a small area at the base of the brain, receives danger signals from other parts of the brain. The hypothalamus releases a hormone that acts on the pituitary gland.

R The pituitary gland secretes a hormone that stimulates the adrenal glands.

3 The adrenal glands secrete adrenaline. *Adrenaline* is the "emergency hormone" that prepares the body to respond to a stressor.

Physical Symptoms
- Dilated pupils
- Increase in perspiration
- Faster heart rate and pulse
- Rise in blood pressure
- Faster respiration rate
- Narrowing of arteries to internal organs and skin
- Increased blood flow to muscles and brain
- Increase in muscle tension
- Release of blood sugar, fats, and cholesterol

Stress and Your Health

Main Idea Ongoing stress affects all aspects of your health.

The physical changes that take place in your body during the stress response can take a toll on your body. Prolonged stress can lead to a **psychosomatic response,** *a physical reaction that results from stress rather than from an injury or illness.* Some of the physical effects of stress include

W
- headache,
- a weakened immune system,
- high blood pressure,
- bruxism, clenching the jaw or grinding the teeth, and
- digestive disorders.

Mental/emotional and social effects of stress include difficulty concentrating, irritability, and mood swings. Using alcohol or drugs to relieve stress may create more problems, if the person begins abusing these substances.

Lesson 1   Understanding Stress   **95**

Academic Integration

Science Scientists have known for decades that people under long-term stress are at increased risk of illnesses ranging from the common cold to cancer. Recent research has found a physiological mechanism to explain this connection between stress and illness. The study found that adults under continuous stress (due to caring for an Alzheimer's patient) had significantly increased blood levels of the immune system chemical interleukin-6. This chemical has been shown in other studies to be linked with heart disease, cancer, and other diseases. The problem may be worsened by overeating and smoking, which are common behaviors in people under stress, because both behaviors also increase blood levels of interleukin-6. Share this information with students, and ask them to learn about the role of interleukin-6 in the immune system.

LESSON 1

Real World CONNECTION

Answers to Activity

1. 348
2. 60
3. Sample answer: I worry about who my teachers will be. I cope by trying to learn about the classes from other students.

❸ ASSESS/CLOSE

Assessment Resources

📁 **FAST FILE ACTIVITIES**
Lesson 1 Quiz

💿 *ExamView Assessment Suite* CD-ROM

Visit glencoe.com for:
Online Quizzes
Online Learning Center

Progress Monitoring

Reteaching
Have pairs of students define *stress* and *stressor* and to use both terms in a sentence showing how they are related.

Enrichment
Ask students to write two paragraphs describing examples of teens under stress.

G❍ Online

Have students visit **glencoe.com** and complete the Interactive Study Guide for this lesson.

Real World CONNECTION

How Stressed Out Are You?

School is a cause of stress for many teens. In a study that examined what worried teens most about going back to school, nearly a third named schoolwork. Almost as many teens reported that they were worried about social concerns and physical appearance issues. The results of the study found that

▸ 32 percent reported schoolwork issues.

▸ 30 percent reported social issues.

▸ 25 percent reported physical appearance issues.

▸ 3 percent reported extracurricular issues.

▸ 10 percent reported no worries about returning to school.

Identifying the causes of stress in your life is the first step to handling it. If you know the cause, you can figure out how to prevent it or at least reduce its effects on you.

Activity Mathematics

The study received completed surveys from 600 teens.

1. How many teens felt that issues other than schoolwork caused them stress?

2. How many teens experienced no worries about returning to school?

3. **Writing** What worries you about returning to school? How do you cope with the stress of new classes?

Concept Number and Operations: Percents A percent is a ratio comparing a number to 100. It can also be represented as a fraction with 100 as the deonominator. To find the percent of a number, change the percent to a fraction or decimal, then multiply by the number.

LESSON 1 ASSESSMENT

After You Read

Reviewing Facts and Vocabulary

1. Define the word *perception*.

2. What are three cognitive stressors for teens?

3. Identify the two body systems involved in the stress response.

Thinking Critically

4. **Synthesize.** Identify one way that stress has had a positive effect on your performance.

5. **Analyze.** Explain how a person in an extremely high-stress situation is able to accomplish an incredible feat of strength, such as lifting a car to free a person trapped underneath.

Applying Health Skills

6. **Analyzing Influences.** Describe ways that peer influence might increase the amount of stress that teens experience.

Writing Critically

7. **Expository.** Write a paragraph describing the positive and negative effects that stress has on your emotions.

G❍ Online

Visit **glencoe.com** and complete the Interactive Study Guide for this lesson.

LESSON 1 ASSESSMENT ANSWERS

1. The act of becoming aware through the senses
2. Poor self-esteem, personal appearance, not fitting in
3. Nervous and endocrine systems
4. Sample answer: Stress motivated me to practice more.
5. During the second stage of the stress response, a person briefly experiences more strength and endurance.

6. Sample answer: Peer influence might lead teens to feel pressure to do things that go against their values, which would increase their stress.
7. Answers will vary but should include examples of both positive and negative effects of stress on emotions.

Managing Stress

Real Life Issues

Dealing with Stress. Kevin recently enrolled in a new school. He feels overwhelmed by the change and has not yet made any friends. Almost every day, he complains of head-aches. His parents have noticed he has become irritable and sulks in his room after school.

Writing *Write a letter to Kevin. Give him some tips that you think might help him deal with the stress that comes with changing schools.*

When Stress Becomes a Problem

Main Idea Identifying what is stressful is the first step in learning how to manage stress.

You are keenly aware of stress when its cause is obvious, such as when you're late for an appointment, your computer crashes while you're doing homework, or when you realize that you've left the materials you need to complete a project at home. When you know the source of stress, you can find ways to resolve the problem. Unfortunately, people often don't recognize the stressors in their lives. Many times, people recognize that they're feeling stressed only after the stress has begin to affect their health.

The effects of stress are *additive,* meaning they build up over time. Unless you find ways of managing stress, it will take a physical and mental toll on you. An increasing number of teens are experiencing **chronic stress,** *stress associated with long-term problems that are beyond a person's control.* For these individuals, stress has become a constant burden that can last for months.

Fortunately, there are positive actions you can take to deal with stress. Although you can't eliminate all stress from your life, you can manage it. The trick is to learn strategies to keep stress from building up and to deal with individual stressors effectively.

GUIDE TO READING

BIG Idea *You can manage stress by learning skills to reduce the amount and impact of stress in your life.*

Before You Read

Create a Cluster Chart. Draw a circle and label it "Stress-Management Skills." Use surrounding circles to define and describe this term. As you read, continue filling in the chart with more details.

Stress Mgmt.

New Vocabulary

▶ chronic stress (p. 97)
▶ relaxation response (p. 99)

Review Vocabulary

▶ stress management skills (Ch.2, L.1)
▶ resilient (Ch.3, L.1)

Managing Stress

① FOCUS

GUIDE TO READING

BIG Idea You can learn skills to reduce your stress and its impact on your life. **Ask Students:** *How do you reduce stress?* (Sample answers: By playing video games; by riding my bike)

Before You Read

Cluster Chart Students' cluster charts may vary, but they should include strategies that help prevent stress and strategies that help lessen the impact of stress.

Main Idea

When Stress Becomes a Problem Identifying what is stressful is the first step in learning how to manage stress. **Ask Students:** *What are some common problems, situations, or events that cause stress?* (Sample answer: test at school)

Real Life Issues

Have students read the scenario. **Ask Students:** *Why might it be stressful to change schools?* (Sample answer: not having friends) After students write their letters, call on volunteers to identify other life changes that are likely to be stressful (e.g., starting college, parents divorcing, birth of a child).

Cooperative Learning

Discussing Chronic Stress Divide the class into several groups, and ask students in each group to brainstorm reasons why chronic stress is a growing problem for teens. Then ask groups to share their ideas. (Students might say, for example, that today's teens are faced with new environmental problems that they cannot control, such as the threat of terrorism and the reality of global warming.) Use their ideas to stimulate a class discussion on the problem of chronic stress in teens and ways it might be addressed.

2 TEACH

Stress-Management Techniques It's possible to develop strategies to both avoid and reduce stress. **Ask Students:** *What is an example of a stressor that can be avoided?* (Sample answer: putting off a project until the last minute)

FITNESS ZONE

This exercise incorporates questions from the lesson with physical activity:

- Take a piece of paper and crunch it up into a ball.
- Have the entire class stand in a circle.
- Pass the ball around and say "hot potato." The person who has the ball must then answer a question about the lesson.

HS Health Skills Practice

Refusal Skills Ask the class to brainstorm situations in which using refusal skills could help a teen avoid stress (e.g., being asked by a classmate to help cheat on a test; feeling pressured by peers to take on too many activities). Call on volunteers to demonstrate how to use refusal skills in one of the situations. Discuss how using refusal skills could help avoid unnecessary stress in that situation. **OL**

FITNESS ZONE

With school, work, and everything else, my friends and I can get really stressed out. I found that working out is the best stress reliever. When I'm feeing really stressed, I go for a run, swim, or just shoot some baskets on my own. Afterward, I always feel less stressed out. For more fitness tips, visit the Online Fitness Zone at glencoe.com.

Stress-Management Techniques

Main Idea You can develop strategies to both avoid and reduce your stress.

Stress-management skills help you manage stressors in a healthful, effective way. Some skills involve strategies to prevent stress. Others focus on coping with the impact of stress.

Avoiding and Limiting Stress

Avoiding situations that cause stress is the easiest way to reduce its effects. If you're unable to avoid a stressor, you can try to restrict or limit the amount of stress you're exposed to. These are effective strategies you can try:

- **Use refusal skills.** Determine whether you have time for a new activity before agreeing to take it on. If the new activity will add to your stress, use refusal skills to say no. You will learn about refusal skills in Chapter 8. **HS**

- **Plan ahead.** Manage your time wisely by planning ahead. Think about how stressed you feel before a test. **Figure 4.4** lists ways to reduce stress when studying for and taking tests.

- **Think positively.** We can't control everything in our lives, but we *can* control how we respond to events. A positive outlook limits stress by shifting your perception and the way you react to a stressor. For example, try viewing a typical stressor, like a job interview, as a learning opportunity instead of a threat.

| Figure 4.4 | **Overcoming Test Anxiety** |

Relaxation techniques, such as deep breathing and stretching, can reduce stress.

- Plan for tests well in advance, studying a little each night.
- Learn to outline material, highlighting and numbering important points to learn them quickly.
- During a test, do some deep breathing. Get comfortable in your chair. Use positive self-talk such as "I can do this!" or "Way to go!"
- Answer all the questions you are sure of, then go back and answer the ones that are more difficult.
- After getting your corrected test back, examine your mistakes. If you don't understand the correction, ask your teacher.

Skills for the 21st Century

Self-Management Skills Share these self-management tips with students to help them use time to their advantage and avoid the stress of having too little time:

- **Keep a log.** For at least a week, keep track of how you are actually spending your time. Use the results to identify ways you can use time more wisely.

- **Use a calendar.** Record all the demands on your time in one place. Remember to leave adequate time for sleeping, eating, grooming, socializing, and relaxing.

- **Plan ahead.** Use your calendar to record start dates as well as due dates. For example, if a paper is due in three weeks and it usually takes you one week to write a paper, make the start date two weeks before the due date. That way, if something unexpected comes up, you should still have enough time to finish the paper.

■ **Figure 4.5** Planning ahead can help you avoid or limit stress. *What other actions can you take to manage stress?*

• **Avoid tobacco, alcohol, and other drugs.** Using tobacco, alcohol, and other drugs in an attempt to relieve stress will actually harm the body and cause more stress.

Handling Stress and Reducing Its Effects

Some stressors may be unavoidable. Some days you may be running late for school because the weather is bad, or the bus had a flat tire. If you have a part-time job, your boss might be stressed himself on some days, which makes your workday stressful. For stressors that are unavoidable, try to find ways to reduce their negative effects. To lower the impact of stress on your health, try these tips:

• **Practice relaxation techniques.** Deep breathing, thinking pleasant thoughts, stretching, taking a warm bath, getting a massage, and even laughing can relieve your stress. Practicing these **techniques** regularly can help you achieve a **relaxation response**, *a state of calm.* **Figure 4.6** describes a relaxation technique.

• **Redirect your energy.** When intense energy builds up from stress, the best thing to do is use that energy in a constructive way. You can put your nervous energy to good use by working on a creative project, going for walk or a swim, jogging, riding your bike, or playing a game of pickup basketball.

READING CHECK

Explain How can refusal skills help you avoid stress?

Academic Vocabulary

technique *(noun):* a method of accomplishing a desired aim

Figure 4.6 — Progressive Muscle Relaxation

By practicing these relaxation techniques daily, you can prepare yourself to manage stress when it occurs.

Breathe deeply and slowly throughout the process.
1. Loosen your clothing and get comfortable. Lie down or relax in a comfortable chair.
2. Tighten the muscles in your toes. Hold for a count of 10. Relax.
3. Flex the muscles in your feet. Hold for a count of 10. Relax.
4. Move slowly up your body, tensing and then relaxing the muscles in your legs, abdomen, back, shoulders, arms, neck, and face.

Lesson 2 Managing Stress **99**

 Universal Access

Clarifying Misconceptions
Some students may think that the more they talk about problems, the more upset and stressed out they will become. Ask the class to identify benefits of talking about problems with people you trust. (Sample answers: You won't feel so alone; expressing feelings may help you feel better; other people may be able to help you solve your problems.) **BL** **OL**

W Writing Strategy

Handling Test Anxiety Have students read about lowering the impact of stress. Have them write a dialogue in which one teen is giving advice to another on how to best overcome anxiety regarding an upcoming test. Make sure students include the tips listed. **OL**

READING CHECK

Answer By helping you avoid taking on more than you have time for

Academic Vocabulary

Technique Explain that the term technique was borrowed from the French language. Challenge the class to identify other English words that come from the French language. (Sample answers: boutique, café, chef, beret)

Teacher to Teacher

Tom Williams, health educator • Fayetteville High School, Fayetteville, AR

Health Triangle and Stress When teaching stress management techniques I think it is important to have the students examine their social, mental/emotional and physical elements of health. Have the students draw a triangle and label the elements of health in each section, then write out what they feel causes their stress. For example: physical—body image, complexion, social—boyfriend/girlfriend relationships, lack of friends, mental/emotional—schoolwork, grades, parents. Hopefully recognizing the symptoms of their stressors can better prepare them to manage their stress that will be with them throughout their life.

Health Skills Activity

Stress Management: When Demands Are Too High

NHES Standard 7 Students will demonstrate the ability to practice health-enhancing behaviors and avoid or reduce health risks.

Objectives

- Identify specific stress management techniques.
- Implement a plan for managing stress.

Teaching Strategies

- After students read the activity, have them list all Juan's commitments.
- Discuss how setting priorities can help determine which stressors can be avoided or limited.

Assessment

Using the list below, student work should provide comprehensive evidence of the following criteria to achieve the highest score:

√ Identifies stressors

√ Lists ways stressors can be avoided

√ Clearly describes stress-management techniques

READING CHECK

Answer Getting adequate rest, getting regular physical activity, and eating nutritious foods

---

Health Skills Activity

Stress Management

When Demands Are Too High

Juan has too many commitments and is beginning to feel the effects of stress. He writes for the school paper, volunteers on the yearbook committee, plays on the basketball and soccer teams, and is working hard to maintain a B+ average. At home, he helps take care of his younger brother and earns an allowance by doing chores such as cleaning out the garage and taking care of the family pets. On weekends, he works at a local bookstore to earn extra money. Juggling all of his responsibilities has become more and more difficult. Now his girlfriend wants him to spend more time with her.

Writing Write a letter to Juan suggesting ways that he could manage his stress. Use the following questions to guide your thinking.

1. What are Juan's stressors?
2. Which stressors, if any, can he avoid or prevent? How?
3. Which stressors can he limit? How?
4. Which stress-management techniques can help Juan deal with his stress?

- **Seek support.** Sometimes just talking about your problem can make you feel better. When you feel stressed, try confiding in someone you trust, such as a parent, guardian, sibling, teacher, or close friend. They can provide you with an objective view and valuable advice.

Staying Healthy and Building Resiliency

Main Idea Taking care of your health is essential to stress management.

READING CHECK

Explain What three self-maintenance habits can reduce your level of stress?

In addition to learning stress-management skills, developing habits that maintain your general health will also help reduce the effects of stress. These self-maintenance habits help you deal with stress in positive ways. They can also play a role in preventing stress, reducing stress, and helping your mind and body recover from stress.

Get Adequate Rest Too little sleep can affect your ability to concentrate. This can affect schoolwork, athletics, and even relationships. By contrast, adequate sleep can help you face the challenges and demands of the next day. Using time-management skills will allow you to get the eight to nine hours of sleep that you need each night.

Teens Want to Know

How Can I Build Resiliency? Studies have found that resilient people tend to:

- Take time to have fun and relax.
- Act quickly to address problems.
- Assume problems can be solved.
- Turn to others for support.

- See setbacks as challenges.
- Believe they can reach their goals.

Try to adopt these ways of thinking and acting, and you will be on your way to building resiliency.

Get Regular Physical Activity Participating in regular physical activity benefits your overall health whether or not you are feeling the effects of stress. Physical activity can release pent-up energy and clear your mind. Done regularly, exercise increases your energy level and your endurance. It helps you sleep better, too.

Eat Nutritious Foods Eating a variety of healthful foods and drinking plenty of water not only helps your body function properly, but it also reduces the effects of stress. In contrast, poor eating habits can contribute to stress, causing weakness, fatigue, and a reduced ability to concentrate. Overeating and undereating can also put your body under stress. Beverages high in caffeine and sugar, such as coffee drinks or quick-energy drinks, can increase the effects of stress. You'll learn more about good nutrition in Chapters 10 and 11.

By including self-maintenance and stress-management strategies in your daily routine, you can become more resilient. This means you're able to adapt effectively and recover from disappointment, difficulty, or crisis. For example, you would probably feel disappointed if you didn't win the part you wanted in the school play. A resilient teen would bounce back from this disappointment and work harder for the next audition. Resiliency helps you handle difficulties and challenges in healthful ways and achieve long-term success in spite of negative circumstances.

 **Online**

For more practice with vocabulary, go to the Interactive Health Tutor at glencoe.com.

 ASSESS/CLOSE

Assessment Resources

📁 *FAST FILE* **ACTIVITIES**
Lesson 2 Quiz

💿 *ExamView*
Assessment Suite CD-ROM

Visit glencoe.com **for:**
Online Quizzes
Online Learning Center

Progress Monitoring

Reteaching
Call on students to give examples of stressors. For each example, call on other students to identify stress-management techniques that would be appropriate for managing that stressor.

Enrichment
Arrange for students to interview a massage therapist to find out how massage helps people relax. Have students give an oral report to the class about what they learn.

LESSON 2 **ASSESSMENT**

After You Read

Reviewing Facts and Vocabulary

1. What is *chronic stress*?
2. Identify four strategies to avoid or limit stress.
3. Identify three relaxation techniques.

Thinking Critically

4. **Synthesize.** It's Wednesday, and Ariana's biology test is on Friday. As she sits down to study, her friend Conner calls and asks her to go out. How might Ariana balance her activities and manage her stress?
5. **Describe.** Explain the role of positive thinking as a stress-management strategy.

Applying Health Skills

6. **Practicing Healthful Behaviors.** Some of the habits that you practice to maintain overall health can also help manage stress. Design a poster illustrating the habits that can help you manage stress.

Writing Critically

7. **Personal.** Evaluate your own wellness in regard to stress. Write a paragraph to explain your assessment.

 Online

Visit glencoe.com and complete the Interactive Study Guide for this lesson.

Lesson 2 Managing Stress **101**

 Online

Have students visit glencoe.com and complete the Interactive Study Guide for this lesson.

LESSON 2 ASSESSMENT ANSWERS

1. Stress associated with long-term problems that are beyond a person's control
2. Use refusal skills; plan ahead; think positively; avoid tobacco, alcohol, and other drugs
3. *Any three:* Deep breathing, thinking pleasant thoughts, stretching, taking a warm bath, getting a massage, laughing
4. Sample answer: Ariana should consider whether she has scheduled enough time to study. If she hasn't, she should use refusal skills to turn down Connor's offer. If she has, she could go out to relieve her stress.
5. Positive thinking helps you change the way you perceive a stressor. It can help reduce the amount of stress from a stressor by making it seem like less of a threat.
6. Should include getting enough sleep, exercising regularly, and healthful eating
7. Answers will vary.

Coping with Loss and Grief

1 FOCUS

BIG Idea Understanding the grieving process can help a person cope with loss. **Ask Students:** *What is grief?* (Sample answer: Feelings you have when you lose someone close to you)

Before You Read

Vocabulary Cards Students should create flashcards for the new vocabulary terms, using definitions based on their current knowledge. For example, they might define *stages of grief* as "steps you go through after a loss."

Main Idea

Acknowledging Loss In order to get over a loss, it's important to accept that the loss has happened. **Ask Students:** *Why might it be hard to accept that a loss has happened?* (Because it causes painful emotions)

Real Life Issues

Have students read the scenario. **Ask Students:** *If you were in Kelly's place, what could your friends do that would make you feel better?* (Sample answers: Call and ask how I'm doing; try to get me involved in doing things I enjoy.) Call on volunteers to read their dialogues to the class.

102

GUIDE TO READING

BIG Idea *Understanding the grieving process helps you cope with loss and manage your feelings in healthy ways.*

Before You Read
Create Vocabulary Cards. Write each new vocabulary term on a separate note card. For each term, write a definition based on your current knowledge. As you read, fill in additional information related to each term.

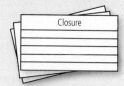

Closure

New Vocabulary
▶ stages of grief (p. 103)
▶ closure (p. 103)
▶ coping (p. 103)
▶ mourning (p. 104)
▶ traumatic event (p. 105)

Coping with Loss and Grief

Real Life Issues ....

Losing a Close Relative. Kelly has always been close to her grandfather. Every weekend they would spend time together, taking walks, watching movies, playing chess, or just talking. He has just passed away at the age of 92. Kelly misses him terribly and feels there is a big hole in her life.

Writing *If you were Kelly's friend, how might you comfort her as she tries to cope with the loss of her grandfather? Write a dialogue between you and Kelly in which you offer support and sympathy.*

Acknowledging Loss

Main Idea Acknowledging a loss is one way to help begin the healing process.

You have probably experienced a loss that left you feeling sad. Perhaps you moved to a new city and left behind good friends. You may have even experienced the death of someone you love. Everyone experiences loss during their lives and the grief that it brings. For example, you may have felt the pain of rejection, the breakup of a relationship, or the death of a pet, friend, or family member. Maybe you had to move or change schools and miss the friends you left behind.

Grieving is a common and natural reaction to any loss that brings on strong emotions. Loss feels hurtful, but it does not have to be harmful. Immediately after the loss, you may feel that your life will never be the same, and that you may never recover. Again, these feelings are natural. Acknowledging and understanding your grief will help you begin the healing process. This in turn will help you to cope with the loss and manage your feelings.

Myths & Reality

Myths about Grieving

Myth: We grieve only deaths.

Fact: All losses cause grief.

Myth: Grief eventually ends.

Fact: We only learn to live with the loss.

Myth: People should be left alone to grieve.

Fact: Grieving people need the support of others.

Expressing Grief

Main Idea The grieving process can help people accept the loss and start to heal.

Feelings of loss are very personal. Some people feel sadness, guilt, or even anger. Some may talk about their loss; others may want to be alone. Sometimes people experience several or all of these emotions.

The Grieving Process

While everyone grieves in their own way, Swiss-American psychiatrist Elisabeth Kübler-Ross noted that the grieving process includes **stages of grief**, *a variety of reactions that may surface as an individual makes sense of how a loss affects him or her.* Not everyone goes through each stage, and the order may be different for each person. Here are the stages:

 8 stages

HS

- **Denial or Numbness.** It may be difficult to believe the loss has occurred.
- **Emotional Release.** The loss is recognized. This stage often involve periods of crying.
- **Anger.** The person uses anger because he or she feels powerless and unfairly deprived.
- **Bargaining.** As the reality of the loss sets in, the person may promise to change if what was lost can be returned.
- **Depression.** Beyond the feelings of sadness, feelings of isolation, alienation, and hopelessness may occur.
- **Remorse.** The person may become preoccupied with thoughts about how the loss could have been prevented.
- **Acceptance.** The person faces the reality of the loss, and experiences **closure**, or the *acceptance of a loss.*
- **Hope.** Remembering becomes less painful, and the person begins to look ahead to the future.

Experiencing and accepting your feelings during grieving is necessary for healing. These feelings are part of **coping**, or *dealing successfully with difficult changes in your life.*

 READING CHECK

Identify List the eight stages of grief.

■ **Figure 4.7** Grieving is a process that you need not experience alone. *How might receiving comfort and support help you through a loss?*

Lesson 3 Coping with Loss and Grief **103**

② TEACH

Main Idea

Expressing Grief The grieving process can help people accept the loss and start to heal. **Ask Students:** *What are some of the feelings people may go through after experiencing a major loss?* (Sample answer: sadness, anger, regret)

HS Health Skills Practice

Communication Skills Communicating feelings can be difficult, especially when the feelings are painful, but it's necessary to express feelings in order to heal from a loss. Ask students to assume that a close friend has moved away and they are moving through the stages of grief over the loss. Have students select one stage of grief and write a letter to the friend describing the feelings they would have if they were in that stage of grief. In their letters, students should use "I" messages and clearly express their emotions. Call on volunteers to read their letters to the class. Ask other students to try to identify which stage of grief each student wrote about. **OL**

READING CHECK

Answer Denial or numbness, emotional release, anger, bargaining, depression, remorse, acceptance, hope

Caption Answer

Figure 4.7 Sample answer: It might help me feel less alone and isolated.

English Language Coach

Understanding Gerunds Explain that many English verbs can be turned into nouns, called gerunds, by adding *-ing*. Give familiar examples, such as *run/running* and *write/writing*. Point out that the final consonant of a verb may be doubled (as in *running*) or the final "e" may be dropped (as in *writing*) before *-ing* is added. Have students find several nouns on this or nearby pages that end in *-ing* (e.g., *grieving, bargaining, remembering, coping*). Ask them to identify the base verb and to define both the verb and its gerund.

■ **Figure 4.8** Memorial services and sites help people grieve and show respect. *What are other ways to remember a loved one?*

Coping with Death

Main Idea Coping with death involves receiving and showing support.

Death is one of the most painful losses we can experience. Even if a person dies after a long illness, it's likely that the survivors will grieve. If the death was sudden or traumatic, the survivors may also experience shock.

Most people respond to loss by **mourning,** *the act of showing sorrow or grief.* Mourning includes talking about the person, experiencing the pain of the loss, and searching for meaning. It may be difficult for some people to move out of the mourning process. Dwelling on things that can't be changed will only add to your hurt. Instead, try to think about how the relationship was positive in your life. **CA**

Showing Empathy

Grieving alone makes the process more difficult. The friendship and support of others who are also grieving may make the process easier. If you can't talk to family and other loved ones, try talking to a supportive friend.

If you know someone who is grieving, there are ways you can show support.

- Help the person to recall happy, positive memories. **W**
- Be a sympathetic listener, and use silence when appropriate. Sometimes, just nodding your head shows that you understand what the person is saying.
- Don't rush the grieving process or attempt to **resolve** the person's grief in one day. Remember, no one can lead another person through this process or hurry through it.

Go Online

Explore glencoe.com and complete the Student Web Activity on grief and coping with loss.

Academic Vocabulary

resolve *(verb):* to deal with successfully

Promoting School Wellness

Memorializing Traumatic Events If students go through the traumatic loss of someone they know, such as a teacher or fellow student, a school memorial can help them through the healing process. Memorials are a way to express grief and bring closure. They can include writing cards and holding candle-lighting ceremonies. Activities that help prevent similar tragedies in the future may be especially effective memorials. Help other school personnel appreciate the importance of memorializing traumatic events, not only those that may occur in your own school but in other schools around the nation.

Community Support

A person's cultural background also influences grieving. Common mourning rituals, such as memorial services, wakes, and funerals are events that celebrate the life of the person who has died. Telling stories or describing why the person was special can help you move through the grieving process. The clergy and mental health professionals who specialize in grief can also provide support.

Coping with Traumatic Events

Main Idea Support from family, friends, and community resources can help individuals recover from a traumatic event.

A **traumatic event** is *any event that has a stressful impact sufficient to overwhelm your normal coping strategies.* Traumatic events are sudden and shocking, such as accidents, violent assaults, suicides, and natural disasters. After a traumatic event, you may question your sense of security and confidence. Seek support from family members, friends, and community groups and agencies to help you manage your shock and grief. Also, trying to resume your normal activities can help you through the grieving process.

READING CHECK

Explain What are ways to support someone who is grieving?

LESSON 3 ASSESSMENT

After You Read

Reviewing Facts and Vocabulary

1. Identify the stages of grief.
2. Define the term *coping*.
3. List three examples of a traumatic event.

Thinking Critically

4. **Analyze.** How might coping with a death resulting from a long-term illness differ from coping with a sudden death caused by an accident?
5. **Apply.** Recall a story of personal loss that you read about in a book or saw in a movie. Write a paragraph that describes the process of grieving that the main character went through.

Applying Health Skills

6. **Communication Skills.** Write a letter expressing caring and empathy to a friend who is grieving for a loved one.

Writing Critically

7. **Expository.** Write a paragraph describing ways that people in the community and community support groups can help someone who is coping with a loss.

Go Online

Visit **glencoe.com** and complete the Interactive Study Guide for this lesson.

Lesson 3 Coping with Loss and Grief **105**

Main Idea
Coping with Traumatic Events
Family, friends, and community resources help the recovery process.
Ask Students: *Why are traumatic events so hard to deal with?* (They are unexpected.)

---

③ ASSESS/ CLOSE

Assessment Resources

📁 *Fast File* Activities
Lesson 3 Quiz
 ExamView Assessment Suite CD-ROM

Visit glencoe.com for:
Online Quizzes
Online Learning Center

Progress Monitoring

Reteaching
Have students make up true/false questions based on the main ideas and topic sentences in the lesson. Then ask students to choose partners and quiz each other.

Enrichment
Have students research community programs and services for grieving people. They can start by contacting a state or local health department.

Go Online

Have students visit **glencoe.com** and complete the Interactive Study Guide for this lesson.

105

LESSON 3 ASSESSMENT ANSWERS

1. Denial or numbness, emotional release, anger, bargaining, depression, remorse, acceptance, hope
2. Dealing successfully with difficult changes
3. *Any three:* Accidents, violent assaults, suicides, natural disasters
4. Sample answer: It might be easier to cope with a death resulting from a long-term illness because people have time to prepare emotionally for the death. Sudden death would be more traumatic.
5. Answers will vary depending on the particular books or movies students describe.
6. Letters will vary but should demonstrate empathy.
7. Sample answer: People in the community can participate in mourning rituals, offer support, and help the grieving person move through the grieving process.

Juggling Stress

Assert Yourself

NHES Standard 7 Students will demonstrate the ability to practice health-enhancing behaviors and avoid or reduce risks.

Teaching Objectives

- Analyze how stress impacts health.
- Identify effective stress management techniques.

Teaching Strategies

- You will need six tennis balls for this activity.
- Provide each student with three large index cards. Have students do steps 1 and 2 of the activity.
- When students have completed the first two steps, stand in the front of the room and hold six tennis balls in your hands. Explain that each tennis ball represents a stressor. Have one student come to the front of the class and identify one stressor teens might have. With each stressor, toss a tennis ball so the student can catch it. Continue until all six tennis balls are caught. Discuss how this activity demonstrates the importance of stress management techniques.
- Retrieve all six tennis balls and toss them all at once toward the student. Discuss what happens and how it relates to managing stress.

Assessment

Using a rubric, student work should provide comprehensive evidence of the following criteria to achieve the highest score:

✓ Clearly identifies stressors

✓ Demonstrates techniques to help manage and reduce stress

✓ Implements a plan for managing stress

Hands-On
HEALTH

Activity Juggling Stress

Do you sometimes feel overwhelmed and exhausted trying to juggle everything in your life—school, homework, activities, family and household responsibilities—all at once? This activity will help you identify your stressors and find ways to manage stress.

What You'll Need

- 3 large index cards
- pen or pencil

What You'll Do

Step 1

In the middle of each index card, draw a 1-inch circle. Write one stressor that is currently affecting your life.

Step 2

Your teacher will demonstrate the tennis ball activity. Each of your stressors is like a tennis ball you juggle as you try to balance your daily activities.

Step 3

Select one of your index cards. List four signs or symptoms describing how this particular stressor is currently affecting your health.

Apply and Conclude

Think about the stressors that you identified. List stress-management techniques that you can practice to reduce or manage the stressful situations you identified. Implement your plan and evaluate its effectiveness.

Checklist: Stress-Management Skills

✓ Identification of situations that cause stress

✓ Techniques you can use to avoid stressful situations

✓ Ways to manage stress

✓ Evaluate the effectiveness of the techniques you use to manage stress

Health Literacy

Health Information Most illnesses have psychological and physical components. The relationship between the mind and body, or emotions and physical reactions, is described in commonly used expressions such as *gut wrenching* and *worried sick*. Anxiety and emotional stress can increase the likelihood of physical health problems. An illness is suspected to be a psychosomatic response when the presence of a disease is eliminated by a thorough medical examination, and there is evidence of a psychological problem. It is confirmed when resolution of the problem causes the physical symptoms to disappear. Headaches, abdominal pain, fatigue, and chest pain are common psychosomatic complaints among teens.

To download quizzes and eFlashcards to your PDA, go to **glencoe.com** and click on the Study to Go icon.

LESSON 1

Understanding Stress

Key Concepts

▶ Stress is a natural part of life; everyone experiences stress.
▶ The specific effects of stressors on your life depend on your experiences and perception.
▶ Too much stress can be unhealthful.

Vocabulary

▶ stress (p. 92)
▶ perception (p. 92)
▶ stressor (p. 93)
▶ psychosomatic response (p. 95)

LESSON 2

Managing Stress

Key Concepts

▶ You can manage stress by using refusal skills, planning ahead, thinking positively, and avoiding tobacco, alcohol, and other drugs.
▶ Stress-management techniques include relaxation, redirecting your energy, and seeking support.
▶ Taking care of your health can help you prevent and reduce stress, as well as recover from its effects.

Vocabulary

▶ chronic stress (p. 97)
▶ stress-management skills (p. 98)
▶ relaxation response (p. 99)
▶ resilient (p. 100)

LESSON 3

Coping with Loss and Grief

Key Concepts

▶ Grief is caused by many kinds of loss.
▶ Each person's response to a loss is unique to the situation and to the individual.
▶ Each person goes through stages of grief, although not in any particular order.
▶ Coping with death requires closure.

Vocabulary

▶ stages of grief (p. 103)
▶ closure (p. 103)
▶ coping (p. 103)
▶ mourning (p. 104)
▶ traumatic event (p. 105)

 Online

Students can visit **glencoe.com** to

● review content online with the Online Student Edition.
● test their knowledge of chapter content with Online Quizzes.
● access Interactive Health Tutor for more practice with vocabulary.

Assessment Resources

📁 **FAST FILE ACTIVITIES**
Chapter 4 Test

💿 *ExamView*
Assessment Suite CD-ROM

Visit glencoe.com for:
Audio Chapter Summaries
Online Quizzes

 Tell students to visit **glencoe.com** where they can download quizzes and eFlashcards.

Study Tips

Using Index Cards for Review An effective way for students to review is to write questions on the front of index cards and answers on the back. They can develop questions by rewriting main ideas in the text or their class notes as questions. To use their cards for review, students should shuffle them and then try to answer the questions. They can set aside any cards for which they know the answers. If they cannot recall an answer, they should read the answer on the back of the card and then place the card at the bottom of the stack so they will have to try to answer the question again.

Chapter 4 Assessment Answers

LESSON 1

Vocabulary Review

1. Stress
2. stressor
3. psychosomatic response

Understanding Key Concepts

4. c
5. d
6. b
7. b

Thinking Critically

8. Life situations, environmental stressors, biological stressors, cognitive stressors, and personal behavior
9. Trying an activity for the first time can be stressful because you might experience frustration or worry about whether you can do it or how it will turn out.
10. You may feel less secure and comfortable working with people you don't know, and this could cause you to feel more stress about the project.
11. Mental fatigue can make it hard to concentrate and learn.
12. *Any three:* Headache, upset stomach, muscle aches and tightness, ringing in ears, allergic reactions
13. You may suffer from a weakened immune system, high blood pressure, and skin or digestive disorders.

LESSON 2

Vocabulary Review

14. stress-management techniques
15. resilient
16. relaxation response
17. stress management skills

LESSON 1

Vocabulary Review

Use the vocabulary terms listed on page 107 to complete the following statements.

1. _____ is the reaction of the body and mind to everyday challenges and demands.

2. Anything that causes stress is called a(n) _____.

3. A physical reaction that results from stress rather than from an injury or illness is called a(n) _____.

Understanding Key Concepts

After reading the question or statement, select the correct answer.

4. The amount of stress that you experience mostly relates to
   a. the type of friends that you have.
   b. where you go to school.
   c. your perception of stressors.
   d. how your parents respond to stress.

5. Which of the following is *not* an environmental stressor?
   a. Unsafe neighborhood
   b. TV
   c. Tornado
   d. Personal appearance

6. During which stage of the body's stress response are hormones released?
   a. Resistance
   b. Alarm
   c. Fatigue
   d. Recovery

7. Which of the following is *not* a physical symptom of the alarm response?
   a. Faster heart rate and pulse
   b. Decreased blood flow to muscles and brain
   c. Increase in perspiration
   d. Decrease in blood pressure

Thinking Critically

After reading the question or statement, write a short answer using complete sentences.

8. **Identify.** What are the five categories of stressors?

9. **Infer.** How would trying an activity for the first time affect your stress level?

10. **Synthesize.** Suppose you've been assigned to work on a project with three students you don't know. How might this affect your perception of doing the project?

11. **Analyze.** Describe how mental fatigue that results from stress can affect your ability to study.

12. **Describe.** List three physical symptoms of stress.

13. **Infer.** You've spent three months feeling stressed while studying for an important exam. What impact could this stress have on your health?

LESSON 2

Vocabulary Review

Correct the sentences below by replacing the italicized term with the correct vocabulary term.

14. Using refusal skills, planning ahead, and practicing relaxation techniques are examples of *chronic stress*.

15. You are *relaxed* if you are able to adapt effectively and recover from disappointment, difficulty, or crisis.

16. Practicing stress-management techniques can help you achieve a state of calm, or a *chronic stress*, when stressed.

17. Stress associated with long-term problems beyond one's control is known as *resilient*.

Health eSpotlight VIDEO Wrap-Up

Managing Strong Emotions Have students reread the Health eSpotlight questions at the beginning of the chapter on page 91 and look at their original answers. **Ask Students:** *What do you know now about managing stress and coping with loss that you didn't know before watching the video and reading the chapter?* (Answers will vary but should include information students have learned from the chapter or video.)

Call on volunteers to describe what they have learned and how their responses would change.

Understanding Key Concepts

After reading the question or statement, select the correct answer.

18. Which is not a relaxation technique?
    a. Taking a warm bath
    b. Laughing
    c. Eating a comfort food
    d. Deep breathing

19. One way to prevent taking on an activity that will add to your level of stress is to
    a. procrastinate.
    b. use refusal skills.
    c. think positively.
    d. redirect your energy.

20. Which of the following is *not* a way to redirect energy that may build up as a result of stress?
    a. Going for a walk
    b. Watching TV
    c. Riding your bike
    d. Working on a creative project

21. Which is *not* an effect of physical activity on stress?
    a. Clears your head
    b. Increases energy level
    c. Helps you sleep better
    d. Helps you avoid stress

Thinking Critically

After reading the question or statement, write a short answer using complete sentences.

22. **Explain.** How does identifying personal stressors help in the development of a stress-management plan?

23. **Analyze.** Why are the effects of stress additive? How can additive stressors affect your health?

24. **Synthesize.** What might be some important considerations when planning ahead for a research project that is due in three weeks?

25. **Analyze.** Why shouldn't people smoke cigarettes as a way to relieve stress?

26. **Analyze.** Explain how having resiliency can help you manage your stress.

LESSON 3

Vocabulary Review

Choose the correct term in the sentences below.

27. *Closure / Coping* is acceptance of a loss.

28. *Coping / Mourning* is the act of showing sorrow or grief.

29. A stressful event that overwhelms your coping strategies is called a *traumatic event / stage of grief*.

Understanding Key Concepts

After reading the question or statement, select the correct answer.

30. Which is *not* a stage of grief?
    a. Remorse
    b. Empathy
    c. Acceptance
    d. Denial

31. The needed outcome of grieving is
    a. anger.
    b. sympathy.
    c. remorse.
    d. closure.

32. You can show support to someone who is grieving by
    a. helping the person recall happy memories.
    b. being a sympathetic listener.
    c. not rushing the grieving process.
    d. all of the above.

Understanding Key Concepts

18. c
19. b
20. b
21. d

Thinking Critically

22. You need to identify what is causing you stress so you can take steps to avoid the stressors or handle them.

23. The effects of stress are additive because they build up over time. This can take a toll on both mental and physical health.

24. Sample answer: How much time will I need to research and write the report? What other commitments do I have during this period of time?

25. Smoking can harm health and contribute to stress. It can also create other problems that may be stressful, such as interfering with relationships and causing a financial burden.

26. Sample answer: Resiliency enables you to bounce back from disappointments and other stressful events and situations. If you are resilient, you are less likely to be affected by potential stressors.

LESSON 3

Vocabulary Review

27. Closure
28. Mourning
29. traumatic event

Understanding Key Concepts

30. b
31. d
32. d

ExamView®
Assessment Suite

Create and customize tests in minutes with this convenient digital platform.

- Create differentiated tests quickly and easily.
- All questions correlated to National/State Standards.
- Enhance tests with Document Based Questions (DBQ) and add your own photos or graphics.
- Build tests in both English and Spanish.
- Generate progress reports.

To order, go to **glencoe.com** and search for ISBN 0-07-888173-0.

Assessment

Assessment

33. c
34. d

Thinking Critically

35. Sample answer: rejection, breakup of a relationship, death of a friend or family member, death of a pet

36. Sample answer: remaining open to relationships would mean the person was more likely to receive comfort and support during grieving. Not remaining open would mean that the person would be more likely to grieve alone, making healing more difficult.

37. To heal after a loss, it is necessary to experience and accept all your feelings during the grieving process.

38. The mourning process may be difficult for a person to move out of. Thinking of positive aspects of the relationship and relying on support of family and friends can help the person cope.

39. Mourning rituals help mark the passage of time since the death, help people move through the grieving process, and serve to reconnect people to their ordinary lives.

40. People who are available in a community to respond to survivors of a traumatic event include clergy, mental health professionals, family, and friends.

Assessment

33. During which stage of grief do people make a promise to change if what was lost can be returned?
    a. Denial
    b. Depression
    c. Bargaining
    d. Hope

34. Which of the following strategies can help someone cope with a traumatic event?
    a. Spending time alone
    b. Delaying getting back to a daily routine
    c. Putting off grieving
    d. Seeking support from the community

Thinking Critically

After reading the question or statement, write a short answer using complete sentences.

35. **Describe.** What are four examples of loss that could cause someone to experience the grieving process?

36. **Evaluate.** How do you think the ability or inability to remain open to relationships could affect the way a person responds to loss?

37. **Analyze.** What is necessary in order for healing to occur after a loss?

38. **Explain.** At which stage of the grieving process might a person become unable to move on? What should people do if they have difficulty moving through the stages of grief?

39. **Explain.** How do mourning rituals following a death help individuals during the grieving process?

40. **Identify.** Who is available in a community to respond to the needs of survivors of a traumatic event?

Project-Based ASSESSMENT

The Stages of Grief

Background
We all have to cope with a significant loss sometime in our lives. A best friend may move to another city, or a close family member may pass away. Grieving for someone we loved, such as pets, friends, and family members is natural. The grieving process occurs in stages, and understanding those stages will help you cope with loss.

Task
Research the grieving process. Write a short play about a student grieving over a loss. Have students fill out a questionnaire describing what they learned.

Audience
Students in your class

Purpose
Help students learn about the grieving process.

Procedure
1 Form small groups. Divide the tasks. Some members may want to conduct research and write the play. Others may want to perform in the play.

2 Using the information in Chapter 4 and additional library or Internet resources, research the stages of grief.

3 Write a script for a play about a student who has suffered a significant loss. The play should show the student moving through all the stages of grief.

4 Write a questionnaire about the stages of the grieving process.

5 Perform the play for your classmates.

6 Assess the effectiveness of the play by having students fill out the questionnaire.

Project-Based ASSESSMENT

Step 1 Research Have students research the stages of the grief process using library or Internet resources.

Step 2 Write Ask students to write a script about a teen who has suffered a significant loss and is moving through the stages of grief. Also ask students to write a brief questionnaire about the stages of grief.

Step 3 Perform/Evaluate Give students a chance to perform their play. After the play, the rest of the class should fill out the questionnaire so students can assess the effectiveness of their play.

Visit **glencoe.com** for Project-Based Assessment rubrics.

Math Practice

Interpret Tables. Angelika conducted a survey of 300 students at her school to determine what caused them the most stress. The results of her survey are shown in the table below. Use the table to answer Questions 1–3.

Student Stressors at Washington High	
Greatest Stressor	**Number of Students**
Grades	93
Peer conflict	81
Family issues	64
Work responsibilities	24
After-school activities	8
Personal health	8
Other	18

1. What percentage of students did not feel that work responsibilities were a stressor?
   A. 88%   C. 19%
   B. 76%   D. 92%

2. What number of students reported that family issues caused them the most stress?
   A. 202   C. 192
   B. 78   D. 53

3. What could you conclude from the information given in the table?
   A. Most students are stressed about work responsibilities.
   B. After-school activities are stressors for many teens.
   C. Peer conflict ranked second as the greatest stressor for students surveyed.
   D. Personal health issues are stressful for students.

Go Online

For more test practice, visit glencoe.com and complete the Online Quizzes for Chapter 4.

Reading/Writing Practice

Understand and Apply. Read the letter below, and then answer the questions.

> Dear Maya,
> Things have changed since you moved away. The factory closed and more than 3,000 people are unemployed. I'm sure more people will be leaving town like your family did. Manuel and his family moved, too. Now both of my best friends have left.
> My parents don't want to tell me, but I can tell that things are not good. I overhear them talking, but they clam up whenever I ask anything. Dad has a new job, but he is making less money.
> Please write back and let me know how things are going for you. Do your parents have jobs? Have you made new friends? I miss you!
> Love,
> Isabel

1. Which word *best* describes the tone of this letter?
   A. Angry
   B. Worried
   C. Bitter
   D. Resigned

2. What does this letter reveal most about Isabel?
   A. It's hard for her to make new friends.
   B. She understands life outside her town.
   C. The factory closing led to lost jobs and wages.
   D. She feels stress due to all the changes.

3. Pretend you are Maya and write a reply to Isabel's letter. As Maya, explain what life is like now for you and your family, and how you are dealing with the stress of moving.

National Education Standards
Math: Data Analysis and Probability
Language Arts: NCTE 1, NCTE 3, NCTE 4

Standardized Test Practice

Standardized Test Practice Answers

Math Practice
1. B
2. A
3. C

Reading/Writing Practice
1. B
2. D
3. Answers will vary but should include details about Maya's life and how she is handling stressors associated with her parents losing their jobs and the family moving to a new town.

National Education Standards
Math: Data Analysis and Probability
Language Arts: NCTE 1, NCTE 3, NCTE 4
For the complete Math and Language Arts standards, visit glencoe.com.

Go Online

Online Study Tools
For more test practice, visit glencoe.com and complete the Online Quizzes for Chapter 4.

Test-Taking Tip

Answering Objective Test Questions
When students take objective tests, they should always read the questions carefully. Each question usually contains one or a few key words that make the question true or false or that define a term or missing word. Students should look for and try to identify these key words. When answering matching questions, they should take a few moments to look through the entire list of choices before selecting any answers. Then they should try to find key words in the definitions that determine which words are the correct choices. If they are unsure of some of the questions, they should first answer those that they are sure of. They may be able to answer the others after eliminating most of the choices.

Mental and Emotional Problems

Chapter 5 pages 112–135	Standards		Features
	National	**State/Local**	
	1.12.2, 1.12.8, 3.12.4, 3.12.5, 4.12.4, 8.12.1– 8.12.4		TIME HEALTH • What's On A Label, page 130
30 Min **Lesson 1** **Dealing with Anxiety and Depression** pages 114–117 **BIG Idea** Anxiety and depression are treatable mental health problems.	1.12.2, 1.12.5, 2.12.7, 2.12.9, 3.12.1, 3.12.2, 3.12.4, 3.12.5, 4.12.4, 5.12.1, 5.12.3, 6.12.2, 7.12.2, 7.12.3		*Health Skills* **Activity** • Recognizing Reliable Resources (*Assessing Information*), page 117 Out of Time
30 Min **Lesson 2** **Mental Disorders** pages 118–121 **BIG Idea** Gaining an understanding of mental health disorders builds insight and empathy.	1.12.2, 2.12.7, 2.12.9, 5.12.1, 5.12.3, 7.12.1, 7.12.2, 7.12.3		
30 Min **Lesson 3** **Suicide Prevention** pages 122–125 **BIG Idea** Professional intervention and support from friends and family can often help prevent suicide.	1.12.2, 2.12.7, 2.12.9, 5.12.1, 5.12.4, 7.12.1, 7.12.2, 7.12.3		*Real World* **CONNECTION** • Depression & Suicide, page 125 Out of Time
30 Min **Lesson 4** **Getting Help** pages 126–129 **BIG Idea** Mental health professionals and related agencies provide treatment and support for people with mental health problems.	1.12.1, 1.12.5, 1.12.7, 2.12.3, 2.12.5, 2.12.7, 2.12.9, 3.12.1, 3.12.2, 3.12.4, 4.12.1, 4.12.4		

Key to Ability Levels

Teaching Strategies and activities have been coded for ability level and appropriateness.

AL Activities for students working above grade level

OL Activities for students working on grade level

BL Activities for students working below grade level

EL Activities for English Learners

Chapter 5 Planning Guide

Resources	Lesson Assessment	Technology
Student Activity Workbook TEACH **FAST FILE RESOURCES** Vocabulary Practice TEACH Health Labs EXTEND	Chapter 5 Review Chapter 5 Assessment Standardized Test Practice *ExamView® Assessment Suite* CD-ROM	**Teaching Tools:** *TeacherWorks™* Plus DVD *StudentWorks™* Plus DVD *ExamView® Assessment Suite* CD-ROM Transparency Fitness DVD PowerPoint® DVD Health eSpotlight Video Series DVD
FAST FILE RESOURCES Reading Strategies Activity TEACH Reteaching Activity REVIEW Enrichment Activity EXTEND Health Skills Practice TEACH	Lesson 1 Assessment, page 117 📁 Lesson 1 Quiz *Fast File* *ExamView® Assessment Suite* CD-ROM	**Web-Based Resources:** **Go Online** glencoe.com • Health Podcast Activities • Audio Chapter Summaries (English/Spanish) • Interactive Health Tutor • Health Skills Activities • Vocabulary PuzzleMaker • Parent Letters (English/Spanish) • Lesson Plans • Health Inventories • Online Quizzes • Study-to-Go • Unit Web Projects • Student Web Activities • Fitness Zone Activities
FAST FILE RESOURCES Reading Strategies Activity TEACH Reteaching Activity REVIEW Enrichment Activity EXTEND Health Skills Practice TEACH	Lesson 2 Assessment, page 121 📁 Lesson 2 Quiz *Fast File* *ExamView® Assessment Suite* CD-ROM	
FAST FILE RESOURCES Reading Strategies Activity TEACH Reteaching Activity REVIEW Enrichment Activity EXTEND Health Skills Practice TEACH	Lesson 3 Assessment, page 125 📁 Lesson 3 Quiz *Fast File* *ExamView® Assessment Suite* CD-ROM	
FAST FILE RESOURCES Reading Strategies Activity TEACH Reteaching Activity REVIEW Enrichment Activity EXTEND Health Skills Practice TEACH	Lesson 4 Assessment, page 129 📁 Lesson 4 Quiz *Fast File* *ExamView® Assessment Suite* CD-ROM	

This is the student's backpack solution.

Includes:
- complete Interactive Student Edition
- full audio of English text and Spanish chapter summaries
- allows students to record assignments and track grades.
- links to online activities and additional student resources
- access to all student worksheets and workbooks

Dinah Zike Foldables® Chapter Activity

FOLDABLES® Study Organizer

Refer to the *Dinah Zike Reading and Study Skills for Glencoe Health.* Have students create a six-tab Foldable to record notes on the six types of mental disorders in Lesson 2. Under each tab, they should write definitions and important details about the mental disorder.

Key to Symbols

 Transparencies

 CD-ROM

 glencoe.com

📁 Print Resources

REVIEW activities to review or reinforce content

TEACH activities to teach basic concepts

EXTEND activities to extend or enrich lesson content

Mental and Emotional Problems

Chapter Overview

Chapter 5 focuses on mental and emotional problems, including suicide. It identifies risk factors and warning signs of mental health problems and describes how the problems can be treated.

Lesson 1

Anxiety and depression are two of the most common mental health problems. Stress-management techniques can help people cope with day-to-day anxiety. Depression can be treated by a mental health professional.

Lesson 2

Mental disorders are diseases that can be diagnosed and treated. The disorders are classified into several types, based on their symptoms.

Lesson 3

Certain factors increase the risk of suicide, and warning signs may indicate that a person is considering suicide. Professional help and support from friends and family can often prevent suicide.

Lesson 4

Many types of mental health professionals, agencies, and treatments are available to help people with mental health problems.

▶ **Activating Prior Knowledge**

Call on volunteers to answer the question. (Sample answer: Creating art might help an individual express emotions that are difficult to talk about.)

CHAPTER **5**

Mental and Emotional Problems

Lesson 1

Dealing with Anxiety and Depression

BIG Idea *Anxiety and depression are treatable mental health problems.*

Lesson 2

Mental Disorders

BIG Idea *Gaining an understanding of mental health disorders builds insight and empathy.*

Lesson 3

Suicide Prevention

BIG Idea *Professional intervention and support from friends and family can often help prevent suicide.*

Lesson 4

Getting Help

BIG Idea *Mental health professionals and related agencies provide treatment and support for people with mental health problems.*

Activating Prior Knowledge

Using Visuals Some mental health professionals recommend art therapy as one strategy for coping with problems. Why do you think creating art might help an individual deal with difficult emotions?

112

Universal Access

Differentiated Learning **Glencoe provides teacher support and student materials for all learners in the health classroom.**

- Chapter Summaries in English and Spanish are available online at **glencoe.com**.

- *Fast Files* and related worksheets support reluctant readers.

- Universal Access strategies throughout the Teacher Wraparound Edition and *Fast Files* help you present materials for gifted students, at-risk students, physically impaired students, and those with behavior disorders or learning disabilities.

Chapter Launchers

Health in Action

Discuss the BIG Ideas

Before beginning this chapter, think about how you would answer these questions:

▸ What are some reasons that teens might feel anxiety?

▸ What mental health disorders can you name?

▸ What are some sources of help for people with mental health disorders?

Watch the *Health eSpotlight* Video Series

Signs of Trouble

If a friend was suffering from depression or suicidal thoughts, what would you do?

Assess Your Health

Go Online

Visit glencoe.com and complete the Health Inventory for Chapter 5.

Chapter Launchers

Health in Action

Discuss the BIG Ideas

Assign this activity before students read the chapter. Explain that the purpose of the questions is to help students assess what they already know about mental and emotional problems.

Health eSpotlight
Video Series

 Signs of Trouble

Before Viewing the Video

Ask Students: *How might someone act who is feeling depressed?* (Sample answer: The person might not participate in usual activities or show excitement about upcoming events.)

Go Online

Have students go to **glencoe.com** and take the Health Inventory for Chapter 5.

Chapter Skills

Reading Skills
- Reviewing Facts and Vocabulary, pp. 117, 121, 125, 129
- Reading/Writing Practice, p. 135

Vocabulary
- New Vocabulary, pp. 114, 118, 122, 126
- Reviewing Facts and Vocabulary, pp. 117, 121, 125, 129

BIG Idea

Providing treatment and support to people with mental and emotional problems may help prevent suicide and help them live happy, productive lives.

Health Skills
- Health Skills Activity, p. 117
- Applying Health Skills, pp. 117, 121, 125, 129

Writing Skills
- Real World Connection, p. 125
- Writing Critically, pp. 117, 121, 125, 129
- Reading/Writing Practice, p. 135

113

LESSON 1

Dealing with Anxiety and Depression

① FOCUS

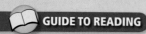

GUIDE TO READING

BIG Idea Mental health problems such as anxiety and depression can be treated.
Ask Students: *What are some common mental health problems?* (Sample answer: depression)

Before You Read

Outline Students' outlines will vary in the details, though the first and second levels of the outline should match the headings and subheadings of the lesson.

Main Idea

Understanding Anxiety It is normal to occasionally react to stress with anxiety. **Ask Students:** *What is anxiety?* (Sample answers: worry, fear) *What situations in your life have caused you to feel anxiety?* (Answers will vary.)

Real Life Issues

Before students start writing, help them develop empathy for Tony. **Ask Students:** *How would you feel if you were Tony?* (Sample answers: worried, upset) Call on a few students to share their completed dialogues with the class.

LESSON 1

GUIDE TO READING

BIG Idea *Anxiety and depression are treatable mental health problems.*

Before You Read

Create an Outline. Look through the lesson to find the headings and subheadings. Write down the headings to make an outline. As you read, fill in details beneath each heading or subheading.

```
I.
   A.
      1.
      2.
   B.
II.
```

New Vocabulary
▶ anxiety (p. 114)
▶ depression (p. 115)
▶ apathy (p. 116)

Review Vocabulary
▶ emotions (Ch.3, L.3)

Dealing with Anxiety and Depression

Real Life Issues

Difficult Times. Tony's parents are separating. He's not surprised because they have been arguing a lot lately. However, he still feels hurt by their decision. Tony is also worried about how his family will get by financially without both of his parents living at home. The constant feelings of sadness and uncertainty are starting to affect other aspects of his life. Tony is tired all the time, has withdrawn from his friends, and has lost his appetite. All he wants to do is stay home alone and sleep.

Writing *Write a dialogue between you and Tony, as if you were Tony's friend. In your conversation, show him empathy and support during this difficult time. What advice might you give him?*

Understanding Anxiety

Main Idea Occasional anxiety is a normal, manageable reaction to many short-term, stressful situations.

Experiencing difficult emotions is a normal part of life. They occur for a variety of reasons, including hormonal changes, relationship issues, grief, or stress. A common feeling is **anxiety**, *the condition of feeling uneasy or worried about what may happen.* You may, for example, feel anxious about an important class presentation.

Occasional anxiety is a natural response to life events. Brief feelings of worry, insecurity, fear, self-consciousness, or even panic are common responses to stress. Usually, once the stressful situation is over, so is the anxiety it created.

Teens Want to Know

How Can I Tell If My Anxiety Is Normal? While occasional anxiety about worrisome events or situations is normal, excessive anxiety that interferes with daily life may indicate an anxiety disorder that needs treatment. Teens should seek help if anxiety causes them to

• have feelings of fear or worry most of the time.

• be easily distracted and have difficulty concentrating.

• have muscle tension and be unable to relax.

• have changes in appetite and trouble falling asleep.

• experience physical symptoms such as headache or upset stomach.

■ **Figure 5.1** Depression can cause a person to withdraw and suffer alone. *Why might this symptom be dangerous?*

Coping with Anxiety

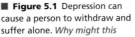

Knowing that anxiety is common doesn't make it easier to manage. Think about the situations that have caused you to be anxious in the past. What can you do in the future to plan ahead so that stress will not build and cause anxiety. The stress-management techniques described in Chapter 4 can help reduce anxiety. Some people use substances such as alcohol or drugs to escape from anxiety. These substances produce a temporary, false sense of relaxation, but can cause other physical, mental/emotional, social, or legal problems.

Understanding Depression

Main Idea Depression can linger or be severe enough to disrupt daily activities.

Depression is *a prolonged feeling of helplessness, hopelessness, and sadness.* Feelings of sadness affect everyone, but depression usually lasts longer and may produce symptoms that do not go away over time. Depression is a serious condition that may **require** medical help. Almost 15 percent of all teens will display some signs of depression. It's one of the most common mental health concerns among teens. Types of depression include *major depression,* which is intense and can last for weeks or months. *Mild depression* has less severe symptoms, but can last for years. *Adjustment disorder* is a reaction to a specific life event. For example, a person may have trouble reaching closure when grieving.

✓ READING CHECK

Identify What is the benefit of using stress management techniques to manage anxiety?

G⊘ Online

))) Listen to the Health Podcast, *The Facts About Depression,* at glencoe.com

Academic Vocabulary

require *(verb):* to demand as necessary

Lesson 1 Dealing with Anxiety and Depression **115**

Writing Strategy

Descriptive Writing Refer students to the warning signs of depression in **Figure 5.2** on page 116. After students read the warning signs, have them write a letter to a friend who has the behavior of a person who shows at least five of the signs. Encour-age students to proofread and edit their letters. Ask students what they would do if the people described were people they knew. Remind students that people with depression should be advised to seek help.

---

❷ TEACH

HS Health Skills Practice

Practicing Healthful Behaviors Explain that stress is a common cause of anxiety, so stress-management techniques can help people cope with anxiety. Ask students to reread the three stress-management techniques on page 98 of Chapter 4. Then call on volunteers to state specific ways to put each technique into practice. BL EL

G⊘ Online

Remind students to visit glencoe.com and listen to the podcast, *The Facts About Depression.*

Main Idea

Understanding Depression
Depression is a prolonged feeling that can interfere with daily life.
Ask Students: *What are some symptoms of depression?* (Sample answers: Feeling sad all the time; crying a lot; unable to concentrate)

AL Active Learning

Other Types of Depression
Explain that there are other types of depression, in addition to the types described in this lesson. They include cyclothymia, atypical depression, postpartum depression, seasonal affective disorder, and premenstrual dysphoric disorder. Have students learn about these other types of depression and create a fact sheet to summarize what they learn. Display their fact sheets in the classroom. OL

Health Skills — Activity

Accessing Information: Recognizing Reliable Resources

NHES Standard 3 Students will demonstrate the ability to access valid information and products and services to enhance health.

Objectives

- Identify sources of information about depression and its treatment.
- Evaluate the reliability of the information using specific criteria.

Teaching Strategies

- Encourage students to find a variety of information sources, such as Web sites, articles, and books.
- Call on volunteers to share some of the information that they think is most reliable. Then ask them to explain why they think the information is reliable.

Assessment

Using this list, student work should provide comprehensive evidence of the following criteria to achieve the highest score:

√ Identifies three or more sources of relevant information

√ Evaluates the reliability of the information according to all three criteria

READING CHECK

Answer A trusted adult, such as a parent, teacher, or school counselor

---

Figure 5.2 — Warning Signs of Depression

Five or more of these symptoms must persist for two or more weeks before a diagnosis of major depression is indicated.

- Persistent sad or irritable mood
- Loss of interest in activities once enjoyed
- Significant change in appetite or body weight
- Difficulty sleeping or oversleeping
- Physical signs of nervousness
- Loss of energy
- Feelings of worthlessness or inappropriate guilt
- Difficulty concentrating
- Recurrent thoughts of death or suicide

Causes and Effects of Depression

Depression can be caused by physical, psychological, or social reasons. A medical condition or illness may cause depression. It may also be caused by psychological reasons, such as surviving a traumatic life event. Finally, social or environmental factors, such as living in poverty or in a physically or emotionally harmful environment may cause depression. **Figure 5.2** lists warning signs of depression. Other symptoms include the following:

- **Changes in thinking.** People who are depressed may have trouble concentrating and making decisions. They may have self-destructive thoughts.
- **Changes in feelings.** People who are depressed may experience **apathy,** or *a lack of strong feeling, interest, or concern.* They may not feel pleasure in things they once enjoyed. They may be sad, or irritable and angry.
- **Changes in behavior.** People with depression may become emotional, and they may begin eating too little or too much. The person may have trouble sleeping and may seem tired. The person might also neglect basic hygiene and withdraw from social situations.

Getting Help for Depression

Main Idea Depression is a treatable illness.

If you recognize signs of depression in yourself or a friend, discuss your concerns with a trusted adult. Depression is serious, but it is treatable. If a friend asks you not to tell anyone that he or she is depressed, it's okay to break that promise. Health professionals can develop a plan to treat depression that may include taking medication, making changes in the home or school environment, or counseling. Treating depression takes time, persistence, and patience.

Go Online

Visit glencoe.com and complete the Student Web Activity on recognizing the signs of depression, and dealing with anxiety.

READING CHECK

Identify Who can a depressed teen ask for help?

More About...

Depression in Teens Between 15 and 20 percent of teens in the U.S. are diagnosed with at least one episode of serious depression during adolescence, and the rate is twice as high in girls as it is in boys. Because depression goes undiagnosed in many teens, the percentage of teens who actually suffer from depression is likely to be considerably higher. Teens with depression are at greater risk for other mental health problems, including anxiety disorders and eating disorders, as well as for further bouts of depression during adulthood.

Health Skills Activity
Accessing Information

Recognizing Reliable Resources

"Hey, Con, how's it going?" Devin asked his close friend Connor as they met up in the hallway. Connor smiled slightly at Devin. "I'm feeling better, thanks," he replied. "I met with my family doctor last week. He was concerned that I was depressed."

"Yeah?" Devin looked interested. "What did he say?"

"He prescribed some medication, and I'm meeting with a mental health specialist tomorrow. This doctor does counseling, so I may be seeing him regularly for a while."

"Good thing you talked to your doctor," said Devin, patting Connor on the shoulder. "See you later."

Still concerned, Devin decided to learn more about depression. He also wanted to find out if there was anything he could do—or shouldn't do—to help his buddy.

Writing List sources of information for depression and its treatment that Devin might use to help Connor. Evaluate the information using the criteria listed below.

1. What are the qualifications of the authors?
2. Is the material backed by a nationally recognized and respected mental health organization?
3. Can the information be confirmed by other sources?

LESSON 1 ASSESSMENT

After You Read

Reviewing Facts and Vocabulary
1. Define the term *anxiety*.
2. What are the causes of depression?
3. Describe changes in thinking that might be effects of depression.

Thinking Critically
4. **Analyze.** Explain the difference between "feeling down or depressed" and "having depression." Provide examples to show the difference.
5. **Synthesize.** If you believe a friend might be depressed, what can you do to help?

Applying Health Skills
6. **Analyzing Influences.** Divide a sheet of paper into three columns. Label the columns "Family," "Friends," and "School." Use this chart to describe how depression can affect each aspect of your life.

Writing Critically
7. **Expository.** Write a paragraph discussing why it is important for someone with depression to get professional help.

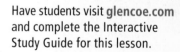

Visit **glencoe.com** and complete the Interactive Study Guide for this lesson.

Lesson 1 Dealing with Anxiety and Depression **117**

 ASSESS/ CLOSE

Assessment Resources

📁 **FAST FILE ACTIVITIES**
Lesson 1 Quiz

💿 *ExamView Assessment Suite* CD-ROM

Visit glencoe.com for:
Online Quizzes
Online Learning Center

Progress Monitoring

Reteaching
Ask students to write a question they have about the lesson. Collect the questions and read them to the class. Call on volunteers to answer the questions.

Enrichment
Have pairs of students write and present skits in which a teen shows signs of depression and a friend offers support and advice.

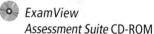

Have students visit **glencoe.com** and complete the Interactive Study Guide for this lesson.

LESSON 1 ASSESSMENT ANSWERS

1. The condition of feeling uneasy or worried about what may happen
2. Physical reasons such as heredity, psychological reasons such as surviving a traumatic event, and environmental factors such as living in poverty
3. Difficulty concentrating and making decisions, forgetfulness, self-critical or self-destructive thoughts
4. "Feeling down" means having feelings of sadness that one can manage. "Having depression" means having a serious illness that requires professional help.
5. Sample answer: I could discuss my concerns with a trusted adult or encourage the person to seek professional help.
6. Charts will vary for each student.
7. Paragraphs will vary but should show that students recognize the importance of getting professional help for depression.

Mental Disorders

Mental Disorders

 ## ① FOCUS

 **GUIDE TO READING**

BIG Idea Learning about mental disorders increases empathy for people with mental health problems. **Ask Students:** *Based on what you learned about depression in Lesson 1, what do you know about mental disorders?* (Sample answers: They may have several causes; they can be treated.)

Before You Read

Vocabulary Cards Students should create a vocabulary card for each of the five new vocabulary terms in the lesson.

Main Idea

Understanding Mental Disorders Mental disorders require diagnosis and treatment. **Ask Students:** *Why do people tend to think of mental disorders differently than they think of other types of illness?* (Sample answer: They know less about mental disorders.)

Real Life Issues

Have students read the scenario. **Ask Students:** *Why do some people respond as Kim did toward people with mental illness?* (Sample answer: They don't understand mental illness.)

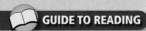 **LESSON 2**

 **GUIDE TO READING**

BIG Idea *Gaining an understanding of mental health disorders builds insight and empathy.*

Before You Read

Create Vocabulary Cards. Write each new vocabulary term on a separate note card. For each term, write a definition based on your current knowledge. As you read, fill in additional information related to each item.

> Mental Disorder

New Vocabulary

▸ mental disorder (p. 118)
▸ stigma (p. 118)
▸ anxiety disorder (p. 119)
▸ mood disorder (p. 120)
▸ conduct disorder (p. 121)

Mental Disorders

Real Life Issues ....

Perceptions of Mental Problems. Jan was in study hall, sitting next to her friend Kim. Kim looks over at a classmate who is sitting by himself. "Brady is really weird," Kim whispers. "He's always alone, and he never talks to anyone. Once I even saw him mumbling to himself. He really creeps me out." Jan knows Brady is coping with some difficult issues and thinks Kim is being insensitive.

Writing *If you were Jan, how would you respond? Write a dialogue in which Jan asks that Kim be more respectful of people showing symptoms of mental problems.*

Understanding Mental Disorders

Main Idea Mental disorders are medical conditions that require diagnosis and treatment.

   Each year, approximately 57.7 million people in the United States are affected by some form of **mental disorder**—*an illness of the mind that can affect the thoughts, feelings, and behaviors of a person, preventing him or her from leading a happy, healthful, and productive life.* That's about one in every four Americans. Many do not seek treatment because they feel embarrassed or ashamed. Others worry about the stigma associated with mental disorders. A **stigma** is *a mark of shame or disapproval that results in an individual being shunned or rejected by others.*

   Many people don't understand that mental disorders are medical conditions, and require diagnosis and treatment just like any physical illness or injury. Learning about mental and emotional problems will help erase the stigma associated with these disorders, and will help encourage people to seek medical help early. Many times, mental and emotional problems cannot be solved without professional help.

Myths & Reality

The Truth About Mental Disorders

Myth: Having a mental disorder means that you are "crazy."

Fact: Mental disorders can affect anyone, and having one does not make you "crazy."

Myth: Having a mental disorder means that you are dangerous to others.

Fact: People with mental disorders are less dangerous than the average person without mental illness.

Myth: Mental disorders cannot be cured.

Fact: With treatment, many people with mental disorders can have a full recovery.

Types of Mental Disorders

Main Idea Mental disorders can be identified by their symptoms.

Mental disorders are medical conditions that can begin as early as childhood. Many times, these problems require help from health professionals.

Anxiety Disorders

An **anxiety disorder** is *a condition in which real or imagined fears are difficult to control.* It is one of the most common mental health problems among children and teens. Reports have shown that as many as 13 **percent** of children between ages 9 and 17 experience an anxiety disorder each year. People with anxiety disorders try to avoid situations that make them feel anxious or fearful. **Figure 5.3** describes five types of anxiety disorders.

Impulse Control Disorders

People with impulse control disorders cannot resist the urge to hurt themselves or others. Impulse control disorders may begin in childhood or the teen years, and can continue into adulthood. People with this disorder may cause physical harm to themselves and others. They may also cause financial harm by overspending and gambling. People with impulse control disorder may also behave in ways that cause them to lose friends. **Figure 5.4** on page 120 provides examples of these disorders.

Academic Vocabulary

percent *(noun):* one part in a hundred

G Online

Go to glencoe.com and complete the Student Web Activity on social phobia and overcoming the fear of social situations.

Figure 5.3	Anxiety Disorders
Phobia	A strong, irrational fear of something specific, such as heights or social situations.
Obsessive-Compulsive Disorder	Persistent thoughts, fears, or urges (obsessions) leading to uncontrollable repetitive behaviors (compulsions). For example, the fear of germs leads to constant hand washing.
Panic Disorder	Attacks of sudden, unexplained feelings of terror. "Panic attacks" are accompanied by trembling, increased heart rate, shortness of breath, or dizziness.
Post-Traumatic Stress Disorder (PTSD)	A condition that may develop after exposure to a terrifying event. Symptoms include flashbacks, nightmares, emotional numbness, guilt, sleeplessness, and problems concentrating.
Generalized Anxiety Disorder (GAD)	Exaggerated worry and tension for no reason. People with GAD startle easily and have difficulty concentrating, relaxing, and sleeping.

Lesson 2   Mental Disorders   **119**

Reading Strategy

Using Graphic Organizers Information may be easier for students to grasp if they create graphic organizers to summarize important points and show relationships among concepts. Work with students to create a graphic organizer, such as a compare/contrast table or a concept map, to show how mental disorders are classified into different types. The graphic organizer should also include symptoms and examples of each type of mental disorder. Urge students to save their completed graphic organizers to use for reviewing lesson content.

② TEACH

Main Idea

Types of Mental Disorders Mental disorders are diagnosed by their symptoms. **Ask Students:** *What symptoms might indicate that a person is depressed? That a person has anxiety?* (Sample answers: Sadness, lack of energy, and apathy; worry, fear, and panic)

Academic Vocabulary

Percent ask a volunteer to read the definition of the word percent to the class. Pose the following question to students: What is 10 percent of 1,000? *(100)* Ask students to come up with another question using the word percent.

U Universal Access

Using Definitions Have students read the definition of *anxiety disorder.* Then have them use the definition to explain how an anxiety disorder is different from temporary sadness. (An anxiety disorder interferes with everyday living.) **BL** **EL**

C Critical Thinking

Inferring After students read about post-traumatic stress disorder, ask them to identify specific events that occurred during their lifetime that are likely to have caused PTSD in many of the events' survivors. (Sample answers: Hurricane Katrina, the Iraq War) **OL**

HS Health Skills Practice

Accessing Information Have students learn more about one of the impulse control disorders listed in **Figure 5.4**. Ask them to find three reliable sources that provide consistent information on the disorder's symptoms, causes, and treatment. Call on volunteers to share their information and sources and also to explain why they think the sources are reliable. OL AL

C Critical Thinking

Analyzing Challenge students to compare and contrast anorexia nervosa with bulimia. (Both are eating disorders. Anorexia is when an individual starves him or herself. Bulimia is when a person eats and then purges.) OL

Caption Answer

Figure 5.5 Sample answer: They can show concern and offer assistance to one another.

Figure 5.4	Impulse Control Disorders
Kleptomania	Unplanned theft of objects
Cutting	Repetitive cutting on parts of the body that can be hidden
Pyromania	Setting fires to feel pleasure or release tension
Excessive Gambling	Continuing to gamble despite heavy losses
Compulsive Shopping	Spending money on items that you can't afford and don't need

HS

Eating Disorders

Eating disorders commonly occur during the teen years. As teens reach puberty, body changes and media images may cause some teens to put pressure on themselves to look a certain way. These teens may develop symptoms of anorexia nervosa, bulimia nervosa, or binge eating disorder. Eating disorders are more common among girls, but can affect boys too. Eating disorders can lead to unhealthful weight loss and death. You will learn more about eating disorders in Chapter 11.

C

Mood Disorders

A **mood disorder** is *an illness that involves mood extremes that interfere with everyday living.* These extremes are more severe than the normal highs and lows everyone experiences. Mood disorders include depression and bipolar disorder. *Bipolar disorder*, or manic-depressive disorder, is marked by extreme mood changes, energy levels, and behavior.

■ **Figure 5.5** Post-traumatic stress disorder may occur in the aftermath of a crisis. *What can community members do to support one another during a crisis?*

Health Literacy

Diagnosing Mental Disorders *The Diagnostic and Statistical Manual of Mental Disorders*, Fourth Edition, or DSM-IV, is the basis of most psychiatric diagnoses. It allows mental health professionals to diagnose and rate patients according to five axes, or dimensions, of mental illness. Axis 1 includes most psychiatric disorders, such as mood disorders, anxiety disorders, and schizophrenia. Axis 2 includes developmental disorders, such as autism and personality disorders. Axis 3 refers to physical conditions that can impact psychiatric disorders. Axis 5 refers to psychosocial stressors that can impair mental and emotional functioning. Axis 5 shows how the other four axes affect the person's life.

Conduct Disorder

Children and teens with **conduct disorder** engage in *patterns of behavior in which the rights of others or basic social rules are violated.* Examples include stealing, cruelty, lying, aggression, violence, truancy, arson, and vandalism. Treatment includes learning to adapt to the demands of everyday life.

Schizophrenia

Schizophrenia (skit-suh-FREE-nee-uh) is a mental disorder in which a person loses contact with reality. Symptoms include delusions, hallucinations, and thought disorders. Schizophrenia affects about one percent of the population. The disease affects both men and women.

People with this disorder behave unpredictably. Professional help and medication are needed to treat the illness successfully.

Personality Disorders

Teens with personality disorders are unable to regulate their emotions. They may feel distressed in social situations or may behave in ways that are distressing to others. The cause of personality disorder is unknown.

 **READING CHECK**

List What are examples of conduct disorder?

 LESSON 2 **ASSESSMENT**

After You Read

Reviewing Facts and Vocabulary

1. Define the term *stigma*. How can a stigma affect your health?
2. Identify the five types of anxiety disorders.
3. Which mental disorder can cause a person to have hallucinations?

Thinking Critically

4. **Evaluate.** Explain why mental disorders should be viewed like any other physical illness. Why is it important not to stigmatize someone with a mental disorder?
5. **Analyze.** Why are eating disorders both a mental health problem and a physical health problem?

Applying Health Skills

6. **Advocacy.** Teens suffering from mental disorders often feel confused, isolated, scared, or ashamed. Create a poster promoting awareness of and empathy toward mental illnesses. Focus on specific ways to be supportive, patient, and understanding.

Writing Critically

7. **Expository.** Choose one of the mental disorders you read about in this lesson. Explain why you chose this particular disorder, and how you would learn more about it

G⊙ Online

Visit **glencoe.com** and complete the Interactive Study Guide for this lesson.

Lesson 2 Mental Disorders **121**

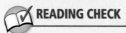 **READING CHECK**

Answer Stealing, cruelty, lying, aggression, violence, truancy, arson, and vandalism

③ ASSESS/ CLOSE

Assessment Resources

📁 *FAST FILE* **ACTIVITIES**
Lesson 2 Quiz

💿 *ExamView Assessment Suite* CD-ROM

Visit glencoe.com for:
Online Quizzes
Online Learning Center

Progress Monitoring

Reteaching
Across the top of the board, write the seven types of mental disorders described in the lesson. Call on students to list specific examples under each type of mental disorder.

Enrichment
Have students use the most recent edition of the *Diagnostic and Statistical Manual of Mental Disorders* to learn about a type of mental disorder that is not covered in the lesson. Ask students to share what they learn in an oral report.

G⊙ Online

Have students visit **glencoe.com** and complete the Interactive Study Guide for this lesson.

LESSON 2 ASSESSMENT ANSWERS

1. Mark of shame or disapproval resulting in a person being shunned or rejected by others
2. Phobia, obsessive-compulsive disorder, panic disorder, post-traumatic stress disorder, generalized anxiety disorder
3. Major depression, dysthymia, adjustment disorder
4. Mental disorders are medical conditions that require diagnosis and treatment just like any physical illness.
5. Eating disorders are mental disorders that can cause serious physical complications.
6. Posters will vary.
7. Answers will vary depending on the mental disorders students choose.

Suicide Prevention

1 FOCUS

GUIDE TO READING

BIG Idea Professional help and support from family and friends may prevent suicide.
Ask Students: *How might the support of family and friends help prevent suicide?* (Sample answer: It might help a suicidal person realize that he or she is loved and valued.)

Before You Read

K-W-L Chart Students' K-W-L charts will vary.

Main Idea

Knowing the Facts About Suicide Certain risk factors increase thoughts of suicide and suicide attempts. **Ask Students:** *What events or situations might increase the risk of suicide?* (Sample answers: Having severe depression; losing a loved one; abusing drugs)

Real Life Issues ·············

Have students read the scenario. **Ask Students:** *What might indicate that Ryan is thinking about suicide?* (He seems depressed, seems not to care about anything anymore, and says that he just wants to get away from it all.)

122

GUIDE TO READING

BIG Idea *Professional intervention and support from friends and family can often help prevent suicide.*

Before You Read

Create a K-W-L Chart. Make a three-column chart. In the first column, list what you **k**now about the prevention of suicide. In the second column, list what you **w**ant to know about the topic. As you read, use the third column to summarize what you **l**earned.

K	W	L

New Vocabulary

▸ alienation (p. 122)
▸ suicide (p. 122)
▸ cluster suicides (p.123)

Suicide Prevention

Real Life Issues ··························

Helping a Friend. Nick's friend Ryan has been feeling down lately. Even though Ryan is a good student, he failed several important tests. As a result, he was suspended from the baseball team. To make matters worse, his girlfriend broke up with him. To Nick, Ryan seems depressed all the time and doesn't care about anything anymore. When Nick tries to talk with him, Ryan says he just wants to get away from it all.

Writing *Write a brief paragraph describing how you might respond to Ryan if you were in Nick's position.*

Knowing the Facts About Suicide

Main Idea Certain risk factors increase thoughts of suicide and suicide attempts.

Most people learn to manage stress in a healthful way. For some people, however, stress can cause **alienation**, *feeling isolated and separated from everyone else.* These people may be unable to cope with difficult life experiences. They may lack the support from family and friends, and be unable to access community resources for help. They may seek to escape from the pain and consider ending their lives.

Suicide is *the act of intentionally taking one's own life.* It is the third leading cause of death for teens ages 15 to 19. Each year, 17 percent of all teens in this age group will consider suicide. More than half will actually attempt it.

Suicide Risk Factors

Among those who commit suicide, two risk factors are common. More than 90 percent are suffering from depression or another mental disorder, or have a history of abusing alcohol or other drugs. Sometimes, both risk factors are present.

122   Chapter 5   Mental and Emotional Problems

Myths & Reality

Dangerous Myths About Suicide

Myth: People who talk about suicide won't really attempt it.

Fact: People who talk about suicide are usually considering it and should be taken seriously.

Myth: When people are determined to commit suicide, nothing can stop them.

Fact: Getting help for suicidal people can prevent them from taking their lives.

Myth: Talking about suicide may give someone the idea to attempt suicide.

Fact: Talking about suicide and where to go for help may help prevent someone from attempting suicide.

■ **Figure 5.6** The Centers for Disease Control and Prevention has asked the media to report fewer details about suicide attempts. *How might this effort help reduce the number of suicides?*

Caption Answer

Figure 5.6 Fewer details in the media might decrease the risk of cluster suicides, as these suicides sometimes occur when teens learn about other teen suicides.

② TEACH

R Reading Strategy

Using Cluster Charts On the board, draw six circles surrounding an inner circle labeled "Suicide." Draw arrows from the six circles pointing at the inner circle. Call on students to fill in the surrounding circles with suicide risk factors from the text. Discuss why each factor increases the chances of a person attempting suicide. **BL**

R Some people use alcohol or other drugs to relieve their depression. Alcohol and drugs, however, have a depressant effect and lower one's inhibitions, making self-destructive behavior more likely. These people usually have more than one risk factor, such as a stressful situation or loss; previous suicide attempts; family history of mental disorders, substance abuse, or suicide; and access to guns.

C Exposure to other teens who have died by suicide is a risk factor that can lead to **cluster suicides**, *a series of suicides occurring within a short period of time and involving several people in the same school or community.* Cluster suicides account for about 5 percent of all teen suicides. Some cluster suicides result from pacts made among peers. In other cluster suicides, the teens may not know one another, but may share an environmental stressor, such as a tragic event in their school or community. Some teens may learn of suicides through the news media.

☑ **READING CHECK**

Describe What are some behaviors that might indicate a person is thinking about suicide?

☑ **READING CHECK**

Answer Behaviors include warnings listed in **Figure 5.7**.

Strategies to Prevent Suicide

Main Idea Recognizing the signs of suicide may help prevent it.

Most suicidal thoughts, behaviors, and actions are expressions of extreme distress. The warning signs of suicide are described in **Figure 5.7** on page 124. A person **displaying** only a few signs may not necessarily be considering suicide. When someone talks about committing suicide—whether it's done in a serious, casual, or even humorous way—*take it seriously.* Any discussion or suggestion about suicide requires immediate attention. Never agree to keep a secret if a friend says he or she is considering suicide. Tell an adult without delay.

Academic Vocabulary

display *(verb):* to make evident

C Critical Thinking

Deducing After students read about cluster suicides and why they occur, challenge the class to deduce ways to lower the risk of cluster suicides. (Sample answers: Help teens deal with shared environmental stressors; limit media coverage of teen suicides.) **OL AL**

Lesson 3 Suicide Prevention **123**

Teacher to Teacher

Marsha Morton • Campbell County High School, Jacksboro, TN

Talking About Suicide When teaching suicide prevention, I use the Jason Foundation program. It is a kit that includes a video and cooperative learning activities based on suicide prevention. The program was developed by Jason's father and brother after his suicide. I show my students the video, then divide them into six groups. Each group discusses a sheet of questions about a different person in the video. I have the students jot down their responses to share with the class. After about 10 minutes I read the questions and let each group give their responses. After the responses are given, we further discuss anything related to suicide that the students want to discuss.

Main Idea

Strategies to Prevent Suicide Suicide prevention depends on recognizing its warning signs. **Ask Students:** *What might tip you off that a friend is thinking about suicide?* (Sample answers: The friend might talk about committing suicide; the friend might act as though nothing matters anymore.)

HS Health Skills Practice

Advocacy Have groups of students create posters describing the warning signs of suicide and what to do if someone shows these signs. Tell students to make their posters eye-catching as well as informative. Display their posters throughout the school. **OL**

W Writing Support

Personal Writing Have students write a dialogue in which they provide support to a friend who is showing warning signs of suicide. In their dialogues, students should follow these steps: initiate a meaningful conversation, show support and ask questions, and try to persuade the friend to seek help. Ask volunteers to enact selected dialogues for the class. Call on others to explain how the support might help. **OL**

Caption Answer

Figures 5.8 They might help suicidal people see that there are other solutions to their problems and that they are not alone.

| Figure 5.7 | **Recognizing the Warning Signs of Suicide** |

The warning signs of suicide should be taken seriously. The more signs exhibited, the more likely it is that the person is thinking about suicide.

▶ Direct statements such as "I wish I were dead."

▶ Indirect statements such as "I can't take it anymore."

▶ Writing poems, song lyrics, or diary entries that deal with death

▶ Direct or indirect suicide threats

▶ An unusual obsession with death

▶ Withdrawal from friends

▶ Dramatic changes in personality, hygiene, or appearance

▶ Impulsive, irrational, or unusual behavior

▶ A sense of guilt, shame, or rejection; negative self-evaluation

▶ Deterioration in schoolwork or recreational performance

▶ Giving away personal belongings

▶ Substance abuse

▶ Complaints about physical symptoms, such as stomachaches, headaches, and fatigue

▶ Persistent boredom and indifference

▶ Violent actions, rebellious behavior, or running away

▶ Intolerance for praise or rewards

Sources: American Academy of Child and Adolescent Psychiatry; National Mental Health Association

READING CHECK

Describe What steps can you take to help someone who may be considering suicide?

■ **Figure 5.8** Suicide survivor support groups are available in most communities. *How might such support groups prevent suicides?*

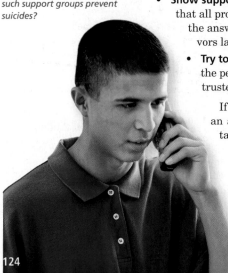

How You Can Help

People who are considering suicide often believe that their death will not matter to anyone. Showing empathy when talking with that person will let him or her know you are concerned. If someone you know may be considering suicide, that person needs help. Try the following:

- **Initiate a meaningful conversation.** Show interest, compassion, patience and understanding. Don't respond by saying "You really don't want to do that," or "Everyone feels sad sometimes."

- **Show support and ask questions.** Remind the person that all problems have solutions, and that suicide is *not* the answer. Tell your friend that most suicide survivors later express gratitude that they did not die.

- **Try to persuade the person to seek help.** Encourage the person to talk with a parent, counselor, or other trusted adult. Offer to go with him to get help.

If you believe a friend may be suicidal, tell an adult, and find out what steps the adult will take. If the adult doesn't seem to believe the threat is serious, talk to other adults until someone takes action. You can also contact community resources, such as a crisis center or suicide hotline. You will learn more about community resources in Lesson 4.

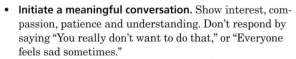

Home and Community

Community Suicide Prevention
Community programs have been developed to help reduce the risk of youth suicide. A nonprofit organization called Suicide Awareness Voices of Education™, or SAVE, has prepared a Community Action Kit that contains all the resources needed to start a suicide awareness and prevention program at the community level. SAVE can be contacted through its Web site. Work with other school personnel to urge community leaders to implement a community program, such as the SAVE program, to reduce the risk of youth suicides in your community.

Real World CONNECTION

Depression and Suicide

Despite the fact that depression is treatable, untreated depression is the leading cause of suicide. As you read in this lesson, people who consider suicide feel that they don't matter to others.

People who appear to have a mental health problem and may be considering suicide need to be encouraged repeatedly to seek help. Among adolescents, nearly 5 percent of 9- to 17-year-olds are believed to have experienced major depression. As many as 7 percent of teens who experience major depression may commit suicide in their young adult years.

What can you, as a friend, do to help prevent suicide? Should you tell someone that a friend has mentioned suicide, even if that friend asked you to keep the information private? What can people in the community do to help prevent suicides?

Activity Reading / Writing

In small groups, create a poster or a printed public service announcement urging teens who may be depressed and considering suicide to seek help. Your poster or public service announcement should provide the following information:

1. Make a clear statement encouraging teens to get help.
2. Remind them that all problems can be solved and that depression is treatable.
3. Encourage them to talk to a parent, teacher, or other trusted adult.
4. Provide contact information for local crisis centers and suicide hotlines.

Real World CONNECTION

Answer to Activity:

Posters and public service announcements will vary, but should urge suicidal teens to seek help and tell them where they can go for help.

3 ASSESS/CLOSE

Assessment Resources

📁 *FAST FILE* ACTIVITIES
Lesson 3 Quiz

💿 *ExamView*
Assessment Suite CD-ROM

Visit glencoe.com **for:**
Online Quizzes
Online Learning Center

LESSON 3 ASSESSMENT

After You Read

Reviewing Facts and Vocabulary

1. Define the term *alienation*.
2. What two risk factors have the strongest association with suicide?
3. Name five warning signs of suicide.

Thinking Critically

4. **Synthesize.** Make a list of three direct statements and three indirect statements that could indicate a teen is considering suicide.
5. **Explain.** Define the term *cluster suicides* and explain why they happen.

Applying Health Skills

6. **Decision Making.** Imagine that you have a friend who is always making negative comments about herself. Use the six steps of decision making to determine what actions to take.

Writing Critically

7. **Descriptive.** Write a note to a teen who has exhibited some suicidal warning behaviors. Use the suggestions listed in the lesson to help the teen rethink his or her situation.

 Online

Visit **glencoe.com** and complete the Interactive Study Guide for this lesson.

Lesson 3 Suicide Prevention **125**

Progress Monitoring

Reteaching

Call on students to go to the board and list warning signs of suicide. Ask students what they should do if someone they know shows these signs.

Enrichment

Ask students to interview a community mental health professional about how to help people who may be considering suicide. Students should summarize what they learn in a brief written report.

 Online

Have students visit **glencoe.com** and complete the Interactive Study Guide for this lesson.

LESSON 3 ASSESSMENT ANSWERS

1. Feeling isolated and separated from everyone else
2. Suffering from a mental disorder; having a history of abusing alcohol or other drugs
3. Any of the five warning signs listed in Figure 5.7
4. Direct statements: "I want to die." "I wish I were dead." "I don't want to live anymore." Indirect statements: "I can't take it anymore." "What's the use?"

5. Cluster suicides occur within a short period of time, involving people in the same school or community. Sometimes teens feel compelled to commit suicide after learning of other teen suicides or making a pact with other teens. Other cluster suicides occur when teens share a common stressor.
6. Answers will vary.
7. Answers will vary.

Getting Help

① FOCUS

GUIDE TO READING

BIG Idea Many professionals and agencies can help people with mental health problems. **Ask Students:** *What types of professionals help people with mental health problems?* (Sample answers: psychologists, counselors)

Before You Read

Cluster Chart Surrounding circles in students' cluster charts should be labeled with the types of mental health professionals listed in the lesson.

Main Idea

When Help Is Needed Recognizing that help is needed is the first step in getting help. **Ask Students:** *Why is it important to encourage teens with symptoms of mental health problems to get help?* (Sample answer: They may not seek help on their own. If left untreated, adolescent mental health problems can lead to problems in adulthood or even suicide.)

Real Life Issues

Have students read the scenario. **Ask Students:** *What is preventing Angie from seeking help?* (She doesn't know who to ask for help, and she's afraid of what the person will think of her.)

LESSON **4**

GUIDE TO READING

BIG Idea *Mental health professionals and related agencies provide treatment and support for people with mental health problems.*

Before You Read

Create a Cluster Chart. Draw a circle and label it "Getting Help." Use surrounding circles to identify professionals in the community who can help individuals with mental health problems. As you read, continue filling in the chart with more details.

New Vocabulary

▶ psychotherapy (p. 128)
▶ behavior therapy (p. 128)
▶ cognitive therapy (p. 129)
▶ family therapy (p. 129)
▶ group therapy (p. 129)
▶ drug therapy (p. 129)

Getting Help

Real Life Issues ....

No One to Turn To. Angie is desperate. She manages to get through each day, but inside she feels as though her life is spiraling out of control. She's confused and tries not to let her fears and frustrations show. Angie knows she needs help, but doesn't know who to ask. She's afraid of what the person will think of her.

Writing *Write a letter to Angie encouraging her to talk to a trusted adult and ask for help. Make sure the tone of your letter is understanding and considerate.*

When Help Is Needed

Main Idea The first step to getting help for a mental health problem is being aware that help is needed.

Many teens with mental health problems do not recognize the seriousness of their condition, or understand that help is available. In fact, most adult mental health disorders have their roots in untreated childhood and adolescent problems. More than half of suicidal youths had symptoms of a mental disorder for more than a year prior to their deaths.

Mental health influences every aspect of a person's life. No one should ever feel embarrassed to talk with someone about mental or emotional problems. Teens should seek help if they experience any of the following:

• Feeling trapped or worrying all the time
• Feelings that affect sleep, eating habits, schoolwork, job performance, or relationships
• Becoming involved with alcohol or other drugs
• Becoming increasingly aggressive, violent, or reckless

Often, friends and family are the first to recognize that a problem is affecting the teen's life and relationships. Their concern may encourage the individual to seek help.

Skills for the **21st** Century

Building Resiliency When teens increase their resiliency, they are better able to cope with the disappointments and other stressors in their lives. The American Psychological Association suggests that schools teach students the following resiliency skills:

• Have friends and be a friend.

• Believe in yourself and what you know and can do.

• Take charge of your behavior and actions.

• Look on the bright side.

• Set new goals and make a plan to reach them.

Overcoming the Stumbling Blocks

Main Idea The benefits of treatment encourage people to overcome a reluctance to get help.

Seeking help for mental health problems can be difficult. However, these problems are *not* easily managed without help. Initially, talking about problems may make a person feel more vulnerable. When asking for help, remember these facts:

- Asking for help is a sign of inner strength. It shows responsibility for one's own wellness.
- Serious disorders, compulsions, and addictions are complex and require professional intervention.
- Sharing your thoughts with an objective, helpful individual can be a great relief.
- Financial help to pay for care may be available.

Where to Go for Help

Main Idea People in your community are available to help.

It takes courage to confront a problem and try to solve it. Talking with a trusted adult, such as a parent, guardian, teacher, or school nurse, can get you started.

Many teens receive help for a mental health problem at school. A counselor or the school nurse can identify and contact support services. Other options for community help are talking with the clergy, and crisis hotlines. Crisis hotlines allow people to talk anonymously. The workers are trained to deal with difficult mental and emotional situations.

Treatment for mental health problems is unique to each individual. Sometimes, a treatment plan may not work. If that happens, talk to someone else. It may be necessary to try several different treatments. People with mental health problems should continue to seek help until they feel better.

READING CHECK

Explain What does asking for help from a mental health professional show?

■ **Figure 5.9** Adults working at a crisis hotline are usually volunteers motivated by the desire to help people who are suffering. *How might a person who is caring and yet objective be helpful during an emotional crisis?*

Lesson 4   Getting Help   **127**

② **TEACH**

Main Idea

Overcoming Stumbling Blocks People may be more likely to seek help if they know that their problems can be treated. **Ask Students:** *Why might people be reluctant to seek help for mental health problems?* (Sample answers: They might feel embarrassed or too vulnerable; they might not realize that their problems can be treated.)

AL Active Learning

Presentation Have students work in small groups to prepare a short computer slide presentation about where to go for help if a teen suffers from a mental health disorder. Challenge students to present the information in a way that's different than the way it's presented in the text. Have each group share its presentation with the class, and if possible, with other students at the same grade level. **OL**

Main Idea

Where to Go for Help Many people in the community can help with mental health problems. **Ask Students:** *Who in your school may be trained to help students with mental health problems?* (counselors, nurses)

Cooperative Learning

Careers in Mental Health Divide the class into groups, and assign each group a different mental health profession described in this lesson. Have all the groups look for the same type of information about their assigned profession, such as educational requirements, nature of the work, salary, and future employment potential. Help students compile the information they gather in a table that has a row for each profession and a column for each type of information. Make copies of the completed table and give one to each student in class.

Caption Answer

Figures 5.9 The person might offer empathy and understanding as well as practical solutions to mental health problems.

U Universal Access

Making Lists Pair students who need extra help with other students. Ask pairs to write a list of what kind of help is available from professionals. Ask partners to share their lists with the class. Discuss the differences between the types of mental health professionals. **BL**

Main Idea

Treatment Methods There are a variety of treatments for mental health problems. **Ask Students:** *Based on what you have already learned about treating depression, what are some ways that mental health problems can be treated?* (Sample answers: therapy, medication)

READING CHECK

Answer Sample answers: Parents, clergy, crisis-hotline volunteers

---

Caption Answer

Figure 5.10 Sample answer: Mental health specialists have expert training and experience in dealing with mental health problems.

READING CHECK

List Name some people who can help teens with mental health problems.

Mental Health Professionals

Help is available from a variety of professionals who work in your community's schools, clinics, hospitals, and family agencies. These specialists are trained to help people with mental and emotional problems, and include the following:

- **Counselor**—a professional who handles personal and educational matters
- **School psychologist**—a professional who specializes in the assessment of learning, emotional, and behavioral problems of schoolchildren
- **Psychiatrist**—a physician who diagnoses and treats mental disorders and can prescribe medications
- **Neurologist**—a physician who specializes in physical disorders of the brain and nervous system
- **Clinical psychologist**—a professional who diagnoses and treats emotional and behavioral disorders with counseling. Some can prescribe medications.
- **Psychiatric social worker**—a professional who provides guidance and treatment for emotional problems in a hospital, mental health clinic, or family service agency

U

Treatment Methods

Main Idea Several methods can be helpful in treating a mental problem.

Mental health professionals may use several treatments depending on their expertise and the needs of the patient. The following are the most commonly used therapy methods.

- **Psychotherapy** is *an ongoing dialogue between a patient and a mental health professional.* The dialogue is designed to find the cause of a problem and devise a solution.
- **Behavior therapy** is *a treatment process that focuses on changing unwanted behaviors through rewards and reinforcements.*

■ **Figure 5.10** A mental health specialist respects a patient's concern for confidentiality. *What are other benefits of seeking help from a mental health specialist?*

Promoting School Wellness

Assessing the School Environment
The psychosocial environment of a school can greatly influence the mental health of students. The World Health Organization (WHO) has developed a tool, called the Psycho-Social Environment (PSE) Profile, to assess a school's psychosocial environment. The PSE Profile is intended to create awareness about the importance of a healthy school psychosocial environment, as well as assess the health of the school's environment. The results of the profile are useful for setting priorities for a healthier school environment. You can read more about this useful tool and how to download it at the WHO Web site.

- **Cognitive therapy** is *a treatment method designed to identify and correct distorted thinking patterns that can lead to feelings and behaviors that may be troublesome, self-defeating, or self-destructive.*
- **Family therapy** focuses on *helping the family function in more positive and* **constructive** *ways by exploring patterns in communication and providing support and education.* Family therapy is most successful when every member of the family attends the sessions.
- **Group therapy** involves *treating a group of people who have similar problems and who meet regularly with a trained counselor.* Group members agree that whatever is said in the group is private. They agree not to discuss information heard during the group with others.
- **Drug therapy** is *the use of certain medications to treat or reduce the symptoms of a mental disorder.* It is sometimes used alone, but is often combined with other treatment methods such as those listed above.

Sometimes a mental health problem is serious enough to require hospitalization. In a hospital, a patient can receive intensive care and treatment from doctors, nurses, and a variety of mental health specialists. When someone is receiving care after being hospitalized, these specialists are available 24 hours a day.

Academic Vocabulary

constructive *(adjective):* promoting improvement or development

 READING CHECK

Explain What types of treatment methods can help those with a mental disorder?

 LESSON 4 **ASSESSMENT**

After You Read

Reviewing Facts and Vocabulary

1. What is *behavior therapy*?
2. Which mental health professional treats physical disorders of the brain?
3. Who might a teen reach out to at school about a mental health problem?

Thinking Critically

4. **Analyze.** What protective factors do you have or can you develop to help you deal with stress in your life?
5. **Synthesizing.** How does developing a positive outlook strengthen your resiliency?

Applying Health Skills

6. **Accessing Information.** Compile a list of local resources for mental health problems. Include mental health professionals, school counselors, hospital emergency rooms, and hotlines.

Writing Critically

7. **Persuasive.** Write an editorial about the importance of seeking help for mental health problems. Include strategies for getting help.

 Online

Visit glencoe.com and complete the Interactive Study Guide for this lesson.

LESSON 4 ASSESSMENT ANSWERS

1. A treatment process that focuses on changing unwanted behaviors through rewards and reinforcements
2. Neurologists treat disorders of the brain.
3. Answers may include: teacher, coach, counselor, or principal.
4. Answers will vary, but may include: asking for help; sharing thoughts with an objective person.
5. It helps develop responsibility for one's wellness.
6. Answers will vary.
7. Editorials will vary, but should include a variety of strategies from the lesson.

 ASSESS/ CLOSE

Assessment Resources

FAST FILE ACTIVITIES
Lesson 4 Quiz

ExamView
Assessment Suite CD-ROM

Visit glencoe.com **for:**
Online Quizzes
Online Learning Center

Progress Monitoring

Reteaching
On the board, write "Help is needed for a mental health problem when ____" and "To get help for a mental health problem, one can ____" Call on students to complete each sentence with a phrase from the lesson that makes the statement true.

Enrichment
Encourage students to learn more about a particular type of therapy, such as behavior therapy, and then present an oral report with examples.

 Online

Have students visit glencoe.com and complete the Interactive Study Guide for this lesson.

What's on a Label

Focus

Motivator
Ask students to recall warning labels they have seen on other prescription drugs (e.g., "may cause drowsiness").

Teach

Interpreting Study Results
Point out that the Columbia University study was not controlled. Teens with depression were not randomly assigned to treatment groups, so it is possible that the teens taking antidepressants were more severely depressed than the other teens in the study. Ask students how this might affect study results. (Suicide attempts in study participants might be related to the severity of their depression rather than to their use of medication.)

Controlled Studies
State that controlled studies of depression have not found antidepressants to increase suicide risk in teens. Call on volunteers to describe how a controlled study might be undertaken to investigate this issue. (Study subjects would be assigned randomly to treatment groups.)

Suicide Rates
Ask students to predict how the teen suicide rate might change if antidepressant use increased suicide risk and more antidepressants were prescribed for teens. (The teen suicide rate would increase.) Explain that increased antidepressant use is actually associated with a decrease in the teen suicide rate. Ask students to state what this finding suggests. (Using antidepressants decreases the risk of suicide.)

TIME HEALTH
SCIENCE & TECHNOLOGY

What's on a LABEL

Not everyone agrees with warning labels on pills to treat depression

People who take pills to treat depression are seeing warning labels on their drugs: The pills might increase the risk of suicide among some users. The warning is there because some experts believe the drugs could actually increase the risk of suicidal behavior in children and teens.

Not everyone agrees with this conclusion, saying that there is not enough evidence to require the warning labels. But those in favor of the labels point to a 2004 Columbia University study. The study reports that out of more than 4,000 children and teens, ages 6 to 18, who took antidepressants, 52 percent were more likely to attempt suicide than their peers who weren't taking medication. In adults, however, no such link was discovered.

What the Study Means

The numbers sound dramatic, but researchers warn that their findings need to be carefully considered. For one thing, the group of patients was a small number on which to make sweeping conclusions. It's also unclear whether the suicidal urge is related more to the medication or to the young person's depression.

Some experts point to other studies that show that the benefits of taking antidepressants outweigh the risks and help to prevent suicides. The debate may continue for years.

Be Aware

Teens just starting to take antidepressants need to be aware of any unusual behavior, especially in the early stages. People on antidepressants should never change or stop treatment without speaking with a doctor. And, most importantly, patients must let doctors know if they are taking any other medications or have any physical or mental illnesses besides depression.

TIME to THINK... | **About Treating Depression**

Some researchers believe meditation may help people with depression by lowering levels of cortisol, a hormone released during stress. Using the Internet or your school's media center, investigate cortisol. Report your findings to the class.

More About...

Cortisol and Depression Scientists have known for decades that people with depression have higher-than-normal blood levels of the stress hormone cortisol. Recent studies have investigated cortisol's role in depression. Results suggest that chronically high blood levels of cortisol may cause some of the symptoms of depression, particularly cognitive symptoms, such as poor concentration and forgetfulness. Cortisol may play this role because it interferes with the functioning of neurotransmitters, including serotonin. However, there is no evidence at this point to indicate that high levels of cortisol actually cause depression.

To download quizzes and eFlashcards to your PDA, go to glencoe.com and click on the Study to Go icon.

LESSON 1

Dealing with Anxiety and Depression

Key Concepts

▶ Seek help if thoughts, emotions, or behaviors affect daily life.
▶ Causes of depression include stressful life events, unhappy family environments, social conditions, and illness.
▶ Depressed people need treatment from a medical or mental health professional.

Vocabulary

▶ anxiety (p. 114)
▶ emotions (p. 114)
▶ depression (p. 115)
▶ apathy (p. 116)

LESSON 2

Mental Disorders

Key Concepts

▶ Education can overcome the stigma of mental illness.
▶ If left untreated, many mental disorders that begin in childhood or adolescence can continue into adulthood.
▶ Anxiety disorders are common disorders that teens experience.

Vocabulary

▶ mental disorder (p. 118)
▶ stigma (p. 118)
▶ anxiety disorder (p. 119)
▶ mood disorder (p. 120)
▶ conduct disorder (p. 120)

LESSON 3

Suicide Prevention

Key Concepts

▶ The two risk factors most associated with suicide are depression and abusing alcohol or other drugs.
▶ Most suicidal thoughts, behaviors, and actions are expressions of extreme distress.
▶ A suicidal teen needs immediate adult intervention.

Vocabulary

▶ alienation (p. 122)
▶ suicide (p. 122)
▶ cluster suicides (p. 123)

LESSON 4

Getting Help

Key Concepts

▶ Help for mental health problems may be available at school or through community resources.
▶ The reluctance to get help can be overcome by recognizing the benefits of treatment.
▶ Mental health professionals can diagnose a mental health problem and devise an appropriate treatment plan.

Vocabulary

▶ psychotherapy (p. 128)
▶ behavior therapy (p. 128)
▶ cognitive therapy (p. 129)
▶ family therapy (p. 129)
▶ group therapy (p. 129)
▶ drug therapy (p. 129)

Chapter 5 Review **131**

Go Online

Students can visit **glencoe.com** to

- review content online with the Online Student Edition.
- test their knowledge of chapter content with Online Quizzes.
- access Interactive Health Tutor for more practice with vocabulary.

Assessment Resources

📁 ***FAST FILE* ACTIVITIES**
Chapter 5 Test

💿 *ExamView Assessment Suite* CD-ROM

Visit glencoe.com for:
Audio Chapter Summaries
Online Quizzes

 Tell students to visit **glencoe.com** where they can download quizzes and eFlashcards.

Study Tips

Remember Through Association It will be easier for students to remember new information if they make a conscious effort to associate it with something they already know. Students should begin to learn new material by asking, "What is this like that I already know and understand?" For example, students can use what they already know about anxiety and depression from Lesson 1 to help them learn the information about anxiety disorders and mood disorders in Lesson 2.

Assessment

Chapter 5 Assessment Answers

LESSON 1

Vocabulary Review
1. depression
2. anxiety
3. apathy

Understanding Key Concepts
4. d
5. b
6. b

Thinking Critically
7. Sample answers: helplessness, hopelessness, and sadness
8. You might have trouble falling asleep, staying asleep, or getting up in the morning.
9. Sample answer: The situation might make someone feel constantly threatened by danger, helpless, and hopeless.
10. Sample answer: You can take care of your health by eating a variety of healthful foods, trying to get plenty of sleep, and exercising regularly.

LESSON 2

Vocabulary Review
11. mood disorders
12. conduct disorder
13. anxiety disorder

Understanding Key Concepts
14. b
15. c
16. d

LESSON 1

Vocabulary Review
Use the vocabulary terms listed on page 131 to complete the following statements.

1. Prolonged feelings of helplessness, hopelessness and sadness can be a sign that you are suffering from _____.
2. Feelings of unease or worrying about what may happen are signs of _____.
3. A lack of strong feeling, interest, or concern is called _____.

Understanding Key Concepts
After reading the question or statement, select the correct answer.

4. Which of the following is *not* a change in behavior one might expect with depression?
   a. Trouble sleeping
   b. Eating too much
   c. Eating too little
   d. Running alone

5. Which of the following is *not* a warning sign of depression?
   a. Boredom
   b. Increased interest in life
   c. Poor concentration
   d. Increased irritability

6. What can you do if you think that you may be depressed?
   a. Start an exercise plan.
   b. Talk to a trusted adult to ask for help.
   c. Change your eating plan.
   d. Start reading about the topic.

Thinking Critically
After reading the question or statement, write a short answer using complete sentences.

7. **Identify.** What are three feelings you may experience when you are depressed?

8. **Explain.** How might depression affect your sleep?
9. **Analyze.** How might community violence cause someone to become depressed?
10. **Discuss.** While being treated for depression, what else can you do to help the healing process?

LESSON 2

Vocabulary Review
Choose the correct term in the sentences below.

11. Illnesses that involve mood extremes that interfere with everyday living are called *mood disorders / stigma.*
12. Patterns of behavior in which the rights of others or basic social rules are violated are typical of a *mental disorder / conduct disorder.*
13. Conditions in which real or imagined fears are difficult to control are called *stigma / anxiety disorder.*

Understanding Key Concepts
After reading the question or statement, select the correct answer.

14. Which is *not* an anxiety disorder?
   a. Phobia
   b. Pyromania
   c. Panic disorder
   d. Post-traumatic stress disorder

15. Kleptomania is
   a. an anxiety disorder.
   b. a mood disorder.
   c. an impulse control disorder.
   d. a conduct disorder.

Health eSpotlight VIDEO Wrap-Up

Have students reread the Health eSpotlight questions at the beginning of the chapter (page 113) and look at their original answers. **Ask Students:** *After reading the chapter and watching the video, would you answer the questions differently?* Call on volunteers to describe how their responses would change.

16. Bipolar disorder is
   a. a conduct disorder.
   b. a personality disorder.
   c. an anxiety disorder.
   d. a mood disorder.

Thinking Critically

After reading the question or statement, write a short answer using complete sentences.

17. Explain. Describe how misconceptions of mental illness can be overcome.

18. Analyze. Explain why some people with a mental disorder may not seek help for their problem.

19. Describe. Identify several examples of anxiety triggers for teens.

20. Infer. Consider the types of problems that people with impulse control disorders have. Explain what problems people with this disorder may face before getting treatment.

LESSON 3

Vocabulary Review

Correct the sentences below by replacing the italicized term with the correct vocabulary term.

21. The act of intentionally taking one's own life is called *alienation*.

22. A series of suicides occurring within a short period of time and involving several people in the same school or community is referred to as *suicide*.

Understanding Key Concepts

After reading the question or statement, select the correct answer.

23. Suicide is the _____ leading cause of teen deaths.
   a. first   b. second
   c. third   d. fourth

24. Of the following risk factors for teen suicide, which should probably be of most concern?
   a. A stressful situation or loss
   b. Substance abuse
   c. Family history of mental disorders
   d. Exposure to other teens who have died by suicide

25. Which is *not* a warning sign of suicide?
   a. Withdrawal from friends
   b. An overwhelming sense of guilt
   c. Persistent indifference
   d. Preoccupation with buying new things

Thinking Critically

After reading the question or statement, write a short answer using complete sentences.

26. Analyze. Explain why drinking alcohol is not an effective way to try to relieve depression.

27. Describe. What are five warning signs of suicide?

28. Explain. Why might cluster suicides occur in a community where the individuals may not even know one another?

29. Evaluate. Explain why it is important never to keep secret a person's threat to commit suicide.

LESSON 4

Vocabulary Review

Use the vocabulary terms listed on page 131 to complete the following statements.

30. A treatment method designed to identify and correct distorted thinking patterns is known as _____.

31. The use of certain medications to treat symptoms of a mental disorder is called _____.

Thinking Critically

17. Misconceptions can be overcome through education about mental illness. Education helps people realize that mental disorders are medical conditions that require diagnosis and treatment, just like any physical illness or injury.

18. Some people with a mental disorder may feel too embarrassed or ashamed to seek help. Others worry about the stigma associated with mental disorders.

19. Anxiety triggers for teens include exams, school performance, personal appearance, peer scrutiny and rejection, and social embarrassment.

20. Before getting treatment, some people with impulse control disorders may face legal problems, such as jail terms, because of criminal acts. Other people with untreated impulse control disorders may face financial problems, because of excessive gambling or compulsive shopping.

LESSON 3

Vocabulary Review

21. suicide
22. cluster suicides

Understanding Key Concepts

23. c
24. b
25. d

Thinking Critically

26. Alcohol has a depressant effect, so it may make symptoms of depression worse. Alcohol also lowers inhibition, so it makes self-destructive behaviors more likely and might increase the risk of suicide by a person with depression.

Assessment

27. Any five of the warning signs listed in **Figure 5.7** on page 124.

28. Individuals who do not know one another might share an environmental stressor such as a tragic event in their school or community, or they might feel compelled to commit suicide after hearing of another suicide.

29. A suicide threat is serious and could lead to a suicide attempt. Not keeping the threat a secret, and instead letting an adult know about it, might prevent a suicide attempt.

LESSON 4

Vocabulary Review

30. cognitive therapy
31. drug therapy

Understanding Key Concepts

32. a
33. c
34. c

Thinking Critically

35. Behaviors include: constant worry; changes in sleep, eating habits, schoolwork, job performance, or relationships; becoming involved with alcohol or other drugs; or acting increasingly aggressive, violent, or reckless.

36. Possible consequences include: unnecessary distress and disruption of life; worsening of the symptoms of the mental disorder and possible suicide; problems continuing into adulthood.

37. Sample answer: Criteria that would be important to me include empathy, trustworthiness, and experience dealing with my particular type of problem.

134

Understanding Key Concepts

After reading the question or statement, select the correct answer.

32. A mental health professional who handles personal and educational matters is a
    a. counselor.
    b. school psychologist.
    c. psychiatrist.
    d. neurologist.

33. A treatment method that uses ongoing dialogue between a patient and a mental health professional is
    a. family therapy.
    b. cognitive therapy.
    c. psychotherapy.
    d. group therapy.

34. Which is *not* true regarding crisis-hotline workers?
    a. They are trained to deal with difficult mental/emotional situations.
    b. They are usually volunteers.
    c. They know about your personal situation.
    d. They allow you to remain anonymous.

Thinking Critically

After reading the question or statement, write a short answer using complete sentences.

35. **Describe.** Identify the behaviors that help you recognize that a friend needs help.

36. **Analyze.** What are the possible consequences of not getting help for an adolescent mental disorder?

37. **Synthesize.** What criteria would be important to you when choosing someone to talk with about a mental health problem?

Project-Based ASSESSMENT

Phobias

Background

A phobia is a strong fear of something specific. For example, *arachnophobia* is a fear of spiders. Other phobias include *agoraphobia*, the fear of being in an open space, or *claustrophobia*, the fear of being in a closed space. Some mental health professionals believe that some phobias are caused by childhood experiences.

Task

Conduct research to learn about different types of phobias. Prepare a poster and oral presentation.

Audience

Students in your class

Purpose

Develop awareness of one kind of mental illness that affects many children, teens, and adults.

Procedure

1. Conduct research at the library or on the Internet to learn more about phobias.

2. Select three to four phobias that you will report on to the class.

3. Identify the kinds of professional help and solutions available for treating specific phobias.

4. Write a summary of each type of phobia, giving as much information as possible.

5. Research and write about what might occur if a person's activities should put him or her near the object or situation that is the source of the phobia.

6. Prepare a poster as part of an oral presentation of your research.

Project-Based ASSESSMENT

Step 1 Research Have students research phobias in medical books and encyclopedias. They should learn about different types of phobias, how people with phobias react, and professional sources of help for people with phobias.

Step 2 Summarize Ask students to write a comprehensive summary of several different types of phobias. Also have students create a poster to show information about phobias.

Step 3 Present Give students a chance to present their research to the class in an oral presentation. Students should use their posters in their presentations.

Visit **glencoe.com** for Project-Based Assessment rubrics.

Math Practice

Understand and Apply. Read the paragraph below, and then answer the questions.

> *Nearly everyone is mildly depressed at some time, but 16 percent of the U.S. population will suffer from major depression in a lifetime. A study was conducted on more than 9,000 people ages 18 and older. Fifty-seven percent of those who had major depression sought help. This rate is almost 40 percent higher than the rate reported 20 years before the study. Even though the number of patients treated is increasing, it is estimated that only 21 percent are receiving adequate care.*

1. If the size of the general population is 200 million people, how many people will experience major depression at some time during their lives?
   - **A.** 32 million
   - **B.** 42 million
   - **C.** 75 million
   - **D.** 92.8 million

2. What function can be used to find the number of people who are seeking help for depression if you know the size of the population with depression? (Hint: The variable N is the number of people seeking help, and P is the size of the population.)
   - **A.** $N = P$
   - **B.** $N = (0.57)(0.16)P$
   - **C.** $N = 0.57P$
   - **D.** $P = 0.16N$

3. Examine the percentages reflecting how many people have major depression, how many of these people seek help, and how many who seek help receive adequate care. Of 20,000 people, how many people would you expect to be receiving adequate care for major depression? Justify your answer.

Go Online

For more test practice, visit glencoe.com and complete the Online Quizzes for Chapter 5.

Reading/Writing Practice

Analyze and Infer. Read the passage below, and then answer the questions.

> *John F. Nash, Jr., is known for his work as a creative mathematician. He is also an example of how one person can succeed in his chosen field even if he is battling a difficult mental health challenge: paranoid schizophrenia.*
>
> *While working at Princeton University in the 1950s, Nash made great strides in a field of mathematics called game theory. This research later earned him a share in the 1994 Nobel Prize in Economics. However, soon after completing this work, he began to suffer what was later diagnosed as paranoid schizophrenia. After taking a break for nearly 30 years, Nash returned to mathematics and now continues to do research and write at Princeton.*

1. What information supports the claim that Nash is successful?
   - **A.** Nash was born in West Virginia.
   - **B.** Nash has paranoid schizophrenia.
   - **C.** Nash stopped his research for 30 years.
   - **D.** Nash won a Nobel Prize in Economics.

2. Why did the author write this passage?
   - **A.** To cite examples of famous people with various mental disorders
   - **B.** To describe how a mathematician came up with his prize-winning research
   - **C.** To explain how schizophrenia affects mental and physical health
   - **D.** To show how a person can be successful in spite of a mental disorder

3. Write a paragraph describing the effects of schizophrenia on a person's mental and emotional health.

National Education Standards
Math: Number and Operations, Problem Solving
Language Arts: NCTE 3, NCTE 4

Standardized Test Practice

Standardized Test Practice Answers

Math Practice
1. A
2. B
3. Of 20,000 people, 16 percent have major depression, 57 percent of these seek help, and 21 percent of those seeking help receive adequate help. Thus, 20,000 people $\times$ $0.16 \times 0.57 \times .021 = 384$ people with major depression are receiving adequate care.

Reading/Writing Practice
1. D
2. D
3. Paragraphs will vary.

National Education Standards

Math: Number and Operations, Problem Solving

Language Arts: NCTE 3, NCTE 4

For the complete Math and Language Arts standards, visit glencoe.com.

Go Online

Online Study Tools
For more test practice, visit glencoe.com and complete the Online Quizzes for Chapter 5.

Test-Taking Tip

Answering Essay Questions Advise students to answer essay questions as directly as possible and to avoid "writing around" the answers. Also, suggest that they pay close attention to the wording of essay questions. For example, if a question asks them to "list" something, they should write a list, not a description. If a question asks them to "compare and contrast" items, they should explain how the items are similar as well as how they are different.

Mental and Emotional Health

Are Teens Overscheduled?

Being involved in extracurricular activities or working at a part-time job while going to school can be a good way for teens to learn useful skills, including time management. Being involved in extracurricular activities can benefit teens in other ways as well. However, having too much to do and not enough time to do it is a major cause of stress. Stress, in turn, can cause mental and emotional problems, such as anxiety and depression.

Signs of Being Overscheduled

Share with students the following signs that a person might be overscheduled:

- Signs of anxiety or depression, such as panic attacks or withdrawal from friends.

- Behavioral or physical changes, such as problems sleeping or frequent headaches.

- Not enough unstructured time to just have fun and to enjoy friends and family.

Benefits of Keeping Busy

Explain that becoming involved in organized activities not only helps teens develop new interests and skills. It may also help their mental and emotional health. Studies show that teens who are busy with extracurricular activities are also more likely to do well in school and to have good family relationships. In addition, they are less likely to use alcohol or other drugs. Therefore, it is beneficial for teens to have at least some involvement in organized activities.

Are Teens Overscheduled?

*T*he high school years can bring many different kinds of stress. Teens today are busier than ever as they try to balance school, athletics and other extracurricular activities, part-time jobs, friendships, dating relationships, and family responsibilities. All these demands can cause a great deal of stress, possibly leading to health problems. Do teens have too many responsibilities? Are they overscheduled? Should parents help teens include free time in their schedule to pursue intersts such as reading, art, or just relaxing? Read on to find out two teens' viewpoints about this issue.

Health Literacy

Organized Activities A recent review of published research found that the average youth aged 5–18 years spends 5 hours per week participating in organized activities (compared with 15 hours watching television). The researchers also found that youth who are involved in organized activities have better mental and emotional health than youth who are not. Even the busiest youth—those who spend at least 20 hours per week in organized activities—tend to have better mental and emotional health than youth who do not participate at all.

Benefits of a Full Schedule

Having a full schedule of different activities can help teens develop new interests and skills because they're always trying new things. Many of these skills, such as multitasking, may help them succeed in college and in the work world. Meeting the challenges of a full schedule can also give teens a sense of accomplishment and build self-esteem.

"I have a busy schedule, and I like it that way. It keeps me challenged, and I don't feel bored. Juggling school, baseball, a job, and time with family and friends also helps prepare me for the real world. It can get stressful sometimes, but that's part of life."

—Jeff Z., age 17

Benefits of a Relaxed Schedule

Having a more relaxed schedule allows teens to devote attention to a few important activities that they really enjoy instead of stretching themselves too thin. A relaxed schedule can help them manage their stress level and avoid stress-related health problems. Also, by not overloading their schedules, teens can better explore their creative interests.

"Some of my friends are stressed all the time because they're trying to do too much. After trying to keep up with schoolwork, studying for SATs, being on sport teams, holding down jobs, and doing chores at home, they don't have any time for themselves. It's important to keep a balance so you don't burn out."

—Alison R., age 16

Activity Beyond the Classroom

1. **Summarize** your thoughts on this issue. Do you think some teens are overscheduled? Why do you think they are trying to do so much? How might this affect their mental and emotional health?

2. **Synthesize** your ideas. Imagine that you are a columnist at a teen magazine. Write an article about balancing responsibilities and activities. Discuss how teens can tell if they are overscheduled, and provide strategies for maintaining an appropriate activity load.

Go Online

For more information about teens and stress, go to glencoe.com.

Teaching Strategies

- **Evaluating Activities** Ask students to list several types of after-school activities in which many teens participate, such as clubs, music groups, sports teams, jobs, and volunteering. Then have students brainstorm potential benefits and drawbacks associated with participation in each type of activity. Ask students which activities they would choose if they were limited to just two or three. Make sure students realize that doing some activities just for fun is important for good health.

- **Calculating Time** Have students calculate how many hours per weekday, on average, they can spend on activities other than attending school. After subtracting their time spent in school from 24 hours, remind them to subtract all the time needed for other necessary activities, including commuting, doing homework and any household chores, basic grooming, eating, and sleeping (9 hours for good health). The time that remains is all the time they have left for other activities. Doing these calculations will help students realize that they are either wasting too much time or trying to do too much in the time they have.

Activity Beyond the Classroom

Writing

1. Sample answer: I think some teens are overscheduled. I think they are trying to do so much in order to improve their chances of getting into a good college. Being overscheduled might cause them stress, which could lead to anxiety or other mental health problems.

2. Articles will vary. Students should include signs of overscheduling, such as anxiety, and also strategies for balancing activities with time, such as calculating the time available for activities.

137

Flexible Technology Solutions

Focus

Health eSpotlight *Video Series*

By Chapter

Chapter 6 Skills for Healthy Relationships
Video 6: It Starts with Respect

Chapter 7 Family Relationships
Video 7: Family First

Chapter 8 Peer Relationships
Video 8: Choices for Healthy Friendships

Chapter 9 Resolving Conflicts and Preventing Violence
Video 9: Preventing Violence, Resolving Conflict

By Lesson

Chapter 6 *Video 6*   For Use With
Segment 6.1   Foundations of a Healthy Relationship .... Lesson 1
Segment 6.2   Respecting Yourself and Others .... Lesson 2
Segment 6.3   Communicating Effectively .... Lesson 3

Chapter 7 *Video 7*   For Use With
Segment 7.1   Healthy Family Relationships .... Lesson 1
Segment 7.2   Strengthening Family Relationships .... Lesson 2
Segment 7.3   Help for Families .... Lesson 3

Chapter 8 *Video 8*   For Use With
Segment 8.1   Safe and Healthy Friendships .... Lesson 1
Segment 8.2   Peer Pressure and Refusal Skills .... Lesson 2
Segment 8.3   Practicing Abstinence .... Lesson 3

Chapter 9 *Video 9*   For Use With
Segment 9.1   Causes of Conflict .... Lesson 1
Segment 9.2   Resolving Conflicts .... Lesson 2
Segment 9.3   Understanding Violence .... Lesson 3
Segment 9.4   Preventing and Overcoming Abuse .... Lesson 4

By Skill

Communication Skills .... Videos   5   **6**   27
Stress Management .... Videos   4   **7**
Refusal Skills .... Videos   **8**   21   24
Conflict Resolution .... Videos   **9**   18

■ Indicates videos featured in the unit that teach the corresponding skill. Other videos listed can also be used to teach that skill.

Teach

Direct lesson plans beyond the classroom with multi-media fitness activities that students can do online, in class, or as a group.

PowerPoint® Presentation

- *Health* eSpotlight videos
- Audio and image bank

FITNESSZONE
Online

Fitness Zone Online is a multi-media resource that helps students find ways to be physically active each day.

- Clipboard Energizer Activities
- Fitness Zone Videos
- Polar Heart Rate Monitor Activities
- Nutrition, Physical Activity, and Injury Prevention Tips
- Links to Nutrition and Physical Activity Resources

Go Online

Online Learning Center

- Student Web Activities
- PuzzleMaker
- Interactive Health Tutor

Podcast Audio Chapter Summaries

Use the audio Podcast Audio Chapter Summaries to teach and review key concepts, and engage students with health content that they can download to a computer or portable MP3 player.

Assess/Close

Help students master chapter and lesson concepts with an integrated technology solution for assessment and performance evaluation.

Go Online

Online Learning Center

- Interactive Study Guides
- Online Quizzes

ExamView® Assessment Suite CD-ROM

Create and customize tests in minutes with this convenient digital platform.

- Create differentiated tests quickly and easily.
- All questions correlated to National/State Standards.
- Enhance tests with Document Based Questions (DBQ) and add your own photos and graphics.
- Build tests in both English and Spanish.
- Generate progress reports.

Enrich

Use these additional digital and online media resources to promote hands-on exploration of health topics covered in the lesson.

Go Online

Online Learning Center

- Interactive Health Tutor
- Vocabulary PuzzleMaker

Study-to-Go

Download a portable version of eFlashcards and Self-Check Quizzes onto your Palm or Pocket PC.

Health Podcasts Activities

Glencoe's "It's Your Health" Podcast Activities provide students with a unique listening and learning experience that takes health education beyond the classroom. Download the audio files and print activities covering a range of current health topics that matter most to teens!

Healthy and Safe Relationships

Students will learn ways to develop healthy relationships. They will also learn how to prevent conflicts and develop skills for dealing with conflicts when they arise.

Health eSpotlight Video Series

At the beginning of each chapter, visit glencoe.com and have students watch the video and do the accompanying print activity.

 Chapter 6
It Starts with Respect

Respect is an important quality in friendships.

 Chapter 7
Family First

Family is a key source of strength.

 Chapter 8
Choices for Healthy Friendships

Saying no is never easy, even if you are making the right decision.

 Chapter 9
Preventing Violence, Resolving Conflict

Coping with conflict is an important skill.

Unit 3 Resources

- Career Corner
- 📁 FAST FILE RESOURCES
- Health Career Research Activity
- Family Involvement Activity
- Community Involvement Activity
- Unit Test

UNIT 3 Healthy and Safe Relationships

Chapter 6
Skills for Healthy Relationships

 It Starts with Respect

Chapter 7
Family Relationships

 Family First

Chapter 8
Peer Relationships

 Choices for Healthy Friendships

Chapter 9
Resolving Conflicts and Preventing Violence

 Preventing Violence, Resolving Conflict

UNIT PROJECT

A Positive Place

Using Visuals Boys & Girls Clubs of America calls itself "The Positive Place for Kids." Four thousand clubs across America offer programs and activities to children and teens in all age groups. Volunteers provide key support to staff.

 To learn more about volunteering for Boys & Girls Clubs of America, go to the Unit Web Project at glencoe.com.

Get Involved. Use community or online resources to locate youth centers in your area. Call or visit one center to find out what kinds of programs and activities it offers. Summarize your findings in a brief report.

138

UNIT PROJECT

Promoting a Positive Place Boys and Girls Clubs serve more than four million boys and girls each year. The clubs offer numerous activities and programs to help young people have fun in a safe environment. The organization was founded in 1906, but served only boys and went by the name Boys Clubs. In 1990, the name was changed to Boys and Girls Clubs of America.

Get Involved Direct students to work in small groups to identify youth centers that serve their community. Have students arrange a visit or make a phone call to learn more about the nearest youth center. Ask students to identify ways that teens can volunteer at the youth center. Have students share what they learned with the class.

"The only way to have a friend is to be one."
— Ralph Waldo Emerson, 19th-century writer and poet

Unit 3 Healthy and Safe Relationships **139**

Activate Prior Knowledge

Ask students these questions before they read the chapter to build on what they already know.

Chapter 6
What are some characteristics of healthy relationships?

(Mutual respect and consideration, honesty, dependability, commitment)

Chapter 7
What is a family and what is its function?

(The family is a basic unit of society. It provides a safe and nurturing environment for its members.)

Chapter 8
What is the difference between peers and friendships?

(Peers are people of similar age who share similar interests. A friendship is a significant relationship between two people.)

Chapter 9
What is the key to personal safety?

(Being able to recognize potentially dangerous situations and learn strategies to avoid them)

Glencoe Exclusive!
TeacherWorks *Plus*
All-In-One Planner and Resource Center

TeacherWorks Plus provides:

- interactive Teacher Wrap-around edition
- click, drag, and drop to plan lessons
- instant access to many print proram resources

How to Get Involved Provide students with these step-by-step instructions on how they can assemble information about volunteer opportunities.

1. Each student should call or visit a youth center to find out more about the services offered there.

2. Have students inquire about opportunities for teens to serve as volunteers at the youth center.

3. Have each student share the information he or she has learned by making a poster to share with other students in the school.

Chapter 6 pages 140–163	Standards		Features
	National	**State/Local**	*Hands-On* **HEALTH**
	1.12.1, 1.12.5, 1.12.8, 4.12.1, 4.12.4, 6.12.1, 8.12.4		• The New Employee *(Communication),* page 158
Lesson 1 **Foundations of a Healthy** **Relationship** pages 142–147 **BIG Idea** Building strong relationships is important to your overall health.	1.12.1, 1.12.7, 2.12.1–2.12.4, 2.12.7, 2.12.8, 4.12.1–4.12.3, 5.12.4–5.12.6, 7.12.1–7.12.3, 8.12.1, 8.12.4		
Lesson 2 **Respecting Yourself and** **Others** pages 148–151 **BIG Idea** You can promote healthy relationships by showing respect for yourself and others in your life.	1.12.7, 2.12.8, 2.12.10, 4.12.2– 4.12.4, 5.12.1, 5.12.2, 5.12.4, 7.12.1, 7.12.2, 7.12.3, 8.12.3, 8.12.4		*Real World* **CONNECTION** • Dealing with a Bully, page 151 (Y) Out of Time
Lesson 3 **Communicating Effectively** pages 152–157 **BIG Idea** Effective communication is a key to building healthy relationships.	1.12.1, 1.12.3, 1.12.5, 2.12.1– 2.12.3, 4.12.1– 4.12.4, 5.12.7, 7.12.1, 7.12.2, 7.12.3, 8.12.2, 8.12.4		*Health Skills* **Activity** • Coping with Criticism *(Communication Skills),* page 157 (Y) Out of Time

Each lesson marked **30 Min**

Key to Ability Levels

Teaching Strategies and activities have been coded for ability level and appropriateness.

AL Activities for students working above grade level   **BL** Activities for students working below grade level

OL Activities for students working on grade level   **EL** Activities for English Learners

Chapter 6 Planning Guide

Resources	Lesson Assessment	Technology
Student Activity Workbook **TEACH** *FAST FILE* **RESOURCES** Vocabulary Practice **TEACH** Health Labs **EXTEND**	Chapter 6 Review Chapter 6 Assessment Standardized Test Practice ⊙ *ExamView® Assessment Suite* CD-ROM	**Teaching Tools:** ⊙ *TeacherWorks™* Plus DVD ⊙ *StudentWorks™* Plus DVD ⊙ *ExamView® Assessment Suite* CD-ROM 🖉 Transparency ⊙ Fitness DVD ⊙ PowerPoint® DVD ⊙ Health eSpotlight Video Series DVD
FAST FILE **RESOURCES** Reading Strategies Activity **TEACH** Reteaching Activity **REVIEW** Enrichment Activity **EXTEND** Health Skills Practice **TEACH**	Lesson 1 Assessment, page 147 📁 Lesson 1 Quiz *Fast File* ⊙ *ExamView® Assessment Suite* CD-ROM	**Web-Based Resources:** Go Online glencoe.com • Health Podcast Activities • Audio Chapter Summaries (English/Spanish) • Interactive Health Tutor • Health Skills Activities • Vocabulary PuzzleMaker • Parent Letters (English/Spanish) • Lesson Plans • Health Inventories • Online Quizzes • Study-to-Go • Unit Web Projects • Student Web Activities • Fitness Zone Activities
FAST FILE **RESOURCES** Reading Strategies Activity **TEACH** Reteaching Activity **REVIEW** Enrichment Activity **EXTEND** Health Skills Practice **TEACH**	Lesson 2 Assessment, page 151 📁 Lesson 2 Quiz *Fast File* ⊙ *ExamView® Assessment Suite* CD-ROM	
FAST FILE **RESOURCES** Reading Strategies Activity **TEACH** Reteaching Activity **REVIEW** Enrichment Activity **EXTEND** Health Skills Practice **TEACH**	Lesson 3 Assessment, page 157 📁 Lesson 3 Quiz *Fast File* ⊙ *ExamView® Assessment Suite* CD-ROM	

This is the student's backpack solution.

Includes:
- complete Interactive Student Edition
- full audio of English text and Spanish chapter summaries
- allows students to record assignments and track grades.
- links to online activities and additional student resources
- access to all student worksheets and workbooks

FOLDABLES® Study Organizer

Dinah Zike Foldables®
Chapter Activity
Refer to the *Dinah Zike Reading and Study Skills for Glencoe Health.* Have students complete the layered-look book Foldable to organize what they learn about building and maintaining healthy relationships.

Skills for Healthy Relationships

Chapter Overview

Chapter 6 focuses on skills that can be used to build and maintain strong and healthy relationships.

Lesson 1

Strong relationships have a positive influence on overall health.

Lesson 2

Showing respect for yourself and others is a way to promote healthy relationships.

Lesson 3

Healthy relationships depend upon effective communication.

▶ **Activating Prior Knowledge**

Have volunteers share words and phrases that would describe the relationships depicted in the photo. For example, students might use the phrases "good friends" or "close relationship." Then lead a discussion of the characteristics that are important in strong and healthy relationships.

Lesson 1
Foundations of a Healthy Relationship

BIG Idea *Building strong relationships is important to your overall health.*

Lesson 2
Respecting Yourself and Others

BIG Idea *You can promote healthy relationships by showing respect for yourself and others in your life.*

Lesson 3
Communicating Effectively

BIG Idea *Effective communication is a key to building healthy relationships.*

Activating Prior Knowledge

Using Visuals Look at the photo on this page. What kind of relationship do these teens seem to have? Discuss the characteristics that you think are most important to a healthy and strong relationship.

140

Universal Access

Differentiated Learning Glencoe provides teacher support and student materials for all learners in the health classroom.

- Chapter Summaries in English and Spanish are available online at glencoe.com.
- *Fast Files* and related worksheets support reluctant readers.

- Universal Access strategies throughout the Teacher Wraparound Edition and *Fast Files* help you present materials for gifted students, at-risk students, physically impaired students, and those with behavior disorders or learning disabilities.

Chapter Launchers

Health in Action

Discuss the **BIG** Ideas

Before beginning this chapter, think about how you would answer these questions:

▶ What relationships in your life are most important?

▶ What makes these relationships special?

▶ What do you do to keep these relationships strong?

Watch the *Health eSpotlight* Video Series

VIDEO

It Starts with Respect

You share relationships with the people around you. Why is respect an important part of any relationship?

Assess Your Health

Go Online

Visit **glencoe.com** and complete the Health Inventory for Chapter 6.

Chapter Launchers

Health in Action

Discuss the **BIG** Ideas

Ask students to think about their responses to the bulleted questions. Have volunteers share their responses, but allow students to keep their responses confidential if they prefer. Remind students that these questions preview the topics covered in the chapter.

Health eSpotlight
Video Series

VIDEO

It Starts with Respect

Before Viewing the Video

Ask Students: *How would you define friendship?* After students have watched the video, discuss what qualities a good friend should have. List the qualities students suggest on the board, and ask students to rank them.

Go Online

Have students go to **glencoe.com** and take the Health Inventory for Chapter 6.

Chapter Skills

Reading Skills
- Reviewing Facts and Vocabulary, pp. 147, 151, 157
- Reading/Writing Practice, p. 163

BIG Idea

Healthy relationships enhance all three sides of the health triangle.

Vocabulary
- New Vocabulary, pp. 142, 148, 152
- Reviewing Facts and Vocabulary, pp. 147, 151, 157

Health Skills
- Health Skills Activity, p. 157
- Applying Health Skills, pp. 147, 151, 157

Writing Skills
- Real World Connection, p. 151
- Writing Critically, pp. 147, 151, 157
- Reading/Writing Practice, p. 163

Foundations of a Healthy Relationship

① FOCUS

GUIDE TO READING

BIG Idea Strong relationships are important to overall health. **Ask Students:** *Who are some individuals with whom you have strong relationships?* (Sample answer: My sister, my aunt, and my best friend)

Before You Read

K-W-L Chart Students' K-W-L charts will vary.

Main Idea

Relationships in Your Life
Individuals play different roles in different types of relationships. **Ask Students:** *How are your relationships with your family members different from your relationships with your friends?* (Sample answer: My relationships with my family members are more long-term than my relationships with my friends.)

Real Life Issues
Before students write their paragraph, have them generate a T-Chart. On one side, have students list consequences of going to the birthday party. On the other side, have students list consequences of going to the music festival. Remind students to consider both positive and negative consequences of each choice.

142

LESSON 1

GUIDE TO READING

BIG Idea *Building strong relationships is important to your overall health.*

Before You Read
Create a K-W-L Chart. Make a three-column chart. In the first column, list what you **k**now about relationships. In the second column, list what you **w**ant to know about this topic. As you read, use the third column to summarize what you **l**earned.

K	W	L

New Vocabulary

▸ relationship (p. 142)
▸ friendship (p. 143)
▸ citizenship (p. 144)
▸ role (p. 144)
▸ cooperation (p. 146)
▸ compromise (p. 146)

Review Vocabulary

▸ interpersonal communication (Ch.2, L.1)

Foundations of a Healthy Relationship

Real Life Issues ....

Family or Friends? Ben's grandmother will be 70 next month, and his family is planning to fly out and celebrate with her. The problem is, the weekend they're going is the same weekend as the annual music festival he always attends with his two best friends. Ben knows his friends will be disappointed if he can't go, but he doesn't want to let his grandmother down either.

Writing *If you were Ben, how would you respond? How can you reassure the people involved that they are important to you? Explain your ideas in a paragraph.*

Relationships in Your Life

Main Idea You have many types of relationships in your life, and you play different roles in all of them.

As you learned in Chapter 3, one of the most basic human needs is the need to belong and to feel loved. Building and maintaining healthy relationships can help you meet this need. A **relationship** is *a bond or connection you have with other people.*

Although some people use the word *relationship* to refer to a romantic involvement, there are actually all kinds of relationships that can be important in your life. For instance, you have relationships with family members, friends, teachers, classmates, and people in your community. All of these relationships can affect your health in ways that may be positive or negative.

Teens Want to Know

What Should I Do If My Parents Don't Like My Friends? Discuss the following strategies that teens can use to deal with this common problem:

• Let your friends and family have a chance to get to know one another.

• Ask your parents to identify what they don't like about a friend. Address your parents' concerns about a friend's appearance, behavior, or attitude.

• Make sure your friends are respectful of your family—it's easy for parents to dislike someone who does not show respect to your family.

Relationships with Family

> Some of the most important relationships in your life are with the family members who share your home, such as parents or guardians, brothers, and sisters. You also have family relationships with other relatives, such as grandparents, aunts, uncles, and cousins. One thing that makes family relationships special is that they last your entire life. The friends you have in high school may not be your friends ten years from now, but your family is your family for life.
>
> Healthy family relationships strengthen every side of your health triangle. Parents or guardians take care of your physical needs for food, clothing, and shelter. The love, care, and encouragement they provide are important to your mental and emotional health. They also help build your social health by teaching you the values and social skills that will guide you in all your other relationships.

AL

Relationships with Friends

> A **friendship** is *a significant relationship between two people that is based on trust, caring, and consideration.* Although you probably have many friends your own age, friendships can form between people of any age. You may choose your friends because you have similar interests, because they share your values, or maybe just because they live nearby. Whatever the reason, good friends can benefit your health in many ways. They have a positive influence on your self-esteem and can help you resist harmful behaviors.

W

■ Figure 6.1 Strong friendships have a positive influence on your health. *What friendships are most important in your life?*

READING CHECK

Explain How can friends benefit your health?

Lesson 1 Foundations of a Healthy Relationship **143**

② TEACH

AL Active Learning

Collage Have students work in pairs to create a collage about relationships with a family member. Provide each pair of students with a large sheet of paper, glue, markers, old magazines, and other appropriate materials. Tell students their collages should include pictures that represent various family members. Have each pair of students present its collage to the class, describing the different types of relationships it illustrates. **BL** **OL**

W Writing Support

Descriptive Writing Ask students to suggest some words that describe friends. For example, students might identify *fun, loyal,* or *caring.* Record their responses on the board. Then have pairs of students write sentences describing friends or friendship. Tell students that the words listed on the board might help them get started. Ask volunteers to share their sentences with the class. **BL** **EL**

Caption Answer

Figure 6.1 Sample answer: My most important friendship is with my next-door neighbor.

Reading Strategy

Finding the Main Idea Explain to students that paragraphs often have one main idea. In some cases, the main idea is explicitly stated. In other cases, it must be inferred from the content of the paragraph as a whole. Ask students to reread the second paragraph under the "Relationships with Family" heading and identify the sentence that states the main idea. (Healthy family relationships strengthen every side of your health triangle.) Have students explain their choices. Then have students work with partners to find the main ideas of three other paragraphs in this lesson.

READING CHECK

Answer Friends have a positive influence on your self-esteem and can help you resist harmful behaviors.

Relationships in Your Community

Being part of a strong community has a positive impact on every aspect of your health. It can promote healthful behaviors and also provide resources to help you when you're in trouble. You reinforce your ties to the community through good **citizenship**—*the way you conduct yourself as a member of the community.* Good citizens work to strengthen their communities by obeying laws, being friendly to neighbors, and helping to improve the places where they live.

C

Roles in Relationships

A **role** is a *part you play in your relationships.* In the course of a single day, you may play many roles with different people. You might be a son or daughter at home, a student at school, a friend when you're hanging out with your buddies, a teammate during gym class, and an employee at an after-school job. For an illustration of how a single person can play many roles, see **Figure 6.2.**

U

Figure 6.2	**Intersecting Relationships**

This diagram illustrates the many overlapping roles that one teen, Felicia, plays in her relationships at home, at school, and in her community. *What different roles do you play in your life?*

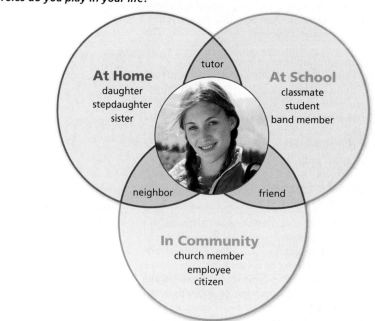

At Home
daughter
stepdaughter
sister

tutor

At School
classmate
student
band member

neighbor

friend

In Community
church member
employee
citizen

R

Home and Community

Staying Informed Explain that good citizens spend time learning about issues of importance in their school, community, state, and country. Have each student choose one issue in their community to learn more about. Issues in communities might be providing parks, improving streets, preventing gang violence, or controlling growth. Suggest that students use newspapers, Internet resources, televised news, or other reliable sources to learn more about the issue they have chosen. Then ask students to summarize what they have learned in a one- or two-paragraph-long written report. Ask students to share their reports with the class.

Sometimes you can even play more than one role with the same person. For instance, when you babysit a younger brother or sister, you temporarily take on the role of caregiver in that relationship. Your role in a relationship can also change over time. For example, someone you work with might become a friend.

Balancing all the different roles in your life can be tricky. You may feel at times that you can't handle all the demands being made on you. In such situations, you may decide that you need to focus more on one relationship right now.

Traits of Healthy Relationships

Main Idea In a healthy relationship, people respect and support each other.

Healthy relationships nurture you. They bring out the best in you and encourage you to make healthful choices in your life. Qualities of healthy relationships include

- **mutual respect.** You treat other people with respect, and they respect you in return. You accept each other's opinions, tastes, and traditions, even if they are different. At times you may agree to disagree instead of trying to force your opinions on each other.
- **caring.** You treat other people with kindness and consideration. During difficult times, you show empathy and support. You're also willing to help out others.
- **honesty.** You are honest and open with others, rather than concealing your thoughts, feelings, or actions.
- **commitment.** You contribute to the relationship and work to keep it strong, even if it means making some sacrifices. You deal with problems in a positive way and are able to overcome them.

Skills for Building Healthy Relationships

It takes work to maintain a healthy relationship. The people involved need to make an effort to understand each other and get along in different situations. Three skills that can help are communication, cooperation, and compromise—sometimes known as the three Cs of healthy relationships.

Communication As you learned in Chapter 2, *interpersonal communication* is the exchange of thoughts, feelings, and beliefs between two or more people. In relationships, people need to understand each other. It's important to learn effective communication skills so you can express your thoughts, feelings, and expectations to others and understand theirs in return. You will learn more about how to communicate well with others in Lesson 3.

■ **Figure 6.3** Communication is more than just talking. It's getting your message across to others and hearing their response. *Describe three different ways you might communicate with someone.*

READING CHECK

Identify What are the characteristics of a healthy relationship?

Lesson 1   Foundations of a Healthy Relationship   **145**

 **HS Health Skills Practice**
Communication Skills Tell students that people often base their style of communication on the particular role they play in a relationship. For example, teens communicate differently with their friends than they do with their teachers. Have each student write three short dialogues in which a teen communicates that he or she needs help with a difficult assignment. One dialogue should be with a parent, one with a friend, and one with a teacher. Have students share their dialogues with the class. **OL**

Main Idea

Traits of Healthy Relationships Respect and support are qualities of healthy relationships.
Ask Students: *What are some ways that support and respect enhance a relationship?* (Sample answer: Relationships that are based on support and respect tend to bring out the best in each person.)

CA Cultural Awareness
Showing Respect Point out to students that showing respect is one quality of a healthy relationship. Explain that this is true in all cultures, but ways of showing respect can vary widely between cultures. Ask students to do research to learn more about behaviors that are considered respectful in cultures other than their own. Have students share what they learned with the class. **OL**

READING CHECK

Answer Mutual respect, caring, honesty, commitment

Caption Answer

Figure 6.3 Sample answer: Talking in person, sending an e-mail, talking on the telephone

Teacher to Teacher

Jia Oliver Jordan • Booker T. Washington Magnet High School, Montgomery, AL

Skills for Healthy Relationships When teaching about the importance of healthy relationships, I have students write down everything they think they want in a personal relationship on a sheet of paper. I have them fold their papers and place them in a basket. Before reading any of the students' responses, I list some of the important factors one should look for in a relationship, i.e., (honesty, trust, friendship, or communication). Then I ask the class if anyone has any questions or comments. Students immediately chime in with comments and this opens our class discussion. I never read aloud their comments to the class; I use them to continue the next class discussion.

AL Active Learning

Comic Strip Have students work in pairs to write and illustrate a comic strip that demonstrates how cooperation can help build a healthy relationship. Show students several models of comic strips to help them get started. Encourage students to use creativity and humor, but remind them to include a clear connection to the lesson content. Display the completed comic strips in the classroom. **EL** **OL** **AL**

R Reading Strategy

Using Context Have students work in pairs to reread the text under each of the six traits of good character to find words or phrases that describe or define each trait. Have students make a list of all six traits and the words and phrases they identified. Then say aloud the traits and call on students to describe or define them using their lists. **BL** **EL**

FITNESS ZONE

Locomotor Sequences

Ask students to develop a workout sequence:

- Each student should think of a sequence of 8 moves or beats.

- Locomotor moves students can use include walking, skipping, galloping, slide-right, slide-left, leaping.

- Allow students to put their movement sequence to music and demonstrate their workout routine.

Caption Answer

Figure 6.4 caring, citizenship

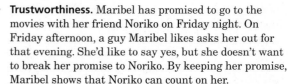

FITNESS ZONE

I always work out with a friend for a couple of reasons. A friend helps keep me motivated when I'm struggling to complete a workout. The other reason is that it's safer to work out with someone else. For more fitness tips, visit the Online Fitness Zone at glencoe.com.

Cooperation Have you ever had to move a heavy desk or other large piece of furniture? Tasks like this are nearly impossible without **cooperation**, *working together for the good of all*. Cooperating with others to reach a common goal can strengthen your relationships. For example, when Jonah and his mom worked together to build a set of shelves for his room, they learned to interact better together and shared a sense of accomplishment in the project.

AL

Compromise Sometimes, when people in relationships want different things, they may decide to compromise. **Compromise** is *a problem-solving method in which each participant gives up something to reach a solution that satisfies everyone.*

The give-and-take of effective compromise strengthens relationships. It allows you to resolve disagreements in a way that everyone can accept. Remember, though, that compromise works only when all the people involved are happy with the solution. You should *not* compromise on things that really matter to you, like your values and beliefs. The art of getting along with others involves knowing when it's appropriate to compromise and when you need to stand your ground.

Character and Relationships

In Chapter 3, you learned about the six traits of good character. Each of these traits contributes in its own way to healthy relationships. Here are examples of how each trait can strengthen a relationship.

R

- **Trustworthiness.** Maribel has promised to go to the movies with her friend Noriko on Friday night. On Friday afternoon, a guy Maribel likes asks her out for that evening. She'd like to say yes, but she doesn't want to break her promise to Noriko. By keeping her promise, Maribel shows that Noriko can count on her.

- **Respect.** Kyle's parents have taught him always to listen when someone else is talking and to avoid interrupting.

■ **Figure 6.4** Demonstrating the traits of good character can strengthen your relationships. *Which traits of good character is this teen showing?*

146   Chapter 6

More About...

Compromise Some teens may think that compromise involves a "winner" and a "loser." Others may think of compromising as arriving at a solution that makes no one happy. Tell students that there are strategies for compromising that avoid both of these negative outcomes. For example, if two friends cannot decide between two activities, good ways to compromise include taking turns or finding a third activity. Ask students to suggest scenarios that would require compromise. For each suggested scenario, have a class discussion of compromises that would have positive outcomes.

By extending this courtesy to each other whenever they talk, Kyle and his parents improve their communication as a family.

- **Responsibility.** While at a party, Tara accidentally knocks over a glass and breaks it. She immediately apologizes to the host, helps clean up the broken glass, and offers to pay to replace it. Her responsible action improves her host's opinion of her.

- **Fairness.** Enrique and his brother take turns using their computer to do schoolwork, send e-mail, and play games. Sharing the computer fairly keeps Enrique and his brother from fighting over it.

- **Caring.** When her friend Carl is having trouble with math, Alison offers to tutor him. Carl considers her a good friend for caring about him and helping him out.

- **Citizenship.** Ruby's family bought a snow blower to help keep the sidewalk and driveway clear. Now, in addition to clearing her own driveway, Ruby offers to do her neighbor's as well. Her actions improve her relationship with her neighbor and her reputation in the community.

> **Academic Vocabulary**
>
> **computer** *(noun):* a device that can store, retrieve, and process data

---

LESSON 1 ASSESSMENT

After You Read

Reviewing Facts and Vocabulary

1. Identify three kinds of relationships you have in your life.
2. Define *citizenship* and give an example of good citizenship.
3. What are the three Cs of healthy relationships?

Thinking Critically

4. **Analyze.** Explain how relationships with family members are important to all three sides of your health triangle.
5. **Synthesize.** Think about your interactions with other people over the course of a day. Analyze these interactions to identify what roles you played in your relationships that day. Summarize your findings.

Applying Health Skills

6. **Advocacy.** Brainstorm a list of ways that students can demonstrate good citizenship at school. Based on these ideas, create a flyer encouraging students to be good citizens of the school community.

Writing Critically

7. **Narrative.** Write a conversation between two characters who share a relationship. In your narrative, show how the communication between these characters affects their relationship in a positive or negative way.

 Online

Visit **glencoe.com** and complete the Interactive Study Guide for this lesson.

LESSON 1 ASSESSMENT ANSWERS

1. Sample answer: Family relationships, friendships, relationships in my community
2. *Citizenship* is the way you conduct yourself as a member of the community. An example of good citizenship is being friendly to neighbors.
3. Communication, cooperation, compromise
4. Sample answer: My family relationships are important to my physical health because my parents take care of my physical needs, such as food. The love my family provides is important to my mental/emotional health. My family enhances my social health by teaching me values.
5. Reponses will vary, but should identify roles in relationships, such as friend, student, and employee.
6. Flyers will vary.
7. Narratives will vary.

---

③ ASSESS/ CLOSE

Assessment Resources

📁 *FAST FILE* **ACTIVITIES**
Lesson 1 Quiz

💿 *ExamView Assessment Suite* CD-ROM

Visit glencoe.com for:
Online Quizzes
Online Learning Center

Progress Monitoring

Reteaching

Have students work in pairs. Have one of the students list the traits of good character aloud, one at a time. After each trait of good character is named, have the other student explain how that trait can strengthen a relationship. After all six traits have been named once, have students reverse roles and repeat the activity.

Enrichment

Have students analyze a story, song, or poem that describes a relationship. Ask students to write a paragraph stating whether or not they think it is a healthy relationship, based on the traits of healthy relationships. Have students cite evidence from the story, song, or poem to support their opinion.

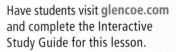 **Online**

Have students visit **glencoe.com** and complete the Interactive Study Guide for this lesson.

147

Respecting Yourself and Others

① FOCUS

GUIDE TO READING

BIG Idea Respecting yourself and others is a way to promote healthy relationships. **Ask Students:** *What are some ways that you can demonstrate self-respect?* (Sample answer: I can avoid unhealthful behaviors.)

Before You Read

T-Chart Students' T-charts will vary.

Main Idea

Respect for Yourself Self-respect strengthens relationships. **Ask Students:** *How can self-respect make a difference in the way you interact with others?* (Sample answer: Self-respect gives me the confidence to meet new people.)

Real Life Issues

Before writing their dialogues, have students consider ways that Marya can respectfully express her disapproval. **Ask Students:** *Have you ever spoken up to show disapproval of someone who is behaving in a way that is disrespectful of others?*

LESSON **2**

GUIDE TO READING

BIG Idea *You can promote healthy relationships by showing respect for yourself and others in your life.*

Before You Read

Create a T-Chart. Draw a two-column chart. Label the left column "Self-Respect" and the right column "Respect for Others." As you read, fill in the columns with information about how each type of respect can improve your relationships.

Self-Respect	Respect for Others

New Vocabulary

▶ prejudice (p. 150)
▶ stereotype (p. 150)
▶ tolerance (p. 150)
▶ bullying (p. 150)
▶ hazing (p. 150)

Review Vocabulary

▶ personal identity (Ch.3, L.2)
▶ values (Ch.2, L.2)

Respecting Yourself and Others

Real Life Issues

Stopping a Bully. While walking down the hall at school, Marya sees Scott intentionally bump into a boy walking in the opposite direction. Scott sneers, "Watch where you're going!" and laughs as the boy scrambles to pick up his dropped books and papers. Marya thinks Scott is acting like a bully, but she isn't sure how to make it clear that she doesn't approve of his behavior.

Writing *Write a dialogue in which Marya lets Scott know how she feels about his disrespectful behavior.*

Respect for Yourself

Main Idea Self-respect will strengthen your relationships.

Having self-respect is an important foundation for developing and maintaining healthy relationships. When you respect yourself, you're more likely to seek out relationships with people who treat you with respect. Self-respect makes you less likely to let other people talk you into taking risks that could harm your health.

The Need for Strong Values

During your teen years, you may be searching for your *personal identity*—your sense of who you are and where you belong in the world. Along the way, you may change your appearance or experiment with different interests and hobbies. You may also be struggling to develop your personal values system. *Values*, as you have learned, are the beliefs, ideas, and attitudes about what is important that help guide the way you live.

◆ Promoting School Wellness

Providing a Respectful Environment
A coordinated school health program includes the promotion of a healthy school environment. One component of a healthy school environment is respectful interactions.

Students should be encouraged to treat one another and the school staff respectfully at all times. Staff members can model respectful interactions in the way they treat one another and the students.

Being unsure of your values can complicate your relationships. If you aren't clear about your values, it's much more difficult to communicate them to others. As a result, the people around you may not be able to tell what is important to you. This could increase the chance that you'll face pressure to participate in unhealthful behaviors.

In contrast, when you are clear about your values, you strengthen your relationships. Other people will know what you believe in and understand what's important to you. Upholding your values shows that you respect yourself, and communicating your values to others can help them respect you too.

Respect for Others

Main Idea It's important to treat people with respect.

You can strengthen your relationships with all the people in your life by treating them with the same respect you'd like them to show you. With strangers and casual acquaintances, you can show respect through common courtesy. You might hold a door open for someone or say "Thank you" to the checker at the grocery store. With close friends and family members, you can show respect in more significant ways:

- **Listen to other people.** Be willing to hear and consider their points of view, even if you disagree with them.
- **Be considerate of others' feelings.** Before you act or speak, consider how it might make the other person feel.
- **Develop mutual trust.** Let others know they can trust you by being honest and dependable. Show that you trust them by believing what they say and confiding in them.
- **Be realistic in your expectations.** For example, you can't expect friends and family members to always make you their top priority.

✓ **READING CHECK**

Explain Why might being unsure about values complicate relationships?

■ **Figure 6.5** Lending your MP3 player to your brother is one way to show that you trust him. *What are some other ways to demonstrate trust?*

② TEACH

W Writing Support

Personal Writing Have a class discussion about the importance of having strong values. Remind students that values are beliefs, attitudes, and ideas about what is important. Then ask students to write a paragraph in which they identify and describe three of their values. Follow up by asking students to think about ways that they could communicate these values to others. OL AL

✓ **READING CHECK**

Answer If you are unsure about your values, others will also have difficulty understanding them. This may cause problems with communication and respect.

Main Idea

Respect for Others Treating people with respect is important. **Ask Students:** *What are some ways to show respect for others?* (Sample answer: Listening to them when they express their point of view)

Caption Answer

Figure 6.5 Sample answer: Confiding in another person

ELL Support

Suffixes Tell students that suffixes are word endings. Point out that *bullying* and *hazing* have the suffix *-ing.*

Beginning Write the words *bullying* and *hazing* on the board. Have a volunteer underline the suffix in both words. Ask students to identify other words that end in *-ing.*

Intermediate Write *bully-bullying; haze-hazing* on the board. Have students develop other word pairs (such as run-running, talk-talking) that have a similar pattern.

Advanced Have students write sentences using words that end in *-ing.* Have volunteers share their sentences aloud with the class.

149

LESSON 2

Answer It can keep people from getting to know others as individuals.

AL Active Learning

Slogan Lead a class discussion on ways that teens can discourage prejudices and stereotypes and encourage tolerance. Then have each student develop a short slogan promoting tolerance. Remind students that a slogan is a very brief, attention-getting phrase that summarizes a goal, an opinion, or a position. Have students share their completed slogans with the class. OL

HS Health Skills Practice

Advocacy Write the following on the board: *Imagine you are walking down the school hallway. You turn the corner and see one student being bullied by another.* Divide the class into small groups. Ask each group to develop a strategy for advocating for the student who is being bullied. Remind students that advocacy involves communicating a clear, health-enhancing stand and encouraging others to make healthful choices. Have each group share its strategy with the class. BL OL

Caption Answer

Figure 6.6 Sample answer: intimidated

☑ **READING CHECK**

Evaluate Why is prejudice a barrier to healthy relationships?

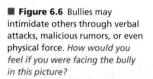

■ **Figure 6.6** Bullies may intimidate others through verbal attacks, malicious rumors, or even physical force. *How would you feel if you were facing the bully in this picture?*

150   Chapter 6   Skills for Healthy Relationships

Tolerance

Sometimes people treat others with disrespect because of prejudice. **Prejudice** is *an unfair opinion or judgment of a particular group of people.* For example, a teen might decide he dislikes all cheerleaders because a cheerleader once turned him down for a date. Some forms of prejudice involve stereotypes. A **stereotype** is *an exaggerated or oversimplified belief about people who belong to a certain group.* Assuming that all boys like sports is an example of a gender stereotype.

Prejudice is a barrier to healthy relationships. It can keep people from getting to know others as individuals. In contrast, demonstrating tolerance can help you build healthy relationships. **Tolerance** is *the ability to accept others' differences.* People who are tolerant value diversity and can appreciate differences in other people's cultures, interests, and beliefs.

AL

Disrespectful Behaviors

Has a fellow student ever picked on you for no reason? Perhaps this person called you names, or even threatened you with physical violence. This disrespectful behavior is an example of **bullying**—*deliberately harming or threatening other people who cannot easily defend themselves.* Bullies may tease their victims, spread rumors about them, or try to keep them out of a group. They may even attack others physically by pushing, shoving, or hitting them.

HS

Some bullies push other people around because it makes them feel superior. They may also do it as a way to feel they are part of a group or to keep from being bullied themselves. As many as one out of four students in the United States gets bullied on a regular basis. Kids and teens who are bullied at school may stay home out of fear. They may even try to harm themselves because the bullying has seriously damaged their self-esteem. Bullying behavior is also harmful to the bullies themselves. They are more likely to drop out of school and to have problems with alcohol or violence.

Hazing, a related problem, means *making others perform certain tasks in order to join the group.* Hazing activities may be physically or emotionally harmful. Examples include yelling or swearing, forcing new group members to go without sleep, physically beating them, or forcing them to drink alcohol. Severe hazing incidents have been known to result in death. Hazing is often meant to humiliate new members or prove that they are inferior to existing members.

Health Literacy

Hazing Hazing is a problem in many high schools, with incoming freshmen and new members of sports teams and music groups as the usual targets. Remind students that hazing is always wrong, even if it is perceived as a tradition and is ignored or condoned by adults. Victims of hazing need to know that most states have anti-hazing laws, and no individual should be demeaned, injured, or harassed in order to join a group. Encourage students who feel pressured to take part in hazing activities to seek help from a trusted adult.

Real World CONNECTION

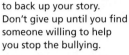

Dealing with a Bully

Stop Bullying Now! is a Web site run by the U.S. Department of Health and Human Services. The site recommends these steps for dealing with a bully:

▶ **Tell a trusted adult.** If you find this difficult to do, try bringing a friend with you to back up your story. Don't give up until you find someone willing to help you stop the bullying.

▶ **Stick with a group.** Bullies prefer to pick on kids or teens who are by themselves a lot. Having a group of friends around you makes you a less desirable target.

▶ **Try standing up to the bully.** Bullies tend to pick on people they see as weaker than themselves. Standing up to the bully shows that you won't be intimidated. Don't exchange insults or threaten a bully. Doing so can make the situation worse.

Activity   Reading / Writing

Work with a small group to write and perform a skit that illustrates the problem of bullying. Your skit should show how the bullied teen deals with the problem in a positive way.

Real World CONNECTION

Writing Activity

Have students work in small groups to write and practice skits about strategies for handling bullies. They should demonstrate positive ways to deal with this problem.

③ ASSESS/ CLOSE

Assessment Resources

📁 **FAST FILE ACTIVITIES**
Lesson 2 Quiz

💿 *ExamView*
Assessment Suite CD-ROM

Visit glencoe.com for:
Online Quizzes
Online Learning Center

Progress Monitoring

Reteaching
Have pairs of students discuss each of the figures and figure caption questions in the lesson. Call on volunteers to summarize the main idea presented in each of the figures.

Enrichment
Have students record instances of prejudices and stereotypes in television shows or popular music they see in one week. Have them share results with the class.

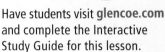

Have students visit **glencoe.com** and complete the Interactive Study Guide for this lesson.

LESSON 2 📖 ASSESSMENT

After You Read

Reviewing Facts and Vocabulary

1. Identify four ways to show respect in your relationships.
2. What are *stereotypes*?
3. List three reasons some teens bully others.

Thinking Critically

4. **Synthesize.** Give an example of how demonstrating strong values can strengthen your relationships with others.
5. **Analyze.** How is bullying different from hazing?

Applying Health Skills

6. **Decision Making.** Ahmed has just made the swim team, but he's concerned about reports that the varsity swimmers haze the new members. Use the decision-making process to analyze how Ahmed might deal with this problem.

Writing Critically

7. **Persuasive.** Write an editorial about the problem of bullying in schools. Your article should encourage students to help create a positive climate in which bullying is not tolerated.

 Online

Visit **glencoe.com** and complete the Interactive Study Guide for this lesson.

LESSON 2 ASSESSMENT ANSWERS

1. Listen to others, be considerate of others' feelings, develop mutual trust, and be realistic in your expectations.
2. *Stereotypes* are exaggerated or oversimplified beliefs about people who belong to a certain group.
3. To make themselves feel superior, to feel they are part of a group, to keep from being bullied themselves
4. Sample answer: If you show that you value your health, your friends will not try to persuade you to put your health at risk.
5. Sample answer: Bullying is often used to exclude someone from a group, while hazing is used to make someone feel included in a group.
6. Sample answer: Ahmed should state the situation, list his options, and weigh the possible outcomes of each option. He should consider his values, make his decision, and then evaluate his decision.
7. Editorials will vary.

Communicating Effectively

1 FOCUS

BIG Idea Healthy relationships require effective communication. **Ask Students:** *What are some qualities that make a person fun to talk to?* (Sample answer: Having a good sense of humor and being a good listener)

Before You Read

Word Web Students' word webs should include words and phrases that describe characteristics of effective communication.

Communication Styles There are three major styles of communication. **Ask Students:** *How does it feel to listen to a person who is pushy, rude, or hostile?* (Sample answer: When someone is rude to me, I don't want to hear what he or she has to say.)

Real Life Issues

Before students write their letters, ask them to think about ways that Erin could express her feelings. **Ask Students:** *Have you ever been in a situation like Erin's? If so, what actions did you take to help solve the problem?* (Sample answer: Yes. I finally called my friend on the phone to discuss the problem.)

LESSON **3**

GUIDE TO READING

BIG Idea *Effective communication is a key to building healthy relationships.*

Before You Read

Create a Word Web. Write the phrase "Effective Communication" in the center of a piece of paper. Jot down characteristics of effective communication. As you read, add more notes to your word web.

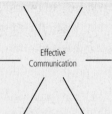

Effective Communication

New Vocabulary

▶ aggressive (p. 152)
▶ passive (p. 152)
▶ assertive (p. 153)
▶ "I" message (p. 154)
▶ active listening (p. 154)
▶ body language (p. 155)

Review Vocabulary

▶ constructive criticism (Ch.3, L.2)

Communicating Effectively

Real Life Issues ....

A Pushy Friend. Erin's friend Louise is the kind of person who always wants to have her own way. When they go out together, Louise decides where they'll go and what they'll do. If Erin offers a suggestion, Louise dismisses it. Erin wants to stay friends with Louise, but she's tired of being pushed around. She wishes she knew how to stand up for herself without being rude.

Writing *Write a letter from Erin to Louise. In it, Erin should discuss how Louise's behavior makes her feel and explain that she'd like to have a say in what they do.*

Communication Styles

Main Idea There are three types of communication styles.

Do you know someone who's like Louise, always insisting on doing things her own way? How about someone who's like Erin, always going along with what other people suggest? These two characters reflect two of the three major styles of communication:

- **Aggressive.** Being **aggressive** means being *overly forceful, pushy, or hostile.* It may involve bullying or intimidation. People with an aggressive communication style may not pay attention to others' thoughts, feelings, or needs.

- **Passive.** Being **passive** means being *unwilling or unable to express thoughts and feelings in a direct or firm manner.* This involves putting other's needs ahead of your own. People may adopt a passive communication style because they dislike conflict and will go out of their way to avoid an argument.

R

Skills for the **21st** Century

Communication The ability to clearly express ideas using different technologies is a skill that will enhance students' performance at school and in the workplace. Have students work in pairs to identify two methods of communication, for example, written mail and e-mail. Have students discuss situations in which they would or would not use these forms of communication. For example, they might not use e-mail to thank someone for a job interview, and they probably wouldn't use written mail to confirm the time to meet a friend. Then lead a class discussion about the similarities and differences among different forms of communication. Emphasize the importance of respect in all forms of communication.

- **Assertive.** Being **assertive** means *expressing your views clearly and respectfully.* Assertiveness involves standing up for your rights and beliefs while also respecting those of others. Dealing with a disagreement in an assertive way can involve negotiating with others to find the best solution to the problem.

Using an assertive communication style will improve your relationships with others. It will help ensure that your own needs are met, along with those of other people.

Ways to Communicate

Main Idea To communicate effectively, you need to learn speaking skills, listening skills, and nonverbal communication.

Communication is a two-way street. It's not enough just to get your messages across to the other person. You also need to understand the messages being sent to you. This includes both verbal and nonverbal messages.

Speaking Skills

The key to good communication is to say what you mean. It's not reasonable to expect other people to read your mind or be able to pick up on subtle hints. If something's on your mind, you need to say what it is. For example, if a friend has hurt your feelings, you need to let that person know as clearly and directly as you can.

■ **Figure 6.7** Communicating assertively makes your relationships run more smoothly. *Which teen in this photo would you say is communicating assertively? How can you tell?*

Lesson 3   Communicating Effectively   **153**

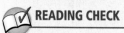
✓ **READING CHECK**

Identify What are the three styles of communication?

✓ **READING CHECK**

Answer Aggressive, passive, and assertive

② TEACH

R Reading Strategy

Organizing Information After students have read the descriptions of passive, aggressive, and assertive communication, make a three-column table on the board. Label one column "Passive," the next "Assertive," and the third "Aggressive." Ask volunteers to come forward and write sentences under the appropriate headings in the table that are examples of the three styles of communication. Once each column contains several sentences, ask students to compare and contrast the three styles of communication. **BL OL**

Main Idea

Ways to Communicate Communicating effectively involves developing good speaking skills, listening skills, and nonverbal communication. **Ask Students:** *How can careful listening help you avoid misunderstandings with friends?* (Sample answer: If you listen carefully, you gather all the information your friend is conveying.)

Caption Answer

Figure 6.7 The teen on the right is communicating assertively. I can tell because the teen is speaking calmly and is trying to calm the others.

Academic Integration

English Writing dialogues can help students practice effective communication. Review with students the following information about correctly writing dialogue.

- Quotation marks are used to enclose direct quotes (someone's exact words).
- Terminal punctuation, such as periods, commas, exclamation points, and ques-

tions marks, is placed before the ending quotation mark.

- Full sentences within quotation marks start with a capital letter.

Have students point out examples of written dialogue in the chapter. Then ask students to practice writing several sentences of dialogue using dialogue in the text as a model.

Caption Answer

Figure 6.8 "I" messages clearly communicate your feelings without placing blame, so a listener is likely to be receptive. "You" messages place blame and can seem like an attack, so people are less willing to listen.

R **Reading Strategy**

Interpreting a Table Have students read the examples of "You" messages and "I" messages in **Figure 6.8**. Then ask students to work in small groups to develop three additional statements for each side of the table. Call on each group to share its results with the class. **BL** **OL**

U **Universal Access**

Listening Skills Stress how important listening skills are when it comes to communication. Have students practice active listening by pairing up. Each student should take turns talking while the partner actively listens. **OL**

Figure 6.8	**"You" Messages and "I" Messages**

Compare the messages in these two columns. *How might a listener react to each message?*

"You" Messages	"I" Messages
"Why can't you ever show up on time?"	"I really don't like to be left waiting—it makes me feel like you don't think I'm important."
"You never listen to anything I say."	"I feel like my suggestions aren't being taken seriously."
"I said I'd take out the trash, and I will! You don't have to nag me about it every five minutes!"	"I'm feeling stressed because I have a big project due tomorrow. I'll take out the trash as soon as I finish working on this."
"You're always taking my CDs without asking."	"It bothers me when I get home and find all my CDs in your room."
"You always ignore me when your other friends are around."	"I feel hurt when I'm left out of a conversation."

Of course, being clear and direct doesn't mean being disrespectful. When people feel that they are being attacked, they may be less willing to listen. One way to make sure you don't sound disrespectful when talking about a touchy subject is to use "I" messages. An **"I" message** is *a statement that focuses on your feelings rather than on someone else's behavior*. Using "I" messages helps you communicate your feelings in a positive way without placing blame on someone else. **Figure 6.8** gives some examples of "I" messages.

Listening Skills

To communicate effectively, listening is just as important as speaking. You can make sure other people's messages get through to you by practicing **active listening**, *paying close attention to what someone is saying and communicating.* Here are some ways to practice active listening:

U

- **Don't interrupt.** Give your full attention to what the speaker is saying.

- **Show interest.** Face the speaker and make eye contact to show that you are paying attention. You can also encourage the speaker by nodding or making comments, such as "I see," "Go on," or "I understand," at appropriate times.

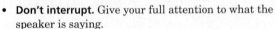

Myths & **Reality**

"You" Messages and "I" Messages

Myth: I need to use a "You" message to get someone to change his or her behavior or actions.

Fact: "I" messages are a more effective way to communicate because they do not place blame. "You" messages seem disrespectful and often this language makes it harder to get your message across.

Myth: "I" messages are a passive way to communicate.

Fact: "I" messages are an assertive style of communication. This type of message allows you to clearly express your thoughts and feelings.

- **Restate what you hear.** Rephrase or summarize the speaker's words to make sure you understand what you're hearing.
- **Ask questions.** Asking questions can help you understand what the speaker is saying. It can also help the speaker clarify her own thoughts and feelings.
- **Show empathy.** Let the other person know that you can relate to his feelings. Try not to pass judgment on the speaker's attitudes and actions.

Nonverbal Communication

Sometimes what you say isn't as important as how you say it. A comment such as "Nice outfit" can actually sound like an insult if it's delivered in a sarcastic tone. Your tone of voice is an example of nonverbal communication.

Your body language can also affect the meaning of the messages you send. **Body language** is *nonverbal communication through gestures, facial expressions, behaviors, and posture.* It includes everything from nodding, which shows that you agree, to turning away, which shows that you aren't listening. **Figure 6.9** shows different examples of body language.

Sometimes you send messages through body language without even realizing it. If you're feeling embarrassed, you may look at the ground instead of at the person you're talking to. In some cases, your body language may even **contradict** what you're saying. For instance, saying "I'm fine" in an angry tone will probably make people think you're anything but fine. Being aware of your body language can help you avoid sending mixed messages that may confuse your listeners.

READING CHECK

Describe What does active listening involve?

Academic Vocabulary

contradict *(verb):* to imply the opposite of

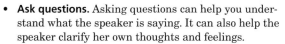

Figure 6.9 Using Body Language

Body language is an important part of nonverbal communication.

"I'm really interested in what you're saying."

"I don't want to talk to you."

"I'm worried."

Lesson 3   Communicating Effectively   **155**

AL Active Learning

Analyzing Listening Skills
Have students observe conversations that occur on television shows over the course of three days. Ask students to make notes of any active listening skills they observe being demonstrated in these conversations. At the end of the three-day period, ask volunteers to share their observations with the class. **OL AL**

READING CHECK

Answer Listening without interrupting or making judgments, showing that you are paying attention, restating what you hear, and asking questions to make sure you understand

C Critical Thinking

Discussing Ask students if they have ever been misunderstood in a letter or e-mail because they were not able to use nonverbal cues such as gestures or tone of voice when they conveyed their message. Then ask students to identify strategies or techniques they use in written communication to replace body language. (For example, spelling out their thoughts more completely or using emoticons to indicate emotions) **OL**

Academic Vocabulary

Contradict Explain that *contra* in *contradict* means "opposite" or "against." Ask students to brainstorm other words that contain the word part *contra-* (Examples include contrary, contrast, and contraceptive.) Then have volunteers use the word *contradict* in spoken sentences.

Cooperative Learning

Active Listening Divide the class into groups of three students: a speaker, an active listener, and an observer. Make a list of topics on the board for students to use. Explain to students that they have two minutes to discuss their first topic. After the speaker has spoken and the listener has paraphrased what has been said, have the observer offer constructive criticism and feedback of the active listening skills that were demonstrated. Repeat the activity two more times so each student has a chance to serve in each role within his or her group.

Health Skills Activity

Communication Skills: Coping with Criticism

NHES Standard 4 Students will demonstrate the ability to use interpersonal communication skills to enhance health and avoid or reduce health risks.

Objectives

- Understand and apply the guidelines for effective communication.
- Demonstrate communication skills to express feelings and bring about positive change.

Teaching Strategies

- Have students review the guidelines for good communication.
- Have students discuss ways that Dennis can express his feelings to Vince.

Assessment

Using this list, student work should provide comprehensive evidence of the following criteria to achieve the highest score:

√ Demonstrates a clear understanding of how to apply the guidelines for effective communication
√ Speaks calmly and clearly
√ Uses "I" messages
√ Shows respect and empathy
√ Listens carefully, and asks appropriate questions

Offering Useful Feedback

Main Idea Offering constructive feedback can improve your relationships with others.

Even in a strong relationship, every now and then people say or do things that bother other people. You might have a friend who's lots of fun to be around, except for the fact that he always interrupts you when you're talking. If you want your friend to change his behavior, you have to let him know how you feel—but in a way that doesn't come across as a personal attack. In other words, you need to offer constructive criticism, nonhostile comments that point out problems and encourage improvement.

The goal of constructive criticism is to bring about positive changes. Thus, it's counterproductive to give it in an aggressive way. Attacking someone isn't going to encourage him to change. Instead, use "I" messages that focus on the problem, not on the person. To offer constructive criticism, point out a specific problem, explain why it bothers you, and suggest a solution. You might say, "I feel that sometimes my ideas don't get heard. I would like to finish what I'm saying. Then I'll be glad to listen to any responses."

Letting people know how their actions make you feel isn't something you should do only when there's a problem. It's also important to let people know you appreciate what they do for you. If a friend goes out of her way to help you and doesn't get so much as a "thank you," she might feel that her actions went unnoticed or unappreciated. Let the people in your life know you value them. Tell your dad how much you enjoyed a meal that he prepared, or compliment a friend on her artistic skills. A little appreciation can go a long way in strengthening a relationship.

✓ READING CHECK

Explain What is the goal of constructive criticism?

■ **Figure 6.10** Encouraging your friends to pursue their interests is one way to show your appreciation for them. *What are other ways to let people in your life know you value them?*

Teens Want to Know

Why Do I Have Such a Hard Time Accepting Constructive Criticism?

Many teens have a difficult time accepting constructive criticism. One common reaction to constructive criticism is to become defensive. This is perfectly normal. Point out, though, that learning to listen to and cope with constructive criticism will allow them to strengthen relationships and grow as a person. Remind students that constructive criticism has a positive intention. Have students form small groups. Within each group, have students discuss strategies for accepting constructive criticism in positive ways.

Health Skills Activity

Communication Skills

Coping with Criticism

Dennis is working on an important history project with Vince. Unfortunately, Vince seems to think everything Dennis does is wrong. He complained that Dennis wasn't doing any of the writing, but when Dennis did write something, Vince said it was poorly done and rewrote it completely.

Now Vince is complaining that he's doing all the work. Dennis is frustrated because he feels nothing will satisfy Vince. The constant criticism is starting to take a toll on his self-esteem.

Writing Write a dialogue between Dennis and Vince. Dennis should let Vince know how his criticism makes him feel, and ask if Vince can offer more constructive advice. Remember to use the following rules for good communication:

1. Speak calmly and clearly.
2. Use "I" messages.
3. Show respect and empathy.
4. Listen carefully and ask appropriate questions.

LESSON 3 ASSESSMENT

After You Read

Reviewing Facts and Vocabulary

1. What are the three main styles of communication?
2. List three ways to show interest in what another person is saying.
3. Define the term *body language* and give an example.

Thinking Critically

4. **Evaluate.** Leah is an aggressive communicator. When somebody says something she disagrees with, she always says, "You're wrong!" How could Leah's communication style affect her relationships with others?
5. **Synthesize.** In a paragraph, discuss how having strong communication in your relationships can contribute to your personal health and safety.

Applying Health Skills

6. **Analyzing Influences.** Think about different factors that can influence how you communicate with others. Factors may include family, environment, peers, culture, or personality. In a paragraph, discuss how one of these factors affects your personal communication style.

Writing Critically

7. **Narrative.** Write a dialogue in which one character offers constructive criticism to another. Follow the guidelines for giving constructive criticism.

Go Online

Visit **glencoe.com** and complete the Interactive Study Guide for this lesson.

Lesson 3 Communicating Effectively **157**

---

3 ASSESS/ CLOSE

Assessment Resources

 FAST FILE ACTIVITIES
Lesson 3 Quiz

 ExamView Assessment Suite CD-ROM

Visit glencoe.com for:
Online Quizzes
Online Learning Center

Progress Monitoring

Reteaching
Have students use index cards or small slips of paper to make a flash card for each Lesson 3 vocabulary term. Ask students to use their completed flash cards with a partner to review the lesson vocabulary.

Enrichment
Have each student write a ten-question quiz about the content of Lesson 3. After the quizzes are completed, have students exchange quizzes with a partner. Have each student take the quiz he or she receives, then return the quiz to its writer for grading.

Go Online

Have students visit **glencoe.com** and complete the Interactive Study Guide for this lesson.

LESSON 3 ASSESSMENT ANSWERS

1. Aggressive, passive, and assertive
2. Sample answer: Face the speaker, make eye contact, nod or make comments at appropriate times
3. Sample answer: Nonverbal communication through gestures, facial expressions, behaviors, and posture; nodding your head to show agreement with the speaker
4. Sample answer: It might make others reluctant to talk to her at all because they do not want to be attacked.
5. Sample answer: Strong communication can help you tell others that you will not engage in risky behaviors.
6. Paragraphs will vary.
7. Dialogues will vary.

The New Employee

NHES Standard 4 Students will demonstrate the ability to use interpersonal communication skills to enhance health and avoid or reduce health risks.

Teaching Objectives

- Demonstrate effective communication skills to advocate for personal health and safety.
- Utilize role-playing techniques for communicating effectively with others to enhance health.

Teaching Strategies

- Place students into groups of two or three. Provide each group with a minimum of five index cards and have students follow the steps in the activity.
- When students have completed and rehearsed their scripts, instruct them to role-play the situation between Rachel and the manager for the class.
- Instruct the class to write down each effective communication skill they observe during the role-play.
- Lead a class discussion about the use of communication skills and the options Rachel might have if the conditions at work are not resolved in a healthy way after her meeting with the manager.

Assessment

Using a rubric, student work should provide comprehensive evidence of the following criteria to achieve the highest score:

- ✓ Includes clear, organized messages
- ✓ Uses "I" messages
- ✓ Applies listening skills
- ✓ Employs respectful tone
- ✓ Demonstrates appropriate body language

Checklist: Communication Skills

- ✓ Clear, organized message
- ✓ "I" messages
- ✓ Active listening
- ✓ Respectful tone
- ✓ Appropriate body language
- ✓ Reason(s) for the request

Activity The New Employee

Rachel has an after-school job at a local store. A new employee started working there recently, and his behavior is often aggressive and inappropriate. Rachel wants to talk to the manager, but she doesn't know where to begin.

What You'll Need

- paper and pen or pencil
- 5 or more index cards

What You'll Do

Step 1

Review the communication skills outlined in the chapter. On the front of each index card, write one skill that Rachel will need to communicate effectively with her manager. On the back of each card, describe how to use that communication skill in this situation.

Step 2

Arrange the cards in the order that Rachel should use them.

Step 3

Use the index cards to help you write a script in which Rachel discusses her concerns with her manager.

Apply and Conclude

Rehearse and role-play the script with classmates. Make sure that Rachel's needs and feelings are clearly communicated to her manager.

Writing Strategy

Journal Writing Ask students to write a private journal entry reflecting on their own use of communication skills. Encourage them to include specific examples of situations in which their communication skills were ineffective and to describe how stronger communication skills could have led to a different outcome. Suggest that students include in their entry short-term goals for strengthening their communication skills.

To download quizzes and eFlashcards to your PDA, go to **glencoe.com** and click on the Study to Go icon.

LESSON **1**

Foundations of a Healthy Relationship

Key Concepts

▸ Relationships in your life affect all sides of your health triangle.

▸ Important relationships in your life may include family relationships, friendships, and relationships in your community.

▸ Healthy relationships involve mutual respect, caring, honesty, and commitment.

▸ Communication, cooperation, and compromise are important skills for building healthy relationships.

▸ Demonstrating the six traits of good character strengthens your relationships.

Vocabulary

▸ relationship (p. 142)
▸ friendship (p. 143)
▸ citizenship (p. 144)
▸ role (p. 144)
▸ interpersonal communication (p. 145)
▸ cooperation (p. 146)
▸ compromise (p. 146)

LESSON **2**

Respecting Yourself and Others

Key Concepts

▸ Having self-esteem and demonstrating strong values can improve your relationships with other people.

▸ You can strengthen your relationships with all the people in your life by treating them with respect.

▸ Demonstrating tolerance, or the ability to accept others' differences, can help you build healthy relationships.

▸ Bullying and hazing are disrespectful and harmful behaviors.

Vocabulary

▸ personal identity (p. 148)
▸ values (p. 148)
▸ prejudice (p. 150)
▸ stereotype (p. 150)
▸ tolerance (p. 150)
▸ bullying (p. 150)
▸ hazing (p. 150)

LESSON **3**

Communicating Effectively

Key Concepts

▸ You can improve your relationships by communicating assertively, rather than aggressively or passively.

▸ Communication involves speaking, listening, and nonverbal communication such as body language.

▸ Using "I" messages helps you communicate your feelings in a positive way without placing blame on someone else.

▸ Active listening involves paying close attention to what someone is saying and communicating.

▸ Constructive criticism can bring about positive changes by pointing out problems in a nonhostile way.

Vocabulary

▸ aggressive (p. 152)
▸ passive (p. 152)
▸ assertive (p. 153)
▸ "I" message (p. 154)
▸ active listening (p. 154)
▸ body language (p. 155)
▸ constructive criticism (p. 156)

 Go Online

Students can visit **glencoe.com** to

• review content online with the Online Student Edition.

• test their knowledge of chapter content with Online Quizzes.

• access Interactive Health Tutor for more practice with vocabulary.

Assessment Resources

📁 *FAST FILE* ACTIVITIES
Chapter 6 Test

💿 *ExamView*
Assessment Suite CD-ROM

Visit glencoe.com for:
Audio Chapter Summaries
Online Quizzes

 Tell students to visit **glencoe.com** where they can download quizzes and eFlashcards.

Chapter 6 Review **159**

Study Tips

Review Each Day Explain that reviewing lesson content and class notes each day is an excellent way to improve retention of material. Suggest that students spend a short period of time each day rereading class notes from the day. They should also review relevant information from the text. Explain that reviewing material for a short period of time each day is more effective than trying to learn large amounts of material right before a test.

Assessment

Chapter 6
Assessment Answers

LESSON 1

Vocabulary Review

1. relationship
2. Communication
3. compromise

Understanding Key Concepts

4. c
5. a
6. b

Thinking Critically

7. Sample answer: I am a sibling in my relationships with my brothers and sisters. At school, I have the roles of student, peer, and friend.

8. Sample answer: I get along better with others when we work together to meet common goals.

9. Sample answers: I would not be willing to compromise in a situation that goes against my values, such as being asked to help a friend shoplift. I would also be unwilling to compromise about decisions that would affect my health or safety, such as wearing a safety belt in the car.

10. Sample answer: Trustworthiness is a trait of good character. When your friends know that they can count on you, it strengthens your relationships.

LESSON 2

Vocabulary Review

11. Prejudice
12. tolerance
13. bullying

LESSON 1

Vocabulary Review
Choose the correct word in the sentences below.

1. A bond or connection you have with other people is called a *relationship / friendship.*

2. *Communication / Citizenship* lets you express your thoughts, feelings, and expectations to others.

3. In *cooperation / compromise,* each participant gives up something to reach a solution that satisfies everyone.

Understanding Key Concepts
After reading the question or statement, select the correct answer.

4. Which of the following is an example of good citizenship?
   a. Looking after a younger brother or sister
   b. Helping a friend study for a test
   c. Taking part in an effort to clean up a local river
   d. Getting good grades in school

5. Jeanne and her father have very different political views. However, they accept their differences and do not try to change each other's opinions. Which quality of strong relationships does this action show?
   a. Mutual respect   c. Honesty
   b. Caring   d. Commitment

6. Which of the following is an example of compromise?
   a. Sympathizing with a friend who didn't get cast in the school play
   b. Agreeing to babysit your brother on Friday night if your parents will let you stay out later on Saturday
   c. Working with classmates to decorate the school gym for a dance
   d. Complaining to a parent about the amount of homework you have

---

Thinking Critically
After reading the question or statement, write a short answer using complete sentences.

7. **Describe.** Identify and describe three roles you play in your relationships with others.

8. **Explain.** How does cooperation strengthen your relationships?

9. **Evaluate.** Give an example of a situation in which you should *not* be willing to compromise.

10. **Synthesize.** Identify one trait of good character, and give an example of how it can strengthen a relationship.

LESSON 2

Vocabulary Review
Use the vocabulary terms listed on page 159 to complete the following statements.

11. _____ is an unfair opinion or judgment of a particular group of people.

12. People display _____ when they recognize and appreciate the differences among people.

13. Deliberately harming or threatening other people who cannot easily defend themselves is known as _____.

Understanding Key Concepts
After reading the question or statement, select the correct answer.

14. Teens who respect themselves probably will choose friends who
   a. are the smartest students in the class.
   b. participate in a wide variety of school activities.
   c. share all of their beliefs, tastes, and values.
   d. treat them with respect.

Health eSpotlight | VIDEO | Wrap-Up

It Starts with Respect Have students reread the Health eSpotlight questions at the beginning of the chapter (page 141) and look at their original answers. **Ask Students:** *Now that you have read the chapter and* *watched the video, how would you respond differently about the qualities of a good friend?* Call on volunteers to describe how their responses would change.

15. Which of the following statements is *not* an example of prejudice?
   a. I get nervous when I'm in large groups of strangers.
   b. I think kids from private schools are stuck-up.
   c. I don't want girls on our baseball team because they can't throw.
   d. I want to be friends only with Asian American kids because they're such good students.

16. Which of the following is *not* an example of bullying?
   a. Repeatedly making fun of the way a classmate talks
   b. Threatening to beat up a student if he doesn't hand over his lunch money
   c. Refusing to accept someone into your group unless she wears a certain brand of clothing
   d. Shoving a younger kid on the school bus

17. If you are being bullied at school, you should
   a. just ignore the bully until she goes away.
   b. stay home from school to avoid the bully.
   c. get a group of friends to gang up on the bully and attack him.
   d. tell a trusted adult about the problem and ask for help.

Thinking Critically

After reading the question or statement, write a short answer using complete sentences.

18. **Discuss.** How might you demonstrate respect in your relationship with a teacher?

19. **Explain.** In what ways can prejudice harm relationships?

20. **Analyze.** Explain how bullying can be harmful both to victims and to bullies themselves.

21. **Evaluate.** At Corinne's school, students who are new to the drama club usually get assigned to sing in the chorus or paint the sets. In contrast, more experienced students get the lead roles in the plays. Is this an example of hazing? Explain why or why not.

 **LESSON 3**

Vocabulary Review

Correct the sentences below by replacing the italicized term with the correct vocabulary term.

22. Trying to get your own way through bullying or intimidation is an example of *passive* communication.

23. Someone using *assertive* communication is unwilling or unable to express his thoughts and feelings.

24. When you use *body language*, you focus on your own feelings rather than on someone else's behavior.

Understanding Key Concepts

After reading the question or statement, select the correct answer.

25. Some of the friends in your group want to go out for Thai food, but you don't like Thai food. Which of the following would be an assertive way to respond?
   a. Tell them Thai food is not your favorite and politely suggest an alternative.
   b. Go with them for Thai food, but don't eat anything.
   c. Just go along with whatever the group wants.
   d. Insist on going for Mexican food instead.

26. Which of the following skills is *not* a part of active listening?
   a. Listening without interrupting
   b. Making eye contact with the speaker
   c. Asking questions for clarification
   d. Using "I" messages

Understanding Key Concepts

14. d
15. a
16. c
17. d

Thinking Critically

18. Sample answer: Pay attention in class and complete assignments on time.

19. Sample answer: It can keep people from getting to know others as individuals.

20. Sample answer: Victims of bullies may feel fearful all the time, develop low self-esteem, or even try to hurt themselves. Bullies are more likely to drop out of school and to have problems with alcohol or violence.

21. No, because the students are not required to do harmful or humiliating tasks in order to join the group. Parts are simply assigned on the basis of experience.

LESSON 3

Vocabulary Review

22. aggressive
23. passive
24. "I" messages

Understanding Key Concepts

25. a
26. d
27. b
28. d

ExamView®
Assessment Suite

Create and customize tests in minutes with this convenient digital platform.

- Create differentiated tests quickly and easily.
- All questions correlated to National/State Standards.
- Enhance tests with Document Based Questions (DBQ) and add your own photos or graphics.
- Generate progress reports.
- Build tests in both English and Spanish.

To order, go to **glencoe.com** and search for ISBN 0-07-888173-0.

Assessment

Thinking Critically

29. Assertive communication is best because it helps ensure that your needs and the needs of others are met.

30. You send messages to others through speaking and through body language. You receive messages from others by listening and by reading their body language.

31. Sample answer: Listen without interrupting, except to say "I see" to show you're listening. Ask questions such as "How do you feel about it?" Show empathy by letting her know you understand how she feels.

32. Sample answers: "I" messages focus on the problem, not on the person. Because "I" messages do not attack the other person, he or she may be more willing to listen to the feedback.

27. If you stand with your hands on your hips and your lips in a frown while someone is talking, what message might you be sending with your body language?
    a. "I'm really interested in everything you're saying."
    b. "I'm feeling angry."
    c. "I'm embarrassed about something."
    d. "I don't feel like listening to you right now."

28. Which of the following is an example of constructive criticism?
    a. "Do you always have to leave all your junk out in the hall?"
    b. "I can't stand the way you interrupt me all the time."
    c. "Haven't you ever heard of knocking? You're always barging into my room!"
    d. "Next time, would you mind calling first to let me know you're coming over?"

Thinking Critically

After reading the question or statement, write a short answer using complete sentences.

29. **Evaluate.** Which communication style will most enhance your relationships? Explain how.

30. **Analyze.** Describe the roles that speaking, listening, and body language play in communication.

31. **Synthesize.** A friend calls to tell you that she just broke up with her boyfriend. Explain how you might use active listening in this situation.

32. **Explain.** Why are "I" messages an important part of constructive criticism?

Project-Based ASSESSMENT

Effective Communication Skills

Background
As you've learned, effective communication involves strong speaking and listening skills. An understanding of nonverbal communication, such as tone of voice and body language, is also necessary.

Task
Write and perform two skits showing different methods of communication. The first skit should show how someone with weak communication skills may end up sending mixed messages. The second skit should demonstrate how using effective communication skills can prevent the problems shown in the first skit.

Audience
Students in your class

Purpose
Demonstrate and practice communication skills.

Procedure
1. Make a list of barriers to effective communication.
2. Use the list to draft a skit in which a teen experiences problems in communication, such as sending mixed messages.
3. Next, make a list of effective communication strategies.
4. Based on this list, write a second skit in which the teen avoids communication problems by using effective strategies.
5. Reread both skits, and make any necessary revisions.
6. Work with classmates to practice and perform your skits.

162   Chapter 6   Assessment

Project-Based ASSESSMENT

Step 1 Make Lists Have each student make a list of ineffective communication skills and use the list to write a draft of the first skit. Then students should make a list of effective communication skills and write a draft of the second skit.

Step 2 Revise Have students reread and revise their skits. Then have them work in small groups to practice and perform their skits for the class.

Step 3 Evaluate Evaluate each set of skits based on how well they contrast the use of ineffective communication skills with the use of effective communication skills.

Visit **glencoe.com** for Project-Based Assessment rubrics.

Math Practice

Calculate Percentages. Bullying occurs more frequently among middle school students, but it also happens in high school. This diagram shows the estimated number of students affected by bullying.

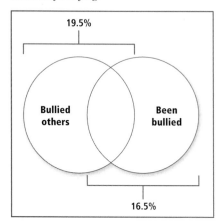

1. About 6% of all students have both bullied other students and have been the victim of a bully. From this information and the diagram, what percentage of students have either been bullied or have bullied another student, but not both?
   A. 3.5%   **C.** 30%
   B. 6%   **D.** 36%

2. Suppose there are 842 students in your school. Using the percentages shown in the diagram, estimate the number of students in your school who have bullied another student.
   A. 25   **C.** 139
   B. 51   **D.** 164

3. Using the percentages given above, explain how you would determine the number of students in your school who have neither bullied another student nor been bullied.

For more test practice, visit glencoe.com and complete the Online Quizzes for Chapter 6.

Reading/Writing Practice

Understand and Apply. Read the passage below, and then answer the questions.

1.	Will:	Hey, Jim, are you busy on Sunday? We could catch the afternoon showing of that new action movie.
2.	Jim:	Actually, I saw that last week with my brother.
3.	Will:	Well, that's the only movie I want to see.
4.	Jim:	Oh, it's okay. I don't mind seeing it again.
5.	Will:	Good. Meet me there at one.
6.	Jim:	Um, I have church that day, so that will be cutting it close . . . but don't worry about it.
7.	Will:	Who's worried?

1. What does line 3 reveal about Will's personality?
   A. He does not like movies.
   B. He treats his friends with respect.
   C. He is used to getting his own way.
   D. He is unwilling to express his thoughts and feelings.

2. Jim could best be described as
   A. enthusiastic.
   B. passive.
   C. inconsiderate.
   D. uncommunicative.

3. Rewrite this dialogue with Jim using a more assertive communication style. Your new dialogue should show how being assertive results in an outcome that is more acceptable for both teens.

National Education Standards

Math: Data Analysis, Reasoning
Language Arts: NCTE 1, NCTE 3, NCTE 4

Standardized Test Practice Answers

Math Practice
1. A
2. A
3. D

Reading/Writing Practice
1. C
2. B
3. Dialogues will vary. Each student's dialogue should demonstrate Will and Jim using assertive communication.

National Education Standards

Math: Data Analysis, Reasoning

Language Arts: NCTE 1, NCTE 3, NCTE 4

For the complete Math and Language Arts standards, visit glencoe.com.

Go Online

Online Study Tools
For more test practice, visit glencoe.com and complete the Online Quizzes for Chapter 6.

Test-Taking Tip

Rewriting a Reading Passage Tell students that they may be required to rewrite a reading passage, making specified changes, as a part of a standardized test. In the example on this page, students are directed to rewrite a dialogue to reflect different communication styles. Point out to students that they should always be clear on what changes are required before they begin rewriting. In this case, students are required to change the communication style used by both characters as well as the outcome. Remind students that they should not make changes beyond those that are required.

Chapter 7 pages 164–189	Standards		Features
	National	**State/Local**	
	1.12.1, 2.12.1, 3.12.2, 3.12.4, 3.12.5, 4.12.1, 8.12.3, 8.12.5		TIME HEALTH • A Better House Blend, page 184
Lesson 1 Healthy Family Relationships pages 166–171 **BIG Idea** *Your relationships with family members influence your total health.*	1.12.2, 1.12.4, 2.12.1, 2.12.7, 5.12.1, 8.12.3, 8.12.4		*Real World* CONNECTION • America's Families, page 168 🕐 Out of Time
Lesson 2 Strengthening Family Relationships pages 172–177 **BIG Idea** *Family members support and care for one another, especially during difficult times.*	2.12.1, 4.12.1, 5.12.1, 7.12.1, 7.12.2, 7.12.3, 8.12.2, 8.12.3		*Health Skills* Activity • Family Finances (*Communication*), page 177 🕐 Out of Time
Lesson 3 Help for Families pages 178–183 **BIG Idea** *Families may require outside assistance to deal with serious problems.*	2.12.1, 2.12.10, 3.12.2, 3.12.5, 4.12.4, 8.12.3		**TEENS** Making a Difference • Taking Charge of a Family's Care, page 181

(Left margin labels: 30 Min, 30 Min, 30 Min)

Key to Ability Levels

Teaching Strategies and activities have been coded for ability level and appropriateness.

AL Activities for students working above grade level

OL Activities for students working on grade level

BL Activities for students working below grade level

EL Activities for English Learners

Chapter 7 Planning Guide

Resources	Lesson Assessment	Technology
Student Activity Workbook TEACH *FAST FILE* RESOURCES Vocabulary Practice TEACH Health Labs EXTEND	Chapter 7 Review Chapter 7 Assessment Standardized Test Practice ⊙ *ExamView®* Assessment Suite CD-ROM	**Teaching Tools:** ⊙ *TeacherWorks*™ Plus DVD ⊙ *StudentWorks*™ Plus DVD ⊙ *ExamView®* Assessment Suite CD-ROM ▭ Transparency ⊙ Fitness DVD ⊙ PowerPoint® DVD ⊙ Health eSpotlight Video Series DVD
FAST FILE RESOURCES Reading Strategies Activity TEACH Reteaching Activity REVIEW Enrichment Activity EXTEND Health Skills Practice TEACH	Lesson 1 Assessment, page 171 📁 Lesson 1 Quiz *Fast File* ⊙ *ExamView®* Assessment Suite CD-ROM	
FAST FILE RESOURCES Reading Strategies Activity TEACH Reteaching Activity REVIEW Enrichment Activity EXTEND Health Skills Practice TEACH	Lesson 2 Assessment, page 177 📁 Lesson 2 Quiz *Fast File* ⊙ *ExamView®* Assessment Suite CD-ROM	**Web-Based Resources:** Go Online glencoe.com • Health Podcast Activities • Audio Chapter Summaries (English/Spanish) • Interactive Health Tutor • Health Skills Activities • Vocabulary PuzzleMaker • Parent Letters (English/Spanish) • Lesson Plans • Health Inventories • Online Quizzes • Study-to-Go • Unit Web Projects • Student Web Activities • Fitness Zone Activities
FAST FILE RESOURCES Reading Strategies Activity TEACH Reteaching Activity REVIEW Enrichment Activity EXTEND Health Skills Practice TEACH	Lesson 3 Assessment, page 183 📁 Lesson 3 Quiz *Fast File* ⊙ *ExamView®* Assessment Suite CD-ROM	

This is the student's backpack solution.

Includes:
- complete Interactive Student Edition
- full audio of English text and Spanish chapter summaries
- allows students to record assignments and track grades.
- links to online activities and additional student resources
- access to all student worksheets and workbooks

FOLDABLES® Study Organizer

Dinah Zike Foldables® Chapter Activity

Refer to the *Dinah Zike Reading and Study Skills for Glencoe Health*. Have students complete the pyramid Foldable to show the relationship between family life and the health pyramid. As students read, have them add details about the influence of family relationships on the appropriate side of the Foldable.

Key to Symbols

 Transparencies

 CD-ROM

glencoe.com

 Print Resources

REVIEW activities to review or reinforce content

TEACH activities to teach basic concepts

EXTEND activities to extend or enrich lesson content

Family Relationships

Chapter Overview

Chapter 7 focuses on family relationships and ways that family members can cope with changes in family structure and circumstance.

Lesson 1

Family relationships affect the physical, mental/emotional, and social health of individuals.

Lesson 2

Family members can help one another during difficult times.

Lesson 3

Serious problems that occur within families may require outside assistance to resolve.

▶ **Activating Prior Knowledge**

After students have completed their paragraphs, ask several volunteers to share what they have written with the class. Emphasize that family relationships have a significant influence on all areas of health.

CHAPTER **7**

Family Relationships

Lesson 1

Healthy Family Relationships

BIG Idea *Your relationships with family members influence your total health.*

Lesson 2

Strengthening Family Relationships

BIG Idea *Family members support and care for one another, especially during difficult times.*

Lesson 3

Help for Families

BIG Idea *Families may require outside assistance to deal with serious problems.*

Activating Prior Knowledge

Using Visuals Look at the photo on this page. Based on what you have learned about relationships, write a paragraph explaining how these family members are strengthening their relationship. Discuss the ways their interactions might contribute to their physical, mental/emotional, and social health.

 Universal Access

Differentiated Learning Glencoe provides teacher support and student materials for all learners in the health classroom.

- Chapter Summaries in English and Spanish are available online at **glencoe.com**.
- *Fast Files* and related worksheets support reluctant readers.

- Universal Access strategies throughout the Teacher Wraparound Edition and *Fast Files* help you present materials for gifted students, at-risk students, physically impaired students, and those with behavior disorders or learning disabilities.

Chapter Launchers

Health in Action

Discuss the **BIG** Ideas

Before beginning this chapter, think about how you would answer these questions:

▸ How do you and your family depend on each other?

▸ What helps you and your family through tough times?

▸ Where would you go for help with a family problem?

Watch the *Health eSpotlight* Video Series

Family First

What activities do you enjoy doing with your family?

Assess Your Health

Go Online

Visit glencoe.com and complete the Health Inventory for Chapter 7.

Chapter Launchers

Health in Action

Discuss the **BIG** Ideas

Ask students to think about their responses to the bulleted questions. Tell students that their answers to these questions and questions about family relationships found throughout the chapter may remain confidential.

Health eSpotlight
Video Series

Family First

Before Viewing the Video

Ask Students: *What fun activities have you done with your family in the past?* After students have watched the video, call on a few volunteers to describe a family member whom they admire.

Go Online

Have students go to **glencoe.com** and take the Health Inventory for Chapter 7.

Chapter Skills

Reading Skills
- Reviewing Facts and Vocabulary, pp. 171, 177, 183
- Reading/Writing Practice, p. 189

Vocabulary
- New Vocabulary, pp. 166, 172, 178
- Reviewing Facts and Vocabulary, pp. 171, 177, 183

BIG Idea

Family relationships affect all three sides of the health triangle.

Health Skills
- Health Skills Activity, p. 177
- Applying Health Skills, pp. 171, 177, 183

Writing Skills
- Writing Critically, pp. 171, 177, 183
- Reading/Writing Practice, p. 189

Healthy Family Relationships

1 FOCUS

GUIDE TO READING

BIG Idea Relationships within families affect the physical, social, and mental/emotional health of family members. **Ask Students:** *What are ways that your family can influence your health?* (Sample answer: Enjoying healthy meals together has a positive impact on all three areas of health.)

Before You Read

Organize Information
Students should identify at least one way that families affect each side of the health triangle.

Main Idea

The Family Unit Family members have responsibilities toward one another. **Ask Students:** *What are some responsibilities you have in your family?* (Sample answer: I watch my siblings after school, and I start dinner each day.)

Real Life Issues ···········

Ask students to write their journal entry. **Ask Students:** *Why might Jack feel a mix of emotions at this time?* (Sample answer: Jack might feel happiness about being part of a loving adoptive family, but sadness about not knowing his biological family.)

GUIDE TO READING

BIG Idea Your relationships with family members influence your total health.

Before You Read

Organize Information. Draw a triangle. Label the sides "Physical," "Mental/Emotional," and "Social." As you read, record information about how families affect each area of health.

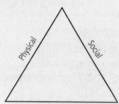

Physical | Social

Mental/Emotional

New Vocabulary

▶ siblings (p. 167)
▶ nuclear family (p. 167)
▶ blended family (p. 167)
▶ extended family (p. 167)
▶ foster care (p. 167)
▶ affirmation (p. 170)

Review Vocabulary

▶ role (Ch.6, L.1)

Healthy Family Relationships

Real Life Issues ·····················

A Family Discovery. Recently, Jack found out that he's adopted. The discovery came as a shock, and now he's starting to question everything he's ever known about himself and his family. Even though he loves his parents and brother and knows they love him too, he still feels confused. He doesn't know whether to think of them as his "real" family anymore, and he also wonders about his biological parents.

Writing *Write a journal entry from Jack's point of view. In it, Jack should express his feelings about being adopted and reflect on how this discovery could affect his life.*

The Family Unit

Main Idea There are many kinds of families, but all family members have certain responsibilities toward each other.

What is a family? The question isn't as simple as it sounds. There are many different types of families. Family members may be related to each other by birth, marriage, or adoption. People in the same family may live together or separately.

No matter who is in your family, your relationships with them are some of the most important in your life. Family relationships have a strong influence on your total health. Healthy families provide support to their members and help children and teens develop the values and skills to become successful members of society. Being part of a strong family can also be an important *protective factor* for teens by helping them avoid behaviors that may put their health at risk. Ultimately, healthy families are the foundation of a healthy society.

More About...

Foster Care More than half a million children in the United States are in foster care. Some are returned to their birth families after a period of time in foster care. Others are adopted, and some remain in foster care until they "age out." The Adoption and Safer Families Act, passed in 1997, places time limits on reunification efforts with the birth family. The goal of this legislation is to help children and teens obtain a permanent family placement in a reasonable amount of time. Have students find out more about legislation, such as The Foster Care Independence Act, designed to assist children and teens who are in foster care. Suggest that students use library or Internet resources for their research.

Types of Families

R

When you think about families, you may picture your own parents or **siblings**, your *brothers and sisters*. To some people, the word *family* suggests a **nuclear family**—*two parents and one or more children living in the same place.* Although this is a common family structure in America, increasing numbers of children live in other types of families:

- **Single-parent families.** These are families with one parent caring for one or more children. A child may live with one parent after a divorce or the other parent's death.

- **Blended families.** These families form when a single parent remarries. A **blended family** consists of *a married couple and their children from previous marriages.* The new couple may also decide to add to their blended family by having more children.

CA

- **Extended families.** An **extended family** is *a family that includes additional relatives beyond parents and children.* Relatives include grandparents, aunts, uncles, and cousins. Some people live with extended family members.

- **Adoptive families.** These families consist of a parent or parents and one or more adopted children. Some families have both biological children and adopted children.

- **Foster families.** **Foster care** is *the temporary placement of children in the homes of adults who are not related to them.* Children may be placed in foster care because of problems like abuse (discussed in Lesson 3). In some cases, foster parents may decide to adopt a child who has been living with them.

READING CHECK

Compare and Contrast How do adoptive families differ from foster families?

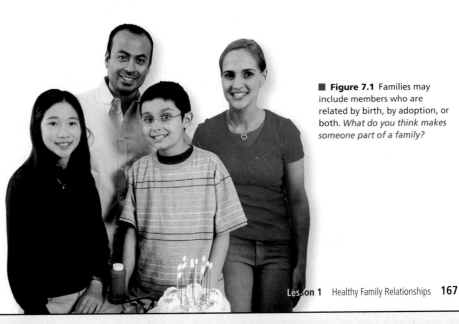

■ **Figure 7.1** Families may include members who are related by birth, by adoption, or both. *What do you think makes someone part of a family?*

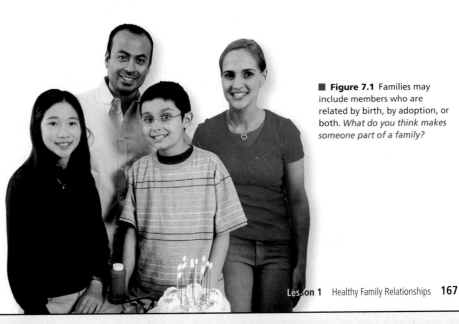

Teacher to Teacher

Colette Dux • El Camino Real High School, Woodland Hills, CA

Family Unit Have students get into groups to create a talk show, play, or skit showing how a family interacts as a *healthy* unit. Let them work in small groups to develop: a family type, a family problem/dilemma, and roles each family member will play. The scene will demonstrate how the family members successfully support each other through the problem. Students should clearly state the problem and include actions that show how each member contributes to the mental/emotional health of the family, i.e., communication, making sacrifices, trusting, finding/seeking counseling, and so on. Allow time for groups to present their scenarios to the class.

---

② TEACH

W Writing Support

Expository Writing Write the following sentence on the board: "Being part of a strong family can be an important protective factor for teens." Explain that a protective factor is anything that helps an individual avoid risk behavior. Lead a class discussion on why family relationships can help teens avoid risk behaviors. Then have students write expository paragraphs that summarize the importance of family as a protective factor. **OL** **AL**

R Reading Strategy

Organizing Information Have students create a table to organize the information about different types of families. Model this activity by making a table with two columns and six rows on the board. Fill in the six types of families in the left column. Then add a brief description of one type of family in the right column. Tell students to make a table like yours and complete the descriptions of each type of family. **EL** **BL** **OL**

CA Cultural Awareness

Family Structure Explain that a person's cultural background may influence his or her family structure. For example, in some cultures, extended and intergenerational families are very common; in other cultures, they are less common. Have students do research using Internet or library resources to learn more about the ways that cultural background influences family structure. **OL**

Caption Answer

Figure 7.1 Sample answer: A feeling of love and commitment

Real World CONNECTION

Answers to Activity Questions

1. Two parents: 88%; Mother only: 8%; Father only: 1%; Other relatives: 3%; Non-relatives: less than 1%.

2. Two parents: 67%; Mother only: 23%; Father only: 5%; Other relatives: 3%; Non-relatives: 1%.

3. Possible answers may include more divorces and acceptance of alternative living arrangements. Accept all reasonable responses.

C Critical Thinking

Applying Information After students have read the information about family interactions, ask: How do responsibilities within the family prepare teens for adulthood? Have students work as a class to brainstorm a list of common responsibilities teens have. For each identified responsibility, ask students to state how it will help a teen prepare for adulthood. **BL OL**

Academic Vocabulary

Authority Have students provide examples of categories of people who are in authority. For example, teacher, police officer. List students' responses on the board. Then ask students to think of situations, such as babysitting, in which they are in authority.

Real World CONNECTION

America's Families

The structure of American families has shifted over the past several decades. The table below shows how the living arrangements of American children under 18 have changed since 1960. Review the statistics, and use the table to answer the questions.

Activity Mathematics

1. In the year 1960, what percentage of all children lived in each type of household?

2. In the year 2005, what percentage of all children lived in each type of household?

3. What factors do you think contributed to the shift in family structure during this 45-year period?

Concept Number and Operations: Percents A percent is a ratio comparing a number to 100. To calculate percentage, divide the given amount by the total amount. Then multiply the answer by 100 and add a percent sign (%).

Living Arrangements of American Children Under 18

Year	Total children under 18	Two parents	Mother only	Father only	Other relatives	Non-relatives
1960	63,727	55,877	5,105	724	1,601	420
1970	69,162	58,939	7,452	748	1,546	477
1980	63,427	48,624	11,406	1,060	1,949	388
1990	64,137	46,503	13,874	1,993	1,421	346
2000	72,012	49,795	16,162	3,058	2,160	837
2005	73,494	49,481	17,225	3,497	2,529	762

Source: U.S. Bureau of the Census

Family Interactions

In a family, each member plays certain roles and has certain responsibilities. In general, parents or guardians are in charge of meeting the family's basic needs, such as food and shelter. Parents also serve as teachers in the family, establishing rules and setting limits to protect their children's health and safety. They teach their children about the reasons for these rules, and teach the values and skills that will guide them in the future.

Children and teens, meanwhile, also have roles and responsibilities. When they are young, their main job is to respect the **authority** of parents or guardians. As they get older, they may take on more responsibilities, such as doing chores or caring for younger siblings. By taking on such tasks, teens can help the family run more smoothly and boost their own self-esteem.

Other relatives play a role in the family as well. For example, grandparents may help care for children and teach them about the family's history. Aunts and uncles may serve as mentors and role models. Cousins who are close in age may be playmates and friends.

Academic Vocabulary

authority (noun): the right to make decisions and give commands

C

Teens Want to Know

Why Do I Have to Follow My Family's Rules? Teens become increasingly independent as they approach adulthood. Resistance to following their family's rules can be a part of this growing independence. Have students form small groups. After they have read the information about the roles and responsibilities of teens in the family, have them develop a three-column chart with their group members. The first column is titled "Family Rule," second and third respectively titled "Positive Consequences of Following Family Rules" and "Negative Consequences of Not Following Family Rules." Have each group share its results with the class.

Your Family and Your Health

Main Idea Your family members contribute to your health.

Being part of a family helps you meet your most basic needs. Beyond that, being part of a healthy family can strengthen all three aspects of your health.

Promoting Physical Health

The most obvious way your family promotes your physical health is by providing for your basic physical needs. Your parents or guardians make sure that you receive food, clothing, and shelter. They also promote your physical health by

- **providing medical care.** When you were young, your parents or guardians took you to the doctor when you were sick. They also made sure you got medical and dental checkups and necessary immunizations.

- **setting limits on behavior.** Do your parents set rules, such as how late you can stay out at night? The purpose of these rules is to promote your safety and health. For instance, setting a curfew can protect you from risky situations and also help make sure you get enough sleep.

- **teaching health skills.** In addition to setting limits on your behavior, your parents helped teach you the skills you needed to control your own behavior as you got older. They may have taught you basic safety skills, such as wearing a helmet when you ride a bike. They may also have encouraged you to develop healthy habits, like eating nutritious foods and engaging in physical activity.

FITNESS ZONE

It feels good to do something nice for someone, and it can be good for your health too. That's why I like to take my little brother and sister to the park to play catch or basketball. I want to be a good role model and teach them just how important exercise is. Besides, the smiles on their faces make it all worthwhile. For more physical activity ideas, visit the Online Fitness Zone at **glencoe.com**.

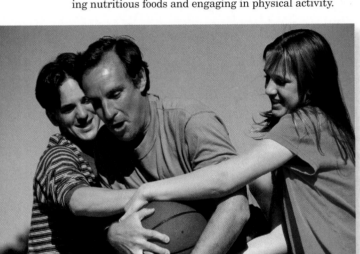

■ **Figure 7.2** By encouraging healthful behaviors such as physical activity, parents and other family members can promote physical health. *What are other ways your family influences your physical health?*

Academic Integration

Math One way that families support physical health is through food. However, the cost of groceries can be a major part of a family's budget. Ask students to work in small groups to generate a grocery list for a family of four for one week. Remind students to include healthy food choices that would promote physical health. Then ask students to use grocery store ads, Internet resources, or a trip to a grocery store to find prices for the items on their lists. Have students calculate the total cost for the groceries on their lists.

Main Idea

Your Family and Your Health
Family members contribute to health. **Ask Students:** *What is one way that you have contributed to the health of another member of your family?* (Sample answer: I help my little sister pack a healthy lunch each day.)

FITNESS ZONE

Brain research indicates that activities including balance, catching a ball, and processing information can improve brain functioning.

- Have students find a partner and stand 5–8 feet apart.
- Ask a question from the text. While asking the question, partner 1 tosses object (scrap paper formed into ball) to partner 2 who answers the question while standing on one foot.

AL Active Learning

Make a Poster Have students make a poster using words, images from magazines, hand-drawn art, or computer-generated art to illustrate ways that families promote health. Encourage students to think beyond the text examples. **EL OL**

Caption Answer

Figure 7.2 Sample answer: My family promotes my physical health by making sure I go to the dentist regularly.

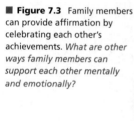

AL Active Learning

Oral Report Ask students to observe toddlers, preschoolers, or elementary-age children in their own family or in a friend or neighbor's family. Tell students to pay special attention to skills such as sharing, conflict resolution, and cooperation. After students have observed the social skills of young children, have them prepare an oral report that identifies ways social skills develop as children get older. **OL**

HS Health Skills Practice

Analyzing Influences As the text points out, families are an important influence on values. Ask students to pair up and to make a list of ways that their family has influenced their values. For example, a student might mention that his parents are polite to others, so he has learned to value good manners. Then ask each student to write a paragraph that summarizes the importance of family in developing values. **BL**

Promoting Mental and Emotional Health

As you get older, you may rely less on your family to meet your physical needs. However, it is likely that your family still plays an important role in meeting your mental and emotional needs. For example, your family can provide a safe environment for you to express and deal with your emotions. Family members can also give you love and support, helping to meet your need to feel that you belong. This sense of belonging, in turn, can help boost your self-esteem.

Your family can also help meet your need to feel valued and recognized by providing **affirmation**. This is *positive feedback that helps others feel appreciated and supported*. For instance, they can celebrate your achievements with you or show appreciation for the ways you help out at home.

Promoting Social Health

Your family also contributes to your social development. In the first few years of your life, family members helped you learn how to communicate and get along with others. As you grew, your family may have helped you learn other important social skills, such as how to cooperate with others and how to resolve conflicts. The social skills you learned from your family will help you make your own way in the world as an independent adult. **AL**

Values One of the most important ways families promote social health is by instilling values. Parents play a significant role in helping children develop core ethical values, including responsibility, honesty, and respect. Learning these values is a key to developing strong character. **HS**

■ **Figure 7.3** Family members can provide affirmation by celebrating each other's achievements. *What are other ways family members can support each other mentally and emotionally?*

Skills for the 21st Century

Collaborative Skills Teamwork, collaboration, and cooperation skills are an aspect of social skills that many teens first learn from their families. These skills are critical to the ability to work productively with others. Have students brainstorm a number of situations in which a family must work together as a team. Ask students to identify skills that are important in these situations, such as showing empathy and listening to diverse ideas. Then ask volunteers to explain how collaboration skills learned at home can be used at school and on the job.

Families can teach values in different ways. One way is by explanation. For instance, if two siblings are fighting over a toy, a parent might sit down with them and explain why it's important to share. Teaching by example can be an even more powerful way to promote good values. Let's say a parent is shopping with a child and receives too much change back for a purchase. By immediately returning the extra money, the parent teaches the child about honesty and fairness. Likewise, parents who demonstrate kindness and respect in their daily behaviors reinforce these same values in their children. By being positive role models, parents and other family members help children develop strong values.

Cultural Heritage Families also promote social health by sharing their culture and traditions. For example, families may light candles together at Kwanzaa or enjoy a barbecue and fireworks on the Fourth of July. Sharing their culture enriches the lives of family members and helps them develop a sense of cultural identity. This awareness of being part of a larger culture can create important social bonds that extend beyond the family.

 READING CHECK

Identify Name two ways families can teach values.

 LESSON 1 **ASSESSMENT**

After You Read

Reviewing Facts and Vocabulary

1. What is a *sibling*?
2. Name three kinds of families.
3. Identify four ways in which families promote the physical health of children and teens.

Thinking Critically

4. **Synthesize.** Explain how the role you play within your family has changed over time.
5. **Analyze.** How does providing affirmation within the family promote mental and emotional health?

Applying Health Skills

6. **Communication Skills.** Work with a classmate to write and perform a scene that shows family members supporting each other mentally and emotionally. The scene should include "I" messages, active listening, and appropriate body language.

Writing Critically

7. **Personal.** Write a personal essay about your family. Describe how you interact, and discuss how family members contribute to each other's total health.

G Online

Visit glencoe.com and complete the Interactive Study Guide for this lesson.

Lesson 1   Healthy Family Relationships   **171**

 CHAPTER 7

LESSON 1

 READING CHECK

Answer By explanation and example

3 ASSESS/ CLOSE

Assessment Resources

📁 *FAST FILE* ACTIVITIES
Lesson 1 Quiz

💿 *ExamView Assessment Suite* CD-ROM

Visit glencoe.com **for:**
Online Quizzes
Online Learning Center

Progress Monitoring

Reteaching
Have students work in pairs. Distribute three index cards to each pair. Ask students to label the index cards *Physical Health*, *Mental/Emotional Health*, and *Social Health*. Then have each pair list ways that families can promote each of these areas of health.

Enrichment
Have students analyze a representation of family life portrayed on television. Instruct them to write an analysis of the television family based on the information presented in this lesson.

 G Online

Have students visit **glencoe.com** and complete the Interactive Study Guide for this lesson.

LESSON 1 ASSESSMENT ANSWERS

1. A *sibling* is a brother or sister.
2. *Any three:* nuclear family, single-parent family, blended family, extended family, adoptive family, foster family
3. Meeting basic physical needs including food, clothing, and shelter; providing medical care; setting limits on behaviors; teaching health skills
4. Sample answer: As a teen, I have more responsibilities in my family than I did as a young child.
5. Sample answer: Affirmation meets people's mental and emotional need to be valued and recognized.
6. Scenes will vary, but should include the listed communication skills.
7. Essays will vary.

Strengthening Family Relationships

1 FOCUS

GUIDE TO READING

BIG Idea Family members can help one another during difficult times. **Ask Students:** *What is a recent time when a member of your family supported you?* (Sample answer: When I was cut from the track team, my sister helped me find other activities that interested me.)

Before You Read

T-Chart Students' T-charts will vary.

Main Idea

Characteristics of Strong Families There are many ways that members of strong families support one another. **Ask Students:** *What is an example of a way that you can show support to members of your family?* (Sample answer: I can encourage my sister as she prepares to try out for the school play.)

Real Life Issues

Remind students about communication skills. **Ask Students:** *Why should Beth communicate her feelings to her parents rather than keeping them to herself?* (Sample answer: Beth will feel better if she shares her feelings with her parents.)

LESSON 2

GUIDE TO READING

BIG Idea Family members support and care for one another, especially during difficult times.

Before You Read

Create a T-Chart. Make a two-column table. Label the columns "Change in Family Structure" and "Change in Circumstances." As you read, fill in each column with examples of changes that can affect families, and strategies strong families can use to deal with these changes.

Change in Structure	Change in Circumstances

New Vocabulary

▶ separation (p. 174)
▶ divorce (p. 174)
▶ custody (p. 174)

Review Vocabulary

▶ stress (Ch.2, L.1)

Strengthening Family Relationships

Real Life Issues ·····························

Dealing with Divorce. Beth has just learned that her parents are getting a divorce. Her father will be moving across town, and she knows she's going to be asked who she wants to live with. Beth is close to both her parents, and she doesn't want to have to choose between them. She'd like to tell her parents how she feels, but she doesn't want to add to their problems.

Writing *Write a dialogue in which Beth discusses her feelings with one or both of her parents. Each character should demonstrate good communication skills.*

Characteristics of Strong Families

Main Idea Strong families support their members in a variety of ways.

Different families interact together in different ways. For example, Joyce's family tends to be reserved around each other. They express their feelings calmly and rationally. When Joyce goes to her friend Ted's house, she's amazed at how openly his family expresses emotions. Ted and his family laugh and cry easily together. They tease each other and get into arguments, but they always make up.

AL

This doesn't mean Ted's family is healthier than Joyce's, or vice versa. They just interact in different ways. The important thing is that both Ted and Joyce feel secure and loved. Both of their families demonstrate traits of strong families:

- **Good communication.** Healthy families share their thoughts and feelings honestly with each other. They listen to each other and demonstrate empathy.

Health Literacy

Listening and Empathy Explain that empathy is "putting yourself in someone else's shoes." When a person listens with empathy, they don't just hear the words the speaker says; they consider the feelings behind the words. Point out that much family conflict and stress could be minimized if family members empathized with one another. Have students make a written plan to practice empathy when interacting with family members. Suggest that they keep a private journal for one week that records times they showed empathy toward family members and how that improved their family relationships.

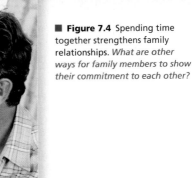

- **Caring and support.** Family members show they love each other through their words and actions. They express appreciation for each other and help each other through difficult times.
- **Respect.** Family members respect each other's opinions, tastes, and abilities. They show consideration by sharing, being courteous, respecting each individual's privacy, and helping out with household tasks.
- **Commitment.** Healthy families make time for each other. They work together to solve problems, and they're willing to make sacrifices for the good of the family.
- **Trust.** In a healthy family, parents earn their children's trust by being honest and keeping their promises. Children show that they are worthy of trust by being honest, loyal, and reliable.

Coping with Change

Main Idea Family members can help each other cope with changes in the family's structure or circumstances.

Families can face a variety of problems, both major and minor. Many of these problems have to do with changes in the family's structure or circumstances. A parent losing a job, for example, or a grandparent's serious illness can lead to long-term stress for the whole family. Even positive events, such as a move or the marriage of a relative, can create stress. Because change is a normal part of life, healthy families must be prepared to deal with changes and help each other cope.

READING CHECK

Identify How can family members show respect for each other?

Lesson 2   Strengthening Family Relationships   **173**

② TEACH

AL Active Learning

Skits Divide the class into five groups. Assign to each group one of the characteristics of strong families. Have the group members write a skit that demonstrates how the assigned characteristic could be expressed within a family. After each group has written its skit, allow practice time, and then have each group perform its skit for the class. BL OL

U Universal Access

English Language Learners Write the following words on the board: *communication, caring, support, respect, commitment,* and *trust.* Have English language learners look up each of these words in a dictionary. If students need assistance, have them work with students who are fluent in English. Ask volunteers to share the definition of a word from the list with the class. EL

Caption Answer

Figure 7.4 Sample answer: By making sacrifices for the good of the family

Main Idea

Coping with Change When a change in family structure or circumstance occurs, family members can help each other cope. **Ask Students:** *What are some kinds of changes that affect families?* (Sample answer: Death, divorce, moving to a new house)

Reading Strategy

Bulleted Lists Point out to students the bulleted list of characteristics of strong families. Explain that a bulleted list is an organized way to present information. In this case, the five characteristics of strong families are printed in boldface, and an explanation of each characteristic follows.

Ask students to brainstorm other ways this information could be organized, for example, in a table or other graphic organizer. Have students work in small groups to develop an alternate strategy for organizing this information. Have each group share its method of organizing the information with the class.

R **Reading Strategy**

Classifying Make a Venn diagram on the board. Label one side "Positive Changes" and the other side "Negative Changes." Ask students to supply examples for each side of the chart. For example, a parent losing his or her job would be classified as a negative change. Some changes, such as a parent's remarriage, may be put on both sides of the chart. After students have supplied a good number of responses, go through the examples one by one. Have students suggest one or two positive strategies for coping with each of the changes. `BL` `OL`

W **Writing Support**

Descriptive Writing Have each student choose one of the changes in family structure described in the text as the basis for a fictional story. Students should write their stories from the perspective of one of the family members, describing the change and the character's feelings about the change. Encourage students to illustrate their completed stories. Remind students that their stories should be proofread and corrected before being turned in. `OL` `AL`

 READING CHECK

Answer Separation is a decision by married people to live apart. Divorce permanently ends the marriage contract.

Changes in Family Structure

The structure of a family changes when someone new joins the family or when a family member moves out of the home. Examples of such changes include birth, adoption, separation, divorce, remarriage, and the death of a family member.

Birth and Adoption Welcoming a new baby or an adopted child into the family is a joyful event. However, adjusting to the new situation isn't always easy. Making room for the new child means that everyone else has to make do with less space at home. Also, as parents devote time and energy to the new child, they may have less time for the other children—and for each other. All these changes can create stress for everyone. Family members can help each other through this time by sharing the responsibility for taking care of the new child. They can also make an effort to find time for each other.

Separation and Divorce Separation and divorce are difficult, especially since they result in a family member leaving the home environment. **Separation** is *a decision by two married people to live apart from each other*. Couples who separate may hope to eventually work out their differences and live together again. **Divorce**, by contrast, is *a legal end to a marriage contract*.

When parents divorce, they need to come to an agreement about where the children will live. **Custody** is *the legal right to make decisions affecting children and the responsibility for their care*. Custody may be granted to only one parent (sole custody) or divided so that both parents share in the child rearing (joint custody). Adapting to either arrangement can be difficult for the children. They may find it hard to go for long periods without seeing one of their parents. In the case of joint custody, they may find it stressful to move back and forth between two homes.

Parents can help their children get through this difficult period by reminding them that both parents still love them. They can also reassure the children that the divorce was not their fault. Children may find it easier to cope if they discuss their feelings with parents and other trusted adults. In some cases, they may want to consider joining a support group for children of divorce. Being part of such a group may help them realize that they are not alone.

Remarriage After a divorce, one or both parents may decide to marry again. A parent may also remarry after the death of a spouse. When a parent remarries, the children must adjust to having, or living with, a stepparent. If the stepparent has children from a previous marriage, all members of the blended family will need time to adjust. Good communication and mutual respect will make this process easier.

W

READING CHECK

Compare and Contrast What is the difference between separation and divorce?

More About...

Blended Families The term *blended family* can be misleading. It implies that the new family mixes into a homogenous unit, and ignores the fact that children may still have ties to the other parent. Teens, in particular, may have a hard time accepting change and adjusting to a new authority figure. Remind students that difficulty adjusting to any family change is normal. Point out resources available to students who need help, such as the school counselor and community agencies, which are discussed in detail in Lesson 3.

■ **Figure 7.5** The remarriage of a parent can bring mixed feelings. *How can teens show support for a parent's decision to remarry?*

Caption Answer

Figure 7.5 Sample answer: This teen is participating in her mother's wedding, which is a sign of support for her mother's remarriage.

Death of a Family Member Perhaps the most difficult change a family can go through is the death of a family member. In Chapter 4, you learned about the feelings of grief that can accompany a death or other loss. Family members can help each other through this difficult time by sharing their feelings and memories about the person they've lost. It's also important for family members to respect each other's feelings and remember that the process of grieving is different for everyone. Joining a support group or seeking help from a counselor may also help those who have lost a loved one recover from their pain.

Changes in Family Circumstances

Changes in a family's **circumstances** can also be a source of stress. Family members can help each other deal with these changes by communicating honestly and showing as much support as possible. Here are some examples of changes in family circumstances:

- **Moving to a new home.** When a family moves, especially over a long distance, family members may miss their old friends and familiar surroundings. Teens may be anxious about making new friends and adjusting to a new school. When a move results from the breakup of a marriage, it can add to the stress already caused by the divorce.

- **Changes in the family's financial situation.** Financial problems can result from the loss of a job, a medical emergency, poor planning, or uncontrolled spending. Not having enough money to pay the bills can be stressful.

Academic Vocabulary

circumstance *(noun):* an event that influences another event

AL Active Learning

Multimedia Presentation Have students work in small groups to prepare a multimedia presentation about experiencing grief after the death of a family member. They should use the information about grief found in Chapter 4, the information about coping with family changes found in this chapter, and Internet or library resources. Students can prepare an oral report with visual aids or a multimedia presentation using a computer and share it with the class. **OL AL**

C Critical Thinking

Predicting Write the word *circumstances* on the board. Ask volunteers to share their ideas about what this word means. Point out to students that changes in family circumstances can be difficult. Ask volunteers to describe what kinds of circumstances could happen that might be stressful. Reassure students that mixed feelings about family changes are normal. **EL OL**

ELL Support

Prefixes Explain that prefixes are word parts that are found at the beginnings of words.

Beginning Write the word *remarriage* on the board. Underline the prefix *re-*. Explain that *re-* means "again." Have students use this information to reinforce the definition of the term *remarriage*.

Intermediate Build on the Beginning activity by asking students to identify other words that contain the prefix *re-*. Examples include: rearrange, regain, reread, retry, and reunify. Students may use dictionaries.

Advanced Have students write three sentences that use words containing the prefix *re-*. Have volunteers share their sentences with the class.

AL Active Learning
Picture Story for Children
Have students work in pairs to develop picture books for young children who are experiencing a change in their family. Have them brainstorm ways to convey ideas for coping to children using words and pictures. Have students share their books with younger students. **OL**

Health Skills Activity

Communication Skills: Family Finances

NHES Standard 4 Students will demonstrate the ability to use interpersonal communication skills to enhance health and avoid or reduce health risks.

Objectives
- Demonstrate communication skills to help cope with a change in family circumstance.
- Utilize skills for communicating effectively with family to enhance health.

Teaching Strategies
- Have students review the guidelines for good communication.
- Ask students to discuss ways that Kenny can effectively communicate his feelings to his parents.

Assessment
Using a rubric, student work should provide comprehensive evidence of the following criteria to achieve the highest score:

√ Speaks calmly and clearly
√ Uses "I" messages
√ Shows respect and empathy
√ Listens carefully, and asks appropriate questions

It can also lead to arguments about how the family's limited funds should be used. Interestingly, a sudden financial gain can also be a source of stress. Unaccustomed wealth can trigger anxiety and confusion as people wonder what to do with the money and whether it's going to change the way people see them.

- **Illness and disability.** A serious illness or disability can disrupt a family's normal routine. One or more family members may need to change their schedules to care for the sick or disabled person. Coping with this situation may be easier if each family member plays a role in caring for the sick or disabled person.
- **Alcohol or other drug abuse.** Substance abuse is one of the most serious problems a family can face. Family members must seek outside help to deal with the situation. Teens may wish to consult teachers, other trusted adults, or organizations such as Alateen. You will learn more about confronting the problem of substance abuse in Chapters 21 and 22.

Coping with Changes

One of the most important strategies for coping with changes in the family is to talk honestly and openly with each other. Just talking about your feelings can help reduce stress. Letting family members know about your needs and wants can also make it easier for them to help you.

You, in turn, can make an effort to support your family members during a difficult period. For example, you can offer to take on more chores and responsibilities at home. You can also make a point of being there for family members if they want to talk.

If this strategy is not enough, family members may find it helpful to talk with someone outside the family, such as a counselor, teacher, or member of the clergy. They can also try to learn more about the situation they're dealing with, either by reading books or by talking with people who have been through similar experiences. Finally, families should be willing to seek professional help if they need it. Lesson 3 discusses resources that can help.

■ **Figure 7.6** Talking with a parent or other trusted adult can help you deal with the stress of family changes. *To whom do you turn when you need to talk?*

Promoting School Wellness

Services for Students Dealing with Family Changes Some of the services offered as a part of a coordinated school health program can assist students who are dealing with changes in their families. Health education, in which students learn about family changes and ways to cope with those changes, is one aspect of coordinated school health that can help these students. Some students may also benefit from counseling and psychological services offered through the school counselors.

Health Skills Activity
Communication Skills

Family Finances

A month ago, Kenny's dad lost his job. Ever since then, his parents have been tense and anxious. They have whispered conversations so the children can't hear them, but Kenny knows they're talking about money. Kenny is worried about how the family is going to manage financially, but he's even more upset that his parents don't trust him enough to talk to him about the problem.

Writing Write a dialogue between Kenny and his parents. In it, Kenny should express his concerns about the family's financial situation and his feelings about being left out of his parents' discussions. Follow these guidelines for good communication:

1. Speak calmly and clearly.
2. Use "I" messages.
3. Show respect and empathy.
4. Listen carefully, and ask appropriate questions.

LESSON 2 ASSESSMENT

After You Read

Reviewing Facts and Vocabulary

1. How can family members demonstrate good communication?
2. What are the two main types of changes that cause stress in families?
3. Identify three situations that can lead to a change in family structure.

Thinking Critically

4. **Analyze.** Compare and contrast the difficulties sole custody and joint custody can pose for teens whose parents are divorced.
5. **Synthesize.** Give an example of a positive or negative event that could cause stress within a family. Explain what strategies the family might use to deal with this stress.

Applying Health Skills

6. **Stress Management.** Think of a stressful family situation. Then list five stress-management techniques that can help you handle this stress.

Writing Critically

7. **Narrative.** Children sometimes go through stages of grief (denial, anger, bargaining, depression, and acceptance) in response to their parents' divorce. Write a story about a teen who goes through several of these stages. Describe how the teen expresses his or her feelings at each stage.

Go Online

Visit **glencoe.com** and complete the Interactive Study Guide for this lesson.

Lesson 2   Strengthening Family Relationships   **177**

---

3 ASSESS/ CLOSE

Assessment Resources

 FAST FILE ACTIVITIES
Lesson 2 Quiz

 ExamView Assessment Suite CD-ROM

Visit glencoe.com for:
Online Quizzes
Online Learning Center

Progress Monitoring

Reteaching
Review the characteristics of strong families with the class. Then ask students to describe how these characteristics can help families as they cope with change.

Enrichment
Have students write a short dialogue between two family members that demonstrates one or more of the characteristics of a healthy family.

Go Online

Have students visit **glencoe.com** and complete the Interactive Study Guide for this lesson.

LESSON 2 ASSESSMENT ANSWERS

1. By sharing their thoughts and feelings honestly with each other, listening to one another, and demonstrating empathy
2. Changes in family structure and in family circumstance
3. Birth or adoption of a child; separation, divorce, remarriage; death of a family member
4. Sole custody can be difficult because the teen seldom sees one parent. Joint custody involves moving between two homes.
5. Sample answer: An illness is a negative event that can cause stress within a family. The family can cope with this stress by sharing the work of caring for the ill family member.
6. Sample answers: Talking with others, getting counseling, getting plenty of physical activity, deep breathing, listening to relaxing music
7. Stories will vary.

① FOCUS

BIG Idea Serious family problems may require outside help. **Ask Students:** *What are some problems that families might not be able to solve on their own?* (Sample answers: Abuse, violence, major financial problems)

Before You Read

Word Web Students' word webs should identify sources of support for families experiencing major problems.

Main Idea

Violence in Families Family violence can cause long-term damage. **Ask Students:** *How do you think family violence could affect the three sides of the victim's health triangle?* (Sample answer: Physical: by causing physical injuries to the victim; Mental/emotional: by damaging the victim's self-esteem; Social: by teaching the victim that violence is an acceptable way to express emotions)

Real Life Issues ....

Have students read the scenario. **Ask Students:** *What are some emotions or feelings that Mark and Sofia may be experiencing?* Remind students to include good communication techniques in their dialogues.

178

BIG Idea *Families may require outside assistance to deal with serious problems.*

Before You Read

Create a Word Web. In the center of a sheet of paper, write the phrase "Sources of Support." As you read, add information about sources of help for families in trouble.

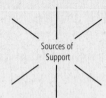

Sources of Support

New Vocabulary

▶ abuse (p. 178)
▶ domestic violence (p. 178)
▶ spousal abuse (p. 178)
▶ child abuse (p. 179)
▶ neglect (p. 179)
▶ elder abuse (p. 179)
▶ cycle of violence (p. 180)
▶ crisis center (p. 182)

Help for Families

Real Life Issues ....

Worried About a Friend. Mark is concerned about his friend Sofia. Sofia says her parents argue a lot, and she thinks her dad hits her mom. One evening, Mark called Sofia to ask her a question about a home-work assignment. He heard her parents arguing in the background. Another time, Mark thought he saw Sofia crying at school.

Writing *Write a dialogue in which Mark encourages Sofia to confide in him and seek help. Make sure Mark uses good communication techniques.*

Violence in Families

Main Idea Violence in families can cause lasting harm.

All families have problems from time to time, and that's normal. In most cases, families can work through their problems with the help of good communication and mutual support. However, some problems are too serious for family members to handle on their own. One of the most dangerous problems a family can face is **abuse**, *the physical, mental, emotional, or sexual mistreatment of one person by another*. When abuse results in *acts of violence involving family members*, it is called **domestic violence**. You will learn more about the different forms of abuse in Chapter 9.

Spousal Abuse

Domestic violence or any other form of abuse directed at a spouse is called **spousal abuse**. This form of violence can occur in all kinds of families, regardless of income, ethnicity, or education level. Spousal abuse can involve physical or sexual violence as well as emotional abuse. Abusers may threaten or intimidate their victims and try to cut them off from family or friends.

Myths & Reality

Domestic Violence

Myth: Child abuse occurs only among lower-income families.

Fact: Child abuse occurs in families of all economic levels.

Myth: Children who misbehave may be to blame if they are abused.

Fact: Children are never to blame for abuse.

Myth: Abused children always want to leave their homes to escape the abuse.

Fact: Children from abusive families may not realize that abuse is not a part of healthy family interactions.

Spousal abuse is a criminal act that can be prosecuted by law. However, this crime often goes unreported. Victims may blame themselves for their partners' abusive behavior, thinking that they somehow deserve the mistreatment. They may also be unwilling to tear the family apart by leaving an abusive spouse. Many fear they will be unable to support themselves or their children if they leave. In some cases, the abuser may threaten to hurt or kill the victim or their children if the spouse attempts to leave.

Child Abuse

HS **Child abuse** is *domestic abuse directed at a child.* It includes any action that harms or threatens a child's health and development. Like spousal abuse, child abuse can be physical, emotional, or sexual. Child abuse may also involve neglect, *the failure to provide for a child's basic needs.* Neglected children may lack adequate food, clothing, shelter, or medical support. Leaving children alone and unsupervised for long periods of time is also a form of neglect.

Parents who abuse their children don't always want to hurt them. Sometimes they simply don't know how to take care of children. Many abusive parents were abused themselves as children and don't know any other way for a family to function. Alcohol and drug abuse also increase the risk of violence in the home. Whatever the reasons behind it, abusing a child is always unacceptable and dangerous.

Elder Abuse

Elder abuse, *the abuse or neglect of older family members,* is a growing problem that often goes unnoticed. Elder abuse can occur both within the family and in institutional settings such as nursing homes. Like children, older family members may suffer physical, emotional, and sexual abuse, as well as neglect. Elder abuse can also be financial. For instance, caregivers may take advantage of elders by manipulating or pressuring them into handing over control of their money and other assets.

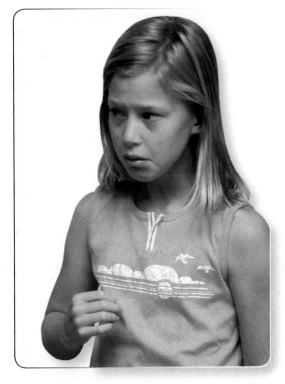

■ **Figure 7.7** Abuse can harm children emotionally as well as physically. *What forms can child abuse take?*

② TEACH

AL Active Learning

Guest Speaker Invite a police officer, other community worker, or school counselor to address the class about the problem of domestic violence. Allow students to submit anonymous, written questions for the speaker. Follow up by having students summarize what they learned about domestic violence by listening to the speaker. **BL OL**

HS Health Skills Practice

Advocacy Have students write an article discussing the effects of child and spousal abuse. The article should urge victims of domestic violence to seek help immediately. Remind students that advocacy involves taking a clear, health-enhancing stand, supporting a position with relevant information, being aware of the audience, and encouraging others to make healthful choices with passion and conviction. **OL AL**

Caption Answer

Figure 7.7 Physical abuse, emotional abuse, sexual abuse, neglect

Cooperative Learning

Careers in Social Work Child abuse and spousal abuse are just two of the many situations that might be handled by a social worker. Explain to students that social work is an excellent career choice for those with a strong desire to help others. Tell students that social workers are employed in many different settings, including hospitals, schools, and family services organizations. Have students work in small groups to research careers in social work. Ask each group to create a poster or prepare an oral report to share its findings with the class.

Academic Vocabulary

Academic Vocabulary

Domestic Review the definition of the word domestic: "of or relating to the household or the family." Have students make a word web with the term domestic violence in the middle. Ask students to add specific types of domestic violence to their word webs.

 **Universal Access**

English Language Learners
Write the phrase *cycle of violence* on the board. Explain that a cycle is a series of events that occur regularly and lead back to a starting point. Have students think of other examples of cycles. (Examples might include the seasons of the year, the rock cycle, the water cycle, the life cycle, and the phases of the moon.) Then ask students to explain why domestic violence often happens in a cycle. **EL**

R **Reading Strategy**

Stopping Abuse Have students make a list of ways domestic violence can be stopped. Be sure students include the three Rs. Ask volunteers to make a list on the board, adding as students share from their own lists. **BL** **OL**

READING CHECK

Answer The pattern of repeating violence or abusive behaviors from one generation to the next

Academic Vocabulary

domestic *(adjective):* of or relating to the household or the family

READING CHECK

Define What is the *cycle of violence?*

Effects of Abuse

Victims of **domestic** abuse may suffer physical injuries, such as bruises, burns, or broken bones. In the worst cases, physical abuse can lead to permanent injury or death. For many victims, however, the emotional scars left by abuse last even longer than the physical injuries. Victims often experience feelings of shame and worthlessness. Abused children may be anxious or depressed and have difficulty in school. Without treatment, abused children often grow up to become abusers themselves. The *pattern of repeating violent or abusive behaviors from one generation to the next* is known as the **cycle of violence**.

Children who live in abusive homes may try to escape by running away. Others are thrown out of their homes by an abusive parent or guardian. Many runaways and "thrownaways" end up living on the street or in the company of predatory adults. They are at risk for drug problems, crime, and continuing physical or sexual abuse.

To avoid these risks, children suffering abuse at home need to seek help from an adult they can trust, such as a relative, teacher, medical professional, or religious adviser. The police can also connect these teens with social services that can help them. Short-term shelters, for instance, can provide a safe place to stay. "Drop-in" services can provide food, clothing, medical attention, and crisis counseling.

Stopping Domestic Abuse

Stopping domestic violence depends on the three Rs: *recognize, resist,* and *report.* The first step is to *recognize* the problem. Victims and others need to be aware that child abuse and domestic violence are crimes. Any claim of abuse should be taken seriously, even if it sounds unbelievable.

Victims of domestic abuse can also *resist* their abusers. If someone tries to harm you, you can try to escape or to prevent the attack. Once you escape, seek help from a trusted adult.

However, resistance may not always be possible. That's why *reporting* the abuse is the third step in putting a stop to it. If you or someone you know is being abused, report the problem to someone who can help you. Try talking to a trusted adult, such as a family member or a school nurse. You can also contact an abuse hotline or a crisis center. Finally, you can go directly to the police. The victim may also require counseling and medical care.

Victims of domestic violence need help. Their abusers need help, too. Through counseling and other strategies, they can learn to manage their feelings and break the cycle of violence. You will learn more about sources of help for victims and abusers in Chapter 9.

180 Chapter 7 Family Relationships

 Home and Community

Help for Runaways Have students work in small groups to find out what resources are available in the community specifically for teens who are at risk for running away or teens who are currently runaways. Ask students to gather information about the resources, services, or programs they find, including contact information and types of services provided. If students are unable to find programs in the local community, have them research national organizations that serve runaways and homeless teens. Have each group share what it learns with the class.

TEENS Making a Difference

Taking Charge of a Family's Care

"It's your own choice to do good."

Ashleigh R., of Ohio, was in the eighth grade when her mother was diagnosed with multiple sclerosis (MS). Ashleigh responded by taking charge of not only her mother's care, but the care of her younger siblings as well. She also did all the housework and kept up with her studies at school.

Today, Ashleigh's mom is in remission. As a result of her mother's courageous battle, Ashleigh wants to become a doctor and find a cure for MS. After finishing high school, Ashleigh plans to attend Ohio State University, and then go on to medical school.

Through it all, Ashleigh has kept a positive attitude. She says, "It's your own choice to do good—it's all in your attitude toward life. Don't just go through life—go for the positive!"

Activity Write your answers to the following questions in your personal health journal.

1. What motivated Ashleigh to "take charge"?
2. List three ways you can help a family member who has a health problem.
3. How do you think maintaining a positive attitude has helped Ashleigh's health?

Sources of Support

Main Idea Communities offer many forms of support to families in crisis.

AL There are many community resources to help families deal with a variety of problems, including abuse. What type of help they need depends on the seriousness of the problem. Some problems, such as domestic violence, may require notifying the police. Others, such as substance abuse, may require medical help. Some sources of help for families facing difficulties include

- family counseling services.
- support groups.
- community services, such as shelters or hotlines.
- law enforcement officials.
- hospitals or clinics.
- faith communities.

TEENS Making a Difference

Answers to Activity Questions

1. Ashleigh's positive attitude and desire to keep her family together.
2. Sample answer: I could be a supportive listener if the ill family member needed to talk.
3. It has kept her from dwelling on the negative aspects of her family's situation.

Main Idea

Sources of Support Families in crisis can find help and support in their communities. **Ask Students:** *If a family you knew needed help, what community resources would you suggest?* (Sample answer: crisis hotline, a counselor, or the police)

AL Active Learning

Role-Play Have students work in pairs to practice calling a hotline for help with a serious family situation. Write the following steps for calling a hotline on the board: 1. Before you call, state the problem to yourself. 2. Make a written list of questions. 3. Rehearse what you will say. 4. During the call, use a pencil and paper to record names and numbers of the services that are suggested to you. **OL** **EL**

Writing Strategy

Letter of Support Have students write a letter to a fictional friend whose family is experiencing a difficult time. In the letter, students should identify at least one resource that may be helpful to the fictional friend. Explain that their letter should provide support and encouragement in a nonjudgmental way. Remind students of the parts of a friendly letter: the heading, the greeting, the body, the closing, and the signature. Have students proofread and correct their letters before turning them in.

181

Figure 7.8 **Support Groups**

These are just a few of the many support groups in the country.

Problem	Organization	Provides Support For
Substance abuse	Alcoholics Anonymous	Alcoholics
	Al-Anon	Family members and friends of alcoholics (subgroup, Alateen, is specifically for younger members)
	Narcotics Anonymous	Drug abusers
Eating disorders	Overeaters Anonymous	Compulsive overeaters
	Eating Disorders Anonymous	People with anorexia, bulimia, or binge eating disorder
Domestic violence	SAFE (Stop Abuse For Everyone)	Victims of domestic violence and abuse
Dealing with grief	Bereaved Parents of the USA	Parents who have lost a child

AL

AL Active Learning

Infomercial Have students examine the information about support groups found in **Figure 7.8**. Then ask students to form small groups. Each group should select one of the support groups mentioned in the figure or another well-known support group. Have each group write a script for an infomercial about the support group. Ask each group to present its infomercial to the class.
OL AL

C Critical Thinking

Inferring Lead students in inferring a list of factors that might deter families from seeking outside support or help with problems. Students might suggest factors such as embarrassment, cost of professional services, fear of the unknown, denial that a problem exists, or lack of knowledge of available services. Follow up with a discussion of strategies for overcoming these barriers to getting help. OL

READING CHECK

Answer *Any three:* Crisis centers or crisis hotlines, faith communities, hospitals or clinics, family counseling services, law enforcement officials, support groups, shelters

Counseling

Family counseling is therapy to restore healthy relationships in a family. Families come in as a group to meet with a counselor, discuss their problems, and seek solutions. Counseling can help some families deal with changes such as separation or divorce. It can also help in cases when one member has a problem that affects the entire family. Such problems may include anger, depression, or substance abuse. Sometimes individual counseling is also beneficial.

C

Support Groups

A support group is several people who are all coping with the same problem. The group meets regularly to discuss their problems and get advice from each other. Support groups can help many people just by reassuring them that they are not alone. **Figure 7.8** lists support groups that deal with various personal or family health issues.

Community Services

Families seeking help may also turn to resources in their community. Troubled family members may seek help from a **crisis center**, *a facility that offers advice and support to people dealing with personal emergencies.* People might turn to a crisis center to help them get through problems such as substance abuse or domestic violence. Some communities also have crisis hotlines. These are special telephone numbers people can call to receive help 24 hours a day.

READING CHECK

Identify Name three places that can provide help for families in crisis.

Teens Want to Know

Will Everyone Find Out If I Seek Help For a Family Problem? One reason that teens may be hesitant to seek help for family problems is a fear that others will find out. Explain to students that support groups have rules that members must maintain confidentiality—that is, members cannot talk about who is in their group or what is discussed in their group. Confidentiality is also the rule with family counseling. Counselors cannot share information about their clients with others. Students should know, however, that if they reveal that they are the victim of abuse, adults may be bound by law to report the abuse.

Communities also provide a variety of other services to families in need. For instance, public or private agencies may offer classes on parenting and conflict resolution. Social services can help provide food, clothing, shelter, and medical care. Public agencies can also help adults find a job or receive job training.

Finally, community services offer help for victims of domestic abuse. Social agencies can remove children from abusive homes and place them in foster care. Victims can also seek help by contacting an organization that deals with domestic violence. Many communities provide shelters where spouses and children can go to escape an abusive home. They may also help victims obtain counseling and legal services.

■ **Figure 7.9** In family counseling, the family meets with the counselor as a group to learn ways to resolve their problems. *Give an example of a problem that a family might seek to solve through family counseling.*

Caption Answer

Figure 7.9 Sample answer: A family going through a divorce might try to resolve custody issues in counseling.

③ **ASSESS/ CLOSE**

LESSON 3 **ASSESSMENT**

After You Read

Reviewing Facts and Vocabulary

1. Identify four different forms of child abuse.

2. Describe the physical and emotional effects of abuse.

3. What is family counseling?

Thinking Critically

4. **Analyze.** Explain how neglect might affect each part of a child's health triangle.

5. **Evaluate.** Hector's dad recently moved out of the house. Hector feels lonely and guilty about his parents' separation. He believes no one understands how he feels. What source of support do you think would be most helpful for Hector, and why?

Applying Health Skills

6. **Accessing Information.** Consult phone directories, bulletin boards, and Web sites to find resources in your community that help families in crisis. Based on your findings, create a brochure that describes sources of support and how to contact them.

Writing Critically

7. **Expository.** Write an article discussing the problem of domestic abuse. Describe the effects of abuse and identify ways victims can seek help.

G⊙ Online

Visit glencoe.com and complete the Interactive Study Guide for this lesson.

Lesson 3   Help for Families   **183**

Assessment Resources

 FAST FILE **ACTIVITIES**
Lesson 3 Quiz

 ExamView Assessment Suite CD-ROM

Visit glencoe.com **for:**
Online Quizzes
Online Learning Center

Progress Monitoring

Reteaching
Have each student write a sentence demonstrating the relationship between two of the vocabulary terms from the lesson. Ask students to share their sentences with the class.

Enrichment
Have each student write a paragraph that summarizes the lesson content. Remind students that their paragraph should include the main ideas from the lesson, but not the details. Have volunteers read their completed paragraphs to the class.

G⊙ Online

Have students visit glencoe.com and complete the Interactive Study Guide for this lesson.

LESSON 3 ASSESSMENT ANSWERS

1. Physical abuse, emotional abuse, sexual abuse, and neglect
2. Physical effects can include injuries, permanent injury, and, in extreme cases, death. Emotional effects include shame, worthlessness, anxiety, and depression.
3. Therapy to restore healthy relationships in a family
4. Physical: lack of clothing, food, or shelter; mental/emotional: feelings of shame;

social: lack of friends
5. Sample answer: Hector would benefit best from a support group made up of other teens who are experiencing a similar problem. In this setting, he would not feel alone and could get support for his specific problem.
6. Brochures will vary.
7. Articles will vary.

A Better House Blend

Focus

Motivator

Ask students to describe some families they are familiar with from television. Have them describe the structures of these families. Then ask students to brainstorm some challenges faced by different kinds of families. Save students' responses for use in the Cooperative Learning activity below.

Teach

Family Changes Point out that the formation of a blended family is a change in family structure that is typically accompanied by a change in family circumstance (a different amount of income and/or a new home). Have students review the information about family changes in the chapter. Then ask students to volunteer positive ways teens could cope with the changes that occur when a blended family forms.

About Strong Families Have students review the traits of strong families (communication, caring and support, respect, commitment, and trust). Ask them to describe ways these traits could be displayed in a blended family. For example, students might mention that teens in a blended family can offer care and support to younger siblings who are having mixed feelings about the parent's remarriage.

Outside Help Ask students to identify types of services that may be helpful to a teen who is struggling to adjust to being part of a blended family. Students will probably suggest family counseling and support groups. Have a discussion of the ways these services could be useful to a teen in a blended family.

A Better HOUSE BLEND

According to the U.S. Census Bureau, fifteen percent of American kids live in a blended, or step, family. And when two families come together, life for everyone is bound to change. Here are some tips to make the blending easier.

Family Matters

Some kids see money spent by parents as scorecards that show who is more loved. If a step-sibling gets something they don't have, arguments about fairness can start. Yet in most families, giving everyone exactly the same thing is impossible to achieve. What to do? Experts say families need to work together to make sure no one feels unloved because they didn't get something a step-sibling may have gotten. No matter who gets what, it's important for siblings to understand that all the children are loved equally.

Discipline is another tricky area. Children in blended families often encounter three or four different sets of rules: those of their biological parents and their stepparent. Whose rules should kids follow? Most experts agree that kids should be disciplined by their biological parents, even if there are different rules within the same household. Over time blended families should try to combine their rules.

Talk It Over

Sometimes families need counseling to help everyone get along. Rachelle and Jillian, 17-year-old stepsisters, tried working out their differences on their own and with their parents, but they couldn't agree. So the two teens spoke to a counselor to help them resolve an argument. One of the girls invited friends over and complained when her stepsister tried to hang out with them. The counselor suggested a rule: Whoever had friends over had a right to privacy in her room, but if they were in a common area, her stepsister could join in. This solved the problem.

Of course, not all blended families have issues that need outside counseling. Differences can ease up as a family becomes truly blended, but that can take anywhere from four to seven years, research shows. Children under age 8 blend the fastest, and those between 9 and 11 the slowest. Experts warn newcomers to blended families to be realistic about what they can expect. No matter what the situation, kids and parents alike will need patience and excellent listening skills. ■

TIME to THINK... **About Family Communication**

Take a poll of your classmates about common family disagreements they may have. Have each of your classmates suggest one or two ways they can resolve their differences. You might try role playing a disagreement and a resolution.

Cooperative Learning

Television Script In the Motivator activity, students were asked to discuss a variety of families they have seen on television. Remind them of their responses. Then have students form small groups to write a script for a 5- to 10-minute-long television segment about a blended family. After the scripts have been written, have each group present its work to the class, either as a skit or in video format.

To download quizzes and eFlashcards to your PDA, go to glencoe.com and click on the Study to Go icon.

LESSON **1**

Healthy Family Relationships

Key Concepts

▸ Your relationships with family members have a strong influence on your total health.

▸ Family members may be related by birth, marriage, or adoption.

▸ All members of a family share responsibility for the family's health.

▸ Families promote physical health by meeting basic physical needs, providing medical care, setting limits on behavior, and teaching health skills.

▸ Family members promote mental and emotional health by giving each other love, support, and affirmation.

▸ Families promote social health by teaching social skills, instilling values, and sharing cultural traditions.

Vocabulary

▸ siblings (p. 167)
▸ nuclear family (p. 167)
▸ blended family (p. 167)
▸ extended family (p. 167)
▸ foster care (p. 167)
▸ role (p. 168)
▸ affirmation (p. 170)

LESSON **2**

Strengthening Family Relationships

Key Concepts

▸ Strong families demonstrate good communication, love and support, respect, commitment, and trust.

▸ Changes in family structure or circumstances can be a major source of stress within families.

▸ Family members can help each other cope with change by talking about their feelings and offering help and support.

Vocabulary

▸ stress (p. 173)
▸ separation (p. 174)
▸ divorce (p. 174)
▸ custody (p. 174)

LESSON **3**

Help for Families

Key Concepts

▸ Abuse in families can be physical, emotional, or sexual.

▸ Victims of abuse include spouses, children, and older relatives.

▸ Families in crisis can seek support from counselors, support groups, crisis centers, and other community services.

Vocabulary

▸ abuse (p. 178)
▸ domestic violence (p. 178)
▸ spousal abuse (p. 178)
▸ child abuse (p. 179)
▸ neglect (p. 179)
▸ elder abuse (p. 179)
▸ cycle of violence (p. 180)
▸ crisis center (p. 182)

Chapter 7 Review **185**

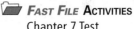
Go Online

Students can visit **glencoe.com** to

• review content online with the Online Student Edition.

• test their knowledge of chapter content with Online Quizzes.

• access Interactive Health Tutor for more practice with vocabulary.

Assessment Resources

📁 **FAST FILE ACTIVITIES**
Chapter 7 Test

💿 *ExamView Assessment Suite* CD-ROM

Visit glencoe.com **for:**
Audio Chapter Summaries
Online Quizzes

Tell students to visit glencoe.com where they can download quizzes and eFlashcards.

Study Tips

Use Graphic Organizers Point out to students that each lesson opener's "Before You Read" feature introduces a graphic organizer that can be used to organize the concepts or vocabulary terms in the lesson. Explain that reviewing these graphic organizers is an effective way to study, because it allows the connections between concepts to be visualized. Suggest that students create additional graphic organizers when reading or reviewing the chapter.

Chapter 7
Assessment Answers

LESSON 1

Vocabulary Review

1. blended family
2. nuclear family
3. Foster care

Understanding Key Concepts

4. c
5. d
6. c
7. a

Thinking Critically

8. Sample answer: To provide safe, temporary homes for children who are in unhealthy or abusive home environments
9. Sample answer: Setting limits can prevent children from engaging in behaviors that could harm their health.
10. Sample answer: Crossing streets safely, brushing teeth regularly
11. Sample answer: Even children who are too young to understand a verbal explanation about values will pick up the behaviors they see in their daily lives.

LESSON 2

Vocabulary Review

12. separation
13. divorce
14. custody

LESSON 1

Vocabulary Review

Correct the sentences below by replacing the italicized term with the correct vocabulary term.

1. A(n) *single-parent family* consists of a married couple and their children from previous marriages.

2. Two parents and one or more children living in the same place form a(n) *extended family*.

3. *Adoption* is the temporary placement of children in the homes of adults who are not related to them.

Understanding Key Concepts

After reading the question or statement, select the correct answer.

4. Relatives such as aunts, uncles, and grandparents are part of a person's
   a. nuclear family.
   b. blended family.
   c. extended family.
   d. foster family.

5. In a family, children are often responsible for
   a. meeting the family's basic needs, such as food and shelter.
   b. setting limits on family members' behaviors.
   c. teaching values and skills.
   d. performing household chores.

6. Parents promote their children's mental and emotional health by
   a. providing for basic needs, such as food, clothing, and shelter.
   b. providing medical care.
   c. providing affirmation.
   d. sharing cultural traditions.

7. Which value might a parent teach a child by making an effort to help a friend?
   a. Caring
   b. Responsibility
   c. Honesty
   d. Citizenship

Thinking Critically

After reading the question or statement, write a short answer using complete sentences.

8. **Describe.** What is one purpose of foster care?

9. **Explain.** How can setting limits on children's behavior promote physical health?

10. **Give Examples.** Name two healthful behaviors children may learn from their parents.

11. **Evaluate.** Why might teaching values by example be more powerful in some cases than teaching by explanation?

LESSON 2

Vocabulary Review

Use the vocabulary terms listed on page 185 to complete the following statements.

12. During a(n) _____, a couple may attempt to work out their problems so that they can live together again.

13. A(n) _____ is a legal end to a marriage contract.

14. After a divorce, sole or joint _____ of the children may be granted to one or both parents.

Health eSpotlight VIDEO Wrap-Up

Family First Have students reread the Health eSpotlight question at the beginning of the chapter (page 165) and look at their original answer. **Ask Students:** *Now that you have read the chapter and watched the video, how would you explain the importance of taking part in activities with family members?* Call on volunteers to describe how their responses would change.

Understanding Key Concepts

After reading the question or statement, select the correct answer.

15. Helping a younger sibling with a difficult school assignment is an example of
    a. good communication.
    b. support.
    c. respect.
    d. trust.

16. Which of the following is an example of a change in family structure?
    a. The birth of a new baby
    b. The loss of a parent's job
    c. A family member's serious illness
    d. Moving to a new home

17. Joint custody is an arrangement in which
    a. the children live with their mother.
    b. the children live with their father.
    c. both parents share responsibility for the children.
    d. the children are placed in foster care.

18. Which of the following is *not* a helpful way to cope with changes in the family?
    a. Talking openly with other family members
    b. Making more of an effort to help out with chores and other responsibilities
    c. Keeping feelings to yourself to avoid worrying family members
    d. Showing empathy for family members' feelings

Thinking Critically

After reading the question or statement, write a short answer using complete sentences.

19. **Describe.** What are five traits of a healthy family?

20. **Compare and Contrast.** Explain how families in movies and TV shows may differ from real families.

21. **Infer.** Why might a divorced parent's remarriage cause mixed feelings for a teen?

22. **Evaluate.** Why can financial gains, as well as losses, be a source of stress for families?

LESSON 3

Vocabulary Review

Choose the correct term in the sentences below.

23. *Cycle of violence / Abuse* is the physical, mental, emotional, or sexual mistreatment of one person by another.

24. Any act of violence involving family members is known as *domestic violence / spousal abuse.*

25. Child *violence / neglect* is the failure to provide for a child's basic needs.

Understanding Key Concepts

After reading the question or statement, select the correct answer.

26. Yelling at or threatening a child is an example of
    a. physical abuse.
    b. emotional abuse.
    c. sexual abuse.
    d. neglect.

27. Older family members are much more likely than young children to suffer
    a. physical abuse.
    b. sexual abuse.
    c. emotional abuse.
    d. financial abuse.

28. If a friend confides that he is being abused, you should
    a. assume the person is just exaggerating.
    b. confront the abuser face-to-face.
    c. keep quiet for fear of putting the victim at further risk.
    d. seek help from a trusted adult.

Chapter 7 Assessment **187**

Understanding Key Concepts

15. b
16. a
17. c
18. c

Thinking Critically

19. Good communication, caring and support, respect, commitment, trust
20. Sample answer: Families in movies and television shows often resolve their conflicts quickly; in real life, problems are usually not resolved in a matter of minutes or hours.
21. Sample answer: The teen might be glad that the parent is in a happy relationship, but might feel disloyal to the other parent for liking the new stepparent.
22. Sample answer: Families may feel uncertain about how to handle their newfound wealth. They may also fear it will change the way others see them.

LESSON 3

Vocabulary Review

23. Abuse
24. domestic violence
25. neglect

Understanding Key Concepts

26. b
27. d
28. d
29. d

Assessment

30. Sample answers: They blame themselves for the abuse; they don't want to tear the family apart; they have nowhere else to go; they cannot support the children on their own; they fear the abuser will find them and hurt them.

31. They believe abuse is a normal part of family life.

32. Sample answer: Unless James has a safe place to go, such as a friend's or relative's home, he puts himself at risk for homelessness, crime, drug problems, and abuse by predatory adults.

33. Counseling involves the help of a trained counselor, while support groups offer help from others facing the same problem.

34. Community services can offer a variety of help, including counseling, support groups, police intervention, shelters, and hotlines. Children may be placed in foster care for protection from domestic abuse.

29. Which type of organization can provide families in need with food, shelter, and medical care?
    a. Counseling services
    b. Support groups
    c. Crisis hotlines
    d. Social services

Thinking Critically

After reading the question or statement, write a short answer using complete sentences.

30. **Analyze.** Explain why some victims of spousal abuse are unwilling to leave their abusers.

31. **Explain.** Why are people who were abused as children more likely to become abusive parents?

32. **Evaluate.** James lives with an abusive, alcoholic parent. He has considered running away from home. What are the possible consequences he might face if he does so?

33. **Compare and Contrast.** What is the main difference between counseling and support groups as a way to deal with family problems?

34. **Explain.** How can community services offer help and support for victims of domestic abuse? Give specific examples.

Project-Based ASSESSMENT

Coping During Times of Stress

Background
A family is a team. For a family to work as a single unit, everyone needs to communicate clearly and carry out their responsibilities. Successful families care for, support, and help each other.

Task
Write a newspaper feature about a fictional family. This family has just survived a natural disaster such as a hurricane or tornado, and the family members are working together and supporting each other through this difficult time.

Audience
Students in your class

Purpose
Help students learn how family support is especially important in times of stress.

Procedure

1. Organize into small groups. Review the information in Chapter 7 about family relationships.

2. Conduct research on families that have survived natural disasters. How does each family member function independently and as part of a group? Obtain examples of what they do to support each other.

3. Identify four or five key points that you want to make in your feature story.

4. Work together to write a newspaper feature about a fictional family supporting each other after a natural disaster. Make sure your key points are clearly explained and supported.

5. Have one member of the group read the feature to the class.

Project-Based ASSESSMENT

Step 1 Choose a Topic Have students form small groups. Have each group review the information in Chapter 7 about family relationships and conduct research about families that have survived natural disasters.

Step 2 Write Article Have students work in their groups to identify five key points they want to make in their newspaper article, write their article, and develop a survey about the key points of the article. Have each group share its article and survey with the class.

Step 3 Evaluate Use the completed surveys to assess the effectiveness of each group's article.

Visit **glencoe.com** for Project-Based Assessment rubrics.

Math Practice

Interpret Statistics. The chart below provides marriage and divorce statistics for the U.S. population in 2004 and 2005. Use the statistics to answer Questions 1–3.

Number of marriages in 2004:	2,279,000
Number of marriages in 2005:	2,230,000
Marriage rate in 2004:	7.8 per 1,000 people
Marriage rate in 2005:	7.5 per 1,000 people
Divorce rate in 2004:	3.6 per 1,000 people
Divorce rate in 2005:	3.7 per 1,000 people

Divorce rates include only 46 states and D.C. Adapted from "Births, Marriages, Divorces, and Deaths: Provisional Data for 2005, table A," *National Center for Health Statistics,* July 2006.

1. By how much did the number of marriages decrease from 2004 to 2005?
   A. 3,000
   B. 30,000
   C. 49,000
   D. 79,000

2. What proportion could be used to estimate the total U.S. population in 2005?
   A. $1,000 - 7.5 = x - 2,230,000$
   B. $1,000 - 7.5 = 2,230,000 - x$
   C. $7.5/1,000 = x/2,230,000$
   D. $7.5/1,000 = 2,230,000/x$

3. According to the marriage statistics, which figure best estimates the total U.S. population in 2005?
   A. 16,725
   B. 223,000,000
   C. 297,300,000
   D. 16,725,000,000

Go Online

For more test practice, visit glencoe.com and complete the Online Quizzes for Chapter 7.

Reading/Writing Practice

Understand and Apply. Read the passage below, and then answer the questions.

> There are four people in my family: me, my mom, and my two older sisters. My mom adopted all three of us when I was very young. I don't remember my birth parents, so this is the only family I've ever known.
>
> Like any other family, we get into arguments sometimes. But we also take care of each other. My sisters help me with homework, and my mom is always there for us.
>
> My mom thinks it's important for my sisters and me to be in touch with our Korean heritage. Even though she's not Korean, she learned to make Korean foods for us. Every year we go to the local heritage festival to celebrate our traditions as a family. It makes me feel valued to know that Mom respects our heritage and doesn't want us to change.

1. In the first sentence, the part after the colon should be changed to read:
   A. me and my mom and my two sisters.
   B. my two older sisters and I and my mom.
   C. my mom, my two older sisters, and me.
   D. I, my mom, and my two sisters.

2. The author mentions arguments to show that
   A. his family is not healthy.
   B. he gets along with his mother but not with his sisters.
   C. his family is supportive and caring.
   D. his family is much like any other.

3. Think about a cultural tradition that you and your family share. Write a short essay describing this tradition and how it helps bring you together as a family.

National Education Standards

Math: Number and Operations, Statistics
Language Arts: NCTE 1, NCTE 3, NCTE 4

Standardized Test Practice

Standardized Test Practice Answers

Math Practice
1. C
2. D
3. C

Reading/Writing Practice
1. C
2. D
3. Essays will vary. Each student's essay should describe a cultural tradition the student shares with his or her family.

National Education Standards

Math: Number and Operations, Statistics

Language Arts: NCTE 1, NCTE 3, NCTE 4

For the complete Math and Language Arts standards, visit glencoe.com.

Go Online

Online Study Tools
For more test practice, visit glencoe.com and complete the Online Quizzes for Chapter 7.

Test-Taking Tip

Get Enough Rest and Eat Breakfast
Tell students that they will perform better on their tests if they have had enough sleep the night before. Explain that 8 hours of sleep is a healthy goal for the night before a major test. Also remind students that a healthy breakfast before the test will boost their energy level and ability to concentrate on the test questions. Point out that a healthy breakfast does not need to include traditional breakfast foods—a sandwich or slice of pizza can also serve as breakfast.

Chapter 8 pages 190–217	Standards		Features
	National	**State/Local**	
	1.12.1, 1.12.7, 2.12.3, 2.12.9, 4.12.2, 4.12.3, 5.12.1, 7.12.1		*Hands-On* **HEALTH** • Assert Yourself (*Communication*), page 212
30 Min **Lesson 1** **Safe and Healthy** **Friendships** pages 192–197 **BIG Idea** Mutual respect and honesty are important charac- teristics of healthy friendships.	1.12.1, 1.12.7, 2.12.3, 4.12.1, 4.12.3, 4.12.4, 5.12.1, 5.12.6, 7.12.1, 7.12.2, 8.12.1, 8.12.2		*Health Skills* **Activity** • When Friendships Change (*Communication Skills*), page 197 Ⓨ Out of Time
30 Min **Lesson 2** **Peer Pressure and Refusal** **Skills** pages 198–204 **BIG Idea** Learning effective refusal skills will help you deal with negative peer pressure.	1.12.8, 2.12.3, 4.12.2, 4.12.3, 5.12.6, 6.12.1, 7.12.1, 7.12.2, 7.12.3, 8.12.1, 8.12.2		**TEENS Making a Difference** • Standing Up for What You Believe, page 201
30 Min **Lesson 3** **Practicing Abstinence** pages 205–211 **BIG Idea** Setting dating limits and practicing abstinence will benefit all three sides of your health triangle.	1.12.1, 1.12.2, 1.12.8, 1.12.9, 2.12.7, 2.12.8, 2.12.9, 4.12.2, 4.12.3, 5.12.3, 5.12.6, 6.12.4, 7.12.1		*Real World* **CONNECTION** • Sexual Content on TV, page 207 Ⓨ Out of Time

Key to
Ability Levels

Teaching Strategies and activities have been coded for ability level and appropriateness.

AL Activities for students working above grade level

OL Activities for students working on grade level

BL Activities for students working below grade level

EL Activities for English Learners

Chapter 8 Planning Guide

TeacherWorks Plus
All-In-One Planner and Resource Center

Resources	Lesson Assessment	Technology
Student Activity Workbook TEACH FAST FILE RESOURCES Vocabulary Practice TEACH Health Labs EXTEND	Chapter 8 Review Chapter 8 Assessment Standardized Test Practice ExamView® Assessment Suite CD-ROM	**Teaching Tools:** TeacherWorks™ Plus DVD StudentWorks™ Plus DVD ExamView® Assessment Suite CD-ROM Transparency Fitness DVD PowerPoint® DVD Health eSpotlight Video Series DVD
FAST FILE RESOURCES Reading Strategies Activity TEACH Reteaching Activity REVIEW Enrichment Activity EXTEND Daily Discussion Notes REVIEW Health Skills Practice TEACH	Lesson 1 Assessment, page 197 Lesson 1 Quiz Fast File ExamView® Assessment Suite CD-ROM	**Web-Based Resources:** Go Online glencoe.com • Health Podcast Activities • Audio Chapter Summaries (English/Spanish) • Interactive Health Tutor • Health Skills Activities • Vocabulary PuzzleMaker
FAST FILE RESOURCES Reading Strategies Activity TEACH Reteaching Activity REVIEW Enrichment Activity EXTEND Daily Discussion Notes REVIEW Health Skills Practice TEACH	Lesson 2 Assessment, page 204 Lesson 2 Quiz Fast File ExamView® Assessment Suite CD-ROM	• Parent Letters (English/Spanish) • Lesson Plans • Health Inventories • Online Quizzes • Study-to-Go • Unit Web Projects • Student Web Activities • Fitness Zone Activities
FAST FILE RESOURCES Reading Strategies Activity TEACH Reteaching Activity REVIEW Enrichment Activity EXTEND Daily Discussion Notes REVIEW Health Skills Practice TEACH	Lesson 3 Assessment, page 211 Lesson 3 Quiz Fast File ExamView® Assessment Suite CD-ROM	

StudentWorks Plus

This is the student's backpack solution.

Includes:
- complete Interactive Student Edition
- full audio of English text and Spanish chapter summaries
- allows students to record assignments and track grades.
- links to online activities and additional student resources
- access to all student worksheets and workbooks

Dinah Zike Foldables®
Chapter Activity
Refer to the *Dinah Zike Reading and Study Skills for Glencoe Health*. Have students complete the Foldable titled "Before You Read." As students read the chapter, have them record main ideas, new terms, and personal experiences on the appropriate pages of their Foldables.

Key to Symbols
 Transparencies   REVIEW activities to review or reinforce content
CD-ROM   TEACH activities to teach basic concepts
glencoe.com   EXTEND activities to extend or enrich lesson content
 Print Resources

Peer Relationships
Chapter Overview

Chapter 8 focuses on types of peer relationships and the positive and negative influence of peer pressure. Dating relationships and the benefits of abstinence until marriage are also discussed.

Lesson 1
The ability to build and maintain significant healthy friendships is an important social skill to develop during the teen years.

Lesson 2
Peer pressure can have a positive or negative influence on a person's actions and behaviors. To resist negative peer pressure, teens need to learn to be assertive and use refusal skills effectively.

Lesson 3
Dating is one way to develop social skills and learn more about oneself. Abstinence from sexual activity is the only 100 percent effective way to prevent pregnancy and sexually transmitted diseases.

▶ Activating Prior Knowledge

After students have discussed their sentences, ask: Why do you choose to spend a lot of time with a particular person? How do you feel when you disagree with that friend? What has caused some of your past friendships to change?

CHAPTER 8 Peer Relationships

Lesson 1
Safe and Healthy Friendships

BIG Idea *Mutual respect and honesty are important characteristics of healthy friendships.*

Lesson 2
Peer Pressure and Refusal Skills

BIG Idea *Learning effective refusal skills will help you deal with negative peer pressure.*

Lesson 3
Practicing Abstinence

BIG Idea *Setting dating limits and practicing abstinence will benefit all three sides of your health triangle.*

Activating Prior Knowledge

Using Visuals The teens in this picture are friends who share similar interests. Write five sentences, each beginning with the words *A true friend is someone who* . . . Discuss your ideas of what characteristics make a true friend.

190

Universal Access

Differentiated Learning Glencoe provides teacher support and student materials for all learners in the health classroom.

- Chapter Summaries in English and Spanish are available online at **glencoe.com**.
- *Fast Files* and related worksheets support reluctant readers.

- Universal Access strategies throughout the Teacher Wraparound Edition and *Fast Files* help you present materials for gifted students, at-risk students, physically impaired students, and those with behavior disorders or learning disabilities.

Chapter Launchers

Health in Action

Discuss the **BIG** Ideas

Before beginning this chapter, think about how you would answer these questions:

▶ Who are your peers?
▶ Why are peer relationships important?
▶ How can peer relationships affect your health?

Watch the *Health eSpotlight* Video Series

Choices for Healthy Friendships

Saying no to your friends is never easy, even if you're making the right decision. How do you deal with peer pressure?

Assess Your Health

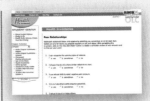

G⊚ Online

Visit glencoe.com and complete the Health Inventory for Chapter 8.

Chapter 8 Peer Relationships **191**

Chapter Launchers

Health in Action

Discuss the **BIG** Ideas

Assign this activity before students read the chapter. Explain that the purpose of the questions is to help students assess their current knowledge of peer relationships.

Health eSpotlight
Video Series

Choices for Healthy Friendships

Before Viewing the Video

Ask Students: *How would you define friendship?* After students have watched the video, call on a few volunteers to describe how they would have responded if they were in Jordan's position.

G⊚ Online

Have students go to **glencoe.com** and take the Health Inventory for Chapter 8.

Chapter Skills

Reading Skills
- Reviewing Facts and Vocabulary, pp. 197, 204, 211
- Reading/Writing Practice, p. 217

Vocabulary
- New Vocabulary, pp. 192, 198, 205
- Reviewing Facts and Vocabulary, pp. 197, 204, 211

BIG Idea

You'll learn about many types of friendships and how to manage problems in friendships.

Health Skills
- Health Skills Activity, p. 197
- Applying Health Skills, pp. 197, 204, 211

Writing Skills
- Writing Critically, pp. 197, 204, 211
- Reading/Writing Practice, p. 217

Safe and Healthy Friendships

① FOCUS

GUIDE TO READING

BIG Idea Students will learn about different types of friendships and how to recognize problems in friendships. **Ask Students:** *What different types of friendships do you have with others?* (Answers will vary but may include casual friends, close friends, or best friends.)

Before You Read

Cluster Chart Students cluster charts will vary. Sample answers may include: Care for, Respect, Trust, Share interests, Honest communication, Sharing joy

Main Idea

Types of Friends Students will form many different kinds of friendships throughout life. **Ask Students:** *What attributes do all healthy friendships share?* (Answers will vary but may include similar beliefs, similar interests or hobbies, and open and honest communication.)

Real Life Issues

Have students read the scenario. **Ask Students:** *Have you ever felt like Jarod or Tom?* Have students write an entry in their Personal Health Journal about a time when a friendship changed. Ask them what strategies they used for handling the change.

GUIDE TO READING

BIG Idea *Mutual respect and honesty are important characteristics of healthy friendships.*

Before You Read

Create a Cluster Chart. Draw a circle and label it "Friendship." Use surrounding circles to define and describe this term. As you read, continue filling in the chart with more details.

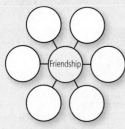

Friendship

New Vocabulary

▶ platonic friendship (p. 194)
▶ clique (p. 195)

Review Vocabulary

▶ peers (Ch.1, L.2)
▶ friendship (Ch.6, L.1)
▶ prejudice (Ch.6, L.2)
▶ stereotypes (Ch.6, L.2)

Safe and Healthy Friendships

Real Life Issues

Maintaining Friendships. Tom and Jarod have been friends since the sixth grade. They promised to join the same clubs and sports teams in high school to stay close friends. Now that they're sophomores, Tom is meeting new friends, and his interests have changed. He wants to try new things but wants to remain friends with Jarod, too.

Writing *If you were Tom, how might you express your concerns? Write a brief letter to Jarod explaining your thoughts and feelings.*

Peer Relationships

Main Idea We will all have many types of friends.

During adolescence, you continue to develop and strengthen your personal identity. The development of your identity will be influenced by many factors, including your peers. Peers are people of similar age who share similar interests. Peer relationships can play an important role in your health and well-being. Your friends and peers may influence you to try new activities, such as joining the debate club or learning to play tennis. These activities, in turn, can promote all aspects of your health.

As you get older, your social groups expand. You may also get a part-time job where you'll meet new people. These opportunities to meet people from different age groups, cultures, races, and religions contribute to your social development. Some of the people you meet during your high school years may become lifelong friends.

Promoting School Wellness

Fostering Friendships One of the components of a successful coordinated school health program includes providing resources that address a student's complete physical, mental, and social well-being. Let students know what kind of information is available at school to foster friendships, increase confidence in making new friends, and help them build strong friendships. Perhaps list some school organizations such as a peer-mentoring program or school clubs that can assist students in developing healthy peer relationships.

Friendships

You will form many kinds of friendships throughout your life. As you learned in Chapter 6, a friendship is a significant relationship between two people. Friends not only enjoy spending time together, they also care for, respect, trust, and show consideration for each other. They also share interests, hobbies, and other friends. Friendships have several common attributes:

- Similar values, interests, beliefs, and attitudes
- Open and honest communication
- Sharing of joys, disappointments, dreams, and concerns
- Mutual respect, caring, and support
- Concern about each other's safety and well-being

You probably have several types of friendships, including casual, close, and platonic friends. With the widespread use of the Internet today, many teens are also forming online friendships.

Casual and Close Friendships A casual friend is someone with whom you share interests but not deep emotional bonds. As you get to know a casual friend better, your relationship may develop into a close friendship. Close friends have strong emotional ties to each other. You feel comfortable sharing your thoughts, feelings, and experiences with a close friend.

When something is bothering you, a close friend offers support and encouragement. She or he listens to your concerns without passing judgment. Close friends also feel comfortable talking about problems that may arise in the friendship.

Academic Vocabulary

attribute *(noun):* a quality or characteristic

Go Online

Go to **glencoe.com** and complete the Student Web Activity on the importance of developing healthy friendships.

■ **Figure 8.1** These teens have a casual friendship based on a common interest. *What interests do you share with the peers you think of as casual friends?*

Lesson 1   Safe and Healthy Friendships   **193**

② TEACH

C Critical Thinking

Discussing Divide the class into several groups, and tell them that they will analyze a friendship in a film, TV show, short story, or poem. Have each group decide what form of media they will examine and choose a friendship to analyze. Then have each group report on the fictional friendship, explaining whether the friendship was healthy or unhealthy. **OL**

Go Online

Have students go to **glencoe.com** and complete the Student Web Activity on the importance of developing healthy friendships.

Academic Vocabulary

Attribute To illustrate the term, choose an object in the classroom, such as a pencil or notebook. Have students identify attributes of the object. Remind students that objects have "tangible" qualities, such as being hard or soft. A person has "intangible" qualities, such as caring and respect. List the attributes on the board.

Caption Answer

Figure 8.1 Answers will vary but may include hobbies, activities, school clubs, interests, or sports.

English Language Coach

Extend Vocabulary Write the words *casual* and *close* on the board. Explain to students who are fluent in languages other than English that these adjectives may be used to describe two different types of friendships. Also explain that there are multiple meanings for the word close. For example, one meaning is to "terminate or end." Regarding friendship, the term means "intimate or familiar."

Then write these incomplete sentences on the board.

"A casual friend is someone _____."

"Close friends have strong _____."

Have students complete each sentence, using concrete examples of how the friendships differ. Ask volunteers to read their sentences aloud.

READING CHECK

Answer Three types of friendships include casual and close, platonic, and online friendships. A casual friendship is based on common interests and a close friendship is based on strong emotional ties. A platonic friendship is based on shared affection between two members of opposite gender who are not considered a couple. An online friendship is based on communication through the Internet.

Main Idea

Building Strong Friendships
Friends can be supportive and loyal.
Ask Students: *What are some traits of healthy relationships?*
(Mutual respect and consideration, honesty, dependability, and commitment)

FITNESSZONE

Tell students to stand up beside their desks. Lead the following energy booster:

- Lift arms above head.
- Bend over, making sure not to hit anyone.
- Try to reach the floor, but be sure NOT to overstretch.
- Repeat five times.

READING CHECK

Describe Identify and describe three types of friendships.

Platonic Friendships Your friends can include both males and females. A **platonic friendship** is *a friendship with a member of the opposite gender in which there is affection, but the two people are not considered a couple*. Platonic friendships can help you understand and become comfortable with members of the opposite gender.

Online Friendships The Internet has created opportunities for new kinds of friendships. Online friendships can be rewarding because you can get to know people in other parts of the world and learn about other cultures and traditions.

Online friendships, however, can be dangerous. For example, online friends may not be truthful. A person who claims to be a teen may really be an adult. When communicating with online friends, keep these guidelines in mind:

- Don't share personal information or pictures of yourself.
- Don't offer your phone number or street address.
- Never arrange a face-to-face meeting.
- Always tell a trusted adult if an online friend suggests you do something that makes you feel uncomfortable.

Building Strong Friendships

Main Idea Good friends offer loyalty, support, and motivation.

As friends grow closer and share more serious thoughts and feelings, friendships may become complex. It's natural for friendships to grow and change, but always remember that healthy relationships are based on:

- mutual respect
- caring
- honesty
- commitment

Friends can reinforce your values and motivate you. Additional traits of a positive friendship include the following:

- **Empathy.** Does your friend consider your needs and feelings? Does she or he demonstrate understanding?
- **Fairness.** Does your friend treat you fairly?
- **Shared interests.** Do you enjoy the same things?
- **Acceptance.** Do you and your friend accept and appreciate each other's differences?
- **Support.** Does your friend support you during difficult times?
- **Loyalty.** Does your friend keep your confidences? Does he or she stay true to your friendship?

FITNESSZONE

My friends and I aren't "sports nuts," but we want to be more active. We asked our PE teacher to suggest some activities. He said we should try noncompetitive activities like walking in the park, playing a round of miniature or disc golf, or just hitting tennis balls (but not keeping score). For more physical activity ideas, visit the Online Fitness Zone at **glencoe.com.**

Home and Community

Cliques There are varying opinions on the nature and value of cliques. Some people feel that exclusive social groups, or cliques, should be banned. Others feel that some cliques, including college fraternities and sororities, are worthwhile—especially when organizing around a good cause. Encourage students to find out how members of their community feel about cliques or groups. Suggest that they interview friends, relatives, and neighbors by asking questions such as: What groups do you consider to be cliques? Do cliques determine social, economic, or political success in your school or community?

■ **Figure 8.2** Friendships can contribute positively to your well-being and enrich your life. *Identify some qualities of strong and healthy friendships.*

Recognizing Problems in Friendships

Main Idea It's important that you know how to recognize problems in a friendship and how to resolve those problems.

Friendships can have a positive or negative effect on you. They are positive when they offer support and encouragement. They have a negative effect if they influence you to engage in harmful activities. To avoid unhealthy friendships, you need to recognize and resolve problems that arise.

Cliques

A **clique** is *a small circle of friends, usually with similar backgrounds or tastes, who exclude people viewed as outsiders.* Often members of a clique share interests, dress similarly, and behave in the same way. Being part of a clique may provide members with a sense of belonging. However, cliques may discourage individual members from thinking for themselves or acting as individuals.

Sometimes, clique members may **exclude** others by showing prejudice. They may make assumptions or judgments about an individual without really knowing him or her. These judgments may include stereotypes, exaggerated or oversimplified beliefs about an entire group of people, such as an ethnic or religious group or a gender.

U

Academic Vocabulary

exclude *(verb):* to prevent or restrict the entrance of

Lesson 1   Safe and Healthy Friendships   **195**

Caption Answer

Figure 8.2 Some qualities of strong and healthy friendships are mutual respect and consideration, honesty, dependability, and commitment.

U Universal Access

Cooperative Learning Pair students who are English proficient with English Language Learners. Have pairs review the new vocabulary terms (for example, platonic friendship, clique, stereotypes) by choosing one term to act out in a short skit or pantomime. Give pairs time to practice their skits. Then ask volunteers to perform their skits for the class. **BL** **EL**

Main Idea

Recognizing Problems It's important to recognize problems in friendships and to resolve those problems. **Ask Students:** *What are some ways that you can tell there is a problem in a friendship?* (Answers will vary but may include feeling envy or jealousy or growing apart from a friend.)

Academic Vocabulary

Exclude Have students provide examples from history of groups that have been excluded from other parts of society. For example, African Americans were forbidden to ride in the front of buses or drink from the same water fountains as Caucasians.

ELL Support

Name and Repeat Write the following words on the board: *exclude, clique, stereotype.* Define each word aloud.

Beginning Use sentences such as "Maria tried to exclude Joanna from their lunch group." Ask students to repeat the sentence. Using the other two words in a sentence, ask students to also repeat.

Intermediate Ask students for sentence examples for each word.

Advanced Have students describe positive and negative influences of cliques.

Communication Skills: When Friendships Change

NHES Standard 4 Students will demonstrate the ability to use interpersonal communication skills to enhance health and avoid or reduce health risks.

Objectives

- Demonstrate refusal skills to enhance health and avoid or reduce health risks.
- Demonstrate strategies to prevent, manage, or resolve interpersonal conflicts without harming oneself or others.

Teaching Strategies

- Discuss the characteristics of a strong friendship. Ask how Dave and Allen reflect these characteristics.
- Ask volunteers to share the endings they have written.

Assessment

Using this list, student work should provide comprehensive evidence of the following criteria to achieve the highest score:

√ Uses "I" messages
√ Speaks calmly and clearly
√ Uses a respectful tone
√ Listens carefully and asks appropriate questions
√ Uses appropriate body language

READING CHECK

Answer Student answers will vary. Remind students that if they end a friendship, end it in a respectful manner.

READING CHECK

Explain What is one way of dealing with feelings of jealousy in a friendship?

■ **Figure 8.3** Talking with a trusted friend can help you deal with difficulties in other peer relationships. *What are some other strategies for handling problems in friendships?*

Managing Feelings of Envy or Jealousy

Another problem that can occur in friendsips is envy or jealousy. Such feelings may arise if one friend compares himself or herself to another friend. Envy and jealousy can harm a friendship. If you feel jealous of a friend, ask yourself the following questions:

- What is making me feel jealous?
- Is my friend deliberately trying to make me feel this way?
- What can I do to manage or reduce these feelings? How can I feel better about myself?
- Are these feelings of jealousy more important than our friendship?
- What positive qualities make this person a good friend?

To overcome feelings of envy or jealousy, remind yourself of your unique talents and the positive aspects of your life. Friendships can survive the occasional feelings of jealousy if individuals focus on the reasons why they became friends.

When Friendships Change

As you grow older, you and a close friend might spend less time together and develop new interests. When close friends grow apart, the friendship may become casual. Other times, you may decide to end a friendship because it is becoming harmful. Here are some reasons for ending a friendship:

- A friend pressures you to do something that is unsafe or goes against your values.
- A friend says hurtful and insulting things to you.
- A friend constantly tries to get you to change your beliefs or actions.

If you decide to end a friendship, communicate your feelings to that friend in a clear and respectful way. Use "I" messages to explain your feelings and reasons for ending the friendship. Let your friend respond with his or her point of view. Although it may be difficult, sometimes ending a friendship is the best decision for both individuals. Remember, you can always talk to another friend or ask a trusted adult for advice about dealing with these situations.

Teens Want to Know

Are Cliques Good or Bad? Cliques, the tight-knit group of friends that form in the preteen and teen years, can be a positive or negative experience. Teens in cliques often lose the opportunities to interact with other peer groups. Cliques can influence a teen to do something that is against his or her values. Often, a clique will be exclusive and encourage its members to belittle students who are not a part of their group. Have students discuss ways to avoid the negative aspects of cliques. Suggest that students become active in several activities and develop variety in their friendships.

Health Skills Activity

Communication Skills

When Friendships Change

Allen ran up to Dave on the way to school. "Dave, what are you doing after school? I'm going out with Eric's group tonight, and they invited you along."

"Sorry, I've got a project to finish," said Dave. "Why do you want to hang out with those guys, anyway? I hear some of them have been in trouble with the police."

"They're fun to be around," Allen said. Then he added angrily, "Why are you so uptight?"

Dave looked at Allen. They had been friends since grade school, but lately Allen seemed to lose interest in doing the things that they used to enjoy together. Allen quit the tae kwon do class and the math study group they were in. Now Allen was spending time with a rough crowd and getting into trouble at school. Dave wondered how he should respond.

Writing Write an ending to the scenario in which Dave communicates to Allen that he thinks their friendship is changing. Make sure Allen knows that Dave has decided to pursue healthier friendships. Use the following tips as a guideline.

1. Use "I" messages.
2. Speak calmly and clearly.
3. Use a respectful tone.
4. Listen carefully and ask appropriate questions.
5. Use appropriate body language.

LESSON 1 ASSESSMENT

After You Read

Reviewing Facts and Vocabulary

1. Define the word *peers*.
2. Define *friendship*. Identify four traits of healthy friendships.
3. List two problems that may affect friendships.

Thinking Critically

4. **Evaluate.** What actions can you take to promote safe and healthy friendships?
5. **Describe.** Name two possible outcomes of lying to a friend. How might this affect the friendship?

Applying Health Skills

6. **Communication Skills.** With a classmate, role-play a scenario in which close friends communicate needs, wants, and emotions in healthful ways.

Writing Critically

7. **Expository.** Write a dialogue in which peers express disagreement about an issue while still showing respect for self and others.

Go Online

Visit glencoe.com and complete the Interactive Study Guide for this lesson.

LESSON 1 ASSESSMENT ANSWERS

1. *Peers* are people of similar age who share similar interests.
2. See page 194.
3. Feelings of envy or jealousy, and growing apart.
4. Responses will vary.
5. The friend could either forgive or the friendship could end.
6. Scenarios will vary.
7. Dialogues will vary.

---

❸ ASSESS/ CLOSE

Assessment Resources

📁 **FAST FILE ACTIVITIES**
Lesson 1 Quiz

💿 *ExamView Assessment Suite* CD-ROM

Visit glencoe.com for:
Online Quizzes
Online Learning Center

Progress Monitoring

Reteaching
Have students work in pairs to perform skits that show how to correctly end a friendship. Then ask volunteers to share their skits with the class.

Enrichment
Have students research the difference between jealousy and envy. Then have them write a fictional letter to a friend, explaining the nature of their envy or jealousy and the steps they have taken to overcome those feelings.

Go Online

Have students visit glencoe.com and complete the Interactive Study Guide for this lesson.

Peer Pressure and Refusal Skills

1 FOCUS

GUIDE TO READING

BIG *Idea* Peer pressure can be positive or negative. Refusal skills can help deal with negative peer pressure. **Ask Students:** *What are two things that you might learn in this lesson?* (Sample answers: Positive peer pressure can motivate you to try new things; there are ways to deal with negative peer pressure.)

Before You Read
Vocabulary Cards Students' definitions will vary. Have students read some aloud.

Main Idea

Peer Pressure Peer pressure can have a positive or negative influence on actions and behaviors. **Ask Students:** *How does your body react when you are under pressure from friends to do something you aren't sure of?* (Answers will vary but may include being restless or out of breath or having sweaty palms. Point out that these reactions demonstrate how peer pressure can affect your physical health.)

Real Life Issues ....

Have students read the Real Life Issues scenario. **Ask Students:** *What is Karen risking if she confronts Ann?* Accept reasonable responses.

198

GUIDE TO READING

BIG *Idea* *Learning effective refusal skills will help you deal with negative peer pressure.*

Before You Read

Create Vocabulary Cards. Write each new vocabulary term on a separate note card. For each term, write a definition based on your current knowledge. As you read, fill in additional information related to each term.

Peer Pressure

New Vocabulary

▸ peer pressure (p. 198)
▸ harassment (p. 199)
▸ manipulation (p. 200)

Review Vocabulary

▸ assertive (Ch.6, L.3)
▸ refusal skills (Ch.6, L.3)
▸ passive (Ch.6, L.3)
▸ aggressive (Ch.6, L.3)

Peer Pressure and Refusal Skills

Real Life Issues ....

Facing Peer Pressure. Karen and Ann met at tryouts for the school gymnastics team. The coach gave each girl a list of fitness tips to prepare for the tryouts. The tips included eating a low-fat diet, getting enough sleep, stretching before each workout, and avoiding tobacco and alcohol use. On the way home, Ann pulled a pack of cigarettes out of her bag and offered one to Karen. Karen doesn't like smoking and really wants to make the team.

Writing *If you were Karen, what would you say to Ann? Write your response in a brief paragraph.*

Peer Pressure

Main Idea Peers can influence how you think, feel, and act.

You are hanging out with friends on a Friday night when someone suggests going to a movie. Everyone agrees, but you aren't sure because the movie ends late. If you stay for the entire movie, you'll miss your curfew. "Come on! It's the weekend!" your friends say. You hesitate, trying to decide what to do.

During the teen years, it's common to experience pressure situations like the one presented above. How you respond to these situations can impact your health and safety. That's why it's important to learn ways to handle pressure from peers. *The influence that people your age may have on you* is called **peer pressure**. Peer pressure can have a positive or negative influence on your actions and behaviors. Evaluating forms of peer pressure and developing strategies for responding to it will help you maintain healthy relationships.

Skills for the *21st* Century

Work Relationships In some jobs, the ability to relate well to peers accounts for 90 percent of job performance and success. In other jobs, relating to others is not quite as essential. List a variety of careers on the board such as a police officer, physician, gardener, telemarketer, computer programmer, writer, teacher, hair stylist, or lab technician. Then divide students into groups or pairs.

For each career, have students list the factors that affect job performance, such as skills and knowledge, punctuality, dependability, honesty, physical strength, efficiency, and social skills. Have them rank the qualities for each job. Invite groups to share their rankings, and discuss where they placed social skills on their list and why.

■ **Figure 8.4** Positive peer pressure can motivate you to try new activities that can benefit all sides of your health triangle. *What are some examples of positive peer pressure that you have experienced?*

Positive Peer Pressure

Peers can influence you in many positive ways. Your peers might inspire you to try a new activity, like an art class, or to try ethnic foods that you've never tasted before. They may also encourage you to participate in community projects, such as a cleanup campaign. Agreeing to work with your peers on a volunteer project benefits your social health because you have the opportunity to interact with others in a positive way. It also benefits the community by providing a cleaner environment. Volunteering to serve food at a homeless shelter or working at a Special Olympics event because a friend does are other examples of positive peer pressure.

Sometimes, positive peer pressure involves *not* participating in risky behaviors or activities. For instance, having friends who do not use tobacco, alcohol, or other drugs may positively influence you to avoid these harmful substances. You can also use positive peer pressure to influence others in healthful ways. You might encourage a peer to try out for the softball team or to study hard for an important test.

Negative Peer Pressure

Peers sometimes pressure others to take part in behaviors or accept beliefs with negative consequences. The members of a clique, for example, may be disrespectful toward people they do not consider acceptable to their group. Such behavior may involve **harassment**, or *persistently annoying others.* Harassment may include hurtful behaviors such as name-calling, teasing, or bullying.

Go Online

))) Listen to the Health Podcast Activity, *Resisting Negative Peer Pressure,* at glencoe.com.

② TEACH

Caption Answer

Figure 8.4 Answers will vary. Students may suggest that a friend pointed out a healthful snack alternative or a fun way to be more physically active.

AL Active Learning

Positive Actions Have pairs brainstorm simple ways in which they can affect positive behaviors in others, such as listening to someone in a nonjudgmental way or not pushing in a crowded line. Have pairs share their ideas with the class. Discuss how even simple actions can have important effects on the mental/emotional health of others. **OL**

Go Online

))) Remind students to visit glencoe.com, listen to the podcast, and complete the Health Podcast Activity, *Resisting Negative Peer Pressure.*

Lesson 2 Peer Pressure and Refusal Skills **199**

Teacher to Teacher

Deborah Tackmann, B.S., M.E.P.D. • North High School, Eau Claire, Wisconsin

Using "I" Messages Students can use this form of communication to share their concerns and feelings with others in a caring and non-judgmental way. Give each student an index card and instruct them to write the following "I" message skill on the card.

I feel_____when you_____because_____and I'd like/I want_____.
Would you consider_____?

Present a realistic situation, such as a friend who has recently been hanging out with people who smoke. Ask students to address that situation using the "I" message skill.

READING CHECK

Answer Answers will vary. Under positive peer pressure, students might list participation in community activities. Negative peer pressures might include disrespect of people outside a certain group, harassment, and manipulation of others.

Main Idea

Resisting Negative Peer Pressure Refusal skills can help deal with negative peer pressure. **Ask Students:** *Have you ever had to say no to a friend? What happened to the relationship?* Students can volunteer situations. Some may say that the friendship was unaffected or that it fell apart.

U **Universal Access**

Reinforcing Concepts Organize the class into groups of three. Assign each group one of the manipulation methods listed in **Figure 8.5**. Within each group, have one student define the technique and have a second student describe an example of how it might be worded. The third student can describe words to counteract or resist the specific manipulation method. Have each group present their summary to the class. EL BL OL

READING CHECK

List What are the differences between positive and negative peer pressure?

Negative peer pressure may also lead some teens to engage in behaviors that go against their values. For instance, a peer might pressure a classmate to help him or her cheat on a test.

Another way that some people exert negative peer pressure is through **manipulation**. This is *an indirect, dishonest way to control or influence other people*. Take a look at **Figure 8.5**, which lists some examples of how people manipulate one another. It is important to discourage this kind of hurtful behavior and to encourage the victim to report the problem to a trusted adult.

Resisting Negative Peer Pressure

Main Idea Practicing refusal skills will help you deal with negative peer pressure.

Peer pressure does not stop at the end of your teen years. Throughout your life, you will experience instances in which peers, including friends and co-workers, try to influence you to behave in a particular way. They might even make direct requests or demands of you.

In some cases, your responses to these siutations will directly affect your health. For example, getting into a car with friends who have been drinking can lead to serious injury or even death. To protect your health and safety, you need to learn effective strategies for resisting negative peer pressure.

One way to resist negative peer pressure is to develop friendships with people who share your values and interests. Friends who have respect for your health and well-being will be less likely to pressure you into doing something that goes against your values. You will also find that it is much easier to resist negative peer pressure when you have supportive friends who stand by you and respect your decision.

Figure 8.5	**Common Methods of Manipulation**

- **Making threats**—promising violence or some other negative consequence if the person does not do what is asked
- **Blackmail**—threatening to reveal some embarrassing or damaging information if the person does not do what is asked
- **Mocking or teasing**—making fun of another person in mean or hurtful ways
- **"Guilt trips"**—making a person feel guilty to get desired results
- **Bargaining**—offering to make a deal to get what one wants
- **Flattery**—using excessive praises to influence another person
- **Bribing**—promising money or favors if the person does what is asked

Health Literacy

Being Health-Literate According to the National Health Education Standards, the four characteristics of a health-literate person are to be

1. a responsible member of society.
2. a self-directed learner.
3. an effective communicator.
4. a critical thinker.

A health-literate teen can convey information about health through a variety of media that includes writing and music. Have students tally incidences of positive and negative peer pressure during one hour of evening television. Students should record how the pressure was used. Have students present their findings to the class.

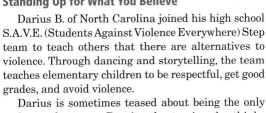

TEENS Making a Difference

"Don't let people get you down."

Standing Up for What You Believe

Darius B. of North Carolina joined his high school S.A.V.E. (Students Against Violence Everywhere) Step team to teach others that there are alternatives to violence. Through dancing and storytelling, the team teaches elementary children to be respectful, get good grades, and avoid violence.

Darius is sometimes teased about being the only male on the team. Despite the teasing, he thinks S.A.V.E. is well worth the effort. "We have a lot of fun and the children like to dance. It gets our message across that there are other things to do than fight and other ways to act than being disrespectful and rude."

If you dare to be different, Darius says: "Keep your head up and don't let people get you down. Helping someone else is always a good thing."

Activity Write your answers to the following questions in your personal health journal.

1. In what ways is Darius a positive role model?
2. How has Darius responded to peer pressure in a positive way?
3. Why is it important to stand up for your beliefs and assert your individuality?

AL

Sometimes, however, the pressure to participate in unsafe or potentially harmful activities can be difficult to resist. When pressured by a friend, many teens worry about hurting the person's feelings or jeopardizing the relationship. They may agree to an activity that goes against their values in an attempt to maintain a friendship or to make new friends.

Another concern that teens have is that refusing to go along with a group may make them appear "uncool." They fear that peers will tease or make fun of them for their decision. Even though these situations may be difficult, it is important to remain firm and stay true to yourself.

CA

Remember, you have the responsibility to make decisions that have the best possible effect on your well-being. In making decisions that involve potentially risky consequences, your health and safety come first. To help you stand your ground when faced with pressure to participate in an activity that is unsafe or goes against your values, you can practice refusal skills. Rehearsing assertive refusals will make it easier to say no when pressure situations arise.

Academic Integration

Math Refusal skills can make it possible to not give in to peer pressure when it comes to drinking alcohol. According to the 2005 Youth Risk Behavior Survey, approximately 13,917 students completed the questionnaire. It was found that 56 percent of high school students did not take a drink of alcohol in the month before the survey.

Pair students, and ask them to calculate the number of students who did not drink alcohol more than once in the 30 days before the survey. (Answer: 7,794 students)

TEENS   Making a Difference

Answers to Activity Questions

1. He has joined S.A.V.E. to spread message to children to get good grades and avoid violence.
2. He believes in not letting people get him down and helping others.
3. Answers will vary. Students might respond by saying that values are important and if you stand up for your individuality, it's a sign of positive self-esteeem.

AL Active Learning

Questionnaire Have students design a questionnaire about the influence of peer pressure on teen behavior. Then have students work in pairs to fill them out. They should summarize and submit the results of the questionnaire in an article to the school newspaper. **AL**

CA Cultural Awareness

Assertive Behavior Review the meaning of the word *assertive* (standing up for rights in a firm but positive way). Explain that *assertive* behavior is interpreted differently across cultures. In some cultures, direct responses, or even direct questions, are looked upon as pushy or rude. Discuss how sensitivity to another's culture should be taken into account when interpreting the actions of others. **BL** **OL**

C Critical Thinking

Brainstorm Ask students to brainstorm times and places in their week when they feel more pressure than others. Record their ideas on the board. Ask students to analyze the information. Is there a pattern? **AL**

R Reading Strategy

Resisting Peer Pressure Ask for volunteers to read aloud the three steps for resisting negative peer pressure. Write each step on the board. Ask volunteers to describe or share ways to help remember these steps. Have students work in small groups to draw a graphic or write a mnemonic that would help them remember the three steps. **BL EL**

Academic Vocabulary

Aspect Have students look up the term aspect in a thesaurus and list two synonyms.

■ **Figure 8.6** Practicing refusal skills will help you deal with negative peer pressure. *How would you say no if someone pressured you to participate in an unsafe activity?*

Academic Vocabulary

aspect *(noun):* a feature or phase of something

Assertive Refusal

When you practice assertive communication, you state your position and stand your ground while acknowledging the rights of others. This is the most effective approach when facing negative peer influences.

Refusal Skills An important **aspect** of being assertive is the ability to demonstrate appropriate refusal skills. Refusal skills are communication strategies that can help you say no when you are urged to take part in behaviors that are unsafe or unhealthy, or that go against your values. Effective refusal skills involve a three-step process:

- **Step 1: State Your Position.** The first step in resisting negative peer pressure is to say no. You need to state your position simply and firmly. When you say no, make sure you really mean it. Combining your words with nonverbal messages, such as those shown in **Figure 8.7**, will make your statement more effective. Having said no, give an honest reason for your response. Your reason may be as simple as, "It goes against my values." Offering a legitimate reason will help strengthen your refusal.

More About...

Saying No The purpose of refusal skills is to be able to say no when in uncomfortable or risky situations. Reinforce these components of an effective no statement:

- Use the word no. Everyone understands its meaning. Combine with a strong nonverbal message such as body language.

Review the body language shown in **Figure 8.7**.

- Suggest an alternate activity or solution.
- Stay firm with your position. Don't let anyone persuade you.

Have students write an effective refusal skills scenario.

- **Step 2: Suggest Alternatives.** When a peer asks you to take part in an activity with which you are uncomfortable, try suggesting another activity. For example, if a friend wants to go to a party where there is no adult supervision, you might say, "No, let's go to the movies instead." By offering an alternative, you create an opportunity to spend time with your friend in a way that makes you comfortable. Keep in mind that your suggestion is most effective if it takes you away from the dangerous or unpleasant situation.

- **Step 3: Stand Your Ground.** Even after you refuse, some peers may continue trying to persuade you to join in. Make it clear that you mean what you said. Use strong body language and maintain eye contact, but do not touch the other person or become physical in any way. If this doesn't work, remove yourself from the situation. Simply say, "I'm going home," and walk away.

When you're faced with negative peer pressure, refusal skills can help you avoid unsafe situations. Learning and practicing these steps will help you deal with high-pressure situations in a way that keeps you safe and healthy. Knowing that you made the decision to protect your safety and uphold your values will make you feel good about resisting negative peer pressure.

Go Online

Visit glencoe.com and complete the Student Web Activity on resisting negative peer pressure.

| Figure 8.7 | **Body Language and Assertive Refusal** |

Reinforce the meaning of your words with appropriate body language.

Shaking your head is one way to communicate no.

Raising your hands in a "Stop" or "No way" signal tells others that you are not interested.

If the other person continues to pressure you, you can walk away from the situation.

Cooperative Learning

Write a Script Review the three steps for effective refusal skills. As a class, brainstorm a list of situations in which students would need to use these steps. In groups of three, have students write a script that uses one of the listed scenarios. Each script should incorporate dialogue that clearly describes the scene and makes use of the steps described on these pages. Have interested groups act out their scripts. Encourage them to use assertive body language as part of their presentation.

U Universal Access
Connecting to the Real World
Pose this question: *What are some alternative activities you would suggest?* Head a class discussion on some positive activities. EL

HS Health Skills Practice
Practice Refusal Skills Have students discuss what is going on in **Figure 8.7**. Ask students to think about how effective the refusal method might be if other body language were used, such as smiling, shrugging the shoulders, mumbling, or looking away while trying to say and mean no. Have student pairs act out both effective and noneffective uses of body language. EL BL

W Writing Strategy
Using Refusal Skills Present the class with several scenarios involving negative peer pressure. For example, a teen might pressure a peer to stay out past curfew. For each scenario, have students write out how the teen uses refusal skills. Students may write in a dialogue format or in paragraphs. OL

Go Online

Have students visit glencoe.com and complete the Student Web Activity on resisting negative peer pressure.

READING CHECK

Answer Using assertive refusal skills shows that the individual has or can show enough confidence to interact in a conflict situation without harming himself or herself or others.

③ ASSESS/ CLOSE

Assessment Resources

📁 *FAST FILE* ACTIVITIES
Lesson 2 Quiz

💿 *ExamView*
Assessment Suite CD-ROM

Visit glencoe.com **for:**
Online Quizzes
Online Learning Center

Progress Monitoring

Reteaching

- Have students write a detailed outline of the three refusal skill steps.
- Ask students to role-play a situation where one student effectively resists negative peer pressure.

Enrichment

Present the class with this scenario: a teen might pressure another teen to stay out past curfew. Divide the class into groups. For that scenario, have one group provide a passive refusal, another group an aggressive refusal, and the third group an assertive refusal.

READING CHECK

Explain Why is it important to use assertive refusal skills, rather than using passive or aggressive responses?

Passive and Aggressive Responses

Being assertive may take some practice. To some people, a passive response to negative peer pressure seems easier. Passive communicators are unwilling or unable to express their thoughts and feelings in a direct or firm manner. Teens who respond passively to peer pressure may believe they are making friends by going along. However, being passive may cause others to view them as pushovers who aren't worthy of respect.

Some people may feel more comfortable with an aggressive response. Such responses are overly forceful, pushy, or hostile. An aggressive way of resisting peer pressure may involve yelling, shouting, shoving, or other kinds of verbal or physical force. Aggressive people may get their way, but most people react to aggressive behavior by avoiding the individual or by fighting back. Either reaction can result in emotional or physical harm to both parties.

Practicing assertive communication is the most effective way to deal with peer pressure. Being assertive shows that you will stand up for your rights, beliefs, and needs. It shows that you respect yourself and those around you.

LESSON 2 ASSESSMENT

After You Read

Reviewing Facts and Vocabulary

1. What is *peer pressure*?
2. Identify two examples of manipulation.
3. How might a friend help you resist negative peer pressure?

Thinking Critically

4. **Describe.** Write a paragraph describing how you would respond to someone who says that being aggressive is the only way to get what you want.
5. **Compare and Contrast.** How are *harassment* and *manipulation* different? How are they similar?

Applying Health Skills

6. **Refusal Skills.** With a classmate, develop a scenario in which peers try to pressure you to use tobacco or alcohol. Demonstrate refusal strategies for resisting this negative peer pressure.

Writing Critically

7. **Expository.** Write an essay analyzing the positive and negative effects of peer pressure. Explain why it is important to learn how to evaluate and respond to peer pressure.

Visit glencoe.com and complete the Interactive Study Guide for this lesson.

204 Chapter 8 Peer Relationships

LESSON 2 ASSESSMENT ANSWERS

1. *Peer pressure* is the influence that people your age may have on you.
2. Answers will vary. Examples include making threats, blackmail, and teasing.
3. Friends who have respect for your health and well-being will be less likely to pressure. They will also be supportive.
4. Responses will vary.

5. Both are forms of negative peer pressure. *Harassment* is persistently annoying another person. *Manipulation* is an indirect, dishonest way to control another person.
6. Scenarios will vary.
7. Essays will vary.

Practicing Abstinence

Real Life Issues

Thinking About Dating. Kayla has a close group of friends. Dan, one of her good friends, recently told her that he wants to date her exclusively. Kayla knows that Dan's been sexually active in the past. She likes Dan but doesn't think she's ready for a serious relationship.

Writing *Write a dialogue in which Kayla expresses her feelings to Dan. Both individuals should be honest and respectful.*

Dating Decisions

Main Idea Personal values and priorities will influence your dating decisions.

During the teen years, you may start thinking about dating. Dating can be a great way to get to know another person. It also provides opportunities to develop social skills, discover new interests, and reaffirm personal values.

Some teens, however, may decide not to date for personal reasons. They might not feel ready or they may have other priorities. **Priorities** are *the goals, tasks, values, and activities that you judge to be more important than others*. Priorities can include focusing on school or spending time with family.

Talking to a parent or other trusted adult can help you decide if you're ready to date. If you decide to date, try to establish healthful dating expectations. Keep the following in mind:

- You and your date deserve to be treated with consideration and respect.
- Be yourself and communicate your thoughts and feelings honestly.
- Never feel pressured to do anything that goes against your values or your family's values.

GUIDE TO READING

BIG Idea *Setting dating limits and practicing abstinence will benefit all three sides of your health triangle.*

Before You Read

Create a K-W-L Chart. Make a three-column chart. In the first column, list what you **k**now about dating and abstinence. In the second column, list what you **w**ant to know about this topic. As you read, use the third column to summarize what you **l**earned.

K	W	L

New Vocabulary

- priorities (p. 205)
- intimacy (p. 206)
- infatuation (p. 206)
- self-control (p. 207)
- sexually transmitted diseases (STDs) (p. 208)

Review Vocabulary

- abstinence (Ch.1, L.3)

Practicing Abstinence

① FOCUS

GUIDE TO READING

BIG Idea All three sides of the health triangle are benefitted by setting dating limits and practicing abstinence. **Ask Students:** *What questions do you think this lesson will answer?* (Questions will vary but may include: Why should teens practice abstinence?)

Before You Read
K-W-L Chart
Students' charts will vary.

Main Idea

Dating Decisions Personal values and priorities influence dating decisions. **Ask Students:** *What are some other dating decisions teens might face?* (Sample answer: whether to date someone older; where to go on a date; whether to go out alone with a date.)

Real Life Issues

Have students read the scenario. **Ask Students:** *What decision must Kayla make?* (Kayla must decide if she wants to date Dan exclusively.) Before students start writing, tell them to apply the remaining five steps of the decision-making process to decide what they would do if they were in Kayla's situation. Students can review the decision-making process on page 42 in Chapter 2.

Writing Strategy

Writing About Priorities After students read the definition of priorities on this page, have them divide a sheet of paper into four columns headed "Goals," "Tasks," "Values," and "Activities." Then ask students to write a list of their own priorities under each heading. After they list their priorities, have them write a paragraph describing how dating fits in with their priorities. For example, is dating one of their priorities? If so, how does it rank compared to their other priorities? If dating is not one of their priorities, does, or would, dating interfere with their priorities? Tell students they may keep their lists and paragraphs private.

LESSON 3

② TEACH

CA Cultural Awareness

Inferring Ask students whether dating is the same among different cultures. For example, is dating in the United States the same as dating in China? Students should be encouraged to share their thoughts with the class. Reinforce the idea that it's okay for cultures to have different dating characteristics. In some cultures, dates are prearranged and supervised by parents or other adult family members. **OL**

Academic Vocabulary

Process Call on a volunteer to use the term in a sentence. Ask other students whether the term was used correctly.

Main Idea

Abstinence There are many ways to help commit to abstinence. **Ask Students:** *What are positive dating relationships based on?* (A positive relationship is based on mutual respect and caring.)

Caption Answer

Figure 8.8 Teens can demonstrate respect for their dates by treating them with consideration, being honest with them, and not pressuring them to do anything that goes against their values or their family's values.

Academic Vocabulary

process *(noun):* a series of actions geared toward an end result

READING CHECK

Explain Why is it important to set dating limits?

■ **Figure 8.8** Positive dating relationships are based on mutual respect and caring. *Identify some ways that teens can demonstrate respect for their dates.*

Setting Limits

Your parents or guardians may set limits regarding your dating relationships. Such limits are intended to protect your health and safety. For example, many parents insist on a curfew, a set time at which teens must be home at night. As you mature, you'll need to set your own limits. Your parents or guardians can guide you through this **process**. It's a good idea to set a limit on the age of the people you date. You'll also need to set limits with your date regarding where you will go, how you will get there, and what you will do when you get there. Setting limits and making them clear before a date will help ensure safe and positive dating experiences.

The most important limit you can set is to practice abstinence. As you learned in Chapter 1, abstinence is a deliberate decision to avoid high-risk behaviors, including sexual activity and the use of tobacco, alcohol, and other drugs. Choosing abstinence will safeguard your health and future.

CA

Abstinence

Main Idea There are many strategies that can help you commit to abstinence.

By choosing abstinence from sexual activity, you are taking responsibility for your well-being. Abstinence does not mean doing without intimacy or physical contact in a close, special friendship. **Intimacy** is *a closeness between two people that develops over time.* You can still express affection and develop intimacy while practicing abstinence. For example, you can hold hands, hug, kiss, and share your thoughts, feelings, and dreams. Keep in mind that it's important not to confuse genuine affection and intimacy with **infatuation**, or *exaggerated feelings of passion.*

Myths & Reality

Teen Dating Decisions

Myth: Every teen has the desire to date and be in a relationship.

Fact: The decisions teens make about dating can significantly affect their health and happiness.

Myth: Practicing abstinence requires no planning and no self-control.

Fact: Teens should be themselves, communicate honestly, and no one should feel pressured to do something that goes against his or her values.

Real World CONNECTION

Sexual Content on TV

Media messages can play an important role in a teen's decisions regarding sexual activity. Studies have shown that adolescents with higher exposure to sexual content on TV are more likely to engage in sexual activity. Consider these statistics:

▶ 64 percent of all television programs contain sexual content.

▶ Of programs with sexual content, 15 percent show abstinence or risk of sexual activity.

Analyzing media messages and comparing them to real-life situations is an important skill to develop. It will help you resist external pressures and stay committed to abstinence.

Activity Mathematics

Assume that 1,500 TV programs were surveyed.

1. How many programs had sexual content?
2. How many programs depicted abstinence or risk of sexual activity?
3. **Writing** Write a short essay describing how the higher rate of sexual content on TV influences teen behavior.

Concept Number and Operations: Percents A percent is a ratio comparing a number to 100. It can also be represented as a fraction with 100 as the denominator. To find a decimal equivalent, divide the percent by 100. To convert a decimal to a percent, multiply it by 100.

Practicing abstinence requires planning and self-control. **Self-control** is *a person's ability to use responsibility to override emotions*. It's normal and healthy to have sexual feelings. You cannot prevent those feelings from occurring, but you can control how you react to those feelings. The following tips can help you maintain self-control and stay firm in your decision to practice abstinence:

- **Set limits for expressing affection.** Think about your priorities and set limits for your behavior before you are in a situation where sexual feelings may build.

- **Communicate with your partner.** Discuss your limits for expressing affection with your dating partner. Clear and honest communication will help your dating partner understand and respect your limits.

- **Talk with a trusted adult.** Ask a trusted adult, such as a parent or guardian, for suggestions on ways to manage your feelings.

- **Seek low-pressure dating situations.** Choose safe dating locations and activities. For example, attend parties only where an adult is present. Try group dating, which can eliminate the pressure to engage in sexual activity.

- **Date someone who respects and shares your values.** A dating partner who respects you and has similar values will understand your commitment to abstinence.

Go Online

For more practice with vocabulary, go to the Interactive Health Tutor at **glencoe.com**.

Real World CONNECTION

Answers to Activity Questions:

1. $1500 \times (64/100) = 1500 \times 0.64 = 960$ programs with sexual content
2. $960 \times (15/100) = 960 \times 0.15 = 144$ programs depicted abstinence or risks of sexual activity
3. Essays will vary.

AL Active Learning

Abstinence Tips Have students create posters that show the five tips for practicing abstinence that are listed on this page. Posters should be creatively designed to attract the attention of other teens. For example, colorful pictures or funny cartoons could be used to illustrate each of the tips. Arrange for students to display their posters in areas of the school where many students will see them. **OL**

U Universal Access

Dating Limits and Abstinence Divide the class into several small groups. Ask group members to discuss how setting other limits on dating, such as curfew and age limits, can help teens practice abstinence. In each group, one student should volunteer to record the group's main ideas. After the discussion, give volunteers a chance to share their group's ideas with the rest of the class. **EL BL**

Reading Strategy

Organizing Information Make a T-diagram on the board describing setting limits. Label one side "Setting Limits" and the other side "Not Setting Limits." Ask two or three volunteers to demonstrate examples of setting and not setting limits. Have the class identify and categorize each example. Then have students brainstorm other examples of setting and not setting limits.

READING CHECK

Answer Students may answer with any three: Set limits for expressing affection; communicate with your partner; talk with a trusted adult about ways to manage your feelings; seek low-pressure dating situations; date someone who respects and shares your values.

Writing Support

Dating Dos and Don'ts Have students make a table entitled "Avoiding Risk Situations." The table should have two columns, one headed "Do" and the other headed "Don't." Ask students to fill in the two columns with relevant information from this page. Tell them to state the Dos and Don'ts in simple declarative sentences, such as, "Do find out where you're going," and "Don't use alcohol or other drugs."
BL

Main Idea

Considering the Consequences Abstinence from sexual activity has a positive effect on all sides of a teen's health triangle. **Ask Students:** *How could the consequences of sexual activity positively affect all sides of a teen's health triangle?* (Abstinence prevents pregnancy, physical health; allows teens to emotionally mature, mental/emotional health; and allows teens to develop new friendships, social health.)

Caption Answer

Figure 8.9 Other benefits of group or double dates might include feeling safer in a group and sharing costs with more people.

READING CHECK

Identify List three behaviors that can help you maintain self-control in a dating situation.

■ **Figure 8.9** Going out in a group can reduce some of the pressures of dating. *What are other benefits of group dates or double dates?*

208

Avoiding Risk Situations

Some dating situations may increase your chances of being pressured to participate in sexual activity or other high-risk behaviors. Before you go on a date, know where you're going and what you will be doing. Find out who else will be there, and discuss with your parents or guardians what time they expect you home. Here are additional precautions:

- **Avoid places where alcohol and other drugs are present.** The use of alcohol or other drugs impairs judgment. People under the influence of these substances are more likely to engage in high-risk behaviors. Prevent such situations by not using alcohol or other drugs and by avoiding people who use these substances.

- **Avoid being alone with a date at home or in an isolated place.** You may find it more difficult to maintain self-control when you are home alone or in an isolated place with a date. These situations also increase the risk of being forced into a sexual act against your will.

W

Considering the Consequences

Main Idea Abstinence from sexual activity has a positive effect on all sides of your health triangle.

Sexual activity carries serious consequences. It is illegal for an adult to have sexual contact with someone under the age of consent. Consent laws, which vary from state to state, make it illegal for an unmarried minor to engage in sexual activity. For example, if a state's age of consent is 18, two 17-year-olds who engage in sexual activity would be breaking the law. Sexual activity can also harm a teen's physical, mental/emotional, and social health.

Effects on Physical Health

Many teens make the decision to practice abstinence because it is the only 100 percent effective method to eliminate health risks associated with sexual activity. These risks include unplanned pregnancy and sexually transmitted diseases. Also known as sexually transmitted infections (STIs), **sexually transmitted diseases (STDs)** are *infectious diseases spread from person to person through sexual contact.*

Health Literacy

Effective Communicator Remind students that being able to communicate effectively is essential for resisting pressure to engage in sexual activity. Help students practice refusal skills to say no to sexual activity.

Write their refusals on the board. Then ask students to comment on the effectiveness of each refusal. Stress the importance of learning refusal skills.

Unplanned Pregnancy Every year in the United States, about one million teenage girls become pregnant. Female teens who have begun to ovulate are physically able to have babies. A pregnancy can result even if teens are engaging in sexual activity for the first time. A teen who becomes pregnant may not obtain the prenatal care that protects her life and that of the growing baby. Her partner may lack the maturity needed to support her during the pregnancy.

Sexually Transmitted Diseases Each year, about half of the diagnosed cases of STDs occur among teens and young adults between the ages of 15 and 24. Although many STDs can be treated and cured if diagnosed early, some STDs have no cure. If left untreated, some STDs can cause sterility in males and infertility in females. This means that a person may never be able to have a child. Other STDs, such as the herpes virus and HIV/AIDS, have no cure. In the case of AIDS, the disease can be fatal.

Effects on Mental/Emotional Health

In general, teens are not prepared for the emotional demands of a sexual relationship. Teens who engage in sexual activity before reaching emotional maturity may experience

- hurt because partners are not committed as in a marital relationship.
- guilt because teens are usually not truthful to their parents about being sexually active.
- loss of self-respect because sexual activity goes against personal and family values.
- regret and anxiety, if sexual activity results in an unplanned pregnancy or an STD.

Effects on Social Health

Engaging in sexual activity can negatively affect a teen's relationships with other people. Sexually active teens may deprive themselves of the opportunity to pursue new interests or friendships. The decision to engage in sexual activity can also harm a teen's relationships with family members. Parents who discover that their teen is sexually active may express disappointment and worry. These feelings can cause tension in the family. In addition, teens who are sexually active risk an unplanned pregnancy. Teen parents face many challenges, such as providing financial and emotional support for their child. Teens who become parents may have to put their own education and career plans on hold.

■ **Figure 8.10** Learning the facts about STDs and other negative consequences of sexual activity will help you make informed dating decisions. *How might contracting an STD affect a teen's mental/emotional and social health?*

✔ **READING CHECK**

Recall What are two health risks associated with sexual activity?

CHAPTER 8

LESSON 3

✔ **READING CHECK**

Answer Unplanned pregancy and sexually transmitted diseases.

AL Active Learning

Video Show Challenge small groups of students to create short video dramas that show negative effects of sexual activity on a teen's mental/emotional health. Give students a chance to present their videos to the class. Ask the class to vote on the video that is most effective in showing negative consequences. Arrange to show the winning video at a school assembly. **AL**

C Critical Thinking

Health Department Resources Ask a few students to contact their municipal or county health department to learn about any programs or other resources that address teen pregnancy and the spread of STDs among teens. Then have the students write a joint report on how the health department tries to deal with these problems in their community. Make several copies of the report and encourage the rest of the class to read it. **AL**

Caption Answer

Figure 8.10 Contracting an STD might cause feelings of loss, regret, and anxiety.

Academic Integration

Science **Bacterial vs. Viral STDs** Most STDs are caused by either bacteria or viruses. Bacterial STDs include chlamydia, syphilis, and gonorrhea. Viral STDs include hepatitis, HIV/AIDS, herpes, and genital warts. Antibiotics can cure most bacterial STDs but are ineffective against viruses. This is why scientists are working hard to develop vaccines to prevent viral STDs. Ask students to research more about vaccines against the viruses that cause HIV and herpes. Students should share what they learn with the class. **AL**

Main Idea

Committing to Abstinence
Communicating honestly with a dating partner will help with commitment to abstinence. **Ask Students:** *What are some tips to help communicate why abstinence is important?* (Answers may vary but should include choosing a relaxed and comfortable time and place and being clear on reasons for choosing abstinence.)

 **HS** **Health Skills Practice**

Refusal Skills Give pairs of students a chance to practice refusal skills. On the board, write down a hypothetical dating situation in which one partner is pressuring his or her date to go to a college party. Each partner should take turns practicing refusal skills using this hypothetical situation. **BL**

READING CHECK

Answer Communicate values and decisions to a partner and remind oneself of the reasons for choosing abstinence.

Committing to Abstinence

Main Idea Honest communication with your dating partner will help you stay committed to abstinence.

To stay firmly committed to abstinence, continue to remind yourself of the reasons that you chose abstinence. Make sure that you communicate your values and decisions to your dating partner. It can be difficult to talk about abstinence, but the following tips can help make the conversation go more smoothly:

- Choose a relaxed and comfortable time and place.
- Begin on a positive note, perhaps by talking about your affection for the other person.
- Be clear in your reasons for choosing abstinence.
- Be firm in setting limits in your physical relationship.

Using Refusal Skills

Committing to abstinence means not letting a partner, peers, or the media pressure you to do something you don't want to do. Practice the refusal skills that you learned in Lesson 2 to help you stand firm in your decision. Resist pressure to engage in sexual activity by using refusal statements similar to those shown in **Figure 8.11**.

HS

Recommitting to Abstinence

Teens who have been sexually active in the past may feel that they cannot choose to abstain from sexual activity in the future. They may feel pressured to remain sexually active. It is important to understand that choosing abstinence is *always* an option regardless of past experiences. Returning to abstinence is a positive alternative to previous sexual behavior. Teens who recommit to abstinence will feel good about their decision to protect their health and well-being.

READING CHECK

Identify What are two strategies for staying committed to abstinence?

Figure 8.11	Using Refusal Skills to Say No to Peer Pressure

Practicing effective refusal statements will help you resist the pressure to engage in sexual activity.

Pressure Line	**Your Response**
▸ Everybody does it.	▸ No. Not everybody is doing it.
▸ I thought you were cool.	▸ I *am* cool, and the answer's still no.
▸ No one will know.	▸ I'll know, and I'm the one who matters.
▸ If you loved me, you'd do it.	▸ If you loved me, you'd respect my decision.

Home and Community

Community-Based Abstinence Education Reauthorized in 2006, the U.S. Department of Health and Human Services established a program to provide funds for the development of community-based abstinence education projects for teens. Hundreds of projects have been funded since then. Ask students to find out what community-based abstinence projects were funded in their own, or a nearby, community. Students should learn the name of the organization conducting the project, the nature of the project, the population the project serves, and any indicators of the project's success. Give students a chance to share their information with the class. Use the information to stimulate a discussion of the role of communities in promoting teen abstinence.

■ **Figure 8.12** Careful consideration of the negative consequences associated with sexual activity will reinforce the decision to practice abstinence. *What are some of your reasons for practicing abstinence?*

  ASSESS/ CLOSE

Assessment Resources

📁 *FAST FILE* ACTIVITIES
Lesson 3 Quiz

💿 *ExamView*
Assessment Suite CD-ROM

Visit glencoe.com **for:**
Online Quizzes
Online Learning Center

 LESSON 3 ASSESSMENT

After You Read

Reviewing Facts and Vocabulary

1. How is *intimacy* different from *infatuation*?

2. What are three negative consequences of teen sexual activity?

3. Identify ways of resisting persuasive tactics regarding sexual involvement.

Thinking Critically

4. **Synthesize.** What are the benefits of practicing abstinence?

5. **Analyze.** How can teen parenthood harm an individual's social development?

Applying Health Skills

6. **Refusal Skills.** Write a scenario in which a teen is being pressured to engage in sexual activity. The teen should demonstrate effective refusal skills to resist the pressure.

Writing Critically

7. **Personal.** Write an essay describing what your life will be like in ten years. Include an explanation of how practicing abstinence will help you achieve your goals.

G⊙ Online

Visit glencoe.com and complete the Interactive Study Guide for this lesson.

Lesson 3   Practicing Abstinence   **211**

Progress Monitoring

Reteaching
Have students write a paragraph using all the lesson vocabulary terms. Then divide the class into pairs, and ask partners to check each other's paragraphs for errors. Students can correct any errors in their own paragraphs by referring to the lesson.

Enrichment
Ask students to design a Web site on abstinence for teens. Tell the students that they will draw this on paper. The site should be accurate, informative, and creative. It should also contain links to other reliable abstinence Web sites.

LESSON 3 ASSESSMENT ANSWERS

1. *Intimacy* is a closeness between two people that develops over time and *infatuation* is exaggerated feelings of passion.
2. Answers may include unplanned pregnancy, STDs, and loss of self-respect.
3. Being clear in reasons for choosing abstinence, setting limits, using refusal skills.

4. Answers will vary. See pp. 208–209.
5. See pp. 208–209.
6. Scenarios will vary.
7. Essays will vary.

Caption Answer

Figure 8.12 Sample answer: My reasons for practicing abstinence include wanting to avoid pregnancy and STDs, and wanting to maintain self-respect and the respect of my parents.

Assert Yourself

NHES Standard 4 Students will demonstrate the ability to use interpersonal communication skills to enhance health and avoid or reduce health risks.

Teaching Objectives

- Utilize skills for communicating effectively with family, peers, and others to enhance health.
- Demonstrate strategies to prevent, manage, or resolve interpersonal conflicts without harming self or others.

Teaching Strategies

- Review the elements of assertive communication. Contrast this type of communication with passive and aggressive forms of communication.
- Review students' suggested ideas for role-playing before distributing them to the class.
- Distribute approved scenarios, and have pairs role-play the scenario they have been given. Encourage them to use the Communication Skills checklist on this page to help them craft their dialogue.

Assessment

Using a rubric, student work should provide comprehensive evidence of the following criteria to achieve the highest score:

✓ Uses "I" messages
✓ Employs a respectful but convincing tone of voice
✓ Provides an alternative to action
✓ Includes clear, simple statements
✓ Suggests appropriate body language

Hands-On
HEALTH

Activity **Assert Yourself**

Learning to be assertive can help you maintain your commitment to a healthful lifestyle. By practicing assertiveness, you will find it easier to resist negative peer pressure and live according to your personal values. In this activity, you will role-play assertive communication skills.

What You'll Need

- large index cards
- pen or pencil
- paper

What You'll Do

Step 1

With a partner, think of a realistic scenario in which you are being pressured by one or more peers to do something against your values.

Step 2

Write your scenario on an index card, and then trade cards with another pair of students.

Step 3

Role-play the scenario you've received. Use the checklist on this page to make sure you include the elements of assertive communication.

Apply and Conclude

Write a short reflective paper describing how being assertive can help protect your physical, mental/emotional, and social health.

Checklist: Communication Skills

☑ "I" messages

☑ Respectful but convincing tone of voice

☑ Alternative to the action

☑ Clear, simple statement

☑ Appropriate body language

Writing Strategy

Writing a Reflective Paper A reflective paper is used to describe an experience (which may be personal or hypothetical), evaluate that experience, and then reflect on how that experience can be applied in the future. Students should include:

- a scenario in which assertive communication will help one of the participants avoid the effects of negative peer pressure,
- an evaluation of how assertive communication can be used in the situation, and
- the positive effect the assertive communication has on their health triangle.

To download quizzes and eFlashcards to your PDA, go to **glencoe.com** and click on the Study to Go icon.

LESSON 1

Safe and Healthy Friendships

Key Concepts

▶ The friendships you form will depend on several common attributes that you and your friends share.

▶ Friendships can change as you develop new interests and expand your social group.

▶ Using "I" messages when explaining your feelings to a friend is the best way to talk about problems in a friendship.

Vocabulary

▶ peers (p. 192)
▶ friendship (p. 193)
▶ platonic friendship (p. 194)
▶ clique (p. 195)
▶ prejudice (p. 195)
▶ stereotypes (p. 195)

LESSON 2

Peer Pressure and Refusal Skills

Key Concepts

▶ Peer pressure can have a positive or negative influence on your actions and behaviors.

▶ You can resist negative peer pressure by learning to use refusal skills.

▶ Assertive refusal is a positive way to resist negative peer pressure.

▶ Passive and aggressive responses are not effective ways to handle negative peer pressure.

Vocabulary

▶ peer pressure (p. 198)
▶ harassment (p. 199)
▶ manipulation (p. 200)
▶ assertive (p. 202)
▶ refusal skills (p. 202)
▶ passive (p. 204)
▶ aggressive (p. 204)

LESSON 3

Practicing Abstinence

Key Concepts

▶ Some teens may decide that they want to postpone dating.

▶ Group dating gives you the opportunity to socialize with the opposite gender without the pressure of one-on-one dating.

▶ Becoming sexually active can affect your physical, mental/emotional, and social health.

▶ Abstinence from sexual activity is the best choice for teens.

Vocabulary

▶ priorities (p. 205)
▶ abstinence (p. 206)
▶ intimacy (p. 206)
▶ infatuation (p. 206)
▶ self-control (p. 207)
▶ sexually transmitted diseases (STDs) (p. 208)

Chapter 8 Review **213**

Go Online

Students can visit **glencoe.com** to

• review content online with the Online Student Edition.

• test their knowledge of chapter content with Online Quizzes.

• access Interactive Health Tutor for more practice with vocabulary.

Assessment Resources

📁 **FAST FILE ACTIVITIES**
Chapter 8 Test

💿 *ExamView*
Assessment Suite CD-ROM

Visit glencoe.com for:
Audio Chapter Summaries
Online Quizzes

 Tell students to visit **glencoe.com** where they can download quizzes and eFlashcards.

Study Tips

Timed Tests Tell students that most standardized tests are timed. Students should use the clock in the testing room or a watch to keep track of the time. If students see that time is running out and it is clear that they will not complete the entire test, they should skim for questions they know they can answer quickly and accurately.

Chapter 8
Assessment Answers

LESSON 1

Vocabulary Review

1. platonic friendship
2. clique
3. stereotype

Understanding Key Concepts

4. c
5. d
6. b
7. c

Thinking Critically

8. Positive—provides members with a sense of belonging; Negative—discourages individual members from thinking for themselves
9. Answers will vary.
10. Answers will vary.
11. Answers will vary.

LESSON 2

Vocabulary Review

12. harassment
13. assertive
14. refusal skills

Understanding Key Concepts

15. b
16. d
17. a
18. c

LESSON 1

Vocabulary Review

Correct the sentences below by replacing the italicized term with the correct vocabulary term.

1. When two teens of the opposite gender have affection for each other but are not considered a couple, they are said to have a *romantic friendship*.

2. A *peer* excludes people viewed as outsiders.

3. An exaggerated or oversimplified belief about a group of people is called a *judgment*.

Understanding Key Concepts

After reading the question or statement, select the correct answer.

4. Which of the following attributes is *not* necessary for a friendship to work?
   a. Mutual respect
   b. Concern about each other's safety
   c. Identical beliefs and values
   d. Open, honest communication

5. Which of the following statements is true of online friendships?
   a. They're not *real* friends unless you meet them face-to-face.
   b. It's okay to assume that people are who they say they are.
   c. You should exchange photos and personal information.
   d. They can be a rewarding way to meet people from around the world.

6. If you feel envious or jealous of a friend, ask yourself all of the following questions *except*:
   a. What can I do to manage these feelings?
   b. How can I show my friend that I'm just as popular or smart as he or she is?
   c. Why am I feeling envious or jealous?
   d. What positive qualities make this person a good friend?

---

7. If you need to end a friendship, how should you handle the situation?
   a. Give the friend a detailed list of what exactly he or she did wrong.
   b. Give the friend the "silent treatment" until he or she gets the message.
   c. Talk about your own feelings and reasons for ending the friendship.
   d. Have someone else tell the friend that you no longer want to be friends.

Thinking Critically

After reading the question or statement, write a short answer using complete sentences.

8. **Identify.** Name one positive effect and one negative effect of belonging to a clique.

9. **Explain.** How would you tell a friend that your friendship has changed?

10. **Discuss.** Name ways that peers might influence your identity as a teen.

11. **Compare and Contrast.** What qualities do casual friends, close friends, and platonic friends share? How do these social groups differ?

LESSON 2

Vocabulary Review

Use the vocabulary terms listed on page 213 to complete the following statements.

12. Name-calling and bullying are examples of _____.

13. When you stand up for your rights in a firm and positive way, you are being _____.

14. If you are urged to take part in unhealthy behaviors, _____ will help you say no.

Health eSpotlight VIDEO *Wrap-Up*

Dealing With A Bully Have students reread the Health eSpotlight question at the beginning of the chapter on page 191 and look at their original answer. **Ask Students:** *Now that you have read the chapter and watched the video, how would you respond differently if you were being bullied?* Call on volunteers to describe how their responses would change.

Understanding Key Concepts

After reading the question or statement, select the correct answer.

15. Which of the following is an example of positive peer pressure?
    a. Offering friendship in exchange for a favor
    b. Encouraging friends to become volunteers at a homeless shelter
    c. Smoking cigarettes to win approval
    d. Persuading a friend to bully another teen

16. Which of the following behaviors does *not* use manipulation:
    a. Flattering a person to influence her actions
    b. Teasing a person in a hurtful way
    c. Using a "guilt trip" to get desired results
    d. Asking a person to tell you honestly what she thinks

17. Which of the following is *not* part of the three-step process of refusal skills?
    a. Try it once before saying no.
    b. Suggest alternatives.
    c. Stand your ground.
    d. State your position.

18. Shaking your head and raising your hand in a "Stop" signal are examples of:
    a. Peer pressure
    b. Manipulation
    c. Nonverbal assertive refusal
    d. Aggressive behavior

Thinking Critically

After reading the question or statement, write a short answer using complete sentences.

19. **Explain.** What are the risks of responding passively to peer pressure?

20. **Describe.** What behaviors do people use when responding aggressively to peer pressure?

21. **Analyze.** Suppose a group of friends constantly teases a student in your school. How can you show disapproval of this inconsiderate and disrespectful behavior?

22. **Evaluate.** Analyze the similarities and differences between passive, aggressive, and assertive forms of communication.

 **LESSON 3**

Vocabulary Review

Choose the correct term in the sentences below.

23. *Responsibility / Abstinence* is a deliberate decision to avoid high-risk behaviors.

24. The ability to practice responsible behaviors even when you are faced with temptation is called *self-control / priority*.

25. *Infatuation / Intimacy* is the closeness that grows over time between two people who care about each other.

Understanding Key Concepts

After reading the question or statement, select the correct answer.

26. Which of the following statements is true?
    a. STDs can be cured with over-the-counter medications.
    b. Teens under the age of 18 are immune to STDs.
    c. Some STDs have no cure, and some can cause infertility or even death.
    d. The symptoms of all STDs go away after a few months.

27. Which of the following behaviors will help you maintain self-control while dating?
    a. Date someone who respects and shares your values.
    b. Return home from dates before midnight.
    c. Avoid dating someone who goes to your own school.
    d. Limit the number of parties you attend.

Chapter 8 Assessment **215**

Thinking Critically

19. Peers may disrespect you and think you are a pushover.
20. Being overly forceful, pushy, and hostile
21. Stand your ground and be firm.
22. **Passive:** People who have a tendency to give up, give in, or back down without standing up for their rights.
    Aggressive: People who are overly forceful, pushy, hostile, or attacking in their approach.
    Assertive: Using effective refusal skills.

LESSON 3

Vocabulary Review
23. Abstinence
24. self-control
25. Intimacy

Understanding Key Concepts
26. c
27. a

ExamView®
Assessment Suite

Create and customize tests in minutes with this convenient digital platform.

- Create differentiated tests quickly and easily.
- All questions correlated to National/State Standards
- Enhance tests with Document-Based Questions (DBQ) and add your own photos or graphics.
- Build tests in both English and Spanish.
- Generate progress reports.

To order, go to **glencoe.com** and search for ISBN 0-07-888173-0.

Glencoe **Health**

Assessment

28. b

29. d

Thinking Critically

30. When it goes against your personal or family values

31. Places where alcohol and drugs are present; places where you are isolated or alone with a date

32. Sexual activity could result in an unplanned pregnancy, which could interfere with your education and career plans. Sexual activity could result in an STD.

33. Teens and parents can set limits by having a curfew, setting limits on the age of people to date, and setting limits with dates on where to go, how to get there, and what to do on the date.

34. Seeing images that imply sexual activity may convince teens that the behavior is normal and acceptable.

35. Answers will vary.

Assessment

28. A person trying to pressure you into sexual activity would probably *not* say:
   a. "Don't worry, no one will ever know."
   b. "If you feel uncomfortable with this, then we shouldn't do it."
   c. "If you love me, then show it."
   d. "Everyone in school is doing it."

29. Approximately how many teenage girls become pregnant every year in the United States?
   a. 1,000
   b. 10,000
   c. 100,000
   d. 1,000,000

Thinking Critically

After reading the question or statement, write a short answer using complete sentences.

30. **Identify.** When might sexual activity result in a loss of self-respect?

31. **Identify.** What are two *risk situations* that could increase your chances of being pressured into sexual activity?

32. **Describe.** How might engaging in sexual activity have a negative effect on your social health?

33. **Describe.** What are some ways that teens and their parents can set limits for dating relationships?

34. **Discuss.** How are teens' attitudes toward sexual activity influenced by the media and popular culture?

35. **Analyze.** Why is abstinence the best choice for teens? Include information on the social, mental/emotional, and physical benefits of abstinence.

Project-Based ASSESSMENT

Friendship Survey

Background
Your peers are important to your development as an individual. During the teen years, you develop a variety of relationships. Some relationships are casual friendships, while others are close friendships. Dating relationships also develop during this time. Each of these relationships has unique characteristics.

Task
Complete a survey of 15 or more students to find out what characteristics they consider essential for a close friendship.

Audience
Students in your class

Purpose
Find out what qualities your peers believe differentiate a close friendship from other kinds of relationships.

Procedure

1 Use the information in Chapter 8 to develop a list of questions about qualities that are essential for a close friendship. The questions might gauge the importance of each quality as *very important, important,* or *not important.*

2 Select 15 or more students for the survey.

3 Tally the responses.

4 Examine the results, and make a table showing the responses to each question. Determine the qualities that are considered to be most essential for a close friendship. Include a title for the table, and write a summary of your findings.

5 Distribute copies of the table to your classmates.

6 Discuss the results with your class.

Project-Based ASSESSMENT

Step 1 Brainstorm Have students brainstorm ideas for a list of questions related to qualities that are important for a close friendship.

Step 2 Conduct Survey Have students choose 15 people to ask their survey questions. Students should try and ask a wide variety of people.

Step 3 Evaluate Have students develop a table showing the results of their survey. Students should also write a one-paragraph summary analyzing what qualities are important for a close friendship. Make sure their summary includes specific answers from their survey.

Visit **glencoe.com** for Project-Based Assessment rubrics.

Math Practice

Interpret Graphs. The table below shows 12-year trends related to sexual activity among teens in the ninth through twelfth grades. Use the graph to answer the questions.

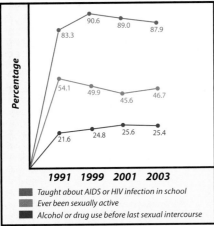

Adapted from the Youth Risk Behavior Survey: 1991–2003, Centers for Disease Control and Prevention.

1. By what percentage has sexual activity among teens decreased between 1991 and 2003?
   A. 10.2   C. 4.3
   B. 7.4   D. 12.6

2. Which year shows the highest rate of teens reporting alcohol use before engaging in sexual activity?
   A. 2001   C. 1991
   B. 1999   D. 2003

3. Identify the years with the lowest and highest percentage of AIDS/HIV education. What is the difference in percentage between the two years?
   A. 3.2   C. 7.3
   B. 6.0   D. 4.5

Go Online

For more test practice, visit glencoe.com and complete the Online Quizzes for Chapter 8.

Reading/Writing Practice

Understand and Apply. Read the passage below, and then answer the questions.

> I have been best friends with Tamara since the first grade. Tamara is nice to me and to other people.
>
> Tamara's kindness shows in many ways. Once she gave her circus tickets to some kids who had never been to the circus. Tamara visits a nearby nursing home at least once a month. She worries about some of the people she has met there because they have no family.
>
> Tamara was a good friend to me when my parents divorced. She listened to me for hours as I talked about how upset I was. She also let me cry and never told me that I was overreacting. I knew that she couldn't do anything to change the situation, but she always made me feel better.

1. How does the author show that Tamara is a good friend?
   A. By comparing Tamara's actions to those of her other friends
   B. By pointing out that Tamara once helped with a canned-food drive
   C. By citing examples of Tamara's kindness
   D. By saying that Tamara does not gossip

2. When Tamara listened to her friend talk about divorce, what characteristics of friendship did she show?
   A. Mutual respect   C. Support
   B. Caring   D. All of the above

3. Describe the qualities that you think make someone a good friend. Give examples and details to support your opinions.

National Education Standards

Math: Number and Operations, Problem Solving
Language Arts: NCTE 1, NCTE 3, NCTE 4

Standardized Test Practice Answers

Math Practice
1. B
2. A
3. C

Reading/Writing Practice
1. C
2. D
3. Answers will vary. Good friends show caring, consideration, mutual respect, and support.

National Education Standards

Math: Number and Operations, Problem Solving.

Language Arts: NCTE 3, NCTE 4.

For the complete Math and Language Arts standards, visit glencoe.com

Go Online

Online Study Tools
For more test practice, visit glencoe.com and complete the Online Quizzes for Chapter 8.

Test-Taking Tip

Review Encourage students to use any extra time after completing a test to review answers. Direct them to look carefully at their answers in order to identify skipped questions or an answer. Let students know that they should try and resist the urge to finish tests quickly. In addition, remind students to check for errors and proofread their writing for spelling mistakes.

Chapter 9 pages 218–247	Standards		Features
	National	**State/Local**	
	1.12.3, 4.12.1, 4.12.2, 4.12.3, 4.12.4		**TIME** HEALTH • When Dating Is Dangerous, page 242
30 Min **Lesson 1** **Causes of Conflict** pages 220–223 **BIG Idea** *Knowing why conflicts occur can help you prevent them.*	1.12.1, 1.12.3, 2.12.2, 2.12.4, 2.12.5, 2.12.8, 4.12.2, 4.12.3, 8.12.1, 8.12.3		**TEENS Making a Difference** • A Voice Against Violence, page 222
30 Min **Lesson 2** **Resolving Conflicts** pages 224–228 **BIG Idea** *Conflicts can be resolved through negotiation or mediation.*	4.12.2, 4.12.3, 5.12.1, 5.12.2, 5.12.3, 5.12.5, 7.12.2, 8.12.1, 8.12.4		**Health Skills Activity** • Negotiating with Parents *(Conflict Resolution)*, page 227 ⏱ Out of Time
30 Min **Lesson 3** **Understanding Violence** pages 229–235 **BIG Idea** *Teens need to know about forms of violence and ways to protect themselves.*	1.12.3, 2.12.5, 2.12.7, 4.12.2, 4.12.3, 4.12.4, 5.12.6, 5.12.7, 8.12.1		**Real World CONNECTION** • Violence Among Teens, page 232 ⏱ Out of Time
30 Min **Lesson 4** **Preventing and Overcoming Abuse** pages 236–241 **BIG Idea** *Abuse can cause physical, mental, and emotional damage.*	1.12.1, 1.12.5, 3.12.3, 3.12.4, 4.12.2, 4.12.3, 4.12.4, 8.12.1, 8.12.4		

Key to Ability Levels

Teaching Strategies and activities have been coded for ability level and appropriateness.

AL Activities for students working above grade level

OL Activities for students working on grade level

BL Activities for students working below grade level

EL Activities for English Learners

Resources	Lesson Assessment	Technology
Student Activity Workbook TEACH *FAST FILE* RESOURCES Vocabulary Practice TEACH Health Labs EXTEND	Chapter 9 Review Chapter 9 Assessment Standardized Test Practice ⊙ *ExamView® Assessment Suite* CD-ROM	**Teaching Tools:** ⊙ *TeacherWorks*™ Plus DVD ⊙ *StudentWorks*™ Plus DVD ⊙ *ExamView® Assessment Suite* CD-ROM 🖳 Transparency ⊙ Fitness DVD ⊙ PowerPoint® DVD ⊙ Health eSpotlight Video Series DVD
FAST FILE RESOURCES Reading Strategies Activity TEACH Reteaching Activity REVIEW Enrichment Activity EXTEND Health Skills Practice TEACH	Lesson 1 Assessment, page 223 📁 Lesson 1 Quiz *Fast File* ⊙ *ExamView® Assessment Suite* CD-ROM	**Web-Based Resources:** Go Online glencoe.com • Health Podcast Activities • Audio Chapter Summaries (English/Spanish) • Interactive Health Tutor • Health Skills Activities • Vocabulary PuzzleMaker • Parent Letters (English/Spanish) • Lesson Plans • Health Inventories • Online Quizzes • Study-to-Go • Unit Web Projects • Student Web Activities • Fitness Zone Activities
FAST FILE RESOURCES Reading Strategies Activity TEACH Reteaching Activity REVIEW Enrichment Activity EXTEND Health Skills Practice TEACH	Lesson 2 Assessment, page 228 📁 Lesson 2 Quiz *Fast File* ⊙ *ExamView® Assessment Suite* CD-ROM	
FAST FILE RESOURCES Reading Strategies Activity TEACH Reteaching Activity REVIEW Enrichment Activity EXTEND Health Skills Practice TEACH	Lesson 3 Assessment, page 235 📁 Lesson 3 Quiz *Fast File* ⊙ *ExamView® Assessment Suite* CD-ROM	
FAST FILE RESOURCES Reading Strategies Activity TEACH Reteaching Activity REVIEW Enrichment Activity EXTEND Health Skills Practice TEACH	Lesson 4 Assessment, page 241 📁 Lesson 4 Quiz *Fast File* ⊙ *ExamView® Assessment Suite* CD-ROM	

This is the student's backpack solution.

Includes:
- complete Interactive Student Edition
- full audio of English text and Spanish chapter summaries
- allows students to record assignments and track grades.
- links to online activities and additional student resources
- access to all student worksheets and workbooks

Dinah Zike Foldables® Chapter Activity
Refer to the *Dinah Zike Reading and Study Skills for Glencoe Health.* Ask students to make a bound book Foldable. As students learn about conflict and violence, they can take notes, define terms, record examples, and record personal experiences.

Key to Symbols

 Transparencies   REVIEW activities to review or reinforce content

 CD-ROM   TEACH activities to teach basic concepts

 glencoe.com   EXTEND activities to extend or enrich lesson content

 Print Resources

Resolving Conflicts and Preventing Violence

Chapter Overview

Chapter 9 focuses on the causes of conflict, how conflicts can be resolved through negotiation and mediation, the types and causes of violence, and how to prevent and overcome abuse.

Lesson 1

Understanding the causes of conflicts can help prevent them.

Lesson 2

Negotiation and mediation are tools for resolving conflicts.

Lesson 3

It is important for teens to know the different types of violence and how to protect themselves.

Lesson 4

Damage from abuse can be physical, mental, or emotional.

▶ **Activating Prior Knowledge**

Have students write a paragraph that answers the questions. Then call on volunteers to identify causes of violence in society. Students may mention alcohol and drugs, gang influence, and violence in the media. Call on volunteers to suggest ways that citizens can work to reduce violence and crime in their communities.

CHAPTER **9**

Resolving Conflicts and Preventing Violence

Lesson 1
Causes of Conflict

BIG Idea *Knowing why conflicts occur can help you prevent them.*

Lesson 2
Resolving Conflicts

BIG Idea *Conflicts can be resolved through negotiation or mediation.*

Lesson 3
Understanding Violence

BIG Idea *Teens need to know about forms of violence and ways to protect themselves.*

Lesson 4
Preventing and Overcoming Abuse

BIG Idea *Abuse can cause physical, mental, and emotional damage.*

Activating Prior Knowledge

Using Visuals Describe what is happening in the scene shown on this page. What are some causes of violence in society? What can citizens do to reduce violence and crime?

218

Universal Access

Differentiated Learning Glencoe provides teacher support and student materials for all learners in the health classroom.

- Chapter Summaries in English and Spanish are available online at **glencoe.com**.

- *Fast Files* and related worksheets support reluctant readers.

- Universal Access strategies throughout the Teacher Wraparound Edition and *Fast Files* help you present materials for gifted students, at-risk students, physically impaired students, and those with behavior disorders or learning disabilities.

Chapter Launchers

Health in Action

Discuss the **BIG Ideas**

Before beginning this chapter, think about how you would answer these questions:

▶ What are some conflicts that you've had with people?

▶ How did you resolve these conflicts?

▶ Why do you think some conflicts result in violence?

Watch the *Health eSpotlight* Video Series

Preventing Violence, Resolving Conflict

How do you and your friends settle disagreements? Is this the best way to address problems?

Assess Your Health

G⊘ Online

Visit glencoe.com and complete the Health Inventory for Chapter 9.

Chapter Launchers

Health in Action

Discuss the **BIG Ideas**

Ask students to respond to the questions aloud. Explain that the purpose of the questions is to help them assess their knowledge of what causes conflicts, how conflicts can be resolved, and how and why conflicts become violent.

Health eSpotlight
Video Series

 Preventing Violence, Resolving Conflict

Before Viewing the Video

Ask Students: *What are some ways that everyday conflicts can be prevented?* (Sample answer: Being willing to compromise when a serious conflict looks like it will occur.)

G⊘ Online

Have students go to **glencoe.com** and take the Health Inventory for Chapter 9.

Chapter Skills

Reading Skills
- Reviewing Facts and Vocabulary, pp. 223, 228, 235, 241
- Reading/Writing Practice, p. 247

BIG Idea

Students will learn about the causes of conflict, how to resolve conflicts, and how to prevent and overcome abuse.

Vocabulary
- New Vocabulary, pp. 220, 224, 229, 236
- Reviewing Facts and Vocabulary, pp. 223, 228, 235, 241

Health Skills
- Health Skills Activity, p. 227
- Applying Health Skills, pp. 223, 228, 235, 241

Writing Skills
- Writing Critically, pp. 223, 228, 235, 241
- Reading/Writing Practice, p. 247

219

Causes of Conflict

① FOCUS

GUIDE TO READING

BIG Idea Knowing why conflicts occur can help prevent them. **Ask Students:** *What is the most common cause of conflict in your life?* (Sample answer: Curfew times)

Before You Read

Organize Information
Students' organizers may vary, though each should closely reflect the causes and effects of conflicts.

Main Idea

Understanding Conflicts There are a variety of causes of conflicts. **Ask Students:** *What do you think are the most common causes of conflict among adults?* (Sample answer: Property disputes)

Real Life Issues ● ● ● ● ● ● ●

Ask volunteers to share their paragraphs with the class. **Ask Students:** What kinds of conflicts do you encounter with your friends or family?

LESSON 1

GUIDE TO READING

BIG Idea Knowing why conflicts occur can help you prevent them.

Before You Read

Organize Information.
In the center of your paper, write "Conflict" and circle it. Label the space above this circle "Causes" and the space below it "Effects." As you read, list causes of conflict on the top half of the page, and effects of conflict on the bottom half of the page.

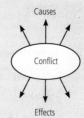

Causes

Conflict

Effects

New Vocabulary

▶ conflict (p. 220)
▶ interpersonal conflicts (p. 220)
▶ escalate (p. 221)

Causes of Conflict

Real Life Issues ●

Conflict Between Friends. As Jesse approaches the movie theater, his friend Lauren storms over to him. "Where have you been?" she demands. "The movie started 15 minutes ago!"
"You said to meet here at two-thirty!" Jesse says defensively. "I told you I had to drop off my sister at the library first."
"I said two o'clock!" insists Lauren. "You're always making excuses for being late!"

Writing *Write a paragraph explaining what you think caused this conflict and how it might have been avoided.*

Understanding Conflicts

Main Idea Conflicts can arise for a variety of reasons.

The term **conflict** refers to *any disagreement, struggle, or fight.* Some conflicts are fairly trivial, such as a squabble between two siblings over control of the TV remote. Others can be serious or even deadly, such as turf wars between rival gangs. *Conflicts between people or groups of people* are known as **interpersonal conflicts**. They tend to arise when one party's needs, wishes, or beliefs clash with those of another party. Interpersonal conflicts can involve groups of any size, from individual people to entire nations. *Internal conflicts,* by contrast, take place within an individual. For example, if your best friend's birthday party and your sister's championship soccer game fell on the same day, you might go through an internal conflict over which event to attend.

Common Causes of Conflict

Interpersonal conflicts can arise for a variety of reasons. Some arise out of misunderstandings. For instance, Lauren and Jesse got angry at each other over a miscommunication.

Skills for the 21st Century

Collaboration Skills Many jobs today require that people from diverse backgrounds work together to complete a project or achieve a goal. Inevitably, when people collaborate, conflicts occur. Have students brainstorm a list of jobs, and write these jobs on the board. Divide the class into small groups. Have each group choose a job from the list and think of a project in that job that would require collaboration. Ask each group to develop a skit in which employees work through a conflict to complete the project. Have groups perform their skits for the class.

Sometimes, misunderstandings occur when an individual **misinterprets** another person's language, gestures, or sense of humor. This type of conflict might occur between people of different cultures or age groups. In other cases, someone deliberately starts a conflict—for example, by insulting or shoving someone else. Causes of conflict include

- **power struggles.** A teen and her parent might have a conflict over how late she is allowed to stay out at night.
- **personal loyalties.** A teen might be angry with his best friend for taking another person's side in an argument.
- **jealousy and envy.** A teen might be upset when her friend starts going out with a boy she likes.
- **property disputes.** A teen might be angry with his brother for borrowing his MP3 player without permission.
- **conflicting attitudes and values.** Two friends might have an argument because one wants to hang out only with the "cool" crowd, while the other wants to be friendly to everyone.
- **lack of respect.** A teen might be rude to a classmate because of a prejudice against that student's ethnic group.

Understanding these causes of conflict may help you avoid some conflicts before they start. If it looks like a conflict is developing, you may be able to keep it from escalating. **Escalate** means *to become more serious.* Conflicts can escalate into fights when emotions get out of control. Feelings such as hurt pride, embarrassment, or the desire for revenge can turn a simple conflict into a situation that could be unsafe for everyone involved. In some cases, it's best to walk away before the conflict escalates.

 READING CHECK

Compare and Contrast How are interpersonal conflicts different from internal conflicts?

■ **Figure 9.1** Conflicts between people can occur for many different reasons. *Which type of conflict does this picture show?*

Lesson 1   Causes of Conflict   **221**

② TEACH

AL Active Learning

Role-Play Divide the class into pairs, and give each pair five minutes to plan a brief role-play that focuses on the development of a conflict between teens as a result of any one of the six listed causes. Then ask pairs to ad lib their role-plays for the class. After each pair makes its presentation, discuss how common such a conflict is and how it could have been avoided. OL

Academic Vocabulary

Misinterpret Ask students to describe examples of instances in their lives when someone has misinterpreted another's words or behavior because of differences in culture or age.

READING CHECK

Answer Interpersonal conflicts are between people or groups, while internal conflicts take place within an individual.

W Writing Support

Compare and Contrast Discuss ways that results of conflicts can be either positive or negative. Have students write a skit to demonstrate what might be a positive result of a conflict when friends argue or get angry with each other. OL AL

Caption Answer

Figure 9.1 The photo shows a property dispute.

English Language Coach

Extend Vocabulary Help students understand the difference between *interpersonal conflicts* and *internal conflicts* by examining the meaning of the two adjectives. Explain that the prefix *inter-* means "between" or "shared between." The word *interpersonal,* then, means "between persons." In contrast, *internal* means "inside." An *internal conflict* is a conflict that happens inside a person. Have students write sentences using the words *interpersonal* and *internal.* Ask volunteers to read their sentences aloud.

TEENS Making a Difference

Answers to Activity Questions

1. Rafael was being bullied.
2. Sample answer: I could join an organization.
3. Answers will vary.

CA Cultural Awareness

Misinterpreting Behavior Attitudes and behaviors can sometimes be misinterpreted among people from different cultures. Ask volunteers to describe such cultural clashes they've seen or experienced. Have English language learners relate instances when conflicts have arisen as a result of cultural differences. Ask these students how changes in attitude and behavior could have prevented these conflicts from occurring. OL EL

U Universal Access

Cooperative Learning Divide the class into pairs, and give each pair a scenario that involves a conflict between teens. For example, two friends are disagreeing over a rumor involving another friend. Have each pair write a dialogue in which they resolve the conflict and show positive results. BL

G Online

Remind students to visit **glencoe.com** and complete the Student Web Activity on how saying you're sorry can be useful in resolving conflicts.

TEENS Making a Difference

"Prevent violence before it starts."

A Voice Against Violence

Rafael G., of North Carolina, knows how it feels to be bullied. That's why he decided to join Students Against Violence Everywhere (SAVE). In his work with SAVE, Rafael raised money to install security cameras and floodlights in hard-to-see areas on campus. His school's SAVE chapter also produced a television segment describing positive ways to respond to violence and crime.

Rafael is proud of the role that SAVE has played in raising awareness about violence. He also recognizes the importance of prevention. "It's better to have a strong force in place to prevent crime or violence before it starts," he says.

Activity Write your answers to the following questions in your personal health journal:

1. What motivated Rafael to join SAVE?
2. What can you do to help reduce or resolve conflicts in your school?
3. What programs does your school have in place to prevent violence?

G Online

Visit **glencoe.com** and complete the Student Web Activity on how saying you're sorry can be useful in resolving conflicts.

Results of Conflict

Conflict is a normal part of life. Because each individual is different, it's inevitable that people will disagree sometimes. Learning to manage conflicts and deal with them before they get out of hand will strengthen all aspects of your health. CA

Sometimes conflict can actually bring about positive results. Working to resolve a conflict can help people improve their communication and problem-solving skills. It can also improve their social health by teaching them how to get along with people who disagree with them. In addition, dealing with conflicts can strengthen relationships. When two people make the effort to work through a conflict together, it shows their commitment to each other. U

Unfortunately, conflicts can also have negative effects. They can be a major source of stress, resulting in problems such as headaches and lost sleep. Conflicts can harm your emotional and social health if they lead to anger, frustration, fear, and emotional pain. In addition, conflicts in the workplace can cause people to lose their jobs. In the worst cases, conflicts can escalate to violence, resulting in serious injury or even death.

More About...

SAVE Students Against Violence Everywhere is a national, nonprofit organization whose mission is to decrease the potential for violence in schools and communities. SAVE was formed in 1989 by a teacher and a student at a high school in North Carolina after another student had been killed trying to stop a fight at a party. Ask volunteers to find out about SAVE activities and report to the class. If there is no SAVE chapter at your school, students may contact the organization through its Web site to find out about SAVE programs.

Preventing Conflicts

It's often easier to prevent a conflict than it is to resolve it. For instance, if you know someone who is always trying to provoke you into an argument, you might decide to avoid that person. If you get involved in a minor disagreement with someone, you can remind yourself that the argument isn't that important in the long run. It's not worth damaging your relationship over something trivial.

Sometimes you can prevent conflicts by adjusting your own behavior. Suppose you have a friend who always forgets to bring money when you go out. Instead of feeling annoyed every time, you might just make a point of reminding this person to stop at the ATM beforehand. Adjusting your attitude can also help. If you tend to interpret any kind of personal remark as an attack on you, you might try to relax and not be bothered so much by what other people say.

■ **Figure 9.2** Reminding a friend who often borrows money to get some cash before you go out is one way to prevent a conflict. *What other ways can you think of?*

LESSON 1 ASSESSMENT

After You Read

Reviewing Facts and Vocabulary

1. Identify two common causes of interpersonal conflicts.
2. How can conflicts be positive?
3. Give an example of how conflicts can negatively affect one's health.

Thinking Critically

4. **Analyze.** How might adapting your behavior help prevent conflicts?
5. **Evaluate.** Discuss the benefits and drawbacks of walking away from a developing conflict.

Applying Health Skills

6. **Analyzing Influences.** How might influences such as environment, culture, media, and personal values affect a conflict between two people?

Writing Critically

7. **Expository.** Write an essay about common teen conflicts. Explain how to prevent some of these conflicts.

Go Online

Visit **glencoe.com** and complete the Interactive Study Guide for this lesson.

LESSON 1 ASSESSMENT ANSWERS

1. Sample answer: Power struggles, property disputes
2. Working through the conflict improves people's communication and problem-solving skills, teaches them how to get along better, demonstrates their commitment to each other, or helps them understand each other better.
3. A conflict at the workplace can cause people to lose their jobs.
4. Sample answer: If you learn ways of adapting a behavior that has been the source of conflict, the behavior will not cause further conflicts.
5. Sample answer: Walking away can prevent the conflict from escalating, but the conflict would not be resolved and could occur again.
6. Answers will vary.
7. Answers will vary.

Caption Answer

Figure 9.2 Sample answer: You could tell the person that you'll pay this time if he or she will pay the next time.

3 ASSESS/CLOSE

Assessment Resources

📁 *FAST FILE* **ACTIVITIES**
Lesson 1 Quiz

💿 *ExamView Assessment Suite* CD-ROM

Visit glencoe.com for:
Online Quizzes
Online Learning Center

Progress Monitoring

Reteaching

Call on students to identify six causes of conflict. Ask volunteers to explain how each conflict could have either positive or negative results.

Enrichment

Ask students to write a short story in which a conflict develops due to one of the six causes of conflict and escalates into a fight. Have students identify positive results from resolving the conflict.

Go Online

Have students visit **glencoe.com** and complete the Interactive Study Guide for this lesson.

LESSON 2

Resolving Conflicts

① FOCUS

GUIDE TO READING

BIG Idea Conflicts can be resolved through negotiation or mediation. **Ask Students:** *What does a negotiation between two people in conflict involve?* (Sample answer: Talking over the causes of the conflict and finding a solution that could satisfy both people)

Before You Read

Venn Diagram Students' Venn diagrams will vary.

Main Idea

Responding to Conflict There are various ways to deal with a conflict. **Ask Students:** *Is it good sometimes to just walk away from a conflict? Explain.* (Sample answer: Yes, walking away can sometimes give people a chance to calm down. However, walking away does not actually resolve the conflict.)

Real Life Issues ···············

Call on volunteers to share their dialogues with the class. As students suggest solutions in their dialogues, point out that both Joe and Maggie have to compromise to find a solution that they both can live with.

LESSON 2

GUIDE TO READING

BIG Idea *Conflicts can be resolved through negotiation or mediation.*

Before You Read

Create a Venn Diagram. Draw two overlapping circles and label them "Negotiation" and "Mediation." As you read, fill in the circles with information about these two methods of resolving conflicts. Traits the two methods have in common should go in the overlapping area.

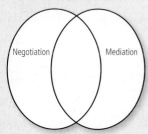

New Vocabulary

▶ negotiation (p. 225)
▶ mediation (p. 226)
▶ confidentiality (p. 227)
▶ peer mediation (p. 228)

Review Vocabulary

▶ conflict resolution (Ch.2, L.1)
▶ compromise (Ch.6, L.1)

Resolving Conflicts

Real Life Issues ··························

Two Teens, One Bathroom. Joe bangs furiously on the bathroom door. "Maggie! You've been in there for half an hour! I need to get ready for school too, you know!"
His sister, Maggie, flings open the door. "You know it takes me longer to get ready," she says. "I have to wash and blow-dry my hair every morning. Give me a break!"
Joe sighs. "Look, we can't go through this every morning. Can't we work out some kind of deal?"

Writing *Continue the dialogue between Joe and Maggie. Have them brainstorm a solution to their conflict.*

Responding to Conflict

Main Idea There are various ways to deal with a conflict.

When you have a conflict with someone, you have two choices: walk away or respond to it. If you think the conflict could escalate and become dangerous, getting out is the best approach. This is also true if you are having trouble managing your own anger. Walking away will give you a chance to calm down so that you can approach the conflict rationally.

However, in many cases, walking away from a conflict will not make it go away. You may stop it from escalating, but the same issue is likely to come up again. Sooner or later, you will need to practice *conflict resolution,* the process of ending a conflict through cooperation and problem solving.

Compromise

You can often resolve minor conflicts with a compromise. If you and your brother disagree about what to watch on TV, you might agree to watch one show and record the other.

Home and Community

Community Mediation Services Many communities have a mediation service provided by the government for disputes between neighbors and for other everyday conflicts. These mediation services provide citizens with a way to settle conflicts without hiring lawyers or using the courts. Ask interested students to investigate local mediation services by calling a local official or the police department. Ask students to find out how citizens can access the services and how much they cost. Have students make a written report of what they find.

However, it can be difficult to reach a compromise when both parties have strong opinions about an issue. In addition, it's unwise to compromise when doing so could have harmful consequences or would go against your values.

Effective Negotiation

Main Idea Negotiation involves finding a solution that both sides can accept.

When conflicts are not resolved, they can get worse, sometimes even resulting in violence. It's important to understand that violence does not solve conflicts. One group may be able to force another to do what it wants, but that does not address the cause of the conflict. As a result, the same conflict is likely to occur again. This may cause the violence to escalate, harming more people. A better strategy is **negotiation**, *the use of communication and, in many cases, compromise to settle a disagreement.*

The Negotiation Process

The negotiation process involves talking, listening, and considering the other party's point of view. Mutual respect is an important factor in a successful negotiation. These are the steps of the negotiation process:

1. Take time to calm down and think over the situation.
2. Let each party take turns explaining its side of the conflict without interruption. Apply good communication skills, such as active listening and using "I" messages.
3. If necessary, ask for clarification to make sure that each party understands the other's position.
4. Brainstorm solutions to the conflict.
5. Discuss the advantages and disadvantages of each solution.
6. Agree on a solution that is acceptable to both sides. The ideal outcome will be a win-win solution. If this is not possible, the two parties may need to compromise.
7. Follow up to see whether the solution has worked for each party.

FITNESS ZONE

Playing sports is a great way to learn how to deal with conflict. In sports, there are disagreements as to whether there was a foul or if someone was out of bounds. When I play ball with my friends, we try to stay cool and discuss the issue. We usually decide to replay the point. After all, we're all friends and we'd like to keep it that way. For more fitness tips, visit the Online Fitness Zone at **glencoe.com.**

■ **Figure 9.3** Compromise can help you resolve simple conflicts, such as whose CD to listen to. *When is it a bad idea to compromise?*

Lesson 2   Resolving Conflicts   **225**

② TEACH

HS Health Skills Practice

Decision Making Have pairs of students think of a conflict between teens and then use the decision-making process to decide whether to walk away or negotiate the conflict. Ask pairs to state the situation in writing and then list the possible outcomes of both options, using the *HELP* strategy in their evaluations. Then have students write down their decision. Ask pairs to share their situations and decisions with the class. **OL**

FITNESS ZONE

Students may be familiar with this activity from sporting events:

- Have students line up in a circle around the classroom.
- One student starts the "wave" beginning in a semi-squat position to fully standing and back to a semi-squat position.
- The wave continues with the next student and so on.
- When the circle has completed, another student begins a new wave with a new movement.

Main Idea

Effective Negotiation In negotiation, a solution must be acceptable to both sides. **Ask Students:** *Why is good communication necessary in settling any conflict?* (Sample answer: So that all parties understand one another's point of view.)

ELL Support

Name and Repeat Write the following words on the board: *compromise, resolve, negotiation, solution.* Define each word aloud.

Beginning Use sentences such as "Both Tiffany and Maria decided to compromise as a way to end their conflict." Ask students to repeat the sentence. Use the other three words in sentences, and ask students to repeat.

Intermediate Ask students for sentence examples for each word.

Advanced Ask students to write sentences using these other forms of the words: *compromised, resolved, negotiate, solve.*

✓ **READING CHECK**

Answer Think it over; let each party explain its side; ask for clarification; brainstorm solutions; compare advantages and disadvantages of each solution; agree on a solution; follow up

U **Universal Access**

Neutrality Explain to students that neutrality means "being for neither one side nor the other." Ask students which person involved in a soccer or football game is neither for one side nor the other. (The referee) Ask students what it means to play a football game on a *neutral* field. (At neither team's home field) Then, point out that a mediation session should take place in a neutral location. **EL** **BL**

Main Idea

The Mediation Process Some conflicts can be resolved through mediation by a neutral third party.

Ask Students: *How could a third person help two people in conflict find some kind of solution?* (Sample answer: A third person might be able to help the two people in conflict communicate with less anger and more respect.)

✓ **READING CHECK**

Describe What are the steps involved in negotiation?

Preparing for Negotiation Successful negotiations require careful planning. Taking these steps ahead of time will increase the chances that negotiation will work:

- **Choose the time and place carefully.** The negotiation should take place at a time when both parties are calm, not impatient or rushed. Arrange to meet in a quiet place on neutral ground—not at the home of either party or in any other place that "belongs" to one side.

- **Check your facts.** Make sure your understanding of the situation is based on accurate information.

- **Plan what you will say.** Think about how to word your statement respectfully. You may wish to rehearse or write down your statement.

U

Tips for Successful Negotiation Staying calm is an important key to successful negotiation. Getting angry or upset could throw off the negotiations. Attack the problem, not each other. Avoid blaming and name-calling.

As you discuss the problem, try to keep an open mind. Listen attentively to what the other side has to say, and try to understand the other party's point of view. Be willing to take responsibility for your role in the conflict, and apologize if you have done something to hurt the other person. Remember, your goal is not to "win," but to find a solution that everyone can accept. Make sure to provide a way out of the conflict that will allow the other person to save face.

The Mediation Process

Main Idea Bringing in a neutral third party to mediate can help resolve some conflicts.

When two parties cannot reach a solution through negotiation, they may consider mediation. **Mediation** is *bringing in a neutral third party to help others resolve their conflicts peacefully.* The word *mediation* literally means "being in the middle." Having a third party "in the middle" helps put some distance between the two opposing parties.

■ **Figure 9.4** Mediation can help people settle interpersonal conflicts. *What qualities would an effective mediator need?*

✕ Promoting School Wellness

Conflicts at School A successful school program often has some structured way for students to work out conflicts. Some schools have adopted peer mediation programs. If your school has such a program, ask volunteers to find out about the details, or have a representative of the program address the class. If there is no peer mediation program in the school, ask volunteers to talk to a school counselor about ways conflicts between students are handled at the school and then report to the class about what they learned.

Health Skills Activity

Conflict Resolution

Negotiating with Parents

Chloe's parents have a strict rule: she isn't allowed to be out past 9 P.M. on a school night and 11 P.M. on weekends. When she was younger, Chloe thought this was reasonable. Now that she's 16, it just doesn't seem fair. All her friends get to stay out later, and it's embarrassing for her to have to leave in the middle of a party. She wants to try negotiating a new curfew with her parents.

Writing Write a dialogue between Chloe and her parents in which they work out an acceptable solution. Follow these negotiation steps:

1. Let each party explain its side.
2. Brainstorm solutions.
3. Discuss the pros and cons of each solution.
4. Agree on an acceptable solution.

The presence of someone who is not on either side reduces the level of confrontation. Mediation can be especially useful for dealing with conflicts that go on for a long time and threaten to disrupt everyday life.

Mediation can be formal or informal. Formal mediation involves the help of a mediator who has special training in resolving conflicts. Informal mediation can be as simple as asking a teacher to help settle a dispute with a classmate. Effective mediation depends on these basic principles:

- **Neutrality.** The mediator must always be an outsider who has no stake in the dispute. The mediation session should also take place in a neutral location.
- **Confidentiality. Confidentiality** means *respecting the privacy of both parties and keeping details secret.* The mediator promises not to reveal anything said by either party during the process.
- **Well-defined ground rules.** Both parties must agree to the rules set by the mediator. In some cases, the mediator may ask the two parties to sign an agreement to work out the problem within a given time frame.

In a typical mediation, each party gets a chance to present its side of the argument. The mediator then summarizes the points made by each side and leads a discussion between the two parties. The mediator does not make judgments or impose solutions. Instead, the solutions must come from the two parties. However, the mediator can help them see the advantages and disadvantages of certain ideas.

 READING CHECK

Compare and Contrast Explain how negotiation and mediation are similar and how they are different as strategies for resolving conflicts.

Lesson 2   Resolving Conflicts   **227**

Writing Strategy

Television Script Ask students to compose a script for a television drama that describes an example of peer mediation. The show should take place in an American high school, and the episode should be about a serious conflict between students that is referred to the school's peer mediation program. Students should include in their script the steps in the peer-mediation process.

Health Skills Activity

Conflict Resolution: Negotiating with Parents

NHES Standard 4 Students will demonstrate the ability to use interpersonal communication skills to enhance health and avoid or reduce health risks.

Objectives

- Demonstrate strategies for resolving a conflict through negotiation and problem solving.
- Demonstrate skills for communicating effectively with family members.

Teaching Strategies

- Review with students the three steps people should take ahead of time to increase the chances that negotiation will work. Ask students to incorporate these steps into their dialogues.
- Ask volunteers to share their dialogues with the class.

Assessment

Using this list, student work should provide comprehensive evidence of the following criteria to achieve the highest score:

√ Explains each side of the conflict without interruption

√ Brainstorms solutions to the conflict

√ Identifies a solution that is acceptable to both sides

√ Includes a follow-up plan

❸ ASSESS/ CLOSE

Assessment Resources

📁 *FAST FILE* **ACTIVITIES**
Lesson 2 Quiz

💿 *ExamView*
Assessment Suite CD-ROM

Visit glencoe.com for:
Online Quizzes
Online Learning Center

Progress Monitoring

Reteaching
Call on students to state the steps of the negotiation process and the steps of the peer-mediation process.

Enrichment
Explain that mediation sessions often require the parties in conflict to sign an agreement—a contract—before the mediation begins. Ask students to work in pairs to create a contract that could be used in peer mediation at their high school.

Have students visit **glencoe.com** and complete the Interactive Study Guide for this lesson.

Peer Mediation

Many schools have started peer mediation programs to help resolve conflicts. **Peer mediation** is *a process in which specially trained students help other students resolve conflicts peacefully.* Typically, peer mediation involves

- **making introductions.** The mediator explains that she will remain neutral and that the session is confidential.
- **establishing ground rules.** Both parties must agree to such rules as listening without interrupting, telling the truth, and addressing each other with respect.
- **hearing each side.** Each student tells his story in turn. The mediator may ask questions and take notes.
- **exploring solutions.** The two sides discuss the situation and propose possible solutions. Each solution is discussed, and both parties try to find an acceptable solution.
- **wrapping it up.** The mediator sums up the agreement. In some cases, both sides sign a written **contract.**

Keep in mind that mediation is not an appropriate solution for every kind of problem in schools. Violence and other crimes, for instance, require action from school administration or legal authorities.

Academic Vocabulary

contract *(noun):* an agreement between two or more parties

LESSON 2 📖 ASSESSMENT

After You Read

Reviewing Facts and Vocabulary

1. List three steps you could take to prepare for a negotiation.
2. When might it be necessary to bring in a mediator to settle a conflict?
3. Give two examples of ground rules in a peer mediation process.

Thinking Critically

4. **Evaluate.** Suppose a friend wants to copy answers off your paper during a test. When you refuse, she gets angry. Explain whether this conflict could be resolved through compromise.
5. **Make Inferences.** Why might peer mediation for students work better than bringing in an adult mediator?

Applying Health Skills

6. **Conflict Resolution.** Luke wants to go to a basketball game, but his parents want him to help out with spring cleaning. Write a dialogue in which they use conflict-resolution techniques to settle this problem.

Writing Critically

7. **Narrative.** Write a short story that centers on a conflict between two teens. Show how the characters resolve their conflict through compromise, negotiation, or mediation.

Go Online

Visit **glencoe.com** and complete the Interactive Study Guide for this lesson.

LESSON 2 ASSESSMENT ANSWERS

1. Choose the time and place carefully, check your facts, and plan what you will say.
2. When the two parties cannot reach a solution through negotiation
3. *Any two:* Listen without interrupting, tell the truth, and address each other with respect.
4. Sample answer: No, because copying is against the rules and against my values and could result in harmful consequences for me if we are caught.
5. Sample answer: Students are more likely to see the peer mediator as a partner in the process rather than as an authority who is there to punish or pass judgment.
6. Students' dialogues should demonstrate how communication and compromise can find a solution to the conflict.
7. Short stories will vary.

Understanding Violence

LESSON **3**

Understanding Violence

Understanding Violence

Real Life Issues

Resisting Gang Influence. Cody has just started high school, and he's alarmed by the presence of gangs at his school. One time, he was mistaken for a member of a gang because he accidentally wore their colors to school. Cody doesn't want to get involved with violence or crime, but sometimes he worries that joining a gang is the only way to fit in and make friends.

Writing *Write a journal entry from Cody's point of view. In it, discuss reasons for avoiding gangs and ideas for healthier alternatives.*

Causes of Violence

Main Idea Weapons, drugs, and gangs are some factors that can contribute to violence.

Violence is *the threatened or actual use of physical force or power to harm another person or to damage property.* Some acts of violence result from interpersonal conflicts that escalate out of control. However, violence can also be random, affecting people who just happen to be in the wrong place at the wrong time.

People may commit violent acts for many reasons. Causes can include

- uncontrolled anger or frustration.
- a need to control others.
- hatred or prejudice against a particular group.
- retaliation or revenge for some past harm, whether real or perceived.

GUIDE TO READING

BIG Idea *Teens need to know about forms of violence and ways to protect themselves.*

Before You Read

Create a Word Web. Write "Violence" in the center of a sheet of paper. As you read the lesson, add information about causes of violence and forms that violence can take.

Violence

New Vocabulary

- violence (p. 229)
- assault (p. 233)
- random violence (p. 233)
- homicide (p. 233)
- sexual violence (p. 234)
- sexual assault (p. 234)
- rape (p. 234)

Review Vocabulary

- prejudice (Ch.6, L.2)
- refusal skills (Ch.2, L.1)

1 FOCUS

GUIDE TO READING

BIG Idea Students will learn about forms of violence and ways to protect themselves. **Ask Students:** *What questions do you think this lesson will answer?* (Sample answer: Why do people become violent with each other? What different forms does violence take?)

Before You Read

Word Web Students' word webs will vary, but should include information from the lesson about causes and forms of violence.

Main Idea

Causes of Violence Factors that contribute to violence include weapons, drugs, and gangs. **Ask Students:** *How would you define violence?* (Answers will vary.)

Real Life Issues

Ask volunteers to share their journal entries. **Ask Students:** *What are some reasons to avoid joining a gang?* (Answers will vary.)

Reading Strategy

Organizing Information Start an outline of Lesson 3 on the board by using the two major heads of the section, "Causes of Violence" and "Types of Violence," for the first level of the outline. Ask students to make an outline of the lesson by using the secondary headings for the next level of the outline. For example, the first secondary heading under "Causes of Violence" is "Alcohol and Drug Use." Students can complete the outline by adding details under these secondary headings, including all bold, highlighted words.

❷ TEACH

R Reading Strategy

Listing Risk Factors Before students begin reading, explain that a risk factor for violence increases a person's chances of becoming violent, though that person may not necessarily become violent. Call on students to suggest risk factors that may make teens more likely to become violent. Write students' ideas on the board. Then, as students read the section, have them compare the risk factors they brainstormed with those they've read about. **BL**

W Writing Support

Risk Factors Emphasize that risk factors make children and teens likely to be involved in violence. Review with students the risk factors listed on this page. Then, have students write a story about a teen who almost becomes violent but whose friends and peers influence that teen not to become involved in violence. **OL AL**

Academic Vocabulary

Insecure Explain that the prefix in- means "not." Someone who is insecure, then, is "not secure"—not confident and not sure of him- or herself. Call on students to explain how they can tell when a teen feels insecure. Write the characteristics that students mention on the board.

Certain risk factors make children and teens more likely to be involved in violence. Children are at a greater risk if their families are poor, have low levels of education, or are involved in illegal activities. For teens, friends and peers play a greater role. Having friends who are involved in violence and crime greatly increases teens' risk of committing violent acts themselves. Fortunately, there are factors that can help protect teens from participating in violence. Teens who are committed to school and have a negative attitude toward crime are less likely to commit acts of violence, even if they have several risk factors. **R**

Alcohol and Drug Use

Studies have found that alcohol, in particular, plays a role in many violent crimes. There are several possible reasons for this connection:

- Drinking and drug use can lower people's self-control. As a result, they may be less likely to restrain their violent impulses.
- Drinking and drug use can damage people's judgment. They may overreact to something they see as a threat or fail to consider the consequences of their actions.
- Teens may engage in violent crimes as a way to get money to buy drugs.
- People who use drugs and drink alcohol are more likely to engage in other high-risk behaviors, such as fighting, carrying weapons, and engaging in unsafe sexual activity.

Some teens actually become involved with violence before they start to use alcohol or drugs. In other words, for some teens, it isn't using drugs and alcohol that makes them violent. Instead, their violent lifestyle puts them at risk for other problems, including substance abuse. **W**

Academic Vocabulary

insecure *(adjective):* not confident or sure

Mental and Emotional Problems

Low self-esteem is another risk factor for violence among teens. Insecure teens may try to use violence to prove themselves. Teens who have had little success in life may use violence as a way of getting back at a system that they think has caused them to fail. In addition, teens with low self-esteem may be more likely to join gangs as a way to belong. Gang membership puts teens at much higher risk for violence.

Stress, depression, and strong emotions such as anger can lead some teens to become violent. Learning to control anger effectively can greatly reduce the risk of violence. Anger-management workshops and counseling can help people learn to deal with anger and avoid lashing out at others.

Health Literacy

Comparing Violence Among Rural vs. Urban Youth Contrary to entertainment media stereotypes, a recent study by the South Carolina Rural Health Research Center showed that there is no significant lower prevalence of violent activities among rural teens when compared to urban and suburban teens. Rural teens, in fact, are more likely to have carried a weapon in the last 30 days. In addition, the study found that rural schools offer fewer teen violence services than urban schools, and rural schools are less likely than urban schools to have security measures to prevent violence.

Availability of Weapons

C

A recent government survey revealed that nearly one in five high school students reported having carried a weapon within the past 30 days. Five percent of all students said they have carried a gun. Access to weapons can increase violence. To protect yourself from the dangers associated with weapons, follow these strategies:

- Do not carry a weapon. People who carry guns are twice as likely to become victims of gun violence.
- If you know that another teen is carrying a weapon, tell a trusted adult, such as a parent or teacher. If necessary, you can contact the authorities anonymously.
- If your parents keep a gun at home, encourage them to equip it with a trigger lock and to store it unloaded in a locked cabinet. (See Chapter 26.)

Violence in the Media

HS

Every day, children and teens are exposed to violent words and images in television, movies, song lyrics, and video games. More than 60 percent of all television shows and nearly 90 percent of top-rated video games contain some violence. In addition, scenes that feature violence often fail to show its harmful consequences. In many cases, the characters who commit violent acts suffer no punishment as a result.

Exposure to violence in the media can influence the way people think about violence. This is especially true for children and teens. Some young people who view scenes of violence may begin to perceive it as normal or even positive. Studies have found that children and teens act more aggressively right after watching violent scenes. Also, children and teens who are aggressive tend to watch more violent television than their less aggressive peers.

■ **Figure 9.5** Children and teens are exposed to violence in the media every day. *How might this exposure influence their behavior?*

READING CHECK

Describe Name three ways for teens to protect themselves from situations involving weapons.

C Critical Thinking

Identifying Cause and Effect
Describe the following scenario to students: A teen boy is in a mall parking lot when a group of boys starts ridiculing him. The lone teen becomes angry and frightened. Instead of getting into his car and driving away, he threatens the group. Ask students how to protect themselves from the dangers associated with weapons. OL

HS Health Skills Practice

Analyzing Influences Bring a newspaper from a large city to class, and read briefly from articles that focus on violent acts. For each, ask students if they have ever viewed anything similar in a movie or on television. Point out that some researchers have found a correlation between watching violence in the media and being aggressive. Have students analyze how much they think this external influence contributes to violence in society. OL

READING CHECK

Answer Do not carry a weapon. If you know another teen is carrying a weapon, tell a trusted adult. If your parents keep a gun at home, encourage them to equip it with a trigger lock and store it unloaded and in a locked cabinet.

Caption Answer

Figure 9.5 It may cause them to act more aggressively.

Lesson 3   Understanding Violence   **231**

Cooperative Learning

TV Violence Survey Divide the class into small groups. Ask each group to conduct a survey of violence on television. Each group should choose four or five shows to watch over the next week, including one children's show. While watching each show, students should note each incidence of violence, describing what happened, whether a weapon was used, and what the outcome was. Have students write an evaluation of what they've observed. Call on groups to report their findings. Discuss how media violence may influence violence in the real world.

Real World CONNECTION

Answers to Activity Questions:

1. 33%

2. All four risk behaviors have declined overall since 1991.

3. Sample answer: Carrying a gun, because it is most likely to result in a homicide

AL Active Learning

Learning About Local Gangs
Have a speaker from the local police department or a social service agency address the class about gang activity in the students' community. Ask the speaker to focus on the illegal activities of gangs, how violence is connected to gangs, how gangs recruit and keep members, and what colors and symbols are used by local gangs. Make sure students have prepared relevant questions to ask the speaker. **BL** **OL**

Go Online

Remind students to visit glencoe.com and complete the Student Web Activity on the increased risk of violence teens experience when they are involved in gangs.

Real World CONNECTION

Violence Among Teens

The National Youth Risk Behavior Survey keeps track of behaviors that put teens' health and safety at risk. The chart below shows how some behaviors related to violence have increased or decreased over time.

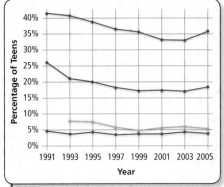

Source: Centers for Disease Control and Prevention, *National Youth Risk Behavior Survey, 1991–2005*

Activity Mathematics

Use the graph to answer the following questions:

1. What percent of teens were involved in a physical fight in 2003?

2. What overall trend can you detect for all four risk behaviors over the 15-year period shown?

3. Which of these behaviors do you think poses the greatest danger to teens? Why?

Concept Data Analysis: Interpreting Graphs
A line graph compares the relationship between two variables. It is an effective tool for showing trends.

- Being in a physical fight (at least once in the past year)
- Carrying a weapon (at least once in the past month)
- Carrying a gun (at least once in the past month)
- Requiring treatment for injuries from a physical fight (at least once in the past year)

Gang Violence

Go Online

Explore glencoe.com and complete the Student Web Activity on the increased risk of violence teens experience when they are involved in gangs.

Youth gangs are groups of teens or young adults who are involved collectively in violent or illegal activity. Gangs are often involved in drug dealing, robbery, and violent attacks on members of rival gangs. Teens who join gangs may be seeking protection from violence or looking for a way to fit in.

Teens who belong to gangs are much more likely than their peers to commit serious or violent crimes. They are also much more likely to become victims of violence. Being part of a gang reduces a teen's chances of graduating from school and finding a steady job. As a result, teen gang members may end up as career criminals.

To avoid gang influence, be aware of gang activity in your area, including the colors and symbols used by various gangs. Doing so will enable you to recognize and steer clear of gang members. It will also help you avoid dressing in a way that could cause you to be mistaken for a gang member. Seek out positive alternatives to gang membership, such as sports or after-school programs. Be prepared to use refusal skills if anyone ever tries to recruit you into a gang.

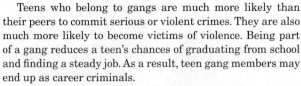

More About...

Gangs Gangs were once considered to be an inner-city problem. Today, gangs have spread to cities and towns throughout the United States. Here are some facts about gangs and gang violence.

- There are more than 24,500 gangs in the United States, and more than 772,500 American teens are members of gangs.

- A gang member is at least 60 times more likely to be killed than non-gang members.

- The average age of gang members is 17–18 years old. About a quarter of gang members are 15–17 years old.

- Only about 6 percent of gang members are female.

- Half to two-thirds of teen gang members leave the gang by the end of their first year.

Types of Violence

Main Idea Violence may be physical or sexual.

R In nearly half of all violent crimes, the victims know their attackers. This rate is higher for certain types of crimes. Victims of sexual attacks, for instance, are very likely to know their attackers, while robberies are typically random.

Assault and Homicide

An **assault** is *an unlawful physical attack or threat of attack.* Assaults range from minor threats to attacks that cause life-threatening injuries. Each year, more than 4 million assaults take place in the United States, and more than one million of those incidents result in injury. Roughly half of all assaults occur between people who know each other. However, assaults may also take the form of **random violence**—*violence committed for no particular reason.*

C If the victim of an assault dies, the crime becomes a **homicide**, *the willful killing of one human being by another.* Teens can protect themselves from assault and homicide by avoiding the risk factors associated with violence in general. That means avoiding drugs, alcohol, weapons, and gangs. You can also work on developing your protective factors. For instance, strengthening your ties to your family and your school can lower your overall risk of violence.

■ **Figure 9.6** Teens who are involved in school activities are at less risk of violence, including assault and homicide. *Why do you think involvement with school can lower teens' risk of violence?*

Teacher to Teacher

Mark Anderson • Cobb County School District, Marietta, GA

Preventing Violence I ask students to write a paragraph about a conflict they have witnessed. I prompt them by asking: Who was involved? What was the conflict about? How was it handled? What was the outcome? Based upon the conflict resolution strategies learned in the chapter, I ask what could have been done differently to prevent it. I encourage them to tell what steps teens can take when they witness conflicts and/or violence among their friends. Sometimes they may be the only one who notices or cares that there is a problem.

Main Idea

Types of Violence Physical and sexual attacks are two forms of violence. **Ask Students:** *What is the difference between a physical attack and a sexual attack?* (Sample answer: A sexual attack includes some form of sexual motivation in the attack, while a physical attack does not.)

R **Reading Strategy**

Types of Violence Have students make a table titled "Types of Violence." The table should have two columns, one headed "Type" and the other headed "Description." In the first column, students should list types of violence, including assault, homicide, sexual harassment, sexual assault, and rape. In the second column, students should use their own words to write brief descriptions to help them remember distinctions as they study and review. **BL** **EL**

C **Critical Thinking**

Assault and Homicide Divide the class into several groups. Tell them they will research statistics on teen violence, specifically causes, incidence, and risk factors. Have each group prepare a report. Ask proficient students to help others in the group as they divide up tasks. **AL** **OL**

Caption Answer

Figure 9.6 Sample answer: Being busy with school activities means less time for being involved in violent activities.

234

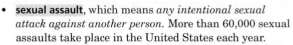

Sexual Violence

You've probably heard of sexual harassment, or unwelcome sexual conduct. This may include jokes, gestures, or physical contact. Sometimes, sexual harassment may escalate to **sexual violence**, *any form of unwelcome sexual contact directed at an individual.* Sexual violence can include

- **sexual assault**, which means *any intentional sexual attack against another person.* More than 60,000 sexual assaults take place in the United States each year.

- **rape**, which is *any form of sexual intercourse that takes place against a person's will.* More than 300,000 females and nearly 93,000 males are raped each year. Rape is one of the crimes least likely to be reported to the police. Survivors of rape may be unwilling to report the crime because of shame or fear.

Sexual violence can affect anyone. However, most victims are female, and most rapists are male. More than half of all female rape victims, and about three-quarters of male victims, are under 18 years old. Of all violent crimes, rape and sexual assault are the ones in which victims are most likely to know their attackers.

Avoiding Sexual Violence A sexual attack can happen anywhere. To help protect yourself, be aware of your surroundings wherever you go. Refuse to go anywhere alone with someone you don't know or trust. Attend parties with friends so you can all watch out for each other. Avoid alcohol and drugs, which can make you an easier target. Finally, trust your instincts. If a situation feels unsafe, don't hesitate to get out of it. For more safety tips, see Chapter 26.

Responding to a Sexual Attack If you are ever sexually attacked, your goal is to survive. In some cases, that may mean resisting the attacker, while in other cases, it may be safer to submit. You may try to stall for time, distract the attacker, or scream to attract attention. Do whatever you need to do to survive the situation.

Reporting a sexual attack right away gives you the best chance of bringing the attacker to justice. To preserve evidence of the attack, do not bathe or brush your teeth until you have been examined. Seek medical help for any injuries and, if appropriate, get tested for pregnancy and sexually transmitted diseases (STDs).

Survivors of rape and sexual assault need time to heal physically and emotionally. They may suffer feelings of fear, guilt, and shame.

■ **Figure 9.7** Counseling can help survivors of sexual violence recover from the experience. *What steps are important to take right after a sexual attack?*

234   **Chapter 9**   Resolving Conflicts and Preventing Violence

---

Teens Want to Know

Can Just Telling a Joke Be Considered Sexual Harassment? Maybe. Schools take unwelcome sexual advances between students very seriously. In 1999, the U.S. Supreme Court held that the school was responsible for being indifferent to the sexual harassment of a fifth-grade-girl by a boy in her class. In that case, the boy repeatedly made unwanted remarks and actions of a sexual nature. Since then, all schools have adopted policies to prevent sexual harassment from occurring. This includes sexual harassment of girls by boys, boys by girls, and same gender harassment.

Many mistakenly blame themselves for the attack. Counseling can help survivors of a sexual attack recover from the experience.

Hate Crimes

A hate crime is any crime motivated chiefly by hatred of or prejudice against a particular group. People may be targeted because of their race, religion, culture, sexual orientation, or other difference. Hate crimes can take many forms:

- **Harassment.** This can include racial slurs, stalking, or attempts to exclude a targeted group from community life.
- **Vandalism.** Perpetrators may use offensive messages or symbols to deface buildings.
- **Arson.** Criminals may blow up or set fire to buildings.
- **Assault and Homicide.** Criminals may physically attack or even kill members of the targeted group.

Hate crimes affect everyone, spreading fear, distrust, and anger throughout the community. The best way to stop hate crimes is to change the attitudes behind them. Practicing and teaching tolerance of other groups can go a long way toward ending these crimes. When a hate crime occurs, community members can condemn the crime and express support for the targeted group. This may prevent the hate violence from escalating.

 READING CHECK

Identify What are some ways of responding to a sexual attack?

 LESSON 3 ASSESSMENT

After You Read

Reviewing Facts and Vocabulary

1. Identify two factors that can contribute to violence.
2. What is *random violence*?
3. Identify two steps you can take to protect yourself from sexual violence.

Thinking Critically

4. **Evaluate.** Why might survivors of rape be reluctant to tell others about the crime?
5. **Analyze.** How can practicing and promoting tolerance help prevent violence?

Applying Health Skills

6. **Refusal Skills.** Write a dialogue between two teens at a party. One teen is trying to persuade the other to go somewhere alone together. The other teen uses refusal skills to avoid the threat of sexual violence.

Writing Critically

7. **Persuasive.** Write an editorial promoting tolerance and condemning hate crimes.

Go Online

Visit **glencoe.com** and complete the Interactive Study Guide for this lesson.

Lesson 3 Understanding Violence **235**

③ ASSESS/CLOSE

Assessment Resources

📁 **FAST FILE ACTIVITIES**
Lesson 3 Quiz

💿 *ExamView*
Assessment Suite CD-ROM

Visit glencoe.com for:
Online Quizzes
Online Learning Center

Progress Monitoring

Reteaching
Have students work in pairs to review the risk factors for violence among children and teens. Then, ask random pairs of students to name a risk factor and explain how that factor may make a teen more likely to commit a violent act.

Enrichment
Ask students to investigate problems associated with gang activity and gang violence both in the United States and in their community. They can use online and library resources and then prepare a written report of what they find.

Go Online

Have students visit **glencoe.com** and complete the Interactive Study Guide for this lesson.

LESSON 3 ASSESSMENT ANSWERS

1. *Any two:* Alcohol and drug use; mental and emotional problems such as low self-esteem, stress, depression, and anger; the availability of weapons; violence in the media; gang violence
2. Violence committed for no particular reason.
3. *Any two:* Be aware of your surroundings; avoid alcohol and drugs; stay in groups and look out for each other; refuse to go anywhere alone with someone you don't know or trust; trust your instincts
4. Sample answer: They may be embarrassed, ashamed, or afraid of the attacker.
5. Sample answer: It can change attitudes that lead to hate crimes.
6. Dialogues will vary.
7. Editorials will vary, but should demonstrate an understanding of the causes and prevention of hate crimes.

Preventing and Overcoming Abuse

1 FOCUS

GUIDE TO READING

BIG Idea Abuse can cause physical, mental, and emotional damage. **Ask Students:** *What different forms of abuse in relationships have you seen on television?* (Sample answer: Family members fighting each other, and some parents screaming at their children)

Before You Read

Organize Information
Students' charts will vary.

Main Idea

Abuse in Relationships Abuse can occur in various forms, all of which are harmful. **Ask Students:** *Why is abuse always harmful?* (It causes either physical or emotional harm to the person being abused.)

Real Life Issues ·············

Have students read the scenario. **Ask Students:** *What could Elena do to protect herself?* (Sample answer: Elena may ask to get out of the car.)

GUIDE TO READING

BIG Idea *Abuse can cause physical, mental, and emotional damage.*

Before You Read

Organize Information. Make a chart with three columns. Label the columns "Physical Abuse," "Emotional Abuse," and "Sexual Abuse." As you read, fill in the columns with examples of each type of abuse, possible effects, and ways to prevent or respond to it.

Physical Abuse	Emotional Abuse	Sexual Abuse

New Vocabulary

▸ physical abuse (p. 237)
▸ emotional abuse (p. 237)
▸ verbal abuse (p. 237)
▸ sexual abuse (p. 237)
▸ stalking (p. 237)
▸ date rape (p. 238)

Review Vocabulary

▸ abuse (Ch.7, L.3)
▸ cycle of violence (Ch.7, L.3)

Preventing and Overcoming Abuse

Real Life Issues ·····················

A Dangerous Date. Elena smiles at Matt as she hops into his car for their date. On the drive, Matt turns and heads in a different direction. "Where are you going?" Elena asks. "The concert's that way."
"Change of plans," Matt says with a sly grin. "There's a party on the other side of town. Some guys figured out how to get into that old abandoned house. I thought it would give us time to be alone." Elena begins to worry. She's afraid that if she and Matt are alone, he might try to take advantage of her sexually.

Writing *Write a conclusion to this story that shows how Elena escapes from this potentially dangerous situation.*

Abuse in Relationships

Main Idea All forms of abuse are extremely harmful.

Abuse is the physical, mental, emotional, or sexual mistreatment of one person by another. In Chapter 7, you learned about abuse in families. However, abuse can also occur in other types of relationships, including dating relationships. A dating relationship may be abusive if one partner

- tries to pressure the other into sexual activity.
- tries to make the relationship serious or exclusive right away.
- acts jealous or possessive.
- tries to control the other's behavior.
- yells, swears, or otherwise emotionally attacks the other.
- threatens the other with physical violence.

236 **Chapter 9** Resolving Conflicts and Preventing Violence

---

More About...

Stalking The effects of stalking can be quite harmful. Many victims come to feel that the stalker is always watching. If a teen is the victim of a stalker, here are steps to take:

- When going out, tell someone where you are going.

- Keep a cell phone with you at all times.
- Keep a record of any contact the stalker has with you. Save letters, notes, voice mail messages, and e-mails from a stalker.
- Memorize the phone numbers of people you can call for help.

Forms of Abuse

Abuse in relationships can take several forms. The most common forms include the following:

- **Physical abuse** is *a pattern of intentionally causing bodily harm or injury to another person.* Examples include hitting, kicking, shoving, biting, pulling hair, and throwing objects at another person. Physical abuse can result in serious injuries. It can also leave the victim emotionally scarred. Victims of physical abuse may respond with violence of their own.

- **Emotional abuse** is *a pattern of attacking another person's emotional development and sense of worth.* One form of emotional abuse is **verbal abuse**, *the use of words to mistreat or injure another person.* Examples include yelling, swearing, and making insults. Abusers may also humiliate their victims, attempt to control their behavior, threaten physical harm, or cut the person off from friends and family members. Emotional abuse can damage self-esteem and lead the victim to feel worthless or helpless. Victims may even come to feel that they deserve the abuse.

- **Sexual abuse** is *a pattern of sexual contact that is forced upon a person against the person's will.* Sexual assault, rape, and trying to pressure someone into sexual activity are examples of sexual abuse. Sexual abuse can harm victims physically and emotionally. It may also put them at risk for pregnancy or disease.

- **Stalking** is *repeatedly following, harassing, or threatening an individual.* Stalkers may follow their victims physically from place to place. They may also harass them by calling or e-mailing repeatedly and sending letters or gifts. More than 1.3 million people are stalked each year in the United States, and most of them know the stalker.

 **READING CHECK**

Synthesize Give an example of verbal abuse.

■ **Figure 9.8** Communicating your sexual limits clearly to the people you date can help protect you from being in an abusive relationship. *What are some harmful effects of abuse?*

Cooperative Learning

Teaching About Abuse Video Review the forms of abuse discussed in Lesson 4. Then, divide the class into groups, and ask each group to make a video about one of the forms of abuse. The purpose of the video is to teach teens about that form of abuse, including what the warning signs are, how the abuse can be avoided or stopped, and what kind of support a victim of the abuse should seek to overcome the effects of the abuse. Have students share their videos with the class.

---

② TEACH

W Writing Support

Describing Abuse Ask a volunteer to read aloud the bulleted list of ways that a partner can be abusive in a dating relationship. Then ask students to write an imaginary scenario about a dating relationship with one of those forms of abuse. Ask for volunteers to read aloud their scenarios, and discuss how prevalent each of these problems is for teens in the community. OL

READING CHECK

Answer Sample answer: Yelling at another person

R Reading Strategy

Brainstorming After students have read about the different forms of abuse in relationships, have them brainstorm an example of emotional abuse. Advise students to not use examples from their own lives. Through discussion of students' examples, clarify the definition of each form of relationship abuse. BL OL

Caption Answer

Figure 9.8 Sample answer: Abuse can damage self-esteem and cause harm to victims both physically and emotionally.

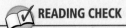 Health Skills Practice

Practicing Healthful Behaviors Describe a teen dating relationship to students in which friends observe the girl becoming depressed and anxious. Friends have heard the girl's boyfriend make insulting comments to her and belittle her intelligence and looks. Ask students to characterize this relationship. (The boy is emotionally abusing the girl.) Then ask if they were the girl's friend, what would they do. (Urge her to end the relationship or seek help from a trusted adult.) **OL**

Main Idea

Date Rape and Acquaintance Rape Date rape is a form of abuse. **Ask Students:** *Why would someone in a dating relationship commit rape?* (Sample answer: Because one of the pair resisted the sexual advances of the other)

U Universal Access

Connecting to the Real World The word *acquaintance* may be unfamiliar to many students, and especially to English language learners. Explain that the term derives from a Latin word meaning "to know." An acquaintance, then, is someone you know—maybe know well or not. Point out that most of the students in school are acquaintances of one another. **EL** **BL**

✓ **READING CHECK**

Answer Acquaintance rape

Academic Vocabulary

partner *(noun):* a member of a couple

Sometimes teens who are in abusive relationships don't realize there is a problem. A boyfriend may think that being jealous and possessive of his girlfriend shows how much he loves her. The girlfriend may accept his efforts to control her as normal. It's important to understand that trying to control a **partner** is not a normal or healthy part of a relationship. **HS**

Protecting Yourself from Abuse

There are several steps you can take to avoid abusive relationships. For starters, you can hang out with others who share your values and treat you with respect. You can also know your own limits with regard to sexual activity and communicate those limits clearly to anyone you date. Avoiding drugs and alcohol is another important step. These substances can impair your ability to make sound decisions.

Know the warning signs of abuse in relationships. If you feel a relationship might be turning dangerous, trust your instincts and get out. If necessary, seek help from someone you trust, such as a parent or teacher. If you feel you are in immediate danger, you can contact the police. Remember that no matter what happens, you are not to blame for anyone else's behavior. You can control only your own actions.

Date Rape and Acquaintance Rape

Main Idea Rape that occurs in dating relationships is a form of abuse.

Sometimes abuse in dating relationships can take the form of sexual violence. **Date rape** occurs when *one person in a dating relationship forces the other person to take part in sexual intercourse.* This is one of the most common forms of rape. More than 40 percent of female rape victims and more than 10 percent of male victims are romantically involved in some way with their attackers. In *acquaintance rape,* the attacker is someone the victim knows casually or considers a friend. This is the form of rape that affects male victims most often. **U**

All forms of rape can harm survivors physically, mentally, and emotionally. Minor injuries, such as scratches and bruises, are common. A smaller percentage of survivors suffer major injuries such as broken bones. Long-term effects include chronic pain, headaches, or stomach problems. Survivors are also at risk for pregnancy and STDs. Rape can trigger feelings of shock, anxiety, guilt, and distrust of others. In the long term, survivors may develop mental and emotional problems, such as depression, eating disorders, or post-traumatic stress disorder (see Chapter 5).

✓ **READING CHECK**

Identify What form of rape most often affects male victims?

Myths & Reality

Date Rape

Myth: If a girl agrees to "make out" with a boy, she is giving implicit permission to "go all the way"—to have intercourse with him.

Fact: Everyone has the right to say no to unwanted sexual activity, no matter what has preceded that refusal.

Myth: Date rape almost always happens between people who have just met each other or don't know each other well.

Fact: It's common for a person to be raped by someone she or he has been dating for a long time.

■ **Figure 9.9** Getting your own drink and always keeping an eye on it can help you avoid date rape drugs. *What other strategies can help prevent date rape?*

Alcohol, Drugs, and Date Rape

Alcohol often plays a role in date rape. Drinking lowers people's inhibitions and impairs their judgment. Both females and males are more likely to be sexually attacked when they've been drinking. In addition, males are more likely to commit sexual attacks when under the influence of alcohol.

AL Some rapists use drugs to subdue their victims. Substances like Rohypnol ("roofies"), GHB, and ketamine are sometimes called "date rape drugs" because they can make someone an easier target. Mixed with food or drink, these drugs are difficult to detect. They work quickly, with effects ranging from drowsiness and dizziness to loss of consciousness. People who've been drugged often cannot remember what happened to them, making it difficult for them to identify attackers.

Avoiding Date Rape

The tips you learned in Lesson 3 on avoiding sexual violence also apply to date rape and acquaintance rape. Specific strategies for avoiding date rape include the following:

R
- Avoid being alone with a dating partner you don't trust or know well, or with anyone who makes you feel uneasy.
- Avoid alcohol and drugs. Stay sober and aware of what's going on around you.
- Be clear about your sexual limits with dating partners.
- Always get your own beverage at parties, and never leave it uncovered or unattended. Don't drink anything that smells or tastes strange.
- Make sure you have a way to get home. Don't depend only on your date for a ride.
- If you start to feel dizzy, disoriented, or otherwise unwell, tell someone you trust and ask for help getting home.

AL Active Learning

Date Rape Drugs Have interested students research statistics on date rape drugs. For each drug, ask students to list the street names it is known by, what the drug looks like, what kind of drug it is, what the most common effects of the drug are, and how soon the drug leaves the system. Have students prepare a written report of what they learn. **AL**

R Reading Strategy

Date Rape Strategies Ask volunteers to read aloud the six strategies for avoiding date rape. For each strategy, have students discuss how easy it would be to implement that strategy when they are among their friends. For each strategy, encourage students to suggest ways it could be used in the social world in which teens live. **BL OL**

Caption Answer

Figure 9.9 Sample answer: Avoid alcohol and drugs; don't depend only on a date for a ride home from a party or social event; tell someone if you experience a warning sign of being drugged.

Writing Strategy

Telling a Friend Ask students to write a letter to a friend who is going out often on dates with many different boys and may be putting herself at risk for violence. In this letter, students should be respectful but informative about strategies the teen should be using to avoid date rape or acquaintance rape.

Main Idea

Overcoming Abuse Survivors of abuse can find help recovering from its effects through counseling. **Ask Students:** *Where can someone who has been abused or raped find help for emotional problems?* (Sample answers: School guidance counselors, members of the clergy, professional counselors)

AL Active Learning

Using Visuals Have students get into groups and create a poster that tells survivors of abuse how they can seek help. Refer students to the list on page 240 for ideas. Encourage students to use magazine cutouts and other creative sources. **BL**

C Critical Thinking

Comparing Have a volunteer read the list of sources of support for survivors of abuse. Then lead a discussion that evaluates each source in terms of what kind of support would be offered and how effective it would be for different situations. For example, students might suggest that the police would be a good source of support in instances of physical abuse or stalking, but not as effective for emotional abuse. **OL**

Caption Answer

Figure 9.10 Listening to and sharing feelings with other survivors can help a survivor understand that he or she is not alone.

Overcoming Abuse

Main Idea Counseling can help survivors of abuse recover from its effects.

Victims of abuse or rape may be reluctant to tell others about what has happened to them. Recognizing that they are not to blame can be the first step in recovering from the experience. People need to understand that all forms of abuse, including rape, are illegal. Reporting the incident to authorities can help prevent future abuse.

Help for Survivors

People who have survived rape or abuse may feel angry, confused, or ashamed. They may withdraw from friends and family or develop symptoms of depression or anxiety. The traumatic experience can lead to a fear of intimacy and an inability to trust others. In the long term, these individuals may be at risk for problems such as alcohol or drug abuse, eating disorders, self-injury, and suicide.

Seeking professional help is the best way to work through these feelings and avoid long-term health consequences. It can be difficult to talk about something as traumatic as rape or abuse. However, talking about the experience in a safe, supportive environment is the best way to move toward healing. Survivors can seek support from sources such as

- parents, guardians, or other trusted adults.
- teachers, coaches, school nurses, or guidance counselors.
- members of the clergy.
- police.
- private physicians or hospital emergency rooms.
- shelters for victims of domestic violence.
- rape crisis centers.
- therapists, counselors, or support groups.

■ **Figure 9.10** Taking part in a support group is one way for survivors of abuse to recover from the experience. *What advantages might a support group have over one-on-one therapy?*

Home and Community

Rape Crisis Centers and Domestic Violence Shelters In many communities there are places where victims of relationship violence can go for help and support, including rape crisis centers and shelters for victims of domestic violence. Have students use a telephone book or an online search engine to identify such sources of support in their community. Ask students to call the center or shelter and make an appointment for an in-person or telephone interview. Advise students to prepare written questions for the interview. Have students share their findings with the class.

Counseling can take several forms. Some survivors of abuse prefer one-on-one sessions with a trained therapist. Others feel more comfortable with support groups where they can share their experiences with other survivors. Being in such a group may help them understand that they are not alone.

Help for Abusers

In cases of abuse, the victim isn't the only one who needs help. Abuse is a learned behavior, and many abusers were once victims of abuse themselves. They need help to break the cycle of violence. Some abusers may see their behavior as normal or justified. They need to recognize that abusing others is wrong and to learn healthier social behaviors. Other abusers understand that their behavior is wrong but feel powerless to stop it. They need to learn that they are responsible for their own behavior, and that with help, they can control their violent impulses.

Counseling can help abusers learn to cope with their emotions in healthier ways. Abusers should recognize that asking for help is an act of courage. Without it, their violent behavior may increase until it destroys their relationships or causes serious harm to someone they love. By getting the help they need, they may be able to save their relationships and stop the cycle from continuing to the next generation.

 READING CHECK

Evaluate Why is it important to report all forms of abuse to authorities?

LESSON 4 **ASSESSMENT**

After You Read

Reviewing Facts and Vocabulary

1. What is *verbal abuse*?
2. Identify two warning signs that a dating relationship may be abusive.
3. Identify two strategies for avoiding date rape.

Thinking Critically

4. **Analyze.** Why should you make sure you have a way to get home from a party or social event other than depending on your date for a ride?
5. **Evaluate.** Why is it beneficial for abusers, as well as survivors of abuse, to seek counseling?

Applying Health Skills

6. **Communication Skills.** Suppose a friend has just confided to you about being in an abusive relationship. Write a dialogue between you and your friend in which you show support and encourage your friend to seek help.

Writing Critically

7. **Creative.** Write a poem or song about the problem of abuse in relationships.

Go Online

Visit glencoe.com and complete the Interactive Study Guide for this lesson.

Lesson 4 Preventing and Overcoming Abuse **241**

 READING CHECK

Answer To help prevent future incidents of abuse

❸ ASSESS/ CLOSE

Assessment Resources

📁 *FAST FILE* ACTIVITIES
Lesson 4 Quiz

 ExamView Assessment Suite CD-ROM

Visit glencoe.com **for:**
Online Quizzes
Online Learning Center

Progress Monitoring

Reteaching
Write the different forms of abuse discussed in the lesson on the board. For each form, call on students at random to explain what kind of abuse takes place and how that form of abuse can either be prevented or overcome.

Enrichment
Have students research laws about stalking in their state and community. Then have them write a newspaper article on what stalking is, what a person can do about it, and how the legal system deals with stalking.

Go Online

Have students visit glencoe.com and complete the Interactive Study Guide for this lesson.

241

LESSON 4 ASSESSMENT ANSWERS

1. The use of words to mistreat or injure another person
2. Sample answer: A date acts possessive, or a date threatens physical harm
3. Sample answer: Avoid alcohol and drugs, and be clear about your sexual limits with people you date.
4. Sample answer: To make sure you can get home safely if your date makes unwanted sexual advances
5. Counseling can help abusers learn to cope with anger in healthier ways and teach them how to communicate better and resolve conflicts peacefully. Counseling may also help them save relationships and stop the abuse cycle from continuing to the next generation.
6. Dialogues will vary.
7. Poems and songs will vary.

When Dating Is Dangerous

Focus

Motivator
Ask students to describe a date between two teens that becomes dangerous for one of them. Record their responses for later discussion.

Teach

Abuse in Dating Relationships
Review with students the list of signs of abuse in a dating relationship, such as when one partner tries to pressure the other into sexual activity or acts jealous or possessive. Explain that young women ages 16–24 experience the highest rates of relationship violence. Abuse in dating relationships isn't simply a problem on first dates or blind dates. Studies have shown that as a dating relationship becomes more serious, the potential for violent behavior increases.

Avoiding Dating Violence
Ask students to describe strategies that can be used to lessen the threat of dating violence. Point out that many of the strategies for avoiding date rape also can be used to avoid other forms of dating violence. Write students' suggestions on the board.

Community Resources
According to the article, one in five high school girls reports being a victim of physical or sexual violence in a dating relationship. Ask students to compile a list of where in their community girls can get confidential help if they are victims of dating violence. Local programs may include a women's support group, a rape crisis center, or a free clinic.

When Dating Is Dangerous

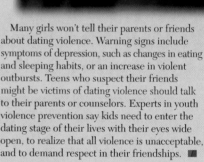

One in five teenage girls reports being a victim of violence by her date.

According to a study by the Harvard School of Public Health, dating during adolescence can be dangerous, especially for girls. The study of 1,977 high school girls shows that 1 in 5 reports being a victim of physical or sexual violence in a dating relationship. Girls reported being hit, slapped, shoved, or forced into sexual activity by dates. Because this is the first study of its kind, it's not clear whether such abuse is on the rise, but Dr. Jay Silverman, author of the report, called the numbers "extremely high."

Pressure to Date
Laura Sessions Stepp, author of *Our Last Best Shot*, isn't surprised by statistics that show a high incidence of violence during dates. "Girls in high school talk a lot about the pressure to have a physical relationship," she says, "and I wonder if 'girl power' makes them think they can handle situations they're not ready for." Sara Stillman, 17, wrote *Soul Searching*, a book for high school girls. She thinks the pressure of having a boyfriend early can push girls into unhealthy relationships.

Many girls won't tell their parents or friends about dating violence. Warning signs include symptoms of depression, such as changes in eating and sleeping habits, or an increase in violent outbursts. Teens who suspect their friends might be victims of dating violence should talk to their parents or counselors. Experts in youth violence prevention say kids need to enter the dating stage of their lives with their eyes wide open, to realize that all violence is unacceptable, and to demand respect in their friendships. ■

TIME to THINK... About Dating Safety

With a small group, develop an ad campaign that promotes safe dating. What easy-to-remember slogan can you create to help teens remember the importance of dating safety? Each group should design one poster with this slogan. With your school's permission, put up the posters around the school.

Writing Strategy

Script Ask students to write a script for a skit that uses many of the strategies for avoiding date rape listed in Lesson 4. Have students imagine a situation in which a teen finds herself in a dating relationship in which she doesn't trust her partner and takes steps to avoid date rape. Encourage students to include the communication skills they've learned, including the use of "I" messages, a respectful tone of voice, and assertive body language. They should also try to include refusal skills in the script.

 To download quizzes and eFlashcards to your PDA, go to glencoe.com and click on the Study to Go icon.

LESSON 1

Causes of Conflict

Key Concepts

▶ Causes of conflict include misunderstandings, power struggles, property disputes, and lack of respect.

▶ Working together to resolve conflicts strengthens relationships.

▶ Conflicts can lead to stress, negative emotions, damaged relationships, financial losses, and violence.

Vocabulary

▶ conflict (p. 220)

▶ interpersonal conflicts (p. 220)

▶ escalate (p. 221)

LESSON 2

Resolving Conflicts

Key Concepts

▶ Compromise is one way to resolve a conflict.

▶ Negotiation is a step-by-step process used to resolve conflicts.

▶ Mediation involves bringing in a neutral third party to help resolve a conflict.

Vocabulary

▶ conflict resolution (p. 224)

▶ compromise (p. 224)

▶ negotiation (p. 225)

▶ mediation (p. 226)

▶ confidentiality (p. 227)

▶ peer mediation (p. 228)

LESSON 3

Understanding Violence

Key Concepts

▶ Substance use, availability of weapons, violence in the media, and gang presence may contribute to violence.

▶ Violent crimes include assault, homicide, and sexual assault.

▶ Following a sexual attack, the most important steps to take are reporting the crime and seeking medical help.

Vocabulary

▶ violence (p. 229)

▶ assault (p. 233)

▶ random violence (p. 233)

▶ homicide (p. 233)

▶ sexual violence (p. 234)

▶ sexual assault (p. 234)

▶ rape (p. 234)

LESSON 4

Preventing and Overcoming Abuse

Key Concepts

▶ Violence in dating relationships is dangerous and unhealthy.

▶ Abuse in relationships can be physical, emotional, or sexual.

▶ Alcohol and drug use can increase the risk of date rape.

▶ Both survivors of abuse and abusers need counseling to overcome the experience and break the cycle of violence.

Vocabulary

▶ physical abuse (p. 237)

▶ emotional abuse (p. 237)

▶ verbal abuse (p. 237)

▶ sexual abuse (p. 237)

▶ stalking (p. 237)

▶ date rape (p. 238)

Chapter 9 Review **243**

Go Online

Students can visit **glencoe.com** to

• review content online with the Online Student Edition.

• test their knowledge of chapter content with Online Quizzes.

• access Interactive Health Tutor for more practice with vocabulary.

Assessment Resources

📁 *Fast File* Activities
Chapter 9 Test

💿 *ExamView Assessment Suite* CD-ROM

Visit glencoe.com **for:**
Audio Chapter Summaries
Online Quizzes

 Tell students to visit glencoe.com where they can download quizzes and eFlashcards.

Study Tips

Correlate Notes with the Textbook

Tell students that taking good notes in class is essential for study and later review in preparing for a test. One way to take effective notes is to correlate the notes taken in class with the related material in the text, since most of what a teacher presents is a review or an enhancement of textbook material. Every day after class, students should review their notes with the textbook at hand, and write next to a note the page number where related material can be found in the text.

Chapter 9 Assessment Answers

LESSON 1

Vocabulary Review

1. *conflict*
2. escalate
3. Interpersonal conflict

Understanding Key Concepts

4. d
5. b
6. a

Thinking Critically

7. Sample answer: Cultural differences might cause people to misunderstand one another. People of different cultures can prevent conflicts by trying to understand one another and by practicing tolerance.
8. Sample answer: Working through a conflict shows commitment to each other, helping the relationship. Conflicts can also cause stress, which harms relationships.
9. Sample answer: You could adjust your behavior by making a habit of reminding the person about your plans.

LESSON 2

Vocabulary Review

10. negotiation
11. Mediation
12. Confidentiality

Understanding Key Concepts

13. a
14. b
15. d

LESSON 1

Vocabulary Review

Use the vocabulary terms listed on page 243 to complete the following statements.

1. The term _____ refers to any disagreement, struggle, or fight.

2. Disagreements can _____ into fights when emotions get out of control.

3. _____ can arise when one party's needs, wishes, or beliefs clash with those of another party.

Understanding Key Concepts

After reading the question or statement, select the correct answer.

4. Which of the following is *not* an example of an interpersonal conflict?
   a. Two friends disagree over which movie to see.
   b. Two rival gangs fight over control of a neighborhood.
   c. Two political parties clash over tax policy.
   d. A teen feels torn between loyalties to two friends who are not on good terms.

5. Keith and Evan used to be best friends. Now they are not speaking to each other because they found out they both like the same girl. The cause of their conflict is
   a. personal loyalties.
   b. jealousy.
   c. conflicting attitudes and values.
   d. lack of respect.

6. Which of the following is a positive result of conflict?
   a. Improved problem-solving skills
   b. Stress
   c. Damaged relationships
   d. Violence

Thinking Critically

After reading the question or statement, write a short answer using complete sentences.

7. **Discuss.** How might cultural differences contribute to interpersonal conflict? What steps could people take to avoid this problem?

8. **Analyze.** Explain how conflicts can both help and harm relationships.

9. **Synthesize.** How could you prevent a friend's frequent forgetfulness from becoming an ongoing source of conflict?

LESSON 2

Vocabulary Review

Correct the sentences below by replacing the italicized term with the correct vocabulary term.

10. Solving a disagreement in a way that satisfies everyone involved is called *escalation*.

11. *Discussion* involves bringing in a neutral third party to help resolve conflicts.

12. *Neutrality* means respecting the privacy of both parties and keeping details secret.

Understanding Key Concepts

After reading the question or statement, select the correct answer.

13. Which of the following conflicts most likely could be resolved through compromise?
    a. The school drama club is split over which of two plays to put on.
    b. One group of parents wants the school to adopt a dress code, but the other doesn't.
    c. A teen wants to buy a used car, but his father objects because the car is unsafe.
    d. One friend makes fun of a boy whom the other likes.

Health eSpotlight Wrap-Up

Preventing Violence, Resolving Conflicts Have students reread the Health eSpotlight questions at the beginning of the chapter (page 219) and look at their original answers. **Ask Students:** *What do you know about disagreements that you didn't know before watching the video and reading the chapter?* Call on volunteers to describe what they have learned and how they would change their responses.

14. Which of the following is *not* a good strategy for negotiation?
    a. Choose the time and place carefully.
    b. Refuse to compromise.
    c. Listen attentively to what the other side has to say.
    d. Be willing to take responsibility for your role in the conflict.

15. For a conflict between two teens who are friends, the best peer mediator would be
    a. the parent of one of the teens.
    b. a teen who is friends with one of them.
    c. a teacher.
    d. a student who does not know either teen well.

Thinking Critically

After reading the question or statement, write a short answer using complete sentences.

16. **Analyze.** Compromise is not always a good way of resolving a conflict. In what type of situation is it unwise to compromise?

17. **Evaluate.** Is a compromise between two parties the ideal outcome of a negotiation? Why or why not?

18. **Explain.** Why is it important for mediators in a conflict to be neutral?

LESSON 3

Vocabulary Review

Choose the correct term in the sentences below.

19. *Violence / Assault* is the use of physical force to harm people or damage property.

20. The willful killing of one human being by another is called *homicide / rape.*

21. The term *sexual violence / sexual assault* refers to any form of unwelcome sexual contact directed at an individual.

Understanding Key Concepts

After reading the question or statement, select the correct answer.

22. Teens are *less* likely to be involved in violence if they
    a. have friends or family who are involved in crime.
    b. use alcohol or drugs.
    c. are committed to school.
    d. have an underprivileged background.

23. Which of the following accurately describes the term *youth gang*?
    a. Teens who hang out together
    b. A major drug ring run by young adults
    c. Two teens who have shoplifted
    d. Teens who commit acts of vandalism and assault as a group

24. In most cases of rape, the victim
    a. does not know the rapist.
    b. is female.
    c. is over 18 years old.
    d. reports the crime to the police.

Thinking Critically

After reading the question or statement, write a short answer using complete sentences.

25. **Analyze.** What are the possible consequences of retaliating for a violent act?

26. **Explain.** How can media violence influence behavior?

27. **Evaluate.** What is the advantage of reporting a sexual attack to the police right away, without bathing or showering first?

LESSON 4

Vocabulary Review

Choose the correct term in the sentences below.

28. *Physical abuse / Emotional abuse* is a pattern of intentionally causing bodily harm or injury to another person.

Chapter 9 Assessment **245**

Thinking Critically

16. When doing so would have harmful consequences or go against your values

17. Sample answer: A compromise is not the ideal outcome because in a compromise both parties give up something. The ideal outcome would be to find a solution in which both parties get what they wanted.

18. Sample answer: The presence of someone who is not on either side reduces the level of confrontation.

LESSON 3

Vocabulary Review

19. Violence
20. homicide
21. sexual violence

Understanding Key Concepts

22. c
23. d
24. b

Thinking Critically

25. Sample answer: If one side retaliates, the other side may strike back, creating a cycle of attacks.

26. Sample answer: Exposure to media violence can influence the way people think about violence. Some young people who watch violence in the media become more comfortable with the idea of violence.

27. Sample answer: Reporting right away preserves the evidence of the attack and increases the chances of bringing the attacker to justice.

Assessment

Assessment

LESSON 4

Vocabulary Review

28. Physical abuse
29. stalking
30. Sexual abuse

Understanding Key Concepts

31. b
32. d

Thinking Critically

33. Sample answer: Verbal abuse harms the victim's emotional development and sense of self-worth.

34. Sample answer: It makes clear what behavior you will and will not accept, eliminating the possibility of a misunderstanding.

35. Survivors may have feelings of anger, shame, anxiety, guilt, and depression. These feelings may prevent them from seeking help. They need to understand that talking about their experience in a supportive, safe place can help the healing process.

29. Repeatedly following, harassing, or threatening an individual is known as *verbal abuse/stalking*.

30. *Sexual abuse/Date rape* is a pattern of sexual contact that is forced upon a person against the person's will.

Understanding Key Concepts

After reading the question or statement, select the correct answer.

31. Trey insists that his girlfriend ask his permission before she goes out with her friends. He also calls to check up on her whenever she's out. His behavior is an example of
    a. physical abuse.
    b. emotional abuse.
    c. sexual abuse.
    d. stalking.

32. Which of the following behaviors can *reduce* your risk of date rape?
    a. Using alcohol or other drugs
    b. Being alone with a date you don't trust or know well
    c. Relying on your date for a ride home
    d. Going to a party with a group of friends

Thinking Critically

After reading the question or statement, write a short answer using complete sentences.

33. **Explain.** Why is verbal abuse considered a form of emotional abuse?

34. **Analyze.** How does knowing your sexual limits and communicating them clearly to the people you date protect you from abuse?

35. **Evaluate.** Why are some survivors of rape or abuse reluctant to seek counseling? What might convince them that counseling can help?

Project-Based ASSESSMENT

Recognizing the Warning Signs of Violence

Background
Recognizing the warning signs of violence can prevent a situation from escalating out of control. Knowing how to prevent a conflict from becoming violent can reduce the risk of injury.

Task
Create a 30-second audio public service announcement (PSA) about the warning signs of violence. Also, create a questionnaire about the effectiveness of the PSA.

Audience
Students in grades 6–8

Purpose
Help students learn how to stay safe by recognizing the warning signs of violent behavior.

Procedure

1 Examine PSAs on other subjects. Write a list of the characteristics that make these PSAs effective.

2 Review the information in Chapter 9 on conflicts and violence.

3 Write a script for the PSA. Have it reviewed by your teacher or a school counselor. Write a brief questionnaire about the message you are trying to get across in your PSA.

4 Present your PSA to a middle school class.

5 Assess the effectiveness of the PSA by having students fill out the questionnaire after listening to the PSA.

Project-Based ASSESSMENT

Step 1 Research Have students use library and online resources to develop a list of warning signs of violence. Also, provide students with examples of good PSAs written for other purposes.

Step 2 Create PSA and Questionnaire Have students write their PSAs and questionnaires of three or four questions.

Step 3 Evaluate Review the script of each PSA and questionnaire before students present to a middle school class. A PSA should be 30 seconds or less, and a well-written PSA will be both informative and memorable. The completed project should include an assessment from middle-school students.

Visit **glencoe.com** for Project-Based Assessment rubrics.

Math Practice

Interpret Tables. A study surveyed teachers at schools that implemented a peer-mediation program. The table below lists some of the problems that teachers reported and the percentage decrease in incidents of those problems since the program began. Use the table to answer Questions 1–3.

Problem	Percentage decrease since implementing program
Expulsions	73%
Assaults	90.2%
Discipline referrals	57.7%

Adapted from *Safe and Drug-Free Schools Program Inventory*, 2002.

1. Which problem decreased the most since the peer-mediation program began?
   A. assaults
   B. conflict
   C. discipline referrals
   D. expulsions

2. If the number of assaults reported before the program began was 150 per year, about how many assaults per year occurred after the program began?
   A. 15
   B. 60
   C. 90
   D. 135

3. A student looking at this table concluded that since the peer-mediation program began, problems decreased by 220.9% (the sum of all three percentages). Why would you question his reasoning?
   A. The percentages do not add up to 100%.
   B. 220.9% is not the sum of all three percentages.
   C. The percentage decreases are not likely related to the peer-mediation program.
   D. There might be overlap in the percentages. For example, assault may lead to expulsion.

Go Online

For more test practice, visit glencoe.com and complete the Online Quizzes for Chapter 9.

Reading/Writing Practice

Understand and Apply. Read the passage below and then answer the questions.

If you have a friend in an abusive relationship, you may be tempted to "rescue" her or him. You may try to persuade your friend to leave the relationship by criticizing the abuser. However, criticizing the abuser may simply make the victim less willing to confide in you.

Ask your friend how she or he feels. Express your concerns in a way that focuses on the abusive behavior rather than on the abuser. You might say, "I'm worried that you're getting hurt," rather than "That jerk doesn't deserve you."

Let your friend know that she or he can always count on you for sympathy and support. That way, when your friend does feel ready to leave the relationship, she or he will be more likely to turn to you for help.

1. The purpose of this piece is
   A. to describe the consequences of abuse.
   B. to discuss ways to prevent abuse.
   C. to let teens know how to help a friend in an abusive relationship.
   D. to list sources of help for abused teens.

2. Which sentence should be added at the beginning of the second paragraph?
   A. Instead, the best approach is to listen without criticizing.
   B. The victim may deny the abuse.
   C. Abuse can destroy self-worth.
   D. Abuse is never acceptable.

3. Write a letter to a fictitious friend who is involved in an abusive relationship. Use the guidelines provided in this passage to offer sympathy and support.

National Education Standards
Math: Number and Operations, Problem Solving
Language Arts: NCTE 1, NCTE 3, NCTE 4

Standardized Test Practice Answers

Math Practice
1. A
2. A
3. D

Reading/Writing Practice
1. C
2. A
3. Letters will vary. Students should use an "I" message to express concern and let the friend know that the writer can be counted on for sympathy and support, whatever the friend decides to do.

National Education Standards

Math: Number and Operations, Problem Solving

Language Arts: NCTE 1, NCTE 3, NCTE 4

For the complete Math and Language Arts standards, visit glencoe.com.

Go Online

Online Study Tools
For more test practice, visit glencoe.com and complete the Online Quizzes for Chapter 9.

Test-Taking Tip

Topic Sentence Explain to students that some questions on standardized tests require them to either write a topic sentence or choose a topic sentence that could be used to introduce a paragraph in a reading passage. Writing or choosing a topic sentence requires a close reading of the paragraph with an eye to discovering its main idea. If the main idea is not clear after a first reading, students should read the passage again, looking for key words and concepts for writing or choosing a topic sentence.

UNIT **3** *Real-World Health*

CAREER CORNER   Social Services Careers

Social Service Careers

Group Activity

- Organize the class into three groups.

- Assign a career to each group, and have a volunteer from each group read the description of his or her assigned career.

- Have members of each group research the educational requirements for their assigned career and where employment is available.

- Encourage members of each group to interview an adult working in their assigned career. Have students submit questions to you for approval before they conduct the interviews.

- Have each group present their findings to the class.

Child Welfare Worker

Child welfare workers help children whose health and well-being are in jeopardy because the child's parents or guardians are not able to take care of them. If a parent or guardian abuses alcohol or other drugs, or abuses a child, a child welfare worker may remove a child from the family and work with the parents to solve their problems.

To help prepare for this career, you can take psychology, sociology, and communications courses in high school. To become a child welfare worker, a bachelor's or master's degree in social work and a license or certificate from your state may be required.

Family Counselor

Family counselors help families find ways to work out their problems and communicate more openly and honestly. They work with family members to overcome issues such as depression, marital problems, and parent-child conflicts. Counselors can help individuals build stronger relationships with their families.

To learn more about becoming a family counselor, take psychology and communications courses in high school. Family counselors are required to have a master's degree in counseling and a license in marriage and family therapy.

Social and Human Services Assistant

A social and human services assistant works under the direction of a social worker, nurse, psychiatrist, psychologist, or a physical therapist. They provide support by assessing a patient's needs and helping that person learn to solve problems.

Social and human services assistants need good communication skills and should demonstrate empathy and understanding. To learn more about this field, take communications, psychology, and sociology classes in high school. A college degree usually is not required, but having a background in the social services field is helpful. In some states, social and human services assistants earn a certificate or an associate's degree.

248   Unit 3   Real-World Health

Skills for the *21st* Century

Communication and Work Good communication is a vital key to success in today's world. Employers seek out individuals with strong communication skills to create a positive work environment. Developing a strong foundation in communicating with others will provide many benefits for students. Discuss with students ways that effective communication skills can enhance student-teacher relationships. Ask students to identify communication skills that they feel they are good at and skillls that might need improvement.

CAREER SPOTLIGHT

CAREER SPOTLIGHT

Health Educator

Elizabeth Jenkins decided to become a health educator when she was in high school. During a teen parenting course, she thought "I could teach this, and teach it better." After completing an internship, she was hired by a high school pregnancy prevention program.

Q. What training do you have?

A. *I completed a Georgia Campaign for Adolescent Pregnancy Prevention program. Then I became a certified nurse assistant so that I could work with school nurses. I earned an associate's degree and am finishing up my bachelor's degree in criminal justice and business administration.*

Q. What are your health goals for the teens you teach?

A. *My main goal is that the teen moms graduate from high school. I encourage these young women to* go to college. I expect all the teens in my school to further their education.

Q. Are you making an impact?

A. *I have teen mothers who have gone to college on scholarships. I know a teen who, after listening to me, left an abusive relationship. I also helped a teen rebuild a relationship with her mother.*

Health Educator

Invite a health educator (or other social worker) to class to talk with students about his or her career.

- Have pairs of students write questions for the educator to answer. After reviewing the questions, provide them to your guest speaker prior to his or her visit to class.

- Suggestions for topics for the educator to address include: How do you help teens? Why did you decide to become a health educator? What do you like best about your career?

Encourage interested students to visit **glencoe.com** for more information on this career.

Activity **Beyond the Classroom**

Writing Social Services Careers.
Visit your school counselor or someone else in the social services field. Ask that person to tell you about his or her career and other related occupations. Invite the person to describe how individuals with these careers help people. Learn what education requirements there are for these jobs. Find out what high school classes you could take now to help prepare for these careers.

Based on what you learn, create a brochure describing two or three social services careers. Include information about how teens can prepare for these careers. Share the brochure with your classmates.

Go Online

For more information, go to the Career Corner link at **glencoe.com**.

Activity **Beyond the Classroom**

Writing Keep students involved in the community and encourage parent participation by assigning the activities on this page for students to work on outside of class. You may want to have students work in groups on the brochure project so that fewer students will need to interview busy school counselors and administrators. Encourage students to be creative in describing and promoting their school's social services. Arrange to display the brochures in the school library, cafeteria, or other space where many students can read them.

Flexible Technology Solutions

Focus

Health eSpotlight Video Series

By Chapter

Chapter 10 Nutrition for Health
Video 10: It's Your Health, It's Your Choice

Chapter 11 Managing Weight and Eating Behaviors
Video 11: Food, Habits, and Choices

Chapter 12 Physical Activity and Fitness
Video 12: Balance and Fitness

By Lesson

Chapter 10 *Video 10*   For Use With

Segment 10.1 The Importance of Nutrition........................ Lesson 1
Segment 10.2 Nutrients .... Lesson 2
Segment 10.3 Healthy Food Guidelines............................ Lesson 3
Segment 10.4 Nutrition Labels and Food Safety .... Lesson 4

Chapter 11 *Video 11*   For Use With

Segment 11.1 Maintaining a Healthy Weight .... Lesson 1
Segment 11.2 Body Image and Eating Disorders .... Lesson 2
Segment 11.3 Lifelong Nutrition...................................... Lesson 3

Chapter 12 *Video 12*   For Use With

Segment 12.1 Benefits of Physical Activity .... Lesson 1
Segment 12.2 Improving Your Fitness .... Lesson 2
Segment 12.3 Planning a Personal Activity Program.......... Lesson 3
Segment 12.4 Fitness Safety and Avoiding Injuries .... Lesson 4

By Skill

Accessing Information .... Videos 2 **10** 14 25
Goal Setting .... Videos **11**
Analyzing Influences .... Videos 1 **12**

■ Indicates videos featured in the unit that teach the
corresponding skill. Other videos listed can also be used
to teach that skill.

Teach

Direct lesson plans beyond the classroom with multi-media fitness activities that students can do online, in class, or as a group.

PowerPoint® Presentation

- *Health* eSpotlight videos
- Audio and image bank

Online

Fitness Zone Online is a multi-media resource that helps students find ways to be physically active each day.

- Clipboard Energizer Activities
- Fitness Zone Videos
- Polar Heart Rate Monitor Activities
- Nutrition, Physical Activity, and Injury Prevention Tips
- Links to Nutrition and Physical Activity Resources

Go Online

Online Learning Center

- Student Web Activities
- PuzzleMaker
- Interactive Health Tutor

Podcast Audio Chapter Summaries

Use the audio Podcast Audio Chapter Summaries to teach and review key concepts, and engage students with health content that they can download to a computer or portable MP3 player.

Assess/Close

Help students master chapter and lesson concepts with an integrated technology solution for assessment and performance evaluation.

Go Online

Online Learning Center

- Interactive Study Guides
- Online Quizzes

ExamView® Assessment Suite CD-ROM

Create and customize tests in minutes with this convenient digital platform.

- Create differentiated tests quickly and easily.
- All questions correlated to National/State Standards.
- Enhance tests with Document Based Questions (DBQ) and add your own photos and graphics.
- Build tests in both English and Spanish.
- Generate progress reports.

Enrich

Use these additional digital and online media resources to promote hands-on exploration of health topics covered in the lesson.

Business Week Health Video Series

- *Is Fortified Food Healthier?*
- *The Slow Burn of Exercising*
- *Video Games Get You in Shape*

Study-to-Go

Download a portable version of eFlashcards and Self-Check Quizzes onto your Palm or Pocket PC.

Health Podcasts Activities

Glencoe's "It's Your Health" Podcast Activities provide students with a unique listening and learning experience that takes health education beyond the classroom. Download the audio files and print activities covering a range of current health topics that matter most to teens!

Nutrition and Physical Activity

This unit will teach students the importance of nutrition and physical activity for good health. They will learn how to make healthful food choices, manage their weight, and improve their fitness with physical activity.

Health *eSpotlight* Video Series

At the beginning of each chapter, visit **glencoe.com** and have students watch the video and do the accompanying print activity.

Chapter 10
It's Your Health, It's Your Choice

Achieving balance and variety in a diet helps maintain healthy eating habits.

Chapter 11
Food, Habits, and Choices

Many teens feel pressured to achieve the "perfect" body, even though this body type isn't the healthiest for everyone.

Chapter 12
Balance and Fitness

Exercise doesn't have to mean spending hours on a treadmill. Many activities teens already enjoy can improve fitness levels.

Unit 4 Resources

- Career Corner
- 📁 FAST FILE RESOURCES
- Health Career Research Activity
- Family Involvement Activity
- Community Involvement Activity
- Unit Test

250

Chapter 10
Nutrition for Health

 It's Your Health, It's Your Choice

Chapter 11
Managing Weight and Eating Behaviors

 Food, Habits, and Choices

Chapter 12
Physical Activity and Fitness

 Balance and Fitness

UNIT PROJECT

Raising Awareness

Using Visuals The American Cancer Society's mission is to "eliminate cancer as a major health problem by preventing cancer, saving lives, and diminishing suffering." The organization raises funds for research into the causes and cures of cancer, and also funds education programs that help people learn how they can reduce their risk for this disease.

Go Online To learn more about the ACS, go to the Unit Web Project at **glencoe.com**.

Get Involved. Do research to learn about organizations in your community that raise funds to fight cancer. Contact one of these organizations to find out how teens can volunteer. Share your findings with your classmates.

250

UNIT PROJECT

Raising Awareness The American Cancer Society is dedicated to providing programs aimed at reducing the risk of cancer, detecting cancer as early as possible, and ensuring proper treatment. There are many ways that students can get involved to help raise awareness. Perhaps suggest that students organize a local school fundraiser such as a 5K race. Students can also contact one of the organizations they've researched to fundraise for them as well.

Get Involved Ask a few students to learn more about The American Cancer Society and volunteering opportunities. Have them locate a local chapter in their community and learn about ways teens can volunteer. Ask them to find out who can volunteer (age) and list a contact person. Display the information in the classroom and encourage other students to read it.

"He who has health has hope; and he who has hope has everything."
—Arabian proverb

Unit 4   Nutrition and Physical Activity   **251**

Activate Prior Knowledge

Ask students these questions before they read the chapter to build on what they already know.

Chapter 10
What do you need to know in order to make wise eating decisions?

(You need to know what factors influence your food choices, as well as what nutrients you need and which foods contain them.)

Chapter 11
What factors determine the appropriate weight for an individual?

(Factors include gender, age, height, and body frame.)

Chapter 12
How can physical activity help control body weight?

(Physical activity can help control body weight by increasing the number of calories that the body burns.)

TeacherWorks Plus provides:

- interactive Teacher Wrap-around Edition
- click, drag, and drop to plan lessons
- instant access to many print program resources

How to Get Involved Provide students with these step-by-step instructions for learning about local food-relief programs and teen volunteering opportunities:

1. Go to The American Cancer Society's Web site and read about volunteering opportunities. Use the Web site's locator to find a local chapter.

2. Locate other cancer-fighting programs. Search the yellow pages under cancer.

3. Contact each local chapter and ask about opportunities for teens to volunteer. Find out if there are any requirements for volunteers that might affect teens, such as minimum age or driver's license requirements.

Chapter 10 pages 252–287	Standards		Features
	National	**State/Local**	
	1.12.1, 1.12.5, 1.12.8, 2.12.2, 2.12.10, 3.12.1, 5.12.6, 6.12.1–6.12.4		*Hands-On* **HEALTH** • What's in the Bag (*Accessing Information*), page 282
Lesson 1 **The Importance of Nutrition** pages 254–257 **BIG Idea** *Learning to make healthful food choices will keep you healthy throughout your life.*	1.12.1–1.12.3, 1.12.5, 1.12.7, 1.12.8, 2.12.2, 2.12.3, 2.12.5, 6.12.1–6.12.4, 7.12.1–7.12.3, 8.12.3		*Health Skills* **Activity** • Food Choices (*Analyzing Influences*), page 257 ⏱ Out of Time
Lesson 2 **Nutrients** pages 258–265 **BIG Idea** *Each nutrient in your diet plays a unique and essential role in keeping you healthy.*	1.12.1, 1.12.2, 1.12.3, 1.12.5, 1.12.7, 3.12.1, 3.12.2, 6.12.1–6.12.4, 7.12.1, 7.12.2, 7.12.3		VIDEO **BusinessWeek** **HEALTH NEWS** • Is Fortified Food Healthier?, page 260
Lesson 3 **Healthy Food Guidelines** pages 266–273 **BIG Idea** *MyPyramid is a tool that can help you choose healthful foods for all your meals and snacks.*	2.12.10, 3.12.2, 3.12.5, 5.12.4, 6.12.2, 6.12.3, 7.12.1, 7.12.2, 7.12.3		*Real World* **CONNECTION** • Evaluate Your Eating Habits, page 270 ⏱ Out of Time
Lesson 4 **Nutrition Labels and Food Safety** pages 274–281 **BIG Idea** *By reading food labels and handling foods safely, you can avoid many food-related health problems.*	1.12.1, 1.12.2, 1.12.5, 1.12.7, 4.12.1, 7.12.1, 7.12.2, 7.12.3, 8.12.1, 8.12.3		

Each lesson marked "30 Min" in the left margin.

Key to Ability Levels **Teaching Strategies and activities have been coded for ability level and appropriateness.**

AL Activities for students working above grade level   BL Activities for students working below grade level

OL Activities for students working on grade level   EL Activities for English Learners

Chapter 10 Planning Guide

Glencoe Exclusive!
TeacherWorks Plus
All-In-One Planner and Resource Center

Resources	Lesson Assessment	Technology
Student Activity Workbook `TEACH` ***FAST FILE* RESOURCES** Vocabulary Practice `TEACH` Health Labs `EXTEND`	Chapter 10 Review Chapter 10 Assessment Standardized Test Practice *ExamView® Assessment Suite* CD-ROM	**Teaching Tools:** *TeacherWorks™* Plus DVD *StudentWorks™* Plus DVD *ExamView® Assessment Suite* CD-ROM Transparency Fitness DVD PowerPoint® DVD Health eSpotlight Video Series DVD
***FAST FILE* RESOURCES** Reading Strategies Activity `TEACH` Reteaching Activity `REVIEW` Enrichment Activity `EXTEND` Health Skills Practice `TEACH`	Lesson 1 Assessment, page 257 Lesson 1 Quiz *Fast File* *ExamView® Assessment Suite* CD-ROM	**Web-Based Resources:** glencoe.com • Health Podcast Activities • Audio Chapter Summaries (English/Spanish)
***FAST FILE* RESOURCES** Reading Strategies Activity `TEACH` Reteaching Activity `REVIEW` Enrichment Activity `EXTEND` Health Skills Practice `TEACH`	Lesson 2 Assessment, page 265 Lesson 2 Quiz *Fast File* *ExamView® Assessment Suite* CD-ROM	• Interactive Health Tutor • Health Skills Activities • Vocabulary PuzzleMaker • Parent Letters (English/Spanish)
***FAST FILE* RESOURCES** Reading Strategies Activity `TEACH` Reteaching Activity `REVIEW` Enrichment Activity `EXTEND` Health Skills Practice `TEACH`	Lesson 3 Assessment, page 273 Lesson 3 Quiz *Fast File* *ExamView® Assessment Suite* CD-ROM	• Lesson Plans • Health Inventories • Online Quizzes • Study-to-Go • Unit Web Projects
***FAST FILE* RESOURCES** Reading Strategies Activity `TEACH` Reteaching Activity `REVIEW` Enrichment Activity `EXTEND` Health Skills Practice `TEACH`	Lesson 4 Assessment, page 281 Lesson 4 Quiz *Fast File* *ExamView® Assessment Suite* CD-ROM	• Student Web Activities • Fitness Zone Activities

StudentWorks Plus

This is the student's backpack solution.

Includes:
- complete Interactive Student Edition
- full audio of English text and Spanish chapter summaries
- allows students to record assignments and track grades.
- links to online activities and additional student resources
- access to all student worksheets and workbooks

GLENCOE HEALTH
StudentWorks Plus

FOLDABLES®
Study Organizer

Dinah Zike Foldables®
Chapter Activity
Refer to the *Dinah Zike Reading and Study Skills for Glencoe Health.* Ask students to make a three-tab book Foldable. As students read the lesson, have them write information under the appropriate tab about how hunger and appetite, emotions, and environment influence their own food choices.

Key to Symbols

Transparencies	`REVIEW` activities to review or reinforce content
CD-ROM	`TEACH` activities to teach basic concepts
glencoe.com	`EXTEND` activities to extend or enrich lesson content
Print Resources	

Nutrition for Health

Chapter Overview

Chapter 10 focuses on the role of nutrition in health. It explains how to make healthful food choices and how to handle foods safely.

Lesson 1

Choosing the right foods is important for lifelong good health. To make healthful food choices, people need to understand the many influences on food choices.

Lesson 2

The body needs six types of nutrients for good health: carbohydrates, proteins, fats, vitamins, minerals, and water. Each type of nutrient has a specific job in the body.

Lesson 3

MyPyramid can help individuals make informed food choices. Guidelines for healthful eating and physical activity include making smart choices from every food group, balancing food and activity, and getting the most nutrition out from the calories you consume.

Lesson 4

Knowing how to read nutrition labels on food packages can help you choose foods wisely. Handling food carefully can help prevent foodborne illnesses.

▶ **Activating Prior Knowledge**

Call on a few volunteers to read their paragraphs to the class. **Ask Students:** *Why are foods such as these good for your health?*

Lesson 1

The Importance of Nutrition

BIG Idea *Learning to make healthful food choices will keep you healthy throughout your life.*

Lesson 2

Nutrients

BIG Idea *Each nutrient in your diet plays a unique and essential role in keeping you healthy.*

Lesson 3

Healthy Food Guidelines

BIG Idea *MyPyramid is a tool that can help you choose healthful foods for all your meals and snacks.*

Lesson 4

Nutrition Labels and Food Safety

BIG Idea *By reading food labels and handling foods safely, you can avoid many food-related health problems.*

Activating Prior Knowledge

Using Visuals Take a look at the photo on this page. How are these teens practicing healthful behaviors? Explain your thoughts in a short paragraph.

252

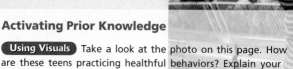

Universal Access

Differentiated Learning Glencoe provides teacher support and student materials for all learners in the health classroom.

- Chapter Summaries in English and Spanish are available online at **glencoe.com**.

- *Fast Files* and related worksheets support reluctant readers.

- Universal Access strategies throughout the Teacher Wraparound Edition and *Fast Files* help you present materials for gifted students, at-risk students, physically impaired students, and those with behavior disorders or learning disabilities.

Chapter Launchers

Health in Action

Discuss the **BIG** Ideas

Before beginning this chapter, think about how you would answer these questions:

▶ What influences your food choices?

▶ Are your eating habits healthful? Why or why not?

Watch the *Health eSpotlight* Video Series

It's Your Health, It's Your Choice

What types of food would you include in a healthy menu to achieve balance and variety?

Assess Your Health

Go Online

Visit **glencoe.com** and complete the Health Inventory for Chapter 10.

Chapter 10 Nutrition for Health **253**

Chapter Launchers

Health in Action

Discuss the **BIG** Ideas

Assign this activity before students read the chapter. Point out that the questions will help them apply what they learn in the chapter to their own food choices and eating habits. Tell students they can keep their answers private.

Health eSpotlight Video Series

It's Your Health, It's Your Choice

Before Viewing the Video

Ask Students: *What kinds of healthful foods do you try and incorporate in your daily diet?* (Answers will vary. Try to give healthful suggestions if students answer with unhealthy choices.)

Go Online

Have students go to **glencoe.com** and take the Health Inventory for Chapter 10.

Chapter Skills

Reading Skills
- Reviewing Facts and Vocabulary, pp. 257, 265, 273, 281
- Reading/Writing Practice, p. 287

Vocabulary
- New Vocabulary, pp. 254, 258, 266, 274
- Reviewing Facts and Vocabulary, pp. 257, 265, 273, 281

BIG Idea

Making nutritious food choices and handling food safely will help keep a person healthy throughout life.

Health Skills
- Health Skills Activity, p. 257
- Applying Health Skills, pp. 257, 265, 273, 281

Writing Skills
- Real World Connection, p. 270
- Writing Critically, pp. 257, 265, 273, 281
- Reading/Writing Practice, p. 287

LESSON **1**

The Importance of Nutrition

1 FOCUS

GUIDE TO READING

BIG Idea Choosing healthful foods is important for lifelong health. **Ask Students:** *How does a person make healthful food choices?* (Answers will vary but may include learning about nutrition.)

Before You Read

K-W-L Chart Students' charts will vary. Sample answer: Know—Nutrition involves the foods you eat; Want to Know—Why the body needs food; Learned: The body needs food for growth, repair, and energy.

Main Idea

Why Nutrition Matters Your choice of foods influences your health and quality of life. **Ask Students:** *How can the foods you choose affect your health?* (Sample answer: If you choose mostly high-fat foods, you might gain weight.)

Real Life Issues

Have students read the scenario. **Ask Students:** *What are some healthful foods that are easy to prepare?* List their ideas on the board, and advise students to consider them for their dialogues.

LESSON **1**

GUIDE TO READING

BIG Idea *Learning to make healthful food choices will keep you healthy throughout your life.*

Before You Read

Create a K-W-L Chart. Make a three-column chart. In the first column, list what you **k**now about nutrition. In the second column, list what you **w**ant to know about this topic. As you read, use the third column to summarize what you **l**earned.

K	W	L

New Vocabulary
▶ nutrition (p. 254)
▶ nutrients (p. 254)
▶ calorie (p. 254)
▶ hunger (p. 255)
▶ appetite (p. 255)

The Importance of Nutrition

Real Life Issues

Making Food Choices. Marcus usually eats dinner with his parents, but sometimes they have to work late. When Marcus is on his own, he often just microwaves a frozen meal. He wishes he knew more about how to fix healthful and satisfying meals for himself.

Writing *Write a dialogue between Marcus and his parents in which he explains his wish for healthful dinners. In the dialogue, Marcus and his parents should come up with ideas for how he can make tasty, healthful meals on his own.*

Why Nutrition Matters

Main Idea The food you eat affects your health and quality of life.

Most people know what foods they like. They may not, however, understand how the body uses food. The food you eat plays a significant role in your total health. What do you think about when you are deciding what to eat? To make healthful food choices, you must first learn about **nutrition**, *the process by which your body takes in and uses food*.

Your body relies on food to provide it with **nutrients**, *substances in food that your body needs to grow, to repair itself, and to supply you with energy*. The energy your body receives from food is measured in calories. A **calorie** is *a unit of heat used to measure the energy your body uses and the energy it receives from food*. The calories in the food you eat provide the energy your body needs for activities such as walking, doing chores, and playing sports.

254 Chapter 10 Nutrition for Health

Home and Community

Eating to Reduce Health Risks As a voluntary project, have students ask a parent or guardian about any health problems that run in their family. They should ask specifically about any conditions related to diet, such as type 2 diabetes, cardiovascular disease, cancer, and osteoporosis. To be relevant, the conditions must occur in fairly close biological relatives, such as parents, grandparents, aunts, or uncles. Suggest that students discuss with family members how eating a variety of healthful foods lifelong can help lower their risk of developing the conditions.

Health Skills Activity

Analyzing Influences

Food Choices

Alex couldn't wait to get home from school the day his brother, Jeff, came home from college. When Alex got home, his brother's car was already parked in front of the house. They talked about school for a couple of minutes before Alex said, "Jeff, Mom said you get to pick what we have for dinner. Should we order a pizza?"

Jeff patted his stomach. "No pizza for me. I've already gained the 'freshman 15,'" referring to the weight gain that many college freshmen experience.

Jeff said that his schedule was different from when he was in high school, and he was finding it hard to start a new routine. His friends often encouraged him to eat even when he wasn't hungry. Alex wonders how Jeff can manage his diet.

Writing Pretend you are Jeff and use the following steps to create a plan analyzing the influences on your diet.

1. Keep a food diary for a week, noting what you eat, when you eat, and what influences your choices.
2. Analyze whether you're eating because of hunger or another reason.
3. Create a healthy eating plan that you can follow.

LESSON 1 ASSESSMENT

After You Read

Reviewing Facts and Vocabulary

1. Name three health problems that good nutrition can help you avoid.
2. What is the difference between *hunger* and *appetite*?
3. Identify two emotions that influence eating when someone isn't hungry.

Thinking Critically

4. **Analyze.** Explain how advertising can influence your food choices.
5. **Evaluate.** Emily can't resist homemade chocolate-chip cookies. What is influencing her behavior? Is this influence healthy?

Applying Health Skills

6. **Stress Management.** Eating when you're not hungry can be a response to stress. List three healthier ways to respond to stress.

Writing Critically

7. **Descriptive.** Write an essay describing two ways in which your family or friends influence your food choices.

Go Online

Visit glencoe.com and complete the Interactive Study Guide for this lesson.

Lesson 1   The Importance of Nutrition   **257**

 ASSESS/ CLOSE

Assessment Resources

 FAST FILE ACTIVITIES
Lesson 1 Quiz

ExamView Assessment Suite CD-ROM

Visit glencoe.com for:
Online Quizzes
Online Learning Center

Progress Monitoring

Reteaching

Have students write a paragraph in which they correctly use all the lesson vocabulary terms. Ask students to exchange paragraphs with a partner and check each other's work.

Enrichment

Ask students to write a short story in which the characters' food choices are influenced by a variety of both internal and external factors. Call on volunteers to read their stories to the class. Ask the rest of the class to identify which factors are involved and evaluate how the factors influence the characters' health.

Go Online

Have students visit **glencoe.com** and complete the Interactive Study Guide for this lesson.

LESSON 1 ASSESSMENT ANSWERS

1. *Any three:* unhealthful weight gain, type 2 diabetes, cardiovascular disease, stroke, certain cancers, osteoporosis
2. *Hunger* is the physical drive to eat when the body needs food. *Appetite* is the psychological desire for food, not based on physical need.
3. Any two emotions, such as those mentioned in the text (e.g., stress, loneliness, boredom)

4. Answers will vary.
5. Emily's eating is being influenced by appetite. It is not healthy because her body does not need the food and eating too much could lead to unhealthful weight gain.
6. Answers will vary.
7. Essays will vary.

Nutrients

① FOCUS

GUIDE TO READING

BIG Idea Each nutrient plays a special role in your body. **Ask Students:** *What are nutrients?* (Substances in food that your body needs)

Before You Read

Cluster Chart Suggest that students draw six circles and use one circle for each type of nutrient.

Main Idea

Giving Your Body What It Needs Each of the six types of nutrients plays a vital role in keeping a person healthy. **Ask Students:** *What is one type of nutrient, and how does it keep you healthy?* (Sample answer: Protein; it keeps you healthy by building strong muscles.)

Real Life Issues

Have students read the scenario. **Ask Students:** *What conflicting advice have you heard about what to eat?* (Sample answer: I heard that you should avoid eating high-fat foods, and I also heard that you should eat oily fish at least twice a week.) Before students write their journal entries, lead them in brainstorming reliable sources of health information.

LESSON 2

GUIDE TO READING

BIG Idea Each nutrient in your diet plays a unique and essential role in keeping you healthy.

Before You Read

Create a Cluster Chart. Draw a circle and label it "Nutrients." Draw circles around it and use these to define and describe this term. As you read, continue filling in the chart with more details.

New Vocabulary

▸ carbohydrates (p. 259)
▸ fiber (p. 259)
▸ proteins (p. 260)
▸ cholesterol (p. 262)
▸ vitamins (p. 262)
▸ minerals (p. 262)
▸ osteoporosis (p. 264)

Nutrients

Real Life Issues

Too Much (Nutrition) Information. Lately, Judy has been getting a lot of advice on what to eat—and all of it is different. First her friend Heather told her you need lots of carbohydrates and little fat. Judy's friend, Rob, said eating certain combinations of foods is a good idea. Then Judy read a magazine article stating that eating too many carbohydrates will cause weight gain. Judy is confused by all the information. She's beginning to feel she should just eat whatever she likes.

Writing *Write a journal entry from Judy's point of view. Have her describe how she will figure out whether the health information she's getting is valid or not.*

Giving Your Body What It Needs

Main Idea Each of the six nutrients has a specific job or vital function to keep you healthy.

Everything you eat contains nutrients. Nutrients perform specific roles in maintaining your body functions. Your body uses nutrients in many ways:

• As an energy source
• To heal, and build and repair tissue
• To sustain growth
• To help transport oxygen to cells
• To regulate body functions

There are six types of nutrients. Three of these types—carbohydrates, proteins, and fats—provide energy. The other three—vitamins, minerals, and water—perform a variety of other functions. Getting a proper balance of nutrients during the teen years can improve your health through adulthood.

More About...

Glucose Storage Excess glucose in the blood is converted to a compound called glycogen by the liver. Each molecule of glycogen consists of many glucose molecules joined together in a complex structure. Most of the glycogen is stored in the liver, but some is stored in skeletal muscles. When the blood glucose level falls, the liver breaks down its stored glycogen. Glucose is released back into the blood and carried to cells throughout the body. These two processes—the synthesis and breakdown of glycogen—work together to keep the level of glucose in the blood relatively constant, giving body cells a steady supply of energy.

Nutrients That Provide Energy

Main Idea Carbohydrates, proteins, and fats provide your body with energy and help maintain your body.

The energy in food comes from three sources: carbohydrates, proteins, and fats. Each gram of carbohydrate or protein provides four calories of energy, while each gram of fat provides nine calories. The body uses these nutrients to build, repair, and fuel itself.

Carbohydrates

R

Carbohydrates are *starches and sugars found in foods, which provide your body's main source of energy.* Most nutrition experts recommend getting 45 to 65 percent of your daily calories from carbohydrates.

C

Types of Carbohydrates There are three types of carbohydrates: simple, complex, and fiber. Simple carbohydrates are sugars, such as fructose (found in fruits) and lactose (found in milk). Sugars occur naturally in fruits, dairy products, honey, and maple syrup. They are also added to many processed foods, such as cold cereals, bread, and bakery products.

Complex carbohydrates, or starches, are long chains of sugars linked together. Common sources include grains, grain products such as bread and pasta, beans, and root vegetables such as potatoes.

The last type of carbohydrate is **fiber**, *a tough complex carbohydrate that the body cannot digest.* Fiber moves waste through your digestive system. Eating foods high in fiber can help you feel full, and may reduce the risk of cancer, heart disease and type 2 diabetes. Experts recommend eating 20 to 35 grams of fiber per day. Good sources of fiber include fruits and vegetables, whole grains, and products made from whole grains, nuts, seeds, and legumes.

Go Online

))) Listen to the Health Podcast Activity *Nutrition* at glencoe.com.

■ **Figure 10.3** These foods are good sources of carbohydrates. *How does your body use carbohydrates?*

---

② TEACH

Main Idea

Nutrients That Provide Energy
Three types of nutrients provide the body with energy: carbohydrates, proteins, and fats. **Ask Students:** *Why does your body need energy?* (For growth, repair, and activity)

R **Reading Strategy**

Organizing Details On the board, start a table entitled *Carbohydrates*, with three columns headed *Sugars, Starches,* and *Fiber,* and three rows labeled *Description, Sources,* and *Roles.* Call on volunteers to fill in the table with relevant details. **BL**

C **Critical Thinking**

Evaluating Tell students that low-carbohydrate weight-loss diets have been popular in recent years. **Ask Students:** *Do you think low-carbohydrate diets are healthful? Why or why not?* (Answers will vary. A moderate eating plan is always healthful.) **OL**

Caption Answer

Figure 10.3 For energy and to help move waste through your digestive system

Go Online

))) Remind students to visit glencoe.com and listen to the Health Podcast Activity, *Nutrition.*

ELL Support

Defining Main Idea Terms The first two Main Ideas in the lesson contain important terms that may be unfamiliar to some students: *vital, function, perform,* and *maintain.* Write these terms on the board and define them, using simple, straightforward definitions, such as "needed" for *vital,* "job" for *function,* "do" for *perform,* and "keep up" for *maintain.*

Beginning Have students repeat the words and their definitions.

Intermediate Repeat the words and ask students to give their definitions.

Advanced Ask students to use each word in a sentence.

259

After students have watched the video, *Is Fortified Food Healthier?,* divide the class into small groups. Have them decide whether fortified foods are helpful when trying to eat a healthy diet. Have students write a paragraph supporting their choice. Make sure students' paragraphs include specific examples.

U Universal Access

Using Visuals Have students find pictures of high-protein foods in old magazines or from the Internet and use them to make posters showing foods that are good sources of protein. Part of the poster should show complete-protein foods, such as meat, eggs, and dairy products. The other part should show incomplete-protein foods, such as whole grains, nuts, and legumes. Display the posters in the classroom. **EL**

W Writing Support

Writing About Analogies Have each student select one of the roles of proteins and write a paragraph describing an analogy that helps explain this role. For example, they might write about bricks in a building as an analogy for the role of proteins as the building material of cells. Call on volunteers to read their paragraphs to the class. **AL**

Caption Answer

Figure 10.4 Meat, eggs, and milk

Is Fortified Food Healthier?
Analyze. Go to glencoe.com and watch the video *Is Fortified Food Healthier?* With a small group, decide whether you think fortified foods are helpful in eating a healthy diet and write a paragraph supporting your choice. Include examples to support your decisions.

■ **Figure 10.4** All these foods are good sources of protein. *Which of these foods provide complete proteins?*

The Role of Carbohydrates Your body uses carbohydrates by breaking them down into their simplest forms. Most of the carbohydrates you consume are turned into a simple sugar called glucose, which is the main source of fuel for the body's tissues. Glucose can be stored in your body's tissue and used later during periods of intense activity.

Benefits of Fiber Although the body cannot digest fiber, it still plays an important role by aiding digestion and reducing the risk of disease. Experts recommend eating 26 grams of total fiber daily for teen girls ages 14 to 18 years, and 38 grams daily for boys the same age.

Proteins

Proteins are *nutrients the body uses to build and maintain its cells and tissues.* They are made up of chemicals called amino acids.

Types of Proteins Your body uses about 20 amino acids that are found in foods. You produce, or synthesize, all but nine of the amino acids. These nine are called essential amino acids because the body must get them from food. The rest are known as nonessential amino acids.

Other proteins are from animal sources—such as meat, eggs, and dairy products—and from soy. They are sometimes called "complete" proteins because they contain all nine essential amino acids. Proteins from plant sources are usually missing one or more of the essential amino acids. However, you can get all the essential amino acids by eating a variety of plant-based foods that are rich in protein. Examples of these foods are grains, nuts, seeds, and legumes.

The Role of Proteins Protein is the basic building material of all your body cells. Muscles, bones, skin, and internal organs are all constructed of protein. Protein helps your body grow during childhood and adolescence. Throughout your life, protein will maintain muscles, ligaments, tendons, and all body cells.

Proteins also do a variety of other jobs in the body. For example, the protein hemoglobin in your red blood cells carries oxygen to all your body cells. Proteins may also function as hormones, chemicals that regulate the activities of your various body systems. Although protein does not supply energy to your body as quickly or easily as carbohydrates do, it can be used as an energy source.

Teen boys ages 14 to 18 should consume about 52 grams of protein per day, and teen girls ages 14 to 18 need 46 grams per day. Between 10 and 15 percent of your total daily calories should come from protein.

Myths & Reality

The Truth About Fats

Myth: All fats are bad for your health.

Fact: Saturated fats and trans fats are bad for your health, but unsaturated fats are essential to the diet because the body cannot make them and needs them for vital functions.

Myth: Eating too much fat causes weight gain.

Fact: Eating too many calories causes weight gain, regardless of whether the excess calories come from fats or other nutrients.

Myth: The best way to lose weight is to cut out fats.

Fact: Although fats have more calories per gram than other nutrients, they are more satisfying and keep you full longer, so eating some fats may actually help you eat less.

Fats

Most of what you hear about fats is how to avoid them. Does this mean you shouldn't eat any fat at all? No. Your body needs a certain amount of fat to function properly. You can, however, choose healthier fats.

Types of Fats Dietary fats are composed of fatty acids, which are classified as either unsaturated or saturated. Fatty acids that the body needs but cannot produce on its own are called essential fatty acids. The fat in all foods is a combination of unsaturated and saturated fats:

- **Unsaturated fats.** Vegetable oils, nuts, and seeds tend to contain larger amounts of unsaturated fats. Eating unsaturated fats in moderate amounts may lower your risk of heart disease.

- **Saturated fats.** Saturated fat is found mostly in animal-based foods such as meat and many dairy products. A few plant oils (palm, coconut, and palm kernel) also contain a lot of saturated fats. Consuming too many saturated fats may increase your risk of heart disease.

- **Trans fats.** These fats are formed by a process called hydrogenation, which causes vegetable oil to harden. As it hardens, the fats become more saturated. Trans fats can be found in stick margarine, many snack foods, and packaged baked goods, such as cookies and crackers. Trans fats can raise your total blood cholesterol level, which increases your risk for heart disease. As a result of the risk of trans fats, the USDA now requires that the amount of trans fats be listed on the nutrition label. Some cities have passed laws limiting or eliminating the use of trans fats in foods prepared in restaurants.

Health Issues of Fats Your body needs a certain amount of fat to carry out its basic functions, however, consuming too much fat can be harmful. Because fatty foods are generally high in calories, consuming a lot of them can lead to unhealthful weight gain and obesity.

The Role of Fats Fats provide a concentrated form of energy. The essential fatty acids are also important to brain development, blood clotting, and controlling inflammation. They also help maintain healthy skin and hair. Fats also absorb and transport fat-soluble vitamins (A, D, E, and K) through the bloodstream.

■ **Figure 10.5** Olive oil is a good source of healthful, unsaturated fat. *Why are unsaturated fats better for your health than saturated fats?*

U Universal Access

Reinforcing Facts Have students write questions about fats on the front of index cards and the answers on the back. Show them how to form questions by selecting and rephrasing topic sentences and other important statements in the lesson. Then ask students to choose partners and quiz each other with their cards. **BL**

R Reading Strategy

Using Graphic Organizers Work with students to create a graphic organizer, such as a spider diagram, to organize and summarize the information on types of fats. The graphic organizer might show the types of fats, their risks or benefits, and the foods in which they are found. **BL**

Caption Answer

Figure 10.5 Unsaturated fats are better for health because they may help decrease the risk of heart disease; saturated fats may increase the risk of heart disease.

Reading Strategy

Visualizing What You Read Some students can better understand and remember information when they visualize what they are reading about. Have students create visuals, such as simple sketches with labels, to summarize what they learn when they read about proteins. For example, students might sketch and label a chain-like structure to show that proteins are made up of linked amino acids. They might draw pictures of foods, such as meat, eggs, and nuts, to show that these foods are good sources of proteins. Have students explain to partners what their visuals mean. If students have trouble remembering details, they should review the relevant information in the text.

LESSON 2

HS Health Skills Practice

Advocacy Have students find a food product, such as margarine, that contains trans fats. Then have them write a letter to the company that makes the product, urging the company to stop using trans fats in its product. Students' letters should describe the negative health effects of trans fats and be persuasive. Check students' letters for accuracy and tone before they mail them. **OL**

Main Idea

Other Types of Nutrients
Vitamins, minerals, and water do not provide energy but perform many important body functions.
Ask Students: *What is one vitamin and one mineral, and what are their roles in the body?* (Sample answer: Vitamin C helps prevent colds; calcium helps build strong bones.)

FITNESSZONE

This activity links actual movement with the material learned in the lesson.

- Have students find a partner.
- One person recaps 5 important pieces of information from the lesson.
- Their partner must make up an action that goes along with each piece.
- For example: Carbohydrates = energy. Student can run in place.

READING CHECK

Cause and Effect
What are the benefits of choosing snacks labeled "no trans fat"?

FITNESSZONE

My doctor says that a lot of teens don't get the nutrients they need because of poor eating habits. Teenagers tend to eat foods high in fat, like fast foods. We need to eat foods like fruits, vegetables, and low-fat dairy products. Now I try to eat the right amount of fruits and veggies every day. For more fitness tips, visit the Online Fitness Zone at glencoe.com.

The calories from fats that your body does not use are stored as body fat. Stored fat, known as adipose tissue, provides insulation for the body. However, carrying too much body fat increases the risk of health problems, such as type 2 diabetes and cardiovascular disease.

In addition, consuming saturated fats can increase the levels of **cholesterol**—*a waxy, fatlike substance*—in your blood. Cholesterol is needed to create cell walls, certain hormones, and vitamin D. However, excess cholesterol in your blood can build up on the insides of the arteries. This raises your risk of heart disease. Trans fats behave like saturated fats and promote cholesterol buildup in your arteries.

Nutrition experts recommend that teens consume less than 25 to 35 percent of their calories from fats because of the health risks associated with fats. Choose healthful unsaturated fats and limit your intake of saturated fats, including trans fats, to less than 10 percent of your total calories.

Other Types of Nutrients

Main Idea Vitamins, minerals, and water do not provide energy, but perform a wide variety of body functions.

Some nutrients do not supply calories but are still necessary for carrying out various body functions. These include vitamins, minerals, and water. Each vitamin and mineral performs a different function in the body.

Vitamins

Vitamins are *compounds found in food that help regulate many body processes*. There are several different vitamins that perform different functions in the body. (See **Figure 10.6** on page 263.)

Vitamin C, folic acid, and the B vitamins are water soluble, meaning they dissolve in water and pass easily into the bloodstream during digestion. The body doesn't store these vitamins; any unused amounts are removed by the kidneys. The fat-soluble vitamins (A, D, E, and K), by contrast, are stored in body fat for later use. If consumed in large amounts, these vitamins can build up in the body to the point where they become harmful.

Minerals

Minerals are *elements found in food that are used by the body*. Because your body cannot produce minerals, it must get them from food. **Figure 10.7** on page 264 lists some of the minerals your body needs and how it uses them.

Teens Want to Know

Do Teens Need Vitamin Supplements?
Teens who regularly choose a variety of healthful foods generally do not need vitamin supplements. Some teens who consistently make poor food choices may benefit from supplements. They should check with their doctor first, however. Ingesting too much of some vitamins can be harmful. Even water-soluble vitamins, such as vitamin C, may cause health problems when taken in excess. Some vitamins also interact with medications. For example, the oral acne drug isotretinoin is a derivative of vitamin A. Taking vitamin A supplements while taking isotretinoin can lead to harmful levels of vitamin A building up in the body.

Figure 10.6 Vitamins

R

Vitamins in yellow boxes are fat soluble. Those in blue boxes are water soluble.

Vitamin/Amount Needed Per Day by Teens Ages 14 to 18	Role in Body	Food Sources
Fat-Soluble Vitamins		
A Teen female: 700 mcg Teen male: 900 mcg	needed for night vision; stimulates production of white blood cells; regulates cell growth and division; helps repair bones and tissues; aids immunity; maintains healthy skin and mucous membranes	carrots, sweet potatoes, tomatoes, fortified cereals, leafy green vegetables, fish, liver, fortified dairy products, egg yolks
D (calciferol) Teen female: 5 mcg Teen male: 5 mcg	helps body use calcium and phosphorus (needed for building bones); aids immune function; helps regulate cell growth	fortified cereals and dairy products, fatty fish such as salmon and tuna **Note:** Your skin naturally produces vitamin D when exposed to sunlight.
E Teen female: 15 mg Teen male: 15 mg	protects cells from damage; aids blood flow; helps repair body tissues	fish, milk, egg yolks, vegetable oils, fruits, nuts, peas, beans, broccoli, spinach, fortified cereals
K Teen female: 75 mcg Teen male: 75 mcg	essential for blood clotting, aids bone formation	green leafy vegetables, vegetable oils, cheese, broccoli, tomatoes
Water-Soluble Vitamins		
B_1 (thiamine) Teen female: 1.0 mg Teen male: 1.2 mg	helps the body use carbohydrates for energy; promotes health of nervous system	enriched and whole-grain cereal products, lean pork, liver
B_2 (riboflavin) Teen female: 1.0 mg Teen male: 1.3 mg	helps the body process carbohydrates, proteins, and fats; helps maintain healthy skin	lean beef, pork, organ meats, legumes, eggs, cheese, milk, nuts, enriched grain products
B_3 (niacin) Teen female: 14 mg Teen male: 16 mg	helps body process proteins and fats; maintains health of skin, nervous system, and digestive system	liver, poultry, fish, beef, peanuts, beans, enriched grain products
B_6 Teen female: 1.2 mg Teen male: 1.3 mg	helps body use proteins and fats; supports immune and nervous systems; helps blood carry oxygen to body tissues; helps break down copper and iron; prevents one type of anemia; helps maintain normal blood sugar levels	organ meats, pork, beef, poultry, fish, eggs, peanuts, bananas, carrots, fortified cereals, whole grains
B_{12} (cobalamin) Teen female: 2.4 mcg Teen male: 2.4 mcg	maintains healthy nerve cells and red blood cells; needed for formation of genetic material in cells; prevents one type of anemia	liver, fish, poultry, clams, sardines, flounder, herring, eggs, milk, other dairy foods, fortified cereals
C (ascorbic acid) Teen female: 65 mg Teen male: 75 mg	protects against infection; promotes healthy bones, teeth, gums, and blood vessels; helps form connective tissue; helps heal wounds	citrus fruits and juices, berries, peppers, tomatoes, broccoli, spinach, potatoes
Folic acid (folate) Teen female: 400 mcg Teen male: 400 mcg	helps body form and maintain new cells; reduces risk of birth defects	dark green leafy vegetables, dry beans and peas, oranges, fortified cereals and other grain products

C

AL

R Reading Strategy

Using Visuals Ask students which three vitamins listed in **Figure 10.6** help maintain healthy skin. (vitamins A, B_2, and B_3) Ask which vitamin listed in the figure is needed for blood clotting. (vitamin K) **BL**

C Critical Thinking

Inferring Call students' attention to the recommended amounts of vitamins for teen boys and girls in **Figure 10.6**. Ask students why teen boys need larger amounts of most vitamins than teen girls. (Sample answer: Because teen boys are typically bigger than teen girls) **BL**

AL Active Learning

Evaluating Vitamin Supplements Bring in two or three different kinds of vitamin supplements. Divide the class into small groups. Ask each group to compare the amounts of vitamins provided by the different vitamin supplements with the amounts needed by teens, as shown in **Figure 10.6**. Give groups a chance to share and discuss their findings. Ask students to find out whether there are any vitamin supplements formulated specifically for teens. **OL**

Writing Strategy

Expository Writing Tell students to assume that they have a younger friend or relative who eats a high-fat diet. Ask them to write a letter to the hypothetical young person, in which they explain the health risks associated with fats. In their letters, students should provide simple descriptions of the different types of fats and straightforward explanations of how they affect health. For the clearest expository writing, advise students to avoid the use of passive voice, overly long or complex sentences, and scientific terminology.

LESSON 2

CA Cultural Awareness

Nondairy Mineral Sources
Point out that dairy products are excellent sources of three of the four minerals listed in **Figure 10.7**. Then explain that people in many cultures do not normally eat dairy products. **Ask Students:** *What other foods can they eat to get the minerals they need?* (Students may identify any of the nondairy food sources listed in the third column of the figure.)
EL **OL**

HS Health Skills Practice

Accessing Information Tell students that the minerals listed in **Figure 10.7** are not the only minerals needed by the body. Have students locate at least two reliable sources of nutrition information. Then have them use the sources to find what other minerals are needed by the body and the roles they play. (Sample answers: Zinc, essential for growth; iodine, needed for a healthy thyroid gland) **AL**

Academic Vocabulary

Reaction Point out the word reaction in the text on this page. Explain that in this context ("chemical reaction") the word has a somewhat different meaning than the one given in the margin of the text. A chemical reaction is the change that occurs when chemicals interact. Call on students to use the word in sentences that demonstrate the different meanings.

READING CHECK

Explain What is the difference between water- and fat-soluble vitamins?

Academic Vocabulary

reaction *(noun):* a response to a stimulus or influence

One mineral that is especially important to your health is calcium. Calcium promotes bone health. Eating calcium-rich foods helps reduce your risk of developing **osteoporosis**, *a condition in which the bones become fragile and break easily.* Osteoporosis is most common in women over the age of 50. You can take action now to prevent the likelihood that you will develop osteoporosis when you're older. Bone mass builds up most rapidly between the ages of ten and 20, reaching its peak around age 30. Eating plenty of calcium-rich foods as a teen can protect your health years down the road.

CA

Water

Water is essential for most body functions. All of the body cells contain water. Water's functions include

- moving food through the digestive system.
- digesting carbohydrates and protein, and aiding other chemical **reactions** in the body.
- transporting nutrients and removing wastes.
- storing and releasing heat.
- cooling the body through perspiration.
- cushioning the eyes, brain, and spinal cord.
- lubricating the joints.

Figure 10.7 **Minerals**

Mineral/Amount Needed Per Day by Teens Ages 14 to 18	Role in Body	Food Sources
Calcium Teen female: 1,300 mg Teen male: 1,300 mg	forms bones and teeth; aids blood clotting; assists muscle and nerve function; reduces risk of osteoporosis	dairy products, calcium-fortified juice, calcium-fortified soy milk and tofu, corn tortillas, Chinese cabbage, broccoli, kale
Phosphorus Teen female: 1,250 mg Teen male: 1,250 mg	produces energy; maintains healthy bones	dairy products, peas, meat, eggs, some cereals and breads
Magnesium Teen female: 360 mg Teen male: 410 mg	maintains normal muscle and nerve function; sustains regular heartbeat; aids in bone growth and energy production	meat, milk, green leafy vegetables, whole grains, nuts
Iron Teen female: 15 mg Teen male: 11 mg	part of a compound in the red blood cells needed for carrying oxygen; aids in energy use; supports immune system	meat, poultry, beans, fortified grain products

HS

264 **Chapter 10** Nutrition for Health

Home and Community

Fluoridating Water Tell students that many communities add the mineral fluoride to drinking water because it helps prevent cavities. However, some people are concerned that fluoride in drinking water might cause health problems, such as certain types of cancer. Have students find out whether their community has fluoridated drinking water. A parent or guardian may know, or they can contact the local water department to find out. Then ask students to interview adult family members about their views on water fluoridation. Are they aware of the benefits and possible risks? Do they think the benefits outweigh the possible risks?

Teen girls need about 9 cups of fluids a day, and teen boys need about 13 cups each day. About 20 percent of your total daily water intake comes from the foods you eat, since all foods contain some water. In most cases, drinking fluids with your meals and any other time you feel thirsty will supply your body with all the water it needs. w

If you are very active, however, you will need to drink even more water to replace what your body loses when you sweat. Make sure to drink extra water before, during, and after exercise, even if you are not feeling thirsty. One important point to remember: if you feel thirsty, you waited too long to take in fluids. You should also drink extra fluids in hot weather to prevent dehydration. Limit your consumption of coffee, tea, and soft drinks that contain caffeine. Caffeine is a substance that eliminates water from your body, so caffeinated drinks can actually make you dehydrated.

■ **Figure 10.8** Water is essential for just about every function in your body. *When should you make sure to drink extra water?*

Caption Answer

Figure 10.8 You should make sure to drink extra water when you are very active and when the weather is very hot.

3 ASSESS/ CLOSE

Assessment Resources

📁 *FAST FILE* ACTIVITIES
Lesson 2 Quiz

💿 *ExamView Assessment Suite* CD-ROM

Visit glencoe.com **for:**
Online Quizzes
Online Learning Center

LESSON 2 📖 **ASSESSMENT**

After You Read

Reviewing Facts and Vocabulary

1. Which nutrients can your body use as sources of energy?

2. What are essential amino acids? From what source do you obtain essential amino acids?

3. How does eating calcium-rich foods as a teen protect your lifelong health?

Thinking Critically

4. **Analyze.** Explain how saturated fats and trans fats may cause illnesses later in life, like heart disease.

5. **Synthesize.** What are the health benefits of eating a variety of fruits and vegetables?

Applying Health Skills

6. **Goal Setting.** Examine your school's weekly lunch menu. List the most healthful food choices available each day. Then use the steps for goal setting to create a healthy eating plan.

Writing Critically

7. **Narrative.** Write a story from the point of view of a nutrient. Have the nutrient describe itself, what it does in the body, and why it is important for health.

 Online

Visit glencoe.com and complete the Interactive Study Guide for this lesson.

Lesson 2 Nutrients **265**

Progress Monitoring

Reteaching
Read how the body uses nutrients on page 258. For each use, call on students to name one or more types of nutrients that fulfill that role.

Enrichment
Ask students to write a basic outline of the lesson. Students' outlines should include the six nutrients.

LESSON 2 ASSESSMENT ANSWERS

1. Carbohydrates, proteins, and fats
2. They are called essential because the body must get them from food.
3. Calcium builds up bone mass and reduces your risk of osteoporosis.
4. Saturated fats and trans fats promote an increased level of blood cholesterol, which builds up on the walls of arteries and interferes with circulation. This can increase your risk of heart disease.
5. Fruits and vegetables are good sources of fiber.
6. Eating plans will vary.
7. Stories will vary, but they should reveal a correct understanding of the selected nutrient, its function in the body, and its role in maintaining good health.

 Online

Have students visit **glencoe.com** and complete the Interactive Study Guide for this lesson.

LESSON 3

Healthy Food Guidelines

1 FOCUS

📖 **GUIDE TO READING**

BIG Idea MyPyramid can help individuals choose healthful meals and snacks.
Ask Students: *What is MyPyramid?* (Sample answer: A diagram that shows you how to choose the right foods for good health)

Before You Read

Outline Check that students have correctly used the headings and subheadings for the appropriate levels of organization in their outlines.

Main Idea

Eating Right and Active Living With MyPyramid, you can use your knowledge of nutrients to select healthful foods. **Ask Students:** *Which two food groups have the widest bands in MyPyramid?* (Grains and vegetables)

Real Life Issues •••••••••

Before students write their paragraphs, lead the class in brainstorming ideas for healthy breakfast items. **Ask Students:** *What are some nutritious breakfast foods that are quick and easy to prepare?* (Sample answers: Cold cereals, fresh fruits, nuts, cheese, yogurt, leftovers)

📖 **GUIDE TO READING**

BIG Idea *MyPyramid is a tool that can help you choose healthful foods for all your meals and snacks.*

Before You Read

Create an Outline. Preview this lesson by scanning the pages. Organize the headings and subheadings into an outline. As you read, fill in your outline with important details.

New Vocabulary

▶ Dietary Guidelines for Americans (p. 266)
▶ MyPyramid (p. 267)
▶ nutrient-dense (p. 269)

Healthy Food Guidelines

Real Life Issues ••••••••••••••••••••

No Time for Breakfast. Ever since she started high school, Tina never seems to have enough time for breakfast. Homework keeps her up late, so when she wakes up the next morning, she barely has time to get dressed and catch the bus. Most mornings in class, she feels weak and sluggish, and by lunchtime she's ravenous. Tina wants to find the time to eat breakfast so she has more energy throughout the day.

Writing *Pretend you are Tina. In a paragraph, write out a plan to fit breakfast into your busy schedule.*

Guidelines for Eating Right and Active Living

Main Idea MyPyramid helps you apply what you know about nutrients to choose healthful foods.

The **Dietary Guidelines for Americans** are *a set of recommendations about smart eating and physical activity for all Americans.* These guidelines, published by the U.S. Department of Agriculture (USDA) and the Department of Health and Human Services (HHS), provide science-based advice for healthful eating. The guidelines also provide information on the importance of active living. This advice can be summed up in three key guidelines:

• Make smart choices from every food group.
• Find your balance between food and activity.
• Get the most nutrition out of your calories.

 Promoting School Wellness

Preventing Childhood Obesity Schools can play an important role in reversing the childhood obesity epidemic by helping students adopt healthful eating habits. One way schools can help is to ensure that students have appealing, nutritious food (and beverage) choices available outside of the school meals program—for example, in vending machines, at concession stands, and for class parties. Some schools have adopted policies to ensure that these foods are healthful. Find out if your school has such a policy. If it does, see whether the policy is being followed, and remind others to follow the policy if necessary. If your school does not have such a policy, work with other concerned staff to promote the development and implementation of one.

Making Smart Choices

U Choosing a variety of foods from each food group will provide all the nutrients your body needs. There are five major food groups: Grains, vegetables, fruits, milk, meats and beans.

MyPyramid Use **MyPyramid**—*an interactive guide to healthful eating and active living*—shown in **Figure 10.9**, to choose foods from all five of the food groups. MyPyramid helps you put the Dietary Guidelines into action.

R Each of the colored bands that run from the tip of the pyramid to the base represents a different food group. The bands differ in width, indicating which foods you need more of than others. The yellow band is for oils, which are not one of the basic food groups. The MyPyramid Web site offers advice on how to choose healthful food sources for the fats you eat.

Go Online

For more vocabulary practice, go to the Interactive Health Tutor at **glencoe.com**.

Figure 10.9   MyPyramid

Each band in MyPyramid stands for a different food group. *Why is the yellow band the narrowest?*

MyPyramid
STEPS TO A HEALTHIER YOU

GRAINS	VEGETABLES	FRUITS	MILK	PROTEINS
Make half your grains whole	Vary your veggies	Focus on fruits	Get your calcium-rich foods	Go lean with protein

---

Academic Integration

Science Remind students that calories measure the amount of energy in food. Then explain how body cells obtain and use that energy. During digestion, food molecules are broken down into simpler molecules. For example, starches are broken down into sugars, including glucose, which provides the fuel for most cells. Each glucose molecule consists of many carbon, hydrogen, and oxygen atoms that are held together by chemical bonds. The energy in glucose is stored in these chemical bonds. When the bonds are broken, during a process called cellular respiration, the energy is released and stored temporarily in another molecule, referred to as ATP. Molecules of ATP store the energy in amounts that are just right for powering cell functions.

---

② TEACH

U Universal Access

Classifying Foods Bring to class a variety of different foods (or alternatively, pictures of foods) in each of the five major food groups. Try to include foods in different states, such as fresh, canned, dried, and frozen fruits. Display the foods on a table and let students examine them. Ask students to try to classify the foods by food group. **BL**

R Reading Strategy

Learning from Visuals Guide students in gleaning important details from the MyPyramid visual in **Figure 10.9**. **Ask students:** *Which food group is represented by the brown band?* (grains) *What are examples of foods in this food group?* (bread, cereal, pasta) Ask questions such as these about the other food groups in MyPyramid to help students learn as much as possible from the visual. **EL**

Caption Answer

Figure 10.9 This is not one of the food groups. It represents oils.

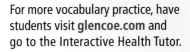
Go Online

For more vocabulary practice, have students visit **glencoe.com** and go to the Interactive Health Tutor.

267

HS Health Skills Practice

Decision Making Write the six decision-making steps on the board, and ask students to write each step on an index card. On the back of each card, they should apply that step to choosing the most healthful food in the food group. For example, on the back of the first card (state the situation), they might write "I want to choose the most healthful food in the grains group." On the back of the second card, they should list several options, such as cereals and breads. In a similar fashion, students should work through and write down the remaining steps to arrive at a decision. **EL**

W Writing Support

Rap Writing Ask interested students to work together to write a rap about the dietary guidelines for choosing healthful foods within each food group. Their rap should include all six recommendations listed on this page. **OL AL**

C Critical Thinking

Applying Tell students that they don't need to visit a farmer's market to find fresh fruits and vegetables. These foods are also available in the produce section of most food stores and supermarkets. Ask students where else in a supermarket they might find fruits and vegetables. (Sample answers: canned food aisle, freezer section, health food section) **BL**

Caption Answer

Figure 10.10 Students can list any types of fruits or vegetables.

✓ READING CHECK

Explain Why are the bands in MyPyramid different sizes?

The steps on the side of the pyramid remind you to be physically active every day. Your level of physical activity should balance out the calories in the foods you eat. The MyPyramid site provides individually tailored advice about your daily calorie needs based on your age, gender, and activity level. **HS**

Your Best Choices Within each food group, some choices are better than others. The Dietary Guidelines offer recommendations for choosing the most healthful foods from each food group: **W**

- **Focus on fruits.** Eat a variety of fruits. Fresh whole fruits that provide fiber are a better choice than fruit juice.

- **Vary your veggies.** Vegetables fall into several categories. These categories include dark green vegetables, such as broccoli, kale, and spinach, and orange vegetables, such as carrots, pumpkin, and winter squash. Try to eat a good mix of different types of vegetables each day. **C**

- **Get your calcium-rich foods.** Low-fat and fat-free dairy products are good choices. Teens should aim to drink three cups a day of low-fat or fat-free milk or an equivalent amount of low-fat yogurt or cheese. If you aren't a milk drinker, you can get your calcium by choosing calcium-fortified foods and beverages.

- **Make half your grains whole.** Get at least three ounces of brown rice or whole-grain cereals, breads, crackers, and pasta each day. When choosing processed foods, such as breads and cereals, check the ingredient label to make sure the grains are described as "whole."

■ **Figure 10.10** The Dietary Guidelines recommend choosing a variety of fruits and vegetables every day. *What fruits or vegetables would you choose for an afternoon snack?*

Teens Want to Know

How Many Calories Do I Need? For a rough estimate of their caloric needs, students can multiply their weight in pounds by the average number of calories burned per pound at their level of activity. Calories burned per pound range from about 12 for someone completely inactive to 20 for someone extremely active. For example, a very active, 130-pound teen might burn 18 calories per pound and need about 2,340 calories a day (130 pounds × 18 calories per pound). An inactive teen of the same weight might burn only 14 calories per pound and need only 1,820 calories a day (130 pounds × 14 calories per pound). If students do these calculations using their own weight and different activity levels, they will see clearly why food must be balanced with physical activity.

- **Go lean with protein.** Choose lean meats and poultry. Prepare them by grilling, baking, or broiling. Proteins, or any foods, that are prepared by frying in oil will add extra fat to your diet. This can increase the risk of overweight and obesity. Also, try getting more of your protein from fish, beans, peas, nuts, and seeds.
- **Limit certain foods.** Avoid foods that are high in fat—especially saturated fats and trans fats. Also, limit foods with salt and added sugars. Remember, it's okay to occasionally enjoy a few foods that are high in sugar, salt, or fat. If you enjoy eating a sweet snack each day, you can use physical activity to burn the extra calories.

Balancing Food and Physical Activity

Even if you eat the right amount and mix of healthful foods, you can still be overweight if you aren't getting enough physical activity. The MyPyramid guidelines recommend that everyone balance the energy in the foods with regular physical activity.

The guidelines recommend that teens should be physically active for 60 minutes almost every day to avoid unhealthy weight gain.

Getting the Most Nutrition Out of Your Calories

Every day your body needs a certain number of calories, depending on your age, your gender, and activity level. If you choose to spend your entire day's calorie needs with a single high-calorie fast-food meal, you may get the right amount of calories, but probably won't get the variety of nutrients your body needs. To make sure you get enough nutrients out of the foods you eat, choose **nutrient-dense** foods. These foods have *a high ratio of nutrients to calories.*

The more nutrient dense a food is, the more nutrients it packs into a given number of calories. For example, a single large carrot and a half ounce of potato chips have about the same number of calories, but the carrot is higher in nutrients. By eating more carrots and fewer potato chips, you will get more nutrients out of the same number of calories.

This doesn't mean that you have to give up all your favorite high-calorie foods. Any food that supplies calories and nutrients can be part of a healthful eating plan. You can plan to include them into your daily eating plan along with healthful, nutrient-dense foods. For example, try eating a small serving of potato chips with a lean, nutritious turkey sandwich with lettuce and tomato and some carrot or celery sticks. If your overall diet is nutrient dense, your eating plan can include an occasional treat.

FITNESSZONE

Part of my fitness plan is to make healthier food choices. For me, that means just a few little changes. When I eat out, I choose healthy substitutes, like grilled chicken instead of fried chicken, or using ketchup and mustard instead of mayonnaise. It's not that hard to substitute, but it's made a big difference to my fitness level. For more fitness tips, visit the Online Fitness Zone at **glencoe.com.**

HS Health Skills Practice

Goal Setting Have students use the six step decision-making process to show how a teen could reach the goal of being physically active for 60 minutes every day. Suggest that students review the steps on page 42 before they begin the activity. Encourage students who currently get too little exercise to follow their plan and try to reach the goal. Caution students who have health problems, are very overweight, or have been very sedentary to get their doctor's approval before starting an exercise program. **BL OL**

C Critical Thinking

Inferring Tell students that nutrient-dense foods are typically low in fats and sugars. Ask students why high-fat foods usually are not nutrient dense. (Fats provide more energy per gram than other nutrients, so high-fat foods are relatively high in calories. To be nutrient dense, a food must be relatively low in calories, so high-fat foods are usually not nutrient dense.) **AL**

AL Active Learning

Food Group Game Organize a group "scrambler." Divide the class into five groups to compete against one another. Provide a list of foods that belong in the five food groups. Have each student group attempt to place all the listed foods in the correct groups as quickly as possible. Students with the fastest time and accuracy win. **OL AL**

Cooperative Learning

Creating Visuals Divide the class into six groups. Tell students that they will be representing the Dietary Guidelines recommendations for choosing the most healthful foods within a food group. Ask the groups to make a visual representation of their assigned guideline. Encourage students to be creative. For example, for the guideline "vary your veggies," students might fill a cornucopia with a variety of plastic vegetables, or they might create a mobile with pictures of colorful vegetables from magazines. Give students a chance to explain their visuals to the class, and then put them on display in the classroom.

Real World **CONNECTION**

Make sure students know the serving sizes of the different types of food in MyPyramid. You can use objects to represent serving sizes for different types of foods. For example, one medium fruit is about the size of a baseball. Students might find that they are not eating enough of some foods, such as fruits and vegetables, or that they are eating too much of other foods, such as fried foods. The steps they list should include healthful food alternatives.

Main Idea

Healthful Eating Patterns The Dietary Guidelines and MyPyramid are flexible enough to allow a variety of healthful eating patterns. **Ask Students:** *What is your idea of a nutritious meal?* (Meals will vary but should include a variety of low-fat foods from all or most food groups. Try to get a diversity of responses.)

HS Health Skills Practice

Practicing Healthful Behaviors Have each student find out his or her daily requirements of foods from each food group at the MyPyramid Web site. Then have students use the information to create an eating plan for a day's worth of meals and snacks. The plan should incorporate the correct number of servings from each food group. Remind students to choose primarily nutrient-dense foods. **OL**

Real World **CONNECTION**

Evaluate Your Eating Habits

MyPyramid shows you how much of the food you eat should come from each food group. So how do you determine how much food you need from each group? The answer depends on you. The MyPyramid Web site can help you evaluate your diet relative to your personal needs, your energy balance, and the Dietary Guidelines. When you visit the MyPyramid Web site, you can enter information about your age, gender, and activity level. The site will then generate a personalized pyramid for you that tells you how much food you should eat from each food group. Visit the MyPyramid site and create your personal pyramid.

Activity **Reading / Writing**

To evaluate your eating habits, keep a food diary for a week. Your food diary should record each food you eat and drink, and the amount you consume.

1. Write down everything you eat, including the type and amount of each food.

2. Compare what you ate each day to the pyramid's recommendations. Did you stay within the pyramid's guidelines, or eat more or less than recommended?

3. In a paragraph, describe how your eating matches up with the guidelines.

4. List some steps to improve your eating habits.

Healthful Eating Patterns

Main Idea You can use MyPyramid and the information in the Dietary Guidelines to plan all your meals and snacks.

Do you like to sit down to three meals a day, or do you prefer to eat six or more smaller meals throughout the day? MyPyramid is flexible enough to adapt to just about any eating style. Some teens find it hard to make healthful choices in certain situations, such as breakfast time, eating on the go, or dining out. With a little planning, however, you can find ways to fit nutritious foods into any lifestyle.

Some people have trouble figuring out how to apply the Dietary Guidelines and MyPyramid to their daily eating plan. One tool that can help is the plate diagram. With this tool, you can **visualize** how a healthful meal might look on your plate. **Figure 10.11** shows a plate diagram for one lunch or dinner. For breakfast, you might leave out the vegetables and high-protein foods and put the starchy food center stage. The colors on the plate match the colors on MyPyramid. For example, orange represents grains, green shows a serving of vegetables, red is fruit, purple is for protein. Milk or other dairy products are shown in the glass.

Academic Vocabulary

visualize *(verb):* to form a mental image of

HS

More About...

Health Benefits of Breakfast The importance of eating a healthful breakfast cannot be overemphasized. In addition to the health benefits listed on this page, people who eat healthful breakfasts tend to have overall higher intakes of nutrients, such as vitamins, and lower intakes of fats. They also tend to have lower blood levels of cholesterol, which may reduce their risk of heart disease. Not surprisingly, regular breakfast eaters live longer, on average, than people who do not eat breakfast.

Figure 10.11 **What's on Your Plate?**

CA The plate diagram can help you visualize how much space you might devote to each type of food. *How might you adapt this diagram to a meal that has different types of foods mixed together, such as pasta with vegetables?*

Starting the Day Off Right

C It's Monday morning, you've overslept, and you have just 20 minutes to get yourself out of bed and out the door. When you're hurried, it can be tempting to skip breakfast. However, you may pay the price later, when your stomach starts growling in the middle of a class. After eight hours of sleep, your body needs to refuel. If you force it to keep going, you will likely run short on energy.

Eating breakfast has many benefits for kids and teens. For example, children who eat breakfast typically do better in school and are less likely to be overweight. You may find it easier to fit breakfast into your schedule if you do some of the prep work the night before. For instance, you can set the table for breakfast before you go to bed. That way, all you have to do in the morning is fill your cereal bowl or put the bread in the toaster. Other ideas for quick and easy breakfasts are instant oatmeal or grits, hard-cooked eggs (which can be cooked the night before), and whole-grain muffins.

 **READING CHECK**

Analyze a Graph
List ways that the plate diagram and the MyPyramid guidelines are consistent?

Lesson 3   Healthy Food Guidelines   **271**

HS Health Skills Practice

Advocacy Ask groups of students to create brochures about the health benefits of eating breakfast and how to choose nutritious breakfast foods. Arrange for student volunteers to set up a table in the cafeteria to display the brochures. The volunteers should also be available during lunch periods to answer any questions other students might have. If possible, provide samples of healthful breakfast foods for other students to try. OL

Caption Answer

Figure 10.12 Answers may vary. All the foods named should be nutritious.

AL Active Learning

Writing a Cookbook Have a group of interested students collect ideas for tasty, healthful snacks from a variety of sources, such as other students, friends, family members, and cookbooks. Ask the group to select the most nutritious, appealing, and interesting choices and write a section of a cookbook called "Sensible Snacks." Urge the group to taste-test their selections before including them in the cookbook. Encourage other students to use the cookbook to get ideas for their own snacks. OL

■ **Figure 10.12** Many different foods can be part of a healthful breakfast. *Name three nontraditional breakfast foods that you might like to try.*

Go Online

Visit glencoe.com and complete the Student Web Activity on selecting foods as part of a nutritious eating plan.

If you simply don't care for traditional breakfast foods, there are plenty of other choices for starting your day off right. For instance, try a whole-grain bagel or toast with peanut butter or melted cheese. A breakfast burrito (eggs, cheese, and salsa on a tortilla) can also be a quick and healthy alternative. Another healthy choic may be to reheat last night's leftover spaghetti for breakfast. **HS**

Sensible Snacks

Healthful snacks can give you energy to keep you going between meals. Enjoying a sensible snack after school, for instance, can keep you from coming to the dinner table so hungry that you eat twice as much as you should. There are plenty of healthful foods that you can easily enjoy when you need a quick bite:

- Fresh fruit
- Cut-up vegetables, such as celery or carrot sticks
- String cheese
- Unsalted nuts
- Air-popped popcorn
- Fat-free yogurt
- Bread sticks

AL

Skills for the *21st* Century

Interpersonal Skills Ask students to assume that they are teachers in a preschool. The board of directors of the preschool wants to save money by providing the children with inexpensive snacks, such as cookies and sweetened drinks. Have students take the position that nutritious snacks, such as fresh fruits and raw vegetables, should be provided instead, regardless of the extra cost. Then ask students to prepare a presentation to the board of directors in which they state and argue for their position. In their presentation, they should explain why their position is more ethical than the board's position. Give students a chance to deliver their presentations to the class.

Eating Right When Eating Out

Making healthful food choices is just as important when you eat away from home. With a little effort, you can find the most healthful, nutrient-dense items on the menu. Here are a few tips to keep in mind:

- **Watch portion sizes.** Restaurant meals have grown larger over the years. If you think the serving size is more than you need, try splitting the meal with a friend or wrapping up the leftovers to take home.
- **Pay attention to how foods are prepared.** Anything fried is likely to be high in fat. Grilled, baked, and broiled foods are healthier choices.
- **Add fresh vegetables and fruits.** The salad bar can be a health-conscious eater's best friend. If the restaurant doesn't have one, order a salad off the menu or ask the server to provide extra lettuce and tomato for your sandwich.
- **Go easy on toppings.** High-fat sauces, mayonnaise, butter, and sour cream add fat and calories to a dish. You can make your meal lighter by asking the restaurant to leave these out or serve them on the side.
- **Don't drink your calories.** Choose water instead of soft drinks to satisfy your thirst without adding extra calories to your meal.

■ **Figure 10.13** Splitting a meal is one way to avoid overeating in a restaurant. *What are other strategies for choosing healthful foods when you go out to eat?*

 LESSON 3 **ASSESSMENT**

After You Read

Reviewing Facts and Vocabulary

1. What are the five basic food groups?
2. What kinds of foods are best to avoid or limit?
3. Provide two examples of nutrient-dense foods.

Thinking Critically

4. **Analyze.** The Dietary Guidelines recommend regular physical activity. Why is this recommendation made?
5. **Synthesize.** Josh ate a cheeseburger, fries, and a soda for lunch. List the foods he could choose for dinner to balance out his lunch.

Applying Health Skills

6. **Accessing Information.** Search for information from credible sources that provide meal planning based on MyPyramid.

Writing Critically

7. **Expository.** Write a description of a meal you had recently. Discuss what foods or cooking methods made this meal healthful or unhealthful.

Gø Online

Visit **glencoe.com** and complete the Interactive Study Guide for this lesson.

Caption Answer

Figure 10.13 Sample answers: Avoid fried foods; order salads; drink water instead of soft drinks

③ ASSESS/ CLOSE

Assessment Resources

📁 **FAST FILE ACTIVITIES**
Lesson 3 Quiz

💿 *ExamView Assessment Suite* CD-ROM

Visit glencoe.com for:
Online Quizzes
Online Learning Center

Progress Monitoring

Reteaching
Ask students to close their books and try to draw a pencil sketch of MyPyramid. Students' pyramids should have five vertical bands, each labeled with one of the five food groups. Have students compare their sketches with **Figure 10.9** and correct any errors.

Enrichment
Challenge students to create a game based on the Dietary Guidelines for Americans. The game should require players to correctly apply the guidelines to make healthful food choices. Students can teach their game to the class.

Gø Online

Have students visit **glencoe.com** and complete the Interactive Study Guide for this lesson.

LESSON 3 ASSESSMENT ANSWERS

1. Grains, vegetables, fruits, milk, and meat and beans
2. Foods high in fats (especially saturated fats and trans fats), salt, and added sugars
3. Sample answers: Low-fat milk, steamed vegetables
4. To maintain a healthy weight, you need to balance the energy in the foods you eat with regular physical activity.
5. Answers will vary.
6. Answers will vary. Make sure students have accessed the most recent version of the Dietary Guidelines for Americans, because the guidelines are updated every five years.
7. Meals will vary, but students' assessments of what made the meals healthful or unhealthful should reflect a correct understanding of nutrients and nutrient needs.

LESSON 4

Nutrition Labels and Food Safety

1 FOCUS

GUIDE TO READING

BIG Idea It's possible to prevent many health problems associated with food by reading food labels and handling foods safely. **Ask Students:** *Aside from excess weight, what other health problems are associated with food?* (Sample answer: Food poisoning and food allergies)

Before You Read

Graphic Organizer Students' graphic organizers should include enough details to show that they understand the tips for keeping food safe.

Main Idea

Nutrition Label Basics Food labels provide essential information. **Ask Students:** *Do you ever read food labels? If so, what information do you look for?* (Sample answers: Number of calories or grams of fat)

Real Life Issues

Have students read the scenario. **Ask Students:** *Why can't Alex just avoid any nuts he might find in the foods, rather than make such a big deal of it?* (Sample answers: The nuts might be ground up so he wouldn't be able to avoid them.)

274

GUIDE TO READING

BIG Idea By reading food labels and handling foods safely, you can avoid many food-related health problems.

Before You Read

Organize Information. Fold a sheet of paper into quarters. Unfold it and label the four sections "Clean," "Separate," "Cook," and "Chill." As you read, fill in the sections with tips about the four steps in food safety.

Clean	Separate
Cook	Chill

New Vocabulary

▶ food additives (p. 275)
▶ foodborne illness (p. 278)
▶ pasteurization (p. 279)
▶ cross-contamination (p. 279)
▶ food allergy (p. 281)
▶ food intolerance (p. 281)

Nutrition Labels and Food Safety

Real Life Issues ....

Food Allergies. Alex is allergic to nuts. If he eats anything that contains nuts, his face swells up and he has to be taken to the hospital. He's learned to read food labels carefully to make sure nothing he eats has nuts in it. His friend Lauren has invited him to her house for dinner with her family. He'd like to say yes, but he knows that if anything they serve has nuts in it, he could be in serious trouble.

Writing *Write a paragraph explaining how you would handle this situation. How can Alex protect his safety and his friend's feelings at the same time?*

Nutrition Label Basics

Main Idea Food labels provide information about the ingredients and nutritional value of foods.

Whenever you buy a package of food, it has a label that tells you about the nutritional value of what's inside. The food label also lists all of the ingredients that were used to prepare the food. Among other things, the food label lists

- the name of the food product.
- the amount of food in the package.
- the name and address of the company that makes, packages, or distributes the product.
- the ingredients in the food.
- the Nutrition Facts panel, which provides information about the nutrients found in the food.

Teens Want to Know

Are Aspartame and Olestra Safe? If students are wondering whether aspartame and olestra are safe, this information may help them decide.

- Most of the safety concerns about aspartame—for example, that it causes brain tumors or other cancers—have been laid to rest by numerous recent studies. There is still concern that aspartame may increase the risk of seizures in people with epilepsy, but this is unlikely when aspartame is consumed in recommended amounts.
- Olestra has been shown to prevent the absorption of fat-soluble vitamins. However, these vitamins are added to foods containing olestra, so there is no net effect on vitamin levels.

Ingredient List

The ingredients in a food appear on the label in descending order by weight. So, the ingredient that makes up the largest share of the weight comes first, followed by the one that makes up the next largest share of the weight, and so on. However, food labels that list several similar ingredients can be misleading. For example, a product that contains three kinds of sweeteners would list each one separately: *high-fructose corn syrup, corn syrup, sugar.* Therefore, the three sweeteners appear farther down on the list than they would if they were all listed as a single ingredient, *sugars.* This may give the impression that the product contains less added sugars than it really does.

Food Additives Some foods contain **food additives,** *substances added to a food to produce a desired effect.* Food additives may be used to keep a food safe for a longer period of time, to boost its nutrient content, or to improve its taste, texture, or appearance. Two food additives that concern some experts are aspartame, a sugar substitute, and olestra, a fat substitute. Many diet soft drinks are sweetened with aspartame. Some potato chips are made with olestra, which passes through the body undigested. Because olestra is not absorbed, some people experience gastrointestinal problems when eating it.

Nutrition Facts

The Nutrition Facts panel provides information about the nutrients found in the food. See **Figure 10.14** on page 276 for an example of a Nutrition Facts panel and the information it contains.

Nutritional Claims

Along with information about specific nutrients, food labels make other types of claims about nutritional value. Federal law gives uniform definitions for the following terms:

- **Free.** The food contains none, or an insignificant amount, of a given component: fat, sugar, saturated fat, trans fat, cholesterol, sodium, or calories. For instance, foods labeled as being "calorie-free" must have fewer than five calories per serving.
- **Low.** You can eat this food regularly without exceeding your daily limits for fat, saturated fat, cholesterol, sodium, or calories. Low-fat foods, for instance, must have three grams or less of fat per serving.
- **Light.** A food labeled as "light" must contain one-third fewer calories, one-half the fat, or one-half the sodium of the original version. On some packages, *light* may refer only to the color of the food, such as light brown sugar.

READING CHECK

Explain Why are additives used in foods?

FITNESS ZONE

After we learned to read food labels in health class, I started checking the label on everything I eat. I'm doing it as part of my overall fitness plan. I was surprised to see that fruit juice is high in calories! It's better to drink water or eat a piece of fruit. For more fitness tips, visit the Online Fitness Zone at **glencoe.com.**

Lesson 4 Nutrition Labels and Food Safety **275**

② TEACH

☑ READING CHECK

Answer To keep foods safe to eat longer, boost their nutrient content, or improve their taste, texture, or appearance

HS Health Skills Practice

Accessing Information Check that students can correctly access information in the food label in **Figure 10.14** on page 276. Have them find specific nutrition facts, such as serving size, number of calories per serving, and grams of fat per serving. Ask students what percent of the Daily Value of carbohydrates the food provides. (8 percent) Remind them that the Daily Value is based on 2,000 calories per day. **EL**

AL Active Learning

Creating Nutrition Facts Panels Challenge groups of students to create Nutrition Facts panels for fictitious food products, using the Nutrition Facts panel in **Figure 10.14** as a guide. Then have groups exchange and check each other's panels. The panels should contain all of the required information and be realistic for the types of food represented. **OL**

Teacher to Teacher

Colette Dux • El Camino Real High School, Woodland Hills, CA

Reading Food Labels To practice reading food labels, I have students bring in food labels from various sources. In groups, students analyze three to four labels based on serving size, number of servings per container, number of calories per serving, the amount and type of fat per serving, protein, carbohydrates (fiber, sugar), and the amount of sodium and cholesterol. Based on what students know about the RDAs and the Dietary Guidelines for Americans, students are to compare their foods and present to the class which are the most/least healthy choices.

C **Critical Thinking**

Evaluating Guide students in evaluating the terms used in nutritional claims. Ask students to research which food has less fat: a food that is "low" in fat or a food that is "reduced" in fat. (It depends on the food. A low-fat food has no more than 3 grams of fat per serving, whereas a reduced fat food has 25 percent less fat than the original version.) **AL**

W **Writing Support**

Descriptive Writing Ask students to write an advertisement for a hypothetical new version of an established food product. Tell them that the new food has 3 grams of fat, no saturated fat or cholesterol, half the sodium of the original food, 20 percent of the Daily Value for fiber, and 10 percent of the Daily Value for protein. Their advertisements should include all the relevant nutritional claims that are defined on this page. (Students' ads should include the claims: low fat, light in sodium, high in fiber, good source of protein, and healthy.) **OL**

Ge Online

Have students visit **glencoe.com** and complete the Student Web Activity on reading and understanding the Nutrition Facts panels.

Ge Online

Explore **glencoe.com** and complete the Student Web Activity on reading and understanding the Nutrition Facts panels on food packages.

- **Reduced.** The food contains 25 percent fewer calories, or 25 percent less of a given nutrient, than the original version. This term may also be worded as *less* or *fewer*. Foods labeled as *reduced* may offer a much healthier option than the original version. The reduced version of a high calorie food may still contain a high number of calories. **C**

- **High.** The food provides at least 20 percent of the daily value for a vitamin, mineral, protein, or fiber. Synonyms for this term include *rich in* and *excellent source of*.

- **Good source of.** The food provides 10 to 19 percent of the daily value for a vitamin, mineral, protein, or fiber. Synonyms for this term include *contains* and *provides*.

- **Healthy.** Foods described as healthy must be low in fat and saturated fat and contain limited amounts of cholesterol and sodium. They must also provide at least 10 percent of the daily value for vitamin A, vitamin C, iron, calcium, protein, or fiber. **W**

Figure 10.14 **Nutrition Facts Panel**

The Nutrition Facts panel gives information about the nutrients found in a food. *Why do consumers need this information?*

Nutrition Facts

Serving Size 30g (about 12 pretzels)
Servings Per Container 30

Amount Per Serving	
Calories 110	Calories from Fat 10

	% Daily Value*
Total Fat 1g	**2%**
Saturated Fat 0g	**0%**
Trans Fat 0g	**0%**
Cholesterol 0mg	**0%**
Sodium 300mg	**13%**
Total Carbohydrate 23g	**8%**
Dietary Fiber 1g	**4%**
Sugars Less than 1g	
Protein 3g	

Vitamin A	0%	•	Vitamin C	0%
Calcium	0%	•	Iron	4%

* Percent Daily Values are based on a 2,000 calorie diet. Your daily values may be higher or lower depending on your calorie needs:

		Less Than		
Total Fat	Less Than	65g	80g
Sat Fat	Less Than	20g	25g
Cholesterol	Less Than	300mg	300mg
Sodium	Less Than	2,400mg	2,400mg
Total Carbohydrate		300g	375g
Dietary Fiber		25g	30g

Calories per gram:
Fat 9 • Carbohydrate 4 • Protein 4

Serving Size and Servings Per Container Used to calculate the nutrient and calorie content of a food.

Calories This section shows the percentage of calories in each serving that come from fat.

Nutrients The amounts of total fat, saturated fat, trans fat, cholesterol, and sodium per serving, measured in grams (g) or milligrams (mg) are listed here.

Vitamins and Minerals This section shows a few major vitamins and minerals, listed as a percentage of your daily needs.

Footnote This section is the same for every product, providing advice on the amounts of certain nutrients that you should consume each day.

Percent Daily Value Daily Value (DV) of a nutrient is a guide to approximately how much of the nutrient you need each day. Percent Daily Value shows the percentage of the DV a serving of the food will provide. The DV is based on the Reference Daily Intakes, or RDIs, which are established by the FDA. DVs for energy-producing nutrients, by contrast, are based on Daily Reference Values (DRVs), which show how much of each nutrient is recommended for a person who consumes 2,000 calories each day.

Caption Answer

Figure 10.14 Consumers need this information to choose foods that provide the nutrients they need and to avoid foods with excess fats, salt, or added sugars.

Health Literacy

Cracking Code Dating An important aspect of health literacy is knowing how to access the information you need to make healthful decisions. To make healthful decisions about food, consumers may need to know how to interpret code dates on food packages. Consumers can contact manufacturers of food products for assistance in translating code numbers to calendar dates. Code dates are typically pack dates, so consumers also need to know the shelf life of different types of products. For example, high-acid canned foods, such as tomatoes, have a shelf life of 12–18 months, whereas most other canned foods have a shelf life of 2–5 years. Consider a can of tuna fish that was packed on November 21, 2008, and has a shelf life of three years. It should be used by November 21, 2011.

Organic Food Labels

In addition to nutritional claims, you may see one other notation on a food label: "USDA Organic." Foods labeled as *organic* are produced without the use of certain agricultural chemicals, such as synthetic fertilizers or pesticides. As well as not containing synthetic fertilizers or pesticides, these foods cannot contain genetically modified ingredients or be subjected to certain types of radiation. The USDA Organic label makes no claims, however, that organic foods are safer or more nutritious than conventionally grown foods.

Open Dating

Many food products have *open dates* on their labels. These dates help you determine how long the food will remain fresh. There are several types of open dates:

- **Sell by dates** show the last day on which a store should sell a product. After this date, the freshness of a food is not guaranteed.
- **Use by** or **expiration dates** show the last day on which a product's quality can be guaranteed. For a short time, most foods are still safe to eat after this date.
- **Freshness dates** appear on **items** with a short shelf life, such as baked goods. They show the last date on which a product is considered fresh.
- **Pack dates** show the day on which a food was processed or packaged. The pack date does not give the consumer an indication of the product's freshness.

Academic Vocabulary

item *(noun):* an object of concern or interest

■ **Figure 10.15** Foods bearing the USDA Organic label are produced without the use of certain agricultural chemicals. *Why might some consumers prefer these foods?*

ORANGE CRANBERRY ORGANIC VINAIGRETTE

TARRAGON DIJON ORGANIC VINAIGRETTE

OLIVE OIL & B... ORGANIC VINAI...

HS Health Skills Practice

Communication Skills Divide the class into two teams. Give food labels with nutrient information from organic food labels to each team. Have one team call out a nutrient listed on a package. In 15 seconds, the other team must name a health benefit of the nutrient and one food where the nutrient can be found. If the team answers correctly, they receive a point. First team to 15 points wins. **OL**

AL Active Learning

Learning About Product Dating Have small groups of students visit a supermarket to find examples of each of the different types of open dates listed on this page. Ask students to make a list of several different products that carry each type of date. Give groups a chance to share their findings with the class. Discuss how different types of food are generally dated. **OL**

Academic Vocabulary

Item Explain that an item is not just any object but usually an object on a list or in a collection, such as an item of food on a shopping list or in a shopping cart. Ask students what the related verb, itemize, means. (to list)

Caption Answer

Figure 10.15 They might think that organic foods are safer than foods produced with chemicals such as pesticides.

ELL Support

Multiple-Meaning Words Point out that several of the words used to make nutritional claims have more than one meaning.

Beginning Use the word *free* in two sentences, one for each meaning of the word. Have students identify which meaning is intended in each sentence.

Intermediate Ask students to identify other nutritional claim words that have more than one meaning. (low, light, high)

Advanced Have students use these other words in sentences that demonstrate their multiple meanings.

C **Critical Thinking**

Inferring Point out that not all foodborne illnesses are caused by pathogens in food. Some are caused by poisons in certain mushrooms or plants. Ask students how this type of foodborne illness is prevented. (By avoiding the mushrooms or plants) **OL**

R **Reading Strategy**

Using Graphic Organizers On the board, create a simple flow chart to help students understand how foodborne illnesses spread. The chart should show the spread of pathogens from unwashed hands to food, and then from the food to the people who eat it. Call on a student to modify the flow chart to show how hand washing could interrupt the spread of pathogens in this way. **BL**

For more vocabulary practice, have students go to the Interactive Health Tutor at **glencoe.com**.

Food Safety

Main Idea Handling food carefully can help you avoid foodborne illnesses and other hazards.

Have you ever seen a sign in a restaurant restroom reminding employees to wash their hands before returning to work? This restaurant policy helps prevent the spread of pathogens that can cause illness. It is one strategy for preventing **foodborne illness**, or *food poisoning*. About 76 million Americans become ill as a result of foodborne illnesses each year.

Foods can contain pathogens, or disease-causing organisms. Sometimes the pathogens produce disease. In other cases, it's the poisons that pathogens produce that cause illness. Some foods, such as certain mushrooms, that don't contain pathogens can still contain or produce poisonous chemicals. To protect yourself against foodborne illnesses learn what causes them and how to keep food safe.

How Foodborne Illness Occurs

Bacteria and viruses cause most cases of foodborne illness. The most common sources are the bacteria *Campylobacter, Salmonella, E. coli,* and a group of viruses known as the Norwalk and Norwalk-like viruses.

Some pathogens are naturally present in healthy animals. *Salmonella* bacteria can infect hens and enter their eggs. Shellfish may pick up bacteria that are naturally present in seawater. Fresh fruits and vegetables may become contaminated if they are washed with water that contains traces of human or animal wastes. Finally, infected humans who handle food can spread pathogens from their own skin to the food or from one food to another.

Some common symptoms of foodborne illness include cramps, diarrhea, nausea, vomiting, and fever. In most cases, people recover from foodborne illness within a few days. Occasionally, symptoms may be severe. Dehydration is one danger of foodborne illness. Fluids lost through vomiting and diarrhea can result in dehydration. If the following symptoms are present, consult a doctor:

- A fever higher than 101.5 degrees F
- Prolonged vomiting or diarrhea
- Blood in the stool
- Signs of dehydration, including a decrease in urination, dry mouth and throat, and feeling dizzy when standing

---

Skills for the 21st Century

Collaborative Skills Have students assume that they and some friends all developed symptoms of food poisoning soon after eating the same food at a local restaurant. They wonder if other people became ill from the food and whether they should do something about it. Ask groups of students to discuss the situation and decide on the socially responsible action to take. Ask groups to share their ideas with the class. (Students might decide that they should contact the local health department about the food poisoning so that other people will not become ill in the future.)

Keeping Food Safe to Eat

Food distributors and the U.S. government take steps to keep pathogens out of the food supply. One important process is pasteurization of milk and juices, which helps prevent *E. coli* infection. **Pasteurization** is *treating a substance with heat to kill or slow the growth of pathogens.* The Dietary Guidelines outline four basic steps for keeping food safe: clean, separate, cook, and chill.

Clean Wash and dry your hands frequently to keep pathogens on your skin from entering food. Be sure to wash your hands for at least 20 seconds with warm water and soap before and after handling food, as well as after using the bathroom, changing a diaper, or handling pets.

Clean utensils and surfaces carefully to prevent **cross-contamination**, *the spreading of pathogens from one food to another.* Wash cutting boards, dishes, utensils, and countertops with hot, soapy water after you finish preparing each food item. Mop up spilled food promptly using a paper towel or a clean cloth that has been washed in hot water.

Finally, wash the food itself. Rinse fresh fruits and vegetables under running water, and rub the surfaces of firm-skinned fruits and vegetables.

Separate The foods most likely to carry pathogens are raw meat, poultry, seafood, and eggs. To avoid cross-contamination, separate these from other foods. Store them separately when shopping and at home. Use separate cutting boards when preparing raw meats, poultry, and fish. After cooking meat, poultry, or fish, transfer the cooked food to a clean platter, rather than putting it back on the plate that held the raw food.

Cook Heating food to a high enough temperature will kill the pathogens that cause foodborne illness. To determine whether meat, poultry, and egg dishes are cooked thoroughly, use a food thermometer to measure the internal temperature (the temperature in the center of the food). **Figure 10.17** on page 280 shows the internal temperatures suggested for different foods.

READING CHECK

Explain Why is it best to always use warm water and soap when washing your hands?

■ **Figure 10.16** Washing hands, produce, utensils, and surfaces carefully is the first step in preventing foodborne illness. *How does this step prevent the spread of pathogens?*

Lesson 4   Nutrition Labels and Food Safety   **279**

AL Active Learning

Learning with Visuals Ask small groups of students to create posters or other visual representations of the four basic steps for keeping food safe. Arrange for students to display their work in the cafeteria and other locations where students eat food at school. **EL**

HS Health Skills Practice

Practicing Healthful Behaviors Point out that, if students usually spend less than 20 seconds washing their hands, they may not be removing all of the pathogens from their skin. Suggest to students that they time themselves the next time they wash their hands. Stress that proper hand washing—including washing for at least 20 seconds—is one of the most important ways to prevent the spread of foodborne illness. **BL OL**

C Critical Thinking

Applying Ask volunteers to apply the tips on this page by demonstrating the correct way to clean kitchen surfaces during food preparation. Call on other students to point out and correct any errors. Discuss with the class how the correct procedures can help prevent cross-contamination. **OL**

Caption Answer

Figure 10.16 To keep pathogens on skin from entering food

Writing Strategy

Writing Fiction Challenge students to write a short story about the spread of a foodborne pathogen due to improper handling of food. Tell students that their stories should be told from the point of view of the pathogen. Stories should demonstrate how foods can become contaminated with a pathogen, what conditions cause the pathogen to grow, how the pathogen infects people, and what symptoms it causes. Make copies of a few of the best stories and hand them out to other students to read.

R Reading Strategy

Understanding Key Phrases
Some students may not understand certain key phrases in the guidelines for safely cooking food. For example, they may not know what it means to "bring a liquid to a boil," to "be opaque," or to "measure internal temperature." Call on volunteers to explain what these three phrases mean. **BL**

U Universal Access

Picturing Foods Have students find and cut out pictures of a variety of foods from magazines. Tell students to include pictures of fresh produce and raw meat, poultry, seafood, and eggs. Display the pictures and ask students to identify foods that must be handled with care to avoid spreading pathogens to other foods. (The raw animal products) Ask students how they would handle these foods if they were buying them in a store. (Sample answers: Wrap them in plastic; put them in a separate bag) **EL**

C Critical Thinking

Explaining Point out the danger zone on the thermometer in **Figure 10.17**. Ask students to explain why it is important to thaw foods in the refrigerator or microwave rather than at room temperature. (So they will pass quickly through the danger zone) Then ask why it is important to refrigerate leftovers as soon as possible. (For the same reason) **OL**

Caption Answer

Figure 10.17 It is called the "danger zone" because this temperature range is neither hot enough nor cold enough to prevent the growth of pathogens that cause foodborne illness.

280

For some foods, you can tell whether they are fully cooked by their appearance. Eggs should be firm, not runny; fish should be opaque and flake easily with a fork. When reheating soups, sauces, or gravy, bring the liquid to a boil. Heat all leftovers to 165 degrees F. When cooking food in a microwave oven, stir and rotate the food periodically to make sure there are no cold spots in which bacteria can survive. **R**

Chill Refrigeration slows the growth of harmful bacteria. Refrigerate or freeze meat, poultry, and other perishable foods as soon as you bring them home from the store. Avoid overpacking the refrigerator; circulating air will help keep the food cool. Divide large amounts of food into small, shallow containers to help it cool more quickly. **U**

Frozen foods should be thawed safely before cooking. Thaw frozen foods in the refrigerator, in a microwave, or under cold running water. Discard any food that has been sitting out at room temperature for two hours or longer—one hour when the temperature is above 90 degrees F.

Figure 10.17 Safe Food Temperatures

The top of this thermometer shows safe temperatures for cooking food, while the bottom shows safe temperatures for storing food. *Why is the area in the middle called the danger zone?* **C**

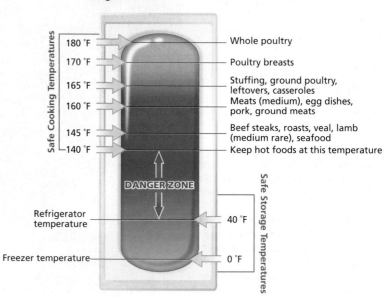

Myths & Reality

Dangerous Food Safety Myths

Myth: Foods containing mayonnaise spoil faster than other foods.

Fact: Commercially prepared mayonnaise contains vinegar or lemon juice, which helps prevent spoilage, so foods without mayonnaise may actually spoil faster.

Myth: You can tell if a food is spoiled because it will smell or taste bad.

Fact: Pathogens and toxins in food may not affect how the food smells or tastes.

Myth: If I sample a food and don't get sick within a couple of hours, then the food must be safe to eat.

Fact: Symptoms of food poisoning may not develop for more than 24 hours after eating a food, so sampling is a dangerous and ineffective way to test food safety.

Food Sensitivities

Keeping pathogens out of food is important for everyone. Some people need to worry about specific foods. Food sensitivities—allergies and intolerances—can make some foods dangerous to eat. A **food allergy** is *a condition in which the body's immune system reacts to substances in some foods.* The most common allergens are found in milk, eggs, peanuts, tree nuts, soybeans, wheat, fish, and shellfish. Food labels are required telling whether a food product contains any of these ingredients or any protein derived from them.

The symptoms of food allergies vary from mild to life threatening. Some people experience skin irritations, such as rashes, hives, or itching while others develop gastrointestinal symptoms such as nausea, vomiting, or diarrhea. The most dangerous allergic reaction is anaphylaxis, a condition in which the throat swells up and the heart has difficulty pumping. Anaphylaxis can be life threatening and requires immediate medical attention.

A **food intolerance**—*a negative reaction to food that doesn't involve the immune system*—is more common than a food allergy. One of the most common is lactose intolerance, which occurs when a person's body does not produce enough of the enzyme needed to digest lactose, a sugar found in milk. People who are lactose intolerant may experience gas, bloating, and abdominal pain.

 READING CHECK

Compare and Contrast What is the difference between a food allergy and a food intolerance?

 LESSON 4 **ASSESSMENT**

After You Read

Reviewing Facts and Vocabulary

1. What does the term *light* mean when used on a food label?
2. What is the difference between a sell by date and a use by date?
3. What is another term that refers to *foodborne illness*?

Thinking Critically

4. **Evaluate.** An instant soup is very low in fat and calories but high in sodium. Can this food be labeled "healthy"? Explain why or why not.
5. **Synthesize.** What are the possible consequences of undercooked eggs?

Applying Health Skills

6. **Practicing Healthful Behaviors.** Summarize the steps for preventing foodborne illnesses. Post the steps in your kitchen as a reminder of food safety.

Writing Critically

7. **Persuasive.** Write an essay that convinces others of the importance of food safety.

Go Online

Visit **glencoe.com** and complete the Interactive Study Guide for this lesson.

LESSON 4 ASSESSMENT ANSWERS

1. The food contains one-third fewer calories, one-half the fat, or one-half the sodium of the original version.
2. A sell by date is the last day on which a store should sell a product. A use by date is the last day on which a product's quality can be guaranteed.
3. Food poisoning
4. No, because foods labeled "healthy" must contain limited amounts of sodium.
5. You might develop a foodborne illness from pathogens in the eggs.
6. Students should summarize the four basic steps for keeping food safe: clean, separate, cook, and chill. Their summaries should enable a reader to follow the steps and keep food safe.
7. Essays will vary.

 READING CHECK

Answer Unlike a food allergy, a food intolerance does not involve the body's immune system.

ASSESS/ CLOSE

Assessment Resources

📁 *FAST FILE* **ACTIVITIES**
Lesson 4 Quiz

💿 *ExamView Assessment Suite* CD-ROM

Visit glencoe.com for:
Online Quizzes
Online Learning Center

Progress Monitoring

Reteaching
On the board, write the four basic steps for handling food safely: Clean, Separate, Cook, and Chill. Call on students to come to the board and fill in details under each step.

Enrichment
Ask students to prepare a lesson plan to teach younger children the basic steps for keeping food safe. If possible, arrange for students to teach their lesson to a class at a lower grade level.

Go Online

Have students visit **glencoe.com** and complete the Interactive Study Guide for this lesson.

What's in the Bag?

NHES Standard 3 Students will demonstrate the ability to access valid information, products, and services to enhance health.

Teaching Objectives

- Analyze the nutritional information provided on food labels
- Demonstrate ability to evaluate nutritional information to make healthful food choices

Teaching Strategies

- Collect nutrition labels prior to this activity.
- Place students into groups of four or five. Give each group one brown paper grocery bag with 7–10 nutrition labels inside. Identify each bag with a number (#1, #2, etc.)
- Have students follow the steps in the hands-on activity "What's in the Bag?"
- Give each group five minutes to analyze the nutrition labels inside the bag and select the healthiest food item. After students have written down their item and three reasons supporting their choice, instruct students to pass the bag clockwise to the next group and repeat the sequence until all groups have analyzed the items in each bag.

Assessment

Using a rubric, student work should provide comprehensive evidence of the following criteria to achieve the highest score:

✓ Cites specific sources

✓ Evaluates the validity of the source of information

✓ Analyzes the nutritional value of foods

✓ Demonstrates rationale for the appropriateness of their choices

---

Hands-On HEALTH

Activity **What's in the Bag?**

Your group is opening a health food store and is looking for healthful foods to stock the store. Working in groups, pass around grocery bags containing nutrition labels. After reviewing the Nutrition Facts information in this chapter, analyze each label, and choose one food item from each bag to add to your store's inventory.

What You'll Need

- paper and pen or pencil
- one brown paper grocery bag per group
- seven to ten nutrition labels per bag

What You'll Do

Step 1

Choose a grocery bag for your group. Analyze the Nutrition Facts panel on each label and choose one.

Step 2

Write down the name of the food item and three reasons to support your group's choice.

Step 3

Exchange the bag with another group. Repeat steps 2 and 3 until you've selected one item from each bag.

Apply and Conclude

Describe your choices to the class. Include the reasons why your group selected each food item for your store.

Checklist: Accessing Information

☑ Did I access specific information from food labels?

☑ Did I use information on the labels to analyze the nutritional values of foods?

☑ Can I show that my choices are healthful?

Health Literacy

Health Literacy Here's one way to get a rough idea of a person's daily calorie needs. If a person is extremely inactive, she would need about 12 calories per pound to stay at that current weight. If a person is involved in a light activity, such as doing homework or household tasks, she needs 15 calories per pound. When someone is moderately active, such as walking briskly or cycling, she needs up to 20 calories per pound. So a moderately active person weighing 140 pounds needs about 2,800 calories a day.

To download quizzes and eFlashcards to your PDA, go to **glencoe.com** and click on the Study to Go icon.

LESSON 1

The Importance of Nutrition

Key Concepts
▶ Nutrients supply your body with energy and help it to grow, repair itself, and function well.
▶ Hunger is a physical need for food. Appetite is a desire to eat.
▶ Family, culture, friends, time, money, and advertising can influence your food choices.

Vocabulary
▶ nutrition (p. 254)
▶ nutrients (p. 254)
▶ calorie (p. 254)
▶ hunger (p. 255)
▶ appetite (p. 255)

LESSON 2

Nutrients

Key Concepts
▶ The six nutrients are carbohydrates, proteins, fats, vitamins, minerals, and water.
▶ Carbohydrates, proteins, and fats provide you with energy.
▶ Vitamins, minerals, and water do not provide energy but are necessary for many body functions and processes.

Vocabulary
▶ carbohydrates (p. 259)
▶ fiber (p. 259)
▶ proteins (p. 260)
▶ cholesterol (p. 262)
▶ vitamins (p. 262)
▶ minerals (p. 262)
▶ osteoporosis (p. 264)

LESSON 3

Healthy Food Guidelines

Key Concepts
▶ The Dietary Guidelines for Americans provide recommendations for healthy eating and regular physical activity.
▶ The five major food groups are grains, vegetables, fruits, milk, and meat and beans.
▶ It is important to eat nutrient-dense foods that have a high ratio of nutrients to calories.

Vocabulary
▶ Dietary Guidelines for Americans (p. 266)
▶ MyPyramid (p. 267)
▶ nutrient-dense (p. 269)

LESSON 4

Nutrition Labels and Food Safety

Key Concepts
▶ Food labels provide information about ingredients, nutritional value, serving sizes, and calories.
▶ Four steps to prevent foodborne illnesses are clean, separate, cook, and chill.
▶ People with food allergies or food intolerances must take special care about the foods they eat.

Vocabulary
▶ food additives (p. 275)
▶ foodborne illness (p. 278)
▶ pasteurization (p. 279)
▶ cross-contamination (p. 279)
▶ food allergy (p. 281)
▶ food intolerance (p. 281)

Chapter 10 Review **283**

  Go Online

Students can visit **glencoe.com** to

• review content online with the Online Student Edition.
• test their knowledge of chapter content with Online Quizzes.
• access Interactive Health Tutor for more practice with vocabulary.

Assessment Resources

📁 **FAST FILE ACTIVITIES**
Chapter 10 Test

💿 *ExamView Assessment Suite* CD-ROM

Visit glencoe.com for:
Audio Chapter Summaries
Online Quizzes

 Tell students to visit **glencoe.com** where they can download quizzes and eFlashcards.

Study Tips

Retaining Facts Although it is important for students to develop analytical skills, they also need to be able to remember facts. Useful techniques for remembering facts include acronyms and acrostics. Acronyms are new words formed with the first letters of a group of words that you are trying to remember. For example, the acronym *CUTS* could be used to remember different types of fats (Cholesterol, Unsaturated fats, Trans fats, and Saturated fats). Acrostics are sentences based on the first letters of a group of words. An example is "cacti sometimes cause cuts," which could be used to remember the steps in keeping food safe: clean, separate, cook, and chill. Repetition of facts is also a good way to reinforce retention.

Assessment

Chapter 10 Assessment Answers

LESSON 1

Vocabulary Review

1. nutrition
2. nutrients
3. calorie

Understanding Key Concepts

4. d
5. a
6. a

Thinking Critically

7. It can lead to unhealthful weight gain.
8. Sample answer: The business executive might choose more expensive foods that are quick to prepare, such as convenience foods. The part-time worker might choose foods that take longer to prepare but are less expensive.
9. Students may mention any specific foods, or occasions involving foods, that are related to a particular culture.

LESSON 2

Vocabulary Review

10. carbohydrates
11. cholesterol
12. Minerals

Understanding Key Concepts

13. b
14. a
15. b

LESSON 1

Vocabulary Review

Use the vocabulary terms listed on page 283 to complete the following statements.

1. The process by which your body takes in and uses food is called _____.

2. Your body relies on food to provide it with the _____ it needs to grow, to repair itself, and to supply you with energy.

3. A _____ is a unit of heat used to measure the energy your body uses and the energy it receives from food.

Understanding Key Concepts

After reading the question or statement, select the correct answer.

4. Which of the following is not a way that choosing healthful foods affects your total health and wellness?
   a. It gives your body the nutrients it needs for growth and development.
   b. It helps you avoid unhealthful weight gain.
   c. It provides fuel for sports and other activities.
   d. It ensures that you will never get sick.

5. Preferring certain foods because you've grown up eating them is an example of the influence of
   a. family.
   b. friends.
   c. money.
   d. advertising.

6. Hearing your stomach growl and feeling tired and lightheaded are signs of
   a. hunger.
   b. appetite.
   c. emotional eating.
   d. mindless eating.

Thinking Critically

After reading the question or statement, write a short answer using complete sentences.

7. **Analyze.** Why is emotional eating harmful?

8. **Synthesize.** How might the food choices of a high-powered business executive with a busy schedule differ from those of a part-time worker?

9. **Discuss.** Give an example of a way in which a person's cultural background could influence that person's food choices.

LESSON 2

Vocabulary Review

Choose the correct word in the sentences below.

10. Your body's main source of energy is *carbohydrates / proteins.*

11. Consuming saturated fats and trans fats can increase the levels of *fiber / cholesterol* in your blood.

12. *Vitamins / minerals* are elements found in food that are used by the body.

Understanding Key Concepts

After reading the question or statement, select the correct answer.

13. Which of the following is not one of the six basic nutrients?
    a. Carbohydrates
    b. Fiber
    c. Protein
    d. Vitamins

14. Your body uses carbohydrates by breaking them down into
    a. sugars.   c. fatty acids.
    b. amino acids. d. water.

Health eSpotlight *Wrap-Up*

It's Your Health, It's Your Choice Have students reread the Health eSpotlight questions at the beginning of the chapter on page 253 and look at their original answers. **Ask Students:** *Now that you have read the chapter and* watched the video, how would you respond differently if you were designing a healthy menu for a friend? Call on volunteers to describe how their responses would change.

15. About what percentage of your daily calories should come from fat?
    a. 10 to 15 percent
    b. Less than 25 to 35 percent
    c. At least 30 percent
    d. 50 to 65 percent

Thinking Critically

After reading the question or statement, write a short answer using complete sentences.

16. **Describe.** How does fiber benefit your body?

17. **Explain.** Why is it dangerous to consume too much of a fat-soluble vitamin?

18. **Explain.** Why does your body need more water when you are very active?

LESSON 3

Vocabulary Review

Use the vocabulary terms listed on page 283 to complete the following statements.

19. The _____ contain recommendations about smart eating and physical activity for all healthy Americans.

20. An interactive guide to healthy eating and active living is the _____.

21. Foods that are _____ have a high ratio of nutrients to calories.

Understanding Key Concepts

After reading the question or statement, select the correct answer.

22. Which food group band in MyPyramid is largest?
    a. Grains
    b. Fruits
    c. Milk
    d. Meat and beans

23. The Dietary Guidelines recommend that teens be physically active for
    a. 20 minutes, three or more times a week.
    b. 30 minutes a day.
    c. 50 minutes, five or more times a week.
    d. 60 minutes a day.

24. Which method of preparation tends to make food high in fat?
    a. Baking
    b. Broiling
    c. Frying
    d. Grilling

Thinking Critically

After reading the question or statement, write a short answer using complete sentences.

25. **Explain.** How can people who don't eat dairy products get enough calcium every day?

26. **Analyze.** Why is it important to include nutrient-dense foods in your daily eating?

27. **Identify.** Give two examples of healthful snacks.

LESSON 4

Vocabulary Review

Correct the sentences below by replacing the italicized term with the correct vocabulary term.

28. *Ingredients* may be used to keep a food fresh longer, to boost its nutrient content, or to improve its taste, texture, or appearance.

29. *Boiling* means treating a substance with heat to kill or slow the growth of pathogens.

30. It is important to clean utensils and surfaces carefully to prevent *foodborne illness*, the spread of pathogens from one food to another.

Thinking Critically

16. It helps move waste through your digestive system, helps promote fullness, prevents overeating, and may reduce the risk of heart disease and type 2 diabetes.
17. Fat-soluble vitamins are stored in body fat, where they can build up to toxic levels.
18. To replace what you lose through sweat

LESSON 3

Vocabulary Review

19. Dietary Guidelines for Americans
20. MyPyramid
21. nutrient dense

Understanding Key Concepts

22. a
23. d
24. c

Thinking Critically

25. By choosing calcium-fortified foods and beverages
26. With nutrient-dense foods, you can get all the nutrients you need without eating more than the recommended number of calories.
27. Answers will vary but should include only nutrient-dense foods. Sample answers: Fresh fruit, cut-up vegetables, string cheese, unsalted nuts, air-popped popcorn, fat-free yogurt, bread sticks

Vocabulary Review

28. Food additives
29. Pasteurization
30. cross-contamination

ExamView®
Assessment Suite

Create and customize tests in minutes with this convenient digital platform.

- Create differentiated tests quickly and easily.
- All questions correlated to National/State Standards.
- Enhance tests with Document Based Questions (DBQ) and add your own photos or graphics.
- Build tests in both English and Spanish.
- Generate progress reports.

To order, go to **glencoe.com** and search for ISBN 0-07-888173-0.

Glencoe
Health

ExamView
Assessment Suite

285

Assessment

Assessment

LESSON 4

Understanding Key Concepts

31. d
32. c
33. b

Thinking Critically

34. The low-fat food must have three grams or less of fat per serving. The reduced-fat food only needs to have 25 percent less fat than the original version of the same food.

35. Cramps, diarrhea, nausea, vomiting, and fever

36. *Any two:* Milk, eggs, peanuts, tree nuts, soybeans, wheat, fish, shellfish

Understanding Key Concepts

After reading the question or statement, select the correct answer.

31. Which of the following is *not* listed in the Nutrition Facts panel?
    a. The number of servings per container
    b. The number of calories per serving
    c. The vitamin and mineral content of the food
    d. The ingredients found in the food

32. Regular ice cream contains 7.5 grams of fat per serving. Ice cream that contains only 5 grams of fat per serving could be described as
    a. light.
    b. low-fat.
    c. reduced-fat.
    d. fat-free.

33. Which of the following is *not* one of the four basic steps for preventing foodborne illness?
    a. Clean
    b. Chop
    c. Cook
    d. Chill

Thinking Critically

After reading the question or statement, write a short answer using complete sentences.

34. **Compare and Contrast.** What is the difference between a food that is labeled "low-fat" and one that is labeled "reduced-fat"?

35. **Identify.** What are the usual symptoms of foodborne illness?

36. **Identify.** Name two foods that are common sources of allergens.

Project-Based ASSESSMENT

The Importance of Nutrients

Background
Nutrients are the substances in food that your body needs. To have a healthful diet, your body needs six basic kinds of nutrients.

Task
You will work in a small group to write and perform a skit about the six basic nutrients.

Audience
Children in elementary grades

Purpose
The purpose of the skit is to inform younger students about the six basic nutrients and how the body uses them. The skit will also show which foods provide the body with each of the nutrients.

Procedure
1. Review the information about the six groups of nutrients discussed in Chapter 5.
2. Write a skit with your group that explains what the basic nutrients are, why the body needs them, and which foods can provide them.
3. Think of a way to dramatize these facts.
4. Select scenery, costumes, and props to enliven the skit.
5. Rehearse your skit, using the costumes and props.
6. Evaluate the skit and make any necessary revisions.
7. Obtain permission to present the skit to classes or children in the elementary grades.

Project-Based ASSESSMENT

Step 1 Review Have students review the information about the six groups of nutrients. Students should work in groups.

Step 2 Write Students should begin writing their skits. Suggest that their dialogue include what nutrients are and why the body needs them.

Step 3 Evaluate Have students rehearse and perform their skits in front of an elementary class. Encourage all students to use costumes and props.

Visit **glencoe.com** for Project-Based Assessment rubrics.

Math Practice

Interpret Tables. To determine which food intake pattern to use, the following table gives an estimate of individual calorie needs. The calorie range for each age/sex group is based on physical activity level, from sedentary to active. *Sedentary* lifestyles include light physical activity. *Active* lifestyles include the equivalent to walking more than 3 miles per day at 3 to 4 miles per hour and the light physical activity typical of day-to-day life.

Calorie Range		
	Sedentary	Active
Females		
14–18	1,800	2,400
19–30	2,000	2,400
Males		
14–18	2,200	3,200
19–30	2,400	3,000

1. What are the approximate calorie needs of a sedentary 16-year-old male?
   A. 1,800 calories   C. 2,200 calories
   B. 2,000 calories   D. 2,400 calories

2. In 2000, the total number of active females age 14–18 in the United States was approximately 4,788,000. This was a 31 percent increase from the total number in 1975. What was the approximate number of active females age 14–18 in 1975?
   A. 274,000   C. 2,245,000
   B. 398,000   D. 3,655,000

3. About 35 percent of a 16-year-old male's calories should come from carbohydrates. Which most closely matches this number?
   A. 1/4   C. 3/5
   B. 1/3   D. 5/7

Go Online

For more test practice, visit glencoe.com and complete the Online Quizzes for Chapter 10.

Reading/Writing Practice

Understand and Apply. Read the passage below and then answer the questions.

> Last weekend, after a game of basketball at the local community center, we all went to get a snack from the vending machine. Everything in the machine was high in fat, salt, or sugar. I put my money back in my pocket. My friends said, "Why don't you want anything?"
>
> Here's why. Last year, my dad found out he has high blood pressure. He's a bit overweight, so his doctor told him to cut out foods high in salt and fat. My parents didn't tell me to stop eating snacks like chips and cookies, but Dad's condition helped me understand that what I eat can affect my health.

1. What was the author's purpose in writing this piece?
   A. To teach friends how to communicate better
   B. To explain that eating better can affect your health
   C. To persuade others to eat cookies rather than chips
   D. To argue that healthy snacks taste better than unhealthy snacks

2. According to this text passage, high blood pressure may be related to
   A. exercising occasionally.
   B. choosing salty foods that are high in fat.
   C. selecting low-fat foods that are salty.
   D. eating foods that are high in fat and salt.

3. Write a paragraph giving your suggestions about how to improve eating habits. Provide details to support your main points.

National Education Standards

Math: Number and Operations, Data Analysis
Language Arts: NCTE 1, NCTE 3, NCTE 4

Standardized Test Practice Answers

Math Practice
1. A
2. D
3. B

Reading/Writing Practice
1. B
2. D
3. Answers will vary but should include only suggestions that promote healthful eating. Students should provide details to support their ideas.

National Education Standards

Math: Number and Operations, Data Analysis

Language Arts: NCTE 1, NCTE 3, NCTE 4

For the complete Math and Language Arts standards, visit glencoe.com.

Go Online

Online Study Tools
For more test practice, visit glencoe.com and complete the Online Quizzes for Chapter 10.

Test-Taking Tip

Previewing Suggest to students that, before they start answering questions on a standardized test, they quickly preview the entire test (if allowed). They can see how the test is organized and estimate how much time they will need to complete each part. They can also identify any parts or questions that they think will be quick and easy to answer. If they complete these items first, they can take more time answering the more difficult questions.

Chapter 11 pages 288–315	Standards		Features
	National	**State/Local**	
	1.12.1, 2.12.5, 3.12.1, 3.12.4, 6.12.1		TIME HEALTH • Craving a Healthy Future, page 310
30 Min **Lesson 1** **Maintaining a Healthy Weight** pages 290–296 **BIG Idea** *Maintaining a healthy weight helps you protect your health and prevent disease.*	1.12.1, 1.12.5, 1.12.7, 3.12.1, 3.12.4, 6.12.4, 7.12.1–7.12.3, 8.12.1–8.12.3		*Real World* CONNECTION • Determining BMI, page 293 Out of Time
30 Min **Lesson 2** **Body Image and Eating Disorders** pages 297–302 **BIG Idea** *Poor body image may lead to unhealthful and harmful eating behaviors.*	1.12.8, 1.12.9, 2.12.5, 2.12.7, 3.12.1, 3.12.4, 5.12.1, 7.12.1, 8.12.1, 8.12.2		
30 Min **Lesson 3** **Lifelong Nutrition** pages 303–309 **BIG Idea** *Nutritional needs will change throughout your life.*	2.12.2, 3.12.1, 4.12.1, 8.12.1, 8.12.4		*Health Skills* Activity • Evaluating Supplements (*Accessing Information*), page 309 Out of Time

Key to Ability Levels

Teaching Strategies and activities have been coded for ability level and appropriateness.

AL Activities for students working above grade level

OL Activities for students working on grade level

BL Activities for students working below grade level

EL Activities for English Learners

Chapter 11 Planning Guide

Resources	Lesson Assessment	Technology
Student Activity Workbook TEACH *FAST FILE* RESOURCES Vocabulary Practice TEACH Health Labs EXTEND	Chapter 11 Review Chapter 11 Assessment Standardized Test Practice 💿 *ExamView® Assessment Suite* CD-ROM	**Teaching Tools:** 💿 *TeacherWorks*™ Plus DVD 💿 *StudentWorks*™ Plus DVD 💿 *ExamView® Assessment Suite* CD-ROM 🕹 Transparency 💿 Fitness DVD 💿 PowerPoint® DVD 💿 Health eSpotlight Video Series DVD
FAST FILE RESOURCES Reading Strategies Activity TEACH Reteaching Activity REVIEW Enrichment Activity EXTEND Health Skills Practice TEACH	Lesson 1 Assessment, page 296 📁 Lesson 1 Quiz *Fast File* 💿 *ExamView® Assessment Suite* CD-ROM	**Web-Based Resources:** Go Online glencoe.com • Health Podcast Activities • Audio Chapter Summaries (English/Spanish) • Interactive Health Tutor • Health Skills Activities • Vocabulary PuzzleMaker • Parent Letters (English/Spanish) • Lesson Plans • Health Inventories • Online Quizzes • Study-to-Go • Unit Web Projects • Student Web Activities • Fitness Zone Activities
FAST FILE RESOURCES Reading Strategies Activity TEACH Reteaching Activity REVIEW Enrichment Activity EXTEND Health Skills Practice TEACH	Lesson 2 Assessment, page 302 📁 Lesson 2 Quiz *Fast File* 💿 *ExamView® Assessment Suite* CD-ROM	
FAST FILE RESOURCES Reading Strategies Activity TEACH Reteaching Activity REVIEW Enrichment Activity EXTEND Health Skills Practice TEACH	Lesson 3 Assessment, page 309 📁 Lesson 3 Quiz *Fast File* 💿 *ExamView® Assessment Suite* CD-ROM	

This is the student's backpack solution.

Includes:
- complete Interactive Student Edition
- full audio of English text and Spanish chapter summaries
- allows students to record assignments and track grades.
- links to online activities and additional student resources
- access to all student worksheets and workbooks

FOLDABLES Study Organizer

Dinah Zike Foldables® Chapter Activity

Refer to the *Dinah Zike Reading and Study Skills for Glencoe Health.* Have students complete the bound book Foldable. Have students use the journal to take notes as they read about maintaining weight, body image and eating disorders, and lifelong nutrition.

Managing Weight and Eating Behaviors

Chapter Overview

Chapter 11 focuses on healthful ways to manage weight, the negative impact of eating disorders, and how nutritional needs change throughout life.

Lesson 1

The ability to manage weight in healthful ways requires an understanding of the methods used to determine a healthy weight range and the factors that impact an individual's food needs.

Lesson 2

Negative body image is a factor that can lead to unhealthy eating behaviors. Eating disorders are dangerous eating behaviors that require treatment by a medical professional.

Lesson 3

Nutritional needs vary through a person's lifetime. There are many factors, such as age, gender, and lifestyle, that can change a person's nutritional requirements.

▶ **Activating Prior Knowledge**

After students have completed their paragraphs, ask: In what ways are these teens taking care of their bodies? What role does nutrition play in helping these teens stay healthy and active?

Lesson 1
Maintaining a Healthy Weight

BIG Idea *Maintaining a healthy weight helps you protect your health and prevent disease.*

Lesson 2
Body Image and Eating Disorders

BIG Idea *Poor body image may lead to unhealthful and harmful eating behaviors.*

Lesson 3
Lifelong Nutrition

BIG Idea *Nutritional needs will change throughout your life.*

Activating Prior Knowledge

Using Visuals Look at the picture on this page. Based on what you see, how does the behavior of these teens contribute to their overall health? Write a paragraph explaining how these teens are taking care of their bodies.

288

Universal Access

Differentiated Learning Glencoe provides teacher support and student materials for all learners in the health classroom.

- Chapter Summaries in English and Spanish are available online at **glencoe.com**.
- *Fast Files* and related worksheets support reluctant readers.

- Universal Access strategies throughout the Teacher Wraparound Edition and *Fast Files* help you present materials for gifted students, at-risk students, physically impaired students, and those with behavior disorders or learning disabilities.

Chapter Launchers

Health in Action

Discuss the BIG Ideas

Before beginning this chapter, think about how you would answer these questions:

▸ What does it mean to have a healthy weight?

▸ Does your weight affect your self-image?

▸ How do your food needs differ from those of your friends?

Watch the *Health eSpotlight* Video Series

Food, Habits, and Choices

How do the media and your family and friends influence your body image?

Assess Your Health

Go Online

Visit glencoe.com and complete the Health Inventory for Chapter 11.

Chapter Launchers

Health in Action

Discuss the BIG Ideas

Have students write a response to each of the bulleted questions before reading the chapter. Suggest that students keep the questions in mind as they read the chapter to help guide their reading. After students have completed the chapter, ask them to revisit their responses to see if any of their responses have changed.

Health eSpotlight Video Series

Foods, Habits, and Choices

Before Viewing the Video

Ask Students: What healthful food options do you choose to eat each day?

Go Online

Have students go to **glencoe.com** and take the Health Inventory for Chapter 11.

Chapter Skills

Reading Skills

- Reviewing Facts and Vocabulary, pp. 296, 302, 309
- Reading/Writing Practice, p. 315

BIG Idea

Students will learn about the ways that eating behaviors can impact their health.

Health Skills

- Health Skills Activity, p. 309
- Applying Health Skills, pp. 296, 302, 308

Writing Skills

- Real World Connection, p. 293
- Writing Critically, pp. 296, 302, 309
- Reading/Writing Practice, p. 315

Vocabulary

- New Vocabulary, pp. 290, 297, 303
- Reviewing Facts and Vocabulary, pp. 296, 302, 309

Maintaining a Healthy Weight

① FOCUS

GUIDE TO READING

BIG Idea Maintaining a healthy weight can protect health and prevent disease.
Ask Students: *Can you identify a way in which a person's weight can impact each side of his or her health triangle?* (Answers will vary.)

Before You Read

Venn Diagram Students' Venn diagrams should include information about maintaining a healthful weight.

Main Idea

The Calorie Connection A consistent weight can be maintained if the number of calories taken in equals the number of calories used.
Ask Students: *What do calories measure?* (Calories are units used to measure the energy in food.)

Real Life Issues ··············

Have students read the Real Life Issues scenario.
Ask Students: *How could Jeffrey's decision impact his health?* (Accept responses that indicate both positive and negative ways in which decisions about weight can impact health.)

290

LESSON 1

GUIDE TO READING

BIG Idea *Maintaining a healthy weight helps you protect your health and prevent disease.*

Before You Read

Create a Venn Diagram. Draw two overlapping circles. Label them "Losing Weight" and "Gaining Weight." As you read, fill in the outer area of each circle with useful tips on the corresponding topic. Fill in the overlapping area with advice that is useful to everyone trying to maintain a healthy weight.

Losing Weight   Gaining Weight

New Vocabulary

▸ metabolism (p. 290)
▸ body mass index (BMI) (p. 291)
▸ overweight (p. 291)
▸ obese (p. 292)
▸ underweight (p. 293)

Maintaining a Healthy Weight

Real Life Issues ··························

Wondering About His Weight. Jeffrey used to be the smallest guy in his class. This year he finally had a growth spurt and grew 6 inches, but his weight doesn't seem to be keeping up with his height. He's happy about being taller, but he's not sure it's normal for him to be so thin. He wonders if his weight is unhealthy and whether he should try to put on some extra weight.

Writing *Write a letter to Jeffrey describing what he can do to figure out whether his weight is healthy and how he can learn to feel comfortable with his changing body.*

The Calorie Connection

Main Idea You maintain your weight by taking in as many calories as you use.

Calories are units used to measure the energy found in food. If you consume more calories than your body needs, you will gain weight. If you use more calories than you take in, you will lose weight. The balance between the calories you take in and those you burn is called energy balance.

Your Energy Balance

Your **metabolism**—*the process by which the body breaks down substances and gets energy from food*—converts the food you eat into fuel. It takes about 3,500 calories to equal 1 pound of body fat. Thus, if you consume 500 fewer calories than you use every day, you will lose 1 pound per week.

 Promoting School Wellness

Nutrition at School One of the components of a successful coordinated school health program is access to healthful meals and other services related to nutrition. Review with students the resources available through the school food program. Information about community-based nutrition related services should also be available through the school. Make students aware of these services, and provide information about these services to students' families several times during the year.

Figure 11.1 Calories in Common Snack Foods

High-Calorie Snack			Lower-Calorie Alternative		
Food Item	**Serving Size**	**Calories**	**Food Item**	**Serving Size**	**Calories**
Potato Chips	1 oz.	155	Pretzels	1 oz.	108
Cola	12 oz.	151	Water	16 oz.	0
Chocolate/caramel candy bar	1.6 oz.	208	Apple	1 medium	70
Chocolate sandwich cookies	6 cookies	282	Granola bar, raisin nut	1 oz.	127
Cream-filled snack cakes	2 (3 oz.)	314	Vanilla yogurt (low-fat)	8 oz.	193

How Many Calories?

As a rule, foods that are high in fat will also be high in calories. A gram of fat contains nine calories while a gram of protein or carbohydrate contains four. Some low-fat foods, however, may also be high in calories. Sugary foods contain more calories than fresh vegetables and fruits, which are higher in water and fiber.

Food preparation also plays a role in how many calories a food delivers. Fried foods, or those served with a cream sauce or otherwise prepared in a way that adds extra fats and sugars, are likely to be high in calories. To control your weight, eat less of high calorie foods or eat them less often. **Figure 11.1** compares the calories of common snack foods.

READING CHECK

Predict What would probably happen if you increased your activity level without eating more food?

Maintaining a Healthy Weight

Main Idea **Body mass index and body composition help you judge whether your weight is healthy.**

To maintain a healthy weight, burn the same amount of calories that are consumed. The right weight for each person is based on several factors, including age, gender, height, body frame, and stage and rate of growth.

Body Mass Index

To learn if your body weight falls into a healthy **range**, calculate your **body mass index (BMI)**—*a measure of body weight relative to height.* Compare it to the charts on page 293 to determine if you're **overweight**—*heavier than the standard weight range for your height*—or at risk for being overweight.

Academic Vocabulary

range *(noun):* the distance between possible extremes

Academic Integration

Math **Word Problems** Use the *Calories in Common Snack Foods* table in **Figure 11.1** in the student text to generate word problems that review math skills. For example, **ask students:** *If you have a granola bar instead of 6 chocolate sandwich cookies, how many fewer calories do you consume?* (155) Have students work in pairs to generate another word problem and solution using the data in the table. Have each pair of students share its problem with the class.

2 TEACH

Main Idea

Maintaining a Healthy Weight Body mass index and body composition can help individuals determine a healthy weight range. **Ask Students:** *Why do healthful weights vary from person to person?* (Healthy weights are based on several factors that vary between individuals, such as height and rate of growth.)

C Critical Thinking

Explaining Direct students' attention to the information in **Figure 11.1**. Ask students to explain why it is important to pay attention to serving size information when you are making lower-calorie, healthy food choices. (Students should note that a large portion of a lower-calorie choice can have as many, or more, calories than the high-calorie snack.) OL

READING CHECK

Answer Sample answer: I would lose weight.

Academic Vocabulary

Range Ask a volunteer to read the definition of the word *range* aloud. Then ask students to use the word range as defined in the text in a written sentence.

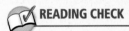

It's important to remember that every teen grows at his or her own rate. It's normal that some of your friends will be taller or shorter than you, and that some will weigh more or less than you.

Body Composition

Although BMI is a quick, handy way to evaluate your weight, it doesn't tell the whole story. A person who is very muscular, for instance, may have a higher BMI but still be healthy. It's also important to consider your body composition—the ratio of fat to lean tissue in your body.

HS

One commonly used method to measure your BMI is called skin-fold testing. It involves measuring the thickness of skin folds at different points on the body to figure out how much fat is stored beneath the skin. This test should be performed by a qualified professional.

CA Cultural Awareness

Lower-Calorie Alternatives
Pair English language learners with English proficient students. Have students volunteer information about or research high-calorie foods and lower-calorie alternatives from two different cultures. Examples include steamed rice as a lower-calorie alternative to fried rice, and salsa as a lower-calorie alternative to guacamole. Have each pair of students prepare a table similar to the table in **Figure 11.1** to display their results. EL OL

READING CHECK

Explain What does body mass index (BMI) measure?

Your Weight and Your Health

> Main Idea Being either overweight or underweight carries health risks.

People whose weight does not fall into a healthy range are at a higher risk for various diseases. Weighing too much can increase your risk for health problems such as heart disease, cancer, asthma, osteoarthritis, gallbladder disease, or type 2 diabetes. Teens who weigh too little may feel weak, tire easily, or have trouble concentrating.

Main Idea

Weight and Health There are health risks associated with being overweight or underweight. **Ask Students:** *What are some health risks associated with a body weight that is not in the healthy range?* (Sample answers include diabetes, cardiovascular disease, and hypertension.)

Weighing Too Much

You've probably heard that more than 13 percent of teens in the United States are overweight. This percentage has tripled since the 1980s. Teens who are overweight may be at risk of becoming **obese**—*having an excess of body fat*. Being obese carries serious health risks.

■ **Figure 11.2** Staying active helps you maintain a healthy weight. *What might happen if these teens spent their afternoons playing video games instead of engaging in physical activity?*

HS Health Skills Practice

Accessing Information Have students work in small groups to find resources available to teens who have questions about their weight, body mass index, or body composition. Ask students to consider a variety of possible sources of information, including information available from health professionals and online. Have each group share one reliable source of information with the class. OL

READING CHECK

Answer Body weight relative to height

Skills for the 21st Century

Advocating for Community Health
Teens who are overweight or obese face health risks related to their weight. Every year, an increasing number of U.S. teens are considered overweight or obese. Have students work in small groups to prepare a poster that lists the short- and long-term health risks of obesity. After students have completed their posters, ask them to research community resources and services that can help combat obesity in teens. Have students share their findings with the class.

Real World CONNECTION

Determining BMI

Here's an example for a 16-year-old male who is 6 feet tall and weighs 182 pounds.

$$182 \div 72 = 2.528$$

$$2.528 \div 72 = .035$$

$$0.035 \times 703 = 24.6$$

$$BMI = 24.6$$

Use this formula to determine your BMI. First, convert your height into inches. Divide your weight in pounds by your height in inches. Divide that result by your height again, and multiply the result by 703.

Look at the charts to the right to determine if you're at risk for being overweight or underweight.

Activity Mathematics

Concept Problem Solving: Make a Plan
Some problems require more than one step to solve. Think through your approach before choosing an operation to use.

G Online

Go to glencoe.com for an online BMI calculator.

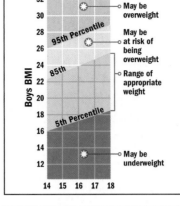

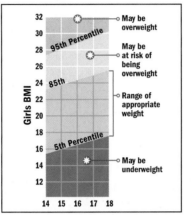

Some people are overweight or obese because of heredity or genetics. Some people may have a slow metabolism, which may lead to weight gain. However, many people who are overweight consume too many calories and get too little physical activity.

Weighing Too Little

Being **underweight**, or *below the standard weight range for your height,* also carries health risks. Some thin people may have trouble fighting off disease. Others are naturally thin because of genetics or because they have a fast metabolism.

Lesson 1   Maintaining a Healthy Weight   **293**

Real World CONNECTION

Answers to Activity Question:

Her BMI is 22.3, which falls into the healthy range. Have students use the online BMI calculator to check the calculations they performed as a part of the Real World Connection activity.

R Reading Strategy

Main Idea and Details Ask for volunteers to read aloud the text under the main head: "Your Weight and Your Health." Then direct students' attention to the two smaller heads: "Weighing Too Much" and "Weighing Too Little." Explain that the information under the two smaller heads provides details related to the main idea. After students have read the section, ask volunteers to share a detail related to the main idea of this section of text. **BL EL**

Cooperative Learning

Multimedia Presentation Divide the class into seven groups. Assign to each group one of the bulleted health risks associated with being overweight (hypertension, cardiovascular disease, type 2 diabetes, osteoarthritis, gallbladder disease, asthma, certain types of cancer). Have the members of each group research how being overweight can lead to that condition. Make sure each group includes one positive health action to take. Each group should prepare a multimedia presentation to share what members learned with the rest of the class. If multimedia technology is not available to students, have each group present a poster, brochure, or oral report.

Universal Access

Reinforcing Vocabulary The vocabulary terms *overweight* and *underweight* may be confusing to students who have limited English. Write the terms *overweight* and *underweight* on the board. Underline the word parts *over-* and *under-*. Explain that the words *over* and *under* are commonly used to describe an object's position. In this case, *over* and *under* are used in a different way. Explain that in these vocabulary terms, *over* and *under* are used to mean "more than" and "less than." **EL**

Caption Answer

Figure 11.3 The range of weights that is considered healthy for any individual depends on many factors that vary between individuals. What is healthy for one person cannot be assumed to be healthy for another.

READING CHECK

Answer A teen may feel weak, tire easily, or have trouble concentrating.

Main Idea

Managing Your Weight A weight-management plan that includes physical activity and healthful foods will help a person maintain weight throughout life.
Ask Students: *Why are both foods and physical activity important parts of a weight-management plan?* (Sample answer: Because weight depends on both the number of calories consumed and the number of calories expended.)

■ **Figure 11.3** There is a wide range of weights that can be considered healthy. *Why should you avoid comparing your weight to that of your friends?*

 READING CHECK

Summarize What health problems may underweight teens have?

Teens may be thin because their bodies are growing very quickly. As their growth slows, their bodies may "fill out." For other teens, however, being too thin can mean that they aren't getting the calories and nutrients their growing bodies need, or that they are exercising excessively to burn calories.

If your BMI suggests that you might be underweight or overweight, get advice from a health care professional about healthful ways to gain or lose weight.

Managing Your Weight

Main Idea Stay physically active and eat healthful foods.

If your weight seems to be in a healthy range, then you probably don't need to worry too much about the number of calories you consume. If you want to lose or gain weight, however, you'll need to adjust either the number of calories you take in, the number you burn through physical activity, or both. The Dietary Guidelines for Americans does not recommend that teens diet. Instead, teens should try to eat a healthful, well-balanced diet every day to reach a healthy weight. Some healthful ways to manage your weight include the following strategies:

- **Target a healthy weight.** Learn your ideal weight range from a health care professional.
- **Set realistic goals.** Eat a consistently healthful diet and exercise regularly.
- **Personalize your plan.** Incorporate foods you enjoy into your daily eating plan.
- **Put your goals and plan in writing.** Write down your goals and your plan.
- **Evaluate your progress.** Track your weight on a weekly basis.

Healthful Ways to Lose Weight

MyPyramid provides information on food groups, recommended amounts, and the importance of physical activity. Here are some points to keep in mind:

- **Choose nutrient-dense foods.** Fruits, vegetables, and whole grains supply nutrients with fewer calories.
- **Watch portion sizes.** Stick to recommended portion sizes for each major food group.
- **Eat fewer foods that are high in fats and added sugars.** These add calories without many nutrients.

Teens Want to Know

Is Gastric Bypass Surgery an Easy Way to Lose Weight? Explain that gastric bypass surgery involves a life-long change in eating habits. After surgery, the stomach can accommodate only small amounts of food. Individuals who have undergone bariatric surgery must limit their food intake for the remainder of their lives. This procedure is used for teens only if other methods for weight loss have been unsuccessful and the health risks caused by the teen's weight are considered greater than the risks of surgery. This method is very controversial in the medical community. Students may have the misconception that this is an easy or "miraculous" way to correct weight problems.

- **Enjoy your favorite foods in moderation.** Try enjoying a small scoop of ice cream less often.
- **Be active.** The information in **Figure 11.5** on page 296 compares the number of calories burned in different types of activity.
- **Tone your muscles.** Since muscle tissue takes more calories to maintain than fat, increasing your muscle mass means that your body will use more calories.
- **Stay hydrated.** Teens should drink between 9 and 13 cups of fluids a day.

Healthful Ways to Gain Weight

If you are trying to gain weight, the following strategies can help. Teens who want to gain weight should try to increase the amount of healthy muscle on their bodies, not fat. To gain healthy weight, continue a regular exercise program while using the strategies listed below.

AL
- **Select foods from the five major food groups that are higher in calories.** Choose whole milk instead of low-fat or fat-free milk.
- **Choose higher-calorie, nutrient-rich foods.** Examples include nuts, dried fruits, cheese, and avocados.
- **Eat nutritious snacks.** Enjoy healthful snacks more often to increase your daily calorie intake.
- **Get regular physical activity.** If you're increasing your calorie intake to gain weight, don't forget exercise. Physical activity will ensure that most of the weight you gain is muscle rather than fat.

■ **Figure 11.4** Your food choices can help you either gain or lose weight. *List three nutritional qualities that make this lunch a good choice for someone trying to lose weight.*

READING CHECK

Explain How is physical activity important to weight loss?

FITNESS ZONE

My dad always says, "If you always do what you always did, you'll always get what you always got." I realized he is saying that if you want to change the outcome, you have to change your behavior. I wanted to get into shape, but skipped workouts and ate junk food. When I changed my behavior, I got what I wanted. Making healthier food choices and exercising regularly improved my fitness level, and I felt a lot healthier. For more fitness tips, visit the Online Fitness Zone at **glencoe.com**.

AL **Active Learning**

Healthy Fast Food Choices
Explain that fast food restaurants have recently experienced pressure from consumers to include more healthful food options on their menus. Have pairs of students research healthy food and drink choices available at one fast food restaurant. They should also include suggestions on how to make the "not-so-healthy" items more healthy. Have each pair present findings to the class.

FITNESS ZONE

Have students do this activity
- Begin with groups of three or four students each forming a line.
- The leader leads her line in an exercise while moving around the room.
- Have leader move to end of the line and next person becomes leader.
- Repeat until all students lead one exercise.

READING CHECK

Answer Physical activity burns calories and helps the body use up excess fat. Strength training exercises can tone the muscles to make the body appear slimmer.

Caption Answer

Figure 11.4 The meal is high in fiber, low in fat, and contains foods from each of the five food groups.

Reading Strategy

Bulleted Lists Direct students' attention to the bulleted list of information found on these pages. Explain that the text following each bullet point is information related to the heading "Healthful Ways to Lose Weight." Tell students that bulleted lists are a way of organizing large amounts of information about a single topic. When a student encounters a bulleted list in the text, he or she should note the heading above the list to find the main idea. Then the student can read the list to learn details related to the main idea. Have students make their own bulleted list under the heading "Different Ways I Can Be More Healthful." Tell them they can include any of the information they have learned so far.

ASSESS/ CLOSE

Assessment Resources

📁 *FAST FILE* ACTIVITIES
Lesson 1 Quiz

💿 *ExamView*
Assessment Suite CD-ROM

Visit glencoe.com for:
Online Quizzes
Online Learning Center

Progress Monitoring

Reteaching

Have students work in pairs to review lists of tips for healthful weight gain and healthful weight loss. Have each pair of students make a T-chart that lists these tips. Ask students to identify a tip that appears on both lists. (Sample answers: Be active/get regular physical activity)

Enrichment

Have students research the portion sizes recommended by MyPyramid for each major food group. Then have students make a poster or other visual model that compares recommended portion sizes to typical serving sizes of various foods that they commonly eat.

Go Online

Have students visit **glencoe.com** and complete the Interactive Study Guide for this lesson.

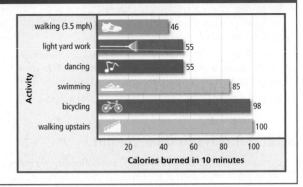

Figure 11.5 Calories Burned During Physical Activity

Physical activity may mean a brief workout. This graph shows how many calories a person weighing 125 to 175 pounds can burn doing each activity for 10 minutes.

Physical Activity and Weight Management

Physical activity can help you lose or maintain a healthy weight. Some added benefits of regular physical activity:

- It helps relieve stress.
- It promotes a normal appetite response.
- It increases self-esteem, which helps you keep your plan on track.
- It helps you feel more energetic.

LESSON 1 **ASSESSMENT**

After You Read

Reviewing Facts and Vocabulary

1. What is *metabolism*?
2. Explain how to calculate your body mass index.
3. List three health problems associated with being overweight and obese.

Thinking Critically

4. **Analyze.** Explain how exercise that builds muscle can help promote loss of body fat.
5. **Synthesize.** Mike is 15 years old. He is 5 feet 9 inches tall and weighs 180 pounds. Explain whether his weight is in a healthy range.

Applying Health Skills

6. **Practicing Healthful Behaviors.** Write a plan describing the strategies you will use to maintain a healthy weight throughout your life.

Writing Critically

7. **Expository.** Write a short article aimed at middle school students describing the causes and effects of overweight and obesity problems among teens.

Go Online

Visit **glencoe.com** and complete the Interactive Study Guide for this lesson.

LESSON 1 ASSESSMENT ANSWERS

1. *Metabolism* is the process by which the body breaks down substances and gets energy from food.
2. Multiply your body weight in pounds by 703, then divide by the square of your height in inches.
3. *Any three:* hypertension, cardiovascular disease, type 2 diabetes, osteoarthritis, gallbladder disease, asthma and other respiratory problems, certain types of cancer
4. Muscle tissue takes more calories to maintain than fat.
5. Mike has a BMI of 26.5, which suggests that he may be at risk of being overweight. Mike should see a healthcare professional to find out whether his weight is due to excess body fat. If so, he should follow healthful steps for losing weight.
6. Plans will vary.
7. Articles will vary.

Body Image and Eating Disorders

Real Life Issues ....

Dealing with Body Image. Lydia has always been comfortable with how she looks. When she started high school this year, however, she started feeling self-conscious about her weight. All of a sudden, none of her clothes seem to fit her, and she's unhappy about being heavier than her friends. She wonders if she should go on a calorie-restricted diet or try liquid meal replacements.

Writing *Write a letter to Lydia offering helpful advice to ease her concerns about her changing body.*

Your Body Image

Main Idea The media and other influences can affect your body image.

When you look in the mirror, do you like what you see? If the answer is yes, that means that your **body image**—*the way you see your body*—is positive. Though many teens like the way they look, many others feel insecure about their changing bodies. During your teen years, you will experience many physical changes at a rapid pace. You may feel unhappy with your body type and wish you were taller, shorter, thinner, shapelier, or more muscular.

Where does body image come from? Some teens may compare their bodies to those of models, athletes, or actors. You should keep in mind that the images shown in the media aren't always realistic. Peers can also influence body image. Overweight or underweight teens may feel pressured by their friends and others to look a certain way.

GUIDE TO READING

BIG Idea *Poor body image may lead to unhealthful and harmful eating behaviors.*

Before You Read

Create a Comparison Chart. Make a chart and label the columns "Anorexia," "Bulimia," and "Binge Eating." Label the rows "Symptoms" and "Health Risks." As you read, fill in the chart with information about these eating disorders.

	Symptoms	Health Risks
Anorexia		
Bulimia		
Binge Eating		

New Vocabulary

- body image (p. 297)
- fad diets (p. 298)
- weight cycling (p. 298)
- eating disorders (p. 300)
- anorexia nervosa (p. 300)
- bulimia nervosa (p. 301)
- binge eating disorder (p. 301)

Lesson 2   Body Image and Eating Disorders   **297**

Body Image and Eating Disorders

1 FOCUS

GUIDE TO READING

BIG Idea A negative body image can lead to a variety of unhealthful eating behaviors, including eating disorders. **Ask Students:** *What are some factors that influence how you think about your body?* (Sample answers: the media, my friends, my parents)

Before You Read

Comparison Chart Students' charts should correctly list the symptoms and health risks associated with anorexia nervosa, bulimia nervosa, and binge eating disorder.

Main Idea

Your Body Image Body image is influenced by many factors, including the media. **Ask Students:** *How is a positive body image related to self-esteem?* (A positive body image can contribute to self-esteem.)

ELL Coach

Vocabulary Support Preview the lesson vocabulary with students by using the following activities.

Beginning Write each Lesson 2 vocabulary term on the board. Pronounce each term aloud for students. Then provide a simple definition for each term. Have students practice pronouncing each term with a partner.

Intermediate Have students use index cards to make a vocabulary flash card for each Lesson 2 vocabulary term. Students can work with a partner to practice pronouncing and defining each term.

Advanced Have students preview each Lesson 2 vocabulary term. Then ask students to use each vocabulary term in a written or spoken sentence.

Real Life Issues ....

Ask volunteers to share their letters with the class. Encourage students to point out examples of constructive advice offered to Lydia.

2 TEACH

R Reading Strategies

Organizing Information Model for students on the board or overhead how to make a cluster chart to organize information. Then ask students to make a blank cluster chart. In the center circle, have students write "Factors that influence body image." Have them add words and phrases that identify factors that influence body image to their charts as they read. **EL BL**

Caption Answer

Figure 11.6 Answers will vary. Students will probably suggest that looking like a magazine model is not a healthy or realistic goal.

READING CHECK

Answer Body image is the way you see your body.

Main Idea

Fad Diets Fad diets are weight-loss plans that promise unrealistic results and promote unhealthy eating habits. **Ask Students:** *Have you ever seen an advertisement for a weight-loss plan that seemed too good to be true? What claims were made about the weight-loss plan's results?* (Answers will vary.)

Academic Vocabulary

Pose Write the following on the board: *Eating behaviors that pose health risks.* Have students identify eating behaviors that pose risks, and record these on the board.

■ **Figure 11.6** Media images may influence teens' views about ideal body types. *Do you think trying to look like magazine models is a realistic or healthy goal?*

READING CHECK

Define What is body image?

Academic Vocabulary

pose *(verb):* to present or set forth

Accepting Yourself

The rapid pace of physical changes you experience during your teen years may affect your body image. Growth spurts may cause some teens to look thin. Hormonal changes may cause other teens to gain weight. Try to accept yourself the way you are, or talk to a parent or other trusted adult about your feelings. You can't change your basic body type, and you could hurt your health if you try. **R**

Fad Diets

Main Idea Fad diets are neither safe nor reliable ways to lose weight.

Teens who want to lose weight may be tempted to try **fad diets,** *weight-loss plans that tend to be popular for only a short time.* Fad diets typically promise quick, easy weight loss. People on these diets may lose weight temporarily, but they usually regain it after going off the diet. As a result, they may fall into **weight cycling,** *a repeated pattern of losing and regaining body weight.*

Fad diets may restrict the types and amounts of foods that you eat, making it difficult to stay on them for a long time. Other fad diets use pills or supplements that seem to offer an easy solution to weight loss. Research has shown that they are not effective. Fad diets can **pose** serious health risks.

In fact, most teens should not diet at all. Teens who feel they may need to lose weight should talk to their doctor before starting any diet plan. In rare circumstances, teens with a serious weight problem may be advised to follow a low-calorie plan, but only under the supervision of a health care professional. In general, teens who want to maintain a healthy weight should follow the nutrition guidelines of MyPyramid and get regular physical activity.

298 Chapter 11 Managing Weight and Eating Behaviors

Home and Community

Weight-Loss Strategies Ask students to find examples of weight-loss plans in magazines or newspapers. Have them compare the weight-loss plans they find to healthy weight-loss strategies they have learned about in this chapter. Then ask students to prepare a written summary that explains why or why not the weight-loss plans they found in magazines or newspapers are healthful ways to lose weight. Have students use their completed summary to explain to a family member the characteristics of healthful weight-loss plans and strategies for evaluating weight-loss plans.

Types of Fad Diets

All fad diets lose their popularity once people realize that they're unhealthy and that they just don't work. Still, certain types of fad diets keep reappearing every few years in a different form. Here are some common ones:

- **Miracle foods.** These plans promise you can "burn fat" by eating lots of a single food or type of food. In reality, there is no single food that can destroy fat. Moreover, eating only certain types of food will not give your body all the nutrients it needs.
- **Magic combinations.** These plans promise that certain foods will trigger weight loss when they're eaten together. The food combinations may be safe to eat as part of an overall healthy diet, but there's no evidence that combining certain foods will lead to weight loss.
- **Liquid diets.** These plans replace solid food with ultra-low-calorie liquid formulas. These diets can lead to dangerous side effects if they are followed incorrectly. However, doctors may recommend them (with medical supervision) for people who are seriously obese.
- **Diet pills.** Some diet pills and supplements claim to suppress your appetite so that you eat less. Others claim to "block" or "flush" fat from the body. Diet pills can be addictive. In addition, they may cause drowsiness, anxiety, a racing heart, or other serious side effects.
- **Fasting.** Fasting deprives the body of needed nutrients and can result in dehydration. Some religious and cultural customs require people to fast for short periods, such as specific days or times of the day during certain months. This kind of short-term fasting is safe for most people.

Recognizing Fad Diets

How can you tell the difference between a fad diet and a legitimate weight-loss plan? Any plan that does not follow the MyPyramid guidelines may deprive your body of nutrients. Plans that promise ultra-fast weight loss (more than 2 pounds a week) are likely to be unsafe or ineffective. Plans that promise you can lose weight without boosting your physical activity also are likely to be unsafe or ineffective. Watch out for such words as *effortless, guaranteed, miraculous, breakthrough, ancient,* or *secret.* Diets that require you to buy certain products rather than choose healthful foods should also raise your suspicions. Finally, be skeptical about claims that "doctors don't want you to know about this weight-loss plan." Ask yourself, "Why would my doctor want to keep me from reaching a healthy weight?"

■ **Figure 11.7** Combining a healthful, lower-calorie eating plan with physical activity is a more reliable way to lose weight than any fad diet. *What are some drawbacks of fad diets?*

READING CHECK

Explain What are some typical characteristics of fad diets?

Lesson 2 Body Image and Eating Disorders **299**

C **Critical Thinking**

Explaining Point out that one common characteristic of all types of fad diets is the tendency for individuals to regain the weight they have lost soon after discontinuing the fad diet. Ask students to explain why most individuals regain the weight they lose on a fad diet. (Most fad diets include eating plans that are not sustainable for long periods of time.) **OL**

AL **Active Learning**

Public Service Announcement Explain that public service announcements, or PSAs, are brief announcements that are broadcast on radio or television. PSAs are often used to promote health and wellness. If possible, provide several current examples of PSAs. Challenge students to work in groups to develop a 30-second radio PSA that warns teens of the health dangers associated with fad diets. Remind students that PSAs must be accurate, persuasive, and attention-grabbing. Have each group share its PSA with the class. **OL** **AL**

Caption Answer

Figure 11.7 Answers will vary. Students will probably suggest that fad diets include eating habits that are not safe or healthful.

English Language Coach

Adjectives Direct students' attention to the words listed in the text that can indicate that an eating plan is a fad diet *(effortless, guaranteed, miraculous, breakthrough, ancient, secret).* Tell students that these words are all adjectives, words that describe a noun or pronoun (in this case, the fad diet). **Ask Students:** *What are some other adjectives that describe fad diets?* (Answers will vary; possible responses include *unsafe, harmful, unreliable, unproven.*)

READING CHECK

Answer Sample answers include: They are popular for short periods of time; they make unrealistic promises.

Go Online

Visit **glencoe.com** and complete the Student Web Activity to learn more about preventing eating disorders.

Eating Disorders

Main Idea Eating disorders are extreme and dangerous eating behaviors that require medical attention.

As you have learned, some types of weight-loss diets are unhealthy. Yet some people eat in ways that are more harmful to their health. They suffer from **eating disorders**—*extreme, harmful eating behaviors that can cause serious illness or even death.* Eating disorders are classified as mental illnesses, and they are often linked to depression, low self-esteem, or troubled personal relationships. Social and cultural forces that emphasize physical appearance can also play a role. Eating disorders often run in families. Research also suggests that genetics may be a factor in the development of eating disorders.

Anorexia Nervosa

Anorexia nervosa is *an eating disorder in which an irrational fear of weight gain leads people to starve themselves.* It mainly affects girls and young women. People with anorexia see themselves unrealistically as overweight even when they are dangerously thin. The disorder affects a person's self-concept and coping abilities. Outside pressures, high expectations, a need to be accepted, and a need to achieve are characteristics associated with anorexia nervosa. Medical specialists say that genetics and other biological factors may also play a role. Often, people with anorexia develop obsessive behaviors related to food, such as

■ **Figure 11.8** People with anorexia can be very thin and still see themselves as overweight. *What are other symptoms associated with anorexia?*

300

- avoiding food and meals.
- eating only a few kinds of food in small amounts.
- weighing or counting the calories in everything they eat.
- exercising excessively.
- weighing themselves repeatedly.

Health consequences of anorexia nervosa are related to malnutrition and starvation. The bones of people with eating disorders may become brittle. Body temperature, heart rate, and blood pressure may drop, and there may be a reduction in organ size. Anorexia nervosa can lead to heart problems and sudden cardiac death.

Bulimia Nervosa

Bulimia nervosa is *an eating disorder that involves cycles of overeating and purging, or attempts to rid the body of food.* People with bulimia regularly go on *binges,* eating a huge amount of food in a single sitting. During the binge they may feel out of control, often gulping down food too fast to taste it. After the binge they purge, forcing themselves to vomit or taking laxatives to flush the food out of their systems. Instead of purging, some people with bulimia may fast or exercise frantically after a binge.

Unlike people with anorexia, bulimia sufferers are typically in the normal weight range for their age and height. However, they share the same fear of weight gain and dissatisfaction with their bodies.

Health consequences of bulimia nervosa include dehydration, sore and inflamed throat, and swollen glands. The teeth of people with bulimia nervosa may become damaged by regular exposure to stomach acid from vomiting. They may also damage their stomach, intestines, or kidneys. In severe cases, the chemical imbalances that result from purging can lead to irregular heart rhythms, heart failure, and death.

Binge Eating Disorder

Binge eating disorder is *an eating disorder in which people overeat compulsively.* They binge in much the same way people with bulimia do, eating large amounts of food in a short period of time. These eating binges generally do not occur as frequently as binges associated with bulimia. During a binge, the person may feel guilty and disgusted about his or her behavior, but feel powerless to stop it. Binge eating disorder is more common in males than any other eating disorder, accounting for more than a third of all cases.

Consequences of binge eating disorder include becoming overweight or obese. People with binge eating disorder do not purge. They can also develop the health problems associated with obesity, including high blood pressure, type 2 diabetes, and cardiovascular disease.

Seeking Help

Eating disorders are serious and dangerous illnesses. People with these disorders need help to overcome them. Medical help may involve counseling, nutritional guidance, a doctor's care, and in extreme cases, a hospital stay.

For anorexia nervosa, the goal of treatment is to restore the patient's body weight to a healthy level. The patient also receives psychological and family therapy. Family members and friends can help by creating a supportive environment and helping the patient learn to eat normally again.

FITNESS ZONE

Some of my friends skip breakfast to lose weight. Some say they don't have the time to eat it. My dad says that he read a magazine article saying that people who eat breakfast every day are more likely to lose weight and keep it off. Eating breakfast gives you an energy boost. It also increases your metabolism, which means that you burn more calories. I think it's so cool that you can actually eat to maintain a healthy weight or lose weight. For more fitness tips, visit the Online Fitness Zone at glencoe.com.

READING CHECK

Compare and Contrast How is binge eating disorder different from bulimia nervosa?

Universal Access

Summarizing Main Ideas Guide students in summarizing the main ideas about each type of eating disorder. On the board, write the following three headings: Anorexia Nervosa, Bulimia Nervosa, and Binge Eating Disorder. Ask students to find information in the text about each of these eating disorders. Have students share words, phrases, or sentences that describe one of these eating disorders and record their responses under the correct heading on the board. After several answers have been provided for each eating disorder, read all of the responses aloud to students. **EL** **BL**

READING CHECK

Answer Individuals with binge eating disorder do not purge after overeating.

FITNESS ZONE

Have students stand back-to-back with a partner. Give each team a small ball, wadded paper, or other small object.

- Have students pass the ball by reaching to one side, exchange ball, twist to one side, and exchange ball again.

- Then have students try other ways to exchange the ball.

Writing Strategy

Write a Dialogue Remind students that individuals with eating disorders often do not recognize or cannot admit that they have a serious problem. Friends and family often play a key role in helping individuals with eating disorders recognize that they need help. After an individual begins receiving treatment for an eating disorder, friends and family continue to play an important role in supporting and encouraging the individual.

Have students work in groups of three or four to write a dialogue that demonstrates ways friends can help and support an individual with an eating disorder who has begun treatment. Have each group share its dialogue with the class. After all dialogues have been shared, encourage students to brainstorm additional ways to offer support to a friend who has an eating disorder.

■ **Figure 11.9** Self-help groups in some communities provide ongoing support for people recovering from eating disorders. *How might being part of such a group be helpful?*

CHAPTER 11
LESSON 2

Caption Answer

Figure 11.9 Sample answer: Individuals recovering from eating disorders can get advice from others who have had similar experiences.

❸ ASSESS/ CLOSE

Assessment Resources

 FAST FILE ACTIVITIES
Lesson 2 Quiz

 ExamView Assessment Suite CD-ROM

Visit glencoe.com for:
Online Quizzes
Online Learning Center

Progress Monitoring

Reteaching
Have students work in pairs to make a written list of characteristics of fad diets. Ask pairs to share one entry from their list with the class.

Enrichment
Have students write a short essay encouraging teens to develop a positive body image. Challenge students to include information about how body image impacts self-esteem.

Go Online

Have students visit **glencoe.com** and complete the Interactive Study Guide for this lesson.

The key to treating bulimia nervosa is to break the cycle of binging and purging. Behavioral therapy can sometimes help with this goal. After that, psychotherapy can address the emotional problems that led to the eating disorder. Similar treatments are used for binge eating disorder.

People with eating disorders often cannot admit that they have a problem. Family members and friends can help them recognize the problem and seek treatment. Some patients end up requiring long-term care to recover. Support groups can help with this process. If you think that you or someone you know may have an eating disorder, your first step might be to talk to a trusted adult, such as a parent, counselor, or school nurse.

LESSON 2 📖 ASSESSMENT

After You Read

Reviewing Facts and Vocabulary

1. List two factors that influence body image.
2. Define *fad diets*.
3. List three types of eating disorders.

Thinking Critically

4. **Synthesize.** How might a poor body image result in an eating disorder?
5. **Evaluate.** If you read an ad in a magazine promising you can lose up to 15 pounds in one month while still eating all your favorite foods, would you think this was a fad diet or a legitimate plan? Explain why.

Applying Health Skills

6. **Analyzing Influences.** Write an essay describing how teen magazines portray teens and their bodies. How might the magazine's pictures affect the body image of teens?

Writing Critically

7. **Narrative.** Write a story about a teen who seeks help for an eating disorder. Describe the symptoms and how the disorder affects the teen's life.

Go Online

Visit **glencoe.com** and complete the Interactive Study Guide for this lesson.

302   **Chapter 11**   Managing Weight and Eating Behaviors

LESSON 2 ASSESSMENT ANSWERS

1. *Any two:* Insecurity about physical changes during adolescence, images in the media, attitudes of friends and family
2. *Fad diets* are weight-loss plans that tend to be popular for only a short time.
3. Anorexia nervosa, bulimia nervosa, binge eating disorder
4. Someone with a poor body image (often linked to poor self-esteem) might always see him- or herself as fat regardless of actual weight and become obsessed with losing weight.
5. This is a *fad diet* because it promises an unrealistic rate of weight loss.
6. Students' essays will vary.
7. Stories will vary.

Lifelong Nutrition

Real Life Issues

A Personal Choice. Miranda is facing a moral dilemma. After spending her summer at a camp where she helped care for farm animals, she's become uncomfortable with the idea of eating meat. She thinks of animals as friends, and she doesn't like the thought of eating them. However, food is an important part of her family's traditions. Miranda is afraid her parents won't understand if she tells them she doesn't want to eat meat anymore.

Writing *Write a dialogue in which Miranda tries to explain to her parents her desire to become a vegetarian.*

Lifelong Nutritional Needs

Main Idea Your age, gender, lifestyle, and health needs can affect your body's food needs.

Everyone has different nutritional needs. An active 16-year-old girl will need more calories and different levels of nutrients than an 80-year-old man. In addition to needing different levels of nutrients, we all have individual nutritional preferences and considerations. People who choose to eat only plant-based foods will select from those food groups. A person with an allergy to nuts will avoid foods that include nuts. There are several factors that affect your nutritional needs, including the following:

- **Age.** During your teen years, your body's calorie needs increase to support your growth. As you get older, your needs will change based on your activity level. You'll learn about the nutritional needs of infants, children, and older adults in Chapters 17 and 18.
- **Gender.** On average, females tend to need fewer calories than males. Throughout their lives, females have a greater need for some nutrients, like iron and calcium.

GUIDE TO READING

BIG Idea *Nutritional needs will change throughout your life.*

Before You Read
Create a Cluster Chart. Draw a circle and label it "Special Nutritional Needs." Draw surrounding circles and use these to describe nutritional needs for vegetarians, athletes, and those with health conditions. As you read, continue filling in the chart with more details.

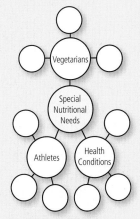

New Vocabulary

▶ vegetarian (p. 304)
▶ dietary supplements (p. 304)
▶ performance enhancers (p. 307)
▶ herbal supplements (p. 308)
▶ megadoses (p. 308)

Lifelong Nutrition

① FOCUS

GUIDE TO READING

BIG Idea Nutritional needs change throughout a person's lifetime. **Ask Students:** *What factors could affect a person's nutritional needs?* (Sample answers: medical conditions, involvement in sports, age)

Before You Read
Cluster Chart Students' charts will vary.

Main Idea

Lifelong Nutritional Needs
There are many factors that affect an individual's nutritional needs. **Ask Students:** *How do the nutritional needs of a teen differ from those of an older adult?* (Sample answer: Teens need more calories because they are still growing and developing.)

Real Life Issues

Have students read the scenario. **Ask Students:** *What concerns might Miranda's parents have about her decision to become a vegetarian?* (Sample answer: Miranda's parents might worry that she will not get all the nutrients she needs if she does not eat meat.) Have volunteers share their completed dialogues with the class.

Teacher to Teacher

Linda Hamrick, Ed.D. • South Side High School, Fort Wayne, IN

Managing Weight and Eating Behaviors Have students develop a one week healthy menu. Instruct them to divide a large piece of construction paper into 21 squares (breakfast, lunch, and dinner down the left side and the days of the week across the top). Students should work with a partner to develop a nutritious menu for the next seven days. I encourage them to include choices such as pizza and fast food items that they would normally eat, but recommend the use of portion control and moderation when choosing foods.

2 TEACH

AL Active Learning

Using MyPyramid Have students explore the advice for vegetarians offered on the MyPyramid website. Ask students to record and share one tip for healthful vegetarian eating they find. OL

C Critical Thinking

Discussing Ask students if all vegetarian eating plans are healthful. (Sample answer: No, just because an eating plan does not include meat does not mean that it is healthful. A vegetarian eating plan that consists of many empty-calorie foods is not healthful.) OL

Caption Answer

Figure 11.10 Eggs, beans, cheese, and peanut butter

 READING CHECK

Answer Vegetarians with lower-fat and high-fiber diets may lower their risk of cardiovascular disease and some cancers.

■ **Figure 11.10** Vegetarians can choose from a wide variety of healthful and tasty foods to meet their protein needs. *Name the foods in each dish that are a source of protein.*

 READING CHECK

Explain What are some potential health benefits of a vegetarian eating style?

Pregnant women also have special nutritional needs. To ensure the health of their babies, pregnant women need extra calcium, iron, and folic acid, along with more calories from food.

- **Activity level.** The more active you are, the more calories your body needs. Very active people need to consume more calories, preferably from nutrient-dense foods, to maintain their weight.

Vegetarian Diets

A **vegetarian** is *a person who eats mostly or only plant-based foods.* There are several different types of vegetarianism. The strictest vegetarians, known as vegans, eat only plant-based foods. Other types of vegetarians include

- Lacto-ovo vegetarians who also eat dairy foods and eggs,
- Lacto vegetarians who add dairy foods to their diet, and
- Ovo vegetarians who include eggs in their diet.

AL

People may choose a meatless diet for many reasons. Many believe a vegetarian diet is more healthful. Still others are vegetarians for religious, cultural, or economic reasons—or because they simply prefer vegetarian foods.

Advantages of the vegetarian eating style are that plant-based foods tend to be lower in saturated fat and cholesterol, and higher in fiber, than most animal-based foods. As a result, a well-planned meatless diet may help reduce the risk of cardiovascular disease and some types of cancer.

Drawbacks of the vegetarian eating style are that plant-based foods tend to be lower in certain nutrients, such as protein, iron, calcium, zinc, and some B vitamins. One nutrient, vitamin B^{12}, is found only in animal-based foods. Some vegetarians may need to take **dietary supplements**—*products that supply one or more nutrients as a supplement to, not a substitute for, healthful foods*—to obtain all the nutrients.

C

More About...

Diabetes In the human body, many chemical reactions are involved in releasing the energy stored in food. Insulin is a hormone produced by the body that is critical to the reactions that release energy from sugars and starches. Type 1 diabetes is a disorder in which the body does not make insulin. This is far less common than type 2 diabetes, in which the body is not able to properly use the insulin it produces. Some individuals with diabetes can manage their symptoms with careful attention to their food consumption; others must take insulin to control their symptoms.

A healthful vegetarian diet contains a variety of foods, including plenty of vegetables, fruits, and whole-grain foods. Choices such as nuts and legumes, as well as eggs and dairy products, can help vegetarians consume enough protein.

Health Conditions

The foods people eat can **trigger** certain diseases or health conditions. People with these conditions may need to avoid or limit certain foods in order to avoid health problems. Below are some of the health conditions that can be affected by foods:

- **Diabetes.** People with diabetes have to monitor their eating carefully to make sure their blood sugar stays in a healthy range. Diabetics who use insulin must tailor the amount of insulin they inject to the amount of carbohydrates in the foods they eat. Others may be able to control their diabetes without medication by carefully controlling the carbohydrates in foods and beverages they consume. Those who are overweight may find that losing weight helps them control their blood sugar.

- **Food allergies.** Food allergies can range from merely annoying to life threatening. People with severe food allergies must avoid the foods and food ingredients they are allergic to. This means checking ingredient lists on packaged foods and quizzing servers at restaurants. This can be difficult, but not nearly as difficult as being rushed to the emergency room.

- **Lactose intolerance.** People with this food intolerance can't easily digest the lactose in milk and some dairy products. Some people with lactose intolerance can control the problem by consuming smaller portions of milk or getting their calcium from cheese and yogurt, which contain less lactose. Some may take lactase (the enzyme needed to digest lactose) in liquid or tablet form when they eat dairy products.

- **Celiac disease.** Also known as gluten intolerance, this condition makes people unable to tolerate a protein called gluten, which is found in wheat, rye, and barley. Oats may also be harmful to those with celiac disease. The only treatment is to avoid these grains and anything made from them, including bread, pasta, and beer.

- **High blood pressure.** Consuming salt can raise a person's blood pressure. This effect is stronger in some individuals than in others. People with high blood pressure are often encouraged to keep their salt intake low.

- **High cholesterol.** People with high cholesterol may need to reduce their intake of saturated fats and trans fats. These fats increase cholesterol production in the body.

Academic Vocabulary

trigger *(verb):* to initiate or set off

Go Online

Listen to the Health Podcast *Fighting Teen Obesity* at glencoe.com.

READING CHECK

Name What are three health conditions that are caused by foods?

HS Health Skills Practice

Advocacy Tell students that high blood pressure is often called the "silent killer" because it can result in heart problems, stroke, or kidney problems with few or no warning symptoms. Have students use library resources, the Internet, or talk to the school nurse to find out more about high blood pressure. Ask students to gather information about blood pressure checks that are offered in the community. Then have students make a poster to share what they learned with other students in the school. **OL AL**

R Reading Strategy

Organizing Information Have students make a two-column table to organize the information about health conditions that are affected by food and nutrition. Tell students to label the left column of their table "Health Condition." Instruct students to list each of the health conditions discussed in the text in the left column. Then have students label the right column "Description." Have students write a one-sentence description of each health condition in the right column of their table. **BL EL OL**

Remind students to visit **glencoe.com** and listen to the Health Podcast *Fighting Teen Obesity.*

Cooperative Learning

Teach a Lesson Have students work in small groups to develop a lesson plan to teach one of the concepts presented in this lesson. Encourage students to use creative methods of teaching, such as a skit or the use of visual aids. Challenge groups to develop a quiz or another way to assess the effectiveness of their lesson. Have each group teach its lesson to the class. Encourage students to identify and describe characteristics of particularly effective lessons.

U Universal Access

Demonstration Use a measuring cup and two empty juice or soda bottles to demonstrate for students the amounts of fluids recommended for teen boys and teens girls each day. As students watch, add nine measuring cups of water to one of the bottles. Explain that this is the amount of fluids recommended for teen girls to consume each day. Place 15 cups of water into the other bottle. Explain that this is the amount of fluid recommended for teen boys to consume each day. **BL** **EL**

Caption Answer

Figure 11.11 Sample answers: fatigue, dizziness, lightheadedness, cramping

AL Active Learning

Consumer Skills Have students collect labels from sports drinks they consume or obtain information on reliable Web sites. Ask students to describe why sports drinks help maintain hydration. Have students determine the sugar content of a variety of sports drinks and identify potential problems that could be caused by excessive sugar intake. **OL** **AL**

Ge Online

Go to **glencoe.com** and complete the Student Web Activity on the dangers of steroids and performance enhancing drugs.

■ **Figure 11.11** Drinking plenty of water during a workout helps you avoid dehydration and keep performing at your peak. *What problems can dehydration cause?*

306   Chapter 11   Managing Weight and Eating Behaviors

Nutrition for Athletes

Eating right affects an athlete's performance. Like everyone else, athletes need a balanced diet that supplies enough nutrients to support health. The most important difference is that when you're very active, you need more calories to provide additional fuel. Teen athletes may need from 2,000 to 5,000 calories per day, depending on their sport and on the intensity, length, and frequency of their training.

Athletes need more protein and carbohydrates than inactive people. They may also need more calories from nutrient-dense foods and foods higher in carbohydrates. These types of foods will help student athletes maintain their energy and keep their weight up for athletic competition.

Making Weight In sports such as wrestling or boxing, your weight is important because you have to compete with others in the same weight class. If your sport requires you to "make weight," you must compete at a weight that's right for you. Your ideal weight will put your BMI in a healthy range and allow you to eat enough to meet your daily nutrient needs.

Some athletes try to compete in a weight class that's too low for them because they think they will have a better chance against smaller opponents. In reality, they are hurting themselves by trying to force their bodies down to a weight that isn't healthy. Extreme measures such as fasting or trying to sweat off extra weight can cause dehydration, harming performance as well as health. If you really do need to lose some weight, stick to a sensible plan that will take off ½ to 1 pound per week.

Hydration

Teen girls should try to drink about 9 cups of noncaffeinated fluids each day, and teen boys should try to drink 13 cups. Student athletes may need more fluids. When you sweat during exercise, your body loses fluids. These fluids must be replaced to avoid dehydration and heatstroke. Dehydration can lead to fatigue, dizziness or light-headedness, and cramping. Becoming dehydrated can lead to an imbalance of *electrolytes*—minerals that help maintain the body's fluid balance. The minerals sodium, chloride, and potassium are all electrolytes. To prevent dehydration, drink water before and after you exercise, and about every 15 minutes or so during a workout.

Myths & Reality

Performance Enhancers

Myth: Taking androstenedione is not harmful, because it is a substance the body produces naturally.

Fact: Androstenedione use has long-term health risks, including impotence in males, increased risk of breast cancer in females, and stunted growth in both males and females.

Myth: Energy drinks are harmless.

Fact: Energy drinks are very popular with teens, and the variety of energy drinks available is increasing rapidly. Most of these drinks contain large amounts of caffeine and sugar. Consumption of energy drinks can lead to symptoms of caffeine overdose, such as irregular heartbeat, dizziness, and sleep disturbances.

Avoiding Performance Enhancers

Some athletes try to gain an extra edge by using performance enhancers—*substances that boost athletic ability.* Many of these substances pose health risks, especially for teens. Using performance enhancers is illegal and has been banned under the rules of many sports organizations. Some of the best-known performance enhancers include the following:

- **Anabolic steroids.** These dangerous drugs, which are illegal without a doctor's prescription, have the same effect as male hormones (known as androgens) in the body. Athletes who take steroids disregard the many health risks in an effort to boost muscle growth. You will learn more about steroids and their risks in Chapter 22.
- **Androstenedione** (better known as "andro"). Andro is a weaker form of the androgens that the body produces naturally. Although some athletes take it to build muscle, its actual benefits are doubtful. Andro has many of the same side effects as steroids, and its use is now banned in professional sports.
- **Creatine.** This compound helps release energy. Some athletes take creatine supplements to give them a quick burst of power and reduce muscle fatigue. However, it can actually hurt athletic performance on account of its side effects, which include cramps and nausea. Using it at high doses may damage the heart, liver, and kidneys.
- **Energy Drinks.** These contain high amounts of caffeine. Energy drinks provide quick energy in an unhealthful way by increasing your heart rate. Using energy drinks to enhance your performance may actually hurt you. Drinking caffeinated beverages may cause your body to lose more fluids, leading to dehydration.

Using any type of performance enhancer, whether it's legal or illegal, is not worth the risk. You can perform at your peak without using performance enhancers by training, eating right, and getting enough rest.

Eating Before a Competition

Eating before a competition provides your body with the energy it needs to get through the competition. Try to eat about three to four hours before a competition so that your stomach is empty by the time you compete.

Before competing, try to choose meals that are high in carbohydrates and low in fat and protein. Fat and protein stay in the digestive system for a longer period of time. Good choices of foods to eat before a competition include pasta, rice, vegetables, breads, and fruits. Also, remember to drink plenty of water before, during, and after the competition.

FITNESS ZONE

I carry healthy snacks in my backpack every day. When I get hungry, I'm not tempted to buy something that's not healthy. An apple or a small bag of carrots are easy to carry. They're healthier than a candy bar or chips, too. For more fitness tips, visit the Online Fitness Zone at glencoe.com.

HS Health Skills Practice

Refusal Skills Have students write a dialogue that shows how refusal skills could be effectively used by a teen who was encouraged to use a performance enhancer. Encourage students to incorporate the STOP formula in their dialogues (Say no in a firm voice, Tell why not, Offer another idea, Promptly leave). Have students work with partners to perform their dialogues for the class. **OL**

W Writing Support

Outline Have students write an outline based on the Avoiding Performance Enhancers section. Students should include main ideas, topic sentences, and supporting details found in the paragraphs. **OL AL**

R Reading Strategy

Finding the Main Idea Write the following sentence from the text on the board: "Using any type of performance enhancers, whether it's legal or illegal, is not worth the risk." Explain that this sentence states the main idea of the information on the page. Ask students to examine the text to find details that support the main idea. Call on volunteers to share what they have found with the class. **BL EL OL**

Academic Integration

English Have students write a letter to an athlete they admire, asking about the athlete's training diet and precompetition meals. Encourage students to write an outline to organize their ideas before they begin writing their letter. Remind students that personal letters contain a heading, a greeting, a body, and a signature. Instruct students to write a draft and proofread for errors before completing their final letter. Ask students to mail their letter. If students receive replies, ask them to share the replies with the class.

Accessing Information: Evaluating Supplements

NHES Standard 3 Evaluate the validity of health information, products and services.

Objectives

- Identify and evaluate reliable sources of information about vitamin supplements.
- Demonstrate the ability to analyze health messages on products.

Teaching Strategies

- Have students work in small groups to evaluate claims found on the Calci-Treat label.
- Tell students to identify the claims listed that can be proved and the ones that are opinions.

Assessment

Using a rubric, student work should provide comprehensive evidence of the following criteria to achieve the highest score:

√ Distinguishes claims that are facts from those that are opinions.
√ Distinguishes claims that require FDA approval from those that do not.
√ Identifies sources of reliable information for confirming claims.

READING CHECK

Answer Sample answer: Strict vegetarians, pregnant or nursing women.

Using Supplements

Main Idea Dietary supplements can help people meet their nutrient needs if they cannot do it with food alone.

Walk down the aisles of any drugstore, and you will see a huge array of dietary supplements. These supplements provide various combinations of vitamins, minerals, protein, and fiber. You may also see **herbal supplements**, which are *dietary supplements containing plant extracts.*

The most important thing to know about supplements is that they are no substitute for eating a variety of healthful foods. Some people, however, may not be able to get all the nutrients they need through food alone. For example, strict vegetarians may use supplements to provide the nutrients they are not getting from animal-based foods. Pregnant or nursing women may use them to make sure they get all the extra nutrients their bodies need. Supplements can also help people who are recovering from illness or taking medications that reduce the body's ability to absorb certain nutrients.

Concerns About Dietary Supplements

Most people who follow a nutritious, well-balanced eating plan, such as the one recommended in MyPyramid, will not need a multivitamin. However, multivitamin and mineral supplements are generally safe to use, as long as you use them correctly. For starters, do not take supplements that provide more than 100 percent of the Daily Values for any nutrient. Taking **megadoses**, or *very large amounts,* of any supplement can be dangerous. Some vitamins, such as A, D, E, and K, can build up in the body and become toxic.

Many herbal supplements raise additional concerns. Some people take these "natural" products because they believe they are a safe alternative to drugs for treating certain conditions. These supplements can still be dangerous. Using the herb ephedra, or ma huang, can lead to a heart attack or stroke. Products containing this herb were banned in 2004. Other herbs, such as kava and comfrey, have been linked to serious liver damage.

The National Institutes of Health (NIH) cautions that herbal supplements are just like drugs. Herbal supplements aren't regulated in the same ways as foods or drugs. However, the U.S. Food and Drug Administration (FDA) can take action to stop the sale of supplements that are unsafe or mislabeled. To be safe, treat supplements with the same caution you'd use with any drug. Check with your health care provider before using any herbal supplements, especially if you are already taking other medications.

■ **Figure 11.12** Supplements can help you meet your needs for specific nutrients, but they cannot take the place of healthful foods. *What are some reasons people might use supplements?*

 READING CHECK

Identify List two kinds of people who might use dietary supplements.

Teens Want to Know

Can Supplements Help Me with Weight Loss? There are many supplements that are advertised as fat burners, metabolism boosters, or appetite suppressants. These products often contain herbal extracts, such as ginseng or chickweed, or other natural materials such as kelp or bee pollen. Explain to students that these products cannot replace healthful eating and exercise as a weight-loss method. Point out that many of the products contain substances that are considered dangerous. Remind students that they should ask a medical professional, such as their family doctor or the school nurse, if they have questions about a specific product.

Health Skills Activity

Accessing Information

Evaluating Supplements

Sanjay knows that teens may need more calcium than adults because their bodies are growing at a fast rate. He's thinking about taking a calcium supplement. Looking in the supplements aisle at the drugstore, he sees that the labels make many types of claims. In his health class, Sanjay learned that certain claims must be reviewed by the FDA. For instance, a product's manufacturers must get FDA approval to claim that their product can prevent or treat any disease. However, FDA approval is not needed for general claims about the product's benefits, such as "promotes circulatory health." Sanjay thinks about which of the Calci-Treat claims can be proven.

CALCI-TREAT

✦ Provides a full day's supply of calcium
✦ Builds strong bones
✦ Helps prevent osteoporosis
✦ Delicious chocolate flavor
✦ Easy to use

Writing Write a paragraph describing how Sanjay could evaluate the claims made on this supplement's label. Consider these questions:

1. Which of the claims can be proved? Which are opinions?
2. Which of these claims require FDA approval? Which might not have received FDA approval?
3. What sources can Sanjay check to confirm the claims made on this label?

LESSON 3 ASSESSMENT

After You Read

Reviewing Facts and Vocabulary

1. What are *dietary supplements*?
2. List three factors that can affect your body's nutrient needs.
3. Why should teen athletes avoid performance enhancers?

Thinking Critically

4. **Analyze.** How would cutting back on food and water affect the performance of a student athlete?
5. **Evaluate.** Is it safe for a vegan to take a daily supplement that provides the recommended dose of iron, calcium, and B vitamins? Explain why.

Applying Health Skills

6. **Advocacy.** Create a flyer telling teens about the dangers of using dietary supplements. Include warnings about specific types of supplements.

Writing Critically

7. **Expository.** Write an article for the school newspaper. In the article, tell teens the right and wrong ways to improve athletic performance.

 Go Online

Visit **glencoe.com** and complete the Interactive Study Guide for this lesson.

Lesson 3   Lifelong Nutrition   **309**

ASSESS/CLOSE

Progress Monitoring

Reteaching
Have students make a flashcard of each of the lesson vocabulary terms. Then ask students to work in pairs to use their flashcards to review the lesson vocabulary.

Enrichment
Have each student create five game-show style questions about the lesson content. Then have volunteers share their questions with the class.

 Go Online

Have students visit **glencoe.com** and complete the Interactive Study Guide for this lesson.

LESSON 3 ASSESSMENT ANSWERS

1. *Dietary supplements* are products that supply one or more nutrients as a supplement to, not a substitute for, healthful foods.
2. Age, gender, activity level
3. Teen athletes should avoid performance enhancers because they pose health risks and many are illegal and/or banned in competitive sports.
4. Athletic performance might suffer if the person is energy-starved or dehydrated.
5. Yes, the use of supplements is safe and reasonable if the person is taking supplements to meet a specific nutritional need and is not taking megadoses.
6. Flyers will vary.
7. How-to columns will vary.

Craving a Healthy Future

Focus

Motivator

Ask students to identify foods that they typically crave. Make a list on the board of their responses. Have students examine the completed list. Ask students: What are some similarities of the foods on the list? What are some differences? (Sample answers: The foods on the list are all high-fat. Some of the foods on the list are sweet, but others are salty.)

Teach

Energy Balance Review with students the information in the chapter about energy balance. Ask students to explain how giving in to a craving for a high-calorie, high-fat food could affect their energy balance. Then have students relate the effect on energy balance to an effect on body weight.

Managing Stress Point out that some experts note a relationship between cortisol and food cravings. Have students make a note of their food cravings for a three-day time period. Tell students to write down the food cravings they experience, and whether or not they eat in response to the craving. Each time students record a craving, have them make a note of their emotions at the time. At the end of the week, ask students whether their data support the idea that stress and cravings are related.

Craving a Healthy Future

Do you crave foods like chocolate or potato chips? Food cravings are common and they can be tough to fight.

Here's a statistic to chew over: The rate of obesity among children and teens has tripled in the past 25 years. What's causing this increase? Some experts point to too much time on the couch and not enough exercise. Others note that working parents are too busy to prepare healthful meals.

According to Dr. Andrew Weil, a health expert, food cravings can also play a part in obesity. Not to worry—there are ways to manage those cravings. Here's what the doctor says:

Q. What causes food cravings?
A. No one is completely sure. One theory is that cravings—especially for energy-packed foods like ice cream and candy—are triggered by cortisol, the hormone released during stress. Once, this reaction might have helped our species survive. In times of scarcity and stress, these cravings would have prompted humans to load up on whatever nutrients they could find.

Today, with energy-dense food available in every convenience store, the same instincts work against us. Stress can lead to overeating.

Q. What can teens do about food cravings?
A. I suggest shifting cravings in healthier directions. For example, choose low-fat chocolate sorbet to satisfy a longing for chocolate ice cream.

Or try breathing exercises to reduce craving-causing stress. Dr. Weil describes one technique: With the tip of your tongue behind your upper front teeth, exhale through your mouth, making a whoosh sound. Inhale through your nose to a count of four. Hold your breath for seven seconds. Exhale completely through your mouth to a count of eight. Repeat the cycle three times.

Finally, remember that totally depriving yourself of your favorite foods often backfires. A better strategy is to indulge moderately and occasionally, perhaps as a way of rewarding yourself for good behavior. ■

TIME to THINK... About Weight

Keep a journal of the foods you eat for one week. Review your eating habits and see if there is anything you can cut out or substitute for overly fattening or unhealthful foods. Do you eat more at stressful times? At certain hours? How could you change your behavior?

 ## Promoting School Wellness

Refrigerator Magnet Have students incorporate a strategy for managing food cravings into a format that could be used as a refrigerator magnet. Point out to students that refrigerator magnets are typically small in size, so their magnet design should contain few words. Explain that pictures or symbols may be used on their magnets as well. Cut paper or index cards into 2 inch by 4 inch rectangles and distribute one of these to each student. Have students write or draw their prepared information on these paper rectangles. Then have students affix small magnets to the back of the paper to create a refrigerator magnet.

To download quizzes and eFlashcards, go to glencoe.com and visit the health page for Chapter 11.

LESSON 1

Maintaining a Healthy Weight
Key Concepts
▶ Body mass index and body composition can help determine whether your weight is healthy.
▶ Being overweight carries health risks such as hypertension, cardiovascular disease, and type 2 diabetes.
▶ Health risks of being underweight include nutrient deficiencies, difficulty fighting off disease, weakness, and tiring easily.
▶ Following nutrition guidelines on MyPyramid and being physically active will help you maintain a healthy weight.

Vocabulary
▶ metabolism (p. 290)
▶ body mass index (BMI) (p. 291)
▶ overweight (p. 291)
▶ obese (p. 292)
▶ underweight (p. 293)

LESSON 2

Body Image and Eating Disorders
Key Concepts
▶ Influences on teens' body image include family, peers, and the media.
▶ Fad diets promise quick and easy weight loss, but they are not a safe and reliable way to lose weight.
▶ Eating disorders, such as anorexia, bulimia, and binge eating, are extreme and dangerous eating behaviors that require professional help.

Vocabulary
▶ body image (p. 297)
▶ fad diets (p. 298)
▶ weight cycling (p. 298)
▶ eating disorders (p. 300)
▶ anorexia nervosa (p. 300)
▶ bulimia nervosa (p. 301)
▶ binge eating disorder (p. 301)

LESSON 3

Lifelong Nutrition
Key Concepts
▶ Your body's nutritional needs depend on such factors as your age, health, and lifestyle.
▶ A vegetarian eating style can offer health benefits if foods are chosen carefully to provide all the nutrients the body needs.
▶ Health conditions, such as diabetes, food allergies, and high blood pressure, can impact food choices.
▶ Athletes need to consume extra calories, drink extra water, and avoid harmful performance enhancers.
▶ In addition to a healthful eating plan, some people take dietary supplements to help meet their nutrient needs.

Vocabulary
▶ vegetarian (p. 304)
▶ dietary supplements (p. 304)
▶ performance enhancers (p. 307)
▶ herbal supplements (p. 308)
▶ megadoses (p. 308)

 Go Online

Students can visit **glencoe.com** to

• review content online with the Online Student Edition.
• test their knowledge of chapter content with Online Quizzes.
• access Interactive Health Tutor for more practice with vocabulary.

Assessment Resources

 FAST FILE ACTIVITIES
Chapter 11 Test

ExamView
Assessment Suite CD-ROM

Visit glencoe.com **for:**
Audio Chapter Summaries
Online Quizzes

 Tell students to visit glencoe.com where they can download quizzes and eFlashcards.

Study Tips

Write a Quiz Suggest that students write a 10-question quiz (with answers) about topics covered in the chapter. Explain that writing quiz questions can help them focus on the key concepts covered in the chapter. Have students exchange their quizzes with a partner. After students have completed the quiz, have them grade their partner's responses. Ask volunteers to share some of their quiz questions and answers with the class.

Chapter 11
Assessment Answers

LESSON 1

Vocabulary Review

1. Body mass index
2. overweight
3. underweight

Understanding Key Concepts

4. d
5. b
6. d
7. c

Thinking Critically

8. If you take in the same number of calories that your body uses, your weight will stay the same.
9. *Any three:* eat larger amounts from the five major food groups; choose some high-calorie, nutrient-rich foods; use your full daily total of discretionary calories; eat often; increase muscle mass
10. Being overweight means having a weight above the standard range. Being obese means having an excess of body fat. People can be overweight without being obese.
11. Physical activity has many other physical and emotional benefits in addition to weight loss.

Vocabulary Review

12. weight cycling
13. Eating disorders
14. Binge eating disorder

LESSON 1

Vocabulary Review

Use the vocabulary terms listed on page 311 to complete the following statements.

1. _____ is a measure of body weight relative to height.

2. Adults who have an excess of body fat may be considered _____.

3. People who are _____ have a BMI that is lower than the healthy range.

Understanding Key Concepts

After reading the question or statement, select the correct answer.

4. How many calories are equivalent to 1 pound of body fat?
   a. 500
   b. 1,000
   c. 2,500
   d. 3,500

5. Measuring the thickness of skin folds at different points on the body is a way to determine your
   a. body mass index.
   b. body composition.
   c. metabolism.
   d. energy balance.

6. Which of the following is *not* a health risk associated with being overweight?
   a. Hypertension (high blood pressure)
   b. Type 2 diabetes
   c. Osteoarthritis (a joint disease)
   d. Anemia (a condition in which the blood cannot carry needed oxygen to the body)

7. A safe, reasonable rate of weight loss is
   a. 1 pound per day
   b. 5 pounds per week
   c. 1/2 to 1 pound per week
   d. 1 to 2 pounds per year

Thinking Critically

After reading the question or statement, write a short answer using complete sentences.

8. **Explain.** How is your weight related to your energy balance?

9. **Identify.** List three healthful steps you could take if you wanted to gain weight.

10. **Compare and Contrast.** What is the difference between being overweight and obese?

11. **Evaluate.** Why is physical activity important for all teens, regardless of weight?

LESSON 2

Vocabulary Review

Correct the sentences below by replacing the italicized term with the correct vocabulary term.

12. A repeated pattern of losing and regaining body weight is called *binge eating*.

13. *Fad diets* are extreme, harmful eating behaviors that can cause serious illness or even death.

14. *Anorexia nervosa* is an eating disorder in which people overeat compulsively.

Understanding Key Concepts

After reading the question or statement, select the correct answer.

15. Which of the following might cause teens to develop a negative body image?
    a. Focusing on their good qualities
    b. Being picked on at school because of the way they look
    c. Being physically active
    d. Having friends with positive attitudes toward their own bodies

---

Health eSpotlight VIDEO *Wrap-Up*

Food, Habits, and Choices Have students reread the Health eSpotlight questions at the beginning of the chapter (page 289) and look at their original answers. **Ask Students:** *Now that you have read the* chapter and watched the video, what are some additional factors that influence the way teens think about their bodies? Call on volunteers to describe how their responses would change.

16. Teens who think they need to lose weight should
    a. take diet pills.
    b. follow a liquid diet.
    c. begin a fast.
    d. consult a doctor.

17. Which of the following is *not* a behavior associated with anorexia nervosa?
    a. Avoiding food and meals
    b. Exercising excessively
    c. Eating a large amount of food in a single sitting
    d. Weighing oneself repeatedly

18. The first step in treating bulimia nervosa is to
    a. break the cycle of binging and purging.
    b. get the patient's weight back to a normal level.
    c. address the emotional problems that led to the eating disorder.
    d. provide nutritional guidance.

Thinking Critically

After reading the question or statement, write a short answer using complete sentences.

19. **Explain.** Why are fad diets generally not safe or reliable ways to lose weight?

20. **Explain.** What makes very-low-calorie diets dangerous for teens?

21. **Analyze.** Identify three signs that distinguish a fad diet from a legitimate weight-loss plan.

22. **Explain.** What are three risks associated with using diet pills?

23. **Compare and Contrast.** How are the eating disorders anorexia and bulimia similar? How are they different?

24. **Compare and Contrast.** How are bulimia and binge eating disorder similar? How are they different?

LESSON 3

Vocabulary Review

Use the vocabulary terms listed on page 311 to complete the following statements.

25. People who eat mostly or only plant-based foods are called _____.

26. _____ are dietary supplements containing plant extracts.

27. Taking a _____, or a very large amount, of any supplement can be dangerous.

Understanding Key Concepts

After reading the question or statement, select the correct answer.

28. Which of the following foods would all vegetarians refuse to eat?
    a. Eggs
    b. Milk
    c. Chicken
    d. Bread

29. People with celiac disease must avoid foods that contain
    a. sugar.
    b. lactose.
    c. gluten.
    d. fiber.

30. Which medical condition may require people to limit their salt intake?
    a. Allergies
    b. Diabetes
    c. High cholesterol
    d. High blood pressure

Chapter 11 Assessment **313**

LESSON 2

Understanding Key Concepts

15. b
16. d
17. c
18. a

Thinking Critically

19. Any weight lost is usually regained, and the diet may not provide adequate energy or nutrients for the body.

20. Low-calorie diets usually do not contain the amount of energy and nutrients teens need for growth.

21. They promise quick, easy weight loss; weight loss is temporary; they use pills or supplements.

22. Any three: addiction, drowsiness, anxiety, increased heart rate

23. People with both disorders are obsessed with food and fear weight gain. However, people with anorexia nervosa eat very little, while those with bulimia nervosa eat large amounts and then purge. Both disorders are dangerous and can be deadly.

24. Bulimia involves cycles of overeating and purging. Binge eating involves compulsive overeating, but less frequently than bulimia.

Vocabulary Review

25. vegetarians
26. herbal supplements
27. megadose

Understanding Key Concepts

28. c
29. c
30. d

ExamView®
Assessment Suite

Create and customize tests in minutes with this convenient digital platform.

- Create differentiated tests quickly and easily.
- All questions correlated to National/State Standards.
- Enhance tests with Document Based Questions (DBQ) and add your own photos or graphics.
- Build tests in both English and Spanish.
- Generate progress reports.

To order, go to glencoe.com and search for ISBN 0-07-888173-0.

Glencoe *Health*

Assessment

Assessment

LESSON 3

Thinking Critically

31. Age, gender, activity level
32. A healthy diet will provide nutrients needed for proper functioning of all body systems and will help you avoid certain diseases.
33. A meatless diet may help reduce the risk of cardiovascular disease and some types of cancer, if chosen carefully. Vegetarians must make an extra effort to get enough of certain nutrients, such as protein, iron, calcium, zinc, and B vitamins.
34. Minerals that help maintain the body's fluid balance are depleted when a person is dehydrated.
35. Supplements cannot provide all of the beneficial substances found in food.
36. Supplements could replace the calcium and vitamin D that Toby cannot obtain by eating dairy products.
37. They disrupt natural muscle development and may cause more fluid loss.

Thinking Critically

After reading the question or statement, write a short answer using complete sentences.

31. **Identify.** List three factors that may influence a person's calorie and nutrient needs.

32. **Analyze.** How can good nutrition enhance your health throughout your life?

33. **Evaluate.** Describe the health advantages and disadvantages of a vegetarian eating style.

34. **Explain.** How are dehydration and electrolyte imbalance related?

35. **Explain.** Why are dietary supplements not a substitute for eating a variety of healthful foods?

36. **Identify Problems and Solutions.** Toby has a milk allergy and is unable to consume dairy products. How might he benefit from dietary supplements?

37. **Describe.** What health problems can result when athletes take performance-enhancement drugs or supplements?

Project-Based ASSESSMENT

Helping a Friend

Background
Eating disorders are a serious medical problem that can result in lifelong health problems and even death. Often, people with eating disorders try to hide the fact from their friends and family. They tend to deny that they have a problem.

Task
With your group of three students, write and perform a short skit that demonstrates how you would talk to a friend who you suspect may have an eating disorder. Encourage your friend to get help. Your skit should also demonstrate ways to obtain help for the friend from a trusted adult.

Audience
Students in your class

Purpose
Practice communicating effectively with your peers and with adults.

Procedure

1 Review the symptoms of eating disorders in your textbook. Choose one eating disorder to focus on in your skit.

2 Develop a script with these characters: a student with a suspected eating disorder, the student's friend, and an adult.

3 Your skit should demonstrate the following:
   a. How to express concern and support
   b. How to tell an adult about the problem
   c. How to make sure your friend receives help

4 When writing your skit, remember that a person with an eating disorder may not accept advice. The person might react to a concerned friend with anger and hostility. Also remember that some adults do not understand the serious nature of eating disorders.

5 Practice your skit and present it to the class.

Project-Based ASSESSMENT

Step 1 Choose a Topic Have each student choose an eating disorder for the focus of his or her skit. Have students become familiar with the symptoms of the eating disorder they choose.

Step 2 Write and Perform a Skit Have each student write a skit. Then ask students to work in small groups to practice and perform their skits.

Step 3 Evaluate As each skit is performed, evaluate its content based on the listed requirements in the Procedure section found in the student text.

Visit **glencoe.com** for Project-Based Assessment rubrics.

Math Practice

Problem Solving. Some math problems require you to read a text passage. Read the text carefully and answer the questions that follow.

> Mohammed's school started a fitness and nutrition program. Mohammed joined the program and developed food and physical activity plans. Exactly two weeks after starting the plan, Mohammed had lost 3 pounds and noticed that he had more energy.
>
> Later that week, Mohammed left school feeling restless. He decided to go for a power walk. He burned 37 calories warming up before he went on the walk and 2.3 calories for every minute of walking once he got started. When Mohammed finished his power walk, he spent 10 minutes cooling down.

1. What was Mohammed's average weight loss per day in the first two weeks of his plan?
   A. 0.21 pounds/day   C. 1.50 pounds/day
   B. 0.67 pounds/day   D. 4/67 pounds/day

2. If x represents the number of minutes Mohammed power walked and y represents how many calories he usually burns cooling down, which expression below could be used to figure out how many total calories he burned on the power walk?
   A. $x(2.3 + 37 + y)$
   B. $(2.3 + 37)(x + y)$
   C. $(2.3 \times y) + 37 + x$
   D. $(2.3 \times x) + 37 + y$

3. Mohammed burned 39 calories during his warm-up, 20 calories during his cool down, and power-walked for 43 minutes. How many total calories did he burn?

Go Online

For more test practice, visit **glencoe.com** and complete the Online Quizzes for Chapter 11.

Reading/Writing Practice

Understand and Apply. Read the passage below and then answer the questions.

> About 50 million Americans begin weight-loss diets each year. Very few—perhaps 5 percent—will manage to keep the weight off. Why? Most people approach weight loss the wrong way. They look for "quick fixes" that will let them lose weight with as little effort as possible. They may put their faith in "magic" weight-loss formulas or combinations of food that will "melt away" the pounds.
>
> The only sensible approach is to cut your calorie intake by following the guidelines in MyPyramid, and getting more physical activity. This plan may not be quick—and it may not be easy—but it will produce lasting results, a promise no other diet can live up to.

1. What is the main idea of this article?
   A. Millions of Americans try to lose weight each year.
   B. Weight-loss diets can be harmful.
   C. Nobody really loses weight by dieting.
   D. Only a sensible plan will result in permanent weight loss.

2. Which sentence could be added to introduce the third paragraph?
   A. There are no shortcuts to weight loss.
   B. Fad diets can help some people.
   C. A healthy weight has many benefits.
   D. For many people, losing weight is impossible.

3. Contrast the realities of fad diets with losing weight by following a plan of healthy eating and physical activity.

National Education Standards

Math: Number and Operations, Problem Solving
Language Arts: NCTE 3, NCTE 4

Standardized Test Practice

Standardized Test Practice Answers

Math Practice
1. C
2. D
3. 148 calories

Reading/Writing Practice
1. D
2. A
3. Answers will vary. Students should note that many people look for a quick and easy solution to weight loss. Responses should include some differences between fad diets and healthful weight loss plans.

National Education Standards

Math: Number and Operations, Problem Solving

Language Arts: NCTE 3, NCTE 4

For the complete Math and Language Arts standards, visit **glencoe.com**.

Go Online

Online Study Tools
For more test practice, visit **glencoe.com** and complete the Online Quizzes for Chapter 11.

Test-Taking Tip

Eliminate Answers Multiple choice questions often include one or more answer choices that can be immediately eliminated because they are obviously incorrect.

After eliminating the obviously incorrect responses, you can spend more time determining which of the remaining answers is correct.

Chapter 12 pages 316–349	Standards: National	Standards: State/Local	Features
Chapter 12 pages 316–349	1.12.1, 1.12.2, 1.12.5, 1.12.8, 6.12.1, 6.12.2, 8.12.1, 8.12.2, 8.12.4		*Hands-On* **HEALTH** • Get Up and Get Fit *(Advocacy)*, page 344
30 Min **Lesson 1** **Benefits of Physical Activity** pages 318–323 **BIG Idea** *Being physically active benefits your total health in a variety of ways.*	1.12.2, 1.12.8, 1.12.9, 2.12.3, 7.12.1, 7.12.2, 7.12.3, 8.12.1, 8.12.2		VIDEO BusinessWeek HEALTH NEWS • Slow Burn of Exercising, page 319 **TEENS Making a Difference** • Giving Others the "Sole" Benefit, page 321
30 Min **Lesson 2** **Improving Your Fitness** pages 324–330 **BIG Idea** *Different types of exercise can help you evaluate and improve the various elements of fitness.*	2.12.8, 5.12.5, 5.12.6, 6.12.1, 6.12.2, 6.12.4, 7.12.1, 7.12.2, 7.12.3, 8.12.1		*Real World* **CONNECTION** • Targeting Cardiovascular Fitness, page 329 Out of Time
30 Min **Lesson 3** **Planning a Personal Activity Program** pages 331–336 **BIG Idea** *Planning your physical activity can help you achieve specific fitness goals.*	1.12.3, 2.12.8, 6.12.2, 6.12.3, 6.12.4, 7.12.1, 8.12.1		***Health Skills*** *Activity* • Identifying Fitness Goals *(Goal Setting)*, page 334 Out of Time
30 Min **Lesson 4** **Fitness Safety and Avoiding Injuries** pages 337–343 **BIG Idea** *It is important to learn how to prevent injuries and respond to them when they occur.*	1.12.2, 1.12.5, 1.12.8, 1.12.9, 6.12.1, 6.12.2, 8.12.1, 8.12.2, 8.12.4		*Real World* **CONNECTION** • Playing It Safe, page 343 Out of Time

Key to Ability Levels

Teaching Strategies and activities have been coded for ability level and appropriateness.

- **AL** Activities for students working above grade level
- **OL** Activities for students working on grade level
- **BL** Activities for students working below grade level
- **EL** Activities for English Learners

Chapter 12 Planning Guide

Glencoe Exclusive!
TeacherWorks Plus™
All-In-One Planner and Resource Center

Resources	Lesson Assessment	Technology
Student Activity Workbook TEACH *FAST FILE* RESOURCES Vocabulary Practice TEACH Health Labs EXTEND	Chapter 12 Review Chapter 12 Assessment Standardized Test Practice ExamView® Assessment Suite CD-ROM	**Teaching Tools:** • TeacherWorks™ Plus DVD • StudentWorks™ Plus DVD • ExamView® Assessment Suite CD-ROM • Transparency • Fitness DVD • PowerPoint® DVD • Health eSpotlight Video Series DVD
FAST FILE RESOURCES Reading Strategies Activity TEACH Reteaching Activity REVIEW Enrichment Activity EXTEND Health Skills Practice TEACH	Lesson 1 Assessment, page 323 Lesson 1 Quiz *Fast File* ExamView® Assessment Suite CD-ROM	**Web-Based Resources:** Go Online glencoe.com • Health Podcast Activities • Audio Chapter Summaries (English/Spanish) • Interactive Health Tutor • Health Skills Activities
FAST FILE RESOURCES Reading Strategies Activity TEACH Reteaching Activity REVIEW Enrichment Activity EXTEND Health Skills Practice TEACH	Lesson 2 Assessment, page 330 Lesson 2 Quiz *Fast File* ExamView® Assessment Suite CD-ROM	• Vocabulary PuzzleMaker • Parent Letters (English/Spanish) • Lesson Plans • Health Inventories
FAST FILE RESOURCES Reading Strategies Activity TEACH Reteaching Activity REVIEW Enrichment Activity EXTEND Health Skills Practice TEACH	Lesson 3 Assessment, page 336 Lesson 3 Quiz *Fast File* ExamView® Assessment Suite CD-ROM	• Online Quizzes • Study-to-Go • Unit Web Projects • Student Web Activities
FAST FILE RESOURCES Reading Strategies Activity TEACH Reteaching Activity REVIEW Enrichment Activity EXTEND Health Skills Practice TEACH	Lesson 4 Assessment, page 343 Lesson 4 Quiz *Fast File* ExamView® Assessment Suite CD-ROM	• Fitness Zone Activities

StudentWorks Plus

This is the student's backpack solution.

Includes:
• complete Interactive Student Edition
• full audio of English text and Spanish chapter summaries
• allows students to record assignments and track grades.
• links to online activities and additional student resources
• access to all student worksheets and workbooks

FOLDABLES Study Organizer

Dinah Zike Foldables® Chapter Activity

Refer to the *Dinah Zike Reading and Study Skills for Glencoe Health*. Ask students to make a four-tab book with tabs labeled "Benefits of Physical Activity," "Improving Fitness," "A Personal Activity Program," and "Fitness Safety." As students read, have them write information about each lesson under the appropriate tab.

Key to Symbols

 Transparencies

 CD-ROM

 glencoe.com

 Print Resources

REVIEW activities to review or reinforce content

TEACH activities to teach basic concepts

EXTEND activities to extend or enrich lesson content

Physical Activity and Fitness

Chapter Overview

Chapter 12 focuses on the benefits of being physically active and specific ways in which to improve personal fitness. Safety precautions associated with physical activity and how to avoid injuries are also discussed.

Lesson 1

Being physically active has physical, mental and emotional, and social benefits. An inactive lifestyle puts one at risk for a variety of health problems.

Lesson 2

There are five elements of fitness that affect one's health in different ways. Different forms of exercise help to improve the different elements of fitness.

Lesson 3

The types of activities one chooses to include in a fitness plan depend on a variety of personal needs. Each exercise session should include a warm-up, a workout, and a cool-down.

Lesson 4

Safety precautions can prevent injuries during physical activity. It is also important to learn how to respond to injuries when they occur.

▶ **Activating Prior Knowledge**

On the board, draw three columns with the headings "Physical," "Mental/Emotional," and "Social." After students have written their paragraphs, call on volunteers to share with the class the ways in which the activity shown in the photo affects the physical, mental/emotional, and social health of the participating teens.

316

Lesson 1

Benefits of Physical Activity

BIG Idea *Being physically active benefits your total health in a variety of ways.*

Lesson 2

Improving Your Fitness

BIG Idea *Different types of exercise can help you evaluate and improve the various elements of fitness.*

Lesson 3

Planning a Personal Activity Program

BIG Idea *Planning your physical activity can help you achieve specific fitness goals.*

Lesson 4

Fitness Safety and Avoiding Injuries

BIG Idea *It is important to learn how to prevent injuries and respond to them when they occur.*

Activating Prior Knowledge

Using Visuals Look at the picture on this page. Based on what you have learned in previous chapters, write a paragraph describing how these teens are affecting their physical, mental/emotional, and social health.

316

Universal Access

Differentiated Learning Glencoe provides teacher support and student materials for all learners in the health classroom.

- Chapter Summaries in English and Spanish are available online at **glencoe.com**.
- *Fast Files* and related worksheets support reluctant readers.

- Universal Access strategies throughout the Teacher Wraparound Edition and *Fast Files* help you present materials for gifted students, at-risk students, physically impaired students, and those with behavior disorders or learning disabilities.

Chapter Launchers

Health in Action

Discuss the **BIG** Ideas

Before beginning this chapter, think about how you would answer these questions:

▸ What physical activities do you enjoy?

▸ How does physical activity fit into your daily life?

▸ Do you consider yourself fit?

Watch the *Health eSpotlight* Video Series

Balance and Fitness

Physical activity can improve fitness and decrease stress. What activities do you enjoy that decrease your stress?

Assess Your Health

Go Online

Visit **glencoe.com** and complete the Health Inventory for Chapter 12.

Chapter 12 Physical Activity and Fitness **317**

Chapter Launchers

Health in Action

Discuss the **BIG** Ideas

Assign this activity before students read the chapter. Explain that the purpose of the questions is to help students assess their current knowledge of physical activity and fitness. If students save their responses to the questions, they can revisit them at the end of the chapter to see how much they have learned.

Health eSpotlight
Video Series

 Balance and Fitness

Before Viewing the Video

Ask Students: *How can physical activity improve your health?* After students have watched the video, call on volunteers to describe how physical activities in their own lives benefit their health.

Go Online

Have students go to **glencoe.com** and take the Health Inventory for Chapter 12.

Chapter Skills

Reading Skills
- Reviewing Facts and Vocabulary, pp. 323, 330, 336, 343
- Reading/Writing Practice, p. 349

BIG Idea

Being physically active improves fitness and has many other health benefits.

Health Skills
- Health Skills Activity, p. 334
- Applying Health Skills, pp. 323, 330, 336, 343

Vocabulary
- New Vocabulary, pp. 318, 324, 331, 337
- Reviewing Facts and Vocabulary, pp. 323, 330, 336, 343

Writing Skills
- Real World Connection, p. 343
- Writing Critically, pp. 323, 330, 336, 343
- Reading/Writing Practice, p. 349

Benefits of Physical Activity

1 FOCUS

BIG Idea Making time for physical activity has mental, emotional, and physical benefits. **Ask Students:** *In what particular ways does being physically active benefit a person?* (Answers will vary but may include feeling good about yourself and others.)

Before You Read

Organize Information
Students' three-column charts will vary. The lists under each column head should reflect the discussion in the lesson about the many different benefits of physical activity.

Main Idea

Physical Activity and Health
Physical activity has many positive effects on one's physical, mental and emotional, and social health. **Ask Students:** *How could being physically active affect your social health?* (Answers will vary but could include being a teammate on a sports team.)

Real Life Issues

Have students brainstorm what they like to do with their friends. **Ask Students:** *What physical activity do you most enjoy doing with friends?* (Accept reasonable responses.)

318

 GUIDE TO READING

BIG Idea *Being physically active benefits your total health in a variety of ways.*

Before You Read

Organize Information.
Divide a sheet of paper into three columns. Label them "Physical," "Mental/Emotional," and "Social." As you read the lesson, fill in the chart by listing how physical activity benefits these three aspects of your health.

Physical	Mental/Emotional	Social

New Vocabulary

▶ physical activity (p. 318)
▶ physical fitness (p. 319)
▶ exercise (p. 319)
▶ sedentary (p. 321)

LESSON 1

Benefits of Physical Activity

Real Life Issues

Trying Something New. Nina and Marianne have been best friends since grade school. When Marianne took up kickboxing last year, Nina was disappointed that her friend had a new activity she didn't share. Marianne kept talking about how much she enjoyed her new sport and encouraging Nina to try it. In the beginning, Nina was hesitant, but she finally decided to take up the sport as well. Now the two friends have another activity they can enjoy together.

Writing *How do your friends affect your choice of sports and other physical activities? Describe an activity that someone you know has influenced you to try.*

Physical Activity and Your Health

Main Idea Physical activity benefits all aspects of your health.

Suppose you decided you were going to do just one thing to improve your health. What one action would you choose? If you're not sure, probably the single most important step you could take would be to lead a physically active life. **Physical activity** is *any form of movement that causes your body to use energy.* It benefits just about every system in your body, and also benefits your mental/emotional and social health.

Physical activity doesn't just mean "working out." It includes all kinds of activities that you do on a daily basis, such as walking to school, cleaning your room, or playing sports with your friends. There are lots of different ways to make physical activity a part of your life and enjoy its many benefits to your health.

Promoting School Wellness

Advancing Activity Schools cannot by themselves be expected to provide all the activities that a teen needs to mature into a healthy adult. Schools can, though, provide programs and facilities that promote participation in physical activities as a way of life. A quality physical education program tries to promote each student's optimum physical, mental and emotional, and social development. Let students know about the variety of programs your school offers. For example, perhaps your school offers after-school activities in the gymnasium or student clubs that focus on physical activities, such as skiing or hiking.

Physical Benefits

AL Being active on a regular basis improves your **physical fitness**, *the ability to carry out daily tasks easily and have enough reserve energy to respond to unexpected demands.* Teens should try for at least 60 minutes of physical activity every day. Depending on what kind of activity you do, it can strengthen your muscles and bones, boost your energy level, or improve your posture. You might feel that committing 60 minutes every day to physical activity will be difficult. Try dividing the time into smaller segments to get your 60 minutes throughout the day.

U You can achieve specific fitness goals through **exercise**, *purposeful physical activity that is planned, structured, and repetitive, and that improves or maintains physical fitness.* All kinds of physical activity—not just exercise—will improve your health. Being physically active can help you maintain a healthy weight and may reduce your risk of many serious diseases. **Figure 12.1** shows the ways in which physical activity can benefit several different body systems and maintain your overall health.

BusinessWeek HEALTH NEWS **VIDEO**

Slow Burn of Exercising

Analyze. Go to glencoe.com and watch the video *The Slow Burn of Exercising.* As a class, discuss slow motion exercises and decide if it is a fitness routine worth trying. Recall what you already know about getting in shape and share your ideas.

| Figure 12.1 | **The Active Body** |

This illustration shows just a few of the ways physical activity makes your body stronger. *Which systems in your body benefit from regular physical activity?*

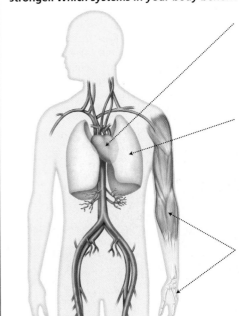

Cardiovascular System
Regular physical activity strengthens the heart muscle so that it pumps blood more efficiently. It reduces blood pressure and lowers the levels of artery-clogging cholesterol.

Respiratory System
As your activity level increases, your lungs begin to work more efficiently, pulling in larger amounts of air and increasing the amount of oxygen delivered to your body. As a result, you can do many activities more easily — for example, running a greater distance without becoming short of breath.

Musculoskeletal System
Physical activity strengthens muscles and bones, reducing your risk of developing fragile bones as you age. Strengthening your bones and muscles can also improve your balance and coordination.

Lesson 1 Benefits of Physical Activity   **319**

C Critical Thinking

Making Connections Make a three-column table on the board, with the column heads "Physical," "Mental/Emotional," and "Social." Ask a volunteer to name a physical benefit of physical activity. Write that benefit in the first column on the board. Then ask for volunteers to name a Mental/Emotional benefit that might be associated with the identified physical benefit. Next ask for a social benefit that might be associated with the physical benefit. For instance, if the physical benefit is maintaining a healthy weight, then the associated mental/emotional benefit might be improved self-esteem, and the social benefit might be confidence in social situations. OL

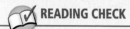 READING CHECK

Answer Physical activity provides stress relief, mood enhancement, better sleep, and improved self-esteem.

Caption Answer

Figure 12.2 Physical activities can be a great way to make new friends and spend time with the friends you have.

READING CHECK

Explain How does physical activity benefit your mental and emotional health?

Mental and Emotional Benefits

Being physically active maintains your physical health and has a positive effect on your mental and emotional health. It can provide the following:

- **Stress relief.** Being active stimulates your body to produce chemicals called endorphins. This results in a feeling of well-being, aids relaxation, and relieves physical pain. Some types of physical activity, such as stretching, can ease muscle tension as well.

- **Mood enhancement.** Have you ever gone out for a walk when you were in a bad mood and returned feeling much better? Physical activity is a natural mood lifter. In addition to endorphins, it promotes the production of other brain chemicals that combat anxiety and depression. For this reason, people with anxiety and depression are advised to get regular physical activity.

- **Better sleep.** Moderate activity at least three hours before bedtime helps you relax and get to sleep more easily.

- **Improved self-esteem.** The physical fitness you develop through increased activity can translate into more self-confidence. It can give you a sense of accomplishment and also help you look and feel your best.

C

Social Benefits

Are you a member of a sports team at school? Do you enjoy hiking or exploring trails in nearby parks? If so, you've probably formed friendships through these activities. Physical activity can be a great way to make new friends and spend time with the friends you already have. Being active as part of a group can help motivate you to stick with your fitness program. It can also help you learn skills that will improve your relationships, such as teamwork and sportsmanship.

■ **Figure 12.2** Taking part in sports can teach teamwork and sportsmanship. *Name other ways physical activity can benefit your social health.*

More About...

Exercise and Mood Physical activity in teens results in more than just strong bones and muscles. Studies have shown that physical activity can help alleviate symptoms of depression, in both adults and teens. Exercise is not a cure for depression, but physical activity can improve symptoms of depression, such as sadness, anxiety, self-doubt, and hopelessness. Health professionals do not know exactly how physical activity reduces these symptoms. Some evidence suggests that exercise increases levels of certain mood-lifting chemicals in the brain. In addition, exercise increases body temperature, which seems to have a calming effect. Ask interested students to research the U.S. Surgeon General's report on how physical activity benefits mood.

TEENS Making a Difference

Giving Others the "Sole" Benefit

"It feels good to help."

Greg W., of California, never realized how much running meant to him until he was diagnosed with a stress fracture in his hip. During his recovery, his injury helped him see the bigger picture. "It made me think about other kids who don't have the chance to run because they can't afford shoes."

Greg started Share Our Soles (SOS), a program that refurbishes used running shoes for kids. After the shoes are donated and collected, Greg cleans and boxes each pair. Then the shoes are picked up by Sports Gift, Inc., and distributed to inner-city areas as close as Los Angeles and as far away as Mexico, Uganda, and the Sudan. "It feels good to help," Greg says. "It's not just me who's making a difference. It's all the people who've made the effort to donate shoes."

Activity Write your answers to the following questions in your personal health journal:

1. Why did Greg start Share Our Soles?
2. What might be some barriers to becoming physically active?
3. List three ways you can promote physical activity in your community.

W The increased self-esteem that comes with physical fitness can help your social life as well. It can give you confidence when meeting new people or dealing with social situations. Finally, physical activity can help you manage stress, rather than letting it build up until it has a negative impact on your relationships.

Go Online

For more practice with vocabulary, go to the Interactive Health Tutor at **glencoe.com**.

Risks of Being Inactive

Main Idea An inactive lifestyle puts you at risk for a variety of health problems.

Despite the many benefits of physical activity, many teens still lead lives that are **sedentary**—*involving little physical activity.* Sedentary teens may spend their free time watching TV, playing video games, or surfing the Internet. All of us **devote** some time to sedentary activities, but being sedentary all the time puts you at risk for a variety of health problems.

Academic Vocabulary

devote *(verb):* to give time or effort to an activity

Lesson 1   Benefits of Physical Activity   **321**

Academic Integration

English Most famous sports figures—ranging from Michael Jordan to Mia Hamm—have either written an autobiography or been the subject of one or more biographies. These books are often well-written and contain insights into not only the achievements of a sports hero but also the struggles that occurred on the road to greatness. Within the life story of a sports champion, there is often a tale of perseverance and success against the odds. Ask a few volunteers to make an annotated list of appealing sports biographies found in the school and local libraries. Have these students share the list with the class. Encourage students to read one of the biographies and write a book report.

TEENS Making a Difference

Answers to Activity Questions

1. Greg feels extremely good in helping others who are less fortunate.
2. Some barriers might include being too busy or not feeling fit enough to do physical activity.
3. Answers will vary. Answers might include asking family members to go for a walk after dinner or encouraging a friend to join a school sports team.

W Writing Support

Personal Writing Have students write a letter to a friend that describes why it is important to be physically fit. Write a sample letter on the board for students who might have difficulty with this activity. Students should exchange letters and proofread before turning them in. **EL**

Main Idea

Risks of Being Inactive An inactive lifestyle puts a person at risk for health problems. **Ask Students:** *What are some activities that take very little physical energy to do?* (Examples may include watching television, playing video games, and surfing the Internet.)

CHAPTER 12

LESSON 1

 AL Active Learning

Daily Log Ask students to keep a daily log of how much time they devote to watching television, playing video games, and communicating on the computer. After several days, ask students to assess their daily logs. Discuss how they could replace sedentary activity with physical activity. **OL**

READING CHECK

Answer By being physically active for 60 minutes every day, or at least most days.

Main Idea

Making Time for Physical Activity There is more than one way to fit physical activity into your daily life. **Ask Students:** *If you didn't have a solid hour during a day to dedicate to being physically active, what could you do to get your daily requirement of physical activity?* (Students can break up their periods of activity. For example, engaging in physical activity for 20 minutes three times during the course of the day.)

READING CHECK

Answer Spreading several shorter periods of activity out over the course of a day and combining physical activity with recreation.

 Caption Answer

Figure 12.3 Answers will vary but may mention any of the social benefits discussed in the lesson, such as making new friends.

READING CHECK

Identify Problems and Solutions How can teens reduce their risk of obesity, cardiovascular disease, and type 2 diabetes?

READING CHECK

Identify List two ways that you can make time for physical activity.

■ **Figure 12.3** Just by turning off the TV and getting out of the house for a little exercise, you can reduce your risk of health problems. *What are other advantages of participating in physical activities?*

322 Chapter 12 Physical Activity and Fitness

Health problems that may result from being sedentary include

- unhealthful weight gain and obesity;
- cardiovascular disease, such as heart attack and stroke;
- type 2 diabetes;
- certain types of cancer;
- asthma and other breathing problems;
- osteoporosis, a condition in which the bones become porous and fragile, making them much more likely to break;
- osteoarthritis, a condition caused by the breakdown of cartilage and bone in the body's joints;
- psychological problems such as stress, anxiety, and depression; and
- premature death.

Increasing your level of physical activity lowers your risk of these health problems. Teens should aim for 60 minutes of physical activity every day, or at least most days.

Making Time for Physical Activity

Main Idea There are several ways to fit physical activity into your daily life.

Setting aside an hour a day for exercise may be difficult for some busy teens. You can get the same benefits from several shorter periods of activity spread out over the course of a day. For example, engaging in 10 minutes of physical activity six times a day provides the same benefits as an hour-long workout. **Figure 12.4** shows some ways you can fit physical activity into your life by choosing active alternatives to the things you do every day. **AL**

Teens Want to Know

I Don't Like Playing Sports—How Can I Be Physically Active? A teen doesn't have to play sports to stop being sedentary and start being physically active. When most people think of becoming physically fit, they think of sweaty, heart-pounding competition. Research shows, though, that when a sedentary person becomes moderately active, the person's health benefits significantly.

Moderate activity doesn't need to include competitive sports. Bicycling and walking briskly with friends are good moderate activities. A method to start becoming more physically active is to make a list of enjoyable ways to replace sedentary activities with moderate physical activities. Then, over the next week the list can be used as a motivator to make time for physical activity.

Figure 12.4 Active Alternatives

Instead of this . . .	Try this . . .
▸ Taking the elevator	▸ Taking the stairs
▸ Using a snowblower	▸ Shoveling snow
▸ Getting a ride to school or to a friend's house	▸ Walking, skating, or riding your bike
▸ Using a shopping cart	▸ Carrying your groceries to the car
▸ Taking the car through a car wash	▸ Washing the car by hand
▸ Playing video or computer games	▸ Playing basketball, soccer, or tennis

HS Health Skills Practice

Advocacy Have students use the information in **Figure 12.4** from the "Try this..." list to make a collage showing alternatives to everyday activities that would increase a teen's level of physical activity. With permission, display the completed collages in the school hallways. OL

③ ASSESS/ CLOSE

Assessment Resources

 FAST FILE ACTIVITIES
Lesson 1 Quiz

 ExamView Assessment Suite CD-ROM

Visit glencoe.com for:
Online Quizzes
Online Learning Center

LESSON 1 **ASSESSMENT**

After You Read

Reviewing Facts and Vocabulary

1. What is the difference between *physical activity* and *exercise*?

2. Name three body systems that benefit from regular physical activity.

3. Identify two types of disease associated with a sedentary lifestyle.

Thinking Critically

4. **Analyze.** Explain how being physically active on a regular basis makes your body better able to respond to physical demands.

5. **Synthesize.** Camilla thinks there's no point in trying to improve her physical fitness because she doesn't have a free hour in her daily schedule for exercise. What advice would you give her?

Applying Health Skills

6. **Stress Management.** Raul is taking several honors classes that require a lot of homework, and often feels stressed. How can he incorporate physical activity into his schedule to help reduce stress?

Writing Critically

7. **Expository.** Write an essay describing what might influence some teens to choose a sedentary lifestyle. Suggest ways to encourage these teens to become more physically active.

Gø Online

Visit **glencoe.com** and complete the Interactive Study Guide for this lesson.

Lesson 1 Benefits of Physical Activity **323**

Progress Monitoring

Reteaching
Have students write a paragraph that describes the benefits of being physically active on a regular basis and the risks of leading a sedentary life.

Enrichment
Have each student write five true-or-false questions about the main ideas and vocabulary terms of this lesson. Then, have students quiz one another using their prepared questions.

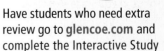

Have students who need extra review go to **glencoe.com** and complete the Interactive Study Guide for this lesson.

LESSON 1 ASSESSMENT ANSWERS

1. *Exercise* is a purposeful kind of physical activity that is planned and *physical activity* is any form of movement that causes the body to use energy.

2. See page 319.

3. Sample answer: cardiovascular disease and type 2 diabetes

4. Regular activity makes the heart and lungs work more efficiently so that they can deliver more oxygen to the body.

5. She could be physically active during several shorter periods over the course of a day or combine physical activity with recreation.

6. Sample answer: He could walk to school or take stairs instead of elevators.

7. Essays will vary.

LESSON 2

Improving Your Fitness

① FOCUS

GUIDE TO READING

BIG Idea Different elements of fitness can help evaluate and improve exercise. **Ask Students:** *One person can easily run 20 kilometers and another can easily lift 200 pounds, yet both are said to be physically fit. How would you describe the type of fitness each person has?* (Sample answers: The person who can easily run 20 kilometers has fit lungs and the person who can easily lift 200 pounds has very strong muscles.)

Before You Read

Comparison Chart
Students' tables will vary.

Main Idea

Elements of Fitness Five elements of fitness affect health in various ways. **Ask Students:** *How would being very strong or being very flexible affect a person's life differently?*

Real Life Issues

Before students begin writing, write a few activities on the board. **Ask Students:** *What are some things you'd like to do if you were extremely fit?* (Accept any reasonable responses.)

324

LESSON 2

GUIDE TO READING

BIG Idea *Different types of exercise can help you evaluate and improve the various elements of fitness.*

Before You Read

Create a Comparison Chart. Draw a chart. Label the columns "Define," "Measure," and "Improve." Label the rows "C/E" (cardio endurance), "M/S" (muscular strength), "M/E" (muscular endurance) and "F" (flexibility). As you read, fill in your chart with information from the lesson.

	Define	Measure	Improve
C/E			
M/S			
M/E			
F			

New Vocabulary

▶ cardiorespiratory endurance (p. 324)
▶ muscular strength (p. 324)
▶ muscular endurance (p. 325)
▶ flexibility (p. 325)
▶ aerobic exercise (p. 327)
▶ anaerobic exercise (p. 328)

Improving Your Fitness

Real Life Issues

Getting Motivated. Malcolm wants to improve his physical fitness. His P.E. teacher suggests making a list of all the activities he'd like to be physically fit enough to do. Malcolm thinks this is a great idea because the list would remind him of his goals and help him stay motivated.

Writing *List two to three activities you would like to be physically fit enough to do. Then pick one of them and write a paragraph about how being able to do this activity would improve your life.*

Elements of Fitness

Main Idea There are five elements of fitness that affect your health in different ways.

Are you physically fit if you can run five miles or do a dozen push-ups in a row? These are two of the five elements of health-related fitness that affect you in different ways.

• **Cardiorespiratory endurance** is *the ability of your heart, lungs, and blood vessels to send fuel and oxygen to your tissues during long periods of moderate to vigorous activity.* By maintaining good cardiorespiratory health, you can run a mile or go on a long hike without tiring. Good cardiorespiratory health lowers your risk of cardiovascular disease.

• **Muscular strength** is *the amount of force your muscles can exert.* You need muscular strength for all kinds of activities that put stress on your muscles, such as lifting, pushing, and jumping.

More About...

Cardiorespiratory Endurance Cardiorespiratory health is an important element in physical fitness. With regular aerobic exercise, the heart becomes stronger and pumps more blood with each beat. During exercise, the arteries dilate—increase in volume—and more blood flows to the body's muscles. With these improvements in the system, both resting heart rate and resting blood pressure decreases. The lungs also benefit from regular exercise. As a person improves cardiorespiratory endurance, fewer breaths are needed to move the same volume of air into and out of the lungs. Breaths become deeper, and that allows more oxygen to reach the parts of the lungs where the oxygen is delivered to the bloodstream. Ask students to investigate how increasing cardiorespiratory endurance affects the body.

- **Muscular endurance** is *the ability of your muscles to perform physical tasks over a period of time without tiring.* Muscular endurance gives you the power to carry out daily tasks without fatigue, such as carrying boxes up and down a flight of stairs.
- **Flexibility** is *the ability to move your body parts through their full range of motion.* If you are flexible, you can touch your toes without bending your legs or put sunscreen on the center of your back. Flexiblility can improve your athletic performance and reduce your risk of muscle strain and other injuries.
- **Body composition**—the ratio of fat to lean tissue in your body—is also an element of fitness. Having low overall body fat reduces your risk of cardiovascular disease and other health problems associated with being overweight.

AL

Evaluating Your Fitness

Main Idea You can use different tests to evaluate each element of your fitness.

So how fit are you? If you're not sure how to answer that, the tests described below may help. Each test measures a different element of fitness. By taking them all, you can figure out how you measure up in each area of fitness.

Measuring Cardiorespiratory Endurance

You can evaluate your cardiorespiratory endurance by doing a three-minute step test. You will need a sturdy bench or step about 12 inches high and a watch or clock with a second hand. Follow this procedure:

1. Step up onto the bench with your right foot. Bring up your left foot. Step back down, right foot first, then left foot.
2. Continue stepping up and back down for three minutes. Try to maintain a steady pace of about 24 steps per minute.
3. After three minutes, take your pulse. To do this, place two fingers of one hand on the wrist of your opposite hand. (Do not use your thumb, which has its own pulse.) Count the number of heartbeats you feel in 15 seconds. Then multiply that number by 4 to determine your pulse rate.

Check your pulse rate against **Figure 12.6** on page 326 to see how you did on the test.

■ **Figure 12.5** The step test is one activity that requires cardiorespiratory endurance. *What are other activities that use this element of fitness?*

READING CHECK

Classify Which elements of fitness would help you run a marathon?

② TEACH

AL Active Learning

Student-Led Learning Divide the class into five groups. Assign each group one of the five elements of fitness. Ask each group to develop a slogan that could be used to advocate for improving its assigned element of fitness. Explain that radio advertisers use catchy slogans to grab listeners' attention. Have each group present its slogan to the class. **BL**

READING CHECK

Answer Cardiorespiratory endurance and muscular endurance

Main Idea

Evaluating Fitness Different tests are used to measure different elements of fitness. **Ask Students:** *If you wanted to check your cardiorespiratory endurance, what would you do?* (Students could do the three-minute step test and check their results against **Figure 12.6**.)

Caption Answer

Figure 12.5 Answers will vary but may include running, hiking, and biking long distances.

Writing Strategy

Evaluating Fitness Ask each student to write an honest evaluation of his or her own fitness. Assure them that this evaluation is personal and will be seen only by them. Students can keep their evaluations in their journals. Explain that when they write their assessment, they should take the perspective of a health-care professional or personal trainer who is describing a new client. With that perspective, students can make an impersonal and impartial assessment of their strengths and weaknesses. Advise students that as they write they should keep in mind the five elements of fitness.

R Reading Strategy

Analyzing a Chart Have students examine **Figure 12.6**. Ask which of these tests measures flexibility? (sit-and-reach) Which measures strength? (push-ups or curl-ups) BL

C Critical Thinking

Alternative Tests After students have read how to measure muscular strength and endurance, point out that curl-ups primarily test abdominal muscles and push-ups primarily test upper-arm and chest muscles. Challenge students to think of two measurements of fitness that test two other muscles in the body. Also ask students to think of a test of these elements for someone who is physically challenged. AL

Caption Answer

Figure 12.7 Sample answer: Having strong abdominal muscles would help in being able to stand or sit straight instead of slouching.

READING CHECK

Answer Both exercises require muscular strength and endurance; curl-ups use abdominal muscles while right-angle push-ups use muscles of the upper body.

Figure 12.6 Fitness Test Scoring Chart

Each of the columns below provides scores for the fitness tests. If you scored at or above the number shown for each of these three tests, you are in good shape. If you scored below the number shown, you need to work on that element of fitness. R

Step Test	Partial Curl-Ups	Right-Angle Push-Ups	Sit-and-Reach Test
Male teens: (heartbeats per minute) 85–95: Excellent 95–105: Good 105–126: Fair 126+: Needs improvement	Boys, ages 13–14: 21	Boys, age 14: 12 Boys, age 15: 14 Boys, age 16: 16 Boys, age 17: 18	Boys: 1 inch
Female teens: (heartbeats per minute) 85–95: Excellent 95–106: Good 106–126: Fair 126+: Needs improvement	Girls, ages 13–14: 18	Girls, ages 14–17: 7	Girls: 3 inches

READING CHECK

Compare and Contrast How are curl-ups and right-angle push-ups alike? How are they different?

Measuring Muscular Strength and Endurance

Different muscle groups require different exercises. The two exercises below will test the strength and endurance of your abdominal muscles and your upper body. After completing each exercise, check **Figure 12.6** to see how you did. C

Partial Curl-Ups Use the following procedure to measure your abdominal strength:

1. Lie on your back with your knees bent and your feet about 12 inches from your backside. Extend your arms forward with your fingers pointing toward your knees.
2. Raise your head and upper body off the floor, sliding your hands forward. Touch your knees with your fingertips.
3. Slowly return to your original position.
4. Continue doing curl-ups at a rate of one every three seconds until you can no longer maintain this pace.

■ **Figure 12.7** Curl-ups measure abdominal strength. *How might building abdominal strength improve your posture?*

The number of curl-ups you can do without tiring is a measure of your abdominal strength and endurance.

Right-Angle Push-Ups The right-angle push-up is one test to gauge your upper body strength and endurance.

1. Lie facedown in the push-up position. Place your hands under your shoulders, with your legs parallel to each other and resting on your toes.

Myths & Reality

Physical Activity

Myth: Thin people are physically fit and have perfect body composition.

Fact: A thin person may be physically fit but not necessarily. Being thin does not mean the ratio of fat to lean tissue is low, and a thin person may have poor cardiorespiratory endurance, muscular strength, muscular endurance, and flexibility.

Myth: Running is the best way to become physically fit.

Fact: There is no best exercise for becoming physically fit. A variety of exercises should be used to address each of the five elements of fitness.

2. Straighten your arms and push up. Keep your back and knees straight. Bend your arms and lower your body until your elbows form a 90-degree angle, with your upper arms parallel to the floor.
3. Repeat this process, doing one push-up every three seconds until you can no longer maintain this pace.

■ **Figure 12.8** Right-angle push-ups are a way of measuring upper body strength and endurance. *What other activities require upper body strength and endurance?*

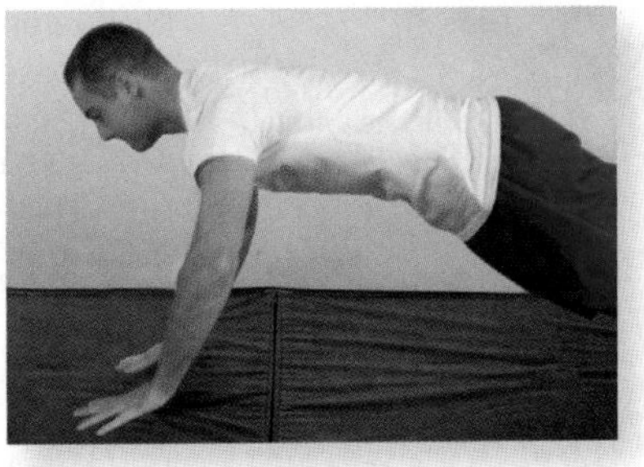

Measuring Flexibility

HS

The sit-and-reach test measures the flexibility of your lower back and hamstring muscles. To set up the test, tape a yardstick to the top of a box with 9 inches protruding over one end.

1. Remove your shoes. Place the box against a wall, or ask someone to hold the box in place, with the yardstick pointing out. Sit on the floor. Place the sole of one foot flat against the side of the box under the yardstick. Bend the other leg at the knee.
2. Extend your arms over the yardstick, with your hands placed one on top of the other, palms down.
3. Reach forward in this manner four times. The fourth time, hold this position for at least one second while a partner records how far you can reach.
4. Switch legs and repeat.

Getting Fit

Main Idea **Use different forms of exercise to improve the various elements of your fitness.**

To improve your overall fitness, you can choose from many different exercises and other activities. Most of these fit into two basic categories: aerobic and anaerobic.

Aerobic exercise includes *all rhythmic activities that use large muscle groups for an extended* **period** *of time.* Aerobic

Academic Vocabulary

period *(noun):* the completion of a cycle

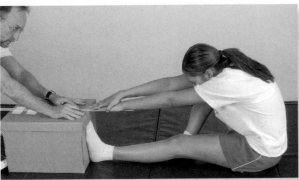

■ **Figure 12.9** The sit-and-reach test measures flexibility in your hips and legs. *What are some benefits of being flexible?*

Caption Answer

Figure 12.8 Sample answer: Both pull-ups and bicep curls with weights require upper-body strength.

HS Health Skills Practice

Practicing Healthful Behaviors Have pairs of students work together to measure each other's flexibility, following the directions of the sit-and-reach test as described in the text. In setting up the test, two or three boxes with yardsticks taped to them could be placed around the classroom. Pairs could take turns using the boxes for the stretch test. Allow students who are reluctant to take the test in front of other students to act as recorder. OL

Caption Answer

Figure 12.9 Being flexible can improve athletic performance and reduce risk of injury.

Main Idea

Getting Fit Different forms of exercise will affect and improve different elements of fitness. **Ask Students:** *If you wanted to improve your cardiorespiratory endurance, why would you choose a daily run instead of lifting weights every day?* (Cardiorespiratory endurance is the most important element to building cardiorespiratory endurance.)

Cooperative Learning

Testing Fitness After students have read about the various tests used to measure the different elements of fitness, divide the class into three groups, one for cardiorespiratory endurance, another for muscular strength, and a third for flexibility. Ask each group to create a video or skit that could be shown to teens for instruction about proper ways to test for its element of fitness. To prepare for the video or skit, each group should write out the appropriate steps. Explain that although the video or skit must be accurate about fitness measurement, it could also be produced in creative and humorous ways in order to appeal to teens.

Academic Vocabulary

Period Call on a volunteer to use the word in a sentence about everyday life, such as time spent in school. Ask other students whether the term was used correctly.

U Universal Access

Fitness Scoring To check for fitness level after doing the tests described in the text, students must be able to interpret the Fitness Scoring Chart in **Figure 12.6**. Help students understand this chart by writing sample results of a fictional student on the board and then calling on volunteers to find where the results fall in each of the columns of the chart. Then, ask students to try and improve their cardiorespiratory endurance over a period of weeks. They should use the Fitness Scoring Chart to record their progress. **BL**

Caption Answer

Figure 12.10 Strength training builds muscles, boosts metabolism, protects joints from injury, increases stamina.

FITNESS ZONE

Have students play with their reaction time.

- Partners face each other
- One partner holds out hands, palms up
- Other partner puts their hands, palms down over their partner's hands
- Person whose hands are on the bottom must try and gently touch the tops of their partners hands.

Go Online

For more practice with vocabulary go to the Interactive Health Tutor at **glencoe.com**.

FITNESS ZONE

My goal this year is to get in great shape, so I started keeping a journal of what I eat and when I work out. With a journal it's easier to stick with my plan because I know exactly what I have to do. My success has kept me motivated. For more physical activity ideas, visit the Online Fitness Zone at **glencoe.com**.

■ **Figure 12.10**
Lifting weights is one form of resistance or strength training. *What are the benefits of strength training?*

exercise raises your heart rate and increases your body's use of oxygen. Jogging, swimming, and riding a bike are examples of aerobic exercise.

Anaerobic exercise involves *intense, short bursts of activity in which the muscles work so hard that they produce energy without using oxygen.* Sprinting and lifting weights are examples of this kind of exercise.

Improving Cardiorespiratory Endurance

Aerobic exercise is important for building cardiorespiratory endurance. Aerobic activities increase your heart rate and pump more blood throughout your body. Over time, your heart and lungs adapt to the demands made by aerobic activity by working more efficiently.

Regular aerobic exercise reduces your risk of cardiovascular disease. It also helps you manage your weight and lower your risk of type 2 diabetes, certain cancers, and other diseases associated with being overweight. The Real World Connection activity explains how to determine your target heart rate when doing aerobic exercise.

Improving Muscular Strength and Endurance

In contrast to aerobic acivity, anaerobic exercises improve muscular strength and endurance. The more the muscles work, the stronger they will become. Exercises that strengthen the muscles are known as resistance or strength training. Free weights, exercise machines, or your own body weight provides resistance. There are three ways to use resistance to work your muscles:

Health Literacy

Steroid Use Anabolic steroids were developed in the 1930s to help build muscles. Today, the main use of anabolic steroids—usually simply called steroids—is as an illegal drug to increase muscle mass and enhance athletic performance. Using steroids to enhance performance can have long-term negative side effects:

- Steroid use in males can cause baldness, the development of breasts, shrinkage

of testicles, and erectile dysfunction (impotence).

- Steroid use in females can cause growth of facial hair and smaller breast size.
- Steroid use in both genders can cause mood swings, outbursts of anger, and nervousness.
- In the long term, steroids cause liver damage and even liver cancer.

- **Isometric exercises** use muscle tension to improve strength with little or no movement of the body part. Pushing against a wall or other immovable object is an example of isometric exercise.
- **Isotonic exercises** combine movement of the joints with contraction of the muscles. Try lifting free weights or doing calisthenics, such as pull-ups, push-ups, and sit-ups. These exercises build flexibility as well as strength.
- **Isokinetic exercises** exert resistance against a muscle as it moves through a range of motion at a steady rate of speed. Various types of weight machines and other exercise equipment provide isokinetic exercise.

Increasing muscle mass boosts your metabolism so your body burns the energy you consume faster. That makes it easier to control your weight.

 READING CHECK

Classify What are the three types of resistance exercise?

Real World CONNECTION

Targeting Cardiovascular Fitness

Your target heart range is the ideal range during aerobic activity. To calculate your target heart range:

1. Multiply your age by 0.7.
2. Subtract this number from 208 to get an estimate of your maximum heart rate. If you are 16 years old, your maximum heart rate will be 197 beats per minute.

3. Multiply this number by 50 percent to get your minimum heart rate for moderately intense activity.
4. Multiply the number in step 2 by 70 percent to get your maximum heart rate for moderately intense activity and the minimum for vigorous activity.
5. Multiply the number in step 2 by 85 percent to get your maximum target heart rate for any physical activity. Exercising above this rate is dangerous.
6. To figure out your heart rate during exercise, take your pulse for six seconds and multiply the result by 10.

Activity Mathematics

Use this procedure to calculate your target heart range for moderate activity and for vigorous activity. Try checking your pulse rate while jogging in place.

Concept Problem Solving: Make a Plan
To solve this problem, change the percent to a fraction or to a decimal, and then multiply by the number.

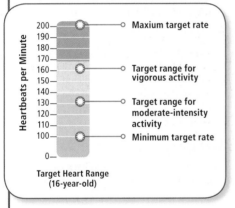

Heartbeats per Minute
200 — Maximum target rate
190
180
170
160 — Target range for vigorous activity
150
140
130 — Target range for moderate-intensity activity
120
110
100 — Minimum target rate
0

Target Heart Range (16-year-old)

Real World CONNECTION

Answers to Activity

Students' ages will vary. Here is the answer for a 16-year-old:

1. $16 \times 0.7 = 11.2$
2. $208 - 11.2 = 197$
3. $197 \times .50 = 98.5$ — Moderate activity target heart range
4. $197 \times .70 = 138$ — Maximum heart rate for rigorous activity
5. $197 \times .85 = 167$ — Target heart range for any physical activity

R Reading Strategy

Discussing After students have read about the three ways to improve muscular strength, ask students to bring in pictures of the three resistance methods, either printed from a strength-training Web site or from a book or magazine. **BL**

 READING CHECK

Answer Isometric exercises, isotonic exercises, and isokinetic exercises

---

Teacher to Teacher

Lee W. Cook • Carey High School, Carey, ID

Measuring Fitness One way I measure the fitness level of our students is to have them participate in the "President's Challenge." This fitness program consists of five individual skills: 1) curl-ups, 2) shuttle run, 3) one-mile walk/run, 4) pull-ups, and 5) V-sit reach. Before students perform any tests, they are taught proper techniques. I also review these skills with them during class. The test results can be sent to the President's Council for awards, or can simply be used as a measurement of fitness.

③ ASSESS/ CLOSE

Assessment Resources

📁 **FAST FILE ACTIVITIES**
Lesson 2 Quiz

💿 *ExamView*
Assessment Suite CD-ROM

Visit glencoe.com for:
Online Quizzes
Online Learning Center

Progress Monitoring

Reteaching
Ask each student to write a paragraph that defines each of the five elements of fitness and also describes what form of exercise could be used to improve each element.

Enrichment
Have students make a pamphlet that explains the difference between aerobic and anaerobic activities, describes the benefits of activities in each category, and classifies common physical activities as one or the other.

Have students visit **glencoe.com** and complete the Interactive Study Guide for this lesson.

When lifting weights, begin each workout with one set of exercises using lighter weights. Gradually increase the amount of weight you use until you are lifting your maximum weight. Warm up before any kind of strength training with gentle aerobic activity, such as jogging or fast walking.

Improving Flexibility

Stretching exercises improve your flexibility, circulation, posture, and coordination, as well as ease stress. It may also reduce your risk of injury during other activities. Do the stretching exercises slowly, holding each stretch for 10 to 30 seconds. Don't bounce. If stretching causes pain you've pushed too far.

Exercise and Bone Strength

Exercise helps increase bone density and lowers the risk of osteoporosis. Weight-bearing exercises work with gravity, and are good for strengthening bones. Strength training, walking, aerobics, and dancing are all weight-bearing exercises.

■ **Figure 12.11** Weight-bearing exercises, which make your body work against gravity, are a way to build bone strength. *What weight-bearing activities do you do on a regular basis?*

LESSON 2 📖 ASSESSMENT

After You Read

Reviewing Facts and Vocabulary

1. What are the five elements of fitness?
2. Which element of fitness does the sit-and-reach test measure?
3. What kind of exercise would you do to improve your cardiorespiratory endurance?

Thinking Critically

4. **Analyze.** How will your target heart range for physical activity change as you grow older? Explain why.
5. **Evaluate.** Carmen wants to get in shape. She is planning to join a gym and use only the weight machines. Is this a good plan? Why or why not?

Applying Health Skills

6. **Goal Setting.** Choose one of the five elements of fitness that you would like to improve. Write out a plan to improve that element of your fitness.

Writing Critically

7. **Personal.** Write a personal journal entry about why fitness is important to you. Describe activities that you can participate in because you are fit, or that would require you to improve your fitness.

G⊙ Online
Visit glencoe.com and complete the Interactive Study Guide for this lesson.

LESSON 2 ASSESSMENT ANSWERS

1. See pages 324–325.
2. Flexibility
3. Aerobic exercise
4. Answers will vary. Example: My target heart rate will be lower because my maximum heart rate will be lower.
5. This is not a good plan because she is not addressing either cardiorespiratory endurance or flexibility.
6. Plans will vary.
7. Journal entries will vary.

Planning a Personal Activity Program

Planning a Personal Activity Program

Real Life Issues

Getting Fit. Pete wants to get in better shape. He has decided to create a fitness plan, but he's not sure where to start. He's not even sure he knows how to determine what a good level of fitness is. He doesn't know which exercises to do, how often he should do them, or how long he should do them.

Writing *If you were Pete, what steps would you take to create an appropriate fitness plan? In a paragraph, describe the steps you would take.*

Your Fitness Plan

Main Idea The physical activities you choose depend on factors such as your fitness goals and the activities you like.

Identifying a specific fitness goal is a good way to get motivated to get in shape. You also need to consider your personal needs, such as your current level of fitness and the resources available to you.

Your Fitness Goals

In Lesson 2, you learned how to measure your level of fitness. This knowledge can serve as a starting point for setting your fitness goals. If you found that you have good cardiorespiratory endurance but not much upper body strength, you might want to make building your upper body strength a goal of your activity plan. If your cardiorespiratory endurance needs to be strengthened, choose exercises that improve this aspect of fitness. Take a look at the Health Skills Activity on page 334 for an example of how to set specific fitness goals.

GUIDE TO READING

BIG Idea *Planning your physical activity can help you achieve specific fitness goals.*

Before You Read

Create Vocabulary Cards. Write each new vocabulary term on a separate note card. For each term, write a definition based on your current knowledge. As you read, fill in additional information related to each term.

Specificity

New Vocabulary

- ▶ specificity (p. 332)
- ▶ overload (p. 332)
- ▶ progression (p. 333)
- ▶ warm-up (p. 334)
- ▶ workout (p. 335)
- ▶ cool-down (p. 335)
- ▶ resting heart rate (p. 336)

① FOCUS

GUIDE TO READING

BIG Idea Students will learn that developing a physical activity plan can help them achieve specific fitness goals.
Ask Students: *Do you have a physical activity goal right now?* (Answers will vary.)

Before You Read

Vocabulary Cards Students' note cards should include the definitions of each of the lesson's new vocabulary terms.

Main Idea

Fitness Plan The physical activities chosen for a fitness plan depend on fitness goals and activities a person likes. **Ask Students:** *What are some physical activities that would be easy to learn to do in this area?* (Answers will vary according to where students live.)

Cooperative Learning

Physical Fitness on the Job Many employers recognize the benefits of having physically fit employees. Benefits can include lower health-care costs, fewer lost work days for workers because of illness, and enhanced productivity at the workplace. As a result, many companies either provide on-site exercise facilities for their workers or offer memberships to health clubs in the community. Ask students to work in pairs to organize a survey of local employers to find out what they do to encourage physical activity among employees. Students can use a phone book and online resources to make a list of companies and then assign pairs of students to make an appointment with a company's Human Resources' office to gather information.

Real Life Issues

Have students read the scenario. **Ask Students:** *What kind of activities do you like to do? Think of action-oriented activities such as skateboarding or playing soccer.* (Answers will vary.)

② TEACH

✓ READING CHECK

Determine When might it be important to consult a doctor before trying a new physical activity?

■ **Figure 12.12** Measuring your resting heart rate is one way to track your fitness. *What is your resting pulse rate now?*

332

Personal Needs

When planning a personal activity program, choose activities that you enjoy and that you can realistically do. The following factors may affect your activity choices:

- **Cost.** Some activities require expensive equipment. Borrow or rent equipment to try a new sport.
- **Where you live.** Choose activities that you can do close to home, and that are best for your region. For example, is your local area flat or hilly? What is the climate like?
- **Your schedule.** Choose activities that fit into your schedule and habits. If you're not a morning person, a morning jog probably won't work for you.
- **Your fitness level.** Start slowly and choose activities that are right for your level of fitness.
- **Your overall health.** Do you have a health condition that may impact your exercise plan, such as asthma? Talk to a doctor before starting a new activity.
- **Personal safety.** When choosing activities, make sure that the environment where you perform the activity is safe.

Types of Activities

Teens should aim to get at least 60 minutes of physical activity most days. Choose different types of activity to meet specific fitness goals and to prevent boredom. An exercise plan can include activities such as walking or biking to school, or playing a pickup basketball or soccer game with friends, as well as competitive sports. Sedentary activities, or those activities that do not require physical activity, should be limited to a small part of your day. **Figure 12.13** shows a page from a fitness journal. The types of physical activities to be included in a fitness journal can include the following:

Moderate-Intensity Physical Activities These count toward your daily dose of physical activity. Examples include walking, climbing stairs, household chores, or yard work.

Aerobic Activities These raise your heart rate. Aim for at least three 20-minute sessions each week of vigorous aerobic activity. Examples include cycling, brisk walking, running, dancing, in-line skating, cross-country skiing, and most team sports.

Strength Training This develops muscle tone. Aim for at least two or three sessions per week of 20 to 30 minutes each, with at least one day off between sessions. Exercises that tone arm muscles include rowing, cross-country skiing, pull-ups, and push-ups. To tone legs, try cycling, running, and skating. Abdominal muscles can be toned by rowing or cycling, and doing abdominal crunches.

Figure 12.13 **A Variety of Physical Activities**

Choose different types of activities to meet specific fitness goals.

Thursday:
 — 20 minutes strength
   training
 — stretching

Friday:
 — walk to school
 — yoga class
 — running

Flexibility Exercises These include stretching for 10 to 12 minutes a day. Examples of flexibility exercises include gymnastics, martial arts, ballet, Pilates, yoga, or stretching.

Principles of Building Fitness

Main Idea Effective fitness plans focus on four principles: specificity, overload, progression, and regularity.

When designing your physical activity program, you will consider your needs and interests. In addition, you should focus on the four key principles of building a fitness plan: specificity, overload, progression, and regularity.

- **Specificity** means *choosing the right types of activities to improve a given element of fitness.* For example, strength-training activities will build muscular strength.

- **Overload** means *exercising at a level that's beyond your regular daily activities.* Increasing the demands on your body will make it adapt and grow stronger.

- **Progression** means *gradually increasing the demands on your body.* Try working a little harder or longer during each session, and more often during the week.

- **Regularity** means *working out on a regular basis.* You need at least three balanced workouts a week to maintain your fitness level. Include different activities to get the recommended hour of physical activity each day.

READING CHECK

Make Inferences
Why do you need to increase the demands on your body over time to build fitness?

U **Universal Access**

Cooperative Learning
Pair students who are English proficient with English language learners. Have pairs review the new vocabulary terms, such as *specificity, progression,* and *overload*. Ask students to use a dictionary together to determine each of the term's definitions. Have pairs write sentences using each of the lesson's new vocabulary terms.
BL **EL**

READING CHECK

Answer If you increase demands on your body, it will adapt by growing stronger.

Main Idea

Principles of Building Fitness
An effective fitness plan is based on the principles of specificity, overload, progression, and regularity.
Ask Students: *Why would regularity be important to a person's fitness plan?* (Answers will vary but may include the idea that unless a program includes regular exercise, a person's fitness level will not improve.)

English Language Coach

Word Forms Explain that English words can take many forms, depending on their use in a sentence or a context. For example, the new vocabulary word *specificity*. The adjectival form of *specificity* is *specific,* as in this sentence: Improving a given element of fitness may depend on the *specific* activity you choose. The verb form of *specificity* is *specify,* as in this sentence: You should *specify* the activity for improving a given element of fitness. Then write these incomplete sentences on the board. "She will _____ the activity needed for muscular endurance" and "A plan to improve cardiorespiratory endurance requires _____ in the exercises chosen to do." Have students complete each sentence.

Health Skills Activity

Goal Setting: Identifying Fitness Goals

NHES Standard 6 Students will demonstrate the ability to use goal-setting skills to enhance health.

Objectives

- Develop a plan to attain a personal health goal that addresses strengths, needs, and risks.

- Implement strategies and monitor progress in achieving a personal health goal.

Teaching Strategies

- List the five goal-setting steps to Wendy's situation. Suggest that students use the list on the board to develop a detailed plan for Wendy.

- Remind students to choose a variety of activities to improve all areas of fitness.

Assessment

Using a rubric, student work should provide comprehensive evidence of the following criteria to achieve the highest score:

√ Sets a realistic goal
√ Identifies five steps to reach the goal
√ Sets up checkpoints to evaluate progress
√ Identifies a reward when the goal has been achieved

Health Skills Activity

Goal Setting Skills

Identifying Fitness Goals

Wendy enjoys playing soccer and is interested in joining her school's team. She's not sure she's in good enough shape to try out though. She has pretty good muscle strength and endurance. But Wendy is concerned about her cardiorespiratory endurance. She always seems to run out of breath sooner than she should, and it sometimes slows her down. She's worried that she won't be able to keep up with the rest of the team or that she can't run around on the field for an hour at a time. She's also not sure she's flexible enough for all the dodging and maneuvering the game involves.

Writing Write a plan for Wendy to achieve her fitness goals. Remember to use the five-step process for goal setting:

1. Identify a specific goal. Write it down.
2. List the steps to reach your goal.
3. Identify potential problems and ways to get support.
4. Set up checkpoints to evaluate your progress.
5. Reward yourself with healthy rewards once you have achieved your goal.

Stages of a Workout

> **Main Idea** An exercise session has three stages: warm-up, workout, and cool-down.

Now that you've defined your fitness goals, chosen your activities, and scheduled time to do them, it's time to get moving. To get your body ready for physical activity and to avoid injuries, include three stages in every exercise session: the warm-up, the workout, and the cool-down.

✓ READING CHECK

Explain What is the purpose of a warm-up?

Academic Vocabulary

instance (verb): to mention as a case or example

Warm-Up

A **warm-up** is *gentle cardiovascular activity that prepares the muscles for work.* Warming up before exercise increases blood flow, delivering needed oxygen and fuel to your muscles. It also gradually increases your pulse rate and body temperature. To warm up, choose an activity that will work the same muscles you're going to use during your workout. For instance, before a run, warm up by walking or jogging slowly.

After warming up your muscles, take a few minutes to stretch. Stretching can prepare your muscles for activity and increase your flexibility.

334 **Chapter 12** Physical Activity and Fitness

Teens Want to Know

Should Teen Girls Avoid Weight Training Because It Builds Bulky Muscles? Weight training, including lifting free weights or using a weight machine, will not build bulky muscles on either teen girls or adult women. Females naturally have smaller muscles than males do. The main reason that men build bulky muscles through weight lifting is because of male hormones, such as testosterone. Girls and women have different hormones, and so building large muscles is very difficult to do. Strength training is very important for girls and women because it improves bone density and helps prevent osteoporosis. Ask students interested in this topic to prepare a report to the class.

Workout

The **workout** is *the part of an exercise session when you are exercising at your highest peak.* Use the **F.I.T.T.** formula when planning your workouts:

- **F: Frequency of workouts.** Schedule at least three exercise sessions a week, but give your body time to rest between workouts. Include other types of physical activity during the week to get an hour of activity each day.

- **I: Intensity of workouts.** Push yourself hard enough to create overload. For aerobic activities, exercise within your target heart range. For strength training, you should feel strain on your muscles, but not pain.

- **T: Type of activity.** Vary your activities throughout the week to build different elements of fitness. If you jog Monday and Wednesday, try lifting weights on Tuesday and Thursday.

- **T: Time (duration) of workouts.** To build cardiovascular fitness, keep your heart rate within your target range for at least 20 minutes. Strength-training sessions should take 20 to 30 minutes, while flexibility can be increased in just 10 minutes of stretching.

Cool-Down

A **cool-down** is *low-level activity that prepares your body to return to a resting state.* The cool-down allows your heart rate, breathing, and body temperature to return to normal gradually. It also reduces strain on your heart and helps prevent muscle soreness. Cool-downs should include five to ten minutes of gentle activity. The cool-down stage is also a good time for stretching.

FITNESS ZONE

One of my friends showed me an exercise that she said would slim down just my thighs. Our coach, though, says there's no such thing as spot reducing. To get in shape, you have to change your eating habits by cutting down on fat and add a well-rounded exercise routine.

■ **Figure 12.14** Stretching your muscles helps prevent injuries. *What stage of a workout is the best time for stretching?*

R Reading Strategy

The F.I.T.T. Formula Explain to students that **F.I.T.T.** is an acronym, a word formed from the first letters of the words in a phrase or the first letters in the first words in a list of phrases. In this case, the acronym comes from the first letters in the first words of four principles that should be kept in mind when planning workouts. Read each of the four principles aloud. Then, say each letter of the acronym aloud, and call on volunteers to explain what the letter stands for. Call on other volunteers to describe why that principle is important in building a fitness program. **BL** **EL**

Caption Answer

Figure 12.14 Cool-down stage

AL Active Learning

Collage Have students work in pairs to create a collage showing a workout and a cool-down. Students can get images from magazines, newspapers, or the Internet. **OL**

Writing Strategy

Fitness Journal Encourage students to dedicate a small notebook for use as a fitness journal. They could also build a spreadsheet on the computer to record data. Assure students that this journal is for their use only and will be kept private. Explain that they should begin the fitness journal with a list of the fitness goals they want to achieve. The rest of the journal should be a daily record of what physical activities they have done that day, with notations about how long they exercised, how much they lifted, how fast they ran a distance, and so on with specifics about the activity. Explain that a main purpose of keeping a record of the specifics is to keep an account of their progression in the activities.

LESSON 3

 READING CHECK

Answer Regular exercise will make your resting heart rate drop.

 ASSESS/ CLOSE

Assessment Resources

📁 *FAST FILE* **ACTIVITIES**
Lesson 3 Quiz

💿 *ExamView*
Assessment Suite CD-ROM

Visit glencoe.com for:
Online Quizzes
Online Learning Center

Progress Monitoring

Reteaching
Have students work in small groups to plan a personal activity program that would appeal to a male teen and another program that would appeal to a female teen in their local area. Have groups trade plans and discuss similarities and differences.

Enrichment
Have students research what it takes to become certified as a personal trainer and where in their community a person can become certified as a personal trainer. Have students present their findings to the class.

G Online

Have students visit **glencoe.com** and complete the Interactive Study Guide for this lesson.

336

Tracking Your Progress

Main Idea Track your progress to see how your fitness level increases over time.

One of the rewards of sticking to a physical activity program is seeing your level of fitness improve over time. You may notice that it takes you less time to walk to and from school, or you may not breathe as hard after climbing stairs.

A fitness journal can help you track your progress. List all of your activities, noting how long you work out, how often, and at what level. You'll see a noticeable difference in your fitness level if you stick with your plan for 12 weeks.

Another figure to list in your fitness journal is your **resting heart rate**—*the number of times your heart beats per minute when you are not active.* Before checking your resting heart rate, sit quietly for at least five minutes. Take your pulse for 15 seconds, then multiply the result by four. A typical pulse rate for teens and adults is between 60 and 100 beats per minute. As your fitness level increases, your resting heart rate will drop.

READING CHECK

Cause and Effect
How does regular exercise affect your resting heart rate?

LESSON 3 📖 ASSESSMENT

After You Read

Reviewing Facts and Vocabulary
1. What personal factors can affect your choice of physical activities?
2. What are the four principles of building fitness?
3. What are the benefits of warming up before exercise and cooling down after exercise?

Thinking Critically
4. **Synthesize.** What activity might you choose if your fitness goals are to increase cardiorespiratory endurance and to strengthen your leg and abdominal muscles? How might increasing your flexibility help you achieve these fitness goals?
5. **Analyze.** How does where you live affect your choice of activities?

Applying Health Skills
6. **Analyzing Influences.** Draw five columns on a sheet of paper, labeled: "Cost," "Location," "Schedule," "Health," and "Safety." Add examples of how each influence might affect your physical activity choices.

Writing Critically
7. **Narrative.** Write a short story about a teen who designs and begins a fitness plan. List three fitness goals for this teen. Describe the types of activities the teen has chosen.

G Online

Visit **glencoe.com** and complete the Interactive Study Guide for this lesson.

LESSON 3 ASSESSMENT ANSWERS

1. Cost, where you live, schedule, fitness level, overall health, personal safety
2. Specificity, overload, progression, and regularity
3. It reduces strain on the heart and can help prevent muscle soreness.
4. Sample answer: Cycling
5. Activities are dependent on features in your local area.
6. Students' charts will vary.
7. Short stories will vary.

Fitness Safety and Avoiding Injuries

Safety First

Main Idea Safety precautions can help you avoid injuries during physical activity.

While getting regular physical activity benefits your health, it is possible to injure yourself. A screening before beginning a physical activity program can identify diseases and disorders that could make it unsafe to participate in some activities. Other ways to protect yourself during exercise are to

- use the correct safety equipment for an activity;
- pay attention to other people, objects, and the weather;
- play or exercise at your skill level and know your limits;
- warm up before exercise and cooling down afterward;
- stay within the areas designated for a given activity;
- obey all rules and restrictions; and
- practice good sportsmanship.

If you become ill or injured during a physical activity, get help immediately.

GUIDE TO READING

BIG Idea *It is important to learn how to prevent injuries and respond to them when they occur.*

Before You Read

Create a T-Chart. Make a two-column chart on paper. Label the left column "Risks" and the right column "Prevention." As you read, fill in information about safety risks involved in different physical activities and prevention steps you can take to protect yourself.

Risks	Prevention

New Vocabulary

- frostbite (p. 339)
- hypothermia (p. 340)
- overexertion (p. 340)
- heat exhaustion (p. 340)
- heatstroke (p. 340)
- muscle cramps (p. 341)
- strains (p. 341)
- sprains (p. 342)

Fitness Safety and Avoiding Injuries

① FOCUS

GUIDE TO READING

BIG Idea Students will learn about how to prevent injuries and respond to them when they occur. **Ask Students:** *What is the most common sports injury among teens?* (The most common injury is an ankle sprain.)

Before You Read

T-Chart Students' T-charts will vary.

Main Idea

Safety First Basic safety precautions can protect a person from injury during physical activity. **Ask Students:** *What are some steps that a person can take to prevent an injury from occurring during exercise?* (Answers will vary. A typical response might mention using the proper equipment and warming up.)

Real Life Issues

Have students read the Real Life Issues scenario. **Ask Students:** *Why is wearing a helmet a good idea for a bike rider?* (Sample answer: A helmet can prevent head injuries in case of an accident in which a rider falls from the bike.)

Writing Strategy

Outlining the Lesson To help students organize the information presented about fitness safety and avoiding injuries, have them make an outline of the lesson. Help them start by writing Lesson 4's two major headings on the board: Safety First and Coping with Injuries. Tell students they should use these headings as the outline's first level. The lesson's secondary headings should form the second level of the outline. On the board, write The Right Equipment as the first secondary heading under Safety First. Explain that students should use the lesson's side headings to form the outline's third level. Under the second- and third-level headings, students can fill in the outline with supporting details, including vocabulary terms and lists of problems and injuries.

LESSON 4

② TEACH

R Reading Strategy

Ways to Protect Yourself
Direct students' attention to the bulleted list of using the right equipment. Ask a volunteer to read aloud the first item about using the correct safety equipment. Then, call on volunteers for examples of how using the correct equipment for an activity helps prevent injuries. Continue down the bulleted list in this way, first asking a volunteer to read the item and then calling on other volunteers for examples. **BL**

VIDEO BusinessWeek
HEALTH NEWS

After students have watched the video, *Video Games Get You in Shape,* have students collaborate in small groups on whether interactive video games can contribute to a healthier society. After allowing time for groups to discuss the question and think of examples, ask a representative from each group to tell the class the group's consensus. Opinions and examples will vary. Encourage informal debate on the issue.

Caption Answer

Figure 12.15 Answers will vary but may include wearing a helmet when bicycling.

VIDEO BusinessWeek
HEALTH NEWS

Video Games Get You in Shape

Analyze. Go to glencoe.com and watch the video *Video Games Get You in Shape.* In a small group, discuss whether you think interactive video games can contribute to a healthier society. Support your ideas with examples and be ready to share your ideas with the class.

■ **Figure 12.15** Using the right safety equipment can protect you from injury during physical activity. *What type of safety equipment is required for your favorite sport?*

The Right Equipment

Using the correct equipment can prevent injury. You might want to rent equipment when trying a new sport. Here are a few specific guidelines:

- Wear well-fitting athletic shoes that are designed for your sport or activity. Wear socks to cushion your feet and keep them dry. Choose comfortable, non-binding clothes that are appropriate for the weather.

- For cycling, always wear a helmet that fits you properly. Make sure the helmet is approved by Snell or ANSI. Use front and rear reflectors if you must ride at night. Wear light-colored clothing with reflective patches.

- For skating or skateboarding, wear a helmet, knee and elbow pads, gloves, and wrist guards.

- For contact sports, male players should wear a cup to protect the groin. For non-contact sports that involve running, they should wear an athletic supporter. Female players should wear sports bras.

- Special adaptive equipment helps those with disabilities take part in a variety of sports, from bowling to golf.

R

Teens Want to Know

How Can I Avoid Being Injured While Skateboarding? Most skateboarding injuries happen when the skateboarder loses his or her balance and falls off the board. The main way to prevent injuries is to wear protective equipment. Here are some more suggestions about how to prevent injuries.

- Use a well-made skateboard that is kept in good condition.

- Avoid skating on irregular or broken surfaces.

- Stay off your skateboard in wet weather.

- Check an area for rocks, potholes, and other hazards before riding there.

Watching the Weather

Check the weather and avoid exercising outside during extreme weather, such as thunderstorms or blizzards.

Cold-Weather Risks Layers of clothing will keep you warm. You can remove layers as you warm up, or add more clothing if the temperature drops. **Figure 12.16** shows how to layer clothing. Follow these tips for cold-weather activity:

- Warm up and cool down, even in cold weather.
- Drink plenty of fluids. Cold air can lead to dehydration.
- Cover your nose and mouth to prevent breathing cold, dry air. If you have asthma, talk to your doctor before exercising outdoors in cold weather.

Two other health risks in cold weather are frostbite and hypothermia. **Frostbite** is *damage to the skin and tissues caused by extreme cold.* The skin becomes pale, hard, and numb. To treat frostbite, go to a warm place and thaw the affected areas with warm (not hot) water. As the skin thaws, it becomes red and painful. If the frostbite is severe or does not respond to treatment, seek medical help.

Go Online

))) Listen to the health podcast titled *Effective Workouts* on a Busy Schedule at glencoe.com.

FITNESS ZONE

I learned how important it is to drink water when I started exercising. It helps prevent dehydration, cleans out the body, and promotes healing. For more fitness tips, visit the Online Fitness Zone at **glencoe.com**.

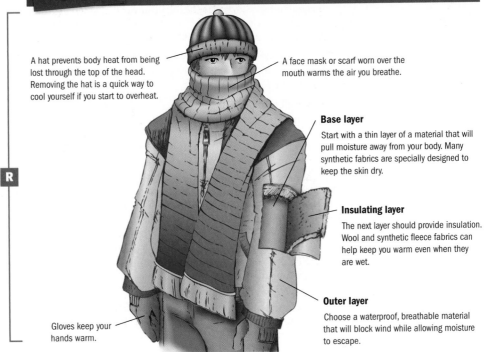

Figure 12.16 Cold-Weather Layering

A hat prevents body heat from being lost through the top of the head. Removing the hat is a quick way to cool yourself if you start to overheat.

A face mask or scarf worn over the mouth warms the air you breathe.

Base layer
Start with a thin layer of a material that will pull moisture away from your body. Many synthetic fabrics are specially designed to keep the skin dry.

Insulating layer
The next layer should provide insulation. Wool and synthetic fleece fabrics can help keep you warm even when they are wet.

Outer layer
Choose a waterproof, breathable material that will block wind while allowing moisture to escape.

Gloves keep your hands warm.

Lesson 4   Fitness Safety and Avoiding Injuries   **339**

CHAPTER 12

LESSON 4

R Reading Strategy

Analyzing a Graphic Direct students' attention to **Figure 12.16** Explain that the purpose of the diagram is to show what to wear to stay safe while being active outside in cold weather. Ask a volunteer to read aloud the description of what a base layer is. **Ask Students:** *What do you have that you could wear as a base layer?* (Accept any reasonable answer. Students might describe a pullover made of a synthetic fabric such as nylon or polyester.) **BL**

Go Online

))) Remind students to visit **glencoe.com**, listen to the podcast, and complete the Health Podcast Activity, *Effective Workouts on a Busy Schedule.*

CA Cultural Awareness

Weather Differences Different countries all over the world have different climates. Ask students to pick one foreign country and find out what the climate is like during the entire year. Students should then write a paragraph or two explaining what kinds of weather precautions they would have to take if they lived in that country and regularly participated in a physical activity. **OL**

English Language Coach

Word Parts Write the word *hypothermia* on the board and draw a line between the *o* and the *t* and another line between the *m* and the *i.* Explain that the prefix *hypo-* means "less than normal." Explain that the word part *therm* means "heat." Explain that the final word part, *-ia,* is a way of saying "relating to having." Ask students to use the meanings of these word parts to define the term *hypothermia* (relating to having less than normal heat). For advanced English learners, point out that the prefix *hyper-* has the opposite meaning of *hypo-.* Ask them to use that information to define the term *hyperactivity* (more than normal activity).

U Universal Access

The Prefix *Over-* Explain to English language learners that the prefix *over-* means "to exceed or surpass." In this context, the prefix *over-* indicates a level above and beyond a safe level. **Ask Students:** *What are three words in the description of hot-weather risks that begin with the prefix* over-*?* (overexertion, overworking, and overheating) **BL** **EL**

Academic Vocabulary

Exposure Explain that exposure to the weather does not apply only to extremes of weather, including the hot sun or a strong wind. Ask students to provide an example of an outdoor activity in which a person has great exposure to the weather and an example of an activity in which a person has very limited exposure. (Sample answer: Swimming wearing a bathing suit, snow skiing wearing heavy clothes, gloves, and a hat)

HS Health Skills Practice

Accessing Information Ask interested students to investigate products that offer sun protection, including sun blocks and sunscreens. Ask them to use and cite reliable online sources. Have them find out how these products protect the skin, and how SPF works. Ask students to make a report of their findings to the class. **AL**

340

Academic Vocabulary

exposure *(noun):* the condition of being unprotected

Hypothermia, or *dangerously low body temperature,* occurs as a result of **exposure** to extreme cold, submersion in cold water, or wearing wet clothing in cold or windy weather. Hypothermia causes drowsiness, weakness, and confusion. Breathing and heart rate slow down, followed by shock and heart failure. Hypothermia requires emergency medical help. Try to warm the victim until help arrives.

Hot-Weather Risks Heavy sweating while exercising in hot weather can lead to dehydration, or excessive loss of water from the body. Drinking fluids before, during, and after physical activity can prevent dehydration. If you're exercising during hot weather, you may also need to replace sodium, chloride, and potassium. Sports drinks will replace these elements.

Hot-weather health problems may lead to **overexertion**, or *overworking the body.* This can cause **heat exhaustion**, *a form of physical stress on the body caused by overheating.* Symptoms include heavy sweating; cold, clammy skin; dizziness, confusion, or fainting; a weak, rapid pulse; cramps; shortness of breath; or nausea or vomiting. To recover, rest in a shady area, douse yourself with cold water, and fan your skin. If you don't feel better within half an hour, seek medical help.

Untreated heat exhaustion can lead to **heatstroke**, *a dangerous condition in which the body loses its ability to cool itself through perspiration.* Heatstroke can cause sudden death. If you recognize symptoms of heatstroke, call for medical help immediately and try to cool the person.

U

Sun and Wind Protection Sun and wind can pose a hazard in both hot and cold weather. Exposure to these elements can lead to the following:

- **Windburn,** or irritation of the skin caused by wind exposure. The skin's protective oil layer is stripped away, leaving it red, dry, and sore. Rubbing lotion into the skin can ease the pain. To reduce your risk of windburn, keep your skin covered and wear lip balm.

- **Sunburn,** a burning of the skin's outer layers. Mild sunburn makes the skin red and painful. Severe sunburn can cause blistering and swelling. Cool and moisturize the skin and take a mild analgesic pain reliever to ease the discomfort. Wear protective clothing when exercising in the sun. Use a sunscreen with a sun protection factor (SPF) of 15 or more, and reapply often. Avoid exercising outside when the sun's rays are most intense.

HS

- **Skin cancer** can result from repeated or prolonged sun exposure. Sunscreens provide protection by blocking UVA, or ultraviolet A, rays, which lead to skin cancer.

Myths & Reality

Treating Injuries

Myth: Putting heat on injuries makes them heal better and faster.

Fact: Placing heat on the injury does not address those problems and may make them worse. Icing an injury acts to reduce swelling and inflammation.

Myth: If you drink water during physical activity, you'll get muscle cramps.

Fact: It is always beneficial to drink water before, during, and after physical activity.

W **Writing Strategy**

Summarize Pair English language learners with students who are more comfortable in the language. Ask each pair to find an article online or in a magazine about a sports celebrity who has successfully treated an injury. Ask each pair to write a brief summary. **OL** **EL**

✓ **READING CHECK**

Answer Dehydration, heat exhaustion, and heatstroke. Drinking plenty of fluids before, during, and after physical activity. Avoiding overexertion can prevent heat exhaustion and heatstroke.

Caption Answer

Figure 12.17 Such adaptive devices give people with disabilities the opportunity of participating in activities that they would not otherwise be able to do.

- **Eye damage** can be caused by exposure to ultraviolet (UV) rays. Wear sunglasses, a wide-brimmed hat in the summer, or UV-absorbing goggles during winter months.

Coping with Injuries

Main Idea You can treat minor sports injuries yourself, but major injuries require professional medical treatment.

You can identify and take action for both minor and major exercise-related injuries.

Minor Injuries

Muscles may become sore after exercise. Applying ice and taking pain relievers can help. Below are other minor injuries related to exercise:

- **Blisters,** fluid-filled bumps caused by friction. Well-fitting shoes and athletic socks can prevent blisters. Cover the blistered area, leave blisters intact, and let them heal.
- **Muscle cramps,** or *sudden and sometimes painful contractions of the muscles,* can occur when muscles are tired, overworked, or dehydrated. Stretching the affected muscle will usually relieve the cramps.
- **Strains** result from *overstretching and tearing a muscle.* Warm up before exercise to reduce the risk of strains. The symptoms are pain, swelling, and difficulty moving the affected muscle. Use the P.R.I.C.E. procedure, outlined in **Figure 12.18** on page 342 to treat strains.

✓ **READING CHECK**

Identify Problems and Solutions Name three health problems that can result from exercising in hot weather and explain how to prevent them.

Main Idea

Coping with Injuries You can treat minor sports injuries by yourself, but major injuries require medical attention. **Ask Students:** *What is a sports injury you could treat at home, and what is an injury that would require you seek medical help?* (Answers will vary. A typical response might mention a muscle strain or a sprain as something that could be treated at home, while a fractured bone must be treated by a medical professional.)

Lesson 4 Fitness Safety and Avoiding Injuries **341**

Writing Strategy

Safety Handbook Have students work in groups of four to write a safety handbook that informs the reader how to be safe and avoid injuries when being physically active. This handbook should include explanations of health risks associated with weather as well as with sports. Ask students to use library or online resources to research information for their pages. Also ask students to make simple line drawings to illustrate concepts. After all groups have finished their pages, compile the pages into a safety handbook.

AL Active Learning

Interviewing Ask a small group of interested students to interview a local physician who treats injuries related to sports and other physical activities. Have these students prepare a list of questions about what injuries are common, how these injuries could be prevented, and how these injuries are treated. Have the students report their findings to the class. **AL**

HS Health Skills Practice

Practicing Healthful Behaviors After students have read about the P.R.I.C.E procedure in **Figure 12.18**, invite one student to come to the front of the class and simulate having just suffered a sprained wrist. Then ask volunteers to explain how the injury should be treated. As the class reaches a consensus on a step in the treatment, invite a volunteer to put that step into action. Make available a splint, a wrap bandage, an Ace bandage, and an ice pack. **OL**

☑ READING CHECK

Answer Protection, rest, ice, compress, and elevate

- **Sprains** are *injuries to the ligaments around a joint* that produce pain, swelling, and stiffness. Use the P.R.I.C.E. procedure to treat minor sprains. If it hurts to move your joint, or you can't put weight on it, see your doctor.
- **Tendonitis** is inflammation and swelling in the tendons. Tendons are bands of fiber that connect muscles to bones. Treatment may include rest, medication, physical therapy, and in rare cases, surgery.

Major Injuries

While some minor injuries may be treated at home, major injuries require medical care. Here are some major injuries:

- **Fractures,** or broken bones, cause severe pain, swelling, bruising, or bleeding. If someone has broken a bone, get medical help immediately. Do not move the victim.
- **Dislocations** occur when a bone pops out of its normal position in a joint. The joint will be painful and may appear misshapen. Call for help immediately.
- **Concussion,** an injury to the brain can result in a severe headache, unconsciousness, or memory loss. A severe concussion can cause brain damage. Signs of brain damage include vomiting, confusion, seizures, or weakness on one side of the body. If any of these symptoms occur, seek medical help immediately.

☑ READING CHECK

Explain What are the steps of the P.R.I.C.E. procedure?

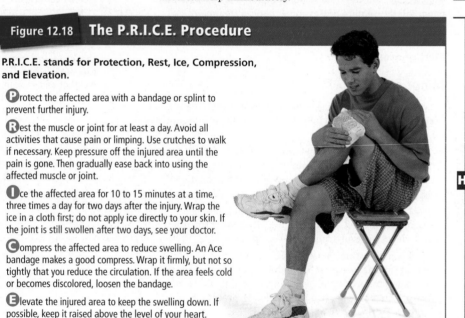

Figure 12.18 **The P.R.I.C.E. Procedure**

P.R.I.C.E. stands for Protection, Rest, Ice, Compression, and Elevation.

Protect the affected area with a bandage or splint to prevent further injury.

Rest the muscle or joint for at least a day. Avoid all activities that cause pain or limping. Use crutches to walk if necessary. Keep pressure off the injured area until the pain is gone. Then gradually ease back into using the affected muscle or joint.

Ice the affected area for 10 to 15 minutes at a time, three times a day for two days after the injury. Wrap the ice in a cloth first; do not apply ice directly to your skin. If the joint is still swollen after two days, see your doctor.

Compress the affected area to reduce swelling. An Ace bandage makes a good compress. Wrap it firmly, but not so tightly that you reduce the circulation. If the area feels cold or becomes discolored, loosen the bandage.

Elevate the injured area to keep the swelling down. If possible, keep it raised above the level of your heart.

342 **Chapter 12** Physical Activity and Fitness

More About...

Concussions A concussion is an injury to the brain that results from a blow to the head, which causes the brain to rock violently back-and-forth within the skull. Concussions are a common injury among teens—about 1 in 10 high school athletes suffer concussions each year. Even mild concussions are taken seriously, and all concussions are considered as mild traumatic brain injuries. Have interested students investigate how concussions are diagnosed and treated.

Real World CONNECTION

Playing It Safe

Sports and other recreational activities are one of the most common causes of injury among teens. In fact, teen athletes get injured at about the same rate as professional athletes do. Many of these injuries could be prevented if teens followed guidelines and safety precautions, and used the proper safety equipment for their sport.

Activity Reading / Writing

With your group, choose a sport or recreational activity to research. Use reliable print and online sources to find injury statistics, precautions for avoiding injuries, and types of protective equipment for this sport.

Use this information to create a poster that educates teens about how injuries occur in this sport and how to stay safe. Show examples of some protective equipment. Your group can draw the poster, or create the poster using a computer graphics program. Hang the poster in the gym or make it available on your school's Web page.

LESSON 4 ASSESSMENT

After You Read

Reviewing Facts and Vocabulary

1. What is the purpose of a health screening? How can it prevent injury during physical activity?

2. How should frostbite be treated? What can you do to prevent frostbite?

3. Name three symptoms of heat exhaustion.

Thinking Critically

4. **Analyze.** What distinguishes major injuries from minor injuries? How can you use the P.R.I.C.E. procedure to treat minor injuries?

5. **Synthesize.** Suppose you are playing Frisbee with some friends, and one of them falls and injures his ankle. How do you deal with the injury?

Applying Health Skills

6. **Practicing Healthful Behaviors.** Design a poster that illustrates the risks of sun and wind exposure. Include strategies for protecting yourself from these risks.

Writing Critically

7. **Expository.** Write a script for a one-minute public service announcement summarizing the importance of using the correct sports equipment. Your announcement should briefly describe the risks of injury.

 Go Online

Visit **glencoe.com** and complete the Interactive Study Guide for this lesson.

Real World CONNECTION

Each group's poster should include information about how injuries occur in the sport they picked and how to stay safe.

③ ASSESS/ CLOSE

Assessment Resources

📁 **FAST FILE ACTIVITIES**
Lesson 4 Quiz

💿 *ExamView Assessment Suite* CD-ROM

Visit glencoe.com for:
Online Quizzes
Online Learning Center

Progress Monitoring

Reteaching
Have students work in teams to create a chart that lists in one column problems and injuries that may result from physical activity and lists in a second column what to do when the problem or injury occurs.

Enrichment
Have students prepare a video that could be used to teach younger students about fitness safety and avoiding injuries.

 Go Online

Have students visit **glencoe.com** and complete the Interactive Study Guide for this lesson.

LESSON 4 ASSESSMENT ANSWERS

1. To check for diseases and disorders that a patient is unaware of
2. By coming in out of the cold and thawing the affected areas with warm water
3. Sample answer: heavy sweating, dizziness, and weak and rapid pulse
4. Minor injuries can be dealt with at home; major injuries require medical care. P.R.I.C.E can be used to treat strains.
5. Sample answer: First, find out how painful the injury is. Severe pain may indicate a fracture, which requires immediate medical help. Less severe pain may indicate a sprain, which can be treated with the P.R.I.C.E procedure.
6. Students' designs will vary.
7. Scripts will vary.

Hands-On HEALTH

Get Up and Get Fit

NHES Standard 8 Students will demonstrate the ability to advocate for personal, family, and community health.

Teaching Objectives

- Identify the physical, mental, emotional, and social benefits of physical fitness.
- Develop a PSA advocating for listeners to make healthful fitness choices.

Teaching Strategies

- Place students in groups of three or four. Each group should have a textbook and access to the Internet.
- Have students begin by reading the instructions for this activity.
- Review effective advocacy skills students can use to promote fitness. Discuss examples of ways to inform listeners and encourage them to make healthful fitness choices.
- Optional: Provide a recording device or have students role-play their PSA to the class.

Assessment

Using a rubric, student work should provide comprehensive evidence of the following criteria to achieve the highest score:

✓ Clear, health-enhancing stand

✓ Support for position with relevant information

✓ Awareness of audience

✓ Encouragement of others to make healthful choices

✓ Passion and conviction

Hands-On HEALTH

Activity **Get Up and Get Fit**

Now that you understand the benefits of fitness, use your knowledge to motivate others. Write a public service announcement (PSA) for a radio show. Conduct research to learn the physical, mental/emotional, and social health benefits of fitness. The PSA script should persuade others to get up and get fit.

What You'll Need

- computers with Internet access
- recording equipment (optional)

What You'll Do

Step 1

Work in groups of three or four. Identify at least five benefits of fitness, and five facts and examples demonstrating the benefits you selected.

Step 2

Write a script featuring at least three examples from your research. Support your position by citing at least one valid resource for each example.

Step 3

Present the PSA to the class as a role-play or a recording.

Apply and Conclude

Ask the entire class for feedback on each PSA. Discuss whether the message was clear, if valid examples were given, and whether the target audience was addressed.

Checklist: Advocacy

☑ Did I take a clear, health-enhancing stand?

☑ Can I support my position with reliable sources?

☑ Did I demonstrate an awareness of our target audience?

☑ Did I deliver the message with enough passion and conviction?

Health Literacy

Exercise Benefits Depression A 2005 study found that exercise is an effective way to treat mild to moderate depression. The study was the first to investigate the effects of exercise alone on depression. Researchers found that 30 minutes of aerobic exercise three times a week for 12 weeks reduced symptoms of depression by almost 50 percent. This is about the same effectiveness as antidepressants or cognitive therapy but without the side effects of expense. Given relatively high rates of depression in teens, this is another important reason to promote physical activity to students.

STUDY TO GO To download quizzes and eFlashcards to your PDA, go to **glencoe.com** and click on the Study to Go icon.

LESSON 1

Benefits of Physical Activity
Key Concepts
▶ Physical activity can benefit all sides of your health triangle.
▶ A sedentary lifestyle increases the risk of health problems.
▶ Several short periods of physical activity throughout the day can have the same benefits as one long workout.

Vocabulary
▶ physical activity (p. 318)
▶ physical fitness (p. 319)
▶ exercise (p. 319)
▶ sedentary (p. 321)

LESSON 2

Improving Your Fitness
Key Concepts
▶ The elements of fitness are five health-related components of fitness.
▶ Aerobic exercise improves cardiorespiratory endurance.
▶ Anaerobic exercises improve muscular strength and endurance.

Vocabulary
▶ cardiorespiratory endurance (p. 324)
▶ muscular strength (p. 324)
▶ muscular endurance (p. 325)
▶ flexibility (p. 325)
▶ aerobic exercise (p. 327)
▶ anaerobic exercise (p. 328)

LESSON 3

Planning a Personal Activity Program
Key Concepts
▶ Consider personal needs when planning a fitness program.
▶ Key fitness principles are specificity, overload, progression, and regularity.
▶ The F.I.T.T. formula will help you plan a successful workout.

Vocabulary
▶ specificity (p. 332)
▶ overload (p. 332)
▶ progression (p. 333)
▶ warm-up (p. 334)
▶ workout (p. 335)
▶ cool-down (p. 335)
▶ resting heart rate (p. 336)

LESSON 4

Fitness Safety and Avoiding Injuries
Key Concepts
▶ Wearing safety equipment will help protect you from injuries.
▶ The P.R.I.C.E. procedure can be used to treat minor injuries.
▶ Major injuries require medical care.

Vocabulary
▶ frostbite (p. 339)
▶ hypothermia (p. 340)
▶ overexertion (p. 340)
▶ heat exhaustion (p. 340)
▶ heatstroke (p. 340)
▶ muscle cramps (p. 341)
▶ strains (p. 341)
▶ sprains (p. 342)

Chapter 12 Review **345**

 Go Online

Students can visit **glencoe.com** to

• review content online with the Online Student Edition.
• test their knowledge of chapter content with Online Quizzes.
• access Interactive Health Tutor for more practice with vocabulary.

Assessment Resources

📁 **FAST FILE ACTIVITIES**
Chapter 12 Test
💿 *ExamView Assessment Suite* CD-ROM
Visit glencoe.com for:
Audio Chapter Summaries
Online Quizzes

 STUDY TO GO Tell students to visit **glencoe.com** where they can download quizzes and eFlashcards.

Study Tips

Study Time Tell students that one way to use study time wisely is to study in the same place and at the same time every day. This strategy eliminates having to decide each day when and where to study. It makes studying a habit. Also important is choosing what the daily time for study will be. Suggest that students choose a time during the day when the body's energy level is high. For most people, that is sometime during daylight hours.

Chapter 12 Assessment Answers

LESSON 1

Vocabulary Review

1. Physical fitness
2. exercise
3. sedentary

Understanding Key Concepts

4. a
5. c
6. d

Thinking Critically

7. Physical activity gives you a chance to meet new people, provides activities to do with friends and family, increases your self-confidence, and helps you learn how to get along with others.
8. Sample answer: Play a sport and combine physical activity with recreation
9. Sample answer: Physical activity improves physical fitness, which in turn improves mental/emotional health by boosting self-esteem, which in turn improves social health by lending confidence in social situations.

LESSON 2

Vocabulary Review

10. cardiorespiratory endurance
11. Flexibility
12. anaerobic exercise

Understanding Key Concepts

13. a
14. c
15. d

LESSON 1

Vocabulary Review

Use the vocabulary terms listed on page 345 to complete the following statements.

1. _____ is the ability to carry out daily tasks easily.

2. To achieve specific fitness goals, use structured, purposeful physical activity, known as _____.

3. People whose lives include little physical activity can be described as _____.

Understanding Key Concepts

After reading the question or statement, select the correct answer.

4. Stronger muscles and bones, and greater energy, are examples of physical activity's
   a. physical benefits.
   b. mental benefits.
   c. emotional benefits.
   d. social benefits.

5. Which of the following is a mental/emotional benefit of physical activity?
   a. Lower blood pressure
   b. Better balance and coordination
   c. Reduced stress
   d. Forming new friendships

6. Which of the following is an example of a sedentary activity?
   a. Taking a walk
   b. Doing household chores
   c. Bowling
   d. Surfing the Internet

Thinking Critically

After reading the question or statement, write a short answer using complete sentences.

7. **Discuss.** Explain how physical activity can improve your social life.

8. **Identify.** Name two ways to fit physical activity into your daily life.

9. **Synthesize.** Give an example of how the physical, mental/emotional, and social benefits of physical activity are interrelated.

LESSON 2

Vocabulary Review

Choose the correct term in the sentences below.

10. Running a mile without stopping is a sign of good *cardiorespiratory endurance / muscular endurance.*

11. *Muscular strength / Flexibility* is the ability to move your body parts through their full range of motion.

12. Sprinting and lifting weights are examples of *aerobic exercise / anaerobic exercise.*

Understanding Key Concepts

After reading the question or statement, select the correct answer.

13. Which of the following is a good test of your cardiorespiratory fitness?
    a. The time it takes to run or walk a mile
    b. How many curl-ups you can do
    c. How heavy a weight you can lift
    d. Whether you can bend over and touch your toes

14. A healthy 30-year-old would have a target heart range between
    a. 60 and 120 beats per minute.
    b. 82 and 133 beats per minute.
    c. 94 and 159 beats per minute.
    d. 101 and 190 beats per minute.

Health eSpotlight VIDEO Wrap-Up

Balance and Fitness Have students reread the Health eSpotlight questions at the beginning of the chapter on page 317 and look at their original answers. **Ask Students:** *What do you now know about what activities to include in a physical fitness pro-gram and how to avoid injury that you didn't know before watching the video and reading the chapter?* Call on volunteers to describe what they have learned and how they would change their responses.

15. Exercises to improve your flexibility are
    a. aerobic exercises.
    b. isometric exercises.
    c. isotonic exercises.
    d. stretching exercises.

Thinking Critically

After reading the question or statement, write a short answer using complete sentences.

16. **Analyze.** Doing 50 curl-ups each day will improve what elements of fitness? What other activities can improve total fitness?

17. **Compare and Contrast.** Explain the different ways that aerobic and anaerobic exercise affect your body composition.

18. **Analyze.** Is swimming a good way to build bone mass? Why or why not?

LESSON 3

Vocabulary Review

Correct the sentences below by replacing the italicized term with the correct vocabulary term.

19. A *stretch* is gentle activity that prepares the muscles for work.

20. The part of an exercise session when you are exercising at your highest peak is called the *cool-down*.

21. Your *target heart rate* is the number of times your heart beats per minute when you are not active.

Understanding Key Concepts

After reading the question or statement, select the correct answer.

22. To build cardiovascular fitness, perform aerobic exercise at least
    a. twice a week for 20 minutes.
    b. three times a week for 20 minutes.
    c. five times a week for 10 minutes.
    d. one hour per day.

23. Which principle of building fitness involves gradually increasing the demands on your body?
    a. Specificity
    b. Overload
    c. Progression
    d. Regularity

24. If you have time to stretch only once during an exercise session, it's best to do it
    a. before warming up.
    b. after warming up.
    c. in the middle of your workout.
    d. while cooling down.

Thinking Critically

After reading the question or statement, write a short answer using complete sentences.

25. **Predict.** Explain what might happen if a teen builds a fitness plan around exercises that he or she strongly dislikes.

26. **Identify.** What are the four elements of the F.I.T.T. formula? How can the four elements help you become fit?

27. **Analyze.** How does your resting heart rate reflect your level of fitness? How does your active heart rate reflect your fitness level?

LESSON 4

Vocabulary Review

Choose the correct word in the sentences below.

28. *Overexertion / Heatstroke* is a dangerous condition in which the body loses its ability to cool itself through perspiration.

29. *Frostbite / Hypothermia* is damage to the skin and tissues caused by extreme cold.

30. Injuries to the ligaments around a joint are known as *strains / sprains*.

Thinking Critically

16. Muscular strength. Aerobic exercise will improve cardiorespiratory endurance and stretching will improve flexibility.

17. Aerobic exercise uses energy and reduces the body's supply of fat. Anaerobic exercise builds muscle, increasing the body's lean tissue.

18. This is not a good plan because swimming is not a weight-bearing exercise.

LESSON 3

Vocabulary Review

19. warm-up
20. workout
21. resting heart rate

Understanding Key Concepts

22. b
23. c
24. d

Thinking Critically

25. The teen will probably not stick to the fitness plan.
26. Frequency, intensity, type, time
27. Resting heart rate drops as fitness level increases.

Vocabulary Review

28. Heatstroke
29. Frostbite
30. sprains

Assessment

Assessment

LESSON 4

Understanding Key Concepts

31. c
32. a
33. d

Thinking Critically

34. A helmet, knee and elbow pads, gloves, and wrist guards
35. Sun exposure can result in sunburn, skin cancer, or eye damage
36. Protect the affected area, rest injured body part, apply ice, compress the affected area, and elevate the injured area.

Understanding Key Concepts

After reading the question or statement, select the correct answer.

31. Drowsiness, weakness, and slowed breathing and heart rate are symptoms of
    a. heat exhaustion.
    b. frostbite.
    c. hypothermia.
    d. concussion.

32. Stretching the affected muscle will usually relieve
    a. muscle cramps.
    b. strains.
    c. sprains.
    d. tendonitis.

33. Which of the following is *not* a major injury?
    a. Fracture
    b. Dislocation
    c. Concussion
    d. Sprain

Thinking Critically

After reading the question or statement, write a short answer using complete sentences.

34. **Describe.** What safety equipment is required for skating or skateboarding?

35. **Explain.** Why is it important to protect yourself from the sun during physical activity?

36. **Describe.** What are the steps in the P.R.I.C.E. procedure?

Project-Based ASSESSMENT

Physical Fitness Mural

Background

Physical fitness is more than just doing exercise and maintaining a healthy, nutritious diet. Physical fitness requires being informed. Accurate information about the importance of physical activity helps individuals to make well-informed decisions about their health.

Task

Organize and create a physical fitness mural to convince other students to incorporate daily physical activity into their lives.

Audience

Students in your school

Purpose

Provide information on physical fitness to your peers.

Procedure

1 Obtain permission to create a physical fitness mural at your school.

2 Brainstorm topics you want presented as part of the physical fitness mural, such as the role of exercise in physical fitness, types of exercises, and nutrition. You may also want to consider physical fitness for people with disabilities.

3 Divide the tasks among group members. Some members may want to do research, while others may want to help design and create the mural.

4 After the mural is completed, ask students to complete a survey to assess its effectiveness. Also ask students what other information they would like about physical fitness.

Project-Based ASSESSMENT

Step 1 Brainstorm Have students brainstorm a list of topics including different types of exercise and fitness-related nutrition.

Step 2 Create Mural As students plan the mural, make sure they keep in mind the dimensions of the space where the mural will be displayed. Have different groups work on different sections of the mural.

Step 3 Evaluate Have students develop a survey of ten questions that could be distributed among students outside the class.

Visit **glencoe.com** for Project-Based Assessment rubrics.

Standardized Test Practice

Math Practice

Calculating Distances. Huntsville High's school-wide olympics will promote physical activity. Races will be run in the gym. For one race, athletes will run one lap around the gym. That distance would be approximately the same as the perimeter of the gym.

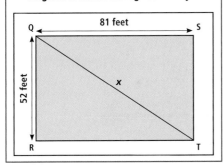

Diagram of Huntsville High School Gym

81 feet

52 feet

Q ─────── S

R ─────── T

x

1. What is the perimeter of the gym?
   - **A.** 1,112 feet
   - **C.** 266 feet
   - **B.** 421 feet
   - **D.** 386 feet

2. One athlete covers about 5 feet every second. If she competed in the race today, approximately how many seconds would it take her to run the one-lap course?
   - **A.** 53 seconds
   - **C.** 532 seconds
   - **B.** 55 seconds
   - **D.** 260 seconds

3. A race across the gym diagonally is represented in the diagram by line x. Line x divides the gym into two congruent right triangles. What is the approximate length, in feet, of line x, the side the two triangles share?
   - **A.** 421.2 feet
   - **C.** 133 feet
   - **B.** 21.60 feet
   - **D.** 96.25 feet

Go Online

For more test practice, visit glencoe.com and complete the Online Quizzes for Chapter 12.

Reading/Writing Practice

Understand and Apply. Read the passage below, and then answer the questions.

> On Sunday, 17-year-old Rosa Martinez completed her first marathon. Her time of 2 hours and 45 minutes won't break any records, but she's proud to have finished the race—in her wheelchair.
>
> "I lost the use of my legs in a car crash three years ago," says Rosa. "I was really depressed, but getting into wheelchair sports inspired me. I started focusing more on what I could do in my chair than on what I couldn't do."
>
> To train for the marathon, Rosa says she did "a lot of aerobic exercises to strengthen my heart and lungs, and a lot of work on my upper body strength."
>
> While she's proud of her achievement, Rosa isn't going to rest on her laurels. She's already looking ahead to next year's marathon, and she's determined to beat her time from this year.

1. In the final paragraph, the phrase "rest on her laurels" means
   - **A.** take a break from exercising.
   - **B.** go on to bigger challenges.
   - **C.** keep doing the same activities.
   - **D.** settle for what she's already achieved.

2. Which of the following would make the best title for this passage?
   - **A.** The Winning Spirit
   - **B.** How to Train for a Marathon
   - **C.** Elements of a Fitness Program
   - **D.** Better Wheelchair Designs

3. Describe the physical and mental qualities that make Rosa a successful athlete. How might she apply these qualities to other aspects of her life?

National Education Standards

Math: Number and Operations, Geometry
Language Arts: NCTE 1, NCTE 3

Standardized Test Practice

Standardized Test Practice Answers

Math Practice
1. C
2. A
3. D

Reading/Writing Practice
1. D
2. A
3. Sample answer: Physical qualities that make Rosa a success include having a high level of physical fitness. Mental qualities include being positive and confident despite her disabilities. These qualities would probably help her be successful both in school and in her social life.

National Education Standards

Math: Number and Operations, Geometry

Language Arts: NCTE 1, NCTE 3

For the complete Math and Language Arts standards, visit glencoe.com.

Go Online

Online Study Tools
For more test practice, visit glencoe.com and complete the Online Quizzes for Chapter 12.

Test-Taking Tip

The Main Idea Remind students that some questions based on a reading passage require them to sum up the main idea of the passage, such as a question that asks for a title to the passage. Finding the main idea of a passage requires reading the entire passage and then reading the entire passage a second time. The purpose of reading the entire passage before answering such a question is to make sure that the reader understands the intent of the passage or the overarching concept that the passage conveys.

Nutrition and Physical Activity

Body Image and the Media

The body shapes of popular models and actors are usually quite different from those of average Americans. According to studies by the National Center for Health Statistics, the average U.S. adult female is about 5 feet, 4 inches tall and weighs about 163 pounds. The average U.S. adult male is about 5 feet, 9 inches tall and weighs about 190 pounds. These are not the characteristics of most actors and models.

The bodies in the media may serve as a motivating force for those who are overweight or live a sedentary life. Yet, these media images often represent an ideal that is unattainable by most people. For example, only a small percentage of women could ever achieve the tall and extremely thin body shape of a fashion model. The genetic makeup of most females make that ideal unattainable. The masculine ideal—muscular, broad-shouldered, and small-waisted—is likewise unattainable for most men because of genetic makeup.

The bodies of adolescents undergo great changes during the teen years, and these changes often increase concerns about body image. For girls, these changes generally go against the media ideal, as girls in their adolescent years often become rounder and increase in body fat. For boys, changes during adolescence can enhance characteristics, including height and strength, that conform to the media ideal. Yet, for most boys the ideal body shape often seen in media images remains an impossible dream.

Body Image and the Media

*I*t's no secret that the average person you see on the street doesn't look like a model in a magazine. The average fashion model is 7 inches taller than the average American woman, yet weighs 23 pounds less. Men in the media also have a typical look: broad-shouldered, narrow-waisted, muscle-clad, and free of body hair. That's far from the look of the average American male.

Some people think the bodies we see in the media are unrealistic and harmful. Others think they represent a healthful ideal. Take a look at what these teens have to say, and then decide how you feel.

Teens Want to Know

How Can I Improve My Body Image?
The best way to improve your body image is to try and concentrate on thinking positively about yourself. Here are some tips to keep in mind:

- Accept that you cannot change your body type. There is no single size or shape that is normal for everyone.
- Try not to compare yourself to others. Your body is your own and special to you.

- If there are features about your body that you can change, such as how physically fit you are, make changes by setting goals for yourself.
- Stop negative thoughts about your body. When you hear negative comments from inside, think about what you like about your body. Build your self-esteem by giving your body at least three complements every day.

Problems with Images in the Media

The "ideal body" presented in the media is exceptionally thin. A typical female fashion model has a body mass index of 16.8—thinner than 98 percent of all women in America, and thin enough to put her health at risk. These media images may be making teen girls dissatisfied with their own appearance. More than half of all teen girls and women say they are unhappy with their bodies. Increasing numbers of males are also unhappy with their body image.

❝Looking at magazines and seeing how perfect everyone's body is makes me feel like my body isn't good enough. When I look around, though, I see that I look pretty much like everyone else. ❞

—Ned R., age 16

Benefits of Images in the Media

In the United States today, 66 percent of adults and 17 percent of teens are overweight. Over 30 percent of adults are considered obese. Health problems related to being overweight include type 2 diabetes and cardiovascular disease. Using models who look more like the typical American could give the impression that being overweight is normal and that it doesn't pose a health risk.

❝When I read magazines, I don't want to see people who look average. Media personalities are people to look up to—an ideal. With the obesity problem in America, media images that only show the average American may set an unhealthy example."

—Joanna L., age 16

Activity | Beyond the Classroom

1. **Investigate** images from a variety of different media, such as magazines, billboards, and television. Take notes on the type of males and females that are pictured.

2. **Survey** other teens to find out how they feel about this issue. Ask: Do you think the bodies you see in the media are healthy? Do they make you feel good or bad about yourself?

3. **Express** your views on this topic. Write a newspaper column summarizing what you've learned from other teens about the effect of media images on body image.

G⊙ Online

For more information about body image and the media, go to **glencoe.com**.

Teaching Strategies

- **Discussion** After students have read about the problems and benefits of images in the media, ask them to relate their own impressions about the teens and adults they see in magazines, on television, and in the movies. Ask students whether they think these models and actors are different from average Americans and, if so, in what ways they are different.

- **Debate** Call on volunteers to read the comments of Ned R. and Joanna L. aloud. Then ask each student to write a paragraph agreeing with one statement or the other, expressing their own thoughts with examples from their own lives. After students have finished writing, call on volunteers to share their paragraphs with the class. Ask first for a student who agrees with Ned R. and then for a student who agrees with Joanna L. Generate a debate by having students argue against the opposing opinion.

Activity | Beyond the Classroom

Writing

1. As a one-night homework assignment, ask students to take notes about what they see in the media. Ask students to share their findings in class the next day.

2. In class discussion, call on volunteers to propose questions for a five-question survey about body image. Write proposed questions on the board. Ask each student to use the questionnaire to interview at least two teens. Call on volunteers to share results with the class.

3. Ask students to write a two- or three-paragraph column that could be published on the opinion page of the local newspaper. Students' conclusions will vary but should draw upon the investigation of images in the media and the survey of other teens.

351

Flexible Technology Solutions
Focus

Health eSpotlight *Video Series*

By Chapter

Chapter 13 Personal Health Care
Video 13: A Healthy You

Chapter 14 Skeletal, Muscular, and Nervous Systems
Video 14: Building a Healthy Body

Chapter 15 Cardiovascular, Respiratory, and Digestive Systems
Video 15: A Look Inside Your Body

Chapter 16 Endocrine and Reproductive Health
Video 16: Your Reproductive Health

By Lesson

Chapter 13 *Video 13* For Use With
Segment 13.1 Healthy Skin, Hair, and Nails .... Lesson 1
Segment 13.2 Healthy Teeth and Mouth.......................... Lesson 2
Segment 13.3 Healthy Eyes and Ears .... Lesson 3

Chapter 14 *Video 14* For Use With
Segment 14.1 The Skeletal System.................................. Lesson 1
Segment 14.2 The Muscular System................................ Lesson 2
Segment 14.3 The Nervous System .... Lesson 3

Chapter 15 *Video 15* For Use With
Segment 15.1 The Cardiovascular and Lymphatic Systems . Lesson 1
Segment 15.2 The Respiratory System .... Lesson 2
Segment 15.3 The Digestive System................................ Lesson 3
Segment 15.4 The Excretory System................................ Lesson 4

Chapter 16 *Video 16* For Use With
Segment 16.1 The Endocrine System............................... Lesson 1
Segment 16.2 The Male Reproductive System .... Lesson 2
Segment 16.3 The Female Reproductive System .... Lesson 3

By Skill

Practicing Healthful Behaviors .... Videos 3 **13** 17 19 23
Accessing Information .... Videos 2 10 **14** 25
Decision Making .... Videos **15** 22 26
Advocacy... Videos **16** 20 28

■ Indicates videos featured in the unit that teach the corresponding skill. Other videos listed can also be used to teach that skill.

Teach

Direct lesson plans beyond the classroom with multi-media fitness activities that students can do online, in class, or as a group.

PowerPoint® Presentation

- *Health* eSpotlight videos
- Audio and image bank

Online

Fitness Zone Online is a multi-media resource that helps students find ways to be physically active each day.

- Clipboard Energizer Activities
- Fitness Zone Videos
- Polar Heart Rate Monitor Activities
- Nutrition, Physical Activity, and Injury Prevention Tips
- Links to Nutrition and Physical Activity Resources

Go Online

Online Learning Center

- Student Web Activities
- PuzzleMaker
- Interactive Health Tutor

Podcast Audio Chapter Summaries

Use the audio Podcast Audio Chapter Summaries to teach and review key concepts, and engage students with health content that they can download to a computer or portable MP3 player.

Assess/Close

Help students master chapter and lesson concepts with an integrated technology solution for assessment and performance evaluation.

Go Online

Online Learning Center

- Interactive Study Guides
- Online Quizzes

ExamView® Assessment Suite CD-ROM

Create and customize tests in minutes with this convenient digital platform.

- Create differentiated tests quickly and easily.
- All questions correlated to National/State Standards.
- Enhance tests with Document Based Questions (DBQ) and add your own photos and graphics.
- Build tests in both English and Spanish.
- Generate progress reports.

Enrich

Use these additional digital and online media resources to promote hands-on exploration of health topics covered in the lesson.

Business Week Health Video Series

- *Brushing Your Teeth Away*
- *Rewiring the Body*

Study-to-Go

Download a portable version of eFlashcards and Self-Check Quizzes onto your Palm or Pocket PC.

Health Podcasts Activities

Glencoe's "It's Your Health" Podcast Activities provide students with a unique listening and learning experience that takes health education beyond the classroom. Download the audio files and print activities covering a range of current health topics that matter most to teens!

Personal Care and Body Systems

Students will learn about personal health care and the major body systems.

Health eSpotlight Video Series

At the beginning of each chapter, visit **glencoe.com** and have students watch the video and do the accompanying print activity.

 Chapter 13
A Healthy You

Puberty causes changes to the body.

 Chapter 14
Building a Healthy Body

Learn how to care for the skeleton, muscular, and nervous systems.

 Chapter 15
A Look Inside Your Body

Maintaining a strong heart is one of the best ways to protect a person's health.

 Chapter 16
Your Reproductive Health

The endocrine system triggers many of the changes in the reproductive system during puberty.

Unit 5 Resources

- Career Corner
- 📁 FAST FILE RESOURCES
- Health Career Research Activity
- Family Involvement Activity
- Community Involvement Activity
- Unit Test

UNIT 5 Personal Care and Body Systems

Chapter 13
Personal Health Care

 A Healthy You

Chapter 14
Skeletal, Muscular, and Nervous Systems

 Building a Healthy Body

Chapter 15
Cardiovascular, Respiratory, and Digestive Systems

 A Look Inside Your Body

Chapter 16
Endocrine and Reproductive Health

 Your Reproductive Health

UNIT PROJECT

Hammering for a Good Cause

Using Visuals **Habitat for Humanity** is an international organization that recruits volunteers and raises funds to build and repair homes for low-income families in the United States and all over the world. Volunteers can raise money, gather building materials, or pick up a hammer and start building.

Go Online To learn more about Habitat for Humanity, go to the Unit Web Project at glencoe.com.

Get Involved. Locate a local organization that uses volunteers to build and repair homes for families in need. Find out how teens can participate. Share your findings with your classmates.

UNIT PROJECT

Hammering for a Good Cause Habitat for Humanity is a worldwide nonprofit organization that provides needy families with decent shelter, one house at a time. Locally run affiliates carry out its work at the community level. Habitat has built more than 255, 000 houses around the world, providing more than 1 million people with shelter.

Get Involved Have students learn how teens can volunteer for a local affiliate of Habitat for Humanity. Ask them to create a school-wide bulletin board to share what they learn.

"The first wealth is health."
—*Ralph Waldo Emerson, 19th-century writer and poet*

Activate Prior Knowledge

Ask students these questions before they read the chapter to build on what they already know.

Chapter 13
What can you do to take care of your skin, teeth, and eyes?

(Sample answer: Bathe daily, brush your teeth after meals, and have regular eye exams.)

Chapter 14
What are the parts of the nervous system?

(The nervous system includes the brain, spinal cord, and nerves throughout the body.)

Chapter 15
How can you protect your cardiovascular and respiratory systems?

(Sample answer: You can exercise regularly and avoid smoking.)

Chapter 16
What is the role of the endocrine system?

(The endocrine system controls other body systems.)

TeacherWorks *Plus* provides:

- interactive Teacher Wrap-around edition
- click, drag, and drop to plan lessons
- instant access to many print program resources

Unit 5   Personal Care and Body Systems   **353**

How to Get Involved Provide students with these step-by-step instructions for learning about teen volunteering opportunities with Habitat for Humanity.

1. Learn more about Habitat for Humanity by visiting their international Web site. Be sure to read about the organization's programs for youth.

2. Use the Web site's search engine to find a local affiliate of Habitat for Humanity.

3. Contact the local affiliate and ask about volunteering opportunities for teens in your community.

4. Create a bulletin board to share what you learn with other students.

Chapter 13 pages 354–379	Standards		Features
	National	**State/Local**	
	1.12.1, 1.12.8, 1.12.9, 2.12.9, 3.12.3, 4.12.1, 7.12.1–7.12.3		TIME HEALTH • Getting Burned—A Trend, page 374
Lesson 1 **Healthy Skin, Hair, and Nails** pages 356–362 **BIG Idea** *Taking care of your skin, hair, and nails helps keep your whole body healthy.*	1.12.1, 1.12.3, 1.12.5, 1.12.9, 2.12.7, 2.12.9, 3.12.1, 3.12.3, 3.12.4, 4.12.1, 5.12.2, 6.12.6, 7.12.1–7.12.3, 8.12.1, 8.12.3		*Health Skills* Activity • Is Tanning Worth the Risk? *(Communication Skills)*, page 359 🕐 Out of Time
Lesson 2 **Healthy Teeth and Mouth** pages 363–366 **BIG Idea** *Your teeth and mouth need care to function well and keep you healthy.*	1.12.1, 1.12.6, 1.12.8, 1.12.9, 2.12.7, 3.12.1, 3.12.4, 7.12.1, 7.12.2, 7.12.3, 8.12.1, 8.12.2		*Real World* CONNECTION • Examining Product Claims, page 366 🕐 Out of Time
Lesson 3 **Healthy Eyes and Ears** pages 367–373 **BIG Idea** *Eyes and ears are sensitive organs that need protective care.*	1.12.1, 1.12.5, 1.12.7–1.12.9, 2.12.7, 3.12.1– 3.12.3, 5.12.6, 5.12.7, 7.12.1– 7.12.3, 8.12.1, 8.12.2		*Health Skills* Activity • Fun in the Sun? *(Decision Making)*, page 369 🕐 Out of Time

(Left column time markers: 30 Min, 30 Min, 30 Min)

Key to Ability Levels

Teaching Strategies and activities have been coded for ability level and appropriateness.

AL Activities for students working above grade level

OL Activities for students working on grade level

BL Activities for students working below grade level

EL Activities for English Learners

Chapter 13 Planning Guide

Resources	Lesson Assessment	Technology
Student Activity Workbook TEACH *FAST FILE* RESOURCES Vocabulary Practice TEACH Health Labs EXTEND	Chapter 13 Review Chapter 13 Assessment Standardized Test Practice ⊙ *ExamView® Assessment Suite* CD-ROM	**Teaching Tools:** ⊙ *TeacherWorks*™ Plus DVD ⊙ *StudentWorks*™ Plus DVD ⊙ *ExamView® Assessment Suite* CD-ROM 🕹 Transparency ⊙ Fitness DVD ⊙ PowerPoint® DVD ⊙ Health eSpotlight Video Series DVD
FAST FILE RESOURCES Reading Strategies Activity TEACH Reteaching Activity REVIEW Enrichment Activity EXTEND Health Skills Practice TEACH	Lesson 1 Assessment, page 362 📁 Lesson 1 Quiz *Fast File* ⊙ *ExamView® Assessment Suite* CD-ROM	**Web-Based Resources:** Go Online glencoe.com • Health Podcast Activities • Audio Chapter Summaries (English/Spanish) • Interactive Health Tutor
FAST FILE RESOURCES Reading Strategies Activity TEACH Reteaching Activity REVIEW Enrichment Activity EXTEND Health Skills Practice TEACH	Lesson 2 Assessment, page 366 📁 Lesson 2 Quiz *Fast File* ⊙ *ExamView® Assessment Suite* CD-ROM	• Health Skills Activities • Vocabulary PuzzleMaker • Parent Letters (English/Spanish) • Lesson Plans • Health Inventories • Online Quizzes
FAST FILE RESOURCES Reading Strategies Activity TEACH Reteaching Activity REVIEW Enrichment Activity EXTEND Health Skills Practice TEACH	Lesson 3 Assessment, page 373 📁 Lesson 3 Quiz *Fast File* ⊙ *ExamView® Assessment Suite* CD-ROM	• Study-to-Go • Unit Web Projects • Student Web Activities • Fitness Zone Activities

StudentWorks Plus

This is the student's backpack solution.

Includes:
- complete Interactive Student Edition
- full audio of English text and Spanish chapter summaries
- allows students to record assignments and track grades.
- links to online activities and additional student resources
- access to all student worksheets and workbooks

FOLDABLES® Study Organizer

Dinah Zike Foldables® Chapter Activity
Refer to the *Dinah Zike Reading and Study Skills for Glencoe Health*. Have students create a layered-look book Foldable to record notes on Lesson 1. Suggest that they label the tabs *Epidermis, Dermis, Hair,* and *Nails*. As they read, have them make notes under the appropriate tabs.

Key to Symbols

 Transparencies   REVIEW activities to review or reinforce content

 CD-ROM   TEACH activities to teach basic concepts

 glencoe.com   EXTEND activities to extend or enrich lesson content

 Print Resources

Personal Health Care

Chapter Overview

Chapter 13 describes how to care for the skin, hair, and nails. It also describes how to take care of the teeth, eyes, and ears.

Lesson 1

Proper care of the skin, hair, and nails is important for keeping the whole body healthy.

Lesson 2

The teeth and mouth need regular care to function well and to help maintain a healthy body.

Lesson 3

The eyes enable vision, and the ears allow hearing and balance. Both are sensitive organs that need to be protected.

▶ Activating Prior Knowledge

After students write their responses, call on a few volunteers to share their ideas about caring for the eyes. (Sample answers: Wear sunglasses on bright days; don't touch your eyes with dirty hands.)

CHAPTER **13**

Personal Health Care

Lesson 1

Healthy Skin, Hair, and Nails

BIG Idea *Taking care of your skin, hair, and nails helps keep your whole body healthy.*

Lesson 2

Healthy Teeth and Mouth

BIG Idea *Your teeth and mouth need care to function well and keep you healthy.*

Lesson 3

Healthy Eyes and Ears

BIG Idea *Eyes and ears are sensitive organs that need protective care.*

Activating Prior Knowledge

Using Visuals The teen in this photo knows the importance of regular exams to keep her eyes healthy. In a few sentences, describe other ways you can take care of your eyes and protect your vision.

354

Universal Access

Differentiated Learning Glencoe provides teacher support and student materials for all learners in the health classroom.

- Chapter Summaries in English and Spanish are available online at **glencoe.com**.
- *Fast Files* and related worksheets support reluctant readers.

- Universal Access strategies throughout the Teacher Wraparound Edition and *Fast Files* help you present materials for gifted students, at-risk students, physically impaired students, and those with behavior disorders or learning disabilities.

Chapter Launchers

Health in Action

Discuss the **BIG** Ideas

Before beginning this chapter, think about how you would answer these questions:

▶ Why are personal hygiene habits so important?

▶ What problems can result from not taking care of your teeth and mouth?

▶ Could you be at risk for hearing problems?

Watch the *Health eSpotlight* Video Series

A Healthy You

How has your attitude towards personal appearance chanced since when you were a child?

Assess Your Health

Go Online

Visit **glencoe.com** and complete the Health Inventory for Chapter 13.

Chapter Launchers

Health in Action

Discuss the **BIG** Ideas

Assign this activity before students read the chapter. Explain that answering the questions will help them recall what they already know about personal health care.

Health eSpotlight Video Series

 A Healthy You

Before Viewing the Video

Ask students: *What kind of personal care do you do?* (Sample answer: Shaving, using deodorant, treating acne)

Go Online

Have students go to **glencoe.com** and take the Health Inventory for Chapter 13.

Chapter Skills

Reading Skills
- Reviewing Facts and Vocabulary, pp. 362, 366, 373
- Reading/Writing Practice, p. 379

Vocabulary
- New Vocabulary, pp. 356, 363, 367
- Reviewing Facts and Vocabulary, pp. 362, 366, 373

BIG Idea

Taking care of the skin, hair, nails, teeth, mouth, eyes, and ears helps to keep these structures healthy and to promote overall good health.

Health Skills
- Health Skills Activity, p. 359
- Applying Health Skills, pp. 362, 366, 373

Writing Skills
- Real World Connection, p. 366
- Writing Critically, pp. 362, 366, 373
- Reading/Writing Practice, p. 379

355

Healthy Skin, Hair, and Nails

1 FOCUS

GUIDE TO READING

BIG Idea Care of the skin, hair, and nails is necessary for good health. **Ask Students:** *What is one way to take care of the skin?* (Sample answer: Keep it clean)

Before You Read

Tables Students' tables may vary but should include important structures of the skin, hair, and nails.

Main Idea

Your Skin Skin protects the body from pathogens, regulates body temperature, and feels sensations. **Ask Students:** *What sensations can you feel with your skin?* (Sample answer: Heat and pain)

Real Life Issues

Have students work in pairs on the dialogue. **Ask Students:** *What are benefits of using sunscreen?* (Preventing sunburn, reducing the risk of skin cancer) Ask a few partners to read their dialogues to the class.

356

GUIDE TO READING

BIG Idea *Taking care of your skin, hair, and nails helps keep your whole body healthy.*

Before You Read

Create a Table. Make a three-column table. Label the columns "Tissue," "Structure," and "Function." In the first column, list "Skin," "Hair," and "Nails." In the second column, describe the important structural features of each. In the third column, write the function of each.

Tissue	Structure	Function

New Vocabulary
- epidermis (p. 356)
- dermis (p. 356)
- melanin (p. 356)
- sebaceous glands (p. 358)
- hair follicles (p. 360)
- melanoma (p. 360)

Healthy Skin, Hair, and Nails

Real Life Issues

Wearing Sunscreen. Trevor knows that sunscreen protects him from the sun's harmful rays. When he snowboards, though, he thinks he won't sunburn in cold weather. He also thinks sunscreen smells like medicine. So even in hotter weather he has decided to stop using it. "In the summer, I won't stay in the sun too long," Trevor tells himself.

Writing *Write a dialogue in which Trevor's friend Max tries to convince him that the benefits of sunscreen make it worthwhile using throughout the year.*

Your Skin

Main Idea Skin protects you from pathogens, regulates your body temperature, and helps you feel sensations.

What's the largest organ on the human body? You may be surprised to learn that the answer is the skin. The skin consists of two main layers, as shown in **Figure 13.1**. The **epidermis** is *the outer, thinner layer of the skin that is composed of living and dead cells.* Just underneath the **dermis** is *the thicker layer of the skin beneath the epidermis that is made up of connective tissue and contains blood vessels and nerves.* Cells in the epidermis make substances called *lipids*, which make your skin waterproof. This waterproofing helps the body maintain a proper balance of water and electrolytes. Other cells produce **melanin**, *a pigment that gives the skin, hair, and iris of the eyes their color*—the more melanin that your body produces,, the darker the skin. The melanin in skin also helps protect the body from harmful ultraviolet (UV) radiation that cause skin cancer.

AL

More About...

Functions of the Skin You may want to share with students these additional functions of the skin:

- Immunity—The dermis contains immune cells called macrophages that destroy invading pathogens.
- Excretion—Excess water and dissolved wastes are excreted in sweat.

- Vitamin D synthesis—The skin makes vitamin D when it is exposed to UV radiation.
- Interpersonal communication—The skin automatically expresses some emotions by blushing or becoming pale.

The skin performs three main functions to keep you healthy:

- **Protection.** The skin protects you from pathogens and internal damage. It acts as a barrier to prevent bacteria and viruses from entering your system. If this barrier is broken by a cut or other wound, the skin repairs itself to keep pathogens from entering the body.
- **Temperature control.** When your body temperature begins to rise, the blood vessels in the skin dilate, allowing heat to escape through the skin's surface. Sweat glands—structures within the dermis that release perspiration through ducts to pores on the skin's surface—cool the skin. If body temperature begins to drop, the blood vessels in the skin constrict, reducing the amount of heat lost and helping to maintain body heat.
- **Sensation.** Touch a hot stove, and your hand immediately pulls back. Why? The skin is a major sense organ. Nerve cells in the dermis act as receptors that are stimulated by changes in the outside environment. These receptors enable you to feel sensations such as pressure, pain, heat, and cold.

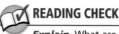 **READING CHECK**

Explain What are the dermis and epidermis?

Figure 13.1 The Skin's Structure

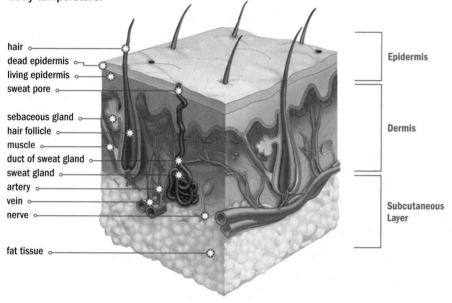

The skin is composed of two main layers, the epidermis and the dermis. These two layers are attached to bones and muscles by the subcutaneous layer, a layer of fat and connective tissue located beneath the dermis. Explain how the skin helps regulate body temperature.

R

hair
dead epidermis
living epidermis
sweat pore

sebaceous gland
hair follicle
muscle
duct of sweat gland
sweat gland
artery
vein
nerve

fat tissue

Epidermis

Dermis

 Subcutaneous Layer

Lesson 1   Healthy Skin, Hair, and Nails   **357**

2 TEACH

AL Active Learning
Practicing Healthful Behaviors
Challenge students to make a drawing of the epidermis, dermis, and subcutaneous layer. Students may use **Figure 13.1** as a reference. **OL**

R Reading Strategy
Using Visuals Point out the three layers of skin in **Figure 13.1**. Call on students to name structures within each layer. Have students find, and read about, each structure in the text. Ask them to explain the role each structure plays in keeping the body healthy. **BL EL**

READING CHECK
Answer The two main layers of the skin: epidermis is the outer, thinner layer; dermis is the thicker layer consisting of blood vessels and nerves.

Caption Answer
Figure 13.1 When body temperature rises, blood vessels in the skin dilate, allowing heat to escape through the skin's surface. Sweat glands also cool the skin by releasing perspiration.

Writing Strategy

Keeping Skin Healthy Students may be reluctant to ask questions about skin hygiene in front of their peers. If they have acne or other skin problems, they may want to avoid calling attention to themselves. Invite students to write any questions they have about skin care on index cards. Collect the cards and select several questions to read aloud. Choose questions that are asked more than once, reveal important misunderstandings, or deal with serious issues. Answer each question or discuss it with the class.

Main Idea

Keeping Your Skin Healthy
Daily care keeps skin healthy. **Ask Students:** *How long does it take to wash your face?* (Sample answer: about a minute) Point out that "not having enough time" is rarely a valid reason for not washing the face twice a day.

U Universal Access

Hands-On Learning After students read about UV protection in the text, provide them with several different sunscreen products to examine. Have them read the labels and choose the product they think is most effective. Call on volunteers to explain their choice. (The most effective product is the one with the highest SPF that blocks both UVB and UVA rays.) **EL** **BL**

HS Health Skills Practice

Analyzing Influences Some people believe that using a tanning bed is safer than outdoor tanning. Ask students to explain how this false belief might influence people to take health risks. Challenge students to think of ways to let the public know that using tanning beds is not safe. (Sample answers: Public service announcements, mandatory notices at tanning salons) **OL**

Caption Answer

Figures 13.2 Answers will vary but may include milk, green and yellow vegetables, or liver.

Go Online

For more vocabulary practice, go to the Interactive Health Tutor at **glencoe.com**.

Academic Vocabulary

remove *(verb):* to get rid of

■ **Figure 13.2** An eating plan rich in vitamin A will promote healthy skin. *Which foods do you enjoy that are a good source of vitamin A?*

358   Chapter 13   Personal Health Care

The dermis is a single thick layer composed of connective tissue, which gives the skin its elastic qualities. **Sebaceous glands,** *structures within the skin that produce an oily secretion called sebum,* are also found in the dermis. Sebum helps keep skin and hair from drying out. Blood vessels in the dermis supply cells with oxygenated blood and nutrients and help remove wastes from body cells.

Keeping Your Skin Healthy

Main Idea A daily routine will keep your skin healthy.

Keeping your skin healthy should be an important part of your daily routine. Some of the ways that you can keep your skin health, include:

- Wash your face every morning and evening with mild soap and water.
- Daily washing, bathing, or showering helps **remove** and slow the growth of bacteria that cause body odor.
- Avoid touching your face with your hands. This can introduce new bacteria to the skin's surface.
- Choose personal skin care products carefully to avoid irritation and the chance of allergic reaction.
- Follow a well-balanced eating plan that is rich in vitamins and minerals, especially vitamin A. Milk, green and yellow vegetables, and liver are good for healthy skin.

UV Protection

Some people believe that tanned skin looks good. A suntan, however, is really a sign that the skin has been damaged by UV rays. When skin is exposed to UV radiation, melanin production is increased. The production in melanin is the skin's way of trying to protecting itself from the UV rays. Prolonged exposure to UV rays can lead to skin cancer. To protect your skin from the sun's damaging rays,

U

- always wear sunscreen on exposed areas of skin. Use an SPF of 15 or higher that blocks both UVB and UVA (the more penetrating) rays. Apply it 15 to 30 minutes before going outside, even on cloudy days.
- wear protective clothing, including hats, long-sleeved shirts, and long pants. UV rays are most intense between 10:00 A.M. and 4:00 P.M., and stronger at higher altitudes.
- wear sunglasses. Exposure to UV rays can damage the eyes, causing burns, cataracts, and even blindness.
- avoid using tanning beds. Tanning beds are not safe, and prolonged exposure can lead to skin cancer.

HS

 Promoting School Wellness

School Sun-Protection Program The World Health Organization (WHO) has developed guidelines for a comprehensive school sun-protection program that includes education, policy, environment, and family and community involvement components.

Many of the ideas included in the program are free, such as scheduling outside physical education classes and sports practices before or after peak UV hours. You can learn more by visiting the WHO Web site and searching "sun protection."

Health Skills Activity

Communication Skills

Is Tanning Worth the Risk?

It's a hot summer day as Shelley walks out of the locker room toward the pool. She has always taken pride in having a deep tan. Lately, however, she's been thinking about her aunt. After years of sun exposure, her aunt is now undergoing skin cancer treatments. Now Shelley doesn't think tanning is such a good idea.

"C'mon, Shelley!" says her friend Raye, motioning to Shelley. "The pool opens in ten minutes. Let's grab the best spots in the sun. School starts in a month, so we have to make the most of every sunny day!"

Shelley hangs back, biting her lip. She'd rather find a spot in the shade. She wants to convince Raye to do the same, but she doesn't want to hurt her friend's feelings.

Writing Compose your thoughts about what Shelley should say in a paragraph or two. Make your argument persuasive enough to change Raye's mind. Use the following tips as a guideline.

1. Use "I" messages.
2. Speak calmly and clearly.
3. Use a respectful tone.
4. Listen carefully and ask appropriate questions.
5. Use appropriate body language.

Body Piercing and Tattooing

Piercing and tattooing practices have been around for thousands of years. Unlike using makeup or changing hair color, however, piercings and tattoos are permanent. Both carry potential health risks because they break the physical barrier of the skin. This can result in infection from bacteria and the transfer of blood-borne pathogens from viruses such as hepatitis B, hepatitis C, and HIV through nonsterile needles. The American Dental Association also warns that oral piercing can damage your mouth and teeth. The decision to get a tattoo or piercing may also impact your social health, by limiting future job opportunities and relationships.

Skin Problems

Many skin problems can affect your self image, but are not life threatening. Check with a health care professional before purchasing any skin care product to make sure it's right for you. Common skin problems include

- **Acne.** When pores in the skin get clogged, bacteria causes inflammation, and pus forms. To treat acne, wash your face gently twice a day, apply over-the-counter treatments, and avoid using oily products or too much makeup. Touching and picking may cause scarring. Extreme cases may require prescription medication.

Go Online

Visit glencoe.com and complete the Student Web Activity on the health risks of getting a tattoo or piercing.

Lesson 1 Healthy Skin, Hair, and Nails **359**

Health Skills Activity

Communication Skills: Is Tanning Worth the Risk?

NHES Standard 4 Students will demonstrate the ability to use interpersonal communication skills to enhance health and avoid or reduce health risks.

Objectives

- Demonstrate persuasive communication skills to reduce health risks.
- Demonstrate strategies to resolve interpersonal conflicts without harming self or others.

Teaching Strategies

- Discuss the health benefits of avoiding sun exposure.
- Ask volunteers to read their paragraphs to the class.

Assessment

Using a rubric, student work should provide comprehensive evidence of the following criteria to achieve the highest score:

√ Uses "I" messages
√ Speaks calmly and clearly
√ Uses a respectful tone
√ Listens carefully and asks appropriate questions
√ Uses appropriate body language

Academic Integration

Science Tattooing involves one of the body's main protective barriers—the skin. Point out that tattooing may result in the transfer of viruses such as hepatitis B, hepatitis C, and HIV. Tattooing also puts a person at risk for skin infections if the needle is infected.

Ask students to write a short report comparing and contrasting the various risk factors and treatment options of getting a tattoo. Students should focus on the possible skin disorders and infections. Encourage them to use reliable sources of information.

W Writing Support

Descriptive Writing Ask students to write a list of adjectives that come to mind when they think about acne and a list of adjectives they would use to describe themselves if they had an acne outbreak. Have students hand in their lists anonymously. Select several lists at random and read them to the class. Call on volunteers to explain—based on the adjectives listed—how acne can affect a teen's self-image. Discuss how thinking of acne as a temporary medical problem—like an allergic reaction or sprained ankle—might help the self-image of teens with acne. **OL**

AL Active Learning

Create a Flip Chart Many skin problems can be diagnosed on the basis of their appearance. Assign different students to find illustrations of the eight skin problems (including melanoma) that are described in the text. Then ask them to create a flip chart with their illustrations. Remind them to label the pictures. Give students a chance to share their flip chart with the rest of the class. **OL**

HS Health Skills Practice

Advocacy Have students make posters of the ABCD's of melanoma shown in **Figure 13.3**. The posters should include information on the seriousness of melanoma and the importance of early diagnosis. Ask students to obtain permission to display their posters in pharmacies, doctors' offices, or clinics in their community. **OL**

✓ READING CHECK

Answer *Any two:* Apply SPF 15 or higher sunscreen, wear protective clothing, use sunglasses, avoid tanning beds

360

- **Warts.** These are caused by a virus and are most commonly found on the hands, feet, and face. They can spread through direct contact with another person's wart.
- **Dermatitis, or eczema.** This is an inflamed or scaly patch of skin, usually from an allergic reaction. Keeping the area well moisturized can help reduce the irritation. A doctor may prescribe medications to treat dermatitis.
- **Fungal infections.** Ringworm and athlete's foot are infections that can be spread by contact with skin or infected clothing, or in public showers. Keep the infected area clean and dry, and treat with over-the-counter medicines.
- **Boils.** These form when **hair follicles**—*sacs or cavities that surround the roots of hairs*—become infected. The tissue becomes inflamed, and pus forms. Bursting or squeezing a boil can spread the infection. Treatment can include draining the pus and taking antibiotics.
- **Vitiligo.** A condition in which patches of skin lose melanin and have no pigment is called Vitiligo (vih-tuh-LY-go). These areas are extremely susceptible to burning when exposed to UV light, so they should always be covered.
- **Moles.** Though most moles are harmless, certain types may develop into **melanoma**, *the most serious form of skin cancer,* which can be deadly. Early detection and treatment are critical in controlling the spread of this cancer. See **Figure 13.3** on how to monitor the appearance of moles. Report any changes to a dermatologist.

✓ READING CHECK

Describe What are two ways to protect your skin from UV rays?

AL

HS

Figure 13.3 **The ABCD's of Melanoma**

Regularly checking the appearance of your moles is important for the early detection of melanoma.

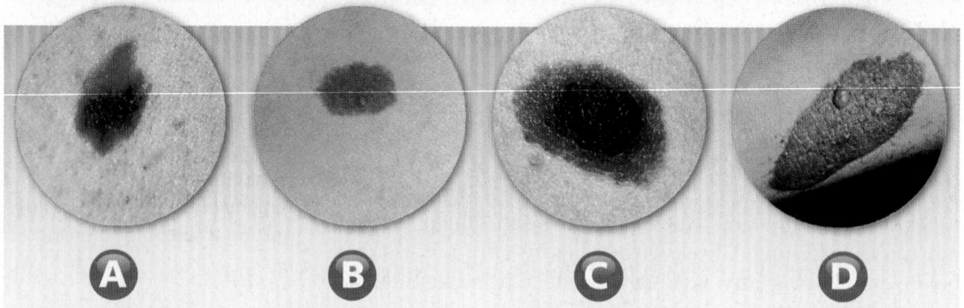

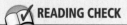

A Asymmetry	B Border Irregularity	C Color	D Diameter
An imaginary line drawn through the center of the mole does not produce matching halves.	Noncancerous moles have smooth edges. Suspect moles often have irregular edges.	Look for moles that are intensely black, possibly with a bluish tint, or that have an uneven color.	Check for moles that are wider across than the width of a pea.

Teens Want to Know

When Should Teens See a Dermatologist for Acne? Severe acne should always be treated by a dermatologist, especially if there are deep, painful lumps in the skin. Less severe acne that does not improve within two months of using over-the-counter treatments may also require professional help. Untreated acne can lead to permanent scars, and early treatment is the best way to prevent them. Prescription medications for acne are stronger and more effective than over-the-counter products. They include:

- benzoyl peroxide gels and creams.
- topical and oral antibiotics.
- isotretinoin, an oral drug used for very severe acne.

Your Hair

Main Idea Your hair protects your skin from UV radiation and helps maintain body heat.

Hair grows on every surface of the skin, except for the palms of the hand and the soles of the feet. You have more than 100,000 hairs on your head alone. Although hair is composed of dead cells, living cells in the epidermis make new hairs and cause hair growth.

Hair helps protect the skin, especially the scalp, from exposure to UV radiation. The eyebrows and eyelashes protect the eyes from dust and other particles. Hair also reduces the amount of heat lost through the skin of the scalp.

Healthy hair begins with a well-balanced diet. Without proper nutrients, hair can become thin and dry. Daily brushing keeps dirt from building up and helps distribute the natural oils in your hair evenly. Regular shampooing will keep your hair healthy. It's best to limit the use of harsh chemical treatments such as dyes, bleach, or permanents. Also, avoid excessive use of heating irons or hot combs. Overexposure to these can cause hair to become dry and brittle.

Hair Problems

Normally, oil produced by sebaceous glands protects the skin from drying out and keeps hair soft and shiny. Dandruff—the dead skin cells that are shed as sticky white flakes when the scalp becomes too dry—usually can be treated with an over-the-counter dandruff shampoo. If itching or scaling persists, consult a health care professional who may prescribe another type of treatment.

C Head lice are tiny parasitic insects that live in the scalp hair of humans. They feed on blood by biting through the skin of the scalp. Lice can infect anyone and are mainly transmitted by head-to-head contact or by using objects such as brushes, combs, or hats that have been used by an infected person. Using a medicated shampoo can kill the organisms. Washing sheets, pillowcases, combs, and hats with hot water and soap, as well as frequent vacuuming at home, can help prevent the spread of head lice or a repeat infection.

FITNESS ZONE

Want healthy hair? I guess we all do! My cousin is learning to be a hair stylist. She says that good nutrition and drinking lots of water helps keep your hair healthy. She says if your body is healthy and well nourished, your hair will be your shining glory. For more fitness tips, visit the Online Fitness Zone at **glencoe.com**.

■ **Figure 13.4** Give your hair daily attention to keep it clean and healthy. *How do you choose hair care products that are right for your hair?*

Lesson 1 Healthy Skin, Hair, and Nails **361**

3 ASSESS/ CLOSE

■ **Figure 13.5** Keeping nails neatly clipped and filed improves your overall appearance. *List three other grooming habits that contribute to a healthy appearance.*

Your Nails

Main Idea Nails help protect your fingers and toes.

Like your hair, your fingernails and toenails are made of closely packed dead cells that contain keratin. Cells beneath the root of the nail divide and multiply, causing the nail to grow. Nails protect and support tissues of fingers and toes.

Good care of the nails includes keeping them clean and evenly trimmed, which helps prevent split nails and hangnails. Use a nail file to shape and smooth nails, and keep cuticles pushed back. A cut, split, or break in the skin around the nail allows pathogens into the body and may lead to infection. Keep the area clean and apply an antibiotic ointment if necessary.

Trim toenails straight across and just slightly above the skin level to reduce the risk of infection and ingrown nails. Keeping nails short also reduces the risk of fungal infections under the nails. Fungal infections can be treated with antifungal medications.

LESSON 1 ASSESSMENT

After You Read

Reviewing Facts and Vocabulary

1. Define the terms *melanin* and *hair follicle.*
2. Explain the causes of acne. How is acne treated?
3. What viruses can you potentially contract through getting a tattoo?

Thinking Critically

4. **Apply.** Taking care to keep your nails clean and trimmed is important. Why might biting your nails be an unhealthy practice?
5. **Synthesize.** Explain how proper skin, hair, and nail care tells others that you care about your appearance.

Applying Health Skills

6. **Analyzing Influences.** Darla wants an eyebrow piercing because the lead singer in her favorite band has one. A friend offered to do the piercing for free. Write a letter to Darla and point out the influences on her choice. Remind her of the health risks.

Writing Critically

7. **Persuasive.** Write a brief dialogue between two teens. One wants to get a shoulder tattoo. The other explains the health and social risks.

Go Online

Visit glencoe.com and complete the Interactive Study Guide for this lesson.

LESSON 1 ASSESSMENT ANSWERS

1. *Melanin* is a pigment that gives the skin, hair, and iris of the eye their color. A *hair follicle* is a sac surrounding the hair root.
2. Acne is caused by clogged skin pores. Treatment includes: washing the face gently twice a day; applying over-the-counter treatment creams; avoiding the use of oily products or too much makeup; not touching and picking at the skin; and prescription medications for extreme cases.
3. Hepatitis B, hepatitis C, and HIV
4. Nail biting can injure the tissue around the nail, which exposes the cuticle to pathogens. Biting your nails also exposes you to dirt and pathogens that are on the skin or under the nails.
5. Sample answer: It shows others that you take time to care for yourself and that you value yourself.
6. Letters will vary.
7. Dialogues will vary.

Healthy Teeth and Mouth

LESSON **2**

Real Life Issues

Preventive Health. Maria is afraid of going to the dentist, even though she knows that getting her teeth cleaned every six months is important to her health. She often makes an appointment, then gets nervous and cancels it. Maria's brother, Juan, overhears her canceling her latest appointment.

Writing *Write a dialogue between Maria and Juan. Juan should try to convince Maria that going to the dentist twice a year is important.*

Your Teeth

Main Idea Every tooth has three main parts.

Having healthy teeth is important for your appearance, but it's also important for your overall physical health. Your teeth break down foods into pieces that are small enough to easily digest. They also help form the shape and structure of your mouth. Your permanent teeth come in gradually, usually beginning when you are about five years old and continuing into young adulthood when your last permanent molars, or wisdom teeth, come in.

Parts of a Tooth

The **periodontium** (per-ee-oh-DAHN-tee-uhm) is *the area immediately around the tooth.* It is made up of the gum, periodontal ligaments, and the jawbone. The periodontium support the tooth and hold it in place. The tooth itself has three main parts: the crown, the neck, and the root, as shown in **Figure 13.6.** The crown is the visible portion of the tooth. It is protected with enamel, a hard substance made of calcium.

GUIDE TO READING

BIG Idea *Your teeth and mouth need care to function well and keep you healthy.*

Before You Read

Make an Outline. Use the headings and subheadings in this lesson to make an outline of what you'll learn. Use this type of format to help you organize your notes.

```
I.
   A.
      1.
      2.
   B.
II.
```

New Vocabulary

▸ periodontium (p. 363)
▸ pulp (p. 364)
▸ plaque (p. 364)
▸ halitosis (p. 365)
▸ periodontal disease (p. 365)
▸ malocclusion (p. 365)

Healthy Teeth and Mouth

1 FOCUS

GUIDE TO READING

BIG Idea Taking care of the teeth and mouth keeps them functioning well and helps maintain the health of the body. **Ask Students:** *What does it mean to have healthy teeth?* (Sample answer: Not having any cavities)

Before You Read

Outline The first and second levels of the outline should match the headings and subheadings of the lesson. Details of the outlines will vary.

Main Idea

Your Teeth A tooth consists of three parts. **Ask Students:** *What is the function of teeth?* (To break food into smaller pieces so it can be swallowed and digested)

Real Life Issues

Have students read the scenario. **Ask Students:** *Why is it important to visit a dentist regularly?* (Sample answer: To treat minor problems before they become major) Call on volunteers to read their dialogues to the class.

English Language Coach

Using Word Parts Write the word *periodontium* on the board, and draw vertical lines to divide it into the following word parts: *peri-* ("around"), *-dont* ("tooth"), and *-ium* ("small mass"). Define the parts and then call on a volunteer to put the definitions together to define *periodontium* ("small mass around a tooth"). Ask students to name and define other words that contain at least two of the word parts. (Sample answers: periodontic, "relating to the area around a tooth;" *periodontist;* "dentist who specializes in treating the areas around the teeth.")

2 TEACH

R Reading Strategy

Using Diagrams Have students sketch and label a tooth like the one in **Figure 13.6**, leaving space under the labels to write the functions of the structures. Then have students find the functions of the structures in the text and add them to their diagram.

READING CHECK

Answer Crown, neck, and root

W Writing Support

Expository Writing Ask students to write a paragraph for young children explaining what plaque is and how it causes cavities. Advise students to avoid difficult words, complex sentences, and passive voice. Remind them to proofread their paragraphs. Call on volunteers to share what they wrote with the class. OL

Main Idea

Keeping Your Teeth and Mouth Healthy You can take steps to keep your teeth and mouth clean and healthy. **Ask Students:** *What do you do to keep your teeth clean?* (Sample answers: Brush after meals, floss daily)

Caption Answer

Figure 13.7 Healthy teeth protect health by helping to digest food and by preventing infection of the periodontium and root.

Figure 13.6 | Cross Section of a Tooth

A protective layer of enamel covers the crown of a tooth. Inside the tooth, blood vessels supply the living tissue with oxygen and nutrients.

- enamel
- dentin
- pulp cavity with nerves and vessels
- gum
- gingiva
- cementum
- periodontal ligaments
- periodontal membrane
- root canal
- bone

Crown

Neck

Root

R

READING CHECK

Identify What are the three parts of the tooth?

■ **Figure 13.7** Healthy teeth are important to your overall health. *Explain how healthy teeth protect your health.*

Beneath the enamel is *dentin,* a layer of connective tissue that contributes to the shape and hardness of a tooth. The **pulp** is *the tissue that contains the blood vessels and nerves of a tooth.* Protected by the overlying layers of dentin and enamel, the pulp extends into the root canal. The neck of a tooth is between the crown and the root.

Keeping Your Teeth and Mouth Healthy

Main Idea You can make choices that help keep your teeth and mouth clean and healthy.

Oral hygiene, which includes brushing and flossing your teeth, is necessary for healthy, clean teeth. The bacteria that naturally inhabit your mouth metabolize the sugars in the foods you eat. They produce an acid that breaks down the protective layer of tooth enamel. Tooth decay occurs when the enamel is destroyed and bacteria penetrate the tooth.

Plaque is *a combination of bacteria and other particles, such as small bits of food, which adheres to the outside of a tooth.* Plaque damages the tooth by coating it, sealing out the saliva that normally protects the tooth from bacteria. If plaque builds up, the acids produced by bacteria break down the tooth enamel, resulting in a hole, or cavity. If decay spreads down to the pulp, the tooth may have to be removed.

W

More About...

Toothbrushes A toothbrush may be the single most important tool for keeping the teeth and gums healthy, so it is important to select the right toothbrush and replace it often. The American Dental Association (ADA) recommends using only soft-bristled toothbrushes, because medium or hard bristles can damage the teeth and gums. The ADA also recommends replacing toothbrushes every three months. Worn toothbrushes do not remove as much plaque as new toothbrushes, and they harbor bacteria that may cause gum disease.

Practicing good oral hygiene can prevent tooth decay and other diseases. Brushing your teeth after eating removes plaque from the surface of the teeth, before bacteria can produce the acid that harms teeth. Flossing between your teeth removes plaque in areas that cannot be reached with the bristles of a toothbrush.

CA To maintain your dental health, visit your dentist regularly. The dentist, or a dental hygienist, will clean your teeth and examine them for signs of decay. Dentists may use sealants to prevent tooth decay. In addition to visiting the dentist regularly, you can take the following steps to keep your teeth and gums healthy:

- Eat a well-balanced diet that includes foods containing phosphorus, calcium, and vitamin C.
- Reduce the number of sugary drinks and snacks you eat.
- Brush your teeth after every meal, and floss daily.
- Get regular dental checkups.
- Wear a mouth guard when you play contact sports or other activities to protect your mouth and teeth.
- Avoid all tobacco products. They stain teeth and cause gums to recede. They also increase the risk of oral cancer.

Tooth and Mouth Problems

Main Idea Neglecting your teeth can result in problems.

Some oral problems are caused by poor hygiene, others by poorly aligned teeth. Be alert to these common problems:

- **Halitosis**, or *bad breath,* can be caused by eating certain foods, poor oral hygiene, smoking, bacteria on the tongue, decayed teeth, and gum disease.
- Gum disease, or **periodontal disease**, *an inflammation of the periodontal structures,* is caused by bacterial infection. When plaque hardens, it builds up *tartar,* a hard, crustlike substance. This causes the gums to become irritated and swollen. This early stage is called *gingivitis* (jin-jih-VY-tis). If left untreated, the bone and tissue that support the teeth are destroyed, and teeth can be lost.
- **Malocclusion** (mal-uh-KLOO-zhun), *a misalignment of the upper and lower teeth,* or a "bad bite," can be caused by crowded or extra teeth, thumb sucking, injury, or heredity. If not treated, malocclusion can lead to decay, and affect a person's speech and ability to chew.
- **Impacted wisdom teeth** sometimes crowd and push on other teeth or become infected. They may need to be removed surgically.

READING CHECK

Cause and Effect Describe how plaque leads to tooth decay.

HEALTH NEWS **VIDEO**

Brushing Your Teeth Away

Analyze. Go to glencoe.com and watch the video *Brushing Your Teeth Away.* Consider the damage that the wrong toothbrush or brushing method can cause. Make a list of ways to reduce the risk of such damage to your teeth and gums.

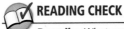

READING CHECK

Describe What are six possible causes of halitosis?

CA **Cultural Awareness**

Dental Health A recent anthropological study found that Americans typically think of dental health problems as cosmetic issues rather than as diseases. For example, Americans tend to put cavities and gum disease in a more superficial category, rather than in the same category as heart disease and diabetes. Discuss how this concept of dental health might negatively influence how well Americans care for their teeth. **OL**

READING CHECK

Answer Plaque coats the teeth, sealing out protective saliva. Bacteria in plaque produce acids that break down tooth enamel and cause tooth decay.

VIDEO **BusinessWeek**
HEALTH NEWS

After students have watched the video, ***Brushing Your Teeth Away,*** call on a volunteer to describe the types of toothbrushes and brushing methods that can damage teeth and gums. Then have students write their lists. When they finish writing, call on students to share their lists with the class.

Main Idea

Tooth and Mouth Problems
Neglecting teeth can result in problems. **Ask Students:** *What are examples of tooth or mouth problems?* (Cavities, crooked teeth, gum disease)

Teacher to Teacher

Joan Davis • Martin Luther King High School, Detroit, MI

A Personal Health Game The idea behind this game is for students to listen to the answers and try to come up with questions pertaining to healthy teeth and mouth.

1. Place five containers on the front table. Label each container with a category and a point value. Place questions inside each container. The higher the point value the more difficult the question.
2. Break the class into two teams (larger classes break into three or four teams).

Each team will have a spokesperson.
3. Each spokesperson will pick a statement out of the container and confer with his classmates on the answer. The spokesperson will give the "answer" in a question.
4. Continue play until all categories are used.

Real World CONNECTION

Answers to Activity:

Information on dental product safety comes from the ADA. Students' reports should contain reliable sources of information.

❸ ASSESS/ CLOSE

Assessment Resources

📁 *FAST FILE* ACTIVITIES
Lesson 2 Quiz

💿 *ExamView*
Assessment Suite CD-ROM

Visit glencoe.com for:
Online Quizzes
Online Learning Center

Progress Monitoring

Reteaching
Have students write sentences using vocabulary terms and check text definitions to be sure they used terms correctly.

Enrichment
Challenge students to prepare a lesson for young children about how and why to take care of the teeth. If possible, arrange for students to present their lessons to classes at the appropriate grade level.

 Online

Have students visit **glencoe.com** and complete the Interactive Study Guide for this lesson.

366

Real World CONNECTION

Examining Product Claims

The toothpaste aisle contains products that make many different claims. Some brands of toothpaste whiten teeth, others prevent cavities, some prevent bad breath, and others combine some or all of these claims. How can you tell if these claims are true?

Check for exaggerated or misleading claims on product labels. Does the label tell you how the product works?

Fresher Breath — Whiter Teeth, Too!

Determine whether the product is safe. Some tooth whiteners, for example, contain abrasives that may cause gum irritation.

Activity Reading / Writing

Investigate the claims made by these toothpaste manufacturers.

1. Begin by finding out what information is reliable. Professional dental associations and nonprofit consumer-protection organizations can be good places to start.

2. Find out what these organizations recommend that all toothpastes should do. Which features are important? Call or e-mail the organizations if necessary.

3. Write a short report on your findings. Cite your sources and explain why you think the claims you support are reliable.

LESSON **2** ASSESSMENT

After You Read

Reviewing Facts and Vocabulary

1. Define the terms *periodontal disease* and *plaque*.
2. What is the pulp of the tooth?
3. Explain how tooth decay happens.

Thinking Critically

4. **Infer.** Dentists may apply a sealant to children's teeth to protect them from decay. How do you think these sealants work?
5. **Compare and Contrast.** Which layers of the tooth are sensitive, and which are not? Explain.

Applying Health Skills

6. **Accessing Information.** Do research at the library or on the Internet to learn more about what an endodontist does.

Writing Critically

7. **Persuasive.** Write a short letter to a younger brother or sister describing the reasons why it's important to brush and floss teeth regularly.

 Online

Visit **glencoe.com** and complete the Interactive Study Guide for this lesson.

LESSON **2** ASSESSMENT ANSWERS

1. *Periodontal disease* is inflammation of the periodontal structures. *Plaque* is a combination of bacteria and other particles that adheres to the outside of a tooth.
2. Tissue that contains the blood vessels and nerves of a tooth
3. If plaque builds up, bacteria thrive in the plaque and produce acids that break down tooth enamel, forming a cavity.
4. Sealants protect teeth from decay by preventing contact with acids from bacteria.
5. Enamel and dentin are not sensitive because they have no nerve tissue. Pulp is sensitive because it has nerve tissue.
6. An endodontist is a dentist who specializes in treating the inside of a tooth.
7. Letters will vary.

Healthy Eyes and Ears

Healthy Eyes and Ears

1 FOCUS

Real Life Issues ....

Playing It Safe. Noah loves music and has an MP3 player. Noah's dad has told him that he can listen on the headphones only if he keeps the volume down to protect his ears. Noah does what his dad asks, but he is tempted to crank up the volume because he enjoys music more when it's played loud.

Writing *Write a short poem or rap lyrics that reinforce the benefits of listening to music at safe levels.*

Your Eyes

Main Idea The eyes and their supporting structures are a complex of parts.

Most of the sensory information that travels to your brain comes from light signals received by your eyes. Structurally, your eyes sit in bony sockets, called orbits, at the front of your skull. A layer of fat cushions each eyeball inside its socket. Another structure is the lacrimal gland, which secretes tears into the eye through ducts. Tears are made of water, salts, mucus, and a substance that protects the eye from infection. As you blink, tears are moved across the surface of the eye. They keep the surface of the eyeball moist and clear of foreign particles.

Parts of the Eye

The eye consists of the optic nerve and three layers of the eyeball wall, as shown in **Figure 13.8.**

- The outermost layer of the eye is made up of the sclera and the cornea. The **sclera** (SKLEHR-uh), *the white part of the eye,* is composed of tough, fibrous tissue that

GUIDE TO READING

BIG Idea Eyes and ears are sensitive organs that need protective care.

Before You Read
Create a K-W-L Chart. Make a three-column chart. In the first column, write what you <u>k</u>now about your eyes and ears. In the second column, write what you <u>w</u>ant to know about them. As you read, fill in the third column describing what you have <u>l</u>earned.

K	W	L

New Vocabulary

- sclera (p. 367)
- cornea (p. 368)
- retina (p. 368)
- auditory ossicles (p. 371)
- labyrinth (p. 371)
- tinnitus (p. 373)

GUIDE TO READING

BIG Idea Eyes and ears are sensitive and need protection.
Ask Students: *What do the eyes need to be protected from?* (Sample answers: Dust, strong light, injuries)

Before You Read
K-W-L Chart Charts will vary.

Main Idea

Your Eyes Eyes and their supporting structures are a complex of parts. **Ask Students:** *What are some structures of the eye?* (Sample answers: Iris and pupil)

Real Life Issues ....

Have students read the scenario. **Ask Students:** *Why is loud music harmful?* (It can damage ears and harm hearing.) Give volunteers a chance to recite their poems or lyrics to the class.

ELL Support

Eye Structures **Point out the most important structures in Figure 13.8 for understanding vision:** *cornea, lens, retina,* **and** *optic nerve.* **Describe the function of each structure.**

Beginning Repeat the functions, and ask students to name the structures.

Intermediate Name the structures, and ask students to state their functions.

Advanced Have students use the names of the structures in original sentences that describe their functions.

② TEACH

U Universal Access

Learning from Visuals Instruct students to use their finger to trace the path of light through the eye in **Figure 13.8**. As they trace the path of light, have them name each structure that light passes through. Explain what happens to the light as it passes through each structure. **EL** **BL**

C Critical Thinking

Predicting Ask students to predict how their vision would be affected if the rods or cones in their retinas could not sense light. (If the rods could not sense light, they would be unable to see in dim light; if the cones could not sense light, they would be unable to see color.) **OL**

AL Active Learning

Vision Testing Ask a few volunteers to set up a vision-testing station. Students can go online to find a free eye chart or instructions for making one. If they make a chart, they will need white poster board, a black marker, and a ruler. Students will also need a tape measure and masking tape to measure and mark distances (20 feet and 30 feet) from the eye chart. Have students use their vision-testing station to demonstrate the difference between 20/20 and 20/30 vision. **OL**

Academic Vocabulary

Portion Ask students to read the definition of the word *portion* provided in the text. Then have them work in pairs to develop a sentence or two using the word as it relates to nutrition. Call on each pair to share their sentences with the class.

| Figure 13.8 | **The Eye** |

The eye collects light and sends signals to the brain, where images are formed.

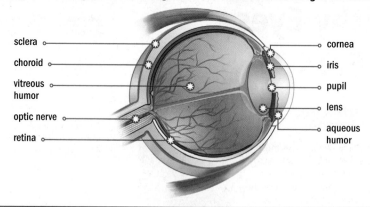

sclera • choroid • vitreous humor • optic nerve • retina • cornea • iris • pupil • lens • aqueous humor

---

protects the inner layers of the eye and supports and shapes the eyeball. At the front of the eye rests the cornea. The **cornea** is *a transparent tissue that bends and focuses light before it enters the lens.*

- Within the middle layer of the eyewall is the *choroid* (KOHR-oid), a thin structure that lines the inside of the sclera. Also within the middle layer is the *iris,* the colored **portion** of the eye that contains the pupil. The color of the iris is genetically determined. The pupil is the hole through which light reaches the inner eye. The muscles of the iris control the size of the pupil. In bright light, the pupil constricts, or dilates; in dim light, it enlarges to let in more light.

- The **retina** is *the inner layer of the eye wall.* The retina contains millions of light-sensitive cells. These cells are called rods and cones, each named for its basic shape. Rods are very sensitive to light and allow us to see in dim light. Cones function in bright light and allow us to see color. When light stimulates these cells, a nerve impulse travels to the brain through the *optic nerve,* which is located at the back of the eye.

Behind the iris and the pupil is the *lens* of the eye. Like the cornea, the lens is transparent and helps refine the focus of images on the retina. The area between the cornea and the lens is filled with a watery fluid called *aqueous humor,* which provides nutrients to the eye. Between the lens and retina there is a cavity filled with a gelatin-like substance called *vitreous humor.* This helps the eyeball stay firm, helps the eye keep its shape, and holds the retina against the choroid.

Academic Vocabulary

portion *(noun):* a part set off from the whole

G❂ Online

For more vocabulary practice, go to the Interactive Health Tutor at **glencoe.com.**

368 Chapter 13 Personal Health Care

Myths & Reality

Eye Myths

Myth: Sitting too close to a television will hurt your eyes.

Fact: This practice may tire the eyes, but there is no evidence that it damages the eyes.

Myth: Children do not need eye exams until they are in school.

Fact: Children should have regular eye exams starting at birth to detect serious eye problems, such as strabismus, which may cause permanent vision loss if not treated.

Myth: Eating carrots will help you have 20/20 vision.

Fact: Carrots contain vitamin A, which is important for eye health and especially for seeing in dim light, but vitamin A does not help vision problems.

Health Skills Activity

Decision Making

Fun in the Sun?

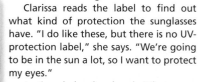

Clarissa's family is going on vacation to a sunny, warm climate, and she wants to buy a new pair of sunglasses. Clarissa and her friend Justine are trying on sunglasses at the mall. Justine encourages Clarissa to buy a particular pair.

"Those look *so* cool on you," says Justine. "You *have* to get them."

Clarissa reads the label to find out what kind of protection the sunglasses have. "I do like these, but there is no UV-protection label," she says. "We're going to be in the sun a lot, so I want to protect my eyes."

Justine shakes her head. "Those sunglasses look the best. C'mon, Clare, which is more important right now—looking great or being healthy?"

Writing Write an ending in which Clarissa decides between looking good and protecting her health. Include what she might do to have it both ways. Apply the six steps of the decision-making process to Clarissa's situation.

1. State the situation.
2. List the options.
3. Weigh the possible outcomes.
4. Consider values.
5. Make a decision and act.
6. Evaluate the decision.

Vision

When light passes through the cornea, pupil, and lens to reach the retina, an image forms. Light rays are first focused by the curved cornea, then later refined by the lens onto the retina. This light stimulates the rods and cones in the retina, sending nerve impulses to the brain through the optic nerve. The brain translates the nerve impulses into images that you recognize.

Your vision may be affected by the way images are produced on the retina. Having clear vision means that the images are produced sharply on your retina. Eye doctors refer to clear, sharp, normal vision as 20/20 vision. This means that you can stand 20 feet away from an eye chart and read the top eight lines. When the images produced on your retina are not clear, an eye doctor will perform tests to determine what type of disorder is affecting your vision. Two common vision disorders are nearsightedness, or *myopia*, and farsightedness, or *hyperopia*.

If you have 20/60 vision, you must be 20 feet from the chart in order to read it the way a person with normal vision can read it from 60 feet. A person with 20/60 vision is said to be nearsighted, which means being able to see close, but not far. Other components of vision include eye coordination, peripheral or side vision, and depth perception.

AL

READING CHECK

Explain How do light signals become images?

Health Skills Activity

Decision Making: Fun in the Sun?

NHES Standard 5 Students will demonstrate the ability to use decision-making skills to enhance health.

Objectives

- Apply the six steps of the decision-making process.
- Generate alternatives to health-related issues.
- Predict the potential health impact of each alternative.

Teaching Strategies

- Explain that UV radiation may increase the risk of macular degeneration and cataracts. Have students read about these two eye problems in **Figure 13.9**.
- Lead the class in brainstorming options for Clarissa that allow her to look good while protecting her health.

Assessment

Using this list, student work should provide comprehensive evidence of the following criteria to achieve the highest score:

√ States the situation
√ Lists options
√ Weighs possible outcomes
√ Considers values
√ Makes a decision and acts on it
√ Evaluates the decision

Academic Integration

Science Challenge students to learn how vitamin A is involved in the functioning of rods and cones in the retina and the transmission of nerve impulses to the brain. Students can search for the information online or in reference books. Ask them to summarize what they learn in a graphic organizer. Give students a chance to explain their graphic organizer to the class. (Graphic organizers should show that vitamin A is part of the pigments in rods and cones that react to light, triggering a series of reactions and other changes that end in a nerve impulse.)

Main Idea

Keeping Your Eyes Healthy
Making healthy choices will keep your eyes healthy. **Ask Students:** *What choices can you make to keep your eyes healthy?* (Sample answers: Wear goggles when there is risk of eye injury; get regular eye exams.)

 Reading Strategy

Comparing and Contrasting
Guide students in using the table in **Figure 13.9** to compare and contrast different eye problems. First ask students to identify the two basic categories of eye problems that are shown in the table. (structural problems and diseases) Then ask students to compare and contrast the causes and treatments of different problems within each category. **BL**

 READING CHECK

Answer Follow a well-balanced eating plan, protect the eyes from injury, rest the eyes frequently, get regular eye exams

W **Writing Support**

Researching Have interested students research and create a report on how best to keep eyes healthy. Instruct students to learn more about other vitamins that may also contribute to eye health. **AL** **OL**

Figure 13.9 **Eye Problems**

Structural Problems	Cause	Treatment
Nearsightedness (myopia) The inability to see distant objects clearly	May occur naturally; cornea is misshaped, or eye is too long.	Contact lenses, eyeglasses, or laser surgery
Farsightedness (hyperopia) The inability see close objects clearly	May occur naturally; cornea is misshaped, or eye is too short.	Contact lenses, eyeglasses, or laser surgery
Astigmatism Blurred vision	May occur naturally; lens or cornea is misshaped.	Contact lenses, eyeglasses, or surgery
Strabismus Eyes off-center, turned inward or outward	Weak eye muscles	Vision therapy, contact lenses, eyeglasses, or surgery
Detached retina Blurred vision or bright flashes of light	Retina has become detached from the choroid due to injury or aging.	Laser surgery to reattach retina

Disease or Vision Problems	Cause	Treatment
Infections and Viruses (such as sties, pinkeye, hepatitis) Swelling, irritation, blurred vision, change in sclera color	Pathogens infect the eye or the tissue around the eye.	Medications such as antibiotics may cure infections. No treatment for viruses.
Glaucoma Cloudy, impaired vision, sometimes permanent eye damage	High pressure inside the eye damages the retina and optic nerve.	Laser treatment; early detection helps minimize damage.
Cataracts Foggy vision	Lens becomes cloudy and cannot focus light.	Surgical removal of old lens and replacement with an artificial lens
Macular degeneration Vision loss	Part of the retina opposite the lens deteriorates due to aging.	No cure exists. Treatment is limited.

READING CHECK

Describe What are four things you can do to keep your eyes healthy?

Keeping Your Eyes Healthy

Main Idea Making healthy choices will keep your eyes healthy.

Eye problems are outlined in **Figure 13.9**. You can practice several healthful behaviors to help keep your eyes healthy.

- **Follow a well-balanced eating plan.** Include foods that contain vitamin A, such as carrots and sweet potatoes. (See **Figure 10.6**, p. 263, for other good sources of this vitamin.) Deficiency in vitamin A could result in night blindness—the inability to see well in dim light.

Health Literacy

LASIK for Teens Many teens would love to put aside their glasses and have their vision problems corrected surgically. However, until recently, LASIK and similar vision-correction surgeries were almost never performed on children and teens, mainly because their vision is still changing. Over the last few years, surgeons have started to perform LASIK surgery on children and teens who have serious visual problems that lenses, eye patches, and similar noninvasive techniques cannot correct. Some eye surgeons predict that LASIK will become more common for teens within the next 10 years, although it is unlikely to be performed as routinely in teens as it is in adults.

- **Protect your eyes.** Wear safety goggles when participating in activities in which your eyes could be injured. Keep dirty hands or other objects away from your eyes to reduce the risk of eye infections and injuries. Avoid sharing eye makeup, which can transmit bacteria. Wear sunglasses that block UV light, and never look directly into the sun or bright lights.
- **Rest your eyes regularly.** Take regular breaks when you are doing close-up work such as using the computer or reading. Looking up and away every 10 minutes or so reduces eyestrain.
- **Get regular eye exams.** Routine eye exams by a health care professional allow certain eye diseases to be detected and treated in their early stages.

Your Ears

Main Idea The inner, middle, and outer ear work together so you can hear.

 The ear can be divided into three main sections, each with its own unique structures. The parts of the ear are shown in **Figure 13.10**, on page 377.

- **The Outer Ear.** The outer ear is the visible part of the ear, called the *auricle*. The auricle channels sound waves into the *external auditory canal,* a passageway about 1 inch long. This canal leads to the remaining portion of the outer ear, called the eardrum. The skin of this canal is lined with tiny hairs and glands that produce wax. The hairs and wax protect the ear from dust and foreign objects. The eardrum, also called the tympanic membrane, is a thin membrane that acts as a barrier between the outer and middle ear.
- **The Middle Ear.** Directly behind the eardrum are the **auditory ossicles**, *three small bones linked together that connect the eardrum to the inner ear.* The auditory ossicles are the smallest bones in the body. The middle ear is connected to the throat by the eustachian tube. When you swallow or yawn, this tube allows pressure to be equalized on each side of the eardrum.
- **The Inner Ear.** *The inner ear,* or **labyrinth**, consists of a network of curved and spiral passages that can be divided into three main parts. The *cochlea,* a spiral-shaped canal, is the area of hearing in the inner ear. The vestibule and the semicircular canals are where balance is controlled.

G♀ Online

Go to **glencoe.com** and complete the Student Web Activity on protecting your hearing from permanent damage.

Main Idea

Your Ears The inner, middle, and outer ear work together to help a person hear. **Ask Students:** *What is hearing?* (sensing sound)

R Reading Strategy

Analyzing a Graphic Have students examine **Figure 13.10**, The Ear, on the next page. Gude students in relating the illustration of parts of the ear to information in the text. Help students identify parts of the middle ear. **Ask Students:** *The middle ear is connected to the throat by what?* (eustachian tube) *What is another name for the eardrum?* (tympanic membrane) **OL**

G♀ Online

Have students visit **glencoe.com** and complete the Student Web Activity on protecting hearing from permanent damage.

Cooperative Learning

Picturing Hearing and Balance Have pairs of students work together to illustrate the parts of the ear and their functions. Assign one student in each pair the parts of the ear involved with hearing and the other student the parts involved with balance. Students should use photos, sketches, diagrams, and text to show how the assigned parts enable hearing or balance. After individual students complete their work, ask partners to collaborate on a poster that shows both functions of the ear. Display the posters in the classroom.

Figure 13.10   The Ear

The ear has two functions: hearing and balance. *Which parts of the ear are involved in hearing?*

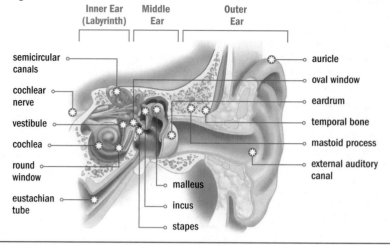

Inner Ear (Labyrinth) — Middle Ear — Outer Ear

semicircular canals
cochlear nerve
vestibule
cochlea
round window
eustachian tube

auricle
oval window
eardrum
temporal bone
mastoid process
external auditory canal

malleus
incus
stapes

Hearing and Balance

Receptors in your inner ear are stimulated by a sound wave. The impulse is then sent to your brain, where it is interpreted as a sound. As these sound waves enter the external auditory canal causing the eardrum to vibrate. The vibrations cause fluid in the cochlea to move, which stimulate receptor cells. These cells send a nerve impulse to the brain, where sound is interpreted. As this is occurring, receptor cells in the vestibule and the semicircular canals send messages to the brain about your sense of balance. Tiny hairs located in the ear sense movement and send nerve impulses to the brain. The brain makes adjustments to maintain balance.

Keeping Your Ears Healthy

Main Idea Caring for your ears helps prevent irritation, injury, infection, and damage to the ears, as well as hearing loss.

To protect your hearing, have your ears examined by a health care professional if you suspect an infection. Middle ear infections can damage the structure of the ear, but can be treated with antibiotics. Other ways to protect your hearing include wearing a hat that covers both the auricles and the earlobes in cold weather. Wear protective gear, such as a batting helmet, when playing sports. Keep foreign objects, including cotton-tipped swabs, out of the ear canal.

■ **Figure 13.11** A health care professional will check your ears during a routine physical examination. *What are other ways to keep your ears healthy?*

Skills for the 21st Century

Personal Responsibility In this lesson, students learn that personal health care depends mainly on individuals taking responsibility for their own health. Point out that some people think corporations should also take responsibility for the health of individuals, for example, by making stereos that cannot be played at very high volumes.

Stimulate a debate on the role of individuals vs. corporations in protecting ears from loud sounds by asking such questions as: Which responsibilities fall to individuals, and which to corporations? Where does corporate responsibility end and individual responsibility begin?

Preventing Hearing Loss

Explsoure to loud noises can can lead to temporary and sometimes permanent hearing loss, or deafness, over time. Hearing loss can be divided into two categories: conductive and sensorineural.

Conductive Hearing Loss In conductive hearing loss, sound waves are not passed from the outer ear to the inner ear, usually because of a blockage or injury to the inner ear. For example, middle-ear infections may cause fluid to build up within the middle ear.

Sensorineural Hearing Loss This problem may result from a birth defect, exposure to noise, growing older, and medication problems. One type of sensorineural hearing loss is **tinnitus**, *a condition in which a ringing, buzzing, whistling, roaring, hissing, or other sound is heard in the ear in the absence of external sound.* To prevent tinnitus, avoid loud music, wear earplugs in noisy environments, and at loud concerts or sporting events. By limiting the length of time you are exposed to loud noise, you reduce the risk of permanent damage.

FITNESS ZONE

I love listening to music when I exercise, but I heard that wearing headphones with the volume turned up can cause permanent hearing loss over time. You might also miss warnings, like a car horn. I turn down the volume. I can still enjoy my music while protecting my hearing and my safety. For more fitness tips, visit the Online Fitness Zone at **glencoe.com**.

LESSON 3 ASSESSMENT

After You Read

Reviewing Vocabulary and Facts

1. What happens to eyes that have cataracts?
2. What is *astigmatism*?
3. Explain the function of the wax and tiny hairs in the ear canal.

Thinking Critically

4. **Infer.** What are four characteristics that you think good safety goggles should have?
5. **Identify.** What are two common activities that would require hearing protection?

Applying Health Skills

6. **Accessing Information.** Conduct research to learn about community health services for people with vision problems. Make a pamphlet that can be used as a reference on the availability of these community services.

Writing Critically

7. **Persuasive.** Write a script or skit featuring two teens. One teen is urging the other to avoid exposure to loud noises to reduce the risk of hearing impairment.

Go Online

Visit **glencoe.com** and complete the Interactive Study Guide for this lesson.

Lesson 3 Healthy Eyes and Ears **373**

LESSON 3 ASSESSMENT ANSWERS

1. The lenses become cloudy and cannot focus light.
2. Blurred vision due to a misshapen cornea or lens
3. Protecting the ear from dust and foreign objects
4. Answers may vary. Sample answer: They should fit well, surround the eye completely, be transparent, and be made of shatter-proof material.
5. Sample answer: Attending a loud rock concert and using a lawn mower
6. Pamphlets will vary.
7. Scripts will vary, but should include facts from the lesson.

Getting Burned by a Trend

Focus

Motivator

Ask students to think of reasons why teens use tanning beds. (Sample answers: To improve their appearance, to fit in with their peers)

Teach

Risk of Melanoma Ask students to recall what they learned about melanoma in Lesson 1. Point out the doubling of melanoma cases in females in their age group since 1975. Add that tanning beds first started being used cosmetically in the early 1970s. Ask students to explain how these two facts might be related. (Sample answer: Use of tanning beds exposes skin to UV radiation, which is the major cause of melanoma.)

Changing Attitudes Ask students why some teens, like Kylie-Ayn in the feature, are more concerned about looking good right now than about protecting their long-term health. (Sample answers: They think nothing bad will happen to them; they feel strong peer pressure to have a tan.) Discuss whether education about the dangers of tanning beds would affect their attitude toward tanning. What else might convince teens that having a tan is not worth the health risks?

Evidence Before students do the Time to Think activity, ask them what evidence they would expect to find if there is a connection between depletion of the ozone layer and increased rates of skin cancer.

TIME HEALTH
SCIENCE & TECHNOLOGY

GETTING BURNED BY A TREND

Effects of too much tanning aren't as far off as you might think—skin cancer is striking more young people.

Kylie-Ayn Kennedy, 16, of Easton, PA, is one of the estimated 2.3 million teens who pop into a tanning parlor at least once a year. She's helping make indoor tanning a $5 billion-a-year business.

Many of these teens go only in the spring to get ready for the prom. More and more, however, are seeking year-round "bronzitude," according to dermatologists. And these experts are alarmed by the risks of so much exposure to ultraviolet (UV) radiation.

Taking Tanning Too Far

Easy access to tanning salons, doctors say, may be contributing to a spike in skin-cancer rates among the young. Cases of melanoma, the most deadly form of skin cancer, has doubled in the U.S. since 1975 among women ages 15 to 29. In 2008, about 2,050 women in this age group were expected to be diagnosed with melanoma.

"Skin cancer used to be something old people got," says Dr. James Spencer, a professor of dermatology at New York City's Mount Sinai School of Medicine. "But now, not a month goes by that I don't see somebody in their 20s. That was unheard of 10 years ago." Doctors worry about the long-term consequences of adolescent tanning. The World Health Organization estimates that up to 60,000 deaths worldwide are caused each year by excessive UV exposure and urges youths under 18 to steer clear of indoor tanning and to always use sunblock or sunscreen if they spend a lot of time outdoors in strong sunlight.

But Kylie-Ayn—and many other teens—shrugs off the downsides. "It may make my skin wrinkle a little bit earlier," she says, "but I'm going to look good while I can." But doctors agree that when it comes to tanning, looking good may come at an extremely high price—your life. ■

TIME to THINK... About Tanning

Is there a relationship between the depletion of Earth's ozone layer and increased rates of skin cancer? Using the Internet and your library's media center, research any connections that may exist between the two and make a list of what evidence you do—or don't—find.

Health Literacy

Tanning Bed Laws Several states and municipalities have passed laws banning tanning bed use by younger teens and children. The laws differ from place to place. For example, the cut-off age may vary, and some laws allow tanning at younger ages with a parent's or guardian's consent. In virtually all cases, however, the laws are difficult to enforce. Have students learn what laws, if any, regulate the use of tanning beds by teens in their state or municipality. Discuss problems in enforcing the laws and reasons why the laws are important.

To download quizzes and eFlashcards to your PDA, go to glencoe.com and click on the Study to Go icon.

LESSON 1

Healthy Skin, Hair, and Nails

Key Concepts

▶ Skin has two main layers, the dermis and epidermis, over a layer of fat and connective tissue.

▶ A well-balanced diet rich in vitamin A is essential to your skin's health.

▶ Wear sunscreen with an SPF of 15 or higher to block UVB and UVA rays.

▶ Your hair protects your scalp from sun exposure and provides warmth.

Vocabulary

▶ epidermis (p. 356)
▶ dermis (p. 356)
▶ melanin (p. 356)
▶ sebaceous glands (p. 358)
▶ hair follicles (p. 360)
▶ melanoma (p. 360)

LESSON 2

Healthy Teeth and Mouth

Key Concepts

▶ A tooth has three main parts: the crown, neck, and root.

▶ The buildup of plaque (bacteria) can lead to cavities.

▶ Periodontal disease begins with the buildup of plaque and tartar.

▶ Good dental care includes proper diet, brushing and flossing, dental checkups, protecting the mouth during sports, and avoiding use of tobacco products.

Vocabulary

▶ periodontium (p. 363)
▶ pulp (p. 364)
▶ plaque (p. 364)
▶ halitosis (p. 365)
▶ periodontal disease (p. 365)
▶ malocclusion (p. 365)

LESSON 3

Healthy Eyes and Ears

Key Concepts

▶ Eyes gather and send light signals to the brain.

▶ Following a well-balanced eating plan, using eye goggles, and getting regular eye exams will protect your vision.

▶ Your ears change sound waves into electrical signals sent to the brain.

▶ To maintain your hearing, keep your ears clean and warm, avoid putting objects in them, protect them during sports, and avoid prolonged loud noise.

Vocabulary

▶ sclera (p. 367)
▶ cornea (p. 368)
▶ retina (p. 368)
▶ auditory ossicles (p. 371)
▶ labyrinth (p. 371)
▶ tinnitus (p. 373)

 Go Online

Students can visit **glencoe.com** to

- review content online with the Online Student Edition.

- test their knowledge of chapter content with Online Quizzes.

- access Interactive Health Tutor for more practice with vocabulary.

Assessment Resources

📁 **FAST FILE ACTIVITIES**
Chapter 13 Test

💿 *ExamView*
Assessment Suite CD-ROM

Visit glencoe.com for:
Audio Chapter Summaries
Online Quizzes

 Tell students to visit **glencoe.com** where they can download quizzes and eFlashcards.

Chapter 13   Review   **375**

Study Tips

Learning New Information Explain to students that they are more likely to learn and remember new information when it has meaning to them and is relevant to their own lives. When students try to learn new material, suggest that they relate the information to something they already know or experiences they have had. For example, encourage students to relate the material in Lesson 3 on the eyes to their own experiences with vision problems, eye exams, and/or corrective lenses.

Assessment

Chapter 13
Assessment Answers

LESSON 1

Vocabulary Review

1. epidermis
2. sweat glands
3. melanin
4. sebaceous glands

Understanding Key Concepts

5. d
6. a
7. b
8. c

Thinking Critically

9. The sun's rays are most intense during this part of the day.
10. Wash your face gently twice a day; use over-the-counter treatment creams or prescription medications; avoid using oily products or too much makeup.
11. A balanced diet provides the nutrients needed to prevent hair from becoming thin and dry.
12. Features include asymmetry, irregular borders, black or uneven color, and diameter greater than the width of a pea.
13. Moles and warts are both skin problems. Moles are harmless spots on skin that contain extra melanin. Warts are sites where surface layers of skin are infected by a virus.

LESSON 2

Vocabulary Review

14. periodontium
15. pulp
16. plaque
17. periodontal disease

LESSON 1

Vocabulary Review

Correct the sentences below by replacing the italicized term with the correct vocabulary term.

1. The *dermis* is the outer, thinner layer of the skin that is composed of living and dead cells.

2. Sweat is produced in the *sebaceous glands*.

3. *Melanoma* is a pigment in the skin.

4. An oily secretion called sebum is produced by the *dermis*.

Understanding Key Concepts

After reading the question or statement, select the correct answer.

5. Which substance cools the skin?
   a. Sebum
   b. Melanin
   c. Dandruff
   d. Sweat

6. What are nails and hair made of?
   a. Keratin
   b. Follicles
   c. Skin
   d. Parasites

7. What is the order of the structure of the skin, going from the inner body to the outer body?
   a. Epidermis, dermis, subcutaneous layer
   b. Subcutaneous layer, dermis, epidermis
   c. Dermis, subcutaneous layer, epidermis
   d. Subcutaneous layer, epidermis, dermis

8. Which of the following is a risk from overexposure to UV radiation?
   a. Hepatitis B
   b. Hepatitis C
   c. Skin cancer
   d. HIV

Thinking Critically

After reading the question or statement, write a short answer using complete sentences.

9. **Describe.** Why should you avoid exposure to the sun between 10:00 A.M. and 4:00 P.M.?

10. **Identify.** List some steps you can take to treat acne.

11. **Explain.** How does a balanced diet help you have healthy hair?

12. **Analyze.** What features make a mole on your skin suspicious? What should you do if you have a suspicious mole?

13. **Compare and Contrast.** What are the similarities and differences between moles and warts?

LESSON 2

Vocabulary Review

Use the vocabulary terms listed on page 375 to complete the following statements.

14. The _____ is the area immediately around the teeth.

15. The part of the tooth that contains the blood vessels and nerves of a tooth is called the _____.

16. The combination of bacteria and other particles that adhere to the ouside of a tooth is called _____.

17. When an inflammation of the periodontal structures occur, you have (a)-_____.

Health eSpotlight VIDEO Wrap-Up

A Healthy You Have students reread the Health eSpotlight question at the beginning of the chapter (page 355). **Ask Students:** *Now that you have read the chapter and watched the video, can you think of other ways your attitude toward personal appearance has changed since you were a kid?* Call on volunteers to describe how their responses would change.

Understanding Key Concepts

After reading the question or statement, select the correct answer.

18. What component of plaque works on sugars to create acids that cause cavities?
    a. Viruses
    b. Bacteria
    c. Moles
    d. Boils

19. Which minerals are most important for healthy teeth?
    a. Phosphorus and calcium
    b. Iron and magnesium
    c. Iron and phosphorus
    d. Magnesium and calcium

20. What is malocclusion?
    a. Bad breath
    b. A crust that forms from unremoved plaque
    c. A source of acids on teeth
    d. A misalignment of teeth

21. What part of the tooth is the connective layer between the enamel and the pulp?
    a. Dentin
    b. Root canal
    c. Periodontal ligaments
    d. Gum

Thinking Critically

After reading the question or statement, write a short answer using complete sentences.

22. **Describe.** What are two functions of the teeth?

23. **Identify.** Why is flossing as important as brushing?

24. **Infer.** Why should you brush your tongue when you brush your teeth?

25. **Predict.** If gingivitis is left untreated, it may destroy the bone tissue that supports the tooth. What may happen to the tooth that is supported by the affected bone?

26. **Analyze.** Why might malocclusion lead to tooth decay?

LESSON 3

Vocabulary Review

Choose the correct term in the sentences below.

27. The *cornea / sclera* is the tough white part of the eye.

28. The *retina / cornea* is the inner layer of the eye wall that contains millions of light-sensitive cells.

29. The *auditory ossicle / labyrinth* is a 1 inch long passageway leading from the outer ear to the eardrum.

30. *Tinnitus / Auditory ossicle* is a ringing or other sound heard in the ear in the absence of external sound.

Understanding Key Concepts

After reading the question or statement, select the correct answer.

31. When you blink, tears move across the surface of the eyeball to
    a. moisten and clean the eye.
    b. reduce glare from sunlight.
    c. give the eye time to adjust to images.
    d. prevent eyestrain.

32. In which disease does abnormal pressure build up inside the eye?
    a. Cataracts
    b. Macular degeneration
    c. Strabismus
    d. Glaucoma

Understanding Key Concepts

18. b
19. a
20. d
21. a

Thinking Critically

22. Teeth break down food into pieces that are small enough to be digested. They also help form the shape and structure of the mouth.
23. Flossing removes plaque between teeth where the bristles of a toothbrush cannot reach.
24. To remove bacteria on the tongue, which can cause bad breath
25. The tooth may become loose and fall out.
26. Teeth that are misaligned may be crowded and difficult to clean, allowing plaque to build up. Areas where plaque builds up may develop cavities.

LESSON 3

Vocabulary Review

27. sclera
28. retina
29. external auditory canal
30. Tinnitus

Understanding Key Concepts

31. a
32. a

ExamView®
Assessment Suite

Create and customize tests in minutes with this convenient digital platform.

- Create differentiated tests quickly and easily.
- All questions correlated to National/State Standards.
- Enhance tests with Document Based Questions (DBQ) and add your own photos or graphics.
- Build tests in both English and Spanish.
- Generate progress reports.

To order, go to **glencoe.com** and search for ISBN 0-07-888173-0.

Assessment

Understanding Key Concepts

33. a
34. d
35. d

Thinking Critically

36. You can have your ears examined and your hearing tested if you suspect an infection; cover the ears with a hat in cold weather; wear protective gear when playing sports; keep foreign objects out of the ears; and avoid prolonged loud noise.

37. The eyes are off-center, turned inward or outward.

38. The pupil; it is a hole in the eye formed by the eye tissues around the pupil.

39. Conductive hearing loss; a buildup of wax can block sound waves from entering the middle ear.

---

33. What refines the focus of an image onto the retina?
    a. The lens
    b. The sclera
    c. The cornea
    d. The choroid

34. Which parts of the ear are involved in balance?
    a. Semicircular canals and vestibule
    b. Round window and eustachian tube
    c. Oval window and incus
    d. Temporal bone and cochlea

35. What object is safe to put in your ear?
    a. A cotton-tipped swab
    b. A pair of tweezers
    c. A small brush
    d. None of the above

Thinking Critically

After reading the question or statement, write a short answer using complete sentences.

36. **Identify.** What can you do now to protect your hearing in the future?

37. **Describe.** What is the effect of strabismus on the eyes?

38. **Infer.** Which important structure of the eye has no solid mass? Explain your answer.

39. **Analyze.** Which kind of hearing loss can result from a buildup of earwax? Explain your answer.

Project-Based ASSESSMENT

Tattoos and Piercings— Risky Business?

Background
Tattoos and body piercing have become popular. Both tattoos and piercings, however, can cause serious health problems if unsanitary needles or methos are used.

Task
Create and draw a cartoon that illustrates the health risks of getting tattoos or body piercings.

Audience
Students in your class

Purpose
Point out specific health risks associated with either tattoos or body piercings. In your cartoon, show how these health risks can affect one or more areas of the health triangle: physical, mental/emotional, or social health. Your cartoon should clearly advocate not getting a tattoo or body piercing.

Procedure

1 Decide whether your cartoon will be about body piercing or tattoos. Using the information in Chapter 13, review the health risks of the procedure you selected.

2 Study the cartoon pages of the newspaper to see how cartoonists use both words and pictures to develop a story.

3 Decide on characters and a story line for your cartoon.

4 Draw a rough draft of the cartoon.

5 Review the cartoon. Does it use words and pictures to clearly convey the story and your message?

6 Draw the final version of your cartoon.

7 Distribute copies of your cartoon to your classmates, and discuss the results.

378 Chapter 13 Assessment

Project-Based ASSESSMENT

Step 1 Decide Have students decide whether their cartoon will be about body piercing or tattoos. Make sure some students choose each practice.

Step 2 Create Students should create characters and story lines that will help them convey health risks of the practice they chose.

Step 3 Draw Remind students to make a rough draft of their cartoon before drawing the final version. Arrange for students to make copies of their cartoons to distribute to classmates.

Visit **glencoe.com** for Project-Based Assessment rubrics.

Math Practice

Interpret Graphs. Use the graph below of a UV Index for four weeks in Orlando and Jacksonville, Florida to answer questions 1–3.

Ultraviolet Index

The United States uses a UV Index (UVI) that goes from 1 to 11. The higher the number on the UVI, the more intense the exposure to UV rays will be on that day at noon. The bar graph below shows the average UVI for four different weeks for Orlando and Jacksonville.

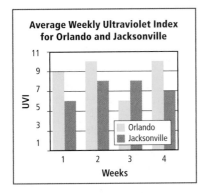

Average Weekly Ultraviolet Index for Orlando and Jacksonville

1. Which of the following statements is a correct interpretation of the bar graph above?
   A. The highest UVI for Jacksonville was 10.
   B. The lowest UVI for Orlando was 5.
   C. The mean UVI for Jacksonville was 7.25.
   D. The median UVI for Orlando was 5.50.

2. Which of these measures of central tendency would make Orlando seem to have as high a UVI as possible for the time span shown?
   A. Mean   C. Range
   B. Median   D. Mode

3. What is the mean UVI for Orlando during these four weeks?
   A. 8.50   C. 7.25
   B. 7.0   D. 7.50

Go Online

For more test practice, visit **glencoe.com** and complete the Online Quizzes for Chapter 13.

Reading/Writing Practice

Understand and Apply. Read the passage below and then answer the questions.

(1) People start exercise programs for many reasons. (2) Some hope to lose weight, while others want to look better. (3) Many people are simply following doctor's orders. (4) But people often find that exercising helps them feel good as well as look good. (5) Here are two simple steps to help you get fit.
(6) Schedule your workout in the same way you schedule any important activity or part of your daily life. (7) Morning works best for most people. (8) Some people however, prefer to exercise later in the afternoon. (9) The important thing is to find the best time and stick to it.

1. Read sentence 6 in the essay. Which revision best supports the organization of the piece?
   A. There are three important things to remember in scheduling a workout.
   B. First, schedule your workout in the same way you schedule any important activity or part of your daily life.
   C. Second, schedule your workout in the same way you schedule any important activity or part of your daily life.
   D. First, it's hard to know where to begin to discuss scheduling workouts.

2. What change in *punctuation* should be made to sentence 8?
   A. Insert a colon after *people*.
   B. Insert a comma after *people*.
   C. Delete the comma after *however*.
   D. Delete the period after *afternoon*.

3. Write a newspaper column that asks and answers three questions from readers of different ages about exercise programs.

National Education Standards
Math: Number and Operations
Language Arts: NCTE 3, NCTE 4

Standardized Test Practice Answers

Math Practice
1. C
2. D
3. C

Reading/Writing Practice
1. B
2. B
3. Answers will vary. Questions might include: How often should I exercise? What exercises increase flexibility?

National Education Standards

Math: Number and Operations

Language Arts: NCTE 3, NCTE 4

For the complete Math and Language Arts standards, visit **glencoe.com**.

Online Study Tools
For more test practice, visit **glencoe.com** and complete the Online Quizzes for Chapter 13.

Test-Taking Tip

Organizing Information for Essays
Suggest that students answer long essay questions by first jotting down a list of topics relevant to the question. This will encourage students to think through their answers. It will also help them remember to include all of the relevant topics after they start writing. Remind students to proofread their answers to essay questions if time allows.

Chapter 14 pages 380–405	Standards		Features
	National	**State/Local**	
	1.12.1, 1.12.5, 1.12.6, 3.12.2, 7.12.1		*Hands-On* **HEALTH** • Good "Housekeeping" (*Accessing Information*), page 400
Lesson 1 The Skeletal System pages 382–386 **BIG Idea** *The skeletal system provides a living structure for the body.*	1.12.1, 1.12.5, 1.12.6, 1.12.8, 4.12.1, 5.12.6, 7.12.1, 8.12.1, 8.12.4		
Lesson 2 The Muscular System pages 387–391 **BIG Idea** *The muscular system enables the limbs and other parts of the body to move.*	1.12.1, 1.12.4, 1.12.5, 4.12.1, 5.12.2, 5.12.6, 7.12.1, 8.12.1		**Health Skills** **Activity** • A Safety Check (*Practicing Healthful Behaviors*), page 391 🕐 Out of Time
Lesson 3 The Nervous System pages 392–399 **BIG Idea** *The nervous system sends messages through the nerves to coordinate all the body's activities.*	1.12.1, 1.12.5, 1.12.6, 3.12.2, 4.12.1, 7.12.1, 7.12.3, 8.12.4		VIDEO **BusinessWeek** **HEALTH NEWS** • Rewiring the Body, page 398

(Lessons each marked 30 Min)

Key to Ability Levels

Teaching Strategies and activities have been coded for ability level and appropriateness.

AL Activities for students working above grade level
OL Activities for students working on grade level
BL Activities for students working below grade level
EL Activities for English Learners

Chapter 14 Planning Guide

Glencoe Exclusive!
TeacherWorks Plus
All-In-One Planner and Resource Center

Resources	Lesson Assessment	Technology
Student Activity Workbook `TEACH` **FAST FILE RESOURCES** Vocabulary Practice `TEACH` Health Labs `EXTEND`	Chapter 14 Review Chapter 14 Assessment Standardized Test Practice ⊙ *ExamView® Assessment Suite* CD-ROM	**Teaching Tools:** ⊙ *TeacherWorks™* Plus DVD ⊙ *StudentWorks™* Plus DVD ⊙ *ExamView® Assessment Suite* CD-ROM ⌨ Transparency ⊙ Fitness DVD ⊙ PowerPoint® DVD ⊙ Health eSpotlight Video Series DVD
FAST FILE RESOURCES Reading Strategies Activity `TEACH` Reteaching Activity `REVIEW` Enrichment Activity `EXTEND` Health Skills Practice `TEACH`	Lesson 1 Assessment, page 386 📁 Lesson 1 Quiz *Fast File* ⊙ *ExamView® Assessment Suite* CD-ROM	**Web-Based Resources:** Go Online glencoe.com • Health Podcast Activities • Audio Chapter Summaries (English/Spanish) • Interactive Health Tutor • Health Skills Activities • Vocabulary PuzzleMaker • Parent Letters (English/Spanish) • Lesson Plans • Health Inventories • Online Quizzes • Study-to-Go • Unit Web Projects • Student Web Activities • Fitness Zone Activities
FAST FILE RESOURCES Reading Strategies Activity `TEACH` Reteaching Activity `REVIEW` Enrichment Activity `EXTEND` Health Skills Practice `TEACH`	Lesson 2 Assessment, page 391 📁 Lesson 2 Quiz *Fast File* ⊙ *ExamView® Assessment Suite* CD-ROM	
FAST FILE RESOURCES Reading Strategies Activity `TEACH` Reteaching Activity `REVIEW` Enrichment Activity `EXTEND` Health Skills Practice `TEACH`	Lesson 3 Assessment, page 399 📁 Lesson 3 Quiz *Fast File* ⊙ *ExamView® Assessment Suite* CD-ROM	

This is the student's backpack solution.

Includes:
• complete Interactive Student Edition
• full audio of English text and Spanish chapter summaries
• allows students to record assignments and track grades.
• links to online activities and additional student resources
• access to all student worksheets and workbooks

Dinah Zike Foldables®
Chapter Activity
Refer to the *Dinah Zike Reading and Study Skills for Glencoe Health.* Have students make a two-tab book Foldable for each of the three lessons in the chapter. In each Foldable, have students record and organize information about the structure and function of one of the body systems discussed.

Key to Symbols

⌨ Transparencies   `REVIEW` activities to review or reinforce content

⊙ CD-ROM   `TEACH` activities to teach basic concepts

 glencoe.com   `EXTEND` activities to extend or enrich lesson content

 Print Resources

CHAPTER **14**

Skeletal, Muscular, and Nervous Systems

Skeletal, Muscular, and Nervous Systems

Chapter Overview

Chapter 14 focuses on the structures and functions of the skeletal system, the muscular system, and the nervous system. Also discussed are how to care for each system and injuries, diseases, and disorders of each system.

Lesson 1

The body's skeletal system, which consists of bones, connective tissue, and joints, provides a framework on which the rest of the body is built.

Lesson 2

The body's muscular system includes both muscles that are under voluntary control and muscles involved in involuntary processes, such as the beating of the heart.

Lesson 3

The body's nervous system is a complex network that allows communication between the brain and the rest of the body.

▶ **Activating Prior Knowledge**

After students have written their paragraphs, call on volunteers to share their thoughts about how stretching and relaxation exercises benefit the skeletal, muscular, and nervous systems.

Lesson 1

The Skeletal System

BIG Idea *The skeletal system provides a living structure for the body.*

Lesson 2

The Muscular System

BIG Idea *The muscular system enables the limbs and other parts of the body to move.*

Lesson 3

The Nervous System

BIG Idea *The nervous system sends messages through the nerves to coordinate all the body's activities.*

Activating Prior Knowledge

Using Visuals As you look at this photo, consider how this teen is improving the health of his skeletal, muscular, and nervous systems. In a short paragraph, describe how physical activity and stretching can benefit your health.

380

Universal Access

Differentiated Learning Glencoe provides teacher support and student materials for all learners in the health classroom.

- Chapter Summaries in English and Spanish are available online at **glencoe.com**.
- *Fast Files* and related worksheets support reluctant readers.

- Universal Access strategies throughout the Teacher Wraparound Edition and *Fast Files* help you present materials for gifted students, at-risk students, physically impaired students, and those with behavior disorders or learning disabilities.

Chapter Launchers

Health in Action

Discuss the **BIG** Ideas

Before beginning this chapter, think about how you would answer these questions:

▸ What exercises strengthen muscles and bones?

▸ How does nutrition affect your muscles and bones?

▸ How can you prevent injuries to the muscular, skeletal, and nervous systems?

Watch the *Health* eSpotlight Video Series

VIDEO

Building a Healthy Body

What steps do you take to keep your skeletal, muscular, and nervous systems healthy?

Assess Your Health

Go Online

Visit **glencoe.com** and complete the Health Inventory for Chapter 14.

Chapter Launchers

Health in Action

Discuss the **BIG** Ideas

Ask students to respond to the questions aloud. Explain that the purpose of the questions is to help them assess their current knowledge of how to maintain and improve the health of their skeletal, muscular, and nervous systems.

Health eSpotlight
Video Series

 *Building a Healthy Body*

Before Viewing the Video

Ask Students: *What are the most important steps a person can take to ensure that the body's bones, muscles, and brain are maintained in good working order?* (Sample answer: Eating a proper diet, exercising regularly, and getting enough sleep)

Go Online

Have students go to **glencoe.com** and take the Health Inventory for Chapter 14.

Chapter Skills

Reading Skills
- Reviewing Facts and Vocabulary, pp. 386, 391, 399
- Reading/Writing Practice, p. 405

BIG Idea

Students will learn about the body's skeletal, muscular, and nervous systems and how to care for them.

Health Skills
- Health Skills Activity, p. 391
- Applying Health Skills, pp. 386, 391, 399

Vocabulary
- New Vocabulary, pp. 382, 387, 392,
- Reviewing Facts and Vocabulary, pp. 386, 391, 399

Writing Skills
- Writing Critically, pp. 386, 391, 399
- Reading/Writing Practice, p. 405

381

The Skeletal System

1 FOCUS

GUIDE TO READING

BIG Idea Students will learn about the structure and function of the skeletal system. **Ask Students:** *What are names of some bones in your body?* (Sample answer: sternum, humerus, femur)

Before You Read

Table Students should list six functions of the skeletal system in the Function column. The list of bones in the Example column may vary, though all major bones of the body should be included.

Main Idea

How the Skeletal System Works The skeletal system consists of bones and connective tissue. **Ask Students:** *What is the evidence that bones are living structures?* (Sample answers: Bone marrow produces blood cells; bones continue to grow until age 25.)

Real Life Issues

Ask volunteers to share their paragraphs with the class. As students mention protective equipment needed for each sport, make lists on the board. Then ask students to explain what injury or injuries each piece of equipment is designed to prevent.

LESSON 1

GUIDE TO READING

BIG Idea *The skeletal system provides a living structure for the body.*

Before You Read

Create a Table. Make a two-column table. Title the first column "Function" and the second column "Example." Write the functions of the skeletal system as listed in the chapter text. As you read, write in the names of specific bones that perform each function.

Function	Example

New Vocabulary

- cartilage (p. 383)
- ossification (p. 383)
- ligament (p. 383)
- tendon (p. 383)
- scoliosis (p. 384)
- osteoporosis (p. 386)

The Skeletal System

Real Life Issues

Speaking on Safety. At his school's health fair, David will give a presentation on the importance of safety gear—including wrist, elbow, and knee pads—when in-line skating or skateboarding. These activities are popular in his neighborhood, but many teens don't wear as much protective equipment as they should.

Writing *Write a paragraph listing the protective equipment needed for in-line skating and skateboarding, and the benefits of using this equipment.*

How the Skeletal System Works

Main Idea The skeletal system consists of bones and connective tissue.

Your skeletal system consists of 206 bones and the attached connective tissues. The bones of the skeleton range in size from the tiniest bone of the inner ear (about 0.25 cm long) to the longest bone of your thigh. The connective tissues cushion the bones, attach bone to bone, and attach bones to muscles.

Your skeletal system has many functions, including

- providing support for the body.
- protecting internal tissues and organs from damage.
- acting as a framework for attached muscles.
- allowing movement of limbs and digits.
- producing new red and white blood cells.
- storing fat and minerals, such as calcium and phosphorus.

Teens Want to Know

Are There Any Differences Between a Male and a Female Skeleton? In general, the male skeleton is somewhat larger than the female skeleton. Also, female pelvic bones are lighter and thinner than male pelvic bones, and the female pelvis is wider than the male pelvis. In other words, women's hips are wider than men's hips. Because women give birth to children, they need wider hips to provide room for the birth canal. This difference in pelvic width develops in puberty, and the wider hips of women are considered a secondary sex characteristic.

Bones

R Bones are made up of living tissues formed into different layers. The outer layer is hard, densely packed, compact bone. Beneath that is spongy bone, a less dense bone with a network of cavities filled with red bone marrow, where blood cells are produced. Some bones also contain yellow bone marrow, a type of connective tissue that stores fat. **Figure 14.1** shows the basic structure of a bone.

Bones are categorized by their shape, as shown in **Figure 14.2**. Shapes include long bones, short bones, flat bones, and irregular bones.

Connective Tissue

There are three types of connective tissue: cartilage, ligaments, and tendons. **Cartilage** is *a strong, flexible connective tissue* that can act as a cushion between two bones to reduce friction. It can also act as a flexible structure for soft parts of the body, such as the tip of the nose or the outer ear. All bones begin in the embryo as cartilage. Early in development, the cartilage hardens. This **ossification** (ah-sih-fih-KAY-shun) is *the process by which bone is formed, renewed, and repaired.*

C Connective tissue can also hold parts of the body together. A **ligament** is *a band of fibrous, slightly elastic connective tissue that attaches one bone to another.* Ligaments attach to bones to create joints. For example, a ligament attaches the two bones of the forearm to each other, forming the pivot joint. A **tendon** is *a fibrous cord that attaches muscle to the bone.* Muscles contract to move parts of the body.

Joints

Joints, such as those shown in **Figure 14.3** on page 384, are points at which bones meet. Some joints, such as the ones between the bones of the skull, do not move. Flexible joints include ball-and-socket joints, hinge joints, pivot joints, and ellipsoidal joints.

Caring for the Skeletal System

Main Idea A healthy diet, exercise, protective gear, and regular checkups are ways to care for your skeletal system.

As you can see in **Figure 14.4** on page 385, your skeletal system supports your entire body. Your overall health depends on the health of your skeletal system. Eat a healthy diet, get regular physical activity, and have regular checkups to keep your skeletal system healthy. Foods high in calcium, vitamin D, and phosphorus help prevent skeletal disorders.

Figure 14.1

Bone Structure

Bone tissue is surrounded by calcium phosphate and other minerals. *Why is calcium important for bone health?*

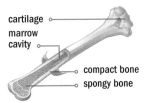

cartilage
marrow cavity
compact bone
spongy bone

Figure 14.2

Bone Shapes

A bone's shape is related to its function. *What are the functions of these bones?*

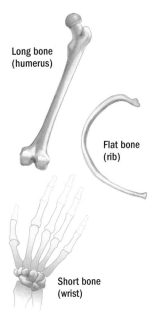

Long bone (humerus)

Flat bone (rib)

Short bone (wrist)

LESSON 1

2 TEACH

R Reading Strategy

Analyzing a Graphic Direct students' attention to the structure of bones in **Figure 14.1**. Then call on students to read aloud each of the functions of the skeletal system listed on the first page of the lesson. For each function, discuss which part of a bone is important in carrying out that function. BL

Caption Answer

Figure 14.1 Calcium-containing minerals make up the nonliving structure of bone tissues.

C Critical Thinking

Comparing and Contrasting On the board, write *ligaments* and *tendons*. Call on volunteers to read aloud the definition of each term. If possible, show students photos of each. Ask students how the two structures are similar and different. (Both are connective tissues that attach to bone. Ligaments connect bones to bones; tendons connect muscles to bones.) OL EL

Caption Answer

Figure 14.2 The humerus provides a framework for the muscles of the upper arm. The wrist bone allows movement of the wrist. The ribs protect internal tissue and organs from damage. The vertebrae provide support for the upper body.

English Language Coach

Extend Vocabulary Explain to students that the term *ossification* is the noun form of the verb *ossify*, which means "to change into bone." These words derive from the Latin root word *os*, which means "bone." Other scientific terms are also formed with the root *os*. *Osteoporosis* is a disease in which bones become weak and brittle. An *osteopath* is a doctor who practices *osteopathy*, a medical therapy that emphasizes bone manipulation. Ask interested students to find out more about osteopathy and osteopaths practicing in the community.

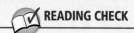
READING CHECK

Answer Sports such as football and hockey that involve falling or hitting, which could lead to bone fractures.

AL Active Learning

Connecting to the Real World
Invite an orthopedic technician to visit the class to make a brief presentation about different kinds of fractures and the casts applied to stabilize them. Ask the technician to bring casting materials for students to see. Instruct students to be prepared to ask relevant questions. **OL**

U Universal Access

Note Taking Have students make a notebook of the different injuries to joints. For each injury, have students write a definition in their own words. Require beginning English learners to learn the words *injury* and *joint*. **BL**

Main Idea

Understanding Skeletal Problems Disorders and injuries can be caused by improper care of the skeletal system. **Ask Students:** *What is a common injury to the skeletal system, and what is done to treat the injury?* (Sample answer: A bone fracture; a cast is used to stabilize the bone while it heals.)

Caption Answer

Figure 14.3 The hip joint is a ball-and-socket joint, which allows movement in all directions. The knee joint is a hinge joint, which allows a joint to bend and straighten.

384

READING CHECK

Extend What kind of sports might require protective gear to protect your skeletal system?

Figure 14.3

Joints

The structure of a joint relates to the type of motion it can produce. *What kind of motion do these joints produce?*

Hip (ball-and-socket joint)

Knee (hinge joint)

During regular checkups, your doctor can screen you for skeletal disorders such as **scoliosis**, *a lateral or side-to-side curvature of the spine.* Weight-bearing exercise such as walking or weight training helps bones stay strong. Wearing protective gear during sports reduces the risk of bone fractures.

Understanding Skeletal Problems

> **Main Idea** Injuries and disorders harm the skeletal system.

Poor nutrition, infections, sports injuries, and poor posture can lead to problems of the skeletal system. Degenerative disorders such as osteoporosis can also cause problems.

Fractures A fracture is any type of break in a bone. In some fractures, called compound fractures, the broken end of the bone breaks through the skin. In a simple fracture, the broken bone does not break through the skin. Fractures are also classified by the pattern of the break:

- **Hairline fractures:** if parts of the bone do not separate.
- **Transverse fractures:** when the fracture is completely across the bone.
- **Comminuted fractures:** pictured in **Figure 14.5** on page 386, when the bone shatters into more than two pieces.

AL

Injuries to Joints Injuries to joints can occur from overuse, strain, or disease. The following are typical joint injuries:

- **Dislocation** results when a bone slips out of place, tearing the ligaments that attach the bone at the joint. A doctor may reset a joint and immobilize it until ligaments heal.
- **Torn cartilage** can result from a sharp blow to a joint or a severe twisting of a joint. Arthroscopic surgery can remove pieces of the damaged cartilage.
- **Bursitis** results from the painful inflammation of bursa, a fluid-filled sac that helps reduce friction in joints.
- **Bunions** are painful swellings of the bursae in the first joints of big toes. Wearing ill-fitting shoes can make bunions worse. Large bunions may require surgery.
- **Arthritis** is the inflammation of a joint, resulting from an injury, natural wear and tear, or autoimmune disease.

U

Repetitive Motion Injury Prolonged, repeated movements such as sewing or computer work can damage tissues. *Carpal tunnel syndrome* occurs when ligaments and tendons in the wrist swell, causing numbness, a tingling sensation in the thumb and forefinger, pain, and weakness in the hand.

◆▶ Promoting School Wellness

Calcium-Rich Foods in the Cafeteria
A successful school health program includes offering appealing meals that accommodate the nutrition needs of students, including meeting the federal dietary guidelines for calcium. The recommendation for teens is 1,300 mg of calcium daily—the equivalent of about four cups of milk. Teens who don't drink milk must consume other calcium-rich foods, such as yogurt, broccoli, or calcium-fortified juices. Ask interested students to talk to the school's nutritionist about calcium-rich foods offered at school and then prepare a list of these foods for the class.

Figure 14.4 The Skeletal System

Your bones continue to grow, both in length and in thickness, until approximately age 25. At this age, bones usually stop growing, but may continue to thicken. *What is the process by which bones are formed?*

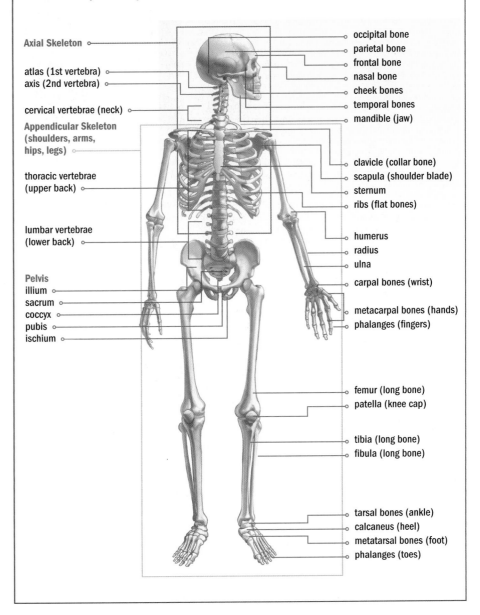

Axial Skeleton

atlas (1st vertebra)
axis (2nd vertebra)

cervical vertebrae (neck)

Appendicular Skeleton
(shoulders, arms,
hips, legs)

thoracic vertebrae
(upper back)

lumbar vertebrae
(lower back)

Pelvis
illium
sacrum
coccyx
pubis
ischium

occipital bone
parietal bone
frontal bone
nasal bone
cheek bones
temporal bones
mandible (jaw)

clavicle (collar bone)
scapula (shoulder blade)
sternum
ribs (flat bones)

humerus
radius
ulna
carpal bones (wrist)

metacarpal bones (hands)
phalanges (fingers)

femur (long bone)
patella (knee cap)

tibia (long bone)
fibula (long bone)

tarsal bones (ankle)
calcaneus (heel)
metatarsal bones (foot)
phalanges (toes)

HS Health Skills Practice

Practicing Healthful Behaviors Ask interested students to create a pamphlet explaining the bones in the leg and foot. The pamphlet should also teach people how to prevent osteoporosis. The pamphlet should include recommendations for foods that are high in calcium, vitamin D, and phosphorus as well as a list of weight-bearing physical activities. **AL**

Writing Strategy

Writing About Skeletal Care After students have read about caring for the skeletal system and the problems that can result from improper care, ask them to write a paragraph setting goals for how they will take better care of their bones. These goals might focus on eating a healthy diet that includes calcium-rich foods, participating in regular physical activity that includes weight-bearing exercises, and wearing protective gear when playing sports. Tell students they may keep their paragraphs private.

Caption Answer

Figure 14.5 Sample answer: Bones need nutrients to grow and strengthen. Poor nutrition can lead to weaker bones that are more likely to break.

❸ ASSESS/ CLOSE

Assessment Resources

 FAST FILE ACTIVITIES
Lesson 1 Quiz

 ExamView
Assessment Suite CD-ROM

Visit glencoe.com for:
Online Quizzes
Online Learning Center

Progress Monitoring

Reteaching
Direct students' attention to the labeled skeletal system in **Figure 14.4**. Then, call on students at random to name various bones.

Enrichment
Ask students to use online resources to investigate how simple fractures and compound fractures are treated, including whether surgery is required, what kind of cast is used to stabilize the fractures, and how long fractures take to heal. Have students report their findings to the class.

G⊙ Online

Have students visit **glencoe.com** and complete the Interactive Study Guide for this lesson.

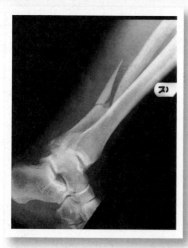

■ **Figure 14.5** Good nutrition and taking safety precautions can help avoid breaks, like the comminuted fracture shown here. *How might poor nutrition lead to a bone fracture?*

Osteoporosis is *a condition in which there is a progressive loss of bone tissue.* Bones weaken and become brittle. This disease affects millions of older Americans. Bone tissue loss is a natural part of aging, but healthful behaviors during your teen years can reduce your risk of developing osteoporosis later in life. A bone scan (in which X-rays measure bone density) can detect signs of osteoporosis. Eating foods containing calcium, vitamin D, and phosphorus will help bones remain strong and healthy. Regular weight-bearing physical activity, such as walking and weight training, stimulates bone cells to increase bone mass.

G⊙ Online

Go to **glencoe.com** and complete the Student Web Activity on the function and composition of the human skeleton.

LESSON **1** 📖 ASSESSMENT

After You Read

Reviewing Facts and Vocabulary

1. How does the skeletal system affect other body systems?
2. How do bones form?
3. How can you help avoid injury to your bones and joints?

Thinking Critically

4. **Analyze.** Some people are allergic to lactose, which is found in milk and many other dairy products. How can lactose-sensitive people get enough calcium for maintaining a healthy skeletal system?
5. **Evaluate.** How might behaviors that you practice as a teen affect your skeletal system later in life?

Applying Health Skills

6. **Accessing Information.** Conduct research to learn more about injury prevention related to activities that teens enjoy. Prepare a pamphlet or poster showing teens how they can avoid injuries.

Writing Critically

7. **Descriptive.** Write a paragraph describing three or more ways in which you have made healthy choices to protect your skeletal system this week.

G⊙ Online

Visit **glencoe.com** and complete the Interactive Study Guide for this lesson.

386 **Chapter 14** Skeletal, Muscular, and Nervous Systems

LESSON **1** ASSESSMENT ANSWERS

1. Students should list the six functions described in the lesson.
2. All bones begin in the embryo as cartilage. Early in development, the cartilage hardens into bone through ossification.
3. Eating a healthy diet, getting regular exercise, wearing protective gear during physical activity, and getting regular checkups
4. Sample answer: They can add other calcium-rich foods, such as yogurt, broccoli, or calcium-fortified juices, to their diet.
5. Answers may vary but should include eating a healthy diet and doing weight-bearing activities regularly.
6. Pamphlets will vary but should include accurate information about the skeletal system, with citation of reliable sources.
7. Paragraphs will vary.

The Muscular System

What Muscles Do

Main Idea The muscular system allows for voluntary and involuntary movements.

Like rubber bands, muscles are elastic; they stretch to allow a wide range of motion. This elasticity allows muscles to move the bones or organs to which they are attached. In this way, your muscular system allows you to move.

You might think that muscles work only when you do things such as pick up an object, catch a ball, or walk across a room. Some muscles in your body, however, are always at work. Even when you are sleeping, muscles help you breathe, make your heart beat, and move food through your digestive system. These involuntary processes occur without your knowing it. At other times, such as when you play the piano, make a dash toward first base, or shoot a basketball, you are using muscles that are under conscious, or voluntary, control. You are aware that you are controlling them. Without the use of both voluntary and involuntary muscles, you would not be able to perform these functions.

BIG Idea *The muscular system enables the limbs and other parts of the body to move.*

Before You Read

Create a K-W-L Chart. Make a three-column chart. In the first column, list what you **k**now about the muscular system. In the second column, list what you **w**ant to know about this topic. As you read, use the third column to summarize what you **l**earned about the topic.

K	W	L

New Vocabulary

▸ smooth muscles (p. 388)
▸ skeletal muscles (p. 388)
▸ flexor (p. 388)
▸ extensor (p. 388)
▸ cardiac muscle (p. 388)
▸ tendinitis (p. 389)
▸ hernia (p. 390)

The Muscular System

① FOCUS

GUIDE TO READING

BIG Idea Students will learn about how the muscular system produces voluntary and involuntary movements, about caring for the muscular system, and about problems of the muscular system. **Ask Students:** *What are the names of some prominent muscles of the body?* (Sample answer: biceps, triceps, hamstrings, abdominal muscles)

Before You Read

K-W-L Chart Students' K-W-L charts will vary, but should include an accurate summary of the lesson content in the third column.

Main Idea

What Muscles Do Both voluntary and involuntary movements are carried out by the muscular system. **Ask Students:** *Which muscles function without a person thinking about them?* (Sample answer: Heart, or cardiac muscle; muscles of the digestive system)

Real Life Issues

Ask volunteers to share their paragraphs with the class. Benefits of the fitness plan may include improving cardiorespiratory endurance and developing a closer friendship between Misaki and Cara.

Cooperative Learning

Mural of Bones and Muscles Divide the class into groups, assigning each group an area of the body, including the head, chest and abdomen, back, arms, and legs. Ask each group to make a labeled illustration on poster board combining the bones and muscles of their assigned body area.

For example, the illustration for arms should include both the bones and the muscles of an arm, including the wrist and hand. Groups may use **Figure 14.4** and **Figure 14.8** for reference. Display all posters together on a classroom wall.

② TEACH

Main Idea

How Muscles Work Muscles are made up of long, fibrous cells that contract and relax. **Ask Students:** *What causes a muscle to shorten or stretch?* (Sample answer: Nerve impulses, or signals from the nervous system)

AL Active Learning

Modeling Movements Divide the class into small groups, and have each group identify the flexor and extensor in a movement from a common physical activity, such as kicking a soccer ball, throwing a football, or bouncing a basketball. Have groups draw the movement, labeled with arrows and the names of muscles, and explain their drawings to the class. **OL**

Caption Answer

Figure 14.6 The muscle in the upper thigh—the flexor— is the hamstring.

 READING CHECK

Answer Skeletal muscles are voluntary striated muscles, while cardiac muscle is involuntary striated muscle.

Figure 14.6

Muscle Movement

Skeletal muscles work in pairs to produce movement. *Which muscle in your upper thigh is the flexor?*

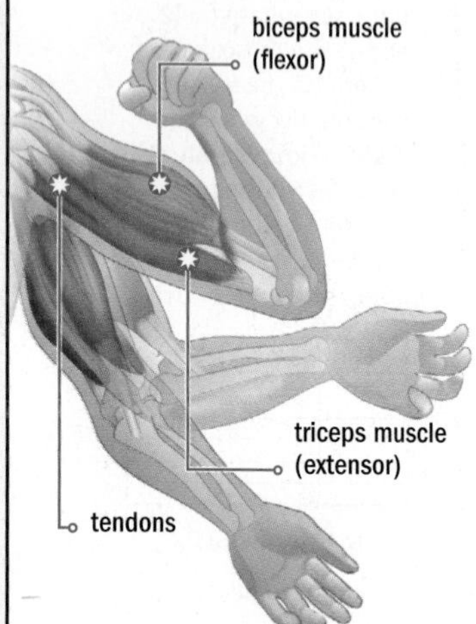

Muscle Movement

- biceps muscle (flexor)
- triceps muscle (extensor)
- tendons

READING CHECK

Explain What are the two types of striated muscle, and how do they differ?

How Muscles Work

Main Idea Muscles consist of long, fibrous cells that can shorten and stretch to make muscles move.

A muscle is made up of hundreds of long cells called muscle fibers. Major muscles in the body are made up of hundreds of bundles of these fibers. When these bundles are stimulated by nerve impulses, or signals, they contract, or shorten. When they relax, the bundles extend, or stretch. Some nerves stimulate many muscle fibers, especially large muscles such as your calf muscle or your biceps. In other areas, such as your eyes, a single nerve may provide impulses to only two or three muscle fibers.

Types of Muscles

The body contains three types of muscle tissue: smooth muscle, skeletal muscle, and cardiac muscle.

- **Smooth muscles** are *muscles that act on the lining of the body's passageways and hollow internal organs.* These muscles can be found in the digestive tract, the urinary bladder, the lining of the blood vessels, and the passageways that lead into the lungs. Smooth muscles are involuntary muscles.

- **Skeletal muscles** are *muscles attached to bone that cause body movements.* Skeletal muscle tissue has a *striated,* or striped, appearance under a microscope. Most of your muscle tissue is skeletal, and almost all skeletal muscles are under voluntary control. Skeletal muscles often work together and perform opposite actions to produce a movement. One muscle contracts while the other muscle relaxes. An example of this can be seen in **Figure 14.6**, which shows the biceps and triceps muscles of the upper arm. To bend and straighten your arm at the elbow, these muscles have opposite jobs. The **flexor** is *the muscle that closes a joint.* In this example, the biceps is the flexor. The **extensor** is *the muscle that opens a joint.* In this case, the triceps is the extensor. When the biceps contracts, the triceps extends and the joint closes. When the biceps extends, the triceps contracts and the joint opens. Identify other opposing skeletal muscles that appear in The Skeletal Muscles illustration, **Figure 14.8** on page 390. **AL**

- **Cardiac muscle** is *a type of striated muscle that forms the wall of the heart.* Cardiac muscle is involuntary and is responsible for the contraction of your heart. The heart contracts rhythmically about 100,000 times each day to pump blood throughout your body.

More About...

Skeletal Muscles Skeletal muscles are composed of long cells called fibers. When skeletal muscles are exercised forcefully, such as by lifting weights, the muscle fibers become enlarged and increase in diameter. Weight lifting produces no new muscle fibers, though. Just as muscles can be enlarged through exercise, they atrophy, or decrease in size, if they aren't used. For example, if a cast is put on a broken arm, the muscles in the arm rapidly decrease in size. Once the cast is removed, the muscles can again increase in size through exercise.

Caring for Your Muscles

Main Idea Eating a healthy diet and getting regular exercise will help you care for your muscular system.

AL
Physical activity will keep your muscles strong and healthy. Muscles that remain unused for long periods of time will atrophy, or decrease in size and strength. Muscle tone is the natural tension in the fibers of a muscle. The following tips can help you care for your muscular system and maintain muscle tone:

- Get regular exercise.
- Eat high protein foods to build muscle.
- Practice good posture to strengthen back muscles.
- Use proper equipment and wear appropriate clothing to protect muscles during any physical activity.
- Warm up properly and stretch before exercising, and cool down after exercising to prevent injury.

Understanding Muscular Problems

Main Idea Caring for the muscular system can help prevent health problems and injuries.

Your muscles might be sore after strenuous activity, such as an all-day hike or bike ride. Although it can be painful, muscle soreness is usually temporary. However, other problems of the muscular system can be more serious. The recovery time varies according to the type and severity of the injury or disease.

- **Bruises** are areas of discolored skin that appear after an injury, usually a blow to the body. The injury causes the blood vessels beneath the skin to rupture and leak, resulting in a bruise. Large bruises can be treated with an ice pack to reduce initial swelling.

- **Muscle strains or sprains** result when muscles are stretched or partially torn from overexertion. Apply ice to strains to reduce swelling, and rest the affected area.

- **Tendinitis**, or *the inflammation of a tendon,* can be the consequence of injury, overuse, or natural aging. Treatment includes ultrasound or anti-inflammatory medication to reduce pain and swelling.

 READING CHECK

Identify What types of foods are good for the muscular system, and why?

■ **Figure 14.7** Prepare your muscles by stretching before beginning a workout. *What injuries can be prevented by warming up before working out?*

Lesson 2   The Muscular System   **389**

CHAPTER 14

LESSON 2

Main Idea

Caring for Your Muscles Caring for the muscular system includes eating a proper diet and getting regular exercise. **Ask Students:** *What can a person do to keep the muscular system healthy?* (Sample answer: Lift weights, eat a diet sufficient in protein)

AL **Active Learning**

Game Show Have each student write one question about caring for muscles. Have students identify the category to which their question belongs. Use the questions to play a game of *Jeopardy!* You might divide the class into several groups that compete against each other. **OL**

 READING CHECK

Answer Foods that are high in protein help build muscles.

Main Idea

Understanding Muscular Problems Improper care of the muscular system can result in problems. **Ask Students:** *Name a common injury to the muscular system.* (Sample answer: A muscle strain)

Caption Answer

Figure 14.7 Muscle strains can occur if the muscles are not properly warmed up.

Academic Integration

Science In physical science, machines that have only one movement are classified as simple machines. One type of simple machine is the lever. Each lever has an input force, an output force, and a fulcrum. There are three classes of levers, depending on the location of the fulcrum relative to the input and output forces. All three are found in the human body. Ask interested students to investigate the levers in the human body and make diagrams showing the input force, output force, and fulcrum of each class of lever.

Practicing Healthful Behaviors: A Safety Check

NHES Standard 7 Students will demonstrate the ability to practice health-enhancing behaviors and avoid or reduce health risks.

Teaching Objectives

- Examine the effects of health behaviors on the muscular system.
- Develop injury prevention strategies.

Teaching Strategies

- Review with students the body's major muscle groups, using **Figure 14.8**.
- Evaluate the accuracy of each guide and suggest revisions before giving a go-ahead to print copies.

Assessment

Using this list, student work should provide comprehensive evidence of the following criteria to achieve the highest score:

√ Includes three to five general tips for safe weight lifting or resistance training
√ Identifies and describes at least one weight-bearing exercise for every major muscle group
√ Lists appropriate clothing along with when and where to work out, safe exercise procedures, and how to use equipment properly
√ Uses textbook and other reliable sources of information
√ Produces an attractive and useful guide

390

- A **hernia** occurs when *an organ or tissue protrudes through an area of weak muscle.* Hernias commonly occur in the abdomen from straining to lift a heavy object. Surgery is usually recommended, and may be required, to repair hernias.
- **Muscular dystrophy** is an inherited disorder in which skeletal muscle fibers are progressively destroyed. There is no cure, but with early detection, muscle weakness can be delayed through exercise programs.

READING CHECK

Compare and Contrast How does muscular dystrophy differ from the other muscular problems listed?

Figure 14.8   The Skeletal Muscles

The major muscle groups include the arms, legs, back, abdomen, shoulders, and chest. What functions do the facial muscles have?

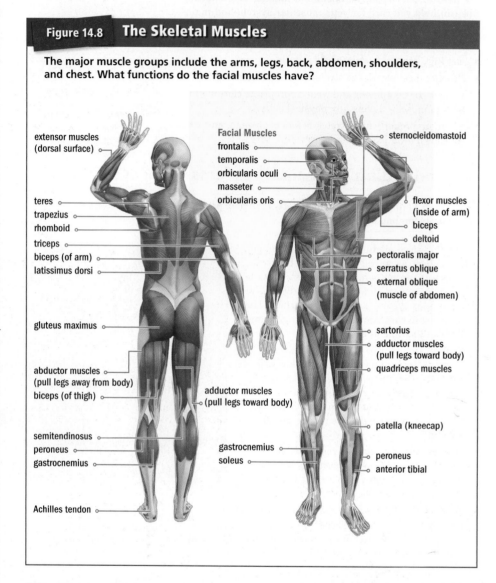

Home and Community

Sports Medicine Centers Many communities have sports medicine centers, clinics that specialize in treating injuries of the skeletal and muscular systems. A sports medicine center may also sponsor educational programs for the public. Ask interested students to use a telephone book or an online search engine to find out whether their community has a sports medicine center. Have students visit the center to find out what the facility provides in the way of treatment and education. Ask students to share their findings with the class.

Health Skills Activity

Practicing Healthful Behaviors

A Safety Check

One day after gym class, Quentin brought up the idea of weight training to his friend Tony.

"I read an article that said strength training builds muscle and helps burn fat," Quentin said.

"Well, I'm all for that," Tony replied. "I think we need to talk to a pro, though. You can get hurt if you lift weights the wrong way."

Quentin's father belongs to a fitness center close to the school. He arranges an appointment for the boys to talk to a professional strength coach. The strength coach shows them both how to use the equipment safely and effectively. As each piece of equipment is explained, Quentin and Tony decide to make a checklist to help them keep track of all the safety tips for each exercise.

Writing Write a checklist of safety tips for weight training:

1. Use a separate page for each exercise. Begin with general safety tips.
2. Include one weight-bearing exercise for every major muscle group.
3. Describe correct techniques, when and where to work out, and how to use equipment properly.
4. Make copies, stapling the pages together, to make a guide for the school gymnasium.

LESSON 2 ASSESSMENT

After You Read

Reviewing Facts and Vocabulary

1. What are the functions of the muscular system?
2. Where is smooth muscle found?
3. What is a *hernia*? How can you get one?

Thinking Critically

4. **Apply.** What muscles are important for playing baseball? How can you protect these muscles from injury?
5. **Analyze.** How can you prevent muscle strains when you are participating in a new physical activity?

Applying Health Skills

6. **Decision Making.** Danielle strained her arm muscle. Her coach says it should heal by the gymnastics meet next week. Danielle wants to go kayaking this weekend. Describe Danielle's decision-making steps.

Writing Critically

7. **Narrative.** Write a story from the point of view of a muscle. Have the muscle describe itself, what it does in the body, how it works and the care it requires.

Go Online

Visit **glencoe.com** and complete the Interactive Study Guide for this lesson.

Lesson 2 The Muscular System **391**

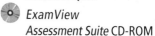 **ASSESS/ CLOSE**

Assessment Resources

📁 *FAST FILE* **ACTIVITIES**
Lesson 2 Quiz

💿 *ExamView Assessment Suite* CD-ROM

Visit glencoe.com for:
Online Quizzes
Online Learning Center

Progress Monitoring

Reteaching
Ask students to write a paragraph that identifies the three types of muscle tissue and gives an example of each type.

Enrichment
In Chapter 12, students learned about muscle cramps, the sudden and often painful contractions of muscles. Ask students to research why muscle cramps occur, how to prevent cramping, and what to do if a muscle cramps during physical activity.

Go Online

Have students visit **glencoe.com** and complete the Interactive Study Guide for this lesson.

LESSON 2 ASSESSMENT ANSWERS

1. The muscular system allows for voluntary and involuntary movements.
2. Smooth muscle is found in the lining of the body's passageways and hollow internal organs, such as in the digestive tract, the urinary bladder, the lining of the blood vessels, and passageways into the lungs.
3. A *hernia* is when an organ or tissue protrudes through an area of weak muscle. A hernia in the abdomen can be caused by straining to lift a heavy object.
4. Sample answer: Biceps and quadriceps. Proper diet and regular exercise can help protect those muscles.
5. Warm up properly.
6. Answers will vary but should incorporate the six step decision-making process.
7. Stories will vary.

The Nervous System

① FOCUS

GUIDE TO READING

BIG Idea Students will learn about how the nervous system coordinates all the body's activities, about caring for the nervous system, and about diseases and disorders of the nervous system. **Ask Students:** *What are the main parts of the nervous system?* (Sample answer: The brain, the spinal cord, and the nerves throughout the body)

Before You Read

Outline Student outlines may vary in the details, though the structure of each outline should match the headings and subheadings of the lesson.

Main Idea

How the Nervous System Works The nervous system coordinates all of the activities of the body. **Ask Students:** *What is the main function of the nervous system?* (Sample answer: Allowing communication between the brain and all other areas of the body)

Real Life Issues

Have volunteers share their journal entries with the class. A typical description of using touch to avoid danger might be feeling how hot the water is before getting into a shower.

LESSON 3

GUIDE TO READING

BIG Idea *The nervous system sends messages through the nerves to coordinate all the body's activities.*

Before You Read

Create an Outline. Preview this lesson by scanning the pages. Organize the headings and subheadings into an outline. As you read, fill in the outline with important details.

```
I.
  A.
    1.
    2.
  B.
II.
```

New Vocabulary

▸ neurons (p. 393)
▸ cerebrum (p. 394)
▸ cerebellum (p. 395)
▸ brain stem (p. 396)
▸ epilepsy (p. 399)
▸ cerebral palsy (p. 399)

The Nervous System

Real Life Issues ....

Feeling the Heat. It's Petra's turn to clean the stovetop. She remembers that her sister just heated up some milk to make hot chocolate. The electric burner does not appear to be hot. Still, Petra knows that a burner can still be warm enough to burn. She carefully holds her hand 2 inches over the burner to feel for heat. It feels cool enough, so she safely wipes down the stove.

Writing *Write a brief journal entry describing the ways you use your sense of touch. How does your sense of touch help you avoid danger?*

How the Nervous System Works

Main Idea The nervous system coordinates all of the activities in the body.

Your nervous system is a complex network that allows communication between the brain and parts of the body. It stores information and coordinates all activities, from breathing or digesting food to sensing pain and feeling fear. The brain, spinal cord, and nerves work together, transmitting messages between organs, tissues, and cells.

The nervous system has two main divisions. The *central nervous system* (CNS) consists of the brain and spinal cord. The *peripheral nervous system* (PNS) gathers information from inside and outside your body. It includes nerves that extend from the brain, spinal cord, and sensory receptors, such as those in the skin that sense pressure, temperature, or pain. The CNS receives messages from the nerves in the PNS, interprets them, and sends out a response.

U

Health Literacy

Medicine and the Nervous System
The branch of medicine that focuses on the study of the nervous system is called neurology. A neurologist is a medical doctor who diagnoses and treats patients with diseases and disorders of the brain, spinal cord, and nerves. Pediatric neurologists specialize in nervous system diseases and disorders in children. A neurosurgeon specializes in surgery related to neurological diseases. Pediatric neurosurgeons specialize in surgery of children with neurological problems, such as head deformities, spine deformities, brain or spine injuries, and birth injuries related to the nervous system.

Understanding Neurons

Main Idea Neurons transmit messages from the brain and spinal cord to the rest of the body.

Neurons, or *nerve cells*, transmit messages to and from the spinal cord and brain. The three types of neurons—sensory neurons, motor neurons, and interneurons—are classified by function. Sensory neurons carry messages from receptors in the body to the CNS. Motor neurons carry messages from the CNS back to muscles or glands in response to an impulse. Interneurons communicate with and connect other neurons. **Figure 14.9** illustrates the nerve impulse. A neuron consists of three main parts:

- The **cell body** of a neuron contains the nucleus, which regulates the production of proteins within the cell. Unlike other cells in the body, neurons have limited ability to repair damage or replace destroyed cells.

- **Dendrites** are branched structures that extend from the cell body in most neurons. Dendrites receive information and transmit impulses toward the cell body.

- **Axons** transmit impulses away from the cell body and toward another neuron, muscle cell, or gland.

READING CHECK

Explain How is the cell body important to a nerve cell?

R

| Figure 14.9 | **The Nerve Impulse** |

A nerve impulse begins when a sensory receptor is stimulated. The impulse travels to the CNS and is interpreted with the help of an interneuron. Then an impulse is sent to a muscle cell or gland in response to the stimulus.

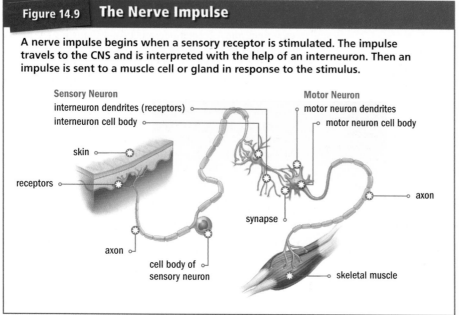

Sensory Neuron
interneuron dendrites (receptors)
interneuron cell body
skin
receptors
axon
cell body of sensory neuron

Motor Neuron
motor neuron dendrites
motor neuron cell body
axon
synapse
skeletal muscle

② TEACH

Main Idea

Understanding Neurons Neurons transmit messages from the brain and spinal cord to the rest of the body. **Ask Students:** *What is the function of a nerve cell?* (Sample answer: A nerve cell transmits messages, or signals, through the nervous system.)

U Universal Access

Peripheral To help students understand the major division in the structure of the nervous system, explain that *peripheral* comes from a Greek word meaning "to carry around." *Perimeter*, meaning "the outer limits of an area," is another common word from the same root. The peripheral nervous system is the part of the nervous system outside the central nervous system. **EL** **BL**

R Reading Strategy

Analyzing a Graphic Have students examine the Nerve Impulse graphic, **Figure 14.9**. **Ask Students:** *What are two components of motor neurons?* (motor neuron dentrites and motor neuron cell body) *What happens when a sensory receptor is stimulated?* (a nerve impulse begins) **OL**

READING CHECK

Answer The cell body contains the nucleus, which regulates the production of proteins in the cell.

ELL Support

Name and Repeat Write the following words on the board: *nerve, neuron, nervous.* Define each word aloud.

Beginning Use sentences such as "The central nervous system consists of the brain and spinal cord." Ask students to repeat the sentence. Use the other two words in a sentence, again asking students to repeat.

Intermediate Ask students for sentence examples for each word.

Advanced Have students use a dictionary to investigate meanings of *nerve* and *nervous* as used in common speech. Ask students to write sentence examples of each word using these nonscientific meanings.

393

Main Idea

Central Nervous System The two organs that make up the central nervous system are the brain and the spinal cord. **Ask Students:** *Where does the spinal cord connect to the brain?* (Sample answer: At the base, or bottom, of the brain)

C Critical Thinking

Making Inferences Discuss with students that the brain can be without oxygen for only four to five minutes before serious damage occurs. Reminding them that blood carries oxygen from the lungs to the brain, have students infer why, in emergency situations, moving air into and out of the lungs and keeping the heart beating are so important. (The supply of oxygen to the brain must be continued for a person to survive.) **OL**

FITNESSZONE

Use a balled up piece of paper in place of a ball for this activity:

- Have students get into groups of two. Each pair should face each other.

- Each pair should have a balled up piece of paper.

- First person performs an exercise while the other mirrors.

- Have students alternate and switch.

- For example weave a Figure 8 between the legs, or circle the ball around the waist.

The Central Nervous System

Main Idea The central nervous system is made up of the brain and spinal cord.

The two organs that make up the CNS—the brain and spinal cord—send and receive impulses to and from nerves in the body. **Figure 14.10** shows how nerves extend to various parts of the body.

The spinal cord is a long column of nerve tissue about the thickness of your index finger. The tissue of the spinal cord is surrounded by several **layers** of connective tissue called the spinal meninges. The meninges, along with the vertebrae—the bones of the spine—help protect the spinal cord. The spinal cord is also bathed in cerebrospinal fluid that absorbs shock and nourishes the nerve tissue.

An adult human brain weighs up to 3 pounds and rests in the protective cavity formed by the bones of the skull. Like the spinal cord, the brain is protected from injury by layers of cranial meninges and cerebrospinal fluid. The brain depends on oxygen to survive. It can last for only four to five minutes without oxygen before suffering irreversible damage.

Academic Vocabulary

layer *(noun):* one thickness or fold spread over or under another

FITNESSZONE

Have you ever heard the expression "use it or lose it"? That's really true for keeping your brain healthy. Researchers at Harvard say that moving helps keep the brain healthy as well as the body. Now, when I feel like I've been sitting too long while studying, I get up and move around for a couple of minutes. It really helps when getting ready for a test. For more fitness tips, visit the Online Fitness Zone at glencoe.com.

Sections of the Brain

The brain, shown in **Figure 14.11** on page 396, coordinates and controls the activities of the nervous system. Your brain helps you to receive and process messages; to think, remember, reason, and feel emotions; and to coordinate muscle movements. The brain has three main divisions: the cerebrum, the cerebellum, and the brain stem. **C**

The Cerebrum The **cerebrum** (seh-REE-brum) is *the largest and most complex part of the brain.* Billions of neurons in the cerebrum are the center of conscious thought, learning, and memory. The cerebrum's right and left sides, or hemispheres, communicate with each other to coordinate movement. The right hemisphere controls the left side of the body, and the left hemisphere controls the right side of the body. The left hemisphere is the center of language, reasoning, and critical thinking skills. The right hemisphere is the center for processing music and art and comprehending spatial relationships. Each hemisphere has four lobes: **U**

- **The frontal lobe** controls voluntary movements and has a role in the use of language. The prefrontal areas are thought to be involved with intellect and personality.

- **The parietal lobe** is involved with sensory information, including feelings of heat, cold, pain, touch, and body position in space.

394 **Chapter 14** Skeletal, Muscular, and Nervous Systems

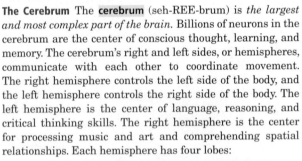

More About...

A Teen's Brain Using MRIs, researchers have been studying how the human brain grows and develops. Studies suggest a major growth spurt up to about age 3, with a second one just before puberty. By ages 10 to 12, the brain has most of the building blocks needed for learning, though most scientists think the brain is not fully formed until the early 20s. The last part of the brain to mature is the region responsible for impulse control and moral judgment, perhaps explaining why many teens take risks and push boundaries.

- **The occipital lobe** controls the sense of sight.
- **The temporal lobe** contains the sense of hearing and smell, as well as memory, thought, and judgment.

W

The Cerebellum The **cerebellum** (ser-eh-BEL-um) is *the second largest part of the brain.* It coordinates the movement of skeletal muscles. This area of the brain also continually receives messages from sensory neurons in the inner ear and muscles. It uses this information to maintain the body's posture and balance. Being able to carry out a complex series of muscle movements, such as serving a volleyball or playing the violin, is made possible by the cerebellum.

Figure 14.10 **The Nervous System**

Nerves extend to various parts of the body along the length of the spinal cord. *Which nerves are the longest?*

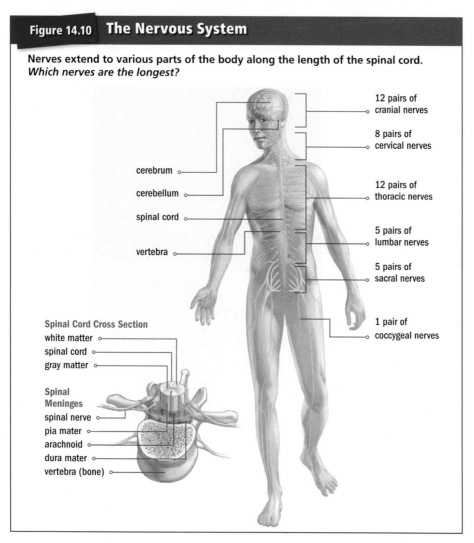

cerebrum
cerebellum
spinal cord
vertebra

12 pairs of cranial nerves
8 pairs of cervical nerves
12 pairs of thoracic nerves
5 pairs of lumbar nerves
5 pairs of sacral nerves
1 pair of coccygeal nerves

Spinal Cord Cross Section
white matter
spinal cord
gray matter

Spinal Meninges
spinal nerve
pia mater
arachnoid
dura mater
vertebra (bone)

Lesson 3 The Nervous System **395**

U **Universal Access**

Brain Hemispheres Explain to students that *hemi-* means "half," and *sphere* is a word for the shape of a ball. Ask students how many lobes, or portions, each hemisphere has. (four) Explain that each lobe has the same name as the part of the skull that protects it. Have students turn to **Figure 14.4** on page 385 and point out the bones that provide protection for the lobes of the right and left hemispheres. **BL** **EL**

Caption Answer

Figure 14.10 The nerves from the spinal cord to the feet

W **Writing Support**

Describing the Cerebellum Ask students who need a challenge to write an article about the cerebellum such as would appear in a popular science magazine. Explain that recent research has discovered that the cerebellum has more significant functions than had previously been thought. Students can illustrate their article with images printed from Web sites. Remind students to cite their sources. **AL**

Reading Strategy

Concept Map Reinforce students' understanding of the organization of the nervous system by making a concept map. Begin by making a circle on the board and writing *Nervous System* within the circle. Draw two lines diagonally beneath that circle to two circles below. Call on volunteers to name the two major divisions of the nervous system, and fill in those circles with *Central Nervous System* and *Peripheral Nervous System*. Have students copy this beginning concept map into their notebooks. Then, have students work in pairs to complete the nervous system concept map.

C Critical Thinking

Inferring Tell students that the brain stem is sometimes called the most basic and primitive part of the brain. Ask students if they can explain that description. (The brain stem is in charge of basic life support functions, such as heartbeat, breathing, reflexive responses, and other involuntary functions.) OL

AL Active Learning

Modeling the Brain Divide the class into small groups, and provide each group with toothpicks, tape, and different colors of modeling clay. Ask each group to make a model of the brain, with labels that name parts and describe functions. Have students use the modeling clay for the different parts, cut up paper for labels, attach the labels to toothpicks with tape, and place the toothpicks into the clay at appropriate places. OL

Caption Answer

Figure 14.11 The cerebellum

Main Idea

Peripheral Nervous System
The peripheral nervous system consists of all the nerves that are not part of the central nervous system.
Ask Students: *What part do the senses play in the nervous system?* (Sample answer: Sensory neurons relay messages from the eyes, ears, nose, tongue, and skin to the central nervous system.)

The Brain Stem The **brain stem** is *a 3-inch-long stalk of nerve cells and fibers that connects the spinal cord to the rest of the brain.* Incoming sensory impulses and outgoing motor impulses pass through the brain stem. It has five parts:

- **The medulla oblongata** regulates heartbeat, respiratory rate, and reflexes such as coughing and sneezing.
- **The pons** helps regulate breathing and controls the muscles of the eyes and face.
- **The midbrain** controls eyeball movement, pupil size, and the reflexive response of turning your head.
- **The thalamus** relays incoming sensory impulses from the eyes, the ears, and from pressure receptors in the skin.
- **The hypothalamus** regulates body temperature, appetite, sleep, and controls secretions from the *pituitary gland,* affecting metabolism, sexual development, and emotions.

📖 READING CHECK

Describe What are the three sections of the brain, and what is the function of each?

The Peripheral Nervous System

Main Idea The peripheral nervous system is made up of the nerves that are not in the brain and spinal cord.

The peripheral nervous system (PNS) carries messages between the CNS and part of the body, signaling internal and external changes. The PNS is made up of the autonomic nervous system and the somatic nervous system.

Figure 14.11 **The Brain**

The brain coordinates all activities of the body. *What part of the brain coordinates muscle movements?*

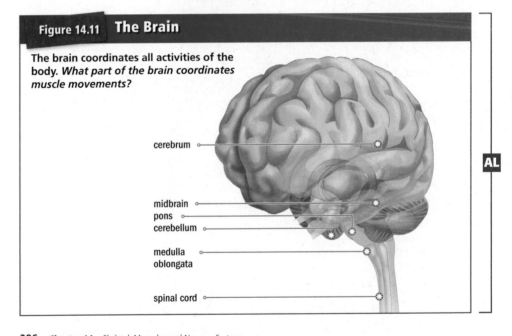

- cerebrum
- midbrain
- pons
- cerebellum
- medulla oblongata
- spinal cord

Myths & Reality

The Brain

Myth: A person uses only 10 percent of his or her brain.

Fact: The reality is that almost all of the brain is in use at all times. For example, diseases that affect only a small part of the brain can be devastating.

Myth: The brain loses brain cells as a person ages and cannot make new brain cells.

Fact: Most areas of the brain do not lose cells as a person ages, and certain areas of the brain regularly make new brain cells.

Figure 14.12 How Your Reflexes Work

Reflexes can prevent injuries such as a burn from a hot stove.

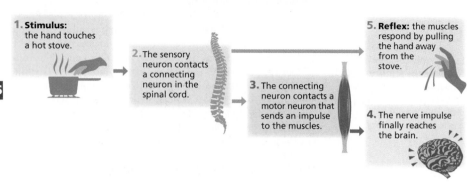

1. **Stimulus:** the hand touches a hot stove.

2. The sensory neuron contacts a connecting neuron in the spinal cord.

3. The connecting neuron contacts a motor neuron that sends an impulse to the muscles.

4. The nerve impulse finally reaches the brain.

5. **Reflex:** the muscles respond by pulling the hand away from the stove.

HS

**HS Health Skills Practice**

Advocacy Have small groups of students make posters about how reflexes work. Give each group a poster board, markers, and pencils. Explain that a poster should use words and drawings to convey the process. Display the posters in the classroom. **OL**

The Autonomic Nervous System

The *autonomic nervous system* controls such involuntary functions as digestion and heart rate. It consists of a network of nerves divided into two smaller networks, the sympathetic nervous system and the parasympathetic nervous system.

- **The sympathetic nervous system** kicks in when you are startled, sending messages that cause your heart rate to increase. Blood vessels in your muscles dilate, allowing greater blood flow. This is the "fight-or-flight" response that prepares you to react in a dangerous situation. **Figure 14.12** illustrates this *reflex,* the body's spontaneous response to a stimulus, as when a doctor tests your knee-jerk reflex by tapping the ligament below your knee during a physical exam.

AL

- **The parasympathetic nervous system** opposes the action of the sympathetic nervous system by slowing body functions. During periods of rest, it slows heartbeat, relaxes blood vessels, and lowers blood pressure to conserve energy. The parasympathetic nervous system stimulates production of saliva and stomach secretions to promote the digestion of food.

The Somatic Nervous System

The *somatic nervous system* involves voluntary responses that are under your control. Sensory neurons relay messages from the eyes, ears, nose, tongue, and skin to the CNS. Motor neurons carry impulses from the CNS to skeletal muscles.

 **READING CHECK**

Describe What happens during the "fight-or-flight" response?

AL Active Learning

Reflexes Have volunteers demonstrate reflex actions for the class. For example, to demonstrate a knee-jerk reflex, ask one student to sit in a chair. Have a second student use the side of a hand to tap the seated student's knee just below the kneecap. Students should observe the lower leg of the seated student reflexively jerk up. **OL**

READING CHECK

Answer Messages from the sympathetic nervous system cause the heart rate to increase and the blood vessels leading to the muscles to dilate, allowing greater blood flow. This prepares a person to react to a dangerous situation.

 ## Teacher to Teacher

Mark Anderson • Cobb County School District, Marietta, GA

Compare and Contrast Reproduce a Venn Diagram for students using three circles, each containing the skeletal, muscular, and nervous systems. Ask students to list similarities in the overlapping circles and list differences in the outer circles. Once finished with individual brainstorming, have students share their work. The relationships between body systems can then be used to add to a Wellness Plan that each student creates.

G Online

Explore glencoe.com and complete the Student Web Activity on the importance of wearing helmets and protective gear when participating in sports.

VIDEO **BusinessWeek**
HEALTH NEWS

Rewiring the Body

Analyze. Watch the video *Rewiring the Body* online at glencoe.com. With a partner, review the pros and cons of using implants to treat diseases such as epilepsy. Do you think these implants are more promising than the traditional treatments?

Caring for Your Nervous System

Main Idea Making healthful choices can protect your nervous system from injury.

Eating a well-balanced diet, exercising regularly, getting enough sleep, and wearing protective devices will protect your nervous system. Always wear a safety belt when in a motor vehicle. Wear a helmet and other protective gear while riding a bicycle, motorcycle, or other open vehicle, or when enjoying a contact sport. Before diving, check the depth of the water. Never dive head first into shallow water or into water where you cannot see the bottom. Finally, drugs and alcohol can permanently damage nerve cells, so avoid using them.

Problems of the Nervous System

Injury to the nervous system affects the immediate tissues, and may lead to other problems, including the following:

- **Headaches.** Headaches can be caused by muscle tension, eyestrain, exposure to fumes, a sinus infection, dehydration, or food allergies. Migraines are recurrent headaches that may be accompanied by sensitivity to light.
- **Head injuries.** Each year, 435,000 American children and teens sustain brain injuries. Types of head injuries include concussion, a temporary loss of consciousness, contusion, a bruising of the brain tissues that causes swelling, and coma, caused by major trauma. **HS**
- **Spinal injuries.** Spinal cord injuries require medical care. Swelling of the spinal cord or the tissue around it can result in temporary loss of nerve function. Permanent nerve damage will result without treatment. If the spinal cord has been severed, paralysis results.

■ **Figure 14.13** Safe behaviors, such as diving only when you know the depth of the water, can reduce your risk of head and spinal injuries. *What other behaviors can protect you from head or spinal injury?*

Skills for the 21st Century

Caring for Those With Alzheimer's Discuss with students the difficult decisions faced by families with parents or grandparents who have Alzheimer's disease, whose mental faculties deteriorate over time. How can these loved ones be cared for at home? Where can they go when home care becomes too difficult? Elicit students' ideas about how to solve these troubling family problems. Then, ask interested students to contact the local chapter of the Alzheimer's Association to find out about programs and facilities available in their community. Have students report their findings to the class.

- **Meningitis.** Meningitis is an inflammation of the spinal and cranial meninges caused by bacterial or viral infection. Meningitis is very serious and can result in death. Symptoms include fever, headache, light and sound sensitivity, and neck stiffness.

Some nervous system diseases are degenerative, which means they occur over time as cells break down. Multiple sclerosis, Parkinson's disease and Alzheimer's are example of degenerative diseases. Other disorders result from injury or brain damage. **Epilepsy** is *a disorder of the nervous system that is characterized by recurrent seizures— sudden episodes of uncontrolled electrical activity in the brain.* Causes include brain damage at birth, infections, head injury, or exposure to toxins. Medications can help control seizures. **Cerebral palsy** refers to *a group of neurological disorders that are the result of damage to the brain before, during, or just after birth or in early childhood.* Physical therapy and medication help patients cope.

■ **Figure 14.14** Multiple sclerosis is an autoimmune disease, often resulting in impaired mobility. *What kinds of activities can you enjoy with someone who has limited voluntary muscle control?*

LESSON 3 ASSESSMENT

After You Read

Reviewing Facts and Vocabulary

1. Where is the nucleus of a neuron located?
2. How can a reflex prevent injury?
3. What are some causes of nervous diseases and disorders?

Thinking Critically

4. **Analyze.** After sustaining a head injury, a patient is having trouble comprehending spatial relationships and controlling the left side of her body. What part of the brain might be damaged?
5. **Compare.** How are the functions of the autonomic nervous system and the somatic nervous system different?

Applying Health Skills

6. **Accessing Information.** Write a one-page report on current research into helping people with degenerative nervous system disorders, such as Parkinson's, multiple sclerosis, or Alzheimer's. Why are these diseases so difficult to treat?

Writing Critically

7. **Expository.** Write a paragraph describing what happens during a reflex action.

 Online

Visit glencoe.com and complete the Interactive Study Guide for this lesson.

Lesson 3   The Nervous System   **399**

LESSON 3 ASSESSMENT ANSWERS

1. The nucleus is located in the cell body.
2. A reflex is a spontaneous response of the body to a stimulus. Reflexes allow a person to respond to and avoid danger.
3. Some diseases of the nervous system are degenerative, while others may result from head injury or neurological problems.
4. The right hemisphere
5. The autonomic nervous system controls involuntary functions, while the somatic nervous system gathers information through sensory neurons.
6. Reports will vary. As part of their reports, students should discuss that these disorders are so difficult to treat because they occur slowly, over time, as tissue and cells break down.
7. Paragraphs will vary.

3 ASSESS/ CLOSE

Assessment Resources

📁 ***FAST FILE* ACTIVITIES**
Lesson 3 Quiz

💿 *ExamView Assessment Suite* CD-ROM

Visit glencoe.com for:
Online Quizzes
Online Learning Center

Progress Monitoring

Reteaching
Have students work with partners to write questions about the important terms and concepts related to the nervous system. Compile these questions and have students use them for review.

Enrichment
Have students use online resources to learn more about epilepsy, including cause, symptoms, and treatment. Also ask students to investigate what actions a person should take if someone with epilepsy has a seizure in a public place.

 Online

Have students visit **glencoe.com** and complete the Interactive Study Guide for this lesson.

Good "Housekeeping"

NHES Standard 3 Students will demonstrate the ability to access valid information and products and services to enhance health.

Teaching Objectives

- Analyze and describe the components and functions of the skeletal, muscular, and nervous systems.
- Demonstrate the ability to access valid information related to health that will enhance the development and maintenance of their skeletal, muscular, and nervous systems.

Teaching Strategies

- Place students in groups of three. Each group will need access to the Internet, a sheet of white paper 3 × 5 feet, and four different colored markers (black, red, blue, and green).
- Allow time for groups to present their silhouettes and explain the health-enhancing behaviors for each system.

Assessment

Using a rubric, student work should provide comprehensive evidence of the following criteria to achieve the highest score:

✓ Cites specific sources
✓ Evaluates the validity of the sources
✓ Gives rationale for the appropriateness of the sources
✓ Identifies at least three health-enhancing behaviors

400

Hands-On
HEALTH

Activity Good "Housekeeping"

Imagine you were building a house that you plan to live in for 100 years. In this activity you will learn how your "house" is built, and how to care for it.

What You'll Need

- a computer with Internet access
- colored markers (black, red, blue, green)
- large sheet of paper

What You'll Do

Step 1

Work in groups to review the chapter. Conduct additional research to learn more about the skeletal, muscular, and nervous systems.

Step 2

Using reliable information that you obtained during your research, draw a life-size silhouette of the human body. Refer to your research, and label one major muscle, one major bone, and one part of the nervous system.

Step 3

Explain the components of each system, how it functions, and steps to keep the system healthy. Cite your sources.

Apply and Conclude

Identify three health-enhancing behaviors that will have a positive impact on your "house" for a lifetime.

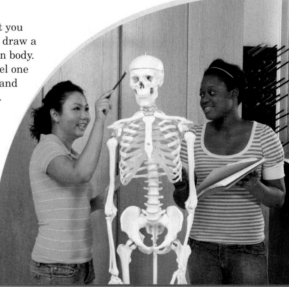

Checklist: Accessing Information

☑ List all of your sources of information.

☑ Evaluate the sources to determine their reliability.

☑ Judge the appropriateness of your sources.

More About...

Medical Illustration Drawing and labeling parts of the body has a long history, and a traditional specialty of commercial art is medical illustration. In recent years medical illustration has been revolutionized by computer technology. Medical illustrators once produced paintings and pen-and-ink drawings. A medical illustrator today needs to be a master of computer art programs in order to produce digital images that can be sent and stored in computers. Despite the new technology, a medical illustrator still needs to have talent and training in the traditional artistic skills of design, composition, color, and lighting. Ask students with artistic talent to try to create labeled illustrations of body components using digital art software.

To download quizzes and eFlashcards to your PDA, go to **glencoe.com** and click on the Study to Go icon.

LESSON **1**

The Skeletal System

Key Concepts
- Your skeletal system consists of bones, cartilage, ligaments, and tendons.
- Bones provide support and protection for the body, provide a framework for muscles, allow movement, produce blood cells, and store nutrients.
- Injuries to the skeletal system include fractures, dislocation of joints, and tears and inflammation of connective tissue.

Vocabulary
- cartilage (p. 383)
- ossification (p. 383)
- ligament (p. 383)
- tendon (p. 383)
- scoliosis (p. 384)
- osteoporosis (p. 386)

LESSON **2**

The Muscular System

Key Concepts
- The muscular system includes smooth, skeletal, and cardiac muscle.
- Extensor and flexor muscles work together to perform opposite actions.
- Proper diet, regular exercise, stretching, and avoiding overexertion will strengthen muscles and prevent injury.

Vocabulary
- smooth muscles (p. 388)
- skeletal muscles (p. 388)
- flexor (p. 388)
- extensor (p. 388)
- cardiac muscle (p. 388)
- tendinitis (p. 389)
- hernia (p. 390)

LESSON **3**

The Nervous System

Key Concepts
- The nervous system enables communication between the brain and all other areas of the body.
- Different parts of the brain are responsible for different functions of the body and different kinds of conscious thought.
- You can avoid injury to your nervous system by practicing healthful behaviors. Use a safety belt, wear a helmet, avoid drug and alcohol use, and check the depth of water before diving.

Vocabulary
- neurons (p. 393)
- cerebrum (p. 394)
- cerebellum (p. 395)
- brain stem (p. 396)
- epilepsy (p. 399)
- cerebral palsy (p. 399)

Go Online

Students can visit **glencoe.com** to

- review content online with the Online Student Edition.
- test their knowledge of chapter content with Online Quizzes.
- access Interactive Health Tutor for more practice with vocabulary.

Assessment Resources

📁 **FAST FILE ACTIVITIES**
Chapter 14 Test

💿 *ExamView*
Assessment Suite CD-ROM

Visit glencoe.com for:
Audio Chapter Summaries
Online Quizzes

 STUDY TO GO Tell students to visit **glencoe.com** where they can download quizzes and eFlashcards.

Chapter 14 Review **401**

Study Tips

Memorization To absorb the information presented in a course of study, students must memorize many facts and concepts. Explain to students that there are some basic techniques that help the memorization of facts. Visualization is one example. As a student reads a fact, he or she should concentrate on a mental image to help remember that fact. For remembering a concept, a good technique is to explain the concept aloud to another student. Another way to remember a concept is to write an explanation in one's own words.

Assessment

Chapter 14 Assessment Answers

LESSON **1**

Vocabulary Review

1. Cartilage
2. tendon
3. scoliosis
4. ossification

Understanding Key Concepts

5. c
6. b
7. b
8. b

Thinking Critically

9. Sample answer: The bones of the skull are thin and flat and therefore function to protect organs. The arm bones are longer than they are wide and therefore function to provide a framework for attached muscles.

10. Sample answer: Attaching bones to bones, ligaments help keep bones from moving too much or falling out of a joint. Tendons attach muscle to bone, allowing entire body parts to move when muscles contract.

11. Sample answer: An activity that requires prolonged, repeated movements can cause damage to tissues.

12. Sample answer: helmet and padding

13. Getting adequate calcium during the teen years and getting weight-bearing exercise is important for building bone mass. This will reduce the risk of developing osteoporosis later in life.

Vocabulary Review

14. flexor
15. Cardiac
16. smooth

LESSON **1**

Vocabulary Review

Use the vocabulary terms listed on page 401 to complete the following statements.

1. _____ is the connective tissue that can act as a cushion between two bones.

2. A fibrous cord called a(n) _____ attaches muscle to bone.

3. A lateral curvature of the spine is called _____.

4. The process by which bone is formed is called _____.

Understanding Key Concepts

After reading the question or statement, select the correct answer.

5. Which of the following is *not* a function of the skeletal system?
   a. Storing minerals and fats
   b. Producing red blood cells
   c. Responding to external stimuli
   d. Protecting internal tissues and organs

6. Which of the following is a condition that involves a progressive loss of bone tissue?
   a. Arthritis
   b. Osteoporosis
   c. Repetitive motion injury
   d. Scoliosis

7. Identify the joint injury that occurs often from natural wear and tear.
   a. Dislocation   c. Bursitis
   b. Arthritis   d. Bunions

8. In a hairline fracture,
   a. the break is completely across the bone.
   b. the two parts of the bone do not separate.
   c. the bone shatters into more than two pieces.
   d. one part of the bone protrudes through the skin.

402 Chapter 14 Assessment

Thinking Critically

After reading the question or statement, write a short answer using complete sentences.

9. **Contrast.** Contrast the shape of the skull bones with the shape of the arm bones, and relate these shapes to their different functions.

10. **Evaluate.** How are tendons and ligaments important for movement?

11. **Analyze.** How can nonrigorous activities, such as typing or sewing, lead to skeletal system injuries?

12. **Apply.** What kinds of protective gear can prevent injuries to the skeletal system?

13. **Analyze.** How will behaviors you practice during your teen years affect your chances of getting osteoporosis later in life?

LESSON **2**

Vocabulary Review

Choose the correct word in the sentences below.

14. A(n) *flexor/extensor* is a muscle that closes a joint.

15. *Smooth/Cardiac* muscle is striated muscle in the heart.

16. All *smooth/skeletal* muscles are under involuntary control.

17. *Tendinitis/Hernia* results when an organ protrudes through an area of weak muscle.

18. A tendon problem resulting from overuse, injury, or natural aging is *tendinitis/hernia*.

Health eSpotlight VIDEO Wrap-Up

Building a Healthy Body Have students reread the Health eSpotlight question at the beginning of the chapter (page 381) and look at their original answer. **Ask Students:** *Now that you have read the chapter and watched the video, how would you respond* *differently about the steps you can take to ensure your body's bones, muscles, and brain are maintained in good order?* Call on volunteers to describe how their responses would change.

Understanding Key Concepts

After reading the question or statement, select the correct answer.

19. Which type of muscle is *not* striated?
    a. Cardiac
    b. Extensor
    c. Flexor
    d. Smooth

20. Where is smooth muscle found?
    a. In the digestive tract
    b. In the walls of the heart
    c. In the triceps and biceps of the arms
    d. In the muscles controlling finger movement

21. How can you improve muscle tone?
    a. Practicing good posture
    b. Getting regular physical exercise
    c. Wearing safety equipment
    d. Eating fruits and vegetables

22. What problem of the muscular system is an inherited disorder?
    a. Hernia
    b. Muscle sprain
    c. Muscular dystrophy
    d. Tendinitis

Thinking Critically

After reading the question or statement, write a short answer using complete sentences.

23. **Connect.** What are some ways that the muscular system works together with other body systems?

24. **Infer.** Consider an injury to a muscle in the thigh. Why might it cause pain when straightening the leg, but not when bending the leg?

25. **Apply.** Why might it be important for the children of a person with muscular dystrophy to be screened for the disease?

26. **Apply.** How can strengthening muscles prevent injury?

LESSON 3

Vocabulary Review

Use the vocabulary terms listed on page 401 to complete the following statements.

27. The _____ coordinates the movement of skeletal muscles.

28. The _____ is the center of conscious thought.

29. Several important voluntary functions, such as breathing and heartbeat, are controlled by _____.

30. _____ is a disorder that is characterized by recurrent seizures.

31. A group of neurological disorders resulting from damage to the brain at birth is called _____.

Understanding Key Concepts

After reading the question or statement, select the correct answer.

32. Which of the following is *not* a part of the brain stem?
    a. Cerebellum
    b. Medulla oblongata
    c. Midbrain
    d. Thalamus

33. What can result from a spinal cord injury?
    a. Concussion
    b. Contusion
    c. Epilepsy
    d. Paralysis

34. Which disease or disorder is *not* degenerative?
    a. Alzheimer's disease
    b. Cerebral palsy
    c. Multiple sclerosis
    d. Parkinson's disease

LESSON 2

17. Hernia
18. tendinitis

Understanding Key Concepts

19. d
20. a
21. b
22. c

Thinking Critically

23. The muscular system allows for voluntary and involuntary movements that help you move and breathe, make your heart beat, and move food through the digestive system.

24. Straightening and bending use different muscles. In this scenario, the injured muscle is being used only to straighten the leg.

25. Screening for muscular dystrophy is important for these people because it is an inherited disorder. With early detection, muscle weakness can be delayed through exercise programs.

26. Sample answer: Strong muscles take longer to overexert, which means they are less likely to get strained.

Vocabulary Review

27. cerebellum
28. cerebrum
29. brain stem
30. Epilepsy
31. cerebral palsy

Understanding Key Concepts

32. a
33. d
34. b
35. c

Create and customize tests in minutes with this convenient digital platform.

- Create differentiated tests quickly and easily.
- All questions correlated to National/State Standards.
- Enhance tests with Document Based Questions (DBQ) and add your own photos or graphics.
- Build tests in both English and Spanish.
- Generate progress reports.

To order, go to **glencoe.com** and search for ISBN 0-07-888173-0.

LESSON 3

Thinking Critically

36. A sensory neuron carries a message from the sensory receptors to the CNS, and a motor neuron carries a message from the CNS back to the muscle that responds.

37. The brain and spinal cord are cushioned in cerebrospinal fluid, covered in protective meninges, and protected by the bones of the skull and vertebrae.

38. Axons transmit impulses away from the cell body and toward another neuron, muscle cell, or gland, while dendrites receive information from other neurons or sensory receptors.

39. Degenerative diseases cause affected cells and tissues to break down or deteriorate and symptoms appear over time making them difficult to treat.

40. The sound stimulates nerves in the ear, which sends a message from the nervous system to the muscles, which will respond by preparing you to react with the fight-or-flight response.

41. It's important to protect the nervous system.

35. What disease or disorder is characterized by sudden episodes of electrical activity in the brain?
 a. Alzheimer's disease
 b. Cerebral palsy
 c. Epilepsy
 d. Parkinson's disease

Thinking Critically

After reading the question or statement, write a short answer using complete sentences.

36. Analyze. How do the central nervous system and peripheral nervous system work together during the motor response to a stimulus?

37. Infer. How does the nervous system protect the brain and spinal cord?

38. Compare. Explain the difference between axons and dendrites.

39. Infer. Why might the symptoms of a degenerative disease of the nervous system be difficult to treat?

40. Describe. What might happen in the nervous system and muscles when a person is surprised by a sudden loud sound like a fire alarm going off nearby?

41. Explain. Why is it important to wear protective gear and to check the depth of water before diving?

Project-Based ASSESSMENT

Sleep and Your Brain

Background
Getting enough sleep means more than resting your body. It's also a time when your brain prepares for the next day. To function at its best, your brain needs to go through five cycles while you sleep. If you don't get enough sleep, you may not go through all five sleep cycles, and both your body and brain won't function at their best the next day.

Task
Create a video showing the importance of sleep to brain functioning.

Audience
Students in your class

Purpose
Help explain the importance of sleep in reenergizing the brain.

Procedure
1 Review the information on the nervous system in Chapter 14.
2 Conduct research to learn about the importance of sleep to brain functions.
3 Create a video presentation lasting two to three minutes on why the brain needs sleep. Use text, sound, figures, photographs, and other elements to make your presentation clear, interesting, and engaging. Also, develop a survey for classmates to fill out on the effectiveness of your video.
4 Show your video to your class.
5 Ask students to complete the survey to learn if they have any additional questions about why the brain needs sleep. The survey should also assess whether your video was effective.

Project-Based ASSESSMENT

Step 1 Research Have students use library and online resources to find reliable information on the importance of sleep to brain function. Remind students to find both information and sounds and images that will make the video engaging.

Step 2 Create the Video Have students create their videos using materials from their research. You may want to have partners or small groups work together on each

video. In addition to the video, students should develop a four- or five-question survey to give to classmates for assessment of the video.

Step 3 Evaluate Each video should contain accurate information about the importance of sleep to brain function.

Visit **glencoe.com** for Project-Based Assessment rubrics.

Math Practice

Interpret Tables. A diet high in calcium and vitamin D can help prevent bone loss or osteoporosis. The table below shows the amount of calcium and vitamin D needed each day for different age groups. Use the table to answer Questions 1–3.

Daily Need for Calcium and Vitamin D

Age Group	Calcium	Vitamin D
0 to 6 months	210 mg	200 IU
7 to 12 months	270 mg	200 IU
1 to 3 years	500 mg	200 IU
4 to 8 years	800 mg	200 IU
9 to 18 years	1,300 mg	200 IU
19 to 50 years	1,000 mg	200 IU
51 to 70 years	1,200 mg	400 IU
Over 70 years	1,200 mg	600 IU

Adapted from *"What Is Osteoporosis?"* National Institutes of Health Osteoporosis and Related Bone Diseases-National Resource Center, March 2006.

1. What is the difference between the Vitamin D daily need for babies, under 12 months, and the daily amount of vitamin D for people over 70?
   - **A.** 200 IU
   - **B.** 400 IU
   - **C.** 600 IU
   - **D.** 800 IU

2. Between which two age groups is there a decrease in the amount of calcium needed?
   - **A.** 0 to 6 months and 7 to 12 months
   - **B.** 4 to 8 years and 9 to 18 years
   - **C.** 9 to 18 years and 19 to 50 years
   - **D.** 19 to 50 years and 51 to 70 years

3. Which group needs the most calcium daily?
   - **A.** 0 to 6 months
   - **B.** 9 to 18 years
   - **C.** Over 50 years
   - **D.** Over 70 years

Go Online

For more test practice, visit glencoe.com and complete the Online Quizzes for Chapter 14.

Reading/Writing Practice

Understand and Apply. Read the passage below, and then answer the questions.

> Each year in the United States, 10,000 new cases of spinal cord injury are reported. These injuries may result from sports or recreational activities, motor vehicle crashes, falls, physical assaults, and gunshot wounds.
>
> Spinal injuries may result in paralysis, or the loss of muscle function and feeling in part of the body. An injury to the upper part of the spinal cord may result in quadriplegia, or paralysis of both upper and lower limbs. Paraplegia, paralysis of both lower limbs, is caused by an injury lower on the spinal column.
>
> Researchers are looking for ways to cure paralysis. Electrical sensors and stimulators can help quadriplegic victims flex their limbs. Possible cures include removal of scar tissue and transplantation of cells that promote nerve growth.

1. What was the author's purpose?
   - **A.** To explain how to cure paralysis
   - **B.** To persuade people to wear helmets
   - **C.** To describe the effects of spinal injuries
   - **D.** To describe different types of paralysis

2. Which sentence best represents the main idea of the second paragraph?
   - **A.** Paralysis can be cured.
   - **B.** There are different degrees of paralysis.
   - **C.** Paralysis can result from accidents.
   - **D.** Paralysis cannot be cured.

3. Write a paragraph persuading a friend to wear a safety belt while riding in a motor vehicle. Provide details about spinal cord injuries to support your main points.

National Education Standards
Math: Number and Operations, Problem Solving
Language Arts: NCTE 3, NCTE 4

Standardized Test Practice

Standardized Test Practice Answers
Math Practice
1. B
2. C
3. B

Reading/Writing Practice
1. C
2. B
3. Paragraphs will vary, but should be persuasive and should include information from the lesson on spinal cord injuries and the consequences of not wearing a safety belt.

National Education Standards

Math: Number and Operations, Problem Solving

Language Arts: NCTE 3, NCTE 4

For the complete Math and Language Arts standards, visit glencoe.com.

Go Online

Online Study Tools
For more test practice, visit glencoe.com and complete the Online Quizzes for Chapter 14.

Test-Taking Tip

Inferring a Purpose Explain to students that some questions on a standardized test may ask them to read a passage and then infer the author's purpose in writing the passage. To understand an author's purpose, a student should read the passage closely and then read it again, the second time with an eye for identifying the main idea of the passage. By understanding the main idea, a student can infer the purpose the author had in mind when writing the piece.

Cardiovascular, Respiratory, and Digestive Systems

Chapter 15 pages 406–439	Standards		Features
	National	**State/Local**	TIME HEALTH
	1.12.1, 7.12.1, 7.12.2, 7.12.3		• A Heart to Last a Lifetime, page 434
30 Min **Lesson 1** **The Cardiovascular and Lymphatic Systems** pages 408–415 **BIG Idea** *The cardiovascular system moves blood through the body, while the lymphatic system circulates lymph throughout the body.*	1.12.1, 1.12.5, 3.12.2, 7.12.1, 7.12.2, 7.12.3, 8.12.1, 8.12.3, 8.12.4		
30 Min **Lesson 2** **The Respiratory System** pages 416–421 **BIG Idea** *The respiratory system provides oxygen to the blood and removes carbon dioxide from the body.*	1.12.1, 1.12.3, 1.12.5, 5.12.6, 7.12.1, 7.12.2, 8.12.1, 8.12.2		*Real World* **CONNECTION** • The Effects of Smoking, page 420
30 Min **Lesson 3** **The Digestive System** pages 422–428 **BIG Idea** *The digestive system provides nutrients and energy for your body through the digestion of food.*	1.12.1, 1.12.5, 6.12.1, 7.12.1, 7.12.2, 7.12.3, 8.12.4		
30 Min **Lesson 4** **The Excretory System** pages 429–433 **BIG Idea** *The excretory system removes wastes from the body.*	1.12.1, 1.12.5, 7.12.2, 7.12.3		

Key to Ability Levels

Teaching Strategies and activities have been coded for ability level and appropriateness.

AL Activities for students working above grade level   **BL** Activities for students working below grade level

OL Activities for students working on grade level   **EL** Activities for English Learners

Chapter 15 Planning Guide

Glencoe Exclusive!
TeacherWorks Plus
All-In-One Planner and Resource Center

Resources	Lesson Assessment	Technology
Student Activity Workbook TEACH **FAST FILE RESOURCES** Vocabulary Practice TEACH Health Labs EXTEND	Chapter 15 Review Chapter 15 Assessment Standardized Test Practice ⊙ *ExamView® Assessment Suite* CD-ROM	**Teaching Tools:** ⊙ *TeacherWorks™* Plus DVD ⊙ *StudentWorks™* Plus DVD ⊙ *ExamView® Assessment Suite* CD-ROM 🕹 Transparency ⊙ Fitness DVD ⊙ PowerPoint® DVD ⊙ Health eSpotlight Video Series DVD
FAST FILE RESOURCES Reading Strategies Activity TEACH Reteaching Activity REVIEW Enrichment Activity EXTEND Health Skills Practice TEACH	Lesson 1 Assessment, page 415 📁 Lesson 1 Quiz *Fast File* ⊙ *ExamView® Assessment Suite* CD-ROM	
FAST FILE RESOURCES Reading Strategies Activity TEACH Reteaching Activity REVIEW Enrichment Activity EXTEND Health Skills Practice TEACH	Lesson 2 Assessment, page 421 📁 Lesson 2 Quiz *Fast File* ⊙ *ExamView® Assessment Suite* CD-ROM	**Web-Based Resources:** Go Online glencoe.com • Health Podcast Activities • Audio Chapter Summaries (English/Spanish) • Interactive Health Tutor • Health Skills Activities
FAST FILE RESOURCES Reading Strategies Activity TEACH Reteaching Activity REVIEW Enrichment Activity EXTEND Health Skills Practice TEACH	Lesson 3 Assessment, page 428 📁 Lesson 3 Quiz *Fast File* ⊙ *ExamView® Assessment Suite* CD-ROM	• Vocabulary PuzzleMaker • Parent Letters (English/Spanish) • Lesson Plans • Health Inventories • Online Quizzes
FAST FILE RESOURCES Reading Strategies Activity TEACH Reteaching Activity REVIEW Enrichment Activity EXTEND Health Skills Practice TEACH	Lesson 4 Assessment, page 433 📁 Lesson 4 Quiz *Fast File* ⊙ *ExamView® Assessment Suite* CD-ROM	• Study-to-Go • Unit Web Projects • Student Web Activities • Fitness Zone Activities

StudentWorks Plus

This is the student's backpack solution.

Includes:
- complete Interactive Student Edition
- full audio of English text and Spanish chapter summaries
- allows students to record assignments and track grades.
- links to online activities and additional student resources
- access to all student worksheets and workbooks

FOLDABLES
Study Organizer

Dinah Zike Foldables®
Chapter Activity
Refer to the *Dinah Zike Reading and Study Skills for Glencoe Health*. Ask students to make a pocket book Foldable. As students learn about the structure and function of each body system, they can record that information on index cards and keep the cards in the appropriate pocket.

Key to Symbols

🕹 Transparencies   REVIEW activities to review or reinforce content

⊙ CD-ROM   TEACH activities to teach basic concepts

〜 glencoe.com   EXTEND activities to extend or enrich lesson content

📁 Print Resources

Cardiovascular, Respiratory, and Digestive Systems

Chapter Overview

Chapter 15 focuses on the cardiovascular, lymphatic, respiratory, digestive, and the excretory systems. Also discussed is how to maintain each system and the problems associated with each system.

Lesson 1

The cardiovascular system, which includes the heart and blood vessels, circulates blood, and the lymphatic system circulates lymph throughout the body.

Lesson 2

The respiratory system, which includes the lungs, supplies oxygen to body cells and carries out the exchange of gases between the body and the environment.

Lesson 3

The digestive system, which includes the stomach and intestines, digests food and provides the nutrients and energy needed by the body's cells.

Lesson 4

The excretory system, which includes the liver and kidneys, removes wastes from the body.

▶ **Activating Prior Knowledge**

Call on volunteers to name activities and write each on the board. **Ask Students:** *What is the function of sweating?* (Sweating is a way that the body releases heat.)

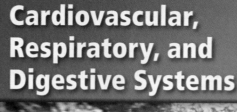
Cardiovascular, Respiratory, and Digestive Systems

Lesson 1

The Cardiovascular and Lymphatic Systems

BIG *Idea* *The cardiovascular system moves blood through the body, while the lymphatic system circulates lymph throughout the body.*

Lesson 2

The Respiratory System

BIG *Idea* *The respiratory system provides oxygen to the blood and removes carbon dioxide from the body.*

Lesson 3

The Digestive System

BIG *Idea* *The digestive system provides nutrients and energy for your body through the digestion of food.*

Lesson 4

The Excretory System

BIG *Idea* *The excretory system removes wastes from the body.*

Activating Prior Knowledge

Using Visuals Regular aerobic activity will strengthen your heart muscle. Name some activities, other than bike riding, that you think might strengthen your heart.

Universal Access

Differentiated Learning Glencoe provides teacher support and student materials for all learners in the health classroom.

- Chapter Summaries in English and Spanish are available online at **glencoe.com**.

- *Fast Files* and related worksheets support reluctant readers.

- Universal Access strategies throughout the Teacher Wraparound Edition and *Fast Files* help you present materials for gifted students, at-risk students, physically impaired students, and those with behavior disorders or learning disabilities.

Chapter Launchers

Health in Action

Discuss the **BIG** Ideas

Before beginning this chapter, think about how you would answer these questions:

▸ When do you feel your heart rate change?

▸ What can cause your breathing to change?

▸ How does your stomach feel after you eat a large meal?

Watch the *Health* eSpotlight Video Series

VIDEO

A Look Inside Your Body

A healthy heart is one way to protect your health. What else can you do to stay healthy?

Assess Your Health

Go Online

Visit glencoe.com and complete the Health Inventory for Chapter 15.

Chapter Launchers

Health in Action

Discuss the **BIG** Ideas

Have students respond to the questions aloud. Explain that the purpose of the questions is to help them assess their current knowledge of the cardiovascular, respiratory, and digestive systems.

Health eSpotlight
Video Series

VIDEO

A Look Inside Your Body

Before Viewing the Video

Ask Students: *What are the most important habits a person can adopt to maintain a healthy cardiovascular system?* (Sample answer: Eating a healthful diet, maintaining a healthy weight, and participating in regular physical activity)

Go Online

Have students go to **glencoe.com** and take the Health Inventory for Chapter 15.

Chapter Skills

Reading Skills
- Reviewing Facts and Vocabulary, pp. 415, 421, 428, 433
- Reading/Writing Practice, p. 439

BIG Idea

You'll learn about the body's cardio-vascular, lymphatic, respiratory, diges-tive, and excretory systems.

Health Skills
- Applying Health Skills, pp. 415, 421, 428, 433

Writing Skills
- Real World Connection, p. 420
- Writing Critically, pp. 415, 421, 428, 433
- Reading/Writing Practice, p. 439

Vocabulary
- New Vocabulary, pp. 408, 416, 422, 429
- Reviewing Facts and Vocabulary, pp. 415, 421, 428, 433

The Cardio-vascular and Lymphatic Systems

① FOCUS

GUIDE TO READING

BIG Idea The cardiovascular system circulates blood, while the lymphatic system circulates lymph throughout the body. **Ask Students:** *What is the main function of the heart?* (To pump blood throughout the body to provide oxygen and nutrients to cells)

Before You Read

T Chart Students' T charts will vary.

Main Idea

Why Blood Circulates The cardiovascular system provides nutrients and oxygen, carries away waste, and helps fight disease.
Ask Students: *Why is the air you breathe important to how the heart functions?* (Sample answer: Oxygen is carried from the lungs to body cells.)

Real Life Issues

Ask volunteers to share their paragraphs with the class.
Ask Students: *What have you already learned about developing a healthy heart?*

GUIDE TO READING

BIG Idea *The cardio-vascular system moves blood through the body, while the lymphatic system circulates lymph throughout the body.*

Before You Read

Create a T Chart. As you read, list the problems of the cardiovascular and lymphatic systems on the left side, under the label "Problems." List preventive health behaviors that can help reduce these problems on the right side, under the label "Prevention."

Problems	Prevention

New Vocabulary

▶ plasma (p. 410)
▶ hemoglobin (p. 410)
▶ platelets (p. 410)
▶ capillaries (p. 412)
▶ lymph (p. 412)
▶ pathogen (p. 412)
▶ blood pressure (p. 413)

The Cardiovascular and Lymphatic Systems

Real Life Issues

The Beat Goes On. Marcos hears the announcement for the boys' 100-yard dash. His pulse quickens. This is it—the moment he's been training for all year. He gets into the starting position. At the sound of the starter pistol, he takes off. His legs are pumping, his lungs are burning, and his heart is racing as he crosses the finish line. He smiles, as the cheers of the crowd tell him he has won.

Writing *Write a persuasive paragraph that explains to a younger person why it's important to practice behaviors that keep your heart healthy.*

Why the Blood Circulates

Main Idea The cardiovascular system provides nutrients and oxygen, carries away wastes, and helps fight disease.

Your heart pumps blood to your body's cells 24 hours a day, even when you're asleep. Your heart accomplishes these important tasks:

• Carrying oxygen from the lungs to body cells
• Absorbing nutrients from food and delivering nutrients to body cells
• Carrying carbon dioxide, a waste gas, from your cells back to your lungs to be exhaled
• Delivering other waste products to the kidneys for removal from the body
• Helping the white blood cells fight disease by attacking infectious organisms

---

Skills for the 21st Century

Communication Skills In today's workplace, a common way to share information related to a company's work is to use presentation software, such as Microsoft's PowerPoint®. To give students practice in this communication skill, have small groups research a topic related to the cardiovascular or lymphatic systems and make a 5- to 10-minute PowerPoint presentation on that topic to the class. Topics might include the structure of the heart, the importance of blood pressure, or functions of the lymphatic system. Students can find information and images online for use in their presentations.

How Blood Circulation Works

Main Idea The cardiovascular system consists of the heart, blood, and blood vessels.

The cardiovascular system depends on the heart and its system of blood vessels to deliver blood throughout the body. If all of your blood vessels were laid end to end, they would stretch over 60,000 miles. That's enough to circle the earth almost two and a half times.

The Heart

Your heart is the muscle that makes the cardiovascular system work. Inside the heart are four chambers. The two top chambers are called the *atria*. The two lower chambers are called *ventricles*. A wall of tissue, the *septum*, separates the four chambers of the heart. Valves between the atria and ventricles allow blood to flow through the chambers.

At the top of the right atrium is an area of muscle that acts as a pacemaker for the heart. Electrical impulses stimulate the atria to **contract**, forcing blood into the ventricles. These electrical impulses travel through the heart to an area between the two ventricles. There they stimulate the muscles of the ventricles to contract, pumping blood out of the heart. Pumping the blood through the heart is only part of the process. **Figure 15.1** shows the pulmonary circulation.

Academic Vocabulary

contract *(verb):* to draw together

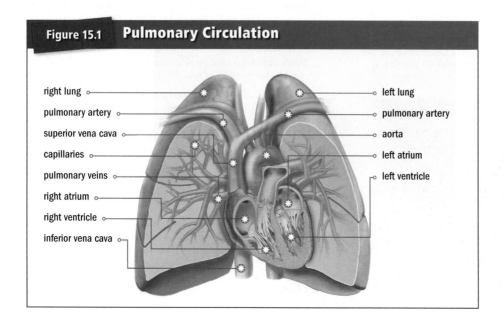

Figure 15.1 **Pulmonary Circulation**

- right lung
- pulmonary artery
- superior vena cava
- capillaries
- pulmonary veins
- right atrium
- right ventricle
- inferior vena cava
- left lung
- pulmonary artery
- aorta
- left atrium
- left ventricle

② TEACH

Academic Vocabulary

Contract To illustrate what occurs when a muscle contracts, make a fist. Then, open the hand to illustrate how a muscle extends as it relaxes. Ask students to identify other meanings for the verb contract that they may encounter in their health studies. (A person may contract a disease.)

Main Idea

How Blood Circulation Works
The cardiovascular system consists of the heart, blood, and blood vessels.
Ask Students: *How many chambers does the human heart have?* (Four; two atria and two ventricles)

Ⓤ Universal Access

Cooperative Learning Pair English proficient students with English language learners. Give students an unlabeled drawing of the four chambers of the heart and the major vessels going to and from the heart. Have each pair work together to add labels and arrows showing how blood flows through, to, and from the heart. Then, make the drawing on the board and ask volunteers to label it, pronouncing each structure correctly. **BL** **EL**

Reading Strategy

Cycle Diagram To reinforce students' understanding of circulation, draw a cycle diagram on the board. Begin with blood flowing to the heart. Ask: *Through what major vessels does blood flow into the heart?* (superior and inferior vena cava) Write *vena cava.* Then ask: *Into which part of the heart* *does the blood in the vena cava flow?* (right atrium) Draw an arrow from *vena cava* and write *right atrium.* Continue until the diagram is complete, naming structures in this order: *vena cava, right atrium, right ventricle, pulmonary arteries, lungs, pulmonary veins, left atrium, left ventricle, aorta, body.*

409

HS Health Skills Practice

Accessing Information Ask students to use an online search engine to find two or three Web sites with accurate information and interesting images of the heart and pulmonary circulation. Tell students that they should look for Web pages associated with universities, hospitals, and government agencies. Ask students to bookmark the Web sites, and give all students opportunities to visit these sites. **OL**

R Reading Strategy

Using Analogies As students read about blood, explain that it is analogous to a fruit smoothie. Both are liquid mixtures made with several different components. In a raspberry smoothie, the raspberries give the smoothie its red color, despite other fruits mixed in. Ask students which component gives blood its color. (The red blood cells) Continue the discussion by calling on volunteers to explain the function of each of blood's components. **OL**

Caption Answer

Figure 15.2 Red blood cells carry oxygen to cells and carbon dioxide away from cells.

How Blood Circulates Pulmonary circulation is the process by which blood moves between the heart and the lungs. During this process, blood that has lost oxygen and picked up carbon dioxide and wastes receives fresh oxygen in the lungs. The oxygen-rich blood is circulated again through the body. **HS**

Blood

Blood is the fluid that delivers oxygen, hormones, and nutrients to the cells and carries away wastes. Blood is made up of the following components:

- **Plasma.** About 55 percent of total blood volume consists of **plasma**, *the fluid in which other parts of the blood are suspended.* Plasma is mainly water, but it also contains nutrients, proteins, salts, and hormones.

- **Red blood cells.** These cells make up about 40 percent of normal blood. They contain **hemoglobin**, *the oxygen-carrying protein in blood.* Hemoglobin contains iron that binds with oxygen in the lungs and releases the oxygen in the tissues. Hemoglobin also combines with carbon dioxide, which is carried from the cells to the lungs. **R**

- **White blood cells.** These cells protect the body against infection. Some white blood cells surround and ingest the organisms that cause disease. Others form antibodies that provide immunity against a second attack from that specific disease. Still other types of white blood cells fight allergic reactions.

- **Platelets.** Platelets are *types of cells in the blood that cause blood clots to form.* When the wall of a blood vessel tears, platelets collect at the tear. They release chemicals that stimulate the blood to produce small thread-like fibers that trap nearby cells and help to form a clot. The clot blocks the flow of blood and dries to form a scab.

■ **Figure 15.2** Millions of each type of blood cell can be found in just 1 milliliter of blood. *What is the main role of red blood cells?*

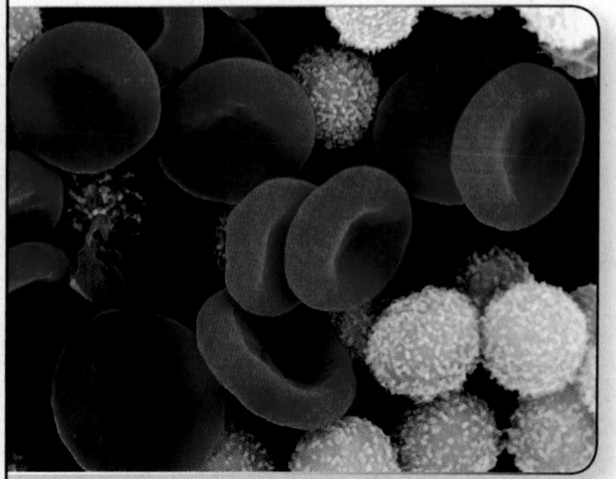

All humans have one of four types of blood: A, B, AB, and O. Each blood type is determined by the presence or absence of certain substances called antigens. Blood types A, B, or AB possess antigens, and a person must receive blood from someone with the same antigen. He or she can, however, receive type O blood, because it contains no antigens. People with type O blood are called universal donors, because anyone can receive their blood. Most blood also carries another substance called the Rh factor. If your blood contains Rh, you are referred to as *Rh positive.* Blood that doesn't have the Rh factor is called *Rh negative.* **AL**

Health Literacy

Natural and Artificial Pacemakers For most people, the normal rhythm of the heart is controlled by the sinoatrial (SA) node, the heart's natural pacemaker. When this natural pacemaker does not function normally, doctors can insert a small, battery-operated artificial pacemaker. With the tip of the pacemaker's lead attached to the wall of the heart, the pacemaker's battery provides an electrical impulse that causes the heart to beat. A sensing device turns the electrical signal off when the heartbeat is above a certain level and on again if the heartbeat slows.

Blood Vessels

R The blood vessels that carry blood throughout the body are shown in **Figure 15.3**. There are three main types of blood vessels: arteries, capillaries, and veins.

- **Arteries** are *blood vessels that carry oxygenated blood away from the heart.* Arteries are vessels that branch into progressively smaller vessels called *arterioles.* The arterioles deliver blood to capillaries.

Figure 15.3 The Cardiovascular System

A network of arteries, veins, and capillaries moves blood throughout the body, providing cells with oxygen and nutrients as well as removing wastes.

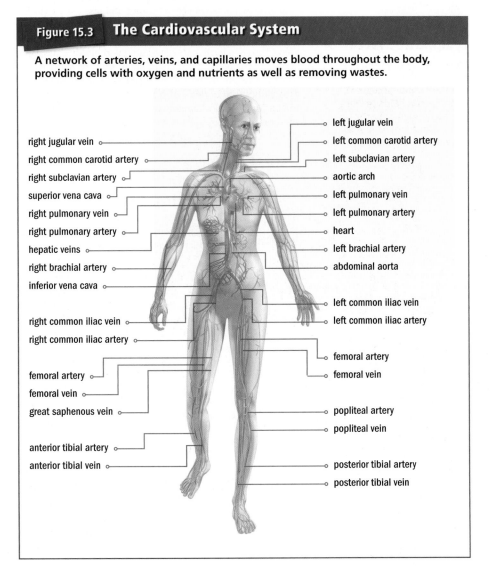

right jugular vein
right common carotid artery
right subclavian artery
superior vena cava
right pulmonary vein
right pulmonary artery
hepatic veins
right brachial artery
inferior vena cava

right common iliac vein
right common iliac artery

femoral artery
femoral vein
great saphenous vein

anterior tibial artery
anterior tibial vein

left jugular vein
left common carotid artery
left subclavian artery
aortic arch
left pulmonary vein
left pulmonary artery
heart
left brachial artery
abdominal aorta

left common iliac vein
left common iliac artery

femoral artery
femoral vein

popliteal artery
popliteal vein

posterior tibial artery
posterior tibial vein

AL Active Learning

Blood Type Grid Divide the class into small groups, and ask each group to make a blood donation grid showing the four blood types. Donors should be listed down the left side of the grid and recipients across the top. If the recipient can accept blood from the donor, have students place an X in the corresponding box. If the recipient cannot accept blood from the donor, the box should be left blank. The completed grid will show that type O is a universal donor. **Ask Students:** *Is there a universal recipient?* (Type AB) **BL OL**

R Reading Strategy

Analyzing a Graphic Using **Figure 15.3**, point out the major vessels mentioned in the description of the heart, including the vena cava and pulmonary arteries and veins. Then ask students to explain why for almost every artery shown in the figure there is a corresponding vein. (Arteries carry oxygenated blood to cells throughout the body. In turn, there must be corresponding veins to carry oxygen-depleted blood back to the heart and lungs.) **OL**

ELL Support

Name and Repeat Write the following words on the board: *arteries, capillaries, veins.* Define each word aloud.

Beginning Use sentences such as "Oxygen-rich blood flows through arteries." Ask students to repeat the sentence. Use the other two words in a sentence, and ask students to also repeat.

Intermediate Ask students for sentence examples for each word.

Advanced Have students write a paragraph that describes the functions of each of the three main types of blood vessels.

Comparing and Contrasting
Ask students how the structures of capillaries and arteries differ. (Capillaries are smaller than arteries, and the walls of capillaries are much thinner than artery walls.) Then ask how their structures contribute to their different functions. (Arteries must be large and thick-walled to carry blood from the heart and withstand the higher blood pressure near the heart. Capillaries must be small with ultra-thin walls to allow gases, nutrients, and wastes to pass through.) **OL**

Main Idea

How Lymph Circulation Works
The lymphatic system helps fight infection and provides immunity to disease. **Ask Students:** *What do white blood cells do?* (Sample answer: They help fight organisms that cause disease.)

W Writing Support

Contrasting Two Networks
By comparing **Figure 15.3** with **Figure 15.4**, students can easily observe similarities between the cardiovascular and lymphatic systems. Ask students to write a paragraph that explains how the two systems differ. (The cardiovascular system includes the heart as a pump, carries blood through its vessels, and provides cells with oxygen and nutrients. The lymphatic system has no pump, carries lymph in its vessels, and helps fight infections.) **OL**

Caption Answer

Figure 15.4 Lymph is moved by the contraction of both the smooth muscles lining the walls of lymph vessels and the surrounding skeletal muscles.

- **Capillaries** are *small vessels that carry blood from arterioles and to small vessels called venules, which empty into veins.* Capillaries form a vast network throughout tissues and organs in the body, reaching almost all body cells. Capillaries near the skin's surface can also dilate, allowing heat to escape the body through the skin. They can also constrict to reduce heat loss if the body temperature drops below normal.

- **Veins** are *blood vessels that return blood to the heart.* While the walls of veins are thinner and less elastic than those of the arteries, they are still able to withstand the pressure exerted by blood flowing through them. The large veins, the *vena cava*, carry deoxygenated blood to the right atrium of the heart. Pulmonary veins carry oxygenated blood to the left atrium. Many veins throughout the body, especially those in the legs, have valves that help prevent the backflow of blood as it is pumped back to the heart. As surrounding muscles contract, they also exert pressure on vein walls, helping to move blood back through the veins.

Figure 15.4

Lymphatic System

The lymphatic system is a system of vessels, much like the cardiovascular system, that helps protect the body against pathogens. *What moves lymph through lymph vessels?*

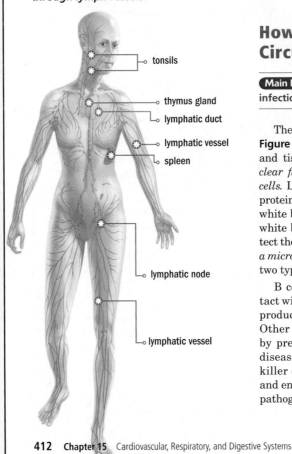

- tonsils
- thymus gland
- lymphatic duct
- lymphatic vessel
- spleen
- lymphatic node
- lymphatic vessel

How Lymph Circulation Works

Main Idea The lymphatic system helps fight infection and provides immunity to disease.

The lymphatic system, shown in **Figure 15.4**, consists of a network of vessels and tissues that move and filter **lymph**, *the clear fluid that fills the spaces around body cells.* Like plasma, lymph contains water and proteins. It also contains fats and specialized white blood cells called lymphocytes. Like the white blood cells in the blood, these cells protect the body against pathogens. A **pathogen** is *a microorganism that causes disease.* There are two types of lymphocytes, B cells and T cells.

B cells multiply when they come in contact with a pathogen. Some of the new B cells produce antibodies that fight the pathogen. Other B cells create an immune response by preventing a second attack of the same disease. There are two main types of T cells, killer cells and helper cells. T cells multiply and enlarge when they come in contact with a pathogen.

Teens Want to Know

What Causes My Lymph Glands to Become Swollen When I'm Sick? The most common cause of swollen lymph nodes is an infection, such as the common cold, strep throat, an ear infection, an abscessed tooth, mumps, measles, and mononucleosis. A lymph node is a bean-shaped capsule of cells, including lymphocytes and macrophages, that attack and capture invading pathogens. During an infection, these capsules become inflamed as they become overwhelmed by invaders. Treatment for swollen lymph nodes usually involves treating the underlying infection.

One type of T cell, killer T cells, release toxins that prevent infections from spreading. Another type of T cell, the helper T cell, activates both the B cells and killer T cells. They also control the body's immune system.

Lymph is filtered by *lymph nodes,* small bean-shaped organs found in lymph vessels. White blood cells within lymph nodes trap and destroy pathogens.

Smooth muscles lining the walls of lymph vessels and surrounding skeletal muscles contract to move lymph toward the heart. Two large lymphatic ducts empty lymph into veins close to the heart, where the lymph is returned to the blood. The lymphatic system also includes certain organs and tissues—such as the spleen, thymus gland, tonsils, adenoids, and appendix—that help protect the body from infection.

Maintaining Your Circulatory Health

Main Idea Healthy habits can help protect the health of the cardiovascular and lymphatic systems.

Many problems with the cardiovascular and lymphatic systems first appear later in life. You can reduce your risk by making healthy decisions throughout your life. Here are some healthful behaviors that should become regular habits:

- Eat a well-balanced diet.
- Maintain a healthy weight.
- Participate in regular aerobic exercise for at least 30 minutes three or four times per week.
- Avoid secondhand smoke and using tobacco products.
- Avoid illegal drug use.
- Get regular medical checkups.

Blood Pressure

Maintaining pressure in the cardiovascular system is important for proper blood circulation. Pressure in arteries is created when the ventricles contract. As blood is forced into the arteries, arterial walls stretch under the increased pressure. When the ventricles relax and refill with blood, arterial pressure decreases. **Blood pressure** is *a measure of the amount of force that the blood places on the walls of blood vessels, particularly large arteries, as it is pumped through the body.*

A blood pressure reading includes two numbers. The first number measures your *systolic pressure*—the maximum pressure as your heart contracts to push blood into your arteries.

READING CHECK

Compare and Contrast How are the cardiovascular and lymphatic systems similar? How are they different?

FITNESS ZONE

I heard that antioxidants provide protection against conditions such as heart disease and cancer. They might even slow down the aging process. I read that researchers at Tufts University in Boston recommend these seven foods in your daily diet: prunes, raisins, blueberries, blackberries, kale, strawberries, and spinach. I should be able to eat at least one of those each day. For more fitness tips, visit the Online Fitness Zone at glencoe.com.

Main Idea

Maintaining Your Circulatory Health Healthy habits can help protect the health of the cardiovascular and lymphatic systems. **Ask Students:** *What steps can you take to keep your circulatory system healthy?* (Sample answers: nutritious eating, maintain a healthy weight, physical activity, avoid tobacco and drugs, get regular checkups)

READING CHECK

Answer Both are a network of vessels that carry liquid. The lymphatic system carries lymph and does not have a pump, while the cardiovascular system carries blood pumped by the heart.

FITNESS ZONE

The Human Machine Arrange students in groups of 5–6 to decide on a machine or piece of equipment with at least four moving parts and a four-beat timing (e.g., truck, blender, washing machine). Each group plans a four-beat timing sequence as follows:

- move every beat (1,2,3,4)
- move every other beat (1, hold, 3, hold)
- move on first beat of 4 (1, hold, hold, hold)
- move 2 times to every beat (1&, 2&, 3&, 4&)

Have the class guess the machine demonstrated by each group.

Cooperative Learning

Make a Poster Review the heart's functions and the habits that can help protect the health of the cardiovascular system. Then, divide the class into small groups and ask each group to design and create a poster that provides information both about the functions of the system and about how to maintain cardiovascular health. Groups can decide which functions and habits they want to highlight. The primary message should be that the cardiovascular system is important and should be taken care of. Place completed posters on the classroom walls.

Cardiovascular System Problems Disorders of the cardiovascular system vary from inherited problems to those that result from illness, diet, or aging. **Ask Students:** *What kinds of heart problems can be inherited?* (Sample answer: Defects in the structure of the heart)

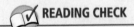

U **Universal Access**

Sound of a Murmur After students have read about heart murmurs, explain that a murmur is a sound that's low and not really distinct. A murmur is what's heard in an auditorium as people talk before a play starts. A listener hears the sound of talking without hearing specific words. Explain that when a doctor listens to a heart murmur, an indistinct "whoosh" or "swish" can be heard. **EL BL**

READING CHECK

Answer anemia

The bottom, or second, number measures your *diastolic pressure*—the pressure at its lowest point when your ventricles relax. A healthy person's blood pressure will vary within a normal range of below 120/80. Exercise and stress will raise blood pressure. Blood pressure that is above 140/90 is considered high and places a strain on the heart. Chronic high blood pressure can cause cardiovascular disease.

Cardiovascular System Problems

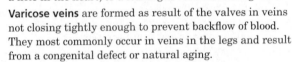 Some cardiovascular problems are inherited; others result from illness, diet, or aging.

These disorders of the cardiovascular system have wide-ranging effects and varying treatments:

- **Congenital heart defects** are conditions of the heart that are present at birth. One common type of congenital heart defect is a septal defect. A hole in the septum allows oxygenated blood to mix with oxygen-depleted blood, affecting the heart's efficiency. Some cases of congenital heart defects result from poor health of the baby's mother during pregnancy. Other cases may be hereditary. Medication and possibly surgery can sometimes repair the affected portion of the heart.

- **Heart murmurs** are abnormal sounds that are made as blood flows through the heart. Some murmurs are due to a hole in the heart, or a leaking or malfunctioning valve.

- **Varicose veins** are formed as result of the valves in veins not closing tightly enough to prevent backflow of blood. They most commonly occur in veins in the legs and result from a congenital defect or natural aging.

- **Anemia** is a condition in which the ability of the blood to carry oxygen is reduced. The blood may contain low numbers of red blood cells or low concentrations of hemoglobin. The most common cause is iron deficiency.

- **Hemophilia** is an inherited disorder. The blood does not clot properly. Bruising and uncontrolled bleeding may occur spontaneously or due to injury. Treatment for hemophilia includes injections that introduce missing clotting proteins into the blood.

- **Leukemia** is a form of cancer in which any one of the different types of white blood cells is produced excessively and abnormally. The abnormal white blood cells do not function properly, making the person susceptible to infection, severe anemia, and possibly uncontrolled bleeding. Chemotherapy, radiation, and bone marrow transplant are all treatment options.

READING CHECK

Cause and Effect What cardiovascular disorder can be avoided through diet?

More About...

Heart Murmurs Through a stethoscope, a heartbeat is heard as two sounds: "lub-DUB." When a heart murmur is present, a "whoosh" or "swish" is also heard. Most heart murmurs are innocent murmurs, meaning they are harmless and do not require treatment. Some heart murmurs, however, indicate a more serious problem, such as a structural defect in the heart from birth. Rheumatic fever and endocarditis, an infection of the inner lining of the heart, are also causes. Ask interested students to find out what doctors do when a heart murmur indicates a serious problem. Students can prepare a written report on what they learn.

Lymphatic System Problems

Main Idea Problems of the lymphatic system can range from mild to life-threatening.

Disorders of the lymphatic system can range from mild to life-threatening. They may be caused by infection or heredity. Lymphatic system disorders include the following:

- **Tonsillitis.** Your tonsils help reduce the number of pathogens entering the body through the respiratory system. If the tonsils become infected, tonsillitis results. It is often treated with antibiotics, or surgery for chronic cases.

- **Immune deficiency.** Immune deficiency results if the immune system is weakened and can no longer protect the body against infection. It may be a congenital condition in which the body cannot make specialized white blood cells, limiting protection against infection. Other causes include HIV, chemotherapy, and sometimes aging.

- **Hodgkin's disease.** Also called Hodgkin's lymphoma, this type of cancer affects the lymph tissue found in lymph nodes and the spleen. Early detection and treatment is essential for recovery. Treatment may include removal of lymph nodes, radiation, and chemotherapy.

 READING CHECK

Apply What is the connection between the immune system and HIV?

LESSON 1 ASSESSMENT

After You Read

Reviewing Facts and Vocabulary

1. Why is the cardiovascular system important to your overall health?
2. What behaviors will help you prevent high blood pressure?
3. What do the blood pressure numbers measure?

Thinking Critically

4. **Infer.** Why are people with type O blood called "universal donors"?
5. **Apply.** Why might lymph nodes become the main site of the body's response to an infection?

Applying Health Skills

6. **Advocacy.** Find out more about heart disease and how to prevent it. What foods and physical activities promote heart health? Design a Web site that promotes heart-healthy behaviors.

Writing Critically

7. Write a paragraph describing three healthy choices you have made to maintain your cardiovascular and lymphatic health.

G⊙ Online

Visit glencoe.com and complete the Interactive Study Guide for this lesson.

 READING CHECK

Answer HIV is a virus in which the immune system can no longer protect the body against infection.

③ ASSESS/ CLOSE

Assessment Resources

📁 FAST FILE ACTIVITIES
Lesson 1 Quiz

 ExamView Assessment Suite CD-ROM

Visit glencoe.com for:
Online Quizzes
Online Learning Center

Progress Monitoring

Reteaching
Ask students to name the functions of the circulatory and lymphatic systems and describe ways these functions are carried out.

Enrichment
Have interested students ask the school nurse to teach them how to use a sphygmomanometer, a device used to measure blood pressure. Then, have these students demonstrate how to measure blood pressure to the class.

G⊙ Online

Have students visit **glencoe.com** and complete the Interactive Study Guide for this lesson.

LESSON 1 ASSESSMENT ANSWERS

1. This system carries oxygen and nutrients to cells, carries carbon dioxide and wastes away from cells, and fights disease through blood cells that fight infection.
2. Maintain a healthy weight with a nutritious, low-salt diet; stay physically active; manage stress; avoid tobacco and drugs.
3. The top number measures systolic pressure against your arteries; bottom shows diastolic pressure, as ventricals relax.
4. Type O blood has no antigens and can therefore be donated to people of any blood type.
5. Lymph nodes filter lymph and contain white blood cells that trap and destroy pathogens to keep them from spreading throughout the body.
6. Web sites will vary. Students should cite reliable sources for information included.
7. Paragraphs will vary.

The Respiratory System

① FOCUS

 GUIDE TO READING

BIG Idea The respiratory system provides oxygen to the blood and removes carbon dioxide from the body. **Ask Students:** *What are the main organs of the respiratory system?* (the lungs)

Before You Read

Note Cards Students should prepare cards for all the respiratory structures.

Main Idea

What Happens During Respiration The main function of the respiratory system is to provide oxygen to the blood and remove carbon dioxide. **Ask Students:** *What happens to air in the lungs when you breathe in and out?* (Sample answer: The oxygen in the air is taken into the body, and carbon dioxide is released from the body.)

Real Life Issues . . . .

Ask volunteers to share their paragraphs with the class. Make a list on the board of activities during which wearing a mask could protect the respiratory system.

 GUIDE TO READING

BIG Idea *The respiratory system provides oxygen to the blood and removes carbon dioxide from the body.*

Before You Read

Prepare Note Cards. On separate index cards, list the various organs of the respiratory system. On the reverse side of each card, write the function of the organ.

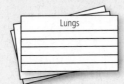

Lungs

New Vocabulary

▶ diaphragm (p. 417)
▶ trachea (p. 417)
▶ bronchi (p. 417)
▶ asthma (p. 420)
▶ tuberculosis (p. 421)
▶ emphysema (p. 421)

The Respiratory System

Real Life Issues . . . .

Breathing Easy. Allison is helping her dad build shelves for the family room. When they are ready to sand the wood, Allison's father asks her to wear a mask like his over her mouth and nose. He explains that sanding sends tiny particles of sawdust into the air that could get into her lungs. The mask blocks the dust so that she can breathe safely.

Writing *Think about a time when you should have worn a mask to protect your respiratory system. Write a paragraph describing the situation. What kind of activity were you doing? How did it affect your mouth, nose, and lungs?*

What Happens During Respiration

Main Idea The respiratory system provides oxygen to the blood and removes carbon dioxide from the body.

The main function of the respiratory system is respiration, the exchange of gases between the body and the environment. In Lesson 1, you learned that carbon dioxide is delivered to the lungs. Your respiratory system removes carbon dioxide from the body and provides it with fresh oxygen. Inhaling and exhaling causes the lungs to expand and deflate slightly.

The process of respiration can be divided into two parts. In *external respiration*, oxygen moves from the lungs into the blood, and carbon dioxide moves from the blood into the lungs. In *internal respiration*, oxygen moves from the blood into the cells, and carbon dioxide moves from the cells into the blood. The continual exchange of gases in both external and internal respiration is essential for survival. Oxygen fuels the brain and allows your body to metabolize food for energy to move muscles.

Home and Community

Avoiding Polluted Air Air pollution can cause serious problems, especially in people with diseases of the respiratory system, in older adults, and in young children. To alert the public to unhealthy air pollution levels, the U.S. Environmental Protection Agency (EPA) developed the Air Quality Index (AQI).

Many newspapers and local television weather broadcasts report the AQI each day, warning if the level of pollutants in the air is high. Have students research the AQI using online resources and write a report of what they find.

How Respiration Works

Main Idea The respiratory system consists of the lungs, trachea, and diaphragm.

Your lungs automatically fill with air and are emptied in a rhythmic way. This rhythm changes with the level of your activity. You've probably noticed that when you do aerobic exercises, like running or fast walking, you tend to breathe harder than when you're sitting still. Breathing is regulated by the brain, which sends impulses to stimulate the muscles involved in respiration. This process provides your body with the oxygen it needs to keep going. It also removes carbon dioxide from the lungs. The lungs are found within the chest cavity and are protected by the ribs. In the base of the chest cavity is the **diaphragm** (DY-uh-fram), *a muscle that separates the chest from the abdominal cavity.*

As you inhale, the diaphragm and the muscles between your ribs contract. This contraction **expands** your chest cavity and your lungs. The pressure inside your lungs is lower than the pressure outside your body, so air naturally flows into your lungs to equalize the pressure. As you exhale, these same muscles relax and your chest cavity decreases. Pressure inside your lungs is higher, so air naturally flows out of your lungs to the outside, the area of lower pressure.

The Lungs

The structure of the lungs can be compared to the structure of a branching tree. Air moves into the lungs through the **trachea** (TRAY-kee-uh), or *the windpipe.* The trachea branches out into two **bronchi** (BRAHN-ky), *the main airways that reach into each lung.* The airways become smaller as they branch out deeper into the lungs. A network of tubes called *bronchioles* brings air closer to the site of external respiration. At the end of each bronchiole are groups of microscopic structures called *alveoli.* Shown in **Figure 15.5** on page 418, alveoli are thin-walled air sacs covered with capillaries. Gas exchange takes place as oxygen and carbon dioxide spread across the walls of the capillaries and alveoli.

Other Respiratory Structures

The respiratory system also includes structures in the upper airways. Air enters and exits your body through the nose and mouth. The membranes of the nose are lined with hairlike structures, called *cilia,* and with cells that produce mucus. The cilia and mucus work together to help prevent foreign particles such as dust, bacteria, and viruses from moving deeper into the respiratory system.

Academic Vocabulary

expand *(verb):* to open up

✓ **READING CHECK**

Explain In what structures does gas exchange take place?

② TEACH

✓ **READING CHECK**

Answer Both involve the exchange of oxygen and carbon dioxide.

Main Idea

How Respiration Works The lungs, trachea, and diaphragm are the main structures of the respiratory system. **Ask Students:** *What structures other than the lungs are involved in breathing?* (Sample answer: the diaphragm and trachea)

W **Writing Support**

Descriptive Writing Ask students to write a first-person story about an oxygen molecule that gets drawn into a person's nose and then down into the lungs. Ask that the story include, in an imaginative way, all of the structures the molecule would pass along the way to an alveolus deep in the lungs, where it changes places with a carbon dioxide molecule in the blood of a capillary. **OL** **AL**

Academic Integration

Science The internal and external respiration of humans and all other animals forms part of a cycle of matter called the carbon cycle. In internal respiration, oxygen is used by cells to break down sugar to produce energy. A by-product of that chemical reaction is carbon dioxide. Through external respiration, that carbon dioxide is released into the air, forming part of Earth's atmosphere. Plants and other producer organisms use the carbon dioxide in air to carry out photosynthesis. Have interested students investigate the carbon cycle and prepare a report for the class.

Figure 15.5   The Respiratory System

U Universal Access

Respiratory Structures As students examine **Figure 15.5**, ask a volunteer to read aloud the annotations of the *epiglottis, larynx,* and *trachea.* Then ask each student to gently run an index finger up and down the neck, feeling the rings of the trachea. Then, ask students to swallow as they keep the finger on the neck. Explain that the movement they feel is the raising of the larynx as the epiglottis closes over the trachea. **BL EL**

Caption Answer

Figure 15.5 Capillaries, pulmonary artery, pulmonary vein

HS Health Skills Practice

Advocating Respiratory Health Display several full-page advertisements from popular teen magazines. Then divide the class into small groups, and ask each group to create a full-page magazine ad that advocates reducing the risk of developing respiratory problems by practicing healthful behaviors. Students might illustrate their ads with original drawings or with images found online. **OL**

The lungs are the principal organs of the respiratory system. *Which structures in the diagram are also parts of the cardiovascular system?*

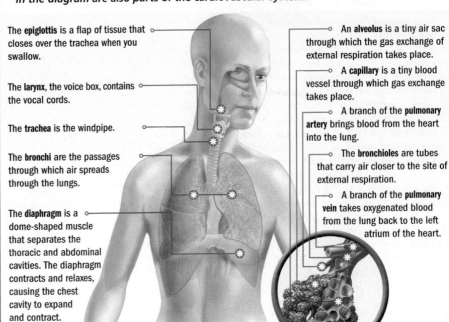

The **epiglottis** is a flap of tissue that closes over the trachea when you swallow.

The **larynx**, the voice box, contains the vocal cords.

The **trachea** is the windpipe.

The **bronchi** are the passages through which air spreads through the lungs.

The **diaphragm** is a dome-shaped muscle that separates the thoracic and abdominal cavities. The diaphragm contracts and relaxes, causing the chest cavity to expand and contract.

An **alveolus** is a tiny air sac through which the gas exchange of external respiration takes place.

A **capillary** is a tiny blood vessel through which gas exchange takes place.

A branch of the **pulmonary artery** brings blood from the heart into the lung.

The **bronchioles** are tubes that carry air closer to the site of external respiration.

A branch of the **pulmonary vein** takes oxygenated blood from the lung back to the left atrium of the heart.

The air that enters the respiratory system is filtered, warmed, and moistened. The air then moves into the *pharynx*, or throat, and then into the *trachea*, or windpipe. The tissue that lines the trachea is also lined with mucus and cilia to trap particles and prevent them from going deeper into the respiratory system.

Other structures that are not directly involved in respiration, but have important functions in the respiratory system, are the larynx and the epiglottis. The *larynx*, or voice box, connects the throat and the trachea. The larynx contains the vocal cords, two bands of tissue that produce sound when air forced between them causes them to vibrate.

The *epiglottis* is a flap of tissue located above the larynx. It folds down to close off the entrance to the larynx and trachea when you swallow. This is an involuntary action that keeps food or drink from entering the respiratory system. If you eat too quickly or talk or laugh while eating, your food may get past the epiglottis and "go down the wrong pipe." The piece of food stimulates the cough reflex to expel the material from your respiratory system.

Promoting School Wellness

Asthma Action Plan The health office of many schools keeps on file an action plan for each student who has asthma. This written plan usually includes a list of medications the student needs and when and how the student should take them. The school may also have a written procedure for handling an asthma attack at school or at a school-sponsored field trip or event. Ask interested students to learn about the school's procedures for caring for students with asthma and write a report on what they learn.

Maintaining Your Respiratory Health

Main Idea Caring for your lungs can prevent many respiratory disorders.

Respiratory problems can affect the functioning of other body systems and, in turn, many other aspects of your daily life. Imagine not being able to climb a flight of stairs without running out of breath. The single most important decision you can make for your respiratory health is not to smoke. Smoking damages all parts of the respiratory system and is the main cause of lung cancer. Smoking can also cause bronchitis and emphysema, and increase the likelihood of asthma in children. Tobacco use also reduces the rate of lung growth in teens. Avoiding tobacco use and exposure to secondhand smoke will decrease your risk. Air pollution also increases the risk of respiratory health problems and certain types of cancers.

Regular physical activity is also important for a healthy respiratory system. Increased respiration during exercise improves the capacity of the lungs to pass oxygen into the blood. Exercise also increases the total amount of air that is moved into and out of your body.

Washing your hands regularly can help prevent infection. Bacteria and viruses can be easily transmitted to the respiratory system when contaminated hands touch the nose or mouth. Limiting your exposure to pollutants in the air, including secondhand or environmental tobacco smoke, can also reduce your risk of developing respiratory disorders.

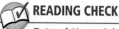

READING CHECK

Extend How might a friend's smoking habit affect your respiratory health?

Respiratory System Problems

Main Idea Problems of the respiratory system can be mild, such as a cold, or serious and even life threatening.

HS

Problems of the respiratory system range from mild infections to disorders that can damage lung tissue and alveoli and prevent proper ventilation. Colds and influenza are common infections of the upper respiratory system. Other infections and disorders affect the lower respiratory tract.

- **Sinusitis** is an inflammation of the tissues that line the sinuses, air-filled cavities above the nasal passages and throat. The inflammation can result from allergies or an infection. Symptoms include nasal congestion, headache, and fever. Treatment includes nasal decongestant drops or sprays and antibiotics.

I like to work out with a friend. During our workouts, we talk. My PE teacher said that when we do aerobic exercises, we should be a little winded but still able to talk or sing. For more fitness tips, visit the Online Fitness Zone at **glencoe.com**.

Main Idea

Maintaining Your Respiratory Health Maintaining respiratory health primarily involves caring for the lungs, and that includes not smoking. **Ask Students:** *What is the most important behavior you should avoid to keep your lungs healthy?* (Smoking)

READING CHECK

Answer Breathing in environmental smoke can damage the respiratory system.

Sports Aerobics Have small groups of students make up their own sports aerobics combinations.

- Each routine must have at least four parts (e.g., shoot, jump, rebound, dribble, pass)
- Groups develop an aerobic routine that can be practiced and repeated.
- Suggest they put routines to music.

Main Idea

Respiratory System Problems Problems with the respiratory system range from mild infections to serious disorders. **Ask Students:** *What is a mild infection of the respiratory system, and what is a more serious disorder?* (Sample answer: A cold is a mild infection; asthma is a serious disorder.)

Writing Strategy

A Story About Improving Respiratory Health Have students write a story about a teen who is always short of breath. In this story, the teen decides to make changes to improve the situation. For example, a sedentary teen may decide to get in shape. The reason for the poor respiratory health and what convinces the teen to change is up to the writer. Each story should conclude, though, with a description of steps the teen takes to improve respiratory health.

Real World CONNECTION

Answers to Activity

Students' opinion articles will vary, though each should include accurate information about the respiratory system. In their research, students should find that tobacco use is a leading cause of preventable death.

R Reading Strategy

Analyzing a Graphic Explain that pollen, dust, dust mites, animal dander, tobacco smoke, and various forms of air pollution are called triggers because they can trigger an asthma attack. Ask students how an inhaler relieves an asthma attack. (The inhaler dispenses medication that dilates, or widens, the airways that have narrowed as a result of the attack.) **OL**

Caption Answer

Figure 15.6 Air pollution could trigger an asthma attack.

C Critical Thinking

Identifying Cause and Effect After students have read about emphysema, ask them what is the most common cause of the destruction of alveoli that occurs in the disease. (Smoking) Then ask what effect the progressive destruction of alveoli would have on a person's breathing. (Because gas exchange occurs in alveoli, a person whose alveoli are progressively destroyed would have more and more trouble exchanging that gas.) **OL**

Real World CONNECTION

The Effects of Smoking

Ari's health teacher, Mrs. Gilcrest, held up a jar filled with a brown, gooey substance. Mrs. Gilcrest told the class that the jar represented the lungs of smokers. The brown sludge represented the amount of tar that gets into a smokers lungs each year from smoking one pack of cigarettes a day. Ari thought about his Uncle Stan, who wears an oxygen tank because he has emphysema and has trouble breathing. "No wonder," thought Ari. "Uncle Stan smoked about a pack of cigarettes a day for as long as I can remember."

Activity Reading / Writing

Conduct research to learn the number of deaths each year that are caused by respiratory illnesses of tobacco users. Write an opinion article to persuade teens to avoid tobacco use. Explain how avoiding tobacco use will reduce the risk of respiratory diseases.

- **Bronchitis** is an inflammation of the bronchi caused by infection or exposure to irritants such as tobacco smoke or air pollution. In bronchitis, the membranes that line the bronchi produce excessive amounts of mucus in the airways. This blocks the airways and leads to symptoms such as coughing, wheezing, and shortness of breath that worsen with physical activity. Treatment includes avoiding exposure to the irritant and taking antibiotics.

R

- **Asthma** (AZ-muh) is *an inflammatory condition in which the trachea, bronchi, and bronchioles become narrowed, causing difficulty breathing.* During an asthma attack, an involuntary contraction of smooth airway muscles leads to chest tightness and breathing difficulty. Acute asthma attacks can be relieved with an inhaler that dispenses medication to dilate, or widen, the airways.

■ **Figure 15.6** An inhaler can relieve an asthma attack. Long-term treatment of asthma includes using medication that reduces inflammation and avoiding substances that can trigger an attack, such as pollen, dust, animal dander, and tobacco smoke. *Why is it important for an asthmatic person to avoid air pollution?*

Myths & Reality

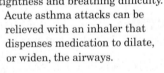

Asthma

Myth: A person can grow out of asthma.

Fact: A person cannot grow out of asthma. For about half of children with asthma, the condition becomes inactive during the teen years. In adulthood, though, asthma symptoms can return.

Myth: A person with asthma can bring on the symptoms at any time just to get attention.

Fact: A person with asthma has no control over when attacks occur, and asthma attacks cannot be faked.

- **Pneumonia** is an inflammation of the lungs commonly caused by a bacterial or viral infection. In a common type of pneumonia, the alveoli swell and become clogged with mucus, decreasing the amount of gas exchange. Symptoms include cough, fever, chills, and chest pain. Bacterial pneumonia is treated with antibiotics.
- **Tuberculosis** is *a contagious bacterial infection that usually affects the lungs.* When a person is infected with tuberculosis, the immune system surrounds the infected area and isolates it. In this inactive stage, which can last for many years, a person doesn't show symptoms. However, if the immune system is weakened by illness or age, the infection can become active. During this active stage, symptoms include cough, fever, fatigue, and weight loss. Treatment includes antibiotics and hospitalization.
- **Emphysema** is *a disease that progressively destroys the walls of the alveoli.* Symptoms include breathing difficulty and chronic cough. Although the symptoms of emphysema can be treated, the tissue damage is permanent. Emphysema is almost always caused by smoking.

C

 READING CHECK

Explain Why can you get tuberculosis from someone who doesn't show any symptoms of the disease?

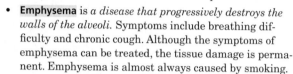 LESSON **2** ASSESSMENT

After You Read

Reviewing Facts and Vocabulary

1. What causes the lungs to fill with air?
2. Which problems with the respiratory system can be caused by smoking?
3. How can washing your hands protect your respiratory system?

Thinking Critically

4. **Compare.** How do internal respiration and external respiration differ?
5. **Apply.** A friend wants to quit smoking. You notice that just walking to school with you leaves her breathing hard. How can you encourage her to quit smoking?

Applying Health Skills

6. **Communication Skills.** Imagine you have a close family member who bicycles to work on major streets during rush hour. During this time, air pollution is at its worst, and a cyclist inhales a lot of it. Write a dialogue in which you encourage the family member to consider the negative effects of this practice. Explain the problems that can result.

Writing Critically

7. **Expository.** Write a paragraph explaining how oxygen and carbon dioxide are exchanged through the respiratory system.

G⊙ Online

Visit glencoe.com and complete the Interactive Study Guide for this lesson.

 READING CHECK

Answer In the inactive stage of tuberculosis, an infected person is without symptoms but can still spread the disease.

3 ASSESS/ CLOSE

Assessment Resources

📁 *FAST FILE* **ACTIVITIES**
Lesson 2 Quiz

💿 *ExamView Assessment Suite* CD-ROM

Visit glencoe.com for:
Online Quizzes
Online Learning Center

Progress Monitoring

Reteaching
Have students work in small groups to write questions about key concepts discussed in Lesson 2. Compile the questions and use them as a basis for discussion.

Enrichment
Have students use online resources to research the cause, symptoms, and treatment of bronchitis. Ask students to present their findings to the class.

G⊙ Online

Have students visit **glencoe.com** and complete the Interactive Study Guide for this lesson.

LESSON **2** ASSESSMENT ANSWERS

1. The contraction of the diaphragm and the muscles between the ribs expand the chest cavity and lungs. The lower pressure inside the lungs causes air to flow in.
2. Bronchitis and emphysema
3. Frequently washing hands helps keep them free of bacteria and viruses that can be easily transmitted to the respiratory system by touching the nose and mouth.
4. During internal respiration, gases are exchanged between blood and cells. During external respiration, gases are exchanged between blood and the lungs.
5. Sample answer: Explain that smoking damages the lungs and causes diseases.
6. Dialogues will vary but should include respiratory problems and air pollution.
7. Paragraphs will vary.

The Digestive System

① FOCUS

GUIDE TO READING

BIG Idea Students will learn about how the digestive system provides nutrients and energy to the body through the digestion of food. **Ask Students:** *What are the main parts of the digestive system?* (Sample answer: The mouth, esophagus, stomach, small intestine, and large intestine)

Before You Read

Chart Students' charts will vary.

Main Idea

What Happens During Digestion Digestion involves breaking down food, absorbing the digested food, and elimination of body wastes. **Ask Students:** *What is involved in breaking down food into a form the body's cells can use?* (The chewing of food and the breaking down of food by digestive juices in the stomach.)

Real Life Issues ....

Ask volunteers to share their descriptions with the class. **Ask Students:** *How would you describe a time when food affected the way you felt?* Most students will describe eating too much at a meal or eating unhealthful foods that made them feel sick. Discuss why students think the foods affected them that way.

422

GUIDE TO READING

BIG Idea The digestive system provides nutrients and energy for your body through the digestion of food.

Before You Read

Create a Chart. Make a three-column chart like the one below. In the first column, list the organs of the digestive system. In the second, describe the function of each organ. In the third, list behaviors that contribute to the health of each organ.

Digestive organ	What it does	How to keep healthy

New Vocabulary

▸ mastication (p. 423)
▸ peristalsis (p. 424)
▸ gastric juices (p. 424)
▸ bile (p. 424)
▸ peptic ulcer (p. 427)
▸ appendicitis (p. 427)

The Digestive System

Real Life Issues ....

Fast-Food Folly. Joey has been looking forward to lunch with his uncle at Joey's favorite fast-food restaurant. He orders a double burger, a side of cheese fries, and a giant-size soda. They share a banana split for dessert. Soon after eating, Joey feels bloated and queasy. Later that afternoon, he feels tired, even though he hasn't done any physical activity. Even after a quick nap in front of the television, he still doesn't feel good. Joey wonders if it has something to do with his lunch.

Writing *Write a description of a time when the food you ate affected the way you felt afterward. Describe how your energy level was affected.*

What Happens During Digestion

Main Idea In digestion, foods are broken down and absorbed as nourishment or eliminated as waste.

The foods you eat provide nourishment. That food and drink, however, must be broken down into smaller nutrients to be absorbed into the blood and carried to the body's cells. The digestive system functions can be divided into three main processes:

- **Digestion** is the mechanical and chemical breakdown of foods within the stomach and intestines for use by the body's cells.
- **Absorption** is the passage of digested food from the digestive tract into the cardiovascular system.
- **Elimination** is the body's expulsion of undigested food or body wastes.

U

More About...

Digestion Digestion varies depending on the nutrient being digested.

- Carbohydrate: Digestion begins in the mouth, where saliva breaks down starch molecules. In the small intestine, an enzyme breaks down those molecules into glucose, which is absorbed into blood.

- Protein: Digestion begins with acid in the stomach and is completed in the small intestine, where proteins are broken down into amino acids that are absorbed by blood.

- Fat: Digestion occurs mainly in the small intestine, where bile acids from the liver dissolve fats and move the smaller molecules into the lining of the small intestine.

How Digestion Works

Main Idea The digestive system consists of the mouth, esophagus, stomach, and intestines.

Digestion includes two processes. The mechanical process involves chewing, mashing, and breaking food down. The chemical process involves secretions produced by digestive organs. **Figure 15.7** shows the organs involved in digestion.

- **Teeth.** The teeth break the food you eat into smaller pieces. **Mastication** (mas-tih-KAY-shun) is *the process of chewing*, which prepares food to be swallowed.

- **Salivary glands.** These glands produce digestive juices. Saliva contains an enzyme that begins to break down the starches and sugars in food into smaller particles.

- **Tongue.** The tongue prepares chewed food for swallowing by shaping it. The *uvula*, a small flap of tissue at the back of the mouth, prevents food from entering the nasal passages. The *epiglottis*, tissue covering the throat, prevents food from entering the respiratory system.

Academic Vocabulary

involve *(verb):* to require as a necessary accompaniment

Figure 15.7 The Digestive System

The organs of the digestive system break down and move food through the body, providing nutrients that are absorbed into the blood and transferred to cells.

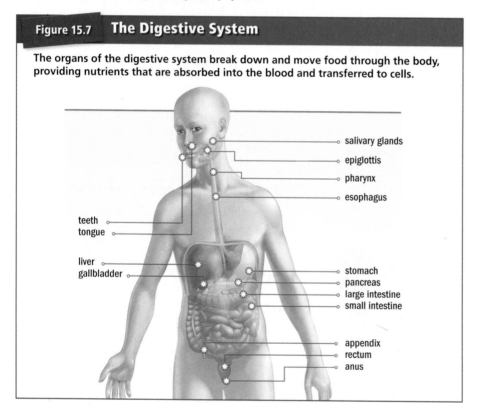

salivary glands
epiglottis
pharynx
esophagus
teeth
tongue
liver
gallbladder
stomach
pancreas
large intestine
small intestine
appendix
rectum
anus

Lesson 3   The Digestive System   **423**

② TEACH

Main Idea

How Digestion Works The mouth, esophagus, stomach, and intestines are involved in the process of digestion. **Ask Students:** *How does digestion of food begin in the mouth?* (Sample answer: Food is broken apart by teeth, then broken down by a chemical in saliva.)

U Universal Access

Three Main Processes Write the three main processes of the digestive system on the board. (Digestion, absorption, elimination) Pronounce each term clearly and have students repeat aloud. Then have volunteers read aloud the description of each process. **BL** **EL**

Academic Vocabulary

Involve Explain that any process involves a series of actions. Ask students to describe what riding a bike involves or kicking a soccer ball involves. Students should describe the actions that make up the process. Point out that because the legs are used to ride a bike or kick a ball, the legs are "involved" in the process, just as various organs are "involved" in digestion.

Teacher to Teacher

Timothy Johnson • Coweta High School, Coweta, OK

System Comparison Highly trained athletes and musicians are similar to the individual systems of the body. When placed on a team, or in a band, an individual has a unique job to perform. Each must work with others to form a more complex "system." Have students select a sports team or musical group. Identify the individual tasks of each athlete or musician. The success of the team, or band, is dependent on the job of each individual. Have students list the ways in which the systems of the body are similar to a team or band.

AL Active Learning

Modeling Peristalsis Divide the class into small groups and provide each group with a length of plastic tubing and a bead or small ball that fits tightly into the tubing. Have each student pinch the tubing above the ball and pull down the tubing. Students will observe that the ball moves down the tubing. Then ask students what process in the digestive system this activity models. (peristalsis) **BL** **OL**

C Critical Thinking

Comparing and Contrasting After students have read about the stomach, ask them what are the three main tasks. (Mixing food with gastric juices, storing partially digested food and liquid, moving food into the small intestine) **OL**

■ **Figure 15.8** The shape of the villi of the small intestine gives them a large surface area to maximize the amount of nutrients they can absorb. *Where do nutrients go once they are absorbed by the small intestine?*

Caption Answer

Figure 15.8 Nutrients go from the capillaries of the villi in the small intestine to the rest of the body by the blood in the cardiovascular system.

The Esophagus

When food is swallowed, it enters the esophagus, the muscular tube about 10 inches long that connects the pharynx with the stomach. Food is moved through the esophagus, stomach, and intestine through **peristalsis** (pare-ih-STAWL-suhs), *a series of involuntary muscle contractions that moves food through the digestive tract.* The action of peristalsis begins as soon as food is swallowed. A sphincter muscle—a circular muscle at the entrance to the stomach—allows food to move from the esophagus into the stomach. **AL**

The Stomach

The stomach is a hollow, sac-like organ enclosed in a wall of muscles. These muscles are flexible and allow the stomach to expand when you eat. The stomach, shown in **Figure 15.9**, has three tasks:

- **Mixing foods with gastric juices. Gastric juices** are *secretions from the stomach lining that contain hydrochloric acid and pepsin, an enzyme that digests protein.* The hydrochloric acid kills bacteria taken in with food and creates an acidic environment for pepsin to do its work. Mucus produced by the stomach forms a protective lining so that the gastric juices do not harm the stomach. **C**

- **Storing partially digested food and liquid.** The stomach holds the food for further digestion before it is moved into the small intestine.

- **Moving food into the small intestine.** As food is digested in the stomach, it is converted to *chyme* (kym), a creamy, fluid mixture of food and gastric juices. Peristalsis moves the chyme into the small intestine through an opening controlled by another sphincter muscle.

The Pancreas, Liver, and Gallbladder

In the small intestine, the juices of two other digestive organs mix with the food to continue the process of digestion. The pancreas produces enzymes that break down the carbohydrates, fats, and proteins in food. Glands in the wall of the intestine produce other enzymes that help this process.

The liver produces another digestive juice—**bile**, *a yellow-green, bitter fluid important in the breakdown and absorption of fats.* Bile is stored in the gallbladder between meals. At mealtimes, it is secreted from the gallbladder into the bile duct to reach the intestine and mix with fats in food. Bile acids dissolve the fats into the watery contents of the intestine. After the fat is dissolved, it is digested by enzymes from the pancreas and the lining of the intestine.

Teens Want to Know

How Does Stomach Stapling Work? Stomach stapling is a common term for a type of surgery called gastric bypass. The surgeon uses surgical staples and a plastic band to make a small pouch at the top of the stomach, where food and liquids are stored. This pouch is not cut off from the rest of the stomach. The purpose of the surgery is to reduce the size of the stomach so that a person can eat only one cup of food before feeling uncomfortably full. Stomach stapling is done only on people who are obese and have tried other methods for losing weight.

Figure 15.9 The Stomach

Digestion continues in the stomach. The three layers of stomach muscles each move in different directions to aid both mechanical and chemical digestion.

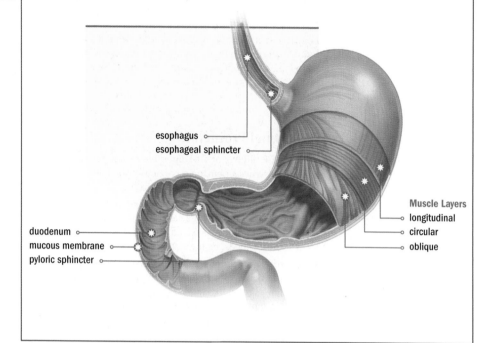

esophagus
esophageal sphincter

duodenum
mucous membrane
pyloric sphincter

Muscle Layers
longitudinal
circular
oblique

The Small and Large Intestines

The small intestine is 20 to 23 feet in length and 1 inch in diameter. It consists of three parts: the *duodenum,* the *jejunum,* and the *ileum.* As chyme enters the duodenum, it contains partially digested carbohydrates and proteins and undigested fats. This mixture is further dissolved by digestive juices secreted from the small intestine, liver, and pancreas.

About 90 percent of all nutrients are absorbed through the small intestine. The inner wall of the small intestine contains millions of fingerlike projections called *villi.* The villi are lined with capillaries that absorb the nutrients. Unabsorbed material leaves the small intestine in the form of liquid and fiber and moves by peristalsis into the large intestine.

The undigested parts of the food—fiber, or roughage—pass into the *colon,* or large intestine. The large intestine is about 2.5 inches in diameter and 5 to 6 feet in length. Its function is to absorb water, vitamins, and salts, and to eliminate waste.

READING CHECK

Interpret What are the differences between the small and large intestines?

Lesson 3   The Digestive System   **425**

W Writing Support
Describing Digestion Have students write a two-paragraph description, illustrated with a labeled drawing, of how digestion works in the stomach. Explain that they should summarize what they read in their text by including only the most important terms and processes. OL

R Reading Strategy
Make a Table On the board, make a table to compare and contrast the small intestine with the large intestine. Create four columns with these headings: Intestine, Size, Position in System, Functions. Have students copy this into their notebooks and then complete the table with information from their text. Call on volunteers to share what they have included in each column of the table. BL OL

READING CHECK

Answer The small intestine is longer and narrower than the large intestine. The small intestine absorbs 90 percent of the nutrients in food, while the large intestine absorbs water, vitamins, and salts from the undigested parts of food.

Academic Integration

Math   Have students convert the length and diameter of both the small and large intestines to metric units.

- The small intestine: 20–25 feet in length and 1 inch in diameter
- The large intestine: 5–6 feet in length and 2.5 inches in diameter

Have students use these conversion factors:

- 1 ft = 30.48 cm = 0.3048 m
- 1 in = 2.54 cm

(Small intestine: 609.6–701.04 cm (6.1–7.0 m) long, 2.54 cm in diameter; Large intestine: 152.4–182.88 cm (1.5—1.8 m) long, 6.35 cm in diameter)

Main Idea

Digestive System Problems A healthy digestive system begins with good eating and hygiene habits. **Ask Students:** *What purpose is served by eating a variety of low-fat, high-fiber foods?* (Sample answer: These foods contribute to the proper functioning of the digestive system.)

Caption Answer

Figure 15.10 Drinking at least eight 8-ounce glasses of water each day and getting regular physical activity.

HS Health Skills Practice

Goal Setting After students read about behaviors that positively affect the digestive system, ask them to keep a log for one week to record how well they practice the five behaviors listed in the text. Logs may be kept confidential. At the end of the week, have students assess how well they maintained their digestive health. Then have them set a long-term goal to improve one or more behaviors and develop an action plan for achieving that goal. **OL**

Digestive System Problems

Main Idea Digestive problems range from indigestion to acute conditions that require immediate medical attention.

Taking care of your digestive system begins with the foods you eat and how you eat them. To maintain your digestive health, eat a variety of low-fat, high-fiber foods, wash your hands before preparing or eating meals, eat slowly and chew your food thoroughly, drink at least eight 8-ounce glasses of water a day, and avoid using food as a way of dealing with your emotions. Some digestive system problems may require medications and a visit to a health professional.

Functional Problems

The functioning of the digestive system may be affected by illness, stress, or eating a particular food. Functional problems of the digestive system include the following:

- **Indigestion** is a feeling of discomfort in the upper abdomen, sometimes with gas and nausea. It can be caused by eating too much food, eating too quickly, eating spicy or high-fat foods, or having a stomach disorder or stress.

- **Constipation** causes the feces to become dry and hard, making bowel movements difficult. It can be caused by not drinking enough water or not consuming enough fiber to move wastes through the digestive system.

- **Heartburn** is a burning sensation in the center of the chest that may rise up to the throat. It results from acid reflux, or the backflow of stomach acid into the esophagus. Using tobacco, alcohol, and aspirin, or eating spicy or greasy foods can cause heartburn.

■ **Figure 15.10** Eating plenty of fruits and vegetables can help prevent constipation. *What other health practices help you avoid constipation?*

Health Literacy

Causes of Peptic Ulcers For decades, most doctors thought that stress, alcohol, and spicy foods were the causes of most peptic ulcers. When an ulcer was diagnosed, the treatment often included advice about lowering the stress level in everyday life and eating bland foods. While too much stress can contribute to the severity of any disease, doctors now know that about 90 percent of peptic ulcers are caused by a type of bacteria, called *Helicobacter pylori*. An antibiotic is used to kill the bacteria.

- **Gas** produced from the breakdown of food is normal. Excessive gas can result in cramps or an uncomfortable feeling of fullness in the abdomen.
- **Nausea** is the feeling of discomfort that sometimes precedes vomiting. Motion sickness, pathogens, some medications, and dehydration can cause nausea.
- **Diarrhea** is the frequent passage of watery feces. It can be caused by bacterial or viral infections, some medications, a change in eating style, overeating, emotional turmoil, or nutritional deficiencies. Dehydration may result with each episode of diarrhea.

CA

Structural Problems

The seriousness of structural problems of the digestive system can vary. Some problems are temporary or easily treated, others are serious and require immediate medical attention.

- **Tooth decay** may make it difficult to chew foods thoroughly. Brushing and flossing teeth daily can prevent tooth decay, along with regular dental checkups.
- **Gastritis** is an inflammation of the mucous membrane that lines the stomach. An increase in the production of stomach acid, use of tobacco or alcohol, bacterial or viral infections, and some medications can cause gastritis. Symptoms include pain, indigestion, decreased appetite, and nausea and vomiting.
- A **peptic ulcer** is *a sore in the lining of the digestive tract.* Peptic ulcers can be caused by a bacterial infection or the overuse of aspirin. Common symptoms include abdominal pain that worsens when the stomach is empty, nausea, and vomiting. Ulcers can cause stomach bleeding.
- **Gallstones** form when cholesterol in bile crystallizes. Gallstones can block the bile duct between the gallbladder and the small intestine. Symptoms of a blockage include pain in the upper right portion of the abdomen, nausea, vomiting, and fever.
- **Lactose intolerance** results from an inability to digest lactose, a type of sugar found in milk and other dairy products. Lactose is normally broken down by the enzyme *lactase.* People who are lactose intolerant do not produce enough lactase. Symptoms include abdominal cramps, bloating, gas, and diarrhea. Soy products are a good replacement for milk or dairy products.

C

- **Appendicitis** is *inflammation of the appendix,* the 3- to 4-inch tube at the tip of the large intestine. It can be caused by a blockage or bacterial infection. Symptoms include pain in the lower right abdomen and a fever.

FITNESS ZONE

I've heard all kinds of advice about how many meals a day you should eat. Everyone seems to have a different opinion about whether we should eat five or six smaller meals a day, or three large ones. It's really a personal decision based on what works best for you. Eating can help speed up your metabolism so you burn more calories. Eating smaller meals throughout the day keeps your body's engine revved up. For more fitness tips, visit the Online Fitness Zone at glencoe.com.

 READING CHECK

Compare Which structural problems of the digestive system can result from bacterial infection?

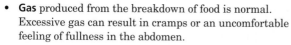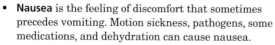

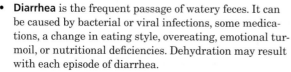

CA Cultural Awareness

Upset Stomach—A Cause of Death In the United States, diarrhea can be a discomfort and minor inconvenience. In the developing world, though, diarrhea is often deadly, especially for children, who suffer dehydration more quickly than adults. Ask interested students to use online resources to investigate the causes of diarrhea in children and what is being done to reduce deaths. **AL**

C Critical Thinking

Lactose Intolerance and Calcium Needs Discuss with students the problems that could arise if a person avoids milk and other dairy products due to lactose intolerance. **Ask Students:** *What are some other nutritional sources of calcium in addition to soy products?* (Sample answer: Some vegetables that are high in calcium, such as broccoli and kale.) Yogurt with active cultures may also be a good source of calcium for some people. **OL**

 READING CHECK

Answer Tooth decay, gastritis, peptic ulcers, and colitis

English Language Coach

Derivation of a Term Write *lactose intolerance* on the board. Point out that the suffix *-ose* is used in chemistry to indicate a type of sugar. Explain that lactose is a type of sugar found in dairy products. Then explain that the second word in the term begins with the prefix *in-*, which means "not." The base word *tolerance* derives from a Latin word meaning "to put up with." A person with lactose intolerance, then, is a person whose digestive system will "not put up with the sugar in dairy products."

ASSESS/ CLOSE

Assessment Resources

 FAST FILE ACTIVITIES
Lesson 3 Quiz

ExamView
Assessment Suite CD-ROM

Visit glencoe.com **for:**
Online Quizzes
Online Learning Center

Progress Monitoring

Reteaching
Have students work with partners to revise the three-column chart they created about the organs of the digestive system.

Enrichment
Have students create ten quiz questions based on lesson content. Then allow students to quiz their classmates.

 **Go Online**

Have students visit **glencoe.com** and complete the Interactive Study Guide for this lesson.

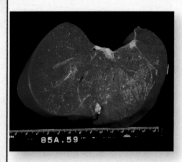

■ **Figure 15.11** Severe damage to the liver from cirrhosis may require a liver transplant. *What are the causes of cirrhosis?*

Decreased appetite, nausea, and vomiting will also occur. The appendix may burst, spreading infection throughout the abdomen, which can lead to death.

- **Colitis** is the inflammation of the large intestine, or colon. It may be caused by bacterial or viral infections. Symptoms can include fever, abdominal pain, and diarrhea that may contain blood.

- **Colon cancer** is the second leading cause of cancer death in the United States. It usually develops in the lowest part of the colon, near the rectum. A low-fat, high-fiber eating plan decreases the risk of colon cancer. Any rectal bleeding should be checked by a medical professional.

- **Hemorrhoids** are veins in the rectum and anus that may become swollen and inflamed. Hemorrhoids may occur with constipation, during pregnancy, and after childbirth. Signs of hemorrhoids include itching, pain, and bleeding.

- **Crohn's disease** causes inflammation of the lining of the digestive tract. Symptoms include diarrhea, weight loss, fever, and abdominal pain. The cause is not known, but seems to be associated with immune system problems.

- **Cirrhosis,** or scarring of the liver tissue, is caused by prolonged heavy alcohol use. Cirrhosis can lead to liver failure and may cause death.

LESSON 3 ASSESSMENT

After You Read

Reviewing Facts and Vocabulary
1. What functions of the digestive system take place in the small intestine?
2. Describe the actions that cause food to move through the digestive tract.
3. What are three behaviors that help prevent indigestion?

Thinking Critically
4. **Evaluate.** What happens to the nutrients in food as it passes through the digestive system?
5. **Apply.** Create a menu with a full day of meals that you can serve to a friend who has lactose intolerance. Make sure that the menu you prepare contains foods high in calcium.

Applying Health Skills
6. **Advocacy.** Write a script for a play for elementary or middle school students on the importance of taking care of their teeth to protect their digestive systems.

Writing Critically
7. **Narrative.** Write a story from the point of view of a piece of food. Have the food describe its path through the digestive system, describing the function of each of the organs it meets.

Go Online

Visit **glencoe.com** and complete the Interactive Study Guide for this lesson.

LESSON 3 ASSESSMENT ANSWERS

1. Digestion and absorption
2. A series of involuntary muscle contractions, called peristalsis
3. Sample answer: Eat less food, eat meals slowly, and chew food thoroughly.
4. Students should describe the process through which food is broken down and mention that about 90 percent of all nutrients are absorbed through the small intestine.
5. Answers will vary but students should include soy products in the meal.
6. Scripts will vary.
7. Stories will vary.

The Excretory System

The Excretory System

The Artificial Kidney. Wendy is on her way to pick up her grandfather who has type 2 diabetes. Ever since his kidneys failed last year, Wendy's grandfather has been going to the clinic for dialysis. When Wendy arrives, her grandfather is not yet ready. At first glance, it looks to Wendy as if her grandfather is giving blood, except the blood goes into a machine instead of a plastic bag. The machine acts like a real kidney, filtering wastes from the blood before returning the blood to her grandfather's body.

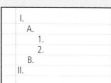

Writing *Write a letter to yourself describing ways you can reduce your risk for type 2 diabetes and prevent kidney failure.*

How Excretion Works

Main Idea The excretory system uses several organs to remove all types of wastes from the body.

Excretion is the process of removing wastes from the body. The body produces wastes in the form of solids, liquids, and gases. These wastes must be removed so that the body can function well.

The Lungs, Skin, and Large Intestine

The lungs expel carbon dioxide when you exhale. Sweating is another form of excretion. When sweat is produced, it removes excess water and salts through the pores. This excretion helps to regulate body temperature. As sweat evaporates on the surface of the skin, it cools the body. Sweating too much, however, can cause dehydration.

BIG Idea *The excretory system removes wastes from the body.*

Before You Read

Create an Outline. Preview this lesson by scanning the pages. Then organize the headings and subheadings into an outline. As you read, fill in the outline with important details.

New Vocabulary

▶ nephrons (p. 430)
▶ ureters (p. 430)
▶ urethra (p. 431)
▶ cystitis (p. 432)
▶ urethritis (p. 432)
▶ hemodialysis (p. 433)

1 FOCUS

GUIDE TO READING

BIG Idea Students will learn about how the excretory system removes wastes from the body. **Ask Students:** *What part of the foods we eat need to be removed from the body?* (Sample answer: The parts that cannot be digested by the digestive system)

Before You Read

Outline Students' outlines will vary in the details, though the first and second levels of the outline should match the headings and subheadings of the lesson.

Main Idea

How Excretion Works The process of removing wastes from the body involves several of the body's organs. **Ask Students:** *How is the respiratory system involved in excretion?* (The respiratory system removes carbon dioxide, a gaseous waste, from the body.)

Real Life Issues ....

Ask volunteers to share their letters with the class. **Ask Students:** *How would your life be different if you were required to go for dialysis several times a week?* (Answers will vary.)

English Language Coach

Naming Excretory Processes Students may have difficulty deciding what terms to use when describing excretory processes. Explain that many common words used for these processes are considered vulgar and offensive and should not be used in school. Other words or phrases may be acceptable within families but may be considered offensive or silly if used in public. Tell students that, in class, the following words should be used for discussing excretion: *urine, urination, feces,* and *bowel movement.* Write these terms on the board, pronounce them clearly, and have students repeat them aloud.

② TEACH

R Reading Strategy

Using Analogies To help students understand excretion, use the analogy of a community waste removal process. **Ask Students:** *What would happen if garbage trucks did not remove trash?* (Trash would build up and overwhelm the people living there.) Explain that the excretory system removes wastes so that cells, tissues, and organs can function. **Ask Students:** *Which excretory organ is like a recycling center?* (The kidneys filter blood to remove wastes and keep materials that the body needs.) **BL**

Caption Answer

Figure 15.12 When skin produces sweat, it removes excess water from the body. If you sweat too much, you may become dehydrated and need to replace lost water.

AL Active Learning

Radio Skit Divide the class into small groups, and give each group 15 minutes to write a script for a radio skit about how excretion works. Explain that the skit can be humorous but should include accurate information about excretion through the skin, lungs, and digestive system. Use a microphone as a prop and ask each group to perform its radio skit for the class. **OL**

Academic Vocabulary

Monitor Ask students who monitors a test in school. (The teacher) Ask what monitors the temperature of the air. (thermostat) Point out that many schools have hall monitors who watch the halls during class periods.

■ **Figure 15.12** The large surface area of your skin allows you to excrete water and salts when you sweat. *Why is it important to drink lots of water on a hot day?*

Solid wastes produced by the digestive system are eliminated through the large intestine. Bacteria that live in the large intestine convert the undigested food materials into a semi-solid mass called *feces*. **AL**

The Liver

The liver plays an important role in the digestive system, and also removes certain toxins from the blood. It is the first organ to receive chemicals absorbed from the small intestine. The liver detoxifies the body by processing and excreting into bile such things as drugs, alcohol, and some cellular waste products.

The Urinary System

The urinary system consists of the kidneys, bladder, ureters, and urethra. The main function of the urinary system is to filter waste and extra fluid from the blood. Urine is liquid waste material excreted from the body. It consists of water and body wastes that contain nitrogen.

The Kidneys The kidneys, shown in **Figure 15.13**, are bean-shaped organs about the size of a fist. They are near the middle of the back, just below the rib cage, one on each side. The kidneys remove waste products from the blood through tiny filtering units called **nephrons** (NEH-frahnz), *the functional units of the kidneys.* Each kidney contains more than a million nephrons. Each nephron consists of a ball formed of small blood capillaries, called a *glomerulus,* which is attached to a small renal tubule that acts as a filtering funnel.

The kidneys adjust the amount of salts, water, and other materials excreted according to the body's needs. In this way, the kidneys **monitor** and maintain the body's acid-base and water balances. When the body becomes dehydrated, the pituitary gland releases *antidiuretic hormone* (ADH). This causes thirst and allows the kidneys to balance the fluid levels.

The Ureters From the kidneys, urine travels to the bladder through the ureters. The **ureters** (YUR-eh-terz) are *tubes that connect the kidneys to the bladder.* Each ureter is about 8 to

Academic Vocabulary

monitor *(verb):* to watch or keep track of

🏔 Home and Community

Organ Transplants Since the days of the first organ transplants in the 1950s, these procedures have become relatively safe and common. The organs most commonly transplanted are kidneys, liver, heart, and lungs. While in many cases kidneys and livers can be transplanted from a living donor, other organs must be removed from a donor who has just died. In the United States, a patient needing an organ from a cadaverous donor must become part of the Organ Procurement and Transplantation Network (OPTN). Ask interested students to investigate how OPTN decides who gets organs.

10 inches long. Muscles in the ureter walls tighten and relax to force urine down and away from the kidneys. Urine is passed from the ureters to the bladder about every 15 seconds.

The Bladder and Urethra The bladder is a hollow muscular organ located in the pelvic cavity. The bladder is held in place by ligaments attached to other organs and the pelvic bones. It stores about 2 cups of urine comfortably for two to five hours. Sphincter muscles help keep urine from leaking. The sphincter muscles close tightly like a rubber band around the opening of the bladder into the **urethra** (yur-EE-thruh), *the tube that leads from the bladder to the outside of the body.*

Maintaining Your Excretory Health

Main Idea Healthful behaviors will help keep your excretory system healthy.

HS

The excretory function removes wastes that can become toxic from the body. Healthy behaviors, like those listed below, will keep your excretory system healthy:

- Drink at least eight 8-ounce glasses of water each day.
- Limit your intake of caffeine and soft drinks, which can increase the amount of water lost through urination.

READING CHECK

Explain What vital body function do the kidneys provide?

Figure 15.13 The Kidney

The kidney, part of the urinary system, performs the vital function of removing wastes from the blood.

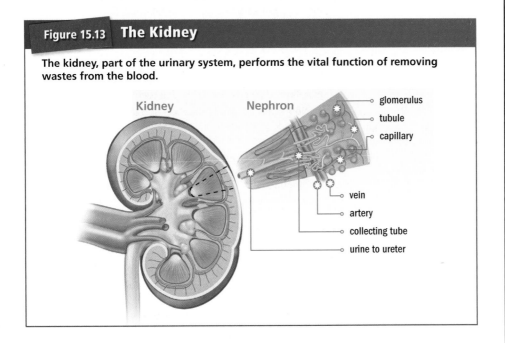

Kidney · Nephron
- glomerulus
- tubule
- capillary
- vein
- artery
- collecting tube
- urine to ureter

READING CHECK

Answer The kidneys remove waste products from the blood.

Main Idea

Maintaining Your Excretory Health Several behaviors can help keep the excretory system healthy. **Ask Students:** *How might drinking plenty of water keep the excretory system healthy?* (Sample answer: Water is part of both urine and the semisolid feces. Without enough water, excreting these wastes would be difficult.)

HS Health Skills Practice

Practicing Healthful Behaviors Point out that to keep the excretory system healthy, a person should drink at least eight 8-ounce glasses of water each day. Ask students to experiment the next day by drinking at least the recommended amount. The day after, call on volunteers to tell how it was to drink this amount of water. Ask students who normally drink less during a day whether drinking more made them feel any different. **OL**

Reading Strategy

Urination Flowchart To help students understand the urinary system, make a flowchart on the board. Begin by asking where urine forms. (Kidneys) Write *Kidneys,* then draw an arrow to the right. Ask: *Through what tubes does urine flow out of the kidneys?* (Ureters) Write *Ureters* and draw an arrow to the right. Ask: *Into what organ do the ureters empty?* (Bladder) Write *Bladder* and draw an arrow to the right. Ask: *What tube leads from the bladder to the outside of the body?* (Urethra) Write *Urethra.* Have students copy this flowchart into their notebooks to use for review.

LESSON 4

Answer Taking in soft drinks can increase the amount of water lost through urination.

Main Idea

Excretory System Problems
Excretory problems can result from several causes, including infection, blockage, and aging. **Ask Students:** *What problems would the body have if the kidneys stopped working properly?* (Sample answer: The kidneys remove wastes from blood and produce urine to be excreted. If the kidneys stopped working properly, wastes would not be removed from blood.)

AL Active Learning

Interviewing Most cities have places such as clinics and hospitals where patients receive hemodialysis. Ask interested students to make an appointment at one of these locations to interview a nurse or technician working there. Students should research online ahead of time to prepare questions about the therapy. They might also ask to observe hemodialysis or take photos of the machine. Have students prepare a presentation to the class about what they learn. **AL**

Go Online

Have students work in pairs to complete the Student Web Activity at glencoe.com on the functioning of the kidneys.

432

Infer Why is it better to drink water rather than soft drinks when you are dehydrated?

Go Online

Explore glencoe.com and complete the Student Web Activity on the functioning of the kidneys.

- Follow a well-balanced eating plan.
- Practice good hygiene to prevent harmful bacteria from causing infection.
- Get regular medical checkups. Report changes in bowel habits and in the frequency, color, or odor of urine.

Excretory System Problems

Main Idea Excretory system problems commonly result from infection or blockage.

Disorders of the excretory system can have several different causes, including infection, blockage of urine, or natural aging. Two common disorders of the urinary system are cystitis and urethritis.

- **Cystitis** (sis-TY-tis) is *inflammation of the bladder*, most often caused by a bacterial infection. Left untreated, the infection can spread to the kidneys.
- **Urethritis** (yur-eh-THRY-tis) is *inflammation of the urethra*. It, too, can be caused by a bacterial infection.

Symptoms of both conditions include burning pain during urination, increased frequency of urination, fever, and possibly blood in urine. Treatment requires a visit to a doctor and may include antibiotics to eliminate infection.

Kidney Problems

Kidney disorders, some of which can be life threatening, should be treated and monitored by a medical professional. Here are some problems that can occur in the kidneys:

- **Nephritis** is the inflammation of the nephrons. Symptoms include a change in the amount of urine produced, fever, and swelling of body tissues.
- **Kidney stones** form when salts in the urine crystallize into solid stones. Kidney stones can move into the ureter, causing pain. They may also block the passage of urine. Smaller stones may be able to pass through naturally. Larger stones can be broken up using shock waves, so they can pass from the body through the ureters and urethra. In some cases, surgery is required to break up the stones.
- **Uremia** is a serious condition associated with decreased blood filtration by the kidneys, leading to abnormally high levels of nitrogen waste products remaining in the blood. These wastes are poisonous to body cells and can cause tissue damage, or death, if allowed to accumulate.

432 Chapter 15 Cardiovascular, Respiratory, and Digestive Systems

More About...

Kidney Stones Kidney stones develop when crystals separate from urine. While urine normally contains chemicals that prevent this from occurring, in some people these chemicals do not work well. Modern treatment often involves extracorporeal shockwave lithotripsy (ESWL). The procedure begins with X-rays or ultrasound to pinpoint the exact location of the stones. Then, a patient reclines in a water bath or on a soft cushion while shock waves travel through skin and body tissues to hit the stone, breaking it down into sand-like particles. Recovery from the procedure usually takes a few days.

Kidney Failure

Kidney failure occurs when the kidneys lose their ability to function. It can be caused by infection, decreased blood flow, or diseases that damage kidney tissue. Here are treatments:

AL

- **Hemodialysis** (HEE-moh-dy-AL-uh-sis) is *a technique in which an artificial kidney machine removes waste products from the blood.* A machine filters the blood. Hemodialysis takes three to five hours and is done three or four times per week, usually in a clinical setting.

- **Peritoneal dialysis** uses the *peritoneum,* a thin membrane that surrounds the digestive organs, to filter the blood. Substances that promote the removal of toxins enter into the abdomen through the catheter and are drained after filtration is complete.

- **Kidney transplant** is another treatment option for chronic kidney failure. This involves the replacement of a nonfunctioning kidney with a healthy kidney from an organ donor. An organ donor allows a healthy organ to be removed from his or her body and surgically placed into a patient who needs a healthy organ.

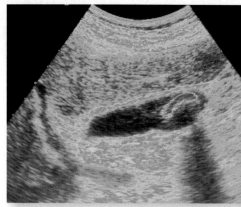

■ **Figure 15.14** Kidney stones larger than 1 cm must be broken up into smaller pieces to pass through the urethra. *How are larger kidney stones broken apart?*

LESSON 4 📖 ASSESSMENT

After You Read

Reviewing Facts and Vocabulary

1. What is the main function of the excretory system? What organs are part of it?

2. How are a *ureter,* a *urethra,* and *urethritis* different?

3. How can you prevent cystitis and urethritis?

Thinking Critically

4. **Evaluate.** What might pain during urination indicate? What should you recommend to a friend who experiences this?

5. **Analyze.** Why is it possible to donate a kidney and survive?

Applying Health Skills

6. **Analyzing Influences.** List the health behaviors that will help teens avoid problems that can affect the urinary system.

Writing Critically

7. **Comparative.** Write a brief paragraph comparing the way a kidney works and the way a hemodialysis machine works.

G⊙ Online

Visit glencoe.com and complete the Interactive Study Guide for this lesson.

Lesson 4   The Excretory System   **433**

Caption Answer

Figure 15.14 Shock waves are used to break stones apart so that they can pass through the urethra.

③ ASSESS/ CLOSE

Assessment Resources

📁 **FAST FILE ACTIVITIES**
Lesson 4 Quiz

 ExamView Assessment Suite CD-ROM

Visit glencoe.com for:
Online Quizzes
Online Learning Center

Progress Monitoring

Reteaching
Call on students to name the four main structures of the urinary system—kidneys, bladder, ureters, and urethra—and describe the function of each.

Enrichment
Have students further investigate how sweating regulates body temperature and why the evaporation of sweat removes heat from the body. Ask students to write a brief report of their findings.

G⊙ Online

Have students visit glencoe.com and complete the Interactive Study Guide for this lesson.

LESSON 4 ASSESSMENT ANSWERS

1. The main function is to remove all types of waste from the body. The organs include the large intestine, lungs, skin, liver, kidneys, and bladder.

2. A *ureter* is a tube that connects a kidney to the bladder. The *urethra* leads from the bladder to outside the body. *Urethritis* is an inflammation of the urethra.

3. Practice good hygiene and personal health to prevent harmful bacteria and infection.

4. Pain may indicate cystitis or urethritis. Treatment requires a visit to the doctor and may include antibiotics.

5. Since each kidney performs the task of filtering waste products from the blood, donors can live normally with one healthy kidney.

6. Students should list five behaviors that help keep the excretory system healthy.

7. Paragraphs may vary.

A Heart to Last a Lifetime

Focus

Motivator

Ask students, "Do you know anyone who has had a heart attack?" Did he or she have any known risk factors for the disease?"

Teach

Risk Factors Studies suggest that family history alone can carry the same weight as the standard risk factors for heart disease. Ask students to research their family history for heart disease. Ask them to examine other factors such as obesity and lifestyle choices in their family that may contribute to their own risk for heart disease. Ask students, "Based on family history, what conclusions can you draw about your need to practice healthy heart habits?"

Healthy Choices Fast food restaurants offer teens a safe place to socialize. As a result, a teen's intake of high-cholesterol foods may reach unhealthy levels. Ask students to compare levels of LDL (bad cholesterol) in hamburgers, chicken nuggets, and a third entree from different fast food restaurants. Are the levels the same? Different? How might you reduce levels and calories when you eat at fast food restauarants? (Sample answers: Hold the salad dressing, don't add cheese, avoid the larger sizes, etc.)

A Heart to Last a Lifetime

Looking to avoid heart disease down the road? Check out these tips that will keep your heart healthy and strong far into the future.

1. Don't Smoke!

Smoking can more than triple a person's chances of having a heart attack. When a smoker quits, that risk is cut in half within 2 years. It takes more than 10 years for the odds to return to nearly normal—so unless you want to waste a decade of your life getting back your health, don't start smoking in the first place.

2. Watch Your Weight

Carrying excess fat, especially around the middle, increases the risk of a heart attack or stroke later on in life. Obesity can also lead to diabetes, a major risk factor in heart disease. Doctors recommend a reduced-calorie diet with lots of vegetables and whole grains, plus at least 30 minutes of moderate aerobic exercise a day.

3. Lower Your Bad Cholesterol

High levels of LDL (bad cholesterol) can tell doctors that heart problems are on the way. Although doctors have focused on levels of LDL, HDL (good cholesterol) may be a better predictor of heart-disease risk. Low levels of HDL might indicate that heart trouble is in the future.

4. Control Blood Pressure

Hypertension makes the heart work harder to move blood through the body and puts those who suffer from it at higher risk of both heart disease and stroke. Teens don't usually have to worry about hypertension. However, if you get short of breath when you exercise, tell a doctor. High blood pressure can be treated with proper diet, exercise, and medication if needed.

5. Reduce Stress

Stress can increase the risk of heart disease and lead to unhealthy habits such as drinking alcohol and eating junk food. Exercise and meditation can reduce stress; so can getting enough sleep every night. If you are feeling stressed out for an extended period of time, talk about it with your parents, teachers, or counselor. ◼

TIME to THINK... **About Cholesterol**

The article mentions LDL and HDL. Research these two kinds of cholesterol and answer the following questions:
1. What do the letters LDL and HDL stand for?
2. What is the difference between LDL and HDL?
3. What are two examples of foods that contain high levels of each?

Health Literacy

Sudden Cardiac Arrest Sudden cardiac arrest (SCA) can cause young athletes to die unexpectedly while participating in sports. SCA is usually caused by abnormality in the heart muscle that was present at birth. Unlike a heart attack, a person experiencing SCA collapses and loses consciousness immediately. Breathing stops and blood pressure and pulse are zero. CPR is not an effective treatment for SCA. However, if the heart receives an immediate electric shock (defibrillation), a normal heartbeat can usually be restored.

STUDY TO GO — To download quizzes and eFlashcards to your PDA, go to glencoe.com and click on the Study to Go icon.

LESSON 1

The Cardiovascular and Lymphatic Systems
Key Concepts
▸ The cardiovascular system includes the heart and blood vessels.
▸ The lymphatic system provides immunity against disease.
▸ Some problems of the cardiovascular system involve congenital heart defects or lifestyle factors.

Vocabulary
▸ plasma (p. 410)
▸ hemoglobin (p. 410)
▸ platelets (p. 410)
▸ capillaries (p. 412)
▸ lymph (p. 412)
▸ pathogen (p. 412)
▸ blood pressure (p. 413)

LESSON 2

The Respiratory System
Key Concepts
▸ The lungs are the principal organs of the respiratory system.
▸ Avoiding tobacco smoke and other pollutants can keep your respiratory system healthy.
▸ Respiratory system problems include bronchitis, asthma, pneumonia, tuberculosis, and emphysema.

Vocabulary
▸ diaphragm (p. 417)
▸ trachea (p. 417)
▸ bronchi (p. 417)
▸ asthma (p. 420)
▸ tuberculosis (p. 421)
▸ emphysema (p. 421)

LESSON 3

The Digestive System
Key Concepts
▸ The functions of the digestive system include digestion, absorption, and elimination.
▸ Digestion includes both mechanical and chemical processes.
▸ Digestive system problems might include indigestion, peptic ulcer, constipation, gallstones, cirrhosis, and colon cancer.

Vocabulary
▸ mastication (p. 423)
▸ peristalsis (p. 424)
▸ gastric juices (p. 424)
▸ bile (p. 424)
▸ peptic ulcer (p. 427)
▸ appendicitis (p. 428)

LESSON 4

The Excretory System
Key Concepts
▸ The lungs, skin, liver, and large intestine remove wastes.
▸ The urinary system consists of the kidneys, bladder, ureters, and urethra, and filters waste and extra fluid from the blood.
▸ Problems of the excretory system include cystitis, urethritis, nephritis, kidney stones, uremia, and kidney failure.

Vocabulary
▸ nephrons (p. 430)
▸ ureters (p. 430)
▸ urethra (p. 431)
▸ cystitis (p. 432)
▸ urethritis (p. 432)
▸ hemodialysis (p. 433)

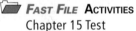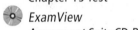

Go Online
Students can visit glencoe.com to
- review content online with the Online Student Edition.
- test their knowledge of chapter content with Online Quizzes.
- access Interactive Health Tutor for more practice with vocabulary.

Assessment Resources
📁 **FAST FILE ACTIVITIES**
Chapter 15 Test
💿 *ExamView Assessment Suite* CD-ROM
Visit glencoe.com for:
Audio Chapter Summaries
Online Quizzes

 Tell students to visit glencoe.com where they can download quizzes and eFlashcards.

Chapter 15 Review **435**

Study Tips

Thinking Ahead Explain to students that it's a good idea to think ahead about what material will likely be tested throughout a course instead of simply cramming the night before a test is given. Point out that a teacher often gives clues about what will be on the test by writing material on the board and by repeating terms and phrases. Students should underline such material as they take notes in class. It's also a good idea to work with other students a few days before a test to write sample test questions and then see if all students in the group can answer those questions.

Chapter 15 Assessment Answers

LESSON 1

Vocabulary Review

1. Plasma
2. Platelets
3. blood pressure

Understanding Key Concepts

4. b
5. a
6. a

Thinking Critically

7. Sample answer: Arteries carry blood away from the heart; aorta. Veins return blood to the heart; vena cava. Capillaries carry blood from arterioles and to venules; capillaries are found throughout the body.

8. Blood carries oxygen to the body's cells. Blood then carries carbon dioxide to the lungs, where fresh oxygen is absorbed and once again circulated through the body.

9. If left untreated, high blood pressure can lead to more dangerous problems of the cardiovascular system, including hardening of arteries, heart attack, and stroke.

10. Anemia is a condition in which the ability of the blood to carry oxygen is reduced, while hemophilia is an inherited disorder in which the blood does not clot properly.

LESSON 2

Vocabulary Review

11. bronchi
12. diaphragm
13. asthma

Understanding Key Concepts

14. a
15. b
16. b

LESSON 1

Vocabulary Review
Use the vocabulary terms listed on page 435 to complete the following statements.

1. _____ is the fluid in which other parts of the blood are suspended.

2. _____ are types of cells in the blood that cause blood clots to form.

3. A measure of the force that blood places on the walls of blood vessels as it is pumped through the body is called _____.

Understanding Key Concepts
After reading the question or statement, select the correct answer.

4. Which of the following is *not* a function of the cardiovascular system?
   a. Getting oxygen from air
   b. Producing red and white blood cells
   c. Removing carbon dioxide from the body
   d. Fighting disease by attacking infections

5. Which of the following is a condition in which the ability of the blood to carry oxygen is reduced?
   a. Anemia   c. Leukemia
   b. Hemophilia   d. Lymphoma

6. Congenital heart defects
   a. are present at birth.
   b. result from poor diet.
   c. affect mainly older people.
   d. can be prevented with regular exercise.

Thinking Critically
After reading the question or statement, write a short answer using complete sentences.

7. **Describe.** Describe and give examples of each type of blood vessel.

8. **Explain.** Explain how blood replaces oxygen with carbon dioxide.

9. **Analyze.** Why is early detection of high blood pressure important?

10. **Contrast.** Explain the difference between anemia and hemophilia.

LESSON 2

Vocabulary Review
Choose the correct word in the sentences below.

11. The *trachea / bronchi* deliver air to and from the lungs.

12. The *diaphragm / trachea* is a muscle that changes the shape of the lungs.

13. In a(n) *bronchitis / asthma* attack, smooth muscles involuntarily contract and cause chest tightness.

Understanding Key Concepts
After reading the question or statement, select the correct answer.

14. Which of the following structures is the smallest?
   a. Bronchioles
   b. Diaphragm
   c. Lungs
   d. Trachea

15. Which behavior is *least* likely to prevent respiratory system problems?
   a. Smoking tobacco
   b. Washing your hands
   c. Getting regular exercise
   d. Eating fruits and vegetables

16. What problem of the respiratory system is almost always caused by smoking?
   a. Bronchitis   c. Pneumonia
   b. Emphysema   d. Tuberculosis

Health eSpotlight *Wrap-Up*

A Look Inside Your Body Have students reread the Health eSpotlight questions at the beginning of the chapter (page 407) and look at their original answers. **Ask Students:** *Now that you have read the chapter and watched the video, how would you respond differently about activities that are good for the heart and how aerobic exercise is good for your whole body?* Call on volunteers to describe how their responses would change.

Thinking Critically

After reading the question or statement, write a short answer using complete sentences.

17. **Describe.** Describe the main function of the respiratory system.

18. **Analyze.** How might increased lung capacity benefit your health?

19. **Describe.** What is sinusitis? What causes it?

20. **Apply.** Why is it important for a person with asthma to avoid known allergens?

LESSON 3

Vocabulary Review

Use the vocabulary terms listed on page 435 to complete the following statements.

21. _____ is the series of muscle contractions that moves food through the digestive tract.

22. The stomach lining secretes _____, which contain hydrochloric acid and pepsin.

23. A(n) _____ is a sore in the lining of the digestive tract that can be caused by bacterial infection.

Understanding Key Concepts

After reading the question or statement, select the correct answer.

24. Which of the following is *not* one of the main functions of the digestive system?
    a. Absorption
    b. Digestion
    c. Elimination
    d. Circulation

25. Which substance is secreted by the liver?
    a. Bile
    b. Chyme
    c. Hydrochloric acid
    d. Mucus

26. Which of these tasks is *not* a function of the stomach?
    a. Storing food
    b. Moving food into the small intestine
    c. Absorbing nutrients from food
    d. Mixing food with gastric juices

27. Which of the following disorders involves a sensitivity to a sugar found in milk and other dairy products?
    a. Cirrhosis
    b. Gastritis
    c. Lactose intolerance
    d. Tooth decay

Thinking Critically

After reading the question or statement, write a short answer using complete sentences.

28. **Describe.** Describe how peristalsis moves food through the digestive tract.

29. **Connect.** What parts of foods do hydrochloric acid, pepsin, and bile work on?

30. **Contrast.** How are the roles of the small intestine and large intestine different?

31. **Analyze.** Why is it important to drink plenty of water when you have diarrhea or constipation?

LESSON 4

Vocabulary Review

Choose the correct word in the sentences below.

32. In *hemodialysis / urethritis,* a machine removes waste products from the blood.

33. The *ureters / nephrons* are the parts of the kidneys that filter blood.

34. The *ureter / urethra* carries urine from the bladder to the outside of the body.

35. *Cystitis / Urethritis* is an inflammation of the bladder caused by bacterial infection.

Thinking Critically

17. The main function is the exchange of gases between the body and the environment.
18. Increased lung capacity means more oxygen intake, and all body cells need oxygen.
19. Sinusitis is an inflammation of the tissues that line the sinuses, which can result from allergies or infection.
20. Allergens can trigger an asthma attack.

LESSON 3

Vocabulary Review

21. Peristalsis
22. gastric juices
23. peptic ulcer

Understanding Key Concepts

24. d
25. a
26. c
27. c

Thinking Critically

28. Peristalsis is like a wave moving through the muscle to push food and fluid through each hollow organ.
29. Hydrochloric acid kills bacteria taken in with food; pepsin digests proteins; and bile dissolves fats.
30. The small intestine absorbs 90 percent of nutrients in food, while the large intestine absorbs water, vitamins, and salts from undigested parts of food.
31. Diarrhea can cause dehydration, and drinking water is needed to replace the water lost. Constipation can be caused by not drinking enough water.

Assessment

LESSON 4

Vocabulary Review

32. hemodialysis
33. nephrons
34. urethra
35. Cystitis

Understanding Key Concepts

36. c
37. c
38. b

Thinking Critically

39. The liver is the first organ to receive chemicals absorbed from the contents of the small intestine.
40. It can prevent harmful bacteria from causing infection.
41. If untreated, either infection could spread.
42. Hemodialysis takes between three to five hours and is done three to four times per week, while a kidney transplant, if successful, allows a patient to live a normal life.

Understanding Key Concepts

After reading the question or statement, select the correct answer.

36. What role does skin play in excretion?
    a. Eliminating solid wastes
    b. Removing carbon dioxide
    c. Removing excess water and salts
    d. Breaking down toxic chemicals

37. Which of the following is *not* a recommended way to maintain the health of the excretory system?
    a. Having regular medical checkups, and reporting problems to your doctor
    b. Practicing good hygiene and personal health care
    c. Increasing your intake of caffeine and soft drinks
    d. Drinking eight 8-ounce glasses of milk each day

38. What problem of the urinary system could require hemodialysis?
    a. Cystitis
    b. Kidney failure
    c. Kidney stones
    d. Nephritis

Thinking Critically

After reading the question or statement, write a short answer using complete sentences.

39. **Infer.** Why might ingesting an unhealthful substance such as alcohol harm the liver first before any other organ?

40. **Analyze.** How does practicing good hygiene maintain the health of the urinary system?

41. **Apply.** Why is it important to address even mild cases of cystitis and urethritis?

42. **Infer.** Why might a patient choose a kidney transplant over hemodialysis?

Project-Based ASSESSMENT

Write a True/False Test

Background
Everyone is familiar with tests. Tests measure your readiness to tackle a new topic or your mastery of a topic. One form of test question is *true/false*. These questions make a statement that must be judged to be either true or false, based on their knowledge of a topic.

Task
Write a 15-question true/false test to assess your classmates' understanding of the information about the urinary and digestive systems.

Audience
Students in your class

Purpose
Accurately and fairly test your classmates' knowledge of the digestive and urinary systems.

Procedure

1. Review examples of true/false test questions provided by your teacher.
2. Carefully review the material on the urinary and digestive systems in the student text.
3. Write your test questions. Make sure you cover each section of the chapter. Consider writing questions that refer to diagrams or illustrations in the text.
4. Review your questions to make sure they are at the appropriate level of difficulty for the majority of your classmates.
5. Prepare an answer key and scoring instructions.
6. Use a word processor to prepare your test, and produce enough copies for the entire class.

438 Chapter 15 Assessment

Project-Based ASSESSMENT

Step 1 Review Have students carefully review the material. They should look for concepts, diagrams, and illustrations that could be used to create 15 true/false questions.

Step 2 Write Test Questions Make sure all students have access to a word processing program to write their questions. Remind students that they should prepare an answer key and scoring instructions.

Step 3 Evaluate Have students or groups distribute their tests. Each test should include 15 true/false questions. Evaluate questions on each test according to whether a question accurately reflects information in the student text and is written clearly and unambiguously.

Visit **glencoe.com** for Project-Based Assessment rubrics.

Math Practice

Interpret Graphs. The bar graph below shows the percentages of high school students who were physically active for at least 60 minutes a day. Use the graph to answer Questions 1–3.

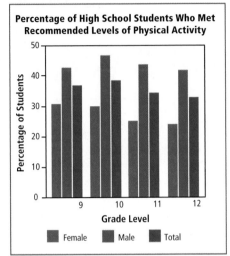

Percentage of High School Students Who Met Recommended Levels of Physical Activity

Adapted from: "Youth Risk Behavior Surveillance—United States, 2005"; Centers for Disease Control and Prevention, June 2006.

1. Which grade level had the lowest levels of physical activity for females?
   A. 9th grade
   B. 10th grade
   C. 11th grade
   D. 12th grade

2. At which grade level did at least half of the total students meet the currently recommended levels of physical activity?
   A. 9th grade
   B. 10th grade
   C. 12th grade
   D. None

3. Write a paragraph describing your general conclusion from the bar graph?

G Online

For more test practice, visit glencoe.com and complete the Online Quizzes for Chapter 15.

Reading/Writing Practice

Understand and Apply. Read the passage below, and then answer the questions.

> (1) Have you ever heard of the influenza epidemic of 1918–1919? (2) Many people died worldwide. (3) In the United States, nearly 800,000 people died. (4) That's more than the number of Americans who died in World War I, World War II, Korea, and Vietnam combined. (5) Influenza viruses still exist. (6) Why doesn't the flu kill as many people today?
> (7) People in the health-care industry today know that they need to tell flu patients some things about how to feel better. (8) One of the most important treatments is simple—drink liquids. (9) People with the flu should drink lots of water, juice, and clear soups.

1. Which sentence below should be added after sentence 5 to support the first paragraph?
   A. Sick people should not drink liquids.
   B. Washing your hands often is important.
   C. Everyone can learn to wash their hands.
   D. You've probably had the flu yourself.

2. Which revision of sentence 7 is the most coherent and focused?
   A. Doctors and nurses need to know how to talk to sick people.
   B. Follow these logical and new rules of flu treatment to be safe.
   C. Health-care professionals understand better how to treat the flu.
   D. To keep you safe from catching the flu, follow simple, new steps.

3. Create a poster using familiar children's book characters, words, and pictures to teach young flu patients to drink lots of liquids.

National Education Standards
Math: Data Analysis, Statistics, and Reasoning
Language Arts: NCTE 1, NCTE 3, NCTE 4

Standardized Test Practice Answers

Math Practice
1. D
2. D
3. Paragraphs will vary, but should show that students understand the importance of physical activity for teens.

Reading/Writing Practice
1. D
2. C
3. Finished posters will vary but should include at least one children's book character, words, and pictures, and should persuade young flu patients to drink fluids.

National Education Standards

Math: Data Analysis, Statistics, and Reasoning

Language Arts: NCTE 1, NCTE 3, NCTE 4

For the complete Math and Language Arts standards, visit glencoe.com.

G Online

Online Study Tools
For more test practice, visit glencoe.com and complete the Online Quizzes for Chapter 15.

Test-Taking Tip

Double Checking Math Answers
Remind students that some standardized tests focus on concepts and operations in mathematics. Explain that in answering math questions, students should double-check their work by asking themselves questions such as: Did I use the correct operation in calculating each of the answers? Do each of the answers I calculated seem reasonable? Did I place the decimal point in the correct position in each of the answers? Did I use the correct units in each of the calculations? Did I use the correct unit in each of the answers?

Chapter 16 pages 440–463	Standards		Features
	National	State/Local	
	1.12.8, 7.12.1, 8.12.1, 8.12.2, 8.12.4		*Hands-On* **HEALTH** • Peer-to-Peer Education (*Communication Skills*), page 458
Lesson 1 **The Endocrine System** pages 442–445 **BIG Idea** *Your endocrine system sends and receives chemical messages that control many body functions.*	1.12.1, 1.12.5, 3.12.4, 6.12.2, 6.12.3, 6.12.4, 7.12.1, 7.12.2, 8.12.4		
Lesson 2 **The Male Reproductive System** pages 446–451 **BIG Idea** *The male reproductive system is a series of organs involved in producing children.*	1.12.1, 1.12.5, 1.12.6, 4.12.1, 7.12.1, 8.12.1, 8.12.4		*Real World* **CONNECTION** • TSE Awareness Campaign, page 451 🕐 Out of Time
Lesson 3 **The Female Reproductive System** pages 452–457 **BIG Idea** *The female reproductive system matures at puberty and enables women to reproduce.*	1.12.1, 1.12.5, 4.12.1, 7.12.1, 7.12.3, 8.12.1, 8.12.4		*Health Skills* **Activity** • Asking Difficult Questions (*Communication Skills*), page 457 🕐 Out of Time

The "30 Min" labels appear beside Lesson 1, Lesson 2, and Lesson 3.

Key to Ability Levels

Teaching Strategies and activities have been coded for ability level and appropriateness.

AL Activities for students working above grade level

OL Activities for students working on grade level

BL Activities for students working below grade level

EL Activities for English Learners

Chapter 16 Planning Guide

Glencoe Exclusive!
TeacherWorks Plus™
All-In-One Planner and Resource Center

Resources	Lesson Assessment	Technology
Student Activity Workbook TEACH FAST FILE RESOURCES Vocabulary Practice TEACH Health Labs EXTEND	Chapter 16 Review Chapter 16 Assessment Standardized Test Practice ⊙ ExamView® Assessment Suite CD-ROM	**Teaching Tools:** ⊙ TeacherWorks™ Plus DVD ⊙ StudentWorks™ Plus DVD ⊙ ExamView® Assessment Suite CD-ROM 🕹 Transparency ⊙ Fitness DVD ⊙ PowerPoint® DVD ⊙ Health eSpotlight Video Series DVD
FAST FILE RESOURCES Reading Strategies Activity TEACH Reteaching Activity REVIEW Enrichment Activity EXTEND Health Skills Practice TEACH	Lesson 1 Assessment, page 445 📁 Lesson 1 Quiz Fast File ⊙ ExamView® Assessment Suite CD-ROM	**Web-Based Resources:** **Go Online** glencoe.com
FAST FILE RESOURCES Reading Strategies Activity TEACH Reteaching Activity REVIEW Enrichment Activity EXTEND Health Skills Practice TEACH	Lesson 2 Assessment, page 451 📁 Lesson 2 Quiz Fast File ⊙ ExamView® Assessment Suite CD-ROM	• Health Podcast Activities • Audio Chapter Summaries (English/Spanish) • Interactive Health Tutor • Health Skills Activities • Vocabulary PuzzleMaker • Parent Letters (English/Spanish) • Lesson Plans • Health Inventories
FAST FILE RESOURCES Reading Strategies Activity TEACH Reteaching Activity REVIEW Enrichment Activity EXTEND Health Skills Practice TEACH	Lesson 3 Assessment, page 457 📁 Lesson 3 Quiz Fast File ⊙ ExamView® Assessment Suite CD-ROM	• Online Quizzes • Study-to-Go • Unit Web Projects • Student Web Activities • Fitness Zone Activities

StudentWorks Plus™

This is the student's backpack solution.

Includes:
- complete Interactive Student Edition
- full audio of English text and Spanish chapter summaries
- allows students to record assignments and track grades.
- links to online activities and additional student resources
- access to all student worksheets and workbooks

Dinah Zike Foldables®
FOLDABLES®
Study Organizer

Chapter Activity
Refer to the *Dinah Zike Reading and Study Skills for Glencoe Health.* Have students make a study organizer Foldable for their notes on the structure and function of the endocrine system. As students read, have them record notes on index cards and store each card in the appropriate pocket.

Key to Symbols

 Transparencies   REVIEW activities to review or reinforce content

 CD-ROM   TEACH activities to teach basic concepts

 glencoe.com   EXTEND activities to extend or enrich lesson content

 Print Resources

Endocrine and Reproductive Health

Chapter Overview

Chapter 16 describes how the endocrine system regulates body functions, including reproduction. Healthful behaviors required to maintain reproductive health are also discussed.

Lesson 1

The endocrine system regulates body functions by sending and receiving chemical messages through the bloodstream.

Lesson 2

When mature, the organs of the male reproductive system function in producing children.

Lesson 3

When the organs of the female reproductive system mature, women are able to bear children.

▶ **Activating Prior Knowledge**

Invite volunteers to explain what the teen in the photo is doing. If necessary, explain that the teen is diabetic and is testing blood to manage the disease. Read the question posed in the text aloud. List students' responses on the board.

CHAPTER **16** **Endocrine and Reproductive Health**

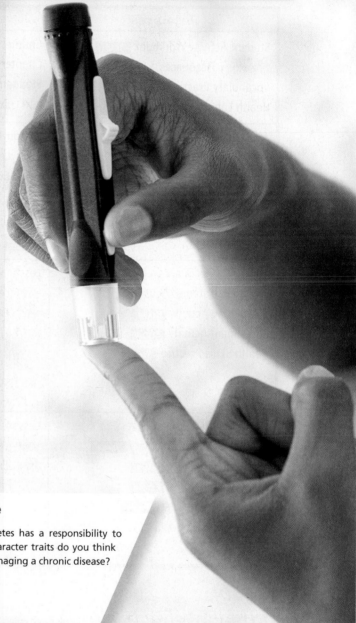

Lesson 1

The Endocrine System

BIG Idea *Your body's endocrine system sends and receives chemical messages that control many body functions.*

Lesson 2

The Male Reproductive System

BIG Idea *The male reproductive system is a series of organs involved in producing children.*

Lesson 3

The Female Reproductive System

BIG Idea *The female reproductive system matures at puberty and enables women to reproduce.*

Activating Prior Knowledge

Using Visuals A teen with diabetes has a responsibility to manage his or her disease. What character traits do you think are important in someone who is managing a chronic disease?

440

 Universal Access

Differentiated Learning Glencoe provides teacher support and student materials for all learners in the health classroom.

- Chapter Summaries in English and Spanish are available online at **glencoe.com**.
- *Fast Files* and related worksheets support reluctant readers.

- Universal Access strategies throughout the Teacher Wraparound Edition and *Fast Files* help you present materials for gifted students, at-risk students, physically impaired students, and those with behavior disorders or learning disabilities.

Chapter Launchers

Health in Action

Discuss the **BIG** Ideas

Before beginning this chapter, think about how you would answer these questions:

▶ What is the purpose of the endocrine system?

▶ Do you recognize the role of hormones during puberty?

▶ What behaviors are essential for the health of the reproductive systems?

Watch the *Health* eSpotlight Video Series

Your Reproductive Health

The endocrine system triggers many changes during puberty. What is the role of hormones?

Assess Your Health

G₀ Online

Visit glencoe.com and complete the Health Inventory for Chapter 16.

Chapter Launchers

Health in Action

Discuss the **BIG** Ideas

Assign this activity before students read the chapter. Explain that the purpose of the questions is to help students assess their current knowledge of endocrine and reproductive health.

Health eSpotlight
Video Series

 Your Reproductive Health

Before Viewing the Video

Ask Students: *What role do you think hormones have in the body?* After students have watched the video, invite volunteers to describe the relationship between the endocrine system and the reproductive system.

G₀ Online

Have students go to **glencoe.com** and take the Health Inventory for Chapter 16.

Chapter Skills

Reading Skills

- Reviewing Facts and Vocabulary, pp. 445, 451, 457
- Reading/Writing Practice, p. 463

Vocabulary

- New Vocabulary, pp. 442, 446, 452
- Reviewing Facts and Vocabulary, pp. 445, 451, 457

BIG Idea

With the direction of the endocrine system, the male and female reproductive systems mature at puberty to produce children.

Health Skills

- Health Skills Activity, p. 456
- Applying Health Skills, pp. 445, 451, 457

Writing Skills

- Real World Connection, p. 451
- Writing Critically, pp. 445, 451, 457
- Reading/Writing Practice, p. 463

The Endocrine System

① FOCUS

GUIDE TO READING

BIG Idea The endocrine system sends and receives hormones to regulate many body functions. **Ask Students:** *What are some parts of the endocrine system?* (Sample answer: Glands such as the pituitary and thyroid)

Before You Read

Flashcards Flashcards should have the name of each endocrine gland and its function as discussed in the lesson.

Main Idea

How the Endocrine System Works The endocrine system includes various organs that regulate body functions. **Ask Students:** *What are hormones?* (Chemical substances carried through the bloodstream that regulate body functions)

Real Life Issues ....

Invite students to discuss the following question. **Ask Students:** *What event happened that made your heart race?* (Accept all reasonable answers.)

LESSON 1

 GUIDE TO READING

BIG Idea Your body's endocrine system sends and receives chemical messages that control many body functions.

Before You Read

Create Flashcards. Write the name of each endocrine gland on the front side of a blank index card. Write the function of each on the reverse side. When you have completed the lesson, partner with a friend and use the cards to check your knowledge.

Name of Gland
Function of Gland

New Vocabulary

▶ endocrine glands (p. 442)
▶ thyroid gland (p. 443)
▶ parathyroid glands (p. 443)
▶ pancreas (p. 443)
▶ pituitary gland (p. 443)
▶ adrenal glands (p. 444)

Review Vocabulary

▶ hormones (Ch.3, L3)

The Endocrine System

Real Life Issues ....

A Close Call. Emily and Laura were walking home at dusk. Right after they stepped into the crosswalk, a car suddenly rounded the corner from behind them. Both girls dashed forward to get out of the way. Emily yelled at the driver to watch out. A few minutes later, Laura said her heart was still racing.

Writing *In a short essay, describe what your body feels like in a situation when you are suddenly startled or frightened.*

How the Endocrine System Works

Main Idea The endocrine system includes various organs that work together to regulate body functions.

Endocrine glands are *ductless or tubeless organs or groups of cells that secrete hormones directly into the bloodstream.* **Hormones** are *chemical substances that help regulate many of your body's functions.* Carried to their destination in the body through the blood, these chemical messengers influence physical and mental responses.

Hormones produced during puberty trigger physical and emotional changes in the body. Growth is controlled by certain hormones, and abnormally high or low amounts of these hormones may contribute to growth disorders. Factors such as stress, infection, and changes in the balance of fluids and minerals in the blood may affect hormone levels. Hormones work to maintain these balances in the body so that important processes and functions work more efficiently. **Figure 16.1** describes the major glands of the endocrine system and the body functions they regulate.

More About...

Glands The body has two different types of glands. Endocrine glands are organs or groups of cells that secrete hormones directly into the bloodstream. The hormones travel through the bloodstream and interact only with body cells that have special target sites that are recognized by the hormone. Each hormone is designed to interact with only certain body cells. Endocrine glands have ducts or tubes that secrete substances in specific areas. For example, salivary glands secrete saliva into the mouth and the pancreas secretes digestive enzymes into the small intestine.

Figure 16.1 The Endocrine System

U The glands of the endocrine system are located throughout the body. Each gland has a particular function.

Hypothalamus The hypothalamus links the endocrine system and the nervous system and stimulates the pituitary gland to secrete hormones.

Pineal gland The pineal gland secretes the hormone *melatonin,* which is thought to affect the onset of puberty, and regulates sleep cycles.

Pituitary gland The **pituitary gland** *regulates and controls the activities of all other endocrine glands.*

Thymus The thymus regulates development of the immune system.

Thyroid The **thyroid gland** *produces hormones that regulate metabolism, body heat, and bone growth.* It produces thyroxine, which regulates the way cells release energy from nutrients.

Parathyroid glands The **parathyroid glands** *produce a hormone that regulates the body's balance of calcium and phosphorus.*

AL

Testes The testes are the male reproductive glands that produce sperm for fertilization.

Ovaries The ovaries are the female reproductive glands that produce the egg cells. The testes and ovaries control the development of secondary sex characteristics during puberty. You'll learn more about how the testes and ovaries play a role in reproduction in Lessons 2 and 3.

Adrenal glands These glands produce hormones that regulate the body's salt and water balance. Secretions from the adrenal cortex and the adrenal medulla stimulate several important body functions and control the body's emergency response.

Pancreas The **pancreas** is *a gland that serves both the digestive and the endocrine systems.* As an endocrine gland, it secretes two hormones—glucagon and insulin—that regulate the level of glucose in the blood.

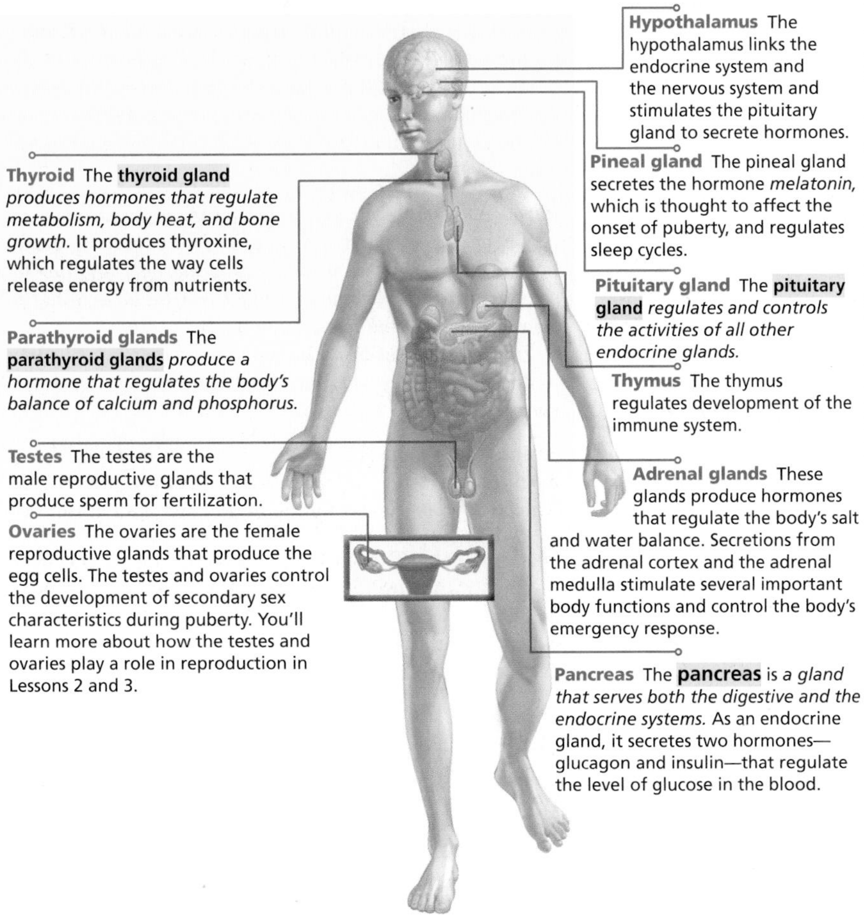

The Pituitary: The Master Gland

Known as the master gland, the pituitary gland has three sections, or lobes: anterior, intermediate, and posterior.

Anterior Lobe The anterior, or front, lobe of the pituitary gland produces these hormones:

- *Somatotropic,* or *growth hormone,* stimulates normal body growth and development by altering chemical activity in body cells.

Lesson 1   The Endocrine System   **443**

2 TEACH

U Universal Access

Using Visuals Pair English language learners with English fluent students. Instruct pairs to use the diagram of the endocrine system in **Figure 16.1** to quiz each other on the location and function of each gland. For example, students can cover up the labels, point to a gland, and state the gland's function for the other student to name. Or, students can cover up the labels, name a gland, and have the other student point to its location and give its function. **EL**

AL Active Learning

Riddles Instruct students to choose four of the glands described in **Figure 16.1**. Have them write a riddle for the gland based on the information given in the figure. Then have students exchange riddles with a partner and guess the endocrine gland. **OL** **AL**

R Reading Strategy

Identifying Cause and Effect As students read about the pituitary gland, have them make a flowchart in which they show how the pituitary gland affects other endocrine glands. Students should also identify the hormones released by these other endocrine glands and their effects on the body. **BL** **OL**

English Language Coach

Anterior vs. Posterior Explain that the adjectives *anterior* and *posterior* are commonly used in anatomy to describe the location of structures. Both words are based on Latin words. The Latin word *ante* means "before." It is used as a prefix in such words as *antechamber* (a small room that acts as an entry to another room). The Latin word *post* means "after or behind." It is used as a prefix in *postpone* (to put after).

W Writing Support

Compare and Contrast Have students write a paragraph to compare and contrast hyperthyroidism and hypothyroidism. Have them look up the meaning of the prefixes *hypo-* and *hyper-* to help them differentiate meaning. Paragraphs should include a topic sentence and supporting details. **AL**

HS Health Skills Practice

Stress Management Explain that stressful situations cause your body to respond in the same way it does when you are frightened. The adrenal gland secretes adrenaline, which increases heartbeat, respiration, and metabolism so that the body is primed to act quickly. Long-term stress can have negative effects. Have students identify the stressors in their lives, such as overscheduling. Suggest that students choose one stressor and identify and practice for one week a stress management technique to help directly relieve the stressor. **OL**

Academic Vocabulary

Intermediate Point out to students that the word *intermediate* as used here does not refer to the size of the pituitary lobe but to its position. Invite three volunteers to stand next to each other. Ask which student is intermediate. (The student in the middle.)

✔ READING CHECK

Answer Thyroid gland: produces hormones that regulate metabolism, body heat, and bone growth. Parathyroid glands: produce a hormone that regulates the body's balance of calcium and phosphorus.

444

Go Online

Visit **glencoe.com** and complete the Student Web Activity on the risks of thyroid disease in teens and young adults.

Academic Vocabulary

intermediate *(adjective):* being at the middle place or stage

✔ READING CHECK

Explain What are the functions of the thyroid gland and the parathyroid glands?

- *Thyroid-stimulating hormone* (TSH) stimulates the thyroid gland to produce hormones.
- *Adrenocorticotropic hormone* (ACTH) stimulates production of hormones in the adrenal glands.
- *Follicle-stimulating hormone* (FSH) and *luteinizing hormone* (LH) stimulate production of all other sex hormones. These two hormones are secreted by the anterior lobe of the pituitary gland during adolescence. They control the growth, development, and functions of the gonads, another name for the ovaries and testes.

In females, FSH stimulates cells in the ovary to produce *estrogen,* a female sex hormone that triggers the development of ova, or egg cells. LH is responsible for ovulation and stimulates ovarian cells to produce *progesterone,* another female sex hormone. The hormone *prolactin* stimulates milk production in females who have given birth.

In males, LH stimulates cells in the testes to produce the male hormone *testosterone.* FSH controls the production of sperm.

Intermediate Lobe The intermediate, or middle, lobe of the pituitary secretes *melanocyte-stimulating hormone* (MSH), which controls the darkening of the pigments in the skin.

Posterior Lobe The posterior, or rear, lobe of the pituitary secretes *antidiuretic hormone* (ADH), which regulates the balance of water in the body. ADH also produces oxytocin, which stimulates the smooth muscles in the uterus during pregnancy, causing contractions during the birth of a baby.

The Adrenal Glands

The **adrenal glands** *help the body deal with stress and respond to emergencies.* They each have two parts, the adrenal cortex and a smaller, inner region called the adrenal medulla, which controls a variety of body functions.

- The **adrenal cortex** secretes a hormone that inhibits the amount of sodium excreted in urine and maintains blood volume and blood pressure. It also secretes hormones that aid in the metabolism of fats, proteins, and carbohydrates. These hormones influence the body's response to stress and play a role in both the immune response and sexual function.
- The **adrenal medulla** is controlled by the hypothalamus and the autonomic nervous system. It secretes the hormones *epinephrine* (also called adrenaline) and *norepinephrine.* Epinephrine increases heartbeat and respiration, raises blood pressure, and suppresses the digestive process during periods of high emotion.

Teens Want to Know

I'm a Late Bloomer. Do I Have an Endocrine Problem? In most cases, teens with delayed puberty are normal. They often have a family history of delayed puberty and require no treatment. However, be sure to talk about your concerns with your doctor.

Sometimes delayed puberty is caused by a pituitary or thyroid gland problem. Other times it's the result of other health issues such as kidney disease, diabetes, or even asthma. The doctor will assess the symptoms and provide treatment if it is required.

Maintaining Your Endocrine Health

Main Idea To keep your endocrine system working at its peak, you need to follow sound health practices.

Your endocrine health is directly related to your overall health. Remember to eat balanced meals to ensure that you get the nutrients you need, and use stress-management techniques. Sleep is also important to endocrine health. Teens need 8½ to 9 hours of sleep every night. Engage in regular physical activity to keep your body strong. Also, have regular medical checkups. Some hormonal disorders have symptoms you may not notice or recognize. A health care professional can perform tests to determine whether your endocrine function is normal.

Certain endocrine disorders can have lifelong effects on your health. Factors such as stress, infection, and changes in the balance of fluid and minerals in the blood can cause hormone levels to fluctuate. In many cases, these situations will correct themselves. Serious problems, including diabetes mellitus, hypothyroidisim, hyperthyroidism, goiter, or overproduction of adrenal hormones may require medication.

■ **Figure 16.2** Hormones produced by the pituitary gland play a significant role in determining height. *What may happen if the pituitary is damaged before adolescence?*

 READING CHECK

Identify What are three ways you can care for your endocrine system?

 LESSON 1 **ASSESSMENT**

After You Read

Reviewing Facts and Vocabulary

1. What are *hormones*?
2. Name the hormone that stimulates normal growth and development.
3. What gland helps regulate the chemicals that control sleep?

Thinking Critically

4. **Infer.** Why do the hormones FSH and LH have different effects in men and women?
5. **Apply.** If the water in your body is not properly balanced, what endocrine gland (or part of a gland) may be malfunctioning?

Applying Health Skills

6. **Self-Management.** Sleep keeps the endocrine system healthy. For one week, log the number of hours you sleep each night. At the end of the week, calculate your average. Create a plan to get the appropriate amount of sleep each night.

Writing Critically

7. **Persuasive.** Write a script for a public service announcement reminding teens that everyone grows at a different rate. Include information about normal growth and genetic influences.

Go Online

Visit glencoe.com and complete the Interactive Study Guide for this lesson.

 READING CHECK

Answer Eat a balanced diet, get plenty of sleep, and manage stress effectively.

③ ASSESS/ CLOSE

Assessment Resources

📁 *FAST FILE* ACTIVITIES
Lesson 1 Quiz

💿 *ExamView Assessment Suite* CD-ROM

Visit glencoe.com **for:**
Online Quizzes
Online Learning Center

Progress Monitoring

Reteaching
Have students create a concept map that displays the glands of the endocrine system, their function, and disorders associated with them.

Enrichment
Have students create a PowerPoint® presentation that describes how hormones work to control body processes.

Go Online

Have students visit **glencoe.com** and complete the Interactive Study Guide for this lesson.

LESSON 1 ASSESSMENT ANSWERS

1. Chemical substances produced in glands that help regulate many body functions
2. Somatotropic hormone
3. Pineal gland
4. The hormones affect the gonads: the ovaries in women and testes in men. These organs respond differently to FSH and LH, so there are different effects in men and women.
5. The posterior lobe of the pituitary gland—it controls water balance in the body.
6. Answers will vary, but students should keep an accurate record of their sleep, and honestly evaluate the amount of sleep they get.
7. Scripts will vary.

LESSON 2

The Male Reproductive System

① FOCUS

GUIDE TO READING

BIG Idea The male reproductive system is a series of organs that function to produce children. **Ask Students:** *About when does the male reproductive system reach maturity?* (Usually between the ages of 12 and 15)

Before You Read

Flow Chart Flow charts should show sperm moving from testes to epididymis to vas deferens to urethra.

Main Idea

How Male Reproductive Works The internal and external organs of the male reproduction system, with the help of hormones, can produce children. **Ask Students:** *What is the male sex hormone?* (Testosterone)

Real Life Issues

Invite volunteers to share their experiences discussing difficult topics with their parents. **Ask Students:** *How would you start a difficult conversation with your mom or dad?* (Accept all reasonable responses.)

446

LESSON 2

GUIDE TO READING

BIG Idea *The male reproductive system is a series of organs involved in producing children.*

Before You Read

Create a Flow Chart. As you read, sketch the path that sperm take through each of the male reproductive organs.

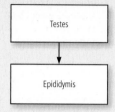

```
┌─────────────┐
│   Testes    │
└─────────────┘
       │
       ▼
┌─────────────┐
│ Epididymis  │
└─────────────┘
```

New Vocabulary

▶ sperm (p. 446)
▶ testosterone (p. 446)
▶ testes (p. 447)
▶ scrotum (p. 447)
▶ penis (p. 447)
▶ semen (p. 447)
▶ sterility (p. 450)

The Male Reproductive System

Real Life Issues ························

Growing Pains. Jack has questions about what he's going through during adolescence. His body is changing, and his moods shift all the time. He's embarrassed to talk to his mom about "guy" problems, but he wants to let her know what's going on with his moods.

Writing *Write a letter to Jack offering suggestions on how to approach his mom and what questions to ask, and advice on getting help from a trusted male adult or his doctor.*

How Male Reproduction Works

Main Idea The male reproductive system includes both external and internal organs that, with the help of hormones, allow physically mature males to produce children.

The two main functions of the male reproductive system are to produce and store **sperm**—*the male gametes,* or reproductive cells—and transfer them to the female's body during sexual intercourse. During the early teen years, usually between the ages of 12 and 15, the male reproductive system reaches maturity. At that time, hormones produced in the pituitary gland stimulate the production of **testosterone,** *the male sex hormone.* Testosterone initiates physical changes that signal maturity, including broadening of the shoulders, development of muscles and facial and other body hair, and deepening of the voice. Testosterone also controls the production of sperm. After puberty begins, a physically mature male is capable of producing sperm for the rest of his life.

More About...

Sperm Formation Sperm begin developing in the seminiferous tubules within the testes during puberty when stimulated by testosterone. Sperm have a head, which carries genetic information, and a short tail that moves the sperm through the male and female reproductive tracts. After forming, the sperm move into the epididymis where they finish developing. It takes four to six weeks for a sperm to move through the epididymis to the vans deferens. Males produce millions of sperm each day, with about 500 million ejected from the body at a time.

External Reproductive Organs

A male's external reproductive organs include the testes, the penis, and the scrotum. The **testes**, also called *testicles*, are *two small glands that secrete testosterone and produce sperm.* They are located in the **scrotum**, *an external skin sac.* The **penis** is *a tube-shaped organ that extends from the trunk of the body just above the testes.* The penis is composed of spongy tissue that contains many blood vessels. When blood flow to the penis increases, it becomes enlarged and erect, causing an erection. Erections are normal body functions that occur more easily and more frequently during puberty. They can occur for no reason.

When the penis becomes erect, semen can be ejected from the body. **Semen** is *a thick fluid containing sperm and other secretions from the male reproductive system.* At the height of sexual arousal, a series of muscular contractions known as *ejaculation* may occur. *Fertilization*—the joining of a male sperm cell and a female egg cell—can result if ejaculation occurs during sexual intercourse.

At birth, the tip of the penis is covered by a thin, loose skin, called the *foreskin.* Some parents choose *circumcision*—surgical removal of the foreskin of the penis—for their male children. In general, circumcision is often chosen for cultural or religious reasons. Sperm cannot live in temperatures higher than the normal body temperature of 98.6 degrees F. The scrotum protects sperm by keeping the testes slightly below the normal body temperature. When body temperature rises, muscles attached to the scrotum relax, causing the testes to lower away from the body. If body temperature lowers, the muscles tighten, moving the testes closer to the body for warmth. Tight clothing that holds the testes too close to the body may interfere with sperm production.

C

R

Go Online

For more vocabulary practice, go to the Interactive Health Tutor at glencoe.com.

READING CHECK

Explain How does fertilization occur?

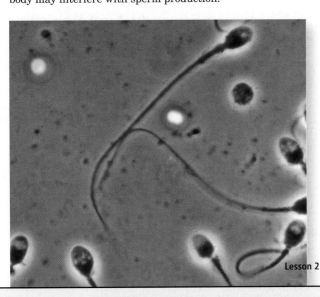

■ **Figure 16.3** Sperm are the male reproductive cells. Millions are produced each day. *What fluid contains sperm?*

② TEACH

C Critical Thinking

Making Connections Have students explain the relationship between the endocrine system and the male reproductive system. Students should identify the hormones that are involved and how the testes are stimulated to secrete testosterone. Ask students to explain the role of the endocrine system in initiating the changes to the male body during puberty. **OL**

Go Online

Encourage students to use the Interactive Health Tutor at **glencoe.com** when they are reviewing vocabulary for this chapter.

R Reading Strategy

Organizing Information As students read about the external and internal reproductive organs of the male reproductive system, instruct them to make a chart or table to organize the name of each structure and its function. Encourage students to use this chart as a study guide. **BL EL**

READING CHECK

Answer When a male sperm cell joins with a female egg cell after ejaculation in sexual intercourse

Caption Answer

Figure 16.3 Semen

ELL Support

Male Reproductive Structures Give students a copy of Figure 16.5, page 449, in which you have removed the labels.

Beginning Provide index cards with the name of each structure. As you say the names aloud, have students find the correct card and point to the structure on the diagram.

Intermediate Give students the index cards and have them point to the structure on

the diagram. Students should read the name of the structure aloud and tell its function.

Advanced Have students write the names of each structure on a copy of **Figure 16.5** and write a sentence that describes its function.

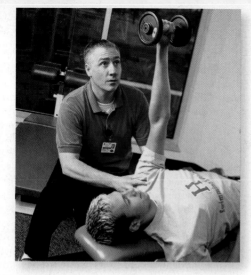

■ **Figure 16.4** Testosterone may spur the development of muscles in adolescence. *What else does testosterone influence?*

Caption Answer

Figure 16.4 The production of sperm, as well as the development of facial and body hair, and a deeper voice

CA Cultural Awareness

Circumcision Explain that the decision parents make to circumcise their infant sons is a personal one. More parents in the United States choose circumcision than parents in European countries. Many parents are questioning the need for circumcision, and often are choosing not to circumcise their infant sons. **OL**

Main Idea

Maintaining Reproductive Health The male reproductive system needs care and monitoring. **Ask Students:** *What is one way to care for the male reproductive system?* (Sample answer: Get regular medical checkups.)

FITNESSZONE

Have students work with partners to try these challenges:

- While standing lift arms to shoulder height and hold for 3 minutes.
- Hold a book between thumb and one finger, hold until it slips out.
- Balance on one foot, alternate touching finger to nose; repeat on other foot.
- Stand and bend both knees slightly, balance in position without bending or straightening.

When a male begins to produce sperm, he may experience nocturnal emissions, an ejaculation that occurs when sperm are released during sleep. This is a normal occurrence to relieve the buildup of pressure as sperm begin to produce during puberty.

Internal Reproductive Organs

Although sperm are produced in the testes, which are suspended outside the body, they must travel through several structures inside the body before they are released. These structures include the vas deferens, the urethra, the seminal vesicles, and the prostate and Cowper's glands. **Figure 16.5** shows the path taken by sperm cells from the testes until they are released from the body.

Maintaining Reproductive Health

Main Idea Male reproductive health involves care and monitoring throughout a male's lifetime.

As with any other body system, the male reproductive system needs care. Ways of caring for the male reproductive system include practicing good personal hygiene, using adequate protection, practicing self-examination, and getting regular medical checkups. **CA**

- **Bathe regularly.** Males should shower or bathe daily, thoroughly cleansing the penis and scrotum. Uncircumcised males should take care to wash under the foreskin.
- **Wear protective equipment.** Use a protective cup or athletic supporter during physical activities to shield the external reproductive organs.

448 **Chapter 16** Endocrine and Reproductive Health

FITNESSZONE

It's really important to me to succeed in whatever I start out to do. I know I need to take care of myself and keep in shape, even when I'm not feeling up to it. I am going out for track this year so I will be motivated to run every day. I know if I choose a sport I really like, I won't give up. For more physical activity ideas, visit the Online Fitness Zone at **glencoe.com**.

◆ Promoting School Wellness

Reproductive Health All schools address reproductive health at some point in their curriculum at various stages of development. While all schools provide basic information about reproductive health in health class, some provide additional information and services. Inform your students of the services and information available to them at your school. Invite the school nurse, counselor, social worker, or any other involved staff member to describe what your school offers in the way of reproductive health information.

Figure 16.5 Male Reproductive System

The internal structures of the male reproductive system work together to promote the delivery of sperm.

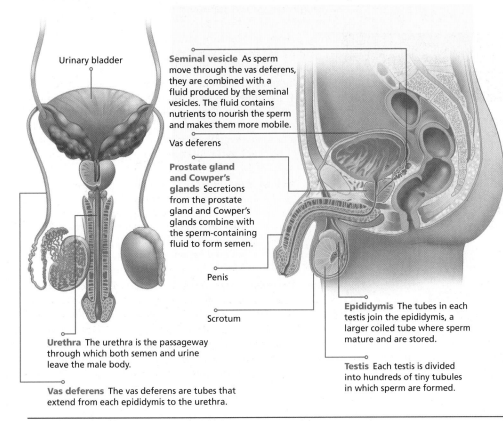

Urinary bladder

Seminal vesicle As sperm move through the vas deferens, they are combined with a fluid produced by the seminal vesicles. The fluid contains nutrients to nourish the sperm and makes them more mobile.

Vas deferens

Prostate gland and Cowper's glands Secretions from the prostate gland and Cowper's glands combine with the sperm-containing fluid to form semen.

Penis

Scrotum

Urethra The urethra is the passageway through which both semen and urine leave the male body.

Vas deferens The vas deferens are tubes that extend from each epididymis to the urethra.

Epididymis The tubes in each testis join the epididymis, a larger coiled tube where sperm mature and are stored.

Testis Each testis is divided into hundreds of tiny tubules in which sperm are formed.

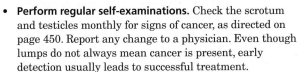 **AL**

- **Practice abstinence.** Abstain from sexual activity before marriage to avoid contracting sexually transmitted diseases (STDs).

- **Perform regular self-examinations.** Check the scrotum and testicles monthly for signs of cancer, as directed on page 450. Report any change to a physician. Even though lumps do not always mean cancer is present, early detection usually leads to successful treatment.

 **W**

- **Get regular checkups.** All males should have regular checkups by a physician every 12 to 18 months. If an abnormality is found, the patient will be referred to a urologist, who specializes in care and problems of the male reproductive system.

READING CHECK

Identify What are the benefits of practicing abstinence to protect the reproductive system?

AL **Active Learning**

Public Service Announcement Have small groups of students work together to create a public service announcement (PSA) that describes how to care for the male reproductive system. Students should include the five methods discussed in the lesson and how they work to maintain good health. Direct students to write a script for the PSA and sketch a few scenes to help convey their idea. Encourage students to use humor, but insist on good taste. **OL**

W **Writing Support**

Personal Writing Have male students write in their personal journals the ways in which they care for their reproductive health. Encourage them to compare their health practices with those recommended in the text. Direct them to complete their journal entry by describing ways they can improve maintaining their reproductive health. **OL**

READING CHECK

Answer By practicing abstinence, you will avoid contracting STDs.

Cooperative Learning

Dangers of Anabolic Steroids Have students work in groups to research and report on the effects of steroid use on the male reproductive system. In their reports, students should explain how the hormones interfere with normal functioning of the system. They should also explain the secondary effects the hormones have on male characteristics and behavior. Have groups write a statement that not only summarizes their findings but also includes their opinion on why steroid use is dangerous. After review, you might wish students to present their statements to the class for discussion.

Male Reproductive System Problems

Main Idea The organs of the male reproductive system can be affected by both functional and structural problems.

Main Idea

Male Reproductive System Problems Both functional and structural problems can affect the organs of the male reproductive system. **Ask Students:** *How do STDs affect the male reproductive system?* (STDs can cause sterility.)

U Universal Access

Classifying Disorders For beginning English language learners, make index cards for the different causes of sterility and one card for the definition of the term. Have students write the term *sterility* and say it aloud. Instruct them to sort through the cards to find the definition of the term. More advanced English language learners can write a sentence that defines the term *sterility*. Then have them list several causes of sterility. **EL**

W Writing Support

Summarizing Have students find out how Lance Armstrong beat testicular cancer. They should use reliable sources of information. **AL**

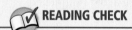 **READING CHECK**

Answer The epididymis might be confused with a lump.

■ **Figure 16.6** Figure skater and Olympic gold medalist Scott Hamilton is a testicular cancer survivor. *What can help detect testicular cancer early so it can be treated more effectively?*

Some problems of the male reproductive system are described below. Males should watch for the signs of these problems, as well as signs of infections from STDs.

- **Inguinal hernia.** An inguinal hernia occurs when part of the intestines push through a tear in the abdominal wall. The tear may be caused by straining the abdominal muscles or lifting heavy objects. Symptoms include a lump in the groin near the thigh, pain in the groin, or blockage of the intestine. Surgery can repair an inguinal hernia.

- **Sterility** is *the inability to reproduce*, as a result of too few sperm or sperm of poor quality. Exposure to X-rays or other radiation, toxic chemicals, and lead, can cause sterility. Other causes include hormonal imbalances, mumps contracted during adulthood, or using certain medications or drugs such as anabolic steroids. STDs can also cause sterility. **U**

- **Testicular cancer.** Testicular cancer can affect males of any age, but occurs most often in males between the ages of 14 and 40. With early detection, most testicular cancer is treatable through surgery, radiation, or chemotherapy. **W**

- **Prostate problems and prostate cancer.** The prostate gland can become enlarged as a result of an infection, a tumor, or age. Early detection of prostate cancer increases survival rates.

How to Do a Testicular Self-Exam (TSE)

The American Cancer Society recommends that males perform a self-exam for testicular cancer once a month.

1. Standing in front of a mirror, look for swelling. Examine each testicle with both hands. Roll the testicle gently between the thumbs and forefingers.

2. Cancerous lumps usually are found on the side of the testicle but can appear on the front. Find the epididymis, the soft tubelike structure behind each testicle, so that you won't mistake it for a lump.

3. Most lumps are not cancerous. If you do find a lump or experience pain or swelling, however, consult a health care professional.

READING CHECK

Explain Why is it important to know where the epididymis is when doing a testicular exam?

Skills for the 21st Century

Interpersonal and Self-Directional Skills Explain to students that social responsibility is acting responsibly with the interests of the larger community in mind. Begin a class discussion on how maintaining reproductive health is a social responsibility. Invite students to agree or disagree with this idea and to give their reasons. Ask students for their opinions about whether or not practicing abstinence is a socially responsible behavior. Be sure they back up their opinions with logical reasons. Point out how abstinence eliminates unwanted pregnancies and stops the spread of sexually transmitted diseases.

Real World CONNECTION

TSE Awareness Campaign

To raise awareness of the importance of performing a monthly testicular self-exam (TSE), you will work with a group to develop an awareness program. Write a script for a public service announcement, design a poster, and create a reminder card.

Here are some facts you may want to use as part of your campaign:

▸ Testicular cancer is most common among men ages 14 to 40.

▸ The disease is four times more likely to occur in white men than in African American men.

▸ Risk factors for testicular cancer include having an undescended testicle or having a personal or family history of testicular cancer.

Activity Reading / Writing

Organize into groups of three or four students. Each group member will create one of the campaign elements—a script, poster, and reminder card. Use information in the text. Group members should work together to make sure that the campaign presents consistent information featuring the same key points.

1. Write a public service announcement script that raises awareness of TSE.

2. Create a poster with the warning signs of testicular cancer. Arrange for permission to place these in the boys' locker room at school.

3. Develop a wallet-size reminder card listing the steps of the testicular self-exam.

Real World CONNECTION

Answer to Activity

Campaigns will vary but should include scripts, posters, and reminder cards that raise awareness of testicular self-exams and give warning signs of testicular cancer.

❸ ASSESS/ CLOSE

Assessment Resources

📁 *FAST FILE* **ACTIVITIES**
Lesson 2 Quiz

💿 *ExamView*
Assessment Suite CD-ROM

Visit glencoe.com **for:**
Online Quizzes
Online Learning Center

Progress Monitoring

Reteaching

Have students make flash cards for each part of the male reproductive system, writing the name of the structure on one side and the function on the other side.

Enrichment

Instruct students to use reliable online resources to learn more about one of the problems of the male reproductive system and prepare a report.

LESSON 2 📖 ASSESSMENT

After You Read

Reviewing Facts and Vocabulary

1. Sperm cannot survive at body temperature. How does the body protect sperm from heat?

2. What is *sterility*?

3. What are the vas deferens?

Thinking Critically

4. **Infer.** How might giving a mumps vaccine to a boy help protect his reproductive health later?

5. **Compare and Contrast.** How might a man's reproductive health concerns change at different periods of his life?

6. **Distinguish.** What is the difference between semen and sperm?

Applying Health Skills

7. **Practicing Healthful Behaviors.** Describe some behaviors that can help males maintain their reproductive health.

Writing Critically

8. **Persuasive.** Write an article persuading males of the need for protective equipment during football and other sports. Describe how shoulder pads, knee pads, and protective cups help prevent injury.

 Online

Visit glencoe.com and complete the Interactive Study Guide for this lesson.

LESSON 2 ASSESSMENT ANSWERS

1. The scrotum holds the testes outside the body so that they are kept at a temperature slightly lower than body temperature.

2. The inability to reproduce

3. Tubes that extend from each epididymis to the urethra

4. Mumps, if contracted as an adult, can cause sterility. A vaccine against mumps can help prevent a mumps infection in an adult and any possible reproductive problems.

5. Sample answer: Males between the ages of 14 and 40 should be careful about testicular cancer. Males over 50 should be checked for signs of prostate cancer.

6. Sperm are the male reproductive cells. Semen is the fluid that contains sperm.

7. Sample answer: Performing TSEs, wearing protective equipment, bathing regularly, abstaining from sexual activity, and getting regular checkups

8. Articles will vary.

Online

Have students visit glencoe.com and complete the Interactive Study Guide for this lesson.

451

The Female Reproductive System

LESSON 3

1 FOCUS

 GUIDE TO READING

BIG Idea The female reproductive system matures at puberty, when pregnancy can occur. **Ask Students:** *Which endocrine gland stimulates the female reproductive system to begin maturing?* (The pituitary gland)

Before You Read

T-Chart Students' T-charts will vary. The parts of the female reproductive system and their functions should reflect the discussion in the lesson.

Main Idea

Female Reproductive Organs
Beginning with the first monthly ovulation at puberty, the organs of the female reproductive system enable women to bear children.
Ask Students: *What is the role of the ovaries in reproduction?* (The ovaries store the ova, or egg cells, and produce female sex hormones.)

Real Life Issues

Before students write the note to Sandra, discuss concrete and healthy ways to deal with teasing. **Ask Students:** *Why shouldn't Sandra feel self-conscious about herself?* (Accept all reasonable answers.)

GUIDE TO READING

BIG Idea *The female reproduction system matures at puberty and enables women to reproduce.*

Before You Read

Create a T-Chart. Set up a T-chart like the one pictured below to organize information about the parts of the female reproductive system and their functions.

Part	Function

New Vocabulary

▶ eggs (p. 452)
▶ ovaries (p. 452)
▶ uterus (p. 452)
▶ ovulation (p. 452)
▶ fallopian tubes (p. 453)
▶ vagina (p. 454)
▶ menstruation (p. 454)
▶ cervix (p. 454)

The Female Reproductive System

Real Life Issues

Being Teased. Jody and her friend Sandra decide to try out for the girls' basketball team at school. Later, however, Sandra tells Jody that she has changed her mind. Sandra is embarrassed to shower and change in the locker room because she's developing at a slower pace than most of the other girls. She's been teased by some of the girls and feels self-conscious in the locker room.

Writing *Write a supportive note to Sandra telling her that all girls mature at various rates. Be sure your note respects Sandra as she is and encourages her to understand she is not alone.*

Female Reproductive Organs

Main Idea The organs of the female reproductive system enable pregnancy to occur with the first monthly ovulation.

The female reproductive system has several functions, including producing female sex hormones and storing the **eggs**, *female gametes or ova (singular: ovum)*. The **ovaries** are *the female sex glands that store the ova and produce female sex hormones.* They are located on each side of the **uterus**, *the hollow, muscular, pear-shaped organ that nourishes and protects a fertilized ovum until birth.* A female at birth has more than 400,000 immature ova. At puberty, the pituitary gland produces hormones that cause these ova to mature. **Ovulation** is *the process of releasing a mature ovum into the fallopian tube each month.*

More About...

Fertilization Timing is critical for successful fertilization to occur. Once the egg ovulates, it survives only 24 hours. This means that sperm must already be present in the fallopian tube before the egg is released. Under ideal conditions, sperm can survive several days in the female reproductive tract. A few days before ovulation, the cervix softens and opens slightly. Cervical mucus increases and becomes transparent and slippery. These changes make it easier for sperm to travel to the fallopian tubes and survive for a couple days before ovulation.

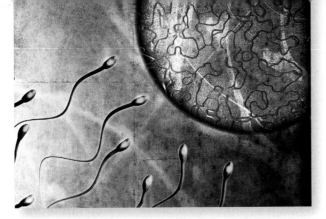

■ **Figure 16.7** Each month, an ovum is released that may unite with sperm, as shown here, in the process of fertilization. *If fertilization occurs, what type of cell is produced?*

② TEACH

R Reading Strategy

Sequencing Have students create a flowchart that shows the movement of an ovum from the ovaries to the uterus. In their flowcharts, students should also include when and where fertilization occurs and what happens to the uterus and the zygote. **BL EL**

Female Reproductive Organs

R The structures of the female reproductive system are shown in **Figure 16.8**. A mature ovum is released from an ovary and moves into one of the two **fallopian tubes**—*a pair of tubes with fingerlike projections that draw in the ovum.*

W

| **Figure 16.8** | **Female Reproductive System** |

The female reproductive system produces egg cells called ova, and each month provides a place for a fertilized ovum to grow.

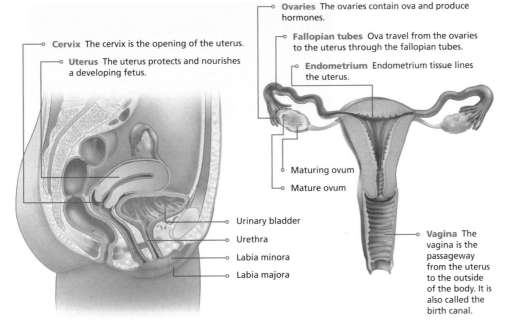

Cervix The cervix is the opening of the uterus.

Uterus The uterus protects and nourishes a developing fetus.

Ovaries The ovaries contain ova and produce hormones.

Fallopian tubes Ova travel from the ovaries to the uterus through the fallopian tubes.

Endometrium Endometrium tissue lines the uterus.

Maturing ovum

Mature ovum

Urinary bladder

Urethra

Labia minora

Labia majora

Vagina The vagina is the passageway from the uterus to the outside of the body. It is also called the birth canal.

Caption Answer

Figure 16.7 A zygote results when fertilization occurs.

W Writing Support

Descriptive Writing Using **Figure 16.8** as a guide, direct students to write a description of how the female reproductive system works. In their descriptions, students should include the names of the organs involved as well as their functions. Students should also include fertilization and how the reproductive system changes to support the developing fetus. Encourage students to write sentences with descriptive details that present a clear picture of the reproductive process. **OL**

Teacher to Teacher

Joan Davis • Martin Luther King High School, Detroit, MI

Reproductive Health Knowledge This is a good introductory activity to find out what the students know about the reproductive system. Break the class into groups of three students. Assign each group a set of vocabulary words related to the reproductive system (male and female). Each group will also have a graphic organizer labeled with the topics: Male, Both, and Female. The students will take the anatomy vocabulary words and place them under the appropriate section. It might be helpful to laminate the terms as well as the graphic organizer. Review with the class the correct answers.

AL Active Learning

Informational Brochure Have small groups of students create an informational brochure that describes to younger female students what happens to their bodies as they mature. Students should include information about menstruation—what it is, what happens to the body, why it happens, and how to manage the changes. Students should target their brochures to adolescents between the ages of 8 and 13. Brochures can include illustrations and should have information that is well organized and easy to understand. OL AL

C Critical Thinking

Inferring Explain that while endocrine hormones control the menstrual cycle, poor nutrition, stress, excessive exercise, low body weight, and illness can affect it. Have students infer why the body does not ovulate in conditions of stress. (The body does not have enough nutrition to support both it and a developing fetus. It is a natural mechanism to ensure that a pregnancy occurs only when conditions are favorable.) OL

READING CHECK

Answer The uterine wall thickens.

Go Online

Visit glencoe.com and complete the Student Web Activity on ways nutrition, age, and alcohol and drug use can affect fertility.

READING CHECK

Describe How does the uterine wall prepare for the zygote?

Tiny hairlike structures called *cilia* work to move the ovum with the help of muscular contractions in the fallopian tubes. Sperm from the male enter the female reproductive system through the **vagina**, *a muscular, elastic passageway that extends from the uterus to the outside of the body.*

If sperm are present in the fallopian tubes, the sperm cell and ovum may unite, resulting in fertilization. The fertilization of an egg by a sperm produces a cell called a *zygote*. When the zygote leaves the fallopian tube, it enters the uterus. The zygote attaches itself to the uterine wall. The uterine wall thickens with blood to nourish the zygote as it grows. The fetus remains in the uterus until birth.

Menstruation

After a female matures, the uterus prepares each month for possible pregnancy. If pregnancy doesn't occur, the thickened lining of the uterus, called the *endometrium,* breaks down into blood, tissue, and fluids. **Figure 16.9** shows the cycle of **menstruation**, *the shedding of the uterine lining.* The endometrium tissues pass through the **cervix**, *the opening to the uterus,* and into the vagina. Females wear sanitary pads or tampons to absorb the blood flow. **AL**

Most females begin their first menstrual cycle between the ages of 10 and 15. The menstrual cycle may be irregular at first. As a female matures, it usually becomes more predictable. Endocrine hormones control the cycle, but poor nutrition, stress, excessive exercise, low body weight, and illness can influence it. Menstruation occurs from puberty until *menopause,* the end of the reproductive years, which usually occurs between the ages of 45 and 55. **C**

Figure 16.9	**The Menstrual Cycle**		
Days 1–8	**Days 9–20**	**Day 21**	**Days 22–30**
Menstruation begins as hormone levels fall.	A new egg cell matures inside the ovary.	The mature egg is released into one of the fallopian tubes.	The egg travels through the fallopian tube to the uterus.

Myths & Reality

Hygiene

Myth: Douches and feminine sprays will keep the vagina fresh and clean.

Fact: Douches and feminine sprays are not needed. The vagina has its own natural cleaning system to flush out bacteria that can cause odors. Douching and spraying can irritate the vagina and cause allergic reactions and infections.

Myth: A tampon can get lost inside the body.

Reality: The tampon will stay in the vagina because the opening of the cervix is too small for a tampon to get through.

Maintaining Reproductive Health

 Main Idea Good hygiene, breast self-exams, and abstinence from sexual activity help female reproductive system health.

Sound health practices, such as those described below, will help females care for their reproductive systems.

- **Bathe regularly.** It is especially important to shower or bathe daily, and change tampons or sanitary pads every few hours during the menstrual period.

- **Have regular medical exams.** Regular medical exams will include a test (Pap smear) for cancerous cells on the cervix, as well as a mammogram to test for breast cancer. Report any pain, discharge, or other signs of infection to your health care provider as soon as possible.

- **Practice abstinence.** Abstain from sexual activity to avoid unplanned pregnancy and STDs.

Breast Self-Exam

Breast cancer is the most common cancer and the second leading cause of death, after lung cancer, for women in the United States. The American Cancer Society recommends that females examine their breasts once a month, right after the menstrual period, when breasts are not tender. Early detection is critical for successful treatment of breast cancer. See **Figure 16.10** and follow these steps:

1. Lie down with a pillow under your right shoulder. Put your right arm behind your head. Place the three middle finger pads of your left hand on your right breast. Move your fingers in a circular motion, pressing first with light, then medium, then firm pressure. Feel for any lumps or thickening in the breast. Follow this process in an up-and-down path over the breast. Be sure to check all of the breast tissue, from the underarm edge to the middle of the chest bone, and from the collarbone to ribs. Repeat, using your right hand on your left breast.

3. Stand in front of a mirror with your hands pressed firmly on your hips. Inspect your breasts for *any* changes in size, shape, or appearance. Look for dimpling, rash, puckering or scaliness of the skin or nipple, or discharge.

4. Next, raise your arms over your head (palms pressed together), and look for changes.

5. Examine your underarms with your arms only slightly raised so you can more easily feel these areas.

READING CHECK

Describe What are three important steps for maintaining reproductive health in females?

Figure 16.10

Breast Self-Exam

In a vertical pattern, check from the underarm to the chest bone, and from the collarbone to the ribs. *How can the underarms be checked?*

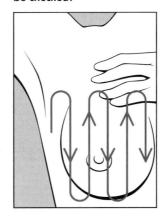

Main Idea

Maintaining Reproductive Health Sound health practices will keep the female reproductive system healthy. **Ask Students:** *What health practices help keep the female reproductive system healthy?* (Regular baths, medical exams, abstinence from sexual activity, breast self-exams)

READING CHECK

Answer Good hygiene, regular medical exams, practice abstinence

HS Health Skills Practice

Communication Skills Invite a health care practitioner to class who specializes in reproductive health and/or teens and development. Before the speaker comes to class, have students write several questions they have about reproduction, reproductive health, and communicating with doctors about sensitive issues. Review the questions, and then have students practice asking the questions to partners before the speaker comes to class. Encourage each student to ask the speaker a question. **OL**

U Universal Access

Writing Sentences Help beginning English language learners create concept maps on ways to keep the female reproductive system healthy. Have students use single words or phrases for the map. They can match pictures or diagrams to words and phrases. **EL**

Caption Answer

Figure 16.10 Check the underarms while standing with the arms only slightly raised so any lumps can be felt more easily.

Writing Strategy

Writing an Owner's Manual Have students write an owner's manual for the female reproductive system. Like all owners' manuals, this manual should include the parts of the female reproductive system and their functions, as well as how to care for these parts. Students should also include a section that describes problems that can occur to the female reproductive system and how these problems can be prevented or solved. Students can include simple illustrations in their manuals for a "parts diagram."

Communication Skills: Asking Difficult Questions

NHES Standard 4 Students will demonstrate the ability to use interpersonal communication skills to enhance health and avoid or reduce health risks.

Objectives

- Explain why it is normal for people to mature at different rates.
- Demonstrate strategies for communicating health concerns.

Teaching Strategies

- Review the ages at which females begin menstruating. Discuss what causes menstruation to begin and reasons why some females start later than others.
- Have pairs of students work together to write the dialogue. Suggest they include "stage instructions" that describe Jenny and Dr. Silvio's body language and tone of voice.

Assessment

Using a rubric, student work should provide comprehensive evidence of the following criteria to achieve the highest score:

√ Use of "I" messages
√ Speaks clearly and calmly
√ Respectful tone of voice
√ Appropriate body language
√ Clear, organized message

FITNESSZONE

Even though my days are really full, I'm committed to getting about 30 minutes of exercise every day. To meet my goal, I started getting up 30 minutes earlier each morning to exercise. My doctor says that exercising in the morning will boost my metabolism. I also seem to have more energy throughout the day. For more fitness tips, visit the Online Fitness Zone at glencoe.com.

Female Reproductive System Problems

Main Idea Several disorders can affect the female reproductive system, and some can lead to infertility.

Both menstrual cramps and premenstrual syndrome are common in females. Toxic shock syndrome is uncommon.

- **Menstrual cramps** sometimes occur at the beginning of a menstrual period. Light exercise or applying a heating pad to the abdominal area may help relieve cramps. If cramps are severe, a health care professional may recommend an over-the-counter or prescription medicine.
- **Premenstrual syndrome (PMS)** is a disorder caused by hormonal changes. Symptoms include anxiety, irritability, bloating, weight gain, depression, mood swings, and fatigue. Regular physical activity and good nutrition may reduce the severity of symptoms.
- **Toxic shock syndrome (TSS)** is a rare but serious bacterial infection that affects the immune system and the liver. It can be fatal. To reduce TSS risk, use tampons with the lowest absorbency and change them often. If symptoms occur, such as fever, vomiting, diarrhea, rash, red eyes, dizziness, and muscle aches, see a doctor.

Infertility and Other Disorders

Infertility in females can have several causes.

- **Endometriosis** occurs when uterine tissue grows in the ovaries, fallopian tubes, or the lining of the pelvic cavity.
- **Sexually transmitted diseases** spread during sexual contact. Untreated STDs, such as gonorrhea and chlamydia, are associated with pelvic inflamatory disease (PID) and may cause infertility. Abstinence from sexual activity until marriage is the only way to avoid STDs.
- **Vaginitis** results in discharge, odor, pain, itching, or burning. *Candida* (yeast infection) and bacterial vaginosis are two common forms of vaginitis.
- **Ovarian cysts** are fluid-filled sacs on the ovary. Small, noncancerous cysts mayc disappear on their own. Larger cysts may have to be removed surgically.
- **Cervical, uterine, and ovarian cancers.** Early sexual activity and STDs such as human papillomavirus (HPV) increase the risk of cervical cancer. Regular exams are important for early detection and treatment. The Food and Drug Administration has approved a vaccine that prevents infection from four strains of the HPV virus.

Teens Want to Know

Why Do I Need a Pelvic Exam? The American College of Obstetricians and Gynecologists recommends that females have their first visit with a gynecologist between the ages of 13 and 15. At this age, the gynecologist will perform a regular health exam and discuss developmental changes. After completing puberty, female adolescents often have pelvic exams to monitor the health and development of the vagina, uterus, and ovaries. Pelvic exams are also done to help prevent sexually transmitted diseases and to deal with menstrual or other reproductive system problems.

Health Skills Activity

Communication Skills

Asking Difficult Questions

Jenny has just arrived for her summer camp physical. She has been a patient of Dr. Silvio's for years and feels comfortable talking with her. Ever since her mother died of cancer last year when Jenny was 13, Jenny and her dad have grown closer. They talk openly about what's on their minds.

As close as she and her dad are, Jenny feels awkward discussing a certain personal problem with him: her menstrual period. She wonders to herself: *Should I tell Dr. Silvio that I haven't started menstruating yet?*

Writing Write a dialogue in which Jenny talks about her concerns. Include a response from Dr. Silvio that is thoughtful and communicates that Jenny has nothing to worry about. Use these guidelines for effective communication.

1. Use "I" messages.
2. Speak calmly and clearly.
3. Be respectful.
4. Listen carefully and ask appropriate questions.
5. Use appropriate body language.

LESSON 3 ASSESSMENT

After You Read

Reviewing Facts and Vocabulary

1. What is the function of the uterus?
2. Distinguish between *ova, ovaries,* and *ovulation.*
3. Identify a kind of cancer of the female reproductive system that is linked to a sexually transmitted disease (STD).

Critical Thinking

4. **Distinguish.** What is the difference between menstrual cramps and PMS?
5. **Infer.** Why do blocked fallopian tubes often result in infertility?

Applying Health Skills

6. **Advocacy.** Create a brochure that educates females about ways to promote reproductive health. Include preventive care such as hygiene, mammograms, and Pap smears.

Writing Critically

7. **Persuasive.** Some students in Mrs. Garcia's class are uncomfortable learning about the reproductive system of the opposite gender. Write a persuasive letter explaining why this education is important.

Go Online

Visit glencoe.com and complete the Interactive Study Guide for this lesson.

Lesson 3 The Female Reproductive System **457**

---

③ ASSESS/ CLOSE

Assessment Resources

📁 **FAST FILE ACTIVITIES**
Lesson 3 Quiz

💿 *ExamView Assessment Suite* CD-ROM

Visit glencoe.com **for:**
Online Quizzes
Online Learning Center

Progress Monitoring

Reteaching
Give students a copy of the female reproductive system from **Figure 16.8** in which all the labels have been removed. Have students write in the name of each part and its function.

Enrichment
Have students get involved in a breast-cancer awareness campaign. Students might participate in or help organize a fundraiser for breast cancer research.

Go Online

Have students visit glencoe.com and complete the Interactive Study Guide for this lesson.

LESSON 3 ASSESSMENT ANSWERS

1. The uterus protects and nourishes a developing fetus.
2. The *ova* are egg cells. The *ovaries* are the female sex glands that store the ova and produce female sex hormones. *Ovulation* is the process of releasing a mature ovum into a fallopian tube each month.
3. Cervical cancer
4. Menstrual cramps occur occasionally at the beginning of a menstrual period. PMS is a disorder that occurs one to two weeks before menstruation that can cause a variety of physical and emotional changes.
5. Fertilization occurs in the fallopian tubes. If they are blocked, sperm cannot reach the ovum.
6. Brochures will vary.
7. Letters will vary.

Peer-to-Peer Education

NHES Standard 4 Students will demonstrate the ability to use interpersonal communication skills to enhance health and avoid or reduce health risks.

Teaching Objectives

- Analyze and describe the components and functions of the male and female reproductive systems.
- Create a presentation on the reproductive systems that is age appropriate and interactive, with a clear and organized message.

Teaching Strategies

- Place students in groups of three or four. Each group will need access to the Internet and the materials listed under What You'll Need.
- Role-play "tough" questions that the sixth-graders might ask of the high school students prior to the peer-to-peer presentation.

Assessment

Using a rubric, student work should provide comprehensive evidence of the following criteria to achieve the highest score:

✔ Interaction among individuals
✔ Clear, organized message
✔ Awareness of audience
✔ Clear, simple language
✔ Appropriate body language

Hands-On
HEALTH

 Activity ## Peer-to-Peer Education

Create a lesson for a class of middle school students to introduce structures, functions, and care of the male and female reproductive systems. Be prepared for "tough" questions that sixth graders might ask. Use communication skills appropriate for that age group.

What You'll Need

- computer with Internet access
- paper and pens or pencils
- poster paper, construction paper, markers, glue, tape, scissors
- props: paper cups, tennis balls, string

What You'll Do

Step 1

Work in groups to research information and outline your presentation. Include facts to support each point.

Step 2

Create visual aids and props, for example, to show how an egg cell passes through the female reproductive system.

Step 3

Include a clear, organized health message. Be sure the language is age appropriate.

Apply and Conclude

Discuss how your presentation will help younger students identify healthful lifestyle behaviors.

Checklist: Communication Skills

☑ Interaction between individuals

☑ Clear, organized message

☑ Respectful tone

☑ Listening skills

☑ Appropriate body language

More About...

Changes During Puberty Puberty usually starts between the ages of 8 and 13 in females and 10 and 15 in males. Along with changes in breast and penis size, adolescents experience hair growth in pubic areas and under the arms. Acne begins, and body odor becomes more noticeable. The body also has a growth spurt and may store a layer of fat. Females will have a mucus discharge from the vagina, and males will get erections. Both become more emotional. They may be overly sensitive or lose their tempers easily.

To download quizzes and eFlashcards to your PDA, go to **glencoe.com** and click on the Study to Go icon.

LESSON 1

The Endocrine System

Key Concepts

- The endocrine glands are organs or groups of cells that secrete hormones into the bloodstream.
- To care for your endocrine system, get plenty of rest, eat well, and avoid stress.
- Problems of the endocrine system include diabetes mellitus, hypothyroidism, goiter, and growth disorders.

Vocabulary

- endocrine glands (p. 442)
- hormones (p. 442)
- thyroid gland (p. 443)
- parathyroid glands (p. 443)
- pancreas (p. 443)
- pituitary gland (p. 443)
- adrenal glands (p. 444)

LESSON 2

The Male Reproductive System

Key Concepts

- The external organs include the penis, testes, scrotum, seminal vesicles, vas deferens, epididymis, prostate and Cowper's glands, and urethra.
- Care of the male reproductive system involves getting medical checkups, bathing regularly, protecting against injury, performing self-exams, and abstaining from sexual activity.
- Problems include inguinal hernias, sterility, and testicular and prostate cancer.

Vocabulary

- sperm (p. 446)
- testosterone (p. 446)
- testes (p. 447)
- scrotum (p. 447)
- penis (p. 447)
- semen (p. 447)
- sterility (p. 450)

LESSON 3

The Female Reproductive System

Key Concepts

- The major structures of the female reproductive system include the ovaries, fallopian tubes, uterus, cervix, and vagina.
- *Menstruation* is the shedding of the uterine lining.
- Breast self-exams should be done in two phases: lying down and standing in front of a mirror.
- Problems include menstrual cramps, PMS, vaginitis, infertility-related disorders such as endometriosis and PID, and cancer.

Vocabulary

- eggs (p. 452)
- ovaries (p. 452)
- uterus (p. 452)
- ovulation (p. 452)
- fallopian tubes (p. 453)
- vagina (p. 454)
- menstruation (p. 454)
- cervix (p. 454)

Go Online

Students can visit **glencoe.com** to

- review content online with the Online Student Edition.
- test their knowledge of chapter content with Online Quizzes.
- access Interactive Health Tutor for more practice with vocabulary.

Assessment Resources

FAST FILE ACTIVITIES
Chapter 16 Test

ExamView
Assessment Suite CD-ROM

Visit glencoe.com for:
Audio Chapter Summaries
Online Quizzes

STUDY TO GO Tell students to visit **glencoe.com** where they can download quizzes and eFlashcards.

Chapter 16 Review **459**

Study Tips

Using the Internet Encourage students to use the resources from the textbook's Web site to review lesson content, quiz themselves, and reinforce vocabulary terms. Demonstrate how to access these materials in class. Consider allowing extra time during the week for students to use the school computer lab to access the Web site, especially if your students do not have access to computers at home.

Chapter 16 Assessment Answers

LESSON 1

Vocabulary Review

1. thyroid gland
2. parathyroid glands
3. pituitary gland

Understanding Key Concepts

4. a
5. c
6. b

Thinking Critically

7. A high salt and water content in the body can raise blood pressure.
8. The pineal gland regulates the production of melatonin, which regulates sleep cycles.
9. Sample answer: Digestion requires a lot of blood flow to the digestive system. Reacting to a dangerous situation requires a lot of blood flow to the limbs and lungs to power the muscles for running.
10. LH stimulates the ovaries to produce progesterone. LH stimulates the testes to produce testosterone.
11. Both secrete hormones. The adrenal cortex secretes a hormone that inhibits the amount of sodium excreted in urine. The adrenal medulla secretes the hormone, epinephrine, which increases heartbeat.

LESSON 2

Vocabulary Review

12. scrotum
13. Semen
14. sterility

LESSON 1

Vocabulary Review

Correct the sentences below by replacing the italicized term with the correct vocabulary term.

1. The *hypothalamus* produces hormones that regulate metabolism, body heat, and bone growth.
2. The *adrenal glands* regulate calcium.
3. The *thymus* regulates and controls the activities of all other endocrine glands.

Understanding Key Concepts

After reading the question or statement, select the correct answer.

4. Which gland links the endocrine system with the nervous system?
   a. Hypothalamus
   b. Pituitary
   c. Pineal
   d. Pancreas

5. What is the main role of the pituitary gland?
   a. Controls sleep
   b. Helps digestion
   c. Regulates other endocrine glands
   d. Adjusts water balance

6. Which gland is involved with the release of epinephrine?
   a. Thyroid
   b. Adrenal glands
   c. Pineal gland
   d. Thymus

Thinking Critically

After reading the question or statement, write a short answer using complete sentences.

7. **Infer.** What might happen if the adrenal glands stop regulating the body's salt and water balance?

---

8. **Analyze.** If you suddenly began having trouble sleeping, how might the pineal gland be involved?

9. **Infer.** Epinephrine helps you respond to dangerous situations. Why might it help to stop digesting food if you are in danger?

10. **Analyze.** What would happen if scientists applied luteinizing hormone to a female's ovary cells and to a male's testes cells?

11. **Compare and Contrast.** Discuss similarities and differences of the adrenal cortex and adrenal medulla.

LESSON 2

Vocabulary Review

Use the vocabulary terms listed on page 459 to complete the following statements.

12. The _____ is the skin sac that holds the testes.

13. _____ is a thick fluid containing sperm from the male reproductive system.

14. The inability to produce children is called _____.

Understanding Key Concepts

After reading the question or statement, select the correct answer.

15. What is an inguinal hernia?
    a. A separation where part of the intestine pushes into the abdominal wall
    b. The inability to reproduce
    c. A type of cancer affecting the prostate
    d. An STD

Health eSpotlight Wrap-Up

Your Reproductive Health Have students reread the Health eSpotlight question at the beginning of the chapter (page 441) and look at their original answer. **Ask Students:** *Now that you have read the chapter* and watched the video, what other functions can you think of that are controlled by hormones? Call on volunteers to describe how their responses would change.

16. How often should males conduct a testicular self-exam?
    a. Once a day
    b. Once a week
    c. Once a month
    d. Once a year

17. Where are sperm formed?
    a. In the urethra
    b. In the epididymis
    c. In the penis
    d. In the testes

18. What is the passageway through which both semen and urine leave the body?
    a. The urethra
    b. The testes
    c. The seminal vesicles
    d. The epididymis

Thinking Critically

After reading the question or statement, write a short answer using complete sentences.

19. **Analyze.** How does the scrotum respond to temperature, and for what purpose?

20. **Identify.** Where are you most likely to find a cancerous lump on a testicle?

21. **Infer.** What should a male infer if he begins to develop facial hair?

22. **Compare and Contrast.** How are testicular cancer and prostate cancer different?

23. **Infer.** Why is it important to see a health care provider right away if a testicular lump is discovered?

LESSON 3

Vocabulary Review

Choose the correct term in the sentences below.

24. The *ovaries / fallopian tubes* produce hormones.

25. *Menstruation / Ovulation* is the process of releasing a mature ovum into the fallopian tube each month.

26. The *cervix / uterus* is the hollow, muscular, pear-shaped organ inside a female's body.

27. *Toxic shock syndrome / Premenstrual syndrome* is a rare but serious bacterial infection.

Understanding Key Concepts

After reading the question or statement, select the correct answer.

28. What type of disease, if left untreated, is associated with pelvic inflammatory disease?
    a. STDs
    b. Vaginitis
    c. Ovarian cancer
    d. Ovarian cysts

29. What is the opening to the uterus called?
    a. Ovum
    b. Bladder
    c. Endometrium
    d. Cervix

30. What happens to the uterine wall as it prepares for a zygote?
    a. The wall shrinks.
    b. The wall dissolves.
    c. The wall thickens.
    d. The wall sheds skin cells.

Chapter 16 Assessment **461**

Understanding Key Concepts

15. a
16. c
17. d
18. a

Thinking Critically

19. When body temperature lowers, muscles attached to the scrotum pull it close to the body. When body temperature rises, these muscles relax and the scrotum lowers away from the body. The scrotum keeps the testes at a temperature slightly lower than body temperature, any warmer and the sperm would not survive.

20. On the sides of the testicle and sometimes on the front

21. That his body is maturing

22. Both are cancers of the male reproductive system. Prostate cancer affects the prostate gland and usually affects men over 50. Testicular cancer affects the testicles and usually affects men from 14 to 40 years of age.

23. If the lump is cancerous, early treatment will often successfully cure it. If it is not treated, the cancer could spread to other tissues.

LESSON 3

Vocabulary Review

24. ovaries
25. Ovulation
26. uterus
27. Toxic shock syndrome

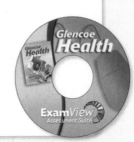

ExamView
Assessment Suite

Create and customize tests in minutes with this convenient digital platform.

- Create differentiated tests quickly and easily.
- All questions correlated to National/State Standards.
- Enhance tests with Document Based Questions (DBQ) and add your own photos or graphics.
- Build tests in both English and Spanish.
- Generate progress reports.

To order, go to **glencoe.com** and search for ISBN 0-07-888173-0.

Glencoe Health

Assessment

Understanding Key Concepts

28. a
29. d
30. c
31. a

Thinking Critically

32. Charlotte might be developing at a faster rate than Karen. Also, the start of menstruation can be delayed if Karen does not practice good nutrition, has a lot of stress in her life, or is ill.

33. By bathing regularly, having regular medical exams, performing breast self-exams, and practicing abstinence, she can avoid infection, disease, and STDs, which could all lead to infertility problems.

34. Because swelling might make lumps harder to identify, and tenderness during the menstrual period might make the exam painful.

35. Changing tampons often and bathing regularly can eliminate the bacteria that cause TSS.

31. How many ova mature each month in a female reproductive system?
    a. 1
    b. 100
    c. 400,000
    d. Millions

Thinking Critically

After reading the question or statement, write a short answer using complete sentences.

32. **Infer.** Charlotte and her friend Karen are the same age. Charlotte has started menstruating, but Karen has not. What could be the cause?

33. **Explain.** How can practicing healthful behaviors help a female maintain a healthy reproductive system and even prevent some infertility problems later in life?

34. **Analyze.** Why is it important for females to conduct a breast exam after a menstrual period ends?

35. **Synthesize.** How can good hygiene help prevent toxic shock syndrome?

Project-Based ASSESSMENT

Care of the Reproductive System

Background
When it comes to serious health issues, teens often think, *It can't happen to me.* Teens are not immune to developing serious health problems, such as those that can affect the male or female reproductive systems. For this project, small groups of students will create a poster providing teens with information on how to prevent reproductive health problems.

Task
Create a poster that illustrates a problem of the reproductive system. (If you are female, select a problem of the female reproductive system; if you are male, choose a problem of the male reproductive system.)

Audience
Students in your school and community

Purpose
Help yourself and other teens become better informed about how to prevent problems related to the male and female reproductive systems.

Procedure

1. Review the student text and choose a particular problem related to your own reproductive system.

2. Research the problem in the library and online. Identify the cause, symptoms, and treatments (historical and present-day), as well as methods by which the probability of experiencing the problem could be reduced.

3. Search through magazines or approved Internet sites to find suitable illustrations. If you wish, supplement these illustrations with drawings of your own.

4. Assemble the relevant information and illustrations in an informative, attractive, well-organized poster.

5. Submit your poster to your teacher. Excellent posters will be displayed in your school and select community locations.

Project-Based ASSESSMENT

Step 1 Research Students should use reliable library and online sources to find the causes, symptoms, treatments (old and new), and ways to reduce the risk of their chosen reproductive problem.

Step 2 Make a Poster Tell students that posters should summarize the reproductive problem they researched with the purpose of better informing other teens. Encourage students to find suitable illustrations that are informative.

Step 3 Evaluate Students' posters should be informative, visually interesting, and well-organized.

Visit **glencoe.com** for Project-Based Assessment rubrics.

Math Practice

Reading Tables. The time between fertilization of an egg by a sperm and birth is a known as a *gestation period*. This amount of time varies from organism to organism. The table gives the average gestation periods (in days) for several different types of animals.

Animal	Gestation Period
Hamster	16.5 days
Ferret	42 days
Coyote	63 days
Lion	108 days
Human	267 days
Horse	337 days
Camel	406 days

1. What is the median of the gestation periods in the table?
   - **A.** 108 days
   - **B.** 177 days
   - **C.** 389.5 days
   - **D.** There is no median because all the numbers are different.

2. The actual gestation period can be stated as a range of days. For a human, that range is from 250 to 285 days. If the value in the table is the average gestation period, the value is the
   - **A.** median.
   - **B.** mode.
   - **C.** mean.
   - **D.** first quartile.

3. Compare the size of each animal listed to its gestation period. Predict the relative gestation period of a rhinoceros. Explain your prediction.

Go Online

For more test practice, visit glencoe.com and complete the Online Quizzes for Chapter 16.

Reading/Writing Practice

Understand and Apply. Read the passage below, and then answer the questions.

Gigantism is a problem of the endocrine system caused when the pituitary gland secretes too much growth hormone during childhood before the bones have completed their growth cycle. As a result, the body's long bones become overdeveloped. The person grows to an abnormally tall height. This very rare disorder can be the result of a tumor in the pituitary gland.

A related disorder, acromegaly (ak-roh-MEG-uh-lee), occurs when the production of growth hormone continues after the normal growth cycle has ended. People with acromegaly experience abnormal growth of bones in the face, hands, feet, and skull.

1. Which outline best represents the passage?
   - **A.** I. Gigantism
       - A. Famous Giants
       - B. Symptoms
   - **B.** I. Endocrine Problems
       - A. Gigantism
       - B. Excessive Growth Hormone
   - **C.** I. Growth Disorders
       - A. Gigantism
       - B. Acromegaly
   - **D.** I. Functions of the Pituitary Gland
       - A. Growth Hormone Production
       - B. Sex Hormone Production

2. In which type of publication would this passage most likely appear?
   - **A.** Encyclopedia
   - **B.** Fictional novel
   - **C.** Letter from a doctor
   - **D.** A pamphlet

3. Write a short story about a person with gigantism. Give details about the disorder.

National Education Standards
Math: Number and Operations
Language Arts: NCTE 3, NCTE 11

Standardized Test Practice Answers

Math Practice
1. A
2. C
3. The trend is for the gestation period to be longer for larger animals. Because a rhinoceros is larger than any animal listed, it could be predicted that its gestation period is longer. (The gestation period for a rhinoceros is 540 days.)

Reading/Writing Practice
1. C
2. A
3. Short stories will vary, but should include details about gigantism.

National Education Standards
Math: Number and Operations
Language Arts: NCTE 3, NCTE 11
For the complete Math and Language Arts standards, visit glencoe.com.

Go Online

Online Study Tools
For more test practice, visit glencoe.com and complete the Online Quizzes for Chapter 16.

Test-Taking Tip

Preparing for Standardized Tests
Students perform better on standardized tests if they are familiar with the format of the test and the types of questions used. Give students practice materials available from the testing company or the state board. Review these materials with students until they become familiar with them. When students sit down before the real test, they will be more comfortable with it.

CAREER CORNER Medical Support Careers

Medical Support Careers

Group Activity

- Divide the class into three groups, and assign each group one of the careers described on this page.

- Have groups research their assigned career. Suggest that students find out more about the educational requirements, potential places of employment, future job potential, and any other aspects of the career that interest them.

- Arrange for two members of each group to interview a person who works in the assigned career. Suggest the partners work together to prepare questions ahead of time that will elicit interesting information about the career, including how the person spends a day on the job.

- Give groups a chance to share what they learned with the class.

Dental Hygienist

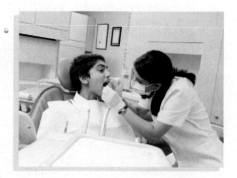

Dental hygienists work in a dentist's office. They record your dental history, examine your mouth and teeth for obvious problems, take X-rays, and clean your teeth. A dental hygienist also teaches you how to take care of your teeth and mouth.

To learn more about becoming a dental hygienist, take science and communications classes in high school. After high school, a dental hygienist must complete a two-year course of study to earn an associate's degree.

Physical Therapy Assistant

Physical therapy assistants work under the supervision of a physical therapist. They help patients practice movements, perform exercises, and learn to use mobility tools such as walkers. Physical therapy assistants must have patience and good communication skills. To learn more about becoming a physical therapy assistant, take human physiology and health classes in high school. Physical therapy assistants may need specialized training through an accredited program, and may need to pass a licensing exam.

Medical Laboratory Technician

A Medical Laboratory Technician (MLT) analyzes blood samples and often specializes in certain areas. In order to be a successful MLT, you must be precise, well organized, and attentive to detail.

To gain a greater understanding of the role of an MLT, take biology, chemistry, physics, and computer classes in high school. Most MLTs need a degree from a one- or two-year accredited program. After completing the required course work, you will need to pass a national certification test to qualify for employment.

Skills for the *21st* Century

ICT Literacy The days when most Americans labored hard on a farm or in a factory are long past. In today's workplace, strong muscles aren't as useful as sharp minds. Workers need to have ICT literacy—the ability to manage and evaluate *I*nformation, *C*ommunicate effectively, and use *T*echnology. This requirement is perhaps nowhere more the case than in medical support careers. Medical therapists and technicians often use advanced technology, evaluate results, and communicate to patients and other medical professionals. Helping students master such digital skills as recording data on a computer, accessing information online, and working confidently with new technology will prepare them for careers in the medical and health fields.

CAREER SPOTLIGHT

Prosthetist

Paul Morton always knew what he wanted to do with his life. "I loved art, I liked to work with my hands, and I wanted to help people. And I grew up watching my dad." It's no wonder that Paul became a prosthetist, just like his dad.

Q. What do you do as a certified prosthetist?

A. *I design, fabricate, and fit artificial limbs for patients. It might be for someone who lost a limb due to diabetes, someone who was born with a missing foot, or someone who was in a car accident.*

Q. Do you need a college degree to do your job?

A. *At my level, yes, you do. But you also can go for special training right after high school and be trained as a prosthetic technician, who focuses* on building artificial limbs to precise specifications.

Q. How is your field changing?

A. *Bionic technology has expanded. There are more opportunities for a person who wants to design and fabricate computer-controlled prosthetic devices.*

Activity — Beyond the Classroom

Writing Exploring Internet Resources. People often think that all medical professionals are doctors or nurses. On the contrary, many other kinds of medical careers exist. Use the Internet to research other careers in the medical or health field. What kinds of medical specialists are there? For example, who takes care of foot problems? Who operates scanning equipment, such as CAT, MRI, and ultrasound machines?

Create a brochure providing information on four careers you identified from your research. Include information on the type of education needed and how each profession helps promote physical health in the community.

Go Online
For more information, go to the Career Corner link at glencoe.com.

Prosthetist

Through a local hospital or clinic, invite a prosthetist or prosthetic technician to address the class about a career in this field.

- Ask the speaker to bring to class an example of a prosthetic device that may be used to help someone who has lost a limb.

- Have students work in small groups to prepare questions in advance for the speaker. After the talk, call on volunteers to ask any questions that remain unanswered.

- Suggestions for topics for the prosthetist or prosthetic technician to address include: How are patients referred to you? How are you able to fit artificial limbs to the great variety of people you see? How do you help people get used to their artificial limbs? What other medical professionals do you work with? What do you like best about your career?

Encourage interested students to visit **glencoe.com** for more information on this career.

Activity — Beyond the Classroom

Writing Have students search online for other careers in the medical or health field. There are many different kinds medical specialists in support positions. For example, a podiatric medial assistant helps a podiatrist take care of foot problems. A radiologic technologist—also called a radiographer—operates scanning equipment. Other careers students might find in an online search include occupational therapists, speech and language therapists, emergency medical technicians, respiratory therapists, recreational therapists, and radiation therapists. You might want to have students work in small groups to do research and then form larger groups to create the brochure.

Flexible Technology Solutions

Focus

Health eSpotlight Video Series

By Chapter

Chapter 17 The Beginning of the Life Cycle
Video 17: Right from the Start

Chapter 18 The Life Cycle Continues
Video 18: Health Through the Life Span

By Lesson

Chapter 17 *Video 17*   For Use With

Segment 17.1 Prenatal Development and Care .... Lesson 1
Segment 17.2 Heredity and Genetics .... Lesson 2
Segment 17.3 Birth Through Childhood........................... Lesson 3

Chapter 18 *Video 18*   For Use With

Segment 18.1 Changes During Adolescence..................... Lesson 1
Segment 18.2 Adulthood, Marriage, and Parenthood......... Lesson 2
Segment 18.3 Health Through the Life Cycle .... Lesson 3

By Skill

Practicing Healthful Behaviors .... **Videos**   3   13   **17**   19   23
Conflict Resolution .... **Videos**   9   **18**

■ Indicates videos featured in the unit that teach the corresponding skill. Other videos listed can also be used to teach that skill.

Teach

Direct lesson plans beyond the classroom with multi-media fitness activities that students can do online, in class, or as a group.

PowerPoint® Presentation

- *Health eSpotlight* videos
- Audio and image bank

FITNESS ZONE Online

Fitness Zone Online is a multi-media resource that helps students find ways to be physically active each day.

- Clipboard Energizer Activities
- Fitness Zone Videos
- Polar Heart Rate Monitor Activities
- Nutrition, Physical Activity, and Injury Prevention Tips
- Links to Nutrition and Physical Activity Resources

Go Online

Online Learning Center

- Student Web Activities
- PuzzleMaker
- Interactive Health Tutor

Podcast Audio Chapter Summaries

Use the audio Podcast Audio Chapter Summaries to teach and review key concepts, and engage students with health content that they can download to a computer or portable MP3 player.

Assess/Close

Help students master chapter and lesson concepts with an integrated technology solution for assessment and performance evaluation.

Go Online

Online Learning Center

- Interactive Study Guides
- Online Quizzes

ExamView® Assessment Suite CD-ROM

Create and customize tests in minutes with this convenient digital platform.

- Create differentiated tests quickly and easily.
- All questions correlated to National/State Standards.
- Enhance tests with Document Based Questions (DBQ) and add your own photos and graphics.
- Build tests in both English and Spanish.
- Generate progress reports.

Enrich

Use these additional digital and online media resources to promote hands-on exploration of health topics covered in the lesson.

Business Week Health Video Series

- *Genetic Issues*
- *Childproofing Your Home*
- *Memory Loss and Technology*

Study-to-Go

Download a portable version of eFlashcards and Self-Check Quizzes onto your Palm or Pocket PC.

Health Podcasts Activities

Glencoe's "It's Your Health" Podcast Activities provide students with a unique listening and learning experience that takes health education beyond the classroom. Download the audio files and print activities covering a range of current health topics that matter most to teens!

Growth and Development

This unit describes the human life cycle, heredity and genetics, and strategies for maintaining good health at all stages of life.

Health eSpotlight Video Series

At the beginning of each chapter, visit **glencoe.com** and have students watch the video and do the accompanying print activity.

 Chapter 17
Right from the Start

Many of our physical features are determined by genetics before we are born.

 Chapter 18
Health Through the Life Span

Our bodies require different diet and exercise programs to meet our evolving needs.

Unit 6 Resources

- Career Corner
- 📁 *FAST FILE* RESOURCES
- Health Career Research Activity
- Family Involvement Activity
- Community Involvement Activity
- Unit Test

UNIT 6 Growth and Development

Chapter 17
The Beginning of the Life Cycle

 Right from the Start

Chapter 18
The Life Cycle Continues

 Health Through the Life Span

UNIT PROJECT

Hunger Relief

Using Visuals **Project Bread** is dedicated to "alleviating, preventing, and ultimately ending hunger in Massachusetts." Project Bread provides funding for food for 400 emergency food programs, school breakfast and lunch programs, and 135 communities throughout Massachusetts. Project Bread's fundraising walk, the Walk for Hunger, attracts more than 50,000 walkers and 2,000 volunteers.

 G₀ Online To learn more about Project Bread, go to the Unit Web Project at **glencoe.com.**

Get Involved. Learn about food banks and hunger relief agencies in your community. Find out how teens can volunteer. Share your findings with the class.

466

UNIT PROJECT

Hunger Relief Project Bread wants to help feed the chronically hungry people of Massachusetts. This organization has volunteers, Walkers, and donors that commit to helping year after year. They work with schools to offer breakfast programs, and fund summer programs so that kids get a nutritious meal when school is out. Their annual Walk for Hunger is extremely successful in raising awareness to this problem.

Get Involved Direct students to work in small groups to identify hunger relief organizations that serve their community. Have students make a phone call to learn more about volunteer opportunities, such as food collection or distribution. Have students identify ways that teens can volunteer at a local hunger relief organization. Ask students to share what they learned with the class.

"All of us need to grow continuously in our lives."
— Les Brown, author and motivational speaker

Activate Prior Knowledge

Ask students these questions before they read the chapter to build on what they already know.

Chapter 17
What are some changes that occur as an infant grows and develops?

(Sample answer: Infants become larger, they develop muscle control, and they start to develop a sense of self.)

Chapter 18
What are some differences between teens and older adults?

(Sample answer: Teens are still growing, while older adults have completed growth.)

Glencoe Exclusive!
TeacherWorks Plus
All-In-One Planner and Resource Center

TeacherWorks Plus provides:

- interactive Teacher Wraparound Edition
- click, drag, and drop to plan lessons
- instant access to many print program resources

Unit 6 Growth and Development **467**

How to Get Involved Provide students with these step-by-step instructions on how they can assemble information about volunteer opportunities.

1. Each student should call or visit a hunger relief organization, such as Project Bread, to find out more about the programs offered and volunteer opportunities.

2. Have students inquire about opportunities for teens to serve as volunteers with the organization. Students should also ask about suggestions for activities, such as food drives.

3. Have each student share the information he or she has learned by making a pamphlet.

The Beginning of the Life Cycle

	Standards		Features
	National	State/Local	
Chapter 17 pages 468–493	1.12.1, 1.12.3, 1.12.4, 1.12.5, 3.12.2, 5.12.2, 5.12.3, 7.12.1, 8.12.4		TIME HEALTH • How DNA Works, page 488
30 Min **Lesson 1** **Prenatal Development and Care** pages 470–477 **BIG Idea** *As a fetus develops during pregnancy, special care needs to be taken to ensure the fetus and mother remain healthy.*	1.12.3, 1.12.5, 1.12.6, 3.12.2, 5.12.2, 5.12.3, 7.12.1, 7.12.2, 7.12.3		Health Skills Activity • Pregnancy Alert *(Decision-Making Skills)*, page 476 Out of Time
30 Min **Lesson 2** **Heredity and Genetics** pages 478–483 **BIG Idea** *Certain traits, such as eye and hair color, come from both parents.*	1.12.4, 1.12.5, 1.12.6, 3.12.2, 8.12.1		VIDEO BusinessWeek HEALTH NEWS • Genetic Issues, page 482
30 Min **Lesson 3** **Birth Through Childhood** pages 484–487 **BIG Idea** *Infancy and childhood are times of great changes and growth.*	1.12.1, 1.12.4, 1.12.5, 1.12.6, 3.12.2, 7.12.1		

Key to Ability Levels

Teaching Strategies and activities have been coded for ability level and appropriateness.

- **AL** Activities for students working above grade level
- **BL** Activities for students working below grade level
- **OL** Activities for students working on grade level
- **EL** Activities for English Learners

Chapter 17 Planning Guide

Glencoe Exclusive!
TeacherWorks *Plus*
All-In-One Planner and Resource Center

Resources	Lesson Assessment	Technology
Student Activity Workbook **TEACH** *FAST FILE* RESOURCES Vocabulary Practice **TEACH** Health Labs **EXTEND**	Chapter 17 Review Chapter 17 Assessment Standardized Test Practice *ExamView® Assessment Suite* CD-ROM	**Teaching Tools:** • *TeacherWorks™* Plus DVD • *StudentWorks™* Plus DVD • *ExamView® Assessment Suite* CD-ROM • Transparency • Fitness DVD • PowerPoint® DVD • Health eSpotlight Video Series DVD
FAST FILE RESOURCES Reading Strategies Activity **TEACH** Reteaching Activity **REVIEW** Enrichment Activity **EXTEND** Health Skills Practice **TEACH**	Lesson 1 Assessment, page 477 Lesson 1 Quiz *Fast File* *ExamView® Assessment Suite* CD-ROM	**Web-Based Resources:** glencoe.com • Health Podcast Activities • Audio Chapter Summaries (English/Spanish) • Interactive Health Tutor • Health Skills Activities • Vocabulary PuzzleMaker • Parent Letters (English/Spanish) • Lesson Plans • Health Inventories • Online Quizzes • Study-to-Go • Unit Web Projects • Student Web Activities • Fitness Zone Activities
FAST FILE RESOURCES Reading Strategies Activity **TEACH** Reteaching Activity **REVIEW** Enrichment Activity **EXTEND** Health Skills Practice **TEACH**	Lesson 2 Assessment, page 483 Lesson 2 Quiz *Fast File* *ExamView® Assessment Suite* CD-ROM	
FAST FILE RESOURCES Reading Strategies Activity **TEACH** Reteaching Activity **REVIEW** Enrichment Activity **EXTEND** Health Skills Practice **TEACH**	Lesson 3 Assessment, page 487 Lesson 3 Quiz *Fast File* *ExamView® Assessment Suite* CD-ROM	

StudentWorks *Plus*

This is the student's backpack solution.

Includes:
• complete Interactive Student Edition
• full audio of English text and Spanish chapter summaries
• allows students to record assignments and track grades.
• links to online activities and additional student resources
• access to all student worksheets and workbooks

FOLDABLES
Study Organizer

Dinah Zike Foldables®
Chapter Activity
Refer to the *Dinah Zike Reading and Study Skills for Glencoe Health.* Have students complete the four-tab book Foldable to organize what they learn about the beginning of the life cycle. As students read, have them add details about the stages of the life cycle under the appropriate tabs.

Key to Symbols

 Transparencies   **REVIEW** activities to review or reinforce content

 CD-ROM   **TEACH** activities to teach basic concepts

 glencoe.com   **EXTEND** activities to extend or enrich lesson content

 Print Resources

The Beginning of the Life Cycle

Chapter Overview

Chapter 17 focuses on the human life cycle from fertilization through childhood.

Lesson 1

During pregnancy, both the mother and the developing fetus require special care.

Lesson 2

Certain traits are passed from parents to children.

Lesson 3

During infancy and childhood, a great amount of growth and change occur.

▶ **Activating Prior Knowledge**

Encourage students to think about ways that strong bonds between a child and his or her parents can affect all three sides of the child's health triangle. Then have students write their sentences as directed. Ask volunteers to share their sentences with the class.

CHAPTER **17**

The Beginning of the Life Cycle

Lesson 1
Prenatal Development and Care

BIG Idea *As a fetus develops during pregnancy, special care needs to be taken to ensure the fetus and mother remain healthy.*

Lesson 2
Heredity and Genetics

BIG Idea *Certain traits, such as eye and hair color, come from both of your parents.*

Lesson 3
Birth Through Childhood

BIG Idea *Infancy and childhood are times of great changes and growth.*

Activating Prior Knowledge

Using Visuals The mother in this photo is bonding with her baby daughter. In a few sentences, describe why it is important for parents to form strong bonds with their children at such a young age.

468

Universal Access

Differentiated Learning Glencoe provides teacher support and student materials for all learners in the health classroom.

- Chapter Summaries in English and Spanish are available online at **glencoe.com**.
- *Fast Files* and related worksheets support reluctant readers.

- Universal Access strategies throughout the Teacher Wraparound Edition and *Fast Files* help you present materials for gifted students, at-risk students, physically impaired students, and those with behavior disorders or learning disabilities.

Chapter Launchers

Health in Action

Discuss the BIG Ideas

Before beginning this chapter, think about how you would answer these questions:

▶ Why is the mother's health important to her fetus during pregnancy?

▶ What role did your parents have in your development?

▶ What changes do infants and children experience?

Watch the *Health eSpotlight* Video Series

Right from the Start

Do you think genetics or the environment has a bigger influence on development?

Assess Your Health

Go Online

Visit **glencoe.com** and complete the Health Inventory for Chapter 17.

Chapter 17   The Beginning of the Life Cycle   **469**

Chapter Launchers

Health in Action

Discuss the BIG Ideas

Assign this activity before students have read the chapter. Explain that the purpose of the questions is to help students assess their current knowledge of the life cycle.

Health eSpotlight
Video Series

 Right from the Start

Before Viewing the Video

Ask Students: *Do you think the similarities among your family members are due to genetic factors or the environment?* After students have watched the video, call on volunteers to discuss factors that influence traits.

Go Online

Have students go to **glencoe.com** and take the Health Inventory for Chapter 17.

Chapter Skills

Reading Skills
- Reviewing Facts and Vocabulary, pp. 477, 483, 487
- Reading/Writing Practice, p. 493

BIG Idea

Many changes occur during the beginning of the life cycle.

Health Skills
- Health Skills Activity, p. 476
- Applying Health Skills, pp. 477, 483, 487

Vocabulary
- New Vocabulary, pp. 470, 478, 484,
- Reviewing Facts and Vocabulary, pp. 477, 483, 487

Writing Skills
- Writing Critically, pp. 477, 483, 487
- Reading/Writing Practice, p. 493

469

Prenatal Development and Care

① FOCUS

GUIDE TO READING

BIG Idea Pregnant females need to take special care to protect their own health and the health of the fetus. **Ask Students:** *What are some ways that pregnant females can protect their health?* (Sample answer: One way that pregnant females can protect their health is by choosing healthful foods.)

Before You Read

Table The first column of students' tables should include actions and substances that could harm the health of a pregnant female and the fetus.

Main Idea

The Very Beginning Humans begin with a single cell formed from one egg and one sperm. **Ask Students:** *How can the health of both the mother and father impact the process of fertilization?* (Sample answer: Fertilization requires a healthy sperm and egg.)

Real Life Issues

Ask volunteers to share information about nutrition they recall from Chapters 10 and 11. **Ask Students:** *What are some foods that are healthful choices for pregnant females?* (Sample answers: Fruits, vegetables, whole-grain breads, dairy products)

470

LESSON 1

GUIDE TO READING

BIG Idea *As a fetus develops during pregnancy, special care needs to be taken to ensure the fetus and mother remain healthy.*

Before You Read

Create a Table. Make a two-column table. Label the first column "Things to Avoid." Label the second column "Things to Do." Fill in the table as you read the lesson.

Things to Avoid	Things To Do

New Vocabulary

▸ fertilization (p. 470)
▸ implantation (p. 470)
▸ embryo (p. 470)
▸ fetus (p. 470)
▸ prenatal care (p. 473)
▸ fetal alcohol syndrome (p. 474)

Review Vocabulary

▸ egg (Ch.16, L.2)
▸ sperm (Ch.16, L.3)

Prenatal Development and Care

Real Life Issues

Eating for Two. Amanda's older sister, Linda, is pregnant and has moved back home while her husband is overseas on a military assignment. Amanda's health class is starting a chapter on healthy pregnancies. Their mother says that good nutrition is very important for a healthy pregnancy, so they decide to plan menus that will be healthy for Linda and her growing baby.

Writing *Create a one-day menu and a shopping list that could help Amanda and her mother plan meals to keep Linda healthy during her pregnancy. Refer to the nutrition information you learned in Chapters 10 and 11.*

The Very Beginning

Main Idea A single cell, formed from one egg and one sperm, can grow into a complex human being.

The human body begins as one microscopic cell that is formed by *the union of a male sperm cell and a female egg cell,* called **fertilization**. This is also known as *conception.* The cell that results from fertilization is called a *zygote.*

The zygote begins to divide and travel through the fallopian tube, as shown in **Figure 17.1**. It divides many times, forming a cluster of cells by the time it reaches the uterus. Within a few days, **implantation**, *the process by which the zygote attaches to the uterine wall,* occurs. After about two weeks, the zygote becomes an **embryo** (EM-bree-oh), *a cluster of cells that develops between the third and eighth week of pregnancy.* This *group of developing cells* is called a **fetus** (FEE-tuhs) after about eight weeks.

Health Literacy

In Vitro Fertilization As students study the process of fertilization, questions about in vitro fertilization may arise. In vitro fertilization is a technique in which eggs and sperm are collected and then combined in a medical laboratory. Eggs that are successfully fertilized are then placed into the mother's fallopian tubes or uterus. The term *in vitro* literally means "in glass," and refers to the fact that the eggs and sperm are combined outside the mother's body. The first in vitro fertilization that resulted in a live birth was performed in 1978.

Figure 17.1 Implantation

Fertilization and implantation occur after an egg is released from the ovary.

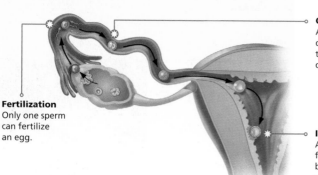

Cell Division
As the zygote travels down the fallopian tube toward the uterus, it divides many times.

Fertilization
Only one sperm can fertilize an egg.

Implantation
About six days after fertilization, the zygote burrows into the lining of the uterus.

The Growing Embryo

The cells of an embryo will continue to divide as it grows. **Eventually**, three layers of tissue are formed. Later, these layers develop into various body systems. One layer becomes the respiratory and digestive systems. A second layer develops into muscles, bones, blood vessels, and skin. The third layer forms the nervous system, sense organs, and mouth.

Two important structures form outside the embryo.

- The *amniotic sac* is a thin, fluid-filled membrane that surrounds and protects the developing embryo.

- The *umbilical cord* is a ropelike structure that connects the fetus with the mother's placenta. The *placenta* is thick, blood-rich tissue that lines the walls of the uterus during pregnancy and nourishes the embryo.

During pregnancy, the blood supply of the mother and the developing embryo are kept separate. Oxygen and nutrients are passed from the mother's blood to the embryo, and waste from the embryo is passed to the mother's blood. These wastes are excreted from the mother's body along with her own body wastes.

Substances that are harmful to a developing embryo can also pass through the umbilical cord. If a pregnant female uses tobacco, alcohol, or other drugs, those substances can cross the placenta and harm the developing embryo.

The time from conception to birth usually takes about 280 days, or nine months. The nine months are divided into three *trimesters* of three months each. **Figure 17.2** on page 472 shows the major changes that occur in each trimester.

Academic Vocabulary

eventually *(adverb):* at an unspecified later time

Teacher to Teacher

Lisa L. Brewer • Scott High School, Taylor Mill, KY

Tobacco and Pregnancy When teaching about the effects of tobacco and pregnancy, I like to use the Smokey Sue Doll. This live example shows how much tar collects from just one cigarette. Smokey Sue is made up of a doll head (with cigarette in her mouth) that sits upon a plastic jar. When Smokey Sue's bulb is pumped, tar collects in a tube where the 'lungs' would be. The tubes can then be passed around to surprise the students with just how much tar comes from just one cigarette. Because of this visual, the students can actually see the effects of cigarettes upon a fetus.

CHAPTER 17

LESSON 1

2 TEACH

R Reading Strategy

Interpreting a Diagram Have students examine **Figure 17.1**. Tell students to sequence the events that are shown in the diagram. Ask them the following questions: What event shown in the diagram occurs first? (fertilization) What happens next? (cell division) Which event in the diagram occurs last? (implantation) **BL OL**

C Critical Thinking

Applying Ideas After students have read the information describing the functions of the umbilical cord and placenta, ask them to discuss the types of substances that can pass from the mother's body to the developing fetus. Have students apply this information to make a list of substances that pregnant females should avoid. **OL**

Academic Vocabulary

Eventually Ask students to read the definition of *eventually* provided in the text. Then have each student write a sentence that uses the word *eventually*. Have students exchange their written sentences with another student to check for correct usage. After the sentences have been peer edited, ask volunteers to share their sentences with the class.

471

C Critical Thinking

Comparing and Contrasting
Direct students' attention to **Figure 17.2**. Ask them to list similarities and differences between the developing fetus in the first and second trimesters of pregnancy. Then have students compare and contrast the developing fetus in the second and third trimesters of pregnancy. OL

U Universal Access

English Language Learners
Write the phrase *multiple births* on the board. Explain that *multiple* means "more than one." Point out that the word part *multi-* is found in many words, such as *multimedia*, *multitasking*, and *multicolor*. Words containing this word part refer to many or more than one. EL

HS Health Skills Practice

Accessing Information Ask students to bring in nutrition panels from a variety of food packages. Have small groups analyze each nutrition panel to find foods that are good sources of calcium, protein, iron, vitamin A, vitamin B complex, and folic acid. Have groups identify foods for a healthful eating plan during pregnancy. OL AL

Figure 17.2 **Stages of Embryonic and Fetal Development**

Fetal development occurs over nine months. The nine months are divided into three trimesters, lasting three months each. An example of a single birth fetus during each trimester of development is shown below.

First Trimester (0 to 14 weeks)	Major Changes	
0–2 weeks	A zygote may float freely in the uterus for 48 hours before implanting. The spinal cord grows. The brain, ears, and arms begin to form. The heart begins to beat.	
3–8 weeks	The embryo is about 1 inch long at 8 weeks. The mouth, nostrils, eyelids, hands, fingers, feet, and toes begin to form. The nervous system and cardiovascular system are functional.	
9–14 weeks	The fetus develops a human profile. Sex organs, eyelids, fingernails, and toenails develop. By week 12 it can make crying motions and may suck its thumb.	
Second Trimester (15 to 28 weeks)	**Major Changes**	
15–20 weeks	The fetus can blink its eyes and becomes more active. The body begins to grow, growth of the head slows and the limbs reach full proportion. Eyebrows and eyelashes develop.	
21–28 weeks	The fetus can hear conversations and has a regular cycle of waking and sleeping. Weight increases rapidly. The fetus is about 12 inches long and weighs a little more than 1 pound. The fetus may survive if born after 24 weeks, but will require special medical care.	
Third Trimester (29 weeks to birth)	**Major Changes**	
29–40 weeks	The fetus uses all five senses and begins to pass water from the bladder. Brain scans have shown that some fetuses dream during their periods of sleep in the eighth and ninth months of development. Approximately 266 days after conception, the baby weighs 6 to 9 pounds and is ready to be born.	

472 Chapter 17 The Beginning of the Life Cycle

Home and Community

Prenatal Care All pregnant females should receive prenatal care, which can be provided by doctors, nurse practitioners, obstetricians, or midwives. Have students work together to compile information about local prenatal clinics and other local sources of help and support for pregnant females. Have students work in small groups to prepare a flyer about sources of prenatal care in their community. Remind students that their flyer should be neat, attractively designed, and contain accurate information.

Multiple Births

In most cases, fertilization results in one embryo. Twins, triplets, and quadruplets, known as *multiple births,* can result when multiple embryos are formed. Identical twins result from a single zygote that splits into two separate embryos with identical traits and the same gender. Fraternal twins occur when two eggs are released and are fertilized by two different sperm. Fraternal twins can be different genders.

A Healthy Pregnancy

Main Idea A pregnant female can maintain the health of her fetus in many different ways.

When a woman learns that she is pregnant, she should begin prenatal care to ensure her health and that of her growing baby. **Prenatal (pree-NAY-tuhl) care** refers to *the steps that a pregnant female can take to provide for her own health and the health of her baby.* Seeing a doctor regularly throughout the pregnancy will provide a new mother with the care and nutritional advice she needs.

What to Eat While Pregnant

An unborn baby receives nourishment from the mother. Pregnant females are encouraged to take prenatal vitamins to provide a balance of nutrients, such as:

- **Calcium** helps build strong bones and teeth, as well as healthy nerves, muscles, and developing heart rhythm.
- **Protein** helps form muscle and other tissue.
- **Iron** makes red blood cells and supplies oxygen to cells.
- **Vitamin A** helps in the growth of cells and bones and in eye development.
- **Vitamin B complex** aids in forming the nervous system.
- **Folic acid** is critical in development of the neural tube, which contains the central nervous system. It's recommended that all females of childbearing age consume 400 to 600 micrograms of folic acid daily.

Most pregnant females need to consume only an addition 300 calories per day to achieve a healthy weight gain during pregnancy. This is equivalent to drinking an extra 2½ cups of low-fat milk per day. Females at a healthy weight before becoming pregnant can gain between 25 and 35 pounds. Gaining too little weight can result in a small, undeveloped baby. Gaining too much weight can result in an early delivery. Extra weight also increases the mother's risk of high blood pressure, diabetes, and varicose veins.

READING CHECK

Describe What are some of the changes that occur during the second trimester?

■ **Figure 17.3** During pregnancy, good nutrition and rest keep both the mother and the developing child healthy. *Why are healthy snacks important to fetal development?*

Lesson 1   Prenatal Development and Care   **473**

READING CHECK

Answer The fetus can blink its eyes and hear conversations, its eyebrows and eyelashes grow, and it can grasp and kick.

Main Idea

A Healthy Pregnancy A pregnant female can protect the health of her developing fetus. **Ask Students:** *What are some ways a pregnant female can help her developing fetus stay healthy?* (Sample answer: eat nutritious foods; avoid alcohol and tobacco)

AL Active Learning

Community Involvement
Hospitals, health clinics, and some health clubs and community centers offer special exercise programs for pregnant females. Have students work in small groups to find out about such programs. Have the students in each group select one program to investigate. Ask students to gather the following information: where and when the program is offered, the cost, and the kinds of physical activity and exercise taught. Have each group share what it has learned with the class. **OL**

Caption Answer

Figure 17.3 Sample answer: Healthy snacks can help a pregnant female avoid gaining too much weight.

Writing Strategy

Expository Writing Ask students to research and write a short report on nutritional requirements related to pregnancy. Suggest that students use library or Internet resources to gather information to include in their report. Remind students that the purpose of expository writing is to help the reader understand a concept. Have students proofread their writing for spelling and grammatical errors before turning it in.

Main Idea

A Healthy Fetus Pregnant females should avoid tobacco, alcohol, drugs, and environmental hazards. **Ask Students:** *What are some environmental hazards that pregnant females should avoid?* (Sample answer: Pregnant females should avoid polluted air.)

C **Critical Thinking**

Inferring Guide students in discussing the information about fetal alcohol syndrome (FAS). Emphasize the serious, lifelong nature of fetal alcohol syndrome. Then ask students to identify why avoiding alcohol altogether is the only safe choice for a female who is pregnant. **OL**

AL **Active Learning**

Class Discussion Have students form small groups. Within each group, have students discuss the following question: Should pregnant females who damage their unborn babies through drug use be held criminally accountable? Why or why not? Have each group of students make notes about its discussion of these questions. **OL** **AL**

G⊙ Online

Have students visit **glencoe.com** and complete the Student Web Activity on the dangers of alcohol consumption during pregnancy.

■ **Figure 17.4** Regular exercise is an important part of a healthy pregnancy. *How can regular physical activity help the health of a pregnant female and the fetus?*

G⊙ Online

Visit **glencoe.com** and complete the Student Web Activity on the dangers of alcohol comsumption during pregnancy.

Fitness During Pregnancy

Physical activity can help a pregnant female maintain a healthy weight during pregnancy. At the end of the pregnancy, it may become more difficult to maintain a fitness program. Before starting any exercise program, an expectant mother should discuss the importance of exercise and exercise programs with her health care provider.

A Healthy Fetus

Main Idea Expectant mothers should avoid tobacco, alcohol, drugs, and environmental hazards.

An expectant mother should avoid substances that can harm her and her fetus. Tobacco, alcohol, and other drugs can be harmful to both mother and baby.

Avoid Tobacco Use

Smoking and using other tobacco products during pregnancy is harmful to the fetus. It is estimated that smoking accounts for up to 30 percent of low-birth-weight babies, 14 percent of premature births, and 10 percent of all infant deaths. Studies suggest that smoking may also affect growth, mental development, and behavior after a child is born. Research by the American Lung Association shows that pregnant females who are exposed repeatedly to secondhand smoke increase the risk of having a low-birth-weight baby.

Avoid Alcohol Use

When an expectant mother uses alcohol, so does her growing fetus. Alcohol passes through the umbilical cord to the fetus. The fetus, however, breaks down alcohol more slowly than the mother. This means that the alcohol level in the fetus's blood is higher, and it remains in the bloodstream for a longer period of time. A severe alcohol-related disorders is **fetal alcohol syndrome** (FAS), *a group of alcohol-related birth defects that includes both physical and mental problems.* Infants born with FAS may have learning, memory, and attention problems, as well as visual and hearing impairments. **C**

Avoid Drug Use

Prescription or over-the-counter medications should be used only with the approval of a doctor or other health care professional. These substances can also harm the fetus.

Myths & Reality

A Healthy Pregnancy

Myth: Pregnant females should avoid physical activity.

Fact: Most pregnant females benefit from regular physical activity. Pregnant females should ask their health care provider about physical activity during a prenatal check-up. Although some should avoid exercise while pregnant, most pregnant females are encouraged to take part in physical activity.

Myth: Pregnant females shouldn't use microwave ovens or cell phones.

Fact: Both microwaves and cell phones are safe to use during pregnancy. Pregnant females should avoid X-rays, however.

Any use of illegal drugs poses a health risk to both the mother and the fetus. Drug abuse can harm the mother's health and make her less able to support the pregnancy. Drugs can also harm the development of the fetus. Infants born to mothers who use drugs may not grow at the same rate as infants born to mothers who do not use drugs. They may have respiratory or cardiovascular problems, mental impairments, or birth defects. In some cases, drug use may lead to the premature birth of the infant, or even a miscarriage. The baby may also be born addicted to the same drugs the mother used during pregnancy.

Avoid Hazards in the Environment

A pregnant female should avoid common hazardous substances in the environment. Family members can help by also being aware of these substances.

- **Lead.** Exposure to lead has been linked to miscarriage, low birth weight, mental disabilities, and behavior problems in children. Lead can be found in the paint of houses built before 1978, and in some glassware or dinnerware.

- **Mercury.** Pregnant females should avoid eating certain types of fish that are known to contain higher than average levels of mercury. These include shark, swordfish, and king mackerel.

- **Smog.** Medical studies have linked air pollution with birth defects, low birth weight, premature birth, stillbirth, and infant death. The greatest period of risk is the second month of pregnancy, when organs are developing.

- **Radiation.** Ionizing radiation, such as that found in X-rays, can affect growth and cause mental retardation.

Pregnant females should also use caution when using household chemicals. They should read all cleaning-product labels, wear gloves, and work in a well-ventilated area.

Complications of Pregnancy

Main Idea A pregnancy may have an unexpected outcome.

Most pregnancies result in the birth of a healthy baby. About 70 percent of all births occur through a vaginal delivery. Pregnancy complications, however, can result in a cesarean delivery, made through an incision in the mother's abdomen.

The complications of pregnancy can also result in a *premature birth*. This type of birth takes place at least three weeks before the due date. Serious complications may lead to *miscarriage*, the spontaneous expulsion of a fetus occurring before the twentieth week of pregnancy. The delivery of a fetus that has died after the twentieth week of pregnancy is called a *stillbirth*.

■ **Figure 17.5** Activities such as painting or using lead-based products should be avoided or done carefully during pregnancy. *Why is it important to keep a room well-ventilated while painting?*

Caption Answer

Figure 17.5 Paint fumes may be harmful to a developing fetus.

Main Idea

Complications of Pregnancy
Complications that can harm the health of the mother and the developing fetus can occur during pregnancy. **Ask Students:** *Why do problems with the mother's health affect the developing fetus?* (Sample answer: The mother's body nourishes the developing fetus, so any problems with the mother's health can affect the ability of her body to provide the nutrients the developing fetus needs.)

R **Reading Strategy**

Summarizing Have English language learners work in pairs with students who are fluent in English. Have each pair summarize the section, Avoid Hazards in the Environment. **EL**

U **Universal Access**

Visual Learners Have students create a word web about complications of pregnancy. Tell students to write the words "Complications of Pregnancy" in the middle of a sheet of paper. As they read the section, have them add words and phrases describing complications of pregnancy to their word webs. **BL**

Cooperative Learning

Bumper Stickers Have students read the information describing the negative impact tobacco smoke has on the developing fetus. Then, have students work in small groups to create a bumper sticker that communicates the message that pregnant women should avoid tobacco smoke. Remind students that advocacy involves taking a clear, health-enhancing stand and encouraging others to make healthful choices. Distribute paper cut to the size of a typical bumper sticker on which students can create their bumper stickers. Ask each group to share its completed bumper sticker with the class.

Health Skills Activity

Decision-Making Skills: Pregnancy Alert

NHES Standard 8 Students will demonstrate the ability to advocate for personal, family, and community health.

Objectives

- Explain the importance of prenatal care and proper nutrition in promoting optimal health for both mother and baby.
- Demonstrate the ability to adapt health messages to the characteristics of a particular audience.

Teaching Strategies

- Have students review the lesson for information on how to have a healthy pregnancy.
- Bring in some prenatal care pamphlets from a doctor's office.

Assessment

Using a rubric, student work should provide comprehensive evidence of the following criteria to achieve the highest score:

- √ Clear, health-enhancing stand
- √ Supports the position with relevant information
- √ Awareness of the audience
- √ Encourages others to make healthful choices
- √ Passion/conviction

READING CHECK

Answer Low birth weight is a leading cause of death in babies under 12 months of age.

Health Skills Activity

Decision-Making Skills

Pregnancy Alert

LeAnn has just discovered she is pregnant with her first child. She and her husband, Walt, are both excited and scared. The thought of having a baby is overwhelming. LeAnn and Walt have begun listing everything they need to do. Both sets of parents are excited about the upcoming birth. They've offered to help buy furniture and to help decorate the baby's room. Still, LeAnn and Walt have a lot to do before the baby is born. After her first prenatal visit to her doctor, LeAnn is more nervous than ever. There are so many things to think about while she is pregnant that she has started to become stressed. What can LeAnn and Walt do together to reduce her anxiety and help her focus on having a healthy pregnancy?

Writing You may know someone who has had an experience just like LeAnn's. Use the information you learned in this lesson to create a pamphlet on ways to plan for a healthy pregnancy. The following tips can be used as a guideline.

1. Identify substances to be avoided during pregnancy.
2. List ways to prepare for pregnancy and birth.
3. Develop strategies to incorporate physical activity.
4. Compare childbirth options.

READING CHECK

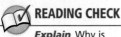

Explain Why is low birth weight a concern?

Sometimes, a medical reason causes a miscarriage or stillbirth. Using tobacco or drugs during pregnancy, however, can increase the risk of miscarriage or stillbirth. Receiving prenatal care during pregnancy can reduce the risk, or severity, of problems during pregnancy. During prenatal care, a doctor may be able to identify medical problems with the fetus before the birth. In some cases, medical care, and even surgery, may be performed on the baby before birth.

Other medical complications result from medical conditions affecting the pregnant female. *Gestational hypertension,* or high blood pressure during pregnancy, may occur after the twentieth week of pregnancy. A severe form of this is *pre-eclampsia.* Symptoms include high blood pressure, swelling, and large amounts of protein in the urine. Preeclampsia can prevent the placenta from getting enough blood to nourish the fetus. Treatment includes reducing blood pressure through bed rest or medication. Hospitalization may be necessary.

An *ectopic pregnancy* results when a zygote implants not in the uterus but in the fallopian tube, abdomen, ovary, or cervix. This makes it impossible for the fetus to receive nourishment and grow. An ectopic pregnancy cannot lead to the birth of a healthy fetus. It is also the number one cause of death in women in the first trimester of pregnancy.

476 Chapter 17 The Beginning of the Life Cycle

More About...

Cesarean Delivery A cesarean delivery is the surgical removal of the fetus through the mother's abdominal wall. Many cesarean deliveries are performed because the baby is too large or the mother's pelvis is too small to allow a vaginal delivery. Fetal distress is another common reason for cesarean deliveries. Recovery from a cesarean delivery usually takes longer than recovery from a vaginal birth. Students may be interested to learn that the term *cesarean* is derived from the name of Julius Cesar. According to legend, Cesar was delivered surgically, however many historians doubt the truth of this legend.

Childbirth

Main Idea The birth of a baby takes place in three steps: labor, delivery, and afterbirth.

Expectant parents must decide where the birth will occur. Most births occur in hospital maternity wards staffed by nurses and doctors, with medical equipment to handle complications. Other options include birthing centers or home births, which offer a more comfortable environment. Midwives may attend home births and births at birthing centers.

As the birth approaches, the fetus becomes more crowded in the uterus. Birth occurs in three steps.

- **Step 1: Labor.** Muscle contractions of the uterus become regular, stronger, and closer together. This causes the cervix—the opening to the uterus—to dilate, or widen.

- **Step 2: Delivery.** Once the cervix is fully dilated, the baby passes through the birth canal and emerges from the mother's body. The baby takes its first breath and cries to clear its lungs of amniotic fluid.

- **Step 3: Afterbirth.** The placenta is still attached to the baby by the umbilical cord. Contractions, although weaker, will continue until the placenta (now called the *afterbirth*) is pushed from the mother's body.

■ **Figure 17.6** The birth of a healthy baby is a joyous event. *What steps can pregnant women take to help ensure a healthy pregnancy and delivery?*

 READING CHECK

Explain During delivery, what must happen before the baby can pass through the birth canal?

 LESSON 1 **ASSESSMENT**

After You Read

Reviewing Facts and Vocabulary

1. Describe an *embryo* and a *fetus*.
2. What is the difference between identical and fraternal twins?
3. What is the relationship between the placenta and the umbilical cord?

Thinking Critically

4. **Evaluate.** How is the diet of a pregnant female important to her growing fetus?
5. **Cause and Effect.** What are some of the risks that may occur if a pregnant female uses tobacco, alcohol, or drugs during her pregnancy?

Applying Health Skills

6. **Accessing Information.** Research library or Internet resources to learn more about gestational hypertension. Explain the warning signs and the need for proper treatment.

Writing Critically

7. **Persuasive.** Write a short essay from the point of view of a fetus persuading its mother to eat healthy foods during pregnancy.

Go Online

Visit **glencoe.com** and complete the Interactive Study Guide for this lesson.

LESSON 1 ASSESSMENT ANSWERS

1. An *embryo* is a cluster of cells that forms between the third and eighth week of pregnancy. This group of cells is called a *fetus* after the eighth week.
2. Identical twins form when one fertilized egg splits into two different embryos. Fraternal twins form when two eggs are fertilized by two different sperm. These individuals are not identical.
3. The umbilical cord connects the fetus to the placenta.

4. The foods a pregnant mother eats nourish the fetus and help it grow. Foods that contain harmful substances or foods that are not fully cooked can harm the fetus.
5. Risks include miscarriage or stillbirth
6. Explanations should include a list of the warning signs of gestational diabetes, including excessive weight gain, hunger, and thirst. Explanations should also note the need for proper treatment.
7. Essays will vary.

Main Idea

Childbirth Labor, delivery, and afterbirth are the three steps of childbirth. **Ask Students:** *Why is the placenta expelled from the mother's body?* (After the baby is born, the placenta is not needed.)

③ ASSESS/ CLOSE

Assessment Resources

📁 **FAST FILE ACTIVITIES**
Lesson 1 Quiz

💿 *ExamView Assessment Suite* CD-ROM

Visit glencoe.com for:
Online Quizzes
Online Learning Center

Progress Monitoring

Reteaching
Have students locate each of the main headings in the text. Ask them to note three facts associated with each main heading. Call on volunteers to share facts with the class.

Enrichment
Have students write a paragraph that summarizes the changes that occur between fertilization and childbirth.

Go Online

Have students visit **glencoe.com** and complete the Interactive Study Guide for this lesson.

LESSON 2

Heredity and Genetics

1 FOCUS

GUIDE TO READING

BIG Idea Some traits are passed from parents to children. **Ask Students:** What are ways that family members can resemble one another? (Sample answer: Sometimes family members have a similar hair color.)

Before You Read

Outline Students' outlines should include each of the headings from the lesson.

Main Idea

Heredity Traits are passed from parents to children. **Ask Students:** Why do the members of some families look very similar to one another? (Sample answer: Traits have been passed from parents to children.)

Real Life Issues ....

Be sensitive to all students during this activity. Encourage students to think about all types of traits that family members share, even if family members are not biologically related. Allow students to write to any adult family member if writing to a parent is not an option.

LESSON 2

GUIDE TO READING

BIG Idea Certain traits, such as eye and hair color, come from both of your parents.

Before You Read

Make an Outline. Use the headings of this lesson to make an outline of what you'll read. Use a format like the one below to help you organize your notes.

```
I.
   A.
      1.
      2.
   B.
II.
```

New Vocabulary

▶ chromosomes (p. 478)
▶ genes (p. 479)
▶ DNA (p. 479)
▶ genetic disorders (p. 481)
▶ amniocentesis (p. 481)
▶ chorionic villi sampling (p. 482)
▶ gene therapy (p. 482)

Review Vocabulary

▶ heredity (Ch.1, L.2)

Heredity and Genetics

Real Life Issues ....

All in the Family. At a family gathering, Samir looks around at the members of his family. Some of them are short, others are tall. A few have straight hair, although most have curly hair. Samir's uncle Manny tells stories about what he and Samir's father did when they were boys. They both liked ice skating, and Samir's father was good at math. Samir is surprised to learn that he and his father have several traits in common.

Writing *Write a letter to your parent. Describe two or three traits that you believe you have in common with other family members.*

Heredity

Main Idea Heredity is the passing of physical traits from parents to their children.

Each one of us inherits traits such as hair and eye color, as well as the shape of your earlobes, from your parents. Inherited traits, however, can also be influenced by the environment. For example, height is an inherited trait, but poor nutrition may limit growth during childhood. Other inherited traits that can be impacted by the environment include body size and the tendency for certain diseases, like diabetes.

Most of the cells in the human body contain a nucleus, or the control center of a cell. Inside each nucleus is a set of **chromosomes** (KROH-muh-sohmz), *thread-like structures found within the nucleus of a cell that carry the codes for inherited traits.* Most of the cells in the human body contain 46 chromosomes that are arranged in 23 pairs.

Skills for the 21st Century

Health and Wellness Awareness One aspect of being a productive citizen is knowing how to access information about factors that affect health. In this lesson, students learn how heredity can influence health. Have students work in small groups to find reliable sources of information about genetic diseases or genetic research. Ask each group to use index cards to identify three reliable sources of information and a summary of the information each source provides. Have groups share their results with the class.

■ **Figure 17.7** Family members often share similar physical traits. *What determines your physical traits?*

Sections of chromosomes, called **genes**, are *the basic units of heredity*. Genes occur in pairs, just like chromosomes. One gene from each pair is inherited from each parent. You have thousands of genes in every cell of your body.

DNA

The chemical unit that makes up chromosomes is called **DNA**, or deoxyribonucleic (dee-AHK-si-ry-boh-noo-KLEE-ik) acid. All living things are made of DNA. DNA is made up of chemical building blocks arranged along a single molecule. Several of these molecules are linked together in a strand to form a DNA sequence, known as the genetic code. When a child is born, that child carries a combination of DNA sequencing from both parents. This DNA contains different proteins that result in individual traits. All the characteristics you have, such as your eye color, the amount of curl in your hair, and your height, are determined by your genetic code. This unique code is a combination of the DNA of both your parents. Only identical twins share the same DNA pattern.

Genetics and Fetal Development

Main Idea Chromosomes from a sperm and an egg unite to carry the hereditary traits from parents.

Passing on traits from parent to child involves genetics. Most human cells have 46 chromosomes, or 23 pairs. However, egg and sperm cells have half that number—23 chromosomes. When a sperm and egg unite during fertilization, the resulting zygote will have 46 chromosomes, 23 from each parent. These chromosomes carry the hereditary traits of the parents, which are passed on to their child. Heredity and the environment can affect human growth and development.

■ **Figure 17.8** DNA like this double helix, look like a long, twisted ladder. Nitrogen bases make up the rungs of this ladder. *What determines your own personal genetic code?*

Lesson 2   Heredity and Genetics   **479**

② TEACH

Caption Answer

Figure 17.7 Sample answer: Physical traits are determined by the genetic code.

AL Active Learning

Make a Model Have students work in small groups to make a three-dimensional model of DNA. Have each group review **Figure 17.8** and locate other pictures of DNA. Then have each group decide on materials for its model. Allow time to construct models. Ask groups to discuss their completed models with the class. **OL** **AL**

Main Idea

Genetics and Fetal Development Hereditary traits are carried from parent to child on chromosomes. **Ask Students:** *In a zygote, how many chromosomes come from each parent?* (23)

W Writing Support

Expository Writing Have students do library or Internet research to learn more about the contributions of Roslyn Franklin, James Watson, and Frances Crick. Have each student write a short report summarizing what he or she has learned. Have students share their reports with the class. **OL** **AL**

Caption Answer

Figure 17.8 Sample answer: The arrangement of nitrogen bases in DNA determines a person's genetic code.

Academic Integration

Science Help students recall that cells, the basic unit of life, form all tissues in the human body. On the board, draw a large circle to represent a cell. Point out that cells are three-dimensional, unlike your drawing, and that body cells have many different shapes. Then, draw a smaller circle inside the first circle. Explain that the smaller circle represents the nucleus, the part of the cell that directs the cell's activities. Within the smaller circle, draw lines to represent chromosomes. Have volunteers label your drawing with the words *cell, nucleus,* and *chromosomes.*

Inferring After students have read the information about cell division, ask them why it is essential that chromosomes are duplicated before each cell division. (If chromosomes were not duplicated before cell division, the number of chromosomes in each cell resulting from cell division would be only half the required number.) BL OL

Caption Answer

Figure 17.9 The father determines gender; only males have an X and Y chromosome.

AL Active Learning

Poster Explain to students that Gregor Mendel, an Austrian priest who lived in the 19th century, studied the inheritance of traits by performing experiments using pea plants. Have students research using library or Internet resources to learn more about Gregor Mendel and his work. Ask students to prepare a poster that uses both text and images to convey information about Mendel's work. Display completed posters in the classroom. AL

A zygote divides many times, ultimately producing the trillions of cells that make up the human body. Between each cell division, each chromosome in the nucleus of the cell copies itself, producing two sets of the 46 chromosomes. The cell then divides, and the two sets of chromosomes separate. Each new cell then contains one complete set of the 46 chromosomes that are identical to the ones found in the first cell of the zygote. **C**

Dominant and Recessive Genes

Each human trait is determined by at least one pair of genes. Some genes are *dominant,* while others are *recessive.* The traits of the dominant genes generally appear in the offspring when they are present. The traits of recessive genes usually appear only when the dominant genes are not present. For example, suppose an individual receives two genes for eye color, one for brown eyes and one for blue eyes. This individual will have brown eyes because the gene for brown eyes is dominant and the gene for blue eyes is recessive. If an individual has blue eyes, that means they have two recessive genes for blue eye color. **AL**

Genes and Gender

One pair of chromosomes determines gender. Females have two chromosomes that look exactly alike; these are called X chromosomes. Males have two different chromosomes, one shorter than the other. The shorter chromosome is the Y chromosome. The longer one is the X chromosome. See **Figure 17.9** to compare X and Y chromosomes.

Since sperm and egg cells contain only half the chromosomes of other cells, these cells have only one sex cell, not two. Because females have only X chromosomes, their egg cells contain only an X chromosome. Sperm, because they come from a male, contain either an X or a Y chromosome. Thus, the sperm from the male determines the gender of a child. If a sperm cell carries the X chromosome, the child will be a girl. If the sperm carries a Y chromosome, the child will be a boy.

■ **Figure 17.9** The body cells of a male have both an X chromosome and a Y chromosome. The body cells of a female have two X chromosomes. *Which parent determines the gender of a child, and why?*

Health Literacy

Polygenic Traits Many human traits are determined by more complicated patterns of inheritance than those described in the student text. For example, students may note that humans have a wide range of heights and skin colors. Obviously this great variation cannot be explained by a simple dominant/recessive inheritance pattern. Explain to students that height and skin color, along with many other traits, are influenced by more than one set of genes. Traits such as height and skin color are also affected by environment. The combination of the influence of several genes and environment lead to the variation of human heights and skin colors.

Genetic Disorders

Main Idea Genetic disorders are caused by defects in genes.

FITNESS ZONE

In 1990, researchers working on the Human Genome Project began to identify all of the genes in human DNA. By 2003, they identified genes that are linked to more than 1,800 diseases. This knowledge can help diagnose, treat, and perhaps even prevent genetic disorders.

A person can inherit genes that contain a *mutation,* or abnormality. The mutation may have little or no effect on the person. These genetic mutations, however, may result in a birth defect or may increase the person's likelihood of developing a disease. These diseases, called **genetic disorders**, are *disorders caused partly or completely by a defect in genes.* Some genetic disorders are apparent at birth. Others may not show up until later in life. **Figure 17.10** lists some common genetic disorders.

Most genetic disorders cannot be cured, but some can be treated. Two technologies used to test for genetic disorders before birth are amniocentesis and chorionic villi sampling.

- **Amniocentesis** (am-nee-oh-sen-TEE-sis) is *a procedure in which a syringe is inserted through a pregnant female's abdominal wall to remove a sample of the amniotic fluid surrounding the developing fetus.* Doctors examine the chromosomes in fetal cells for genetic abnormalities. This test is performed 16 to 20 weeks after fertilization.

I see ads for workout equipment that promise to give me washboard abs, to melt off the fat, or to tone my body in just two minutes a day. Those promises are too good to be true. We are born with our bodies, and we can make the most of what we've got. The best way to get fit is to set goals, eat healthy, and exercise to get into shape. For more fitness tips, visit the Online Fitness Zone at glencoe.com.

Figure 17.10	Common Human Genetic Disorders

Disorder	Characteristics
Sickle-cell anemia	Red blood cells have a sickle shape and clump together; may result in severe joint and abdominal pain, weakness, kidney disease, restricted blood flow
Tay-Sachs disease	Destruction of nervous system; blindness; paralysis; death during early childhood
Cystic fibrosis	Mucus clogs many organs, including lungs, liver, and pancreas; nutritional problems; serious respiratory infections and congestion
Down syndrome	Varying degrees of mental retardation, short stature, round face with upper eyelids that cover inner corners of the eyes
Hemophilia	Failure of blood to clot

Lesson 2 Heredity and Genetics **481**

481

Genetic Disorders Students' familiarity with various genetic disorders may be influenced by their cultural backgrounds. Certain genetic disorders are prevalent in people with specific racial or ethnic backgrounds. For example, sickle-cell anemia primarily affects individuals with ancestors from Africa, India, or the Middle East. The gene for cystic fibrosis is much more commonly carried by individuals with a Caucasian, European background than by individuals of other backgrounds. **OL**

Caption Answer

Figure 17.11 It is important to diagnose very early so modifications can be made to treat the condition.

Main Idea

Battling Genetic Diseases
Researchers are working on techniques that can be applied to treat or correct genetic disorders. **Ask Students:** *How is treating a genetic disorder different from treating an illness such as a cold?* (Sample answer: A genetic disorder is a part of a person's genetic make-up; correcting it requires a change in a gene.)

VIDEO **BusinessWeek**
HEALTH NEWS

After students have watched the video, *Genetic Issues,* lead a class discussion on the ethical debate surrounding the use of human genes in drug development and production. Then have each student write a paragraph supporting his or her opinion on the issue. Remind students to provide clear and logical explanations of their opinions.

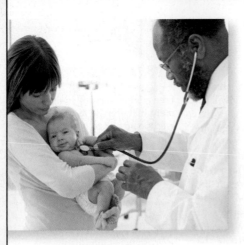

■ **Figure 17.11** Newborns can be checked for certain genetic disorders with the help of some very simple tests. *Why might it be difficult to diagnose a genetic disorder early in life?*

VIDEO **BusinessWeek**
HEALTH NEWS

Genetic Issues

Analyze. Go to glencoe.com and watch the video *Genetic Issues.* As a class, discuss the ethical debate over placing human genes into animals for the purpose of drug development. Examine the issues, and then write a paragraph explaining your personal opinions on the topic.

- **Chorionic villi sampling** (kor-ee-ON-ik VIL-eye), or CVS, is *a procedure in which a small piece of membrane is removed from the chorion, a layer of tissue that develops into the placenta*. The tissue can be examined for genetic disorders or to determine the age and gender of the fetus. The procedure is done around the eighth week of fetal development.

It is also possible to test a child for genetic disorders after birth. For example, many states require that all newborns be tested for phenylketonuria (PKU). If PKU is diagnosed soon after birth, a baby's diet can be altered to stop possible mental retardation caused by this genetic disorder.

Battling Genetic Diseases

Main Idea Research is ongoing to correct genetic disorders.

The information obtained as a result of the Human Genome Project was an important first step in learning more about genetic diseases. With it, scientists have gained a greater understanding of how diseases progress. The information can also be used to identify people who may be susceptible to genetic diseases or disorders. **CA**

Genetic disorders occur when an individual is missing a functioning gene. Without the functioning gene, the body does not produce some of the substances it needs. One experimental treatment, **gene therapy**, is *the process of inserting normal genes into human cells to correct genetic disorders*. Scientists feel that once a defective gene is replaced with a normal gene, the cells can then begin producing the normal gene. At this time gene therapy is experimental. Placing parts of DNA from one organism into another is called *genetic engineering*.

Genetic Counseling

Genetic research has resulted in many ways to diagnose and treat genetic diseases. Genetic counselors can guide families of children with genetic disorders on treatment options. Genetic counseling offers options to people with a family history of some diseases. In Chapter 2, you learned about the importance of keeping a complete family medical history. With this information, genetic counselors can educate families about possible risks for certain diseases and guide families through their options. Having a faulty gene, however, does *not* guarantee the person will get the disease.

More About...

Prenatal Technology Amniocentesis and chorionic villi sampling are just two of the many technologies that can be used to monitor the health of a developing fetus. Another test used to monitor the health of the fetus is a maternal blood test called a triple screen. Results of this test may suggest (but not definitely diagnose) that a fetus has Down syndrome. FISH, or fluorescence in situ hybridization, is a test that uses fluorescent probes to locate specific DNA sequences in cells. This test can be performed on fetal cells to detect the presence of mutations that cause disorders.

■ **Figure 17.12** Genetic research often takes places in a laboratory. *What sort of information might be learned in a genetics laboratory?*

 READING CHECK

Cause and Effect
What happens when a defective gene is replaced by a normal one?

Genetically Engineered Drugs

Genes used to treat diseases are not inserted directly into human beings. They are instead placed into other organisms, causing that organism to produce substances that can be used to treat human diseases and disorders. Though genetic engineering, some vaccines that can prevent disease have been produced.

LESSON 2 ASSESSMENT

After You Read

Reviewing Facts and Vocabulary

1. Define the terms *chromosomes* and *genes*.

2. How many chromosomes are found in most human cells? How many are found in egg and sperm cells?

3. Identify the difference between the chromosomes of a male and the chromosomes of a female.

Thinking Critically

4. **Evaluate.** When might a pregnant woman consider having CVS?

5. **Interpret.** The gene for brown hair is dominant, while the gene for blond hair is recessive. What genes does a brown-haired person have?

Applying Health Skills

6. **Accessing Information.** Use library or Internet resources to learn more about genetic research. Explain how this technology can prevent disease, and how it can impact personal, family, and community health.

Writing Critically

7. **Descriptive.** Write a short essay describing how genetic counseling and gene therapy might change someone's life.

 Go Online

Visit **glencoe.com** and complete the Interactive Study Guide for this lesson.

Lesson 2   Heredity and Genetics   **483**

---

③ ASSESS/ CLOSE

Assessment Resources

📁 *Fast File* Activities
Lesson 2 Quiz

💿 *ExamView Assessment Suite* CD-ROM

Visit glencoe.com **for:**
Online Quizzes
Online Learning Center

Progress Monitoring

Reteaching
Have each student review Lesson 2 and write down three ideas about genetics, genetic disorders, or ways to treat genetic disorders. Then have students review their ideas with a partner.

Enrichment
Have students choose one section of Lesson 2 and prepare a short lesson. Encourage them to do additional research to prepare.

Go Online

Have students visit **glencoe.com** and complete the Interactive Study Guide for this lesson.

LESSON 2 ASSESSMENT ANSWERS

1. *Chromosomes* are found within the nucleus of a cell and carry the codes for inherited traits. The chromosomes contain *genes,* which are the basic units of heredity.

2. Most human body cells have 46 chromosomes, but egg and sperm cells have 23 chromosomes.

3. Males have an X and a Y chromosome. Females have two X chromosomes.

4. Sample answer: A pregnant woman may have CVS if there is a likelihood that her baby will be born with a genetic disorder, such as Down syndrome, Tay-Sachs disease, sickle-cell anemia, cystic fibrosis, or hemophilia.

5. A person with brown hair may have two dominant genes or one dominant gene and one recessive gene.

6. Research will vary.

7. Essays will vary.

483

Birth Through Childhood

① FOCUS

GUIDE TO READING

BIG Idea Change and growth occur during infancy and childhood. **Ask Students:** *What are some ways that you have changed since early childhood?* (Sample answer: I am more independent, and I have grown quite a bit.)

Before You Read

K-W-L Chart The first and second columns of students' charts will vary. The third column should contain accurate information from the lesson.

Main Idea

Childhood Infancy and childhood are composed of four stages. **Ask Students:** *What are some ways that infants are different from children?* (Sample answer: Infants cannot walk well, but children can.)

Real Life Issues ⋯⋯⋯⋯⋯⋯

Before students begin writing their diary entries, ask them to think about activities they enjoyed at age 5, age 8, and age 10. **Ask Students:** *What were some of your favorite pastimes when you were 5 years old?* (Sample answer: When I was 5, I enjoyed riding my bike.)

484

 **GUIDE TO READING**

BIG Idea *Infancy and childhood are times of great changes and growth.*

Before You Read

Create a K-W-L Chart. Make a three-column chart like the one below. In the first column, write what you **k**now about infancy and childhood. In the second column, write what you would **w**ant to know about this topic. As you read, fill in the third column describing what you have **l**earned.

K	W	L

New Vocabulary

▸ developmental tasks (p. 484)
▸ autonomy (p. 485)
▸ scoliosis (p. 486)

Birth Through Childhood

Real Life Issues ⋯⋯⋯⋯⋯⋯⋯⋯⋯⋯⋯⋯⋯

Trip Down Memory Lane. Henry and his parents are going to a family reunion. He's looking forward to seeing his grandparents, aunts, uncles, and cousins, all of whom live in other states. Earlier today he helped his mom put together some photo albums to take on the trip. At one point, she showed him a photo of a young child. It's Henry when he was five years old. He thought back to when he was younger and how he has changed since then.

Writing *Write three entries in Henry's diary as he remembers what he was like at the ages of 5, 8, and 10.*

Childhood

Main Idea Each child passes through four stages of development during infancy and childhood.

Our lives can be divided into eight developmental stages. The first four stages occur during infancy and childhood. Each of the eight stages is associated with certain **developmental tasks**, *events that need to happen in order for a person to continue growing toward becoming a healthy, mature adult.* The developmental tasks for each stage are summarized in **Figure 17.13**.

Infancy

Infancy is the time of fastest growth in a person's life. It is a time of learning: how to eat solid food, how to sit up, how to crawl, and how to walk. Infants also learn to trust others during this time.

Teens Want to Know

Why Should I Learn About Infants and Young Children? Students may wonder how information about infants and young children is relevant to their lives. Point out that many teens are employed as babysitters. A knowledge of the developmental tasks of different stages of childhood is essential for planning appropriate activities for the children they are babysitting. In addition, many teens have younger siblings with whom they interact on a daily basis. If an older sibling understands the developmental tasks associated with different stages, he or she can help the younger sibling develop autonomy.

Figure 17.13 **Stages of Infancy and Childhood**

AL

Each stage of development is associated with a developmental task that involves a person's relationship with other people.

HS

Infancy Birth to 12 months	Early Childhood Ages 1–3	Middle Childhood Ages 4–6	Late Childhood Ages 7–12
Opens and closes hands	Walks well	Dresses and undresses	Puberty may begin
May begin associating sounds with objects	Picks up objects without losing balance	Use utensils to eat for most foods	Sensitivity about body image may begin
Imitates new word sounds	Throws balls overhead, but inaccurately	Becomes more independent	Develops sense of self
May walk a few steps	Draws recognizable pictures	Eager to explore the larger world	Recognizes unique personality traits
Experiences the five basic emotions	Begins showing defiance, disagreement	Craves praise and approval	Sense of competence develops
Forms strong attachment to parents	Behaves affectionately	Self-confidence grows	Becomes aware of dangers in the world
Begins to smile	May wish to help adults	Begins forming friendships	Deeper friendships develop
Wants companionship	Begins being bothered by fears	Becomes more outgoing and talkative	Relationships with parents change
Enjoys company of other children	Desires approval	Respects others' belongings	Begins facing moral decisions
Begins experiencing stranger anxiety	Bosses other children	May want to do things their own way	Peer pressure becomes stronger
Shows strong likes and dislikes	Takes part in brief group activities		

Early Childhood

W

During early childhood, children begin to feel proud of their accomplishments and are eager to try new tasks and to learn new things. During this stage, children also begin to learn to play as part of a group. Parent are encouraged to allow their children to try new things and to test their abilities. This helps a child in the early childhood stage develop a sense of **autonomy,** *the confidence that a person can control his or her own body, impulses, and environment.*

 **READING CHECK**

Infer How can a parent help a child develop a sense of autonomy?

Lesson 3 Birth Through Childhood **485**

② TEACH

AL Active Learning

Interpreting a Chart Direct students' attention to **Figure 17.13**. Divide the class into four groups. Assign each group one of the four stages described in the chart. Ask each group to develop a strategy for teaching other students about its assigned stage of development. After allowing students time to develop strategies, ask each group to teach the rest of the class. OL

HS Health Skills Practice

Accessing Information Have students imagine that a friend's mother is going to have a baby any day and their friend would like to learn more about caring for an infant. Have students work in pairs to find two reliable sources of information about infant care. For each source of information have students write a paragraph that includes the following: a citation of the specific source and a summary of the information provided by the source. OL

W Writing Support

Descriptive Writing After students have read the information describing infancy and the developmental tasks associated with infancy, have them write a paragraph from an infant's point of view. The paragraph should creatively describe what an infant might be thinking or feeling as he or she accomplishes a developmental task associated with infancy. OL AL

Reading Strategy

Paraphrasing Explain to students that paraphrasing—the rephrasing of ideas in their own words—is an effective strategy for understanding and remembering information. Have students select a partner. Each student in the pair should select one paragraph from the text to paraphrase. After each student has shared his or her paraphrased version of the text with his or her partner, ask volunteers to share some of their work with the class.

C Critical Thinking

Predicting Have students read the developmental tasks associated with early, middle, and late childhood. Ask students to predict how a child would be affected if his or her parents consistently expected the child to perform tasks that were beyond the child's level of development. Then ask students to predict how a child would be affected by expectations that were consistently below his or her stage of development. Follow up with a discussion of the development of autonomy that occurs when the parent's expectations of a child match his or her developmental level. **AL**

Caption Answer

Figure 17.14 Infants learn to eat, crawl, and trust others.

Main Idea

Childhood Health Screenings
The health and growth of a child can be monitored by health screenings.
Ask Students: *What health screenings are performed at your school?*
(Sample answer: The school nurse checks our hearing and vision.)

G Online

Have students visit **glencoe.com** and explore early childhood skills development in the Student Web Activity.

■ **Figure 17.14** Infants learn to trust and depend on others. *What do infants learn during the infancy stage of development?*

G Online

Explore glencoe.com and complete the Student Web Activity on the development of physical, mental, and social skills in early childhood.

Middle Childhood

During middle childhood, children learn to initiate play rather than following the lead of others. Children at this stage must be taught to recognize emotions and practice expressing them in appropriate ways

Late Childhood

C

School becomes an important part of a child's life during late childhood. Children learn to get along with their peers, learn about different roles in society, and develop a conscience at this stage.

Childhood Health Screenings

Main Idea Many screening tests are performed in childhood to monitor the health and growth of a child.

Vision and hearing impairments are two problems that can affect a child's ability to learn and develop. Health screenings and immunizations can identify and prevent many problems that can affect development.

Vision and Hearing

Nearly one in every four school-aged children in the United States has a vision problem. The American Academy of Ophthalmology recommends that newborns receive a vision screening and that these screenings continue through childhood. Children may receive regular vision screenings at school. Oftentimes, school aged children do not receive a vision screening until age 18.

As well as vision problems, hearing impairment can also affect a childs ability to learn. Two or three in every 1,000 children in the United States are born with a hearing impairment severe enough to affect their language development. Some states require that infants are screened for hearing loss. Again, some school districts may provide children screenings to identify hearing impairments.

Scoliosis

Scoliosis, *an abnormal lateral, or side-to-side, curvature of the spine,* may begin in childhood and go unnoticed until a child is a teenager. The exact cause of scoliosis is unknown, but it is more common in girls. Many middle schools have developed screening methods to check students for scoliosis.

Promoting School Wellness

Health Services Health screenings are an important part of the health services offered through a coordinated school health program. These screenings can be used to identify and diagnose conditions that can impair development and learning. Examples of screenings routinely offered in schools include vision, hearing, and scoliosis. Some schools also offer screenings for dental health, head lice, obesity, and type 2 diabetes. Family involvement, another component of coordinated school health, is essential when a screening requires a follow-up. Offering referrals to community resources can help increase the number of screenings that result in appropriate follow-up.

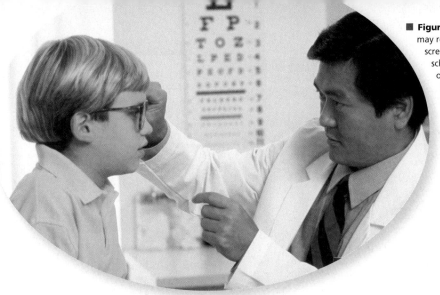

Figure 17.15 Children may receive vision screenings through school, a pediatrician, or a health clinic. *Why is it important to get regular health screenings?*

Other Screenings

Children are tested for lead poisoning yearly until age four. Blood pressure screenings begin after age three. Children with a family history of cholesterol problems or anemia may also be screened for these conditions.

 READING CHECK

Explain Why are students screened for vision and hearing?

LESSON 3 ASSESSMENT

After You Read

Reviewing Facts and Vocabulary

1. What are some *developmental tasks* children learn in early childhood?

2. What is an important part of a child's life during late childhood?

3. What is *scoliosis*?

Thinking Critically

4. **Evaluate.** How can positive parenting affect the autonomy and independence of a child?

5. **Analyze.** What is the result when a parent allows a child autonomy?

Applying Health Skills

6. **Accessing Information.** Research library or Internet resources to learn more about vision and hearing screenings. Explain how these screenings could prevent problems later in life.

Writing Critically

7. **Descriptive.** Write a short essay about the changes a child will face from early childhood to late childhood.

Go Online

Visit glencoe.com and complete the Interactive Study Guide for this lesson.

Caption Answer

Figure 17.15 Regular health screenings can identify health problems that need treatment.

 READING CHECK

Answer Problems with vision and hearing can impact a student's ability to learn.

3 ASSESS/CLOSE

Assessment Resources

📁 *FAST FILE* **ACTIVITIES**
Lesson 3 Quiz

💿 *ExamView*
Assessment Suite CD-ROM

Visit glencoe.com **for:**
Online Quizzes
Online Learning Center

Progress Monitoring

Reteaching
Have students work with a partner to review the information in **Figure 17.13**. Suggest that students take turns asking and answering questions.

Enrichment
Ask students to research health screenings and immunizations available in the community and prepare information cards to share with families.

Go Online

Have students visit **glencoe.com** and complete the Interactive Study Guide for this lesson.

LESSON 3 ASSESSMENT ANSWERS

1. Sample answer: In early childhood, children learn to walk, pick up and throw objects, draw, initiate play, and participate in group activities. They are eager to learn and gain a sense of autonomy.

2. Sample answer: School is an important part of a child's life during late childhood. At school a child learns to get along with peers and learns different social roles.

3. *Scoliosis* is an abnormal side-to-side curvature of the spine more common in girls.

4. Sample answer: Parents who give a child comfort and allow the child control over his or her environment foster a feeling of independence and autonomy in their child. This leads to greater self-confidence.

5. Autonomy allows a child to become comfortable in his or her environment. As a result, the child will be more self-confident in the future.

6. Students' explanations will vary.

7. Essays will vary.

How DNA Works

Focus

Motivator

Ask students if they have ever heard about technologies involving DNA being used in criminal investigations or food production. After students have volunteered responses, explain that technologies involving DNA are used in many ways.

Teach

DNA and Criminal Law Students may be familiar with the process of DNA fingerprinting, which is commonly depicted on television shows about crime investigations. Explain that investigators search a crime scene for blood, hair, sweat, semen, or saliva. These all contain DNA, which investigators can match to a particular suspect. Point out that all humans (except identical twins) have unique DNA sequences, so investigators can be confident in their identifications.

The Human Genome Project
The Human Genome Project began in 1990 with the goal of sequencing the entire human genome. By June 2000, the scientists had assembled a working draft of the entire human genome sequence. Ask students to form small groups to discuss ways that information about the human genome sequence could be applied to improve individual, family, and community health. Have groups share their ideas with the class.

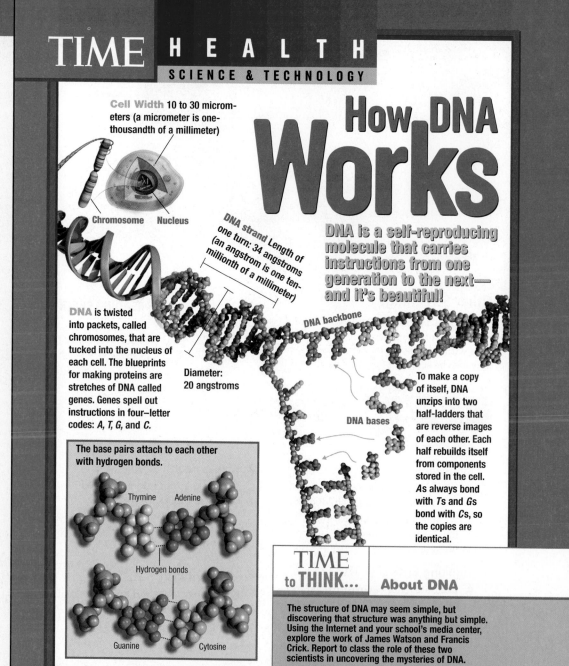

How DNA Works

Cell Width 10 to 30 micrometers (a micrometer is one-thousandth of a millimeter)

Chromosome   Nucleus

DNA strand Length of one turn: 34 angstroms (an angstrom is one ten-millionth of a millimeter)

DNA is a self-reproducing molecule that carries instructions from one generation to the next—and it's beautiful!

DNA backbone

DNA is twisted into packets, called chromosomes, that are tucked into the nucleus of each cell. The blueprints for making proteins are stretches of DNA called genes. Genes spell out instructions in four–letter codes: *A, T, G,* and *C.*

Diameter: 20 angstroms

DNA bases

To make a copy of itself, DNA unzips into two half-ladders that are reverse images of each other. Each half rebuilds itself from components stored in the cell. *A*s always bond with *T*s and *G*s bond with *C*s, so the copies are identical.

The base pairs attach to each other with hydrogen bonds.

Thymine   Adenine

Hydrogen bonds

Guanine   Cytosine

TIME to THINK... About DNA

The structure of DNA may seem simple, but discovering that structure was anything but simple. Using the Internet and your school's media center, explore the work of James Watson and Francis Crick. Report to class the role of these two scientists in uncovering the mysteries of DNA.

More About...

Timeline Have students work in small groups to investigate the history of research involving DNA using library or Internet resources. Ask each group to make a timeline of DNA research that includes at least five major advances in the study of DNA. Provide each group with a long sheet of paper on which to make its timeline. You may want to make a model of a timeline on the board to help students get started. After each group has placed at least five milestones in the study of DNA on its timeline, have students present their work to the class.

To download quizzes and eFlashcards to your PDA, go to glencoe.com and click on the Study to Go icon.

LESSON 1

Prenatal Development and Care

Key Concepts

▶ A human fetus begins with the joining of a female egg and a male sperm.

▶ A pregnant female must avoid tobacco, alcohol, drugs, and environmental hazards.

▶ Expectant parents have many options regarding the location and method of delivery of their baby.

▶ The birth of a baby takes place in three steps: labor, delivery, and afterbirth.

Vocabulary
▶ fertilization (p. 470)
▶ implantation (p. 470)
▶ embryo (p. 470)
▶ fetus (p. 470)
▶ prenatal care (p. 473)
▶ fetal alcohol syndrome (p. 474)

LESSON 2

Heredity and Genetics

Key Concepts

▶ A person's DNA determines his or her individual characteristics.

▶ Children inherit genetic traits from their parents.

▶ Genetic disorders are caused by defects in genes.

▶ Genetic research provides an opportunity to correct some genetic disorders.

Vocabulary
▶ chromosomes (p. 478)
▶ genes (p. 479)
▶ DNA (p. 479)
▶ genetic disorders (p. 481)
▶ amniocentesis (p. 481)
▶ chorionic villi sampling (p. 482)
▶ gene therapy (p. 482)

LESSON 3

Birth Through Childhood

Key Concepts

▶ Infants and children complete a variety of tasks during four stages of development.

▶ Health screenings during childhood can identify problems, and monitor growth and development.

▶ Keeping your health history and your immunizations current is important for your individual health.

Vocabulary
▶ developmental tasks (p. 484)
▶ autonomy (p. 485)
▶ scoliosis (p. 486)

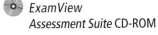

Go Online

Students can visit **glencoe.com** to

- review content online with the Online Student Edition.

- test their knowledge of chapter content with Online Quizzes.

- access Interactive Health Tutor for more practice with vocabulary.

Assessment Resources

📁 **FAST FILE ACTIVITIES**
Chapter 17 Test

💿 *ExamView*
Assessment Suite CD-ROM

Visit glencoe.com **for:**
Audio Chapter Summaries
Online Quizzes

 Tell students to visit glencoe.com where they can download quizzes and eFlashcards.

Study Tips

Use a Timeline Explain that a timeline can be a useful way to organize and study processes, such as the human life cycle, that have a series of sequential steps. Encourage students to make a timeline of the steps of the human life cycle that are described in the chapter. Point out that the timeline can be a useful study tool when students need to review the human life cycle before a test.

Assessment

Chapter 17 Assessment Answers

LESSON 1

Vocabulary Review

1. embryo
2. Prenatal care
3. implantation

Understanding Key Concepts

4. a
5. c
6. d
7. b

Thinking Critically

8. Prenatal care helps ensure the health of both mother and baby.
9. Sample answers: The health of the mother and fetus, whether the parents prefer a birthing center or a hospital
10. Sample answer: A fetus breaks down alcohol more slowly than an adult, and the alcohol level becomes elevated in the fetus' body. The fetus may be born with FAS, a group of physical and mental disabilities that require lifelong care.
11. Identical twins
12. Sample answer: Both are potential complications that might arise during pregnancy. Preeclampsia is a condition that could prevent the placenta from getting enough blood. In many cases, the mother will go on bed rest to ensure the health of the baby. An ectopic pregnancy develops outside the uterus and must be removed from the mother as it can endanger her life.

LESSON 2

Vocabulary Review

13. Genes
14. gene therapy
15. genetic disorders

490

LESSON 1

Vocabulary Review
Correct the sentences below by replacing the italicized term with the correct vocabulary term.

1. A(n) *fetus* is a cluster of cells that develops between the third and eighth week of pregnancy.
2. *Fetal alcohol syndrome* refers to the steps that a pregnant female can take to provide for her own health and the health of her baby.
3. The process by which a zygote attaches to the uterine wall is called *fertilization*.

Understanding Key Concepts
After reading the question or statement, select the correct answer.

4. What is the union of a sperm cell and an egg cell called?
   a. Fertilization
   b. Embryo
   c. Implantation
   d. Trimester
5. Which of the following nutrients helps form the nervous system of an embryo?
   a. Calcium
   b. Vitamin A
   c. Folic acid
   d. Iron
6. Exposure to which of the following may cause birth defects in the second month of pregnancy?
   a. Lead
   b. Mercury
   c. Radiation
   d. Smog

490   Chapter 17   Assessment

---

7. What is the result when a zygote implants in the fallopian tube or ovary?
   a. Preeclampsia
   b. Ectopic pregnancy
   c. Miscarriage
   d. Stillbirth

Thinking Critically
After reading the question or statement, write a short answer using complete sentences.

8. **Analyze.** What is the role of prenatal care in protecting the health of the mother and the fetus?
9. **Evaluate.** What should parents consider when choosing a childbirth method?
10. **Explain.** How can drinking alcohol during pregnancy damage a fetus?
11. **Analyze.** What is the result if one healthy zygote splits into two?
12. **Compare and Contrast.** What are the similarities and differences between preeclampsia and an ectopic pregnancy?

LESSON 2

Vocabulary Review
Use the vocabulary terms listed on page 489 to complete the following statements.

13. _____ are the basic units of heredity.
14. The process of inserting normal genes into human cells to correct genetic disorders is called _____.
15. Disorders caused by a defect in genes are called _____.

Health eSpotlight VIDEO Wrap-Up

Right from the Start Have students reread the Health eSpotlight question at the beginning of the chapter (page 469) and look at their original answer. **Ask Students:** *Now that you have read the chapter and* *watched the video, what information would you add about family similarities and heredity?* Call on volunteers to describe how their responses would change.

Understanding Key Concepts

After reading the question or statement, select the correct answer.

16. How many chromosomes do most human cells have?
   a. 12
   b. 23
   c. 46
   d. 69

17. Where are chromosomes located?
   a. Within the DNA molecule
   b. In genes
   c. In the nucleus of a cell
   d. Outside a cell

18. What is the chemical compound that makes up genetic material?
   a. Genes
   b. DNA
   c. Chromosomes
   d. Genetic code

Thinking Critically

After reading the question or statement, write a short answer using complete sentences.

19. **Explain.** How does genetics play a role in fetal development?

20. **Synthesize.** How might a disorder like sickle-cell anemia be traced to its origin?

21. **Infer.** Why would a brown-eyed parent and a blue-eyed parent have a brown-eyed child?

22. **Predict.** What would a pregnant female expect to find out after having an amniocentesis?

LESSON 3

Vocabulary Review

Use the vocabulary terms listed on page 489 to complete the following statements.

23. The confidence that you can control your own body, impulses, and environment is called _____.

24. _____ are events that need to happen for a person to continue growing toward being a healthy, mature adult.

25. The abnormal lateral curvature of the spine is known as _____.

Understanding Key Concepts

After reading the question or statement, select the correct answer.

26. Which of the following is the time of fastest growth in a person's life?
   a. Infancy
   b. Early childhood
   c. Middle childhood
   d. Late childhood

27. Which of the following may lead to low self-esteem in children?
   a. Overprotective parents
   b. Parents who encourage questions
   c. Parents who encourage autonomy
   d. Attentive parents

28. Which group is more likely to be diagnosed with scoliosis?
   a. Boys
   b. Infants
   c. Girls
   d. Preschoolers

Understanding Key Concepts

16. c
17. c
18. b

Thinking Critically

19. The genes carried in DNA from both parents determine the physical characteristics of the fetus.

20. Certain genes contain mutations, so scientists can identify and trace the abnormal gene.

21. The gene for brown eyes is dominant, and its trait will show up even in the presence of a gene for blue eyes.

22. She could find out if the fetus has any genetic abnormalities, the gender of the fetus, and the age of the fetus.

LESSON 3

Vocabulary Review

23. autonomy
24. Developmental tasks
25. scoliosis

Understanding Key Concepts

26. a
27. a
28. c
29. d

Create and customize tests in minutes with this convenient digital platform.

- Create differentiated tests quickly and easily.
- All questions correlated to National/State Standards.
- Enhance tests with Document Based Questions (DBQ) and add your own photos or graphics.
- Build tests in both English and Spanish.
- Generate progress reports.

To order, go to **glencoe.com** and search for ISBN 0-07-888173-0.

Assessment

Thinking Critically

30. During late childhood, children develop a conscience and social skills, learn to get along with peers, and learn about their roles in society.

31. The child may develop feelings of self-doubt.

32. The child could develop doubts about his abilities, which can lead to low self-esteem.

33. Problems with vision and hearing can lead to developmental problems.

Assessment

29. Which of the following can impact a child's development?
    a. Vision impairments
    b. Hearing impairments
    c. Social factors
    d. All of the above

Thinking Critically

After reading the question or statement, write a short answer using complete sentences.

30. **Analyze.** What developmental tasks are involved as friendships and school become especially important during late childhood?

31. **Infer.** What might happen to a child who is constantly scolded for making a mess or for getting in the way?

32. **Infer.** If a parent is overprotective and does not let a child explore his surroundings, what may happen?

33. **Explain.** Why do most states require that students be screened for hearing and vision problems?

Project-Based ASSESSMENT

Genes Count

Background

In 1962, James Watson, Francis Crick, and Maurice Wilkins received a Nobel Prize for their explanation of the chemical structure of DNA. Since then, our knowledge of genetics and of how the DNA molecule works has increased rapidly. In 1992, research turned to human genome sequencing to identify the location of hundreds of thousands of human genes. (The term *genome* means the genetic material of an organism.)

Task

Conduct research to learn the progress of the Human Genome Project. Develop an oral presentation based on your findings.

Audience

Students in your class

Purpose

Gain an appreciation of the progress that has been made in recent years by researchers working on the Human Genome Project.

Procedure

1. Use a variety of print and online resources to learn the progress of the Human Genome Project and to identify recent advances in genetic research.

2. Based on your findings, write a draft script for an oral presentation.

3. Include information on genetic maps, Summarize the progress that has been made to identify genes that causes specific genetic disorders, and describe how genetic counseling and genetic engineering are used.

4. Compile your notes and prepare an oral report. Assign part of the presentation to each member of your group.

5. Create visual for your presentation.

6. Present your report to your class. Ask for feedback from your peers.

Project-Based ASSESSMENT

Step 1 Research Have each student use library or Internet resources to find out more about the Human Genome Project, gene maps, and ways that researchers learn more about genes that cause specific disorders.

Step 2 Prepare Have students write a first draft of their presentation and review their first draft with you. Have students practice their oral report before they present it to the class. Encourage students to use visual aids to enhance the listeners' understanding of their report.

Step 3 Evaluate Evaluate each oral presentation based on how well it describes the Human Genome Project, gene maps, and ways to identify genes that cause specific disorders.

Visit **glencoe.com** for Project-Based Assessment rubrics.

Standardized Test Practice

Math Practice

Interpret Graphs. The pie chart below shows the number of weeks in a typical 40-week pregnancy designated for each trimester. Use the pie chart to answer questions 1–3.

Stages of Pregnancy

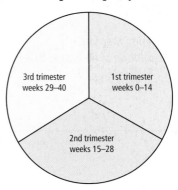

1. According to the information in the pie chart, what percentage of duration of the pregnancy makes up the first trimester?
   A. 14%   C. 35%
   B. 30%   D. 40%

2. The term *zygote* describes the fertilized egg in the first two weeks after conception. For what percentage of a typical 40-week pregnancy is the developing human called a zygote?
   A. 2%   C. 14%
   B. 5%   D. 35%

3. A baby is born early, after only 36 weeks of pregnancy. What percentage of the typical 40-week pregnancy did the baby complete?
   A. 10%   C. 90%
   B. 36%   D. 96%

G⊙ Online

For more test practice, visit **glencoe.com** and complete the Online Quizzes for Chapter 17.

Reading/Writing Practice

Understand and Apply. Read the passage below, and then answer the questions.

> Jean Piaget (1896–1980) was the first theorist to study how children learn. Piaget analyzed facts about the way children develop cognitive abilities. He also conducted studies on the way children develop thinking skills.
>
> One of Piaget's famous studies used pieces of candy to test children's discriminative abilities. Piaget placed equal numbers of the candy into two lines. He spread one line farther apart than the other line. The two- to three-year-olds tested saw that the rows had the same amount of candies, while the three- to four-year-olds tested believed the longer row had more candies.
>
> Piaget's test showed that during this stage of development three to four year olds temporarily lose their ability to problem solve.

1. What is a *theorist*?
   A. A person who solves a problem
   B. A person who writes a story
   C. A person who analyzes a set of facts
   D. A person who uses a large vocabulary

2. The word *discriminative*, used in paragraph two, means which of the following?
   A. Objective
   B. Distinguish
   C. Prejudice
   D. Judicious

3. Considering Piaget's test, why do you think children between ages three to four temporarily lose the ability to solve?

National Education Standards

Math: Number and Operations
Language Arts: NCTE 3, NCTE 4

Standardized Test Practice

Standardized Test Practice Answers

Math Practice
1. C
2. B
3. C

Reading/Writing Practice
1. C
2. B
3. Children temporarily lose their solving abilities because of their overdependence on perception in developing their motor skills.

National Education Standards

Math: Number and Operations

Language Arts: NCTE 3, NCTE 4

For the complete Math and Language Arts standards, visit glencoe.com.

G⊙ Online

Online Study Tools
For more test practice, visit glencoe.com and complete the Online Quizzes for Chapter 17.

Test-Taking Tip

Interpreting Graphs Tell students that they may be required to interpret information that is presented in a graph. In the example on this page, students need to interpret a circle graph in order to answer the questions. Point out to students that they should pre-view the questions, then examine the graph. Remind students to spend time looking at the title and all of the labels on the graph. Then have students reread the questions and use the information in the graph to determine the answers.

Chapter 18 pages 494–517	Standards		Features
	National	**State/Local**	*Hands-On* **HEALTH**
	1.12.2, 2.12.1, 2.12.6, 2.12.8, 4.12.1–4.12.3, 5.12.1, 5.12.3, 7.12.2, 8.12.1, 8.12.4		• Skills for a Happy Marriage *(Conflict Resolution Skills)*, page 512
Lesson 1 **Changes During Adolescence** pages 496–501 **BIG Idea** *Adolescence begins with puberty as a person starts to mature physically, emotionally, and mentally.*	1.12.2, 4.12.1, 4.12.2, 5.12.4, 5.12.5, 5.12.6		
Lesson 2 **Adulthood, Marriage, and Parenthood** pages 502–507 **BIG Idea** *During adulthood, individuals may choose to get married and become parents.*	1.12.2, 1.12.7, 2.12.1, 3.12.2, 7.12.1, 8.12.2		VIDEO **BusinessWeek** **HEALTH NEWS** • Childproofing Your Home, page 506
Lesson 3 **Health Through the Life Cycle** pages 508–511 **BIG Idea** *Middle and late adulthood are times of contribution and reflection.*	1.12.2, 1.12.6, 2.12.10, 3.12.2, 4.12.1, 8.12.4		VIDEO **BusinessWeek** **HEALTH NEWS** • Memory Loss and Technology, page 510

30 Min (Lesson 1)
30 Min (Lesson 2)
30 Min (Lesson 3)

Key to Ability Levels

Teaching Strategies and activities have been coded for ability level and appropriateness.

AL Activities for students working above grade level

OL Activities for students working on grade level

BL Activities for students working below grade level

EL Activities for English Learners

Glencoe Exclusive!
TeacherWorks™ Plus
All-In-One Planner and Resource Center

Resources	Lesson Assessment	Technology
Student Activity Workbook TEACH **FAST FILE** RESOURCES Vocabulary Practice TEACH Health Labs EXTEND	Chapter 18 Review Chapter 18 Assessment Standardized Test Practice ⊙ *ExamView® Assessment Suite* CD-ROM	**Teaching Tools:** ⊙ *TeacherWorks™* Plus DVD ⊙ *StudentWorks™* Plus DVD ⊙ *ExamView® Assessment Suite* CD-ROM 🕹 Transparency ⊙ Fitness DVD ⊙ PowerPoint® DVD ⊙ Health eSpotlight Video Series DVD
FAST FILE RESOURCES Reading Strategies Activity TEACH Reteaching Activity REVIEW Enrichment Activity EXTEND Health Skills Practice TEACH	Lesson 1 Assessment, page 501 📁 Lesson 1 Quiz *Fast File* ⊙ *ExamView® Assessment Suite* CD-ROM	**Web-Based Resources:** **Go Online** glencoe.com • Health Podcast Activities • Audio Chapter Summaries (English/Spanish) • Interactive Health Tutor • Health Skills Activities
FAST FILE RESOURCES Reading Strategies Activity TEACH Reteaching Activity REVIEW Enrichment Activity EXTEND Health Skills Practice TEACH	Lesson 2 Assessment, page 507 📁 Lesson 2 Quiz *Fast File* ⊙ *ExamView® Assessment Suite* CD-ROM	• Vocabulary PuzzleMaker • Parent Letters (English/Spanish) • Lesson Plans • Health Inventories • Online Quizzes
FAST FILE RESOURCES Reading Strategies Activity TEACH Reteaching Activity REVIEW Enrichment Activity EXTEND Health Skills Practice TEACH	Lesson 3 Assessment, page 511 📁 Lesson 3 Quiz *Fast File* ⊙ *ExamView® Assessment Suite* CD-ROM	• Study-to-Go • Unit Web Projects • Student Web Activities • Fitness Zone Activities

This is the student's backpack solution.

Includes:
- complete Interactive Student Edition
- full audio of English text and Spanish chapter summaries
- allows students to record assignments and track grades.
- links to online activities and additional student resources
- access to all student worksheets and workbooks

Dinah Zike Foldables® FOLDABLES® Study Organizer
Chapter Activity
Refer to the *Dinah Zike Reading and Study Skills for Glencoe Health.* Have students create a three-tab book Foldable to record notes about the changes that occur in males and females during adolescence. Students should take notes under the appropriate tabs as they read Lesson 1.

Key to Symbols

🕹 Transparencies   REVIEW activities to review or reinforce content

 CD-ROM   TEACH activities to teach basic concepts

 glencoe.com   EXTEND activities to extend or enrich lesson content

 Print Resources

The Life Cycle Continues

Chapter Overview

Chapter 18 focuses on adolescence and adulthood. It describes the changes of puberty, the responsibilities of marriage and parenthood, and the transitions that occur during each stage of adulthood.

Lesson 1

Adolescence starts with puberty, the period when teens begin to develop certain adult traits. During adolescence, teens strive to develop independence, a sense of identity, and a personal value system.

Lesson 2

Adulthood can be divided into three stages: young, middle, and late adulthood. During young adulthood, many people decide to marry and become parents. Both marriage and parenthood have important responsibilities.

Lesson 3

During middle adulthood, people generally make contributions to others, such as raising a family or contributing to the community. During late adulthood, most people look back and reflect on their lives and accomplishments.

▶ Activating Prior Knowledge

Before students write their answers, have the class brainstorm reasons why participating in the activities in the photo is good for the health of family members in each generation. Make sure students mention reasons relating to all three sides of the health triangle.

Lesson 1
Changes During Adolescence

BIG Idea *Adolescence begins with puberty as a person starts to mature physically, emotionally, and mentally.*

Lesson 2
Adulthood, Marriage, and Parenthood

BIG Idea *During adulthood, individuals may choose to get married and become parents.*

Lesson 3
Health Through the Life Cycle

BIG Idea *Middle and late adulthood are times of contribution and reflection.*

Activating Prior Knowledge

Using Visuals As you look at this photo, identify the different generations in the picture. What are some occasions that might bring generations together? How can maintaining relationships within different generations enhance the lives of each member of a family?

494

Universal Access

Differentiated Learning Glencoe provides teacher support and student materials for all learners in the health classroom.

- Chapter Summaries in English and Spanish are available online at **glencoe.com**.

- *Fast Files* and related worksheets support reluctant readers.

- Universal Access strategies throughout the Teacher Wraparound Edition and *Fast Files* help you present materials for gifted students, at-risk students, physically impaired students, and those with behavior disorders or learning disabilities.

Chapter Launchers

Health in Action

Discuss the **BIG** Ideas

Assign this activity before students read the chapter. Explain that the purpose of the questions is to help them recall what they already know about adolescence and adulthood.

Health eSpotlight
Video Series

Health Through the Life Span

Before Viewing the Video

Ask Students: *What are some physical problems that might occur as you head into late adulthood?* (Sample answers: Heart conditions, joint problems, vision restrictions)

Go Online

Have students go to **glencoe.com** and take the Health Inventory for Chapter 18.

Chapter Launchers

Health in Action

Discuss the **BIG** Ideas

Before beginning this chapter, think about how you would answer these questions:

▸ What sorts of changes occur during adolescence?

▸ How could marriage and parenthood affect your life?

▸ What challenges do adults face in their later years?

Watch the *Health eSpotlight* Video Series

Health Through the Life Span

How might a fitness plan for an older adult be different from one designed for a teen?

Assess Your Health

Go Online

Visit **glencoe.com** and complete the Health Inventory for Chapter 18.

Chapter Skills

Reading Skills
- Reviewing Facts and Vocabulary, pp. 501, 507, 511
- Reading/Writing Practice, p. 517

Vocabulary
- New Vocabulary, pp. 496, 502, 508
- Reviewing Facts and Vocabulary, pp. 501, 507, 511

BIG Idea

People mature into adults during adolescence and continue to go through important changes during adulthood.

Health Skills
- Applying Health Skills, pp. 501, 507, 511
- Hands-On Health, p. 512

Writing Skills
- Writing Critically, pp. 501, 507, 511
- Reading/Writing Practice, p. 517

495

LESSON 1

Changes During Adolescence

1 FOCUS

GUIDE TO READING

BIG Idea Adolescence begins when a person starts to mature physically, emotionally, and mentally. **Ask Students:** *What does it mean to mature?* (Sample answer: To become an adult)

Before You Read

Outline Headings and subheadings of the lesson should comprise the first two levels of students' outlines. Details of the outlines may vary.

Main Idea

Puberty: A Time of Changes
Teens begin moving toward adulthood during puberty. **Ask Students:** *At about what age does puberty begin?* (Sample answer: age 12)

Real Life Issues

Have students read the scenario. **Ask Students:** *Why might it be easier to talk with a person of the same gender about issues relating to puberty?* (Sample answer: A person of the same gender knows what you are going through.)

LESSON 1

GUIDE TO READING

BIG Idea *Adolescence begins with puberty as a person starts to mature physically, emotionally, and mentally.*

Before You Read

Create an Outline. Preview this lesson by scanning the pages. Then, organize the headings and subheadings into an outline. As you read, fill in the outline with important details.

I.
A.
1.
2.
B.
II.

New Vocabulary

▸ adolescence (p. 496)
▸ puberty (p. 496)
▸ cognition (p. 498)

Review Vocabulary

▸ hormones (Ch.3, L.3)

Changes During Adolescence

Real Life Issues ·············

What's Happening to Me? Claire and Seth are fraternal twins who have always been close. Lately, though, Seth doesn't want to spend as much time with Claire. When she asks him about it, Seth says he's going through some physical and emotional changes, and he's unsure what they mean. Claire has been experiencing changes of her own. Even though Seth is her twin, she's uncomfortable talking to him about it.

Writing *Write a letter to a parent or other trusted adult describing the physical and mental/emotional changes you're experiencing. Girls may be more comfortable addressing the letter to another female, and boys may want to address the letter to another male.*

Puberty: A Time of Changes

Main Idea Adolescents begin moving toward adulthood during puberty.

Adolescence, *the period between childhood and adulthood,* is a time of many challenges and changes. Physical growth is one of the most noticeable changes during this period. Children grow, their voices change, and their bodies begin to fill out. After infancy, adolescence is the second fastest period of growth. During adolescence, changes occur in one's mental, emotional, and social life.

The beginning of adolescence is marked by the onset of puberty. **Puberty** is *the time when a person begins to develop certain traits of adults of his or her gender.* Puberty usually begins sometime between the ages of 12 and 18.

Myths & Reality

Myths About Puberty

Myth: The development of pubic hair is the first sign of puberty.

Fact: Pubic hair usually appears before the start of true puberty. It may appear normally in girls as young as 8 and boys as young as 9. Enlargement of the breasts or testes generally indicates that true puberty has begun, and thus, usually occurs later than the appearance of pubic hair.

Myth: Girls have almost finished growing once menstruation begins.

Fact: The average girl grows another 3 inches after menstruation begins. The younger a girl is when she starts menstruating, the more likely she is to grow after menstruation begins.

Hormones are chemical substances produced in glands that help regulate many of the body's functions. Testosterone, the male hormone, and female hormones estrogen and progesterone, create changes that affect teens during puberty.

Physical Changes

One of the most important and **significant** body changes that takes place during puberty is the development of *sex characteristics*. These are the traits related to a person's gender. Primary sex characteristics are directly related to the production of reproductive cells, or *gametes*. The male gametes are *sperm*. The production of sperm by the testes begins at puberty. The female gametes are the *eggs*, or *ova*. At birth, a female's body contains all the eggs she will ever produce. However, the eggs don't mature until puberty begins, with the onset of ovulation. The onset of these changes indicates sexual maturity and the ability to reproduce. You will read more about emotional maturity, which is required to parent a child, in Lesson 2.

Other changes occur during puberty and are associated with secondary sex characteristics. These are summarized in **Figure 18.1**.

Academic Vocabulary

significant *(adjective)*: having meaning

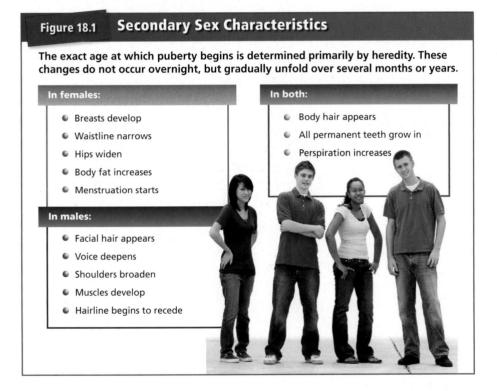

Figure 18.1   Secondary Sex Characteristics

The exact age at which puberty begins is determined primarily by heredity. These changes do not occur overnight, but gradually unfold over several months or years.

In females:
- Breasts develop
- Waistline narrows
- Hips widen
- Body fat increases
- Menstruation starts

In males:
- Facial hair appears
- Voice deepens
- Shoulders broaden
- Muscles develop
- Hairline begins to recede

In both:
- Body hair appears
- All permanent teeth grow in
- Perspiration increases

Lesson 1   Changes During Adolescence   **497**

Teacher to Teacher

Tom Williams, health educator • Fayetteville High School, Fayetteville, AR

The Life Cycle Life changes for most students can be a challenge and creates emotional distress. Guiding students through these changes by creating a table will help them cope during adolescence. Ask students to divide a piece of paper into 6 different sections: Skin, voice, body, hair, teeth, mental, social. Within in each section subdivide into 3 parts and label them (child, adolescent, adult). Have the students write a characteristic for each section corresponding to the particular age group:

Example: Skin

Child 1–12	Adolescent 13–19	Adult 19–29
Clear, soft	oily, acne, hair growth	Clear, shaves facial hair daily

② TEACH

CA Cultural Awareness

Rites of Passage Explain that most cultures hold ceremonies to mark important life transitions including puberty. The Jewish *bar mitzvah* for boys and *bat mitzvah* for girls are examples. Explain that rites of passage give people a ritualized way to cope with stressful life changes and to mark their entry into a new stage of life. Ask a few students to research rites of passage at puberty in other cultures and report back to the class on what they learn. Discuss how the practices might help people cope with the stresses of puberty. **AL**

U Universal Access

Building on Prior Knowledge Help students recall what they learned in Chapter 16 about the male and female reproductive systems. List the following terms on the board and ask students to explain what they mean: *gamete, sperm, testis, egg, ovary, ovulation.* For any terms students cannot recall, have them find and reread relevant passages in Chapter 16. **BL** **EL**

Academic Vocabulary

Significant Explain that the term significant ends in the suffix *-ant*, which is an adjective suffix meaning "being" or "having." Ask the class to think of other adjectives that end in the suffix *-ant*. (Sample answers: important, reluctant, expectant)

R Reading Strategy

Learning from Visuals Guide students in using **Figure 18.2** to learn about the brain. Ask such questions as: Which part of the brain is responsible for planning? (frontal cortex) What does this part do? (It controls planning, strategizing, and reasoning.) Which part of the brain controls emotions? (amygdala) Where is this part located? (At the base of the brain) `BL` `EL`

C Critical Thinking

Explaining After students read about the amygdala in **Figure 18.2**, ask them to explain how reacting emotionally instead of analytically might affect decision making. (Sample answer: You might make decisions without thinking through the consequences of the different options.) Explain that this is one reason why young teens are usually not allowed to make serious decisions on their own. `OL`

FITNESS ZONE

This is a great activity for finger dexterity:

- Have students stand beside their desks.
- Give each student a sheet of paper.
- Have them ball the piece of paper using the fingers of one hand only.
- Students must then see if they can un-crunch the paper, opening it, using only the fingers of that hand.
- Have them try with their other hand.

FITNESS ZONE

I make hundreds of choices every day. From the time I get up until I go to sleep, I choose what to wear, what to eat, and who to hang out with. And, I see how the choices I make can have either a positive or negative impact. That's why one of my easiest choices is working out and eating healthy foods. After all, I deserve the best. For more fitness tips, visit the Online Fitness Zone at glencoe.com.

In any group of teens, there is a variety of body sizes and shapes. Growth rates vary from person to person. Each teen goes through puberty at his or her own pace. There is no real timetable for the physical changes that a teen experiences. Some teens develop the physical characteristics of adults before their friends do. You may experience changes sooner or later than your classmates do, and you may feel uncomfortable about these changes. Just remember that every teen experiences these changes, that they are normal, and that they will resolve themselves as time passes.

Mental and Emotional Changes

As your body goes through dramatic changes during adolescence, your brain is changing as well. By age six, a child's brain is about 95 percent of the size it will be when the child is an adult. The cerebrum, though, continues to develop during adolescence, increasing memory and cognition. **Cognition** is *the ability to reason and think out abstract solutions.* A child sees only a limited number of solutions to a problem.

Figure 18.2   Brain Development in Teens

Over the past 25 years, neuroscientists have discovered a great deal about the human brain. Recent imaging techniques have enabled scientists to examine the brains of people throughout their life spans—including the teen years.

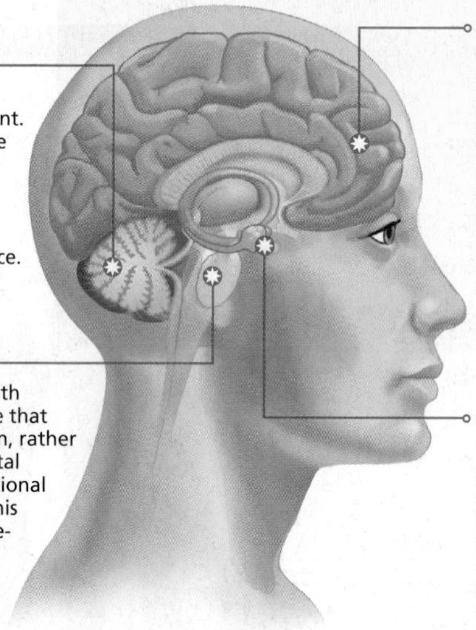

Cerebellum
The cerebellum coordinates muscles and physical movement. Scientists have found evidence that it is also involved in the coordination of thinking processes. The cerebellum undergoes dramatic growth and change during adolescence.

Amygdala
The amygdala is associated with emotion. New studies indicate that teens use this part of the brain, rather than the more analytical frontal cortex that adults use in emotional responses. Scientists believe this might explain why teens sometimes react so emotionally.

Frontal Cortex
The frontal cortex is responsible for planning, strategizing, impulse control, and reasoning. The area undergoes a growth spurt when a child is 11 to 12 years of age. This is followed by a growth period, during which new nerve connections form.

Corpus Callosum
The corpus callosum connects the two sides of the brain. It is thought to be involved in creativity and problem solving. Research suggests that it grows and changes significantly during adolescence.

R

C

498   Chapter 18   The Life Cycle Continues

Teens Want to Know

Am I Developing Normally? Both early- and late-developing teens may worry whether their development is normal. They may be reassured to know that there is great variation in the timing of the events of puberty. For example, for girls, it is normal to begin menstruating as early as age 10 or as late as age 15. For boys, it is normal for the penis to start growing at any age between 10 and 15 years. Teens who fall outside of these normal ranges should be checked by a doctor.

Adolescents become increasingly capable of solving problems in more complex ways. During this stage you will learn to

- anticipate the consequences of a particular action.
- think logically.
- understand different points of view.

W Adolescence is a time of emotional change as well. You may begin to look outward to try to understand yourself and your place in society. Most adolescents begin to search for meaning, personal values, and a sense of self. These new mental and emotional developments can be tied to physical changes and growth in adolescent brains. The brain development of teens is explored in **Figure 18.2**.

Social Changes

HS You may notice that you are also experiencing social changes during adolescence. Friends become a major part of a teen's social experience. As you explore new interests through a variety of classes and extracurricular activities, you'll make new friends and meet people from many cultural and social backgrounds. This is a time when you'll begin to appreciate how ethnic and cultural diversity can enrich your life. Likewise, your peers may challenge what you believe in and what you think is right and wrong. You can practice responsible decision making skills when a friend asks you to do something that goes against your own personal values. In general, strong friendships begin when people realize they share similar goals, experiences, and values.

Accomplishments in Adolescence

Main Idea Adolescents will develop independence, find their identity, and establish their personal values.

You are familiar now with some of the physical, mental, emotional, and social changes that teens experience. These changes are not experienced separately. A teen may be dealing with several issues at the same time. This makes adolescence a wonderful, but often difficult, time of life.

READING CHECK

Describe How does a person change emotionally during adolescence?

■ **Figure 18.3** Friends from different cultural backgrounds share their traditions and cultural interests. *What traditions or interests would you share?*

Academic Integration

Science Technological advances, including the development of CT, PET, and MRI imaging technologies, have greatly increased scientific knowledge, including knowledge of the brain and how it changes during adolescence. Assign a different student to research each of these technologies. Ask them to learn how the technologies work, their pros and cons, and what they have revealed about the developing brain. Have students report their findings to the class.

W **Writing Support**

Descriptive Writing On the board, write "I am ___." Ask students to privately fill in the blank with the first few words or phrases that come to mind (e.g., *I am 16 years old; I am a girl; I am smart.*) Encourage students to reflect on what they wrote. Based on the words or phrases they used, how would they describe their "self"? **OL**

HS **Health Skills Practice**

Decision Making Relate the cognitive skills that develop during adolescence to the steps of the decision-making process. Then ask small groups of students to apply the decision-making process to a hypothetical decision many teens might make, such as whether to date someone older. Afterward, ask group members to explain how using the skills helped them make a good decision. **OL**

Caption Answer

Figure 18.3 Answers will vary but may include traditions or interests that are related to the student's heritage.

Main Idea

Accomplishments in Adolescence During adolescence, teens develop independence, self-identity, and personal values. **Ask Students:** *Why is it important to accomplish these tasks before adulthood?* (Sample answer: Accomplishing the tasks will help you handle adult responsibilities.)

Go Online

Visit glencoe.com and complete the Student Web Activity on the education and training you will need to prepare for jobs as you work toward becoming a self-sufficient adult.

W Writing Support

Creative Writing Ask students to write poems or rap lyrics about teen friendships. Urge students to be creative and expressive. Call on a few volunteers to share what they wrote with the class. Afterward, ask students to deduce from the poems or lyrics some of the roles that friends play in adolescent social development. (Sample answers: friends support your values; they help you deal with problems.) **OL**

HS Health Skills Practice

Practicing Healthful Behaviors Point out that meeting people from diverse backgrounds enriches one's life. Challenge students to think of ways they could meet a greater diversity of people. (Sample answers: Join a new club; find a pen pal in another country) **OL**

Go Online

Have students visit **glencoe.com** and complete the Student Web Activity on the education and training needed to prepare for jobs.

Caption Answer

Figure 18.4 Answers will vary. Some students may not yet have vocational goals.

During adolescence, you will be maturing, and you will accomplish a series of specific developmental tasks that you will find helpful as you make the transition from adolescence to adulthood. Some of these tasks include achieving emotional independence from your parents, developing an identity, and adopting a system of personal values. You will begin to establish career goals, and you will find that practicing healthful, responsible behaviors will help you achieve these goals.

As you recognize the adjustments you are going through, evaluate your progress by asking yourself the questions at the end of each developmental task description below. **W**

- **Emotional and psychological independence.** During adolescence, you may find yourself moving back and forth between wanting independence and wanting the security of your family. Teens who have ongoing, open communication with their parents or guardian have the advantage of seeking advice and feedback about the decisions they need to make. A parent can help teens learn problem-solving skills. When parents or guardians discuss and explain situations, rules, and reasons in the decision-making process, teens learn from their modeling. Your family's support and guidance can help you become more emotionally and socially independent. During this time, you will develop confidence and build your self-esteem as you become more independent. *In what ways are you a different person than you were two years ago?* **HS**

■ **Figure 18.4** Teens begin to make decisions about their future and goals at this stage of their lives. *What are your vocational goals?*

Promoting School Wellness

Role of Schools in Teen Social Development When the social changes of adolescence are coupled with a hostile social environment or lack of social skills, teens may develop social isolation, anxiety, or depression. Schools have a responsibility to create a warm and supportive social environment by promoting inclusion of, and respect for, all students. For example, schools can discourage cliques and adopt a no-tolerance policy for hate messages and bullying. Schools also have a responsibility to help students develop the social skills they need to form healthy relationships and to safely and effectively deal with social aggression. For example, schools can provide students with training in interpersonal-communication, problem-solving, and conflict-resolution skills.

- **Personal value system.** Parents and guardians provide a set of rules for appropriate and inappropriate behavior for younger children. This helped lay the foundation for your own values. You will now begin to assess your values when they differ from the values expressed by your peers and others. *Have you begun to establish personal beliefs and values that enhance your health and well-being? Are you acting in ways that support those standards?*

- **Vocational goals.** The teen years are a time to begin identifying your vocational goals for the future. As you explore the possibilities open to you and develop new interests, you may discover that some of these interests can lead to a career. *Have you set long-term goals and identified steps to reach those goals?*

- **Control over behaviors.** Adolescents make decisions every day about whether to participate in risky behaviors that may harm their health. Considering your values and your short-term and long-term goals will give you a firm basis for making healthful decisions and avoiding risky situations. *Identify two recent events that challenged you to show emotional maturity and avoid a risky behavior.*

 READING CHECK

Identify What are your vocational goals for the future?

 LESSON 1 **ASSESSMENT**

After You Read

Reviewing Facts and Vocabulary

1. Define the terms *adolescence* and *puberty.*

2. What are the reproductive cells of females called? What are those of males called?

3. What are some secondary sex characteristics of males that develop during puberty?

Thinking Critically

4. **Infer.** How does the fact that the cerebrum is still developing during adolescence explain some teenage behavior?

5. **Explain.** During which time frame does adolescent development typically occur?

Applying Health Skills

6. **Refusal Skills.** At times, your peers might encourage you to do something that you know is wrong. Write a scenario describing how you would handle such a situation.

Writing Critically

7. **Persuasive.** Your friend is being asked to participate in an activity that you think is unsafe and unwise. Write a short letter suggesting why you think this is a mistake and how to get out of it. Be encouraging and supportive, but suggest alternatives.

G‍o Online

Visit glencoe.com and complete the Interactive Study Guide for this lesson.

Lesson 1 Changes During Adolescence **501**

 CHAPTER 18

LESSON 1

 READING CHECK

Answer Answers will vary but may include college, vocational school, military training, or other options.

❸ ASSESS/ CLOSE

Assessment Resources

📁 *FAST FILE* ACTIVITIES
Lesson 1 Quiz

💿 *ExamView*
Assessment Suite CD-ROM

Visit glencoe.com **for:**
Online Quizzes
Online Learning Center

Progress Monitoring

Reteaching
Have students turn topic sentences in the lesson into true/false questions. Then ask them to exchange questions with a classmate and try to answer each other's questions.

Enrichment
Ask students to learn more about the role of hormones in puberty in males and females. Give them a chance to share what they learn with the class.

G‍o Online

Have students visit glencoe.com and complete the Interactive Study Guide for this lesson.

LESSON 1 ASSESSMENT ANSWERS

1. *Adolescence* is the period between childhood and adulthood. *Puberty* is the time when a person begins to develop certain traits of adults of his or her gender.

2. Female reproductive cells are called eggs. Male reproductive cells are called sperm.

3. Males: facial hair, deep voice, broad shoulders, muscle development, receding hairline; females: breasts, narrow waistline, wider hips, increased body fat, menstruation

4. Reasoning is controlled by the cerebrum, so adolescents may react emotionally rather than analytically.

5. Puberty usually begins between the ages of 12 and 18, but each teen develops at his or her own rate.

6. Scenarios will vary.

7. Letters will vary.

LESSON 2

Adulthood, Marriage, and Parenthood

① FOCUS

GUIDE TO READING

BIG Idea Adults may choose to marry and become parents. **Ask Students:** *Why should people wait until they are adults to marry?* (Sample answer: Marrying is a big decision that most younger people are not ready to make.)

Before You Read

K-W-L Chart Students' charts will vary. Remind students to fill in the third column as they read.

Main Idea

Maturing Physically and Emotionally Adulthood begins when a person is physically and emotionally mature. **Ask Students:** *What is a sign of physical maturity?* (Sample answer: You stop growing.)

Real Life Issues

Have students read the scenario. **Ask Students:** *What is needed to make a marriage work?* (Sample answers: Responsibility, mutual respect, commitment, hard work) Call on a few volunteers to read their letters to the class.

LESSON 2

GUIDE TO READING

BIG Idea *During adulthood, individuals may choose to get married and become parents.*

Before You Read

Create a K-W-L Chart. Make a three-column chart like the one below. In the first column, write what you **k**now about parenthood. In the second column, write what you **w**ant to know about this topic. As you read, fill in the third column describing what you have **l**earned.

K	W	L

New Vocabulary

▶ physical maturity (p. 502)
▶ emotional maturity (p. 502)
▶ commitment (p. 504)
▶ adoption (p. 505)
▶ self-directed (p. 506)
▶ unconditional love (p. 507)

Review Vocabulary

▶ extended family (Ch.7, L.1)

Adulthood, Marriage, and Parenthood

Real Life Issues

Wedding Bells? Lily's older sister, Maya, will graduate from college at the end of the year. Maya confides in Lily that she and her boyfriend are thinking about getting married as soon as they graduate. Lily likes Maya's boyfriend, but has learned in her health class that marriage is a very big step.

Writing *Write a letter from Lily to Maya, explaining what she thinks marriage involves and why it's an important step that requires a lot of thought.*

Maturing Physically and Emotionally

Main Idea Adulthood is reached when both physical maturity and emotional maturity are achieved.

Most people reach **physical maturity**, *the state at which the physical body and all its organs are fully developed,* in late adolescence or their early twenties. Being physically mature does not make you an adult, however. To be an adult, you need to develop emotionally as well.

Emotional maturity is *the state at which the mental and emotional capabilities of an individual are fully developed.* Emotionally healthy individuals have positive values and goals. They are able to give and receive love, have the ability to face reality and deal with it, and have the capacity to learn from life experiences. Relationships with peers, family, and friends can have a positive effect on a person's physical and emotional health.

More About...

Erikson's Stages of Adulthood The three stages of adulthood described in the text are part of psychologist Erik Erikson's theory of psychosocial development. Erikson was influenced by the "father" of psychology, Sigmund Freud. He revised Freud's ideas regarding psychological influences on personality in early childhood to include social, historical, and cultural influences. He also extended the analysis to cover the entire lifespan, which he divided into eight stages of development. Each stage is characterized by a different conflict that individuals must resolve as they pass through the stage.

Stages of Adulthood

Main Idea Three major stages make up the adult years.

The adult years are made of three different stages. Each stage can be characterized by its own accomplishments and is associated with a goal that involves a person's relationship with other people.

The three stages are as follows:

- **Young adulthood.** This stage lasts from 19 to 40 years of age. The goal of this stage is to develop intimacy. A person in young adulthood tries to develop close personal relationships. Many people will decide to get married and start a family during this stage.

- **Middle adulthood.** This stage occurs between the ages of 40 and 65. The goal here is to develop a sense of having contributed to society. A person in this stage looks outside themselves and cares for others through such activities as grandparenting or volunteering.

- **Late adulthood.** This stage lasts from the age of 65 to death. The goal of a person in this stage is to feel satisfied with his life. A person in this stage tries to understand the meaning and purpose of her life.

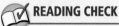

READING CHECK

Infer What positive events can happen during middle adulthood?

■ **Figure 18.5** Your extended family may include aunts, uncles, and grandparents, as well as your parents and brothers or sisters. *Which members of your extended family do you enjoy a close relationship with?*

② TEACH

Main Idea

Stages of Adulthood Adulthood can be divided into three major stages. **Ask Students:** *How do adults change as they get older?* (Sample answers: Their interests and roles change; they age physically.)

R Reading Strategy

Explaining Have students explain how middle adulthood differs from young adulthood and late adulthood. Encourage students to use a table to write down the differences. Other students may want to do a compare and contrast essay. **OL**

READING CHECK

Answer Contributing to society, caring for others

Caption Answer

Figures 18.5 Answers may vary but should include extended family members, such as grandparents, aunts, and uncles.

English Language Coach

Using Noun Suffixes Explain that adjectives can become nouns with the addition of a noun suffix. For example, the adjective mature can become a noun with the suffix *-ity*, which means "quality," or the suffix *-ation*, which means "process." Ask students to add these suffixes to *mature* and define the nouns they form. (*Maturity*, "quality of being mature;" *maturation*, "process of becoming mature")

503

Marriage

Main Idea Marriage is a commitment to share your life with another person.

Most people marry because they fall in love and are ready to enter into a lasting, intimate relationship. Married couples share togetherness and support each other in hard times as well as in good times.

Deciding to Marry

There are differences between a dating relationship and marriage. When a couple agree that marriage may be in their future, their relationship becomes more serious, and they make a deeper **commitment**—*a promise or a pledge*—to each other. They also consider the long-term consequences when making decisions. In this way, the couple show they understand the relationship between mental, emotional, and physical health. If one partner has any doubts or questions about the other partner's reasons for marrying, these questions should be explored and resolved before the marriage actually takes place.

Successful Marriages

The decision to make the commitment to marry is only the first step in a successful marriage. *Marital adjustment*—how well a person adjusts to marriage and to a spouse—depends on the following factors:

- **Communication.** Couples need to be able to share their feelings and express their needs and concerns to each other. Demonstrating communication skills helps couples build and maintain a healthy marriage relationship.
- **Emotional maturity.** Emotionally healthy people try to understand their partner's needs and are willing to compromise. They don't always think of themselves first; they consider what is best for the relationship as a whole.
- **Values and interests.** When couples share similar attitudes about the importance of good health, spirituality, ethical standards, morality, family, and friendships, they spend more time together, which strengthens a marriage.

Resolving Conflict in Marriage

Conflict arises occasionally, even in the strongest marriages, because people can't completely agree on everything all the time. Learning how to get along involves how to recognize causes of these conflicts and finding ways to resolve them so the relationship can be strengthened.

■ **Figure 18.6** Financial concerns are a common problem that married couples face. *What can this couple do to make sure that finances do not become a problem in their relationship?*

Skills for the 21st Century

Parenting Skills In earlier generations, young adults typically lived in extended families, so they could usually turn to older family members when they had questions about parenting. In the 21st century, extended families are uncommon, and many new parents must find other ways to learn parenting skills. One popular option is to take parenting classes. Parenting classes are offered online, at colleges, in many communities, and in some workplaces. Have students find and learn about parenting classes that are available to people in their community. Ask them which class they would choose and why.

Issues that can cause problems in marriages include the following:

- Differences in spending and saving habits
- Conflicting loyalties involving family and friends
- Lack of communication
- Lack of intimacy
- Jealousy, infidelity, or lack of attention
- Decisions about having children and arranging child care
- Abusive tendencies or attitudes

In a successful marriage, partners respect, trust, and care for each other. **Conflicts** are resolved fairly without damaging the self-esteem of either partner. The development of good communication and conflict-resolution skills can help reduce the impact of conflict on a marriage. Sometimes couples need counseling to resolve marital conflict.

Teen Marriage

Some people begin talking about marriage at a young age. In most states it's illegal for a couple to marry before the age of 18 without parental permission. As well as meeting legal requirements, marriage is a step that requires emotional maturity. Emotional maturity enables partners to deal with the problems and decisions of marriage. Most teens are still struggling to figure out their own identity and set goals for the future. It is unlikely that they have had a chance to determine their life path, or what they want in a marriage partner. That's one reason about 60 percent of marriages involving teens end in divorce. Statistics show a high probability that a teen marriage will end in the first few years.

Teens who do get married may soon begin to realize that they have increased responsibilities that interfere with their personal freedoms and their educational or career goals. They may find they do not have enough life experience to make this important and lasting decision. Financial pressures can add stress to the marriage. Marriage difficulties may arise as the newness wears off and teens recognize the responsibilities required to make a successful marriage.

Parenthood

Main Idea Parenting demands many added responsibilities.

Many married couples decide to start a family. Some couples choose to adopt a child. **Adoption** is *the legal process of taking a child of other parents as one's own.* Couples may choose to raise foster children by becoming a legal guardian.

Academic Vocabulary

conflict *(noun):* a competitive or opposing act, or incompatibles

READING CHECK

Identify What are three issues that often cause problems in a marriage?

FITNESS ZONE

Every summer I visit my grandparents. They have a habit of having a mid-afternoon snack. My grandmother calls it "sweets for my sweetie." Their afternoon snack is always something healthy. Gran may cut up an apple and drizzle some chocolate or butterscotch syrup over it. It tastes just like a candied apple, and my grandparents are both in good shape, so I guess it works. For more fitness tips, visit the Online Fitness Zone at at **glencoe.com**.

Academic Vocabulary

Conflict Challenge students to think of synonyms for conflict as the word is used on this page. (Sample answers: Disagreement, argument, fight) Then ask students to identify typical causes of marital conflicts. (Sample answers: Money, jealousy, children)

READING CHECK

Answer *Any three:* Differences in spending and saving habits, conflicting loyalties involving family and friends, lack of communication, lack of intimacy, jealousy, infidelity, lack of attention, decisions about children, abusive tendencies or attitudes

Main Idea

Parenthood People who decide to become parents must accept many new responsibilities. **Ask Students:** *What responsibilities do parents have?* (Sample answer: Parents are responsible for their children's food, shelter, clothing, medical care, and education.)

Lesson 2 Adulthood, Marriage, and Parenthood **505**

Cooperative Learning

Factors That Promote Marital Success
Divide the class into groups of three. Assign each student in a group one of the three factors that help make a successful marriage: communication, emotional maturity, shared values and interests. Ask students to think of an example that demonstrates how their assigned factor contributes to marital success. Then have students in each group share and discuss their examples.

VIDEO BusinessWeek
HEALTH NEWS

After students have watched the video, *Childproofing Your Home,* ask students to choose a partner and discuss with their partner the benefits of childproofing a home. Have partners identify common dangers in the home and think of ways to reduce or eliminate them. Encourage pairs to share their ideas with other students.

 Reading Strategy

Inferring Ask students to use information in the text to write a dialogue between a parent and a teen. The parent is providing guidance for the teen. For example, the teen has just decided to not rejoin the swim team, but the parent gently encourages him or her against that. The parent may advise that doing extracurricular activities helps with the teen's social development. **BL**

C Critical Thinking

Giving Examples Challenge the class to think of examples that show how setting limits on children helps them become self-directed. (Sample answer: If parents limit how much junk food their children eat, the children will learn how to choose healthful foods when they have to make eating decisions on their own.) **OL**

506

■ **Figure 18.7** Setting limits and curfews is one of the responsibilities of being a parent. *What limits do your parents or guardians place on you?*

VIDEO BusinessWeek
HEALTH NEWS

Childproofing Your Home

Analyze. Go to glencoe.com and watch the video *Childproofing Your Home.* With a partner, discuss the benefits of childproofing a home where small children live. Think about common dangers in the home and what steps can be taken to reduce the risk of accidents.

Most parents find raising a child to be both challenging and rewarding, and they take great joy in loving and caring for their children. Prospective parents need to understand the changes in lifestyle and responsibility that will take place before and after the birth of their baby. These responsibilities will continue for many years after birth. Parents must provide protection, food, clothing, shelter, education, and medical care. Parenting also involves providing guidance, instilling values, setting limits, and giving unconditional love.

Providing Guidance

Involved parents will teach children that each individual is responsible for one's own successes and failures. Parents should encourage children and help them develop a sense of pride in their accomplishments. Parents also need to guide and protect their children while teaching them to make their own decisions. Watching children learn to get along with others and solve their own problems is a satisfying experience for a parent. The role of the extended family—grandparents and other family members—is important in promoting a healthy family. When children see family members interacting in a mature, loving, and caring manner, they are more likely to grow up to be healthy and productive.

Instilling Values

Parents with a strong value system may pass these aspects of life on to their children. Children develop a set of *values* as they grow. Values make up the system of beliefs and standards of conduct that people find important and that will guide the way they live. Values help children develop strong character and the ability to resist negative influences they may encounter. Teaching positive values, ethics, and respect for cultural diversity can help children grow to become happy, productive, and mature adults.

Setting Limits

When children learn limits, they become **self-directed**, or *able to make correct decisions about behavior when adults are not present to enforce rules.* The limits parents set for their children during childhood are very different, but just as important, as the limits they set for adolescence. Limits on bedtime, eating habits, and television exposure will change as children get older. Limits on adolescents can include curfews and use of the family car. It is a parent's responsibility to set limits. During the teen years, children will be able to handle more responsibility.

Promoting School Wellness

Counseling and Health Services The school nurse and guidance counselor are excellent resources for students who have questions about their physical, emotional, or social development during adolescence. Invite the school nurse or guidance counselor to speak to the class about the health services offered at the school. Be certain that students know the procedure for making an appointment with the nurse or guidance counselor if they have questions they would like to discuss.

Giving Unconditional Love

Another responsibility of parenthood is providing children with **unconditional love**, *love without limitations or quantifications.* Parents need to show their children love at all times. Receiving unconditional love helps a child thrive by meeting a child's basic needs. Meeting basic needs is part of Maslow's hierarchy of needs, which you learned about in Chapter 3. Before having children, couples should carefully examine the lifelong responsibilities and requirements of being a parent.

Teen Parenting

Becoming a parent is challenging and difficult at any stage in life. This is particularly true when the parents are teenagers. Teens who are pregnant may choose to put their baby up for adoption or raise the child themselves. Consequences of teen parenthood are many, but may include:

- Financial difficulties
- Restrictions on educational and career plans
- Emotional stress
- Limitations on social and personal life

Although parenthood is very rewarding, it also requires maturity. Teens need to consider the responsibilities of parenthood as they make decisions that could alter their lives.

■ **Figure 18.8** Teen parents may feel they are missing part of their own childhood. *What other stresses may impact teen parents?*

 READING CHECK

Explain How do limits change as a child grows older?

 **LESSON 2** **ASSESSMENT**

After You Read

Reviewing Facts and Vocabulary

1. Distinguish between *physical maturity* and *emotional maturity*.
2. How do the goals of young adulthood differ from the goals of middle adulthood?
3. Which factors determine how well a person will adjust to marriage?

Thinking Critically

4. **Predict.** What are some factors that may cause conflict, even in a good marriage?
5. **Identify.** What is a parent giving a child by offering unconditional love?

Applying Health Skills

6. **Accessing Information.** Use print or online resources to research the legal rights and responsibilities of teen parents. Compare and contrast these rights with the rights of adult parents.

Writing Critically

7. **Expository.** Write a short essay explaining the disadvantages of marrying during the teen years.

 Online

Visit glencoe.com and complete the Interactive Study Guide for this lesson.

Caption Answer

Figure 18.8 Answers might include financial difficulties, restrictions on educational and career plans, and emotional stresses.

③ ASSESS/ CLOSE

Assessment Resources

📁 *FAST FILE* ACTIVITIES
Lesson 2 Quiz

💿 *ExamView Assessment Suite* CD-ROM

Visit glencoe.com **for:**
Online Quizzes
Online Learning Center

Progress Monitoring

Reteaching
Ask students to use each of the new vocabulary terms in a sentence that shows the meaning of the term. Have students compare and discuss their sentences with a classmate.

Enrichment
Ask students to create a poster illustrating the three stages of adulthood. Posters should show young, middle, and late adults participating in activities that are typical of their stage of life.

Online

Have students visit **glencoe.com** and complete the Interactive Study Guide for this lesson.

LESSON 2 ASSESSMENT ANSWERS

1. *Physical maturity*: state at which the physical body and organs are fully developed; *emotional maturity*: state at which mental and emotional capabilities are fully developed
2. Goals of young adulthood focus on developing intimacy. Goals of middle age focus on making a contribution to society.
3. Communication skills, emotional maturity, and shared values and interests
4. Answers may vary but might include money, conflicting loyalties, lack of communication or intimacy, jealousy, infidelity, inattention, children, or abuse.
5. Love without limitations, which helps a child thrive by meeting the child's basic needs
6. Teen parents have the same legal rights and responsibilities as adult parents.
7. Essays will vary.

Health Through the Life Cycle

1 FOCUS

GUIDE TO READING

BIG Idea Middle adulthood is a time of making contributions, and late adulthood is a time of reflection. **Ask Students:** *What contributions do people generally make during middle adulthood?* (Sample answers: Performing a job, supporting a family, paying taxes)

Before You Read

Table Students' tables may vary but should correctly identify milestones of middle and late adulthood.

Main Idea

Middle Adulthood Middle adulthood is a time of many changes. **Ask Students:** *What are some changes that might occur in the lives of people in their forties and fifties?* (Sample answer: Children growing up and leaving home)

Real Life Issues

Have students read the scenario. **Ask Students:** *How can writing down feelings help you deal with them?* (Sample answer: It can help you identify and acknowledge the feelings and provide an outlet for expressing them.)

GUIDE TO READING

BIG Idea *Middle and late adulthood are times of contribution and reflection.*

Before You Read

Create a Table. Make a two-column table. Label the first column "Middle Adulthood." Label the second column "Late Adulthood." Fill in the major milestones for each stage as you read the lesson.

Middle Adulthood	Late Adulthood

New Vocabulary

- transitions (p. 508)
- empty-nest syndrome (p. 510)
- integrity (p. 510)

Health Through the Life Cycle

Real Life Issues

Where Did They Go? Anna's grandmother lives less than a mile from Anna and her family. Anna visits her grandmother twice a week on her way home from school. Her grandmother lives alone, and Anna worries that she is lonely. Anna's grandfather died two years ago. Anna has learned in school that writing down your feelings is a good way to begin dealing with them.

Writing *Write a scenario between Anna and her grandmother in which Anna encourages her grandmother to write about her feelings.*

Middle Adulthood

Main Idea Many changes occur during middle adulthood.

Middle adulthood is the stage of development that spans from age 40 to age 65. These years are full of **transitions**, *critical changes that occur at all stages of life*. These changes can include family and individual accomplishments, including children graduating from college, the arrival of the first grandchild, achievement of a satisfying career goal, or recognition of an individual's contribution to the community. These accomplishments can enhance a person's physical, mental, emotional, and social health throughout adulthood.

Health Concerns

Each phase of adulthood has its own unique concerns that affect one's health and well-being. Scientific research continues to bring new discoveries that are advancing disease prevention and improving nutrition for better health.

Home and Community

Community Services for Middle Adults People in middle adulthood may have special challenges, such as caring for aging parents, facing an empty nest, or paying for their children's college education. Services are available in many communities to help people deal with these and other challenges of middle adulthood, ranging from support groups to financial aid. Ask students to learn about any relevant services in their community and share the information with middle-aged family members. Students should encourage family members to make use of the services if they need them or to share the information with other adults who do.

These advances have made a significant difference in the lives of older adults. In general, people nowadays are experiencing a healthier older adulthood. Older adults, however, still have to be aware of the conditions that result from aging.

- **Eyesight** changes with age. The eyes of an adult in this stage may have difficulty bringing images into focus.
- **Hearing** may decrease, particularly if a person was exposed to loud sounds constantly throughout one's life.
- **Muscles and joints** may be affected by arthritis. Arthritis affects nearly half the people over the age of 65.
- **Bones** may become brittle and more likely to break. Osteoporosis most commonly affects older women, but anyone can get osteoporosis.
- **Teeth and gums** can become decayed and diseased without proper care.
- **Heart disease** may occur due to heredity or lifestyle factors, such as a lifetime of too little physical exercise and a diet too high in saturated fat.
- **Cancer** may occur, so it's recommended that adults in this stage get regular screenings.

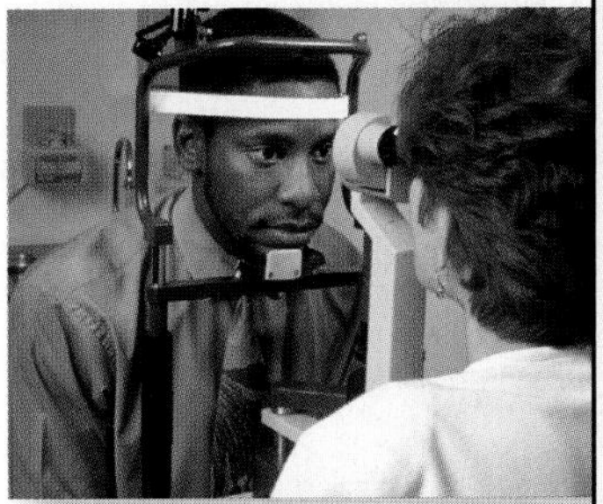

Physical Transitions

As you have learned, physical change doesn't stop when adolescence ends; it continues throughout the life cycle. The rate of change may slow down, however. People in middle adulthood experience physical changes as their bodies begin to age. Females enter *menopause,* or the end of ovulation and menstruation, between the ages of 45 and 55. This means that a woman can no longer become pregnant.

Research indicates that most people who practiced healthful behaviors as teens and young adults, such as weight management, nutritious eating, and regular physical activity, experience better physical health for a longer period. Adults who have developed lifelong healthful habits and continue to be active stay healthy by eating low-fat, high-fiber diets and avoiding tobacco, alcohol, and other drugs. Strength training has been proven to offer significant benefits to most adults. Benefits include increasing muscle mass, preserving bone density, and protecting major joints from injury.

Mental Transitions

Just as physical exercise strengthens the body, mental activities strengthen the brain. Solving puzzles, reading, and playing strategy games provide mental stimulation. An adult who exercises his or her brain remains mentally active. Learning should be a lifelong pursuit. At midlife, many adults begin new careers, return to school, and learn new hobbies.

■ **Figure 18.9** Routine eye exams are part of staying healthy at any age. *How are the lives of middle adults changing?*

Go Online

Explore **glencoe.com** and complete the Student Web Activity on Alzheimer's disease, affecting 4.5 million Americans.

② TEACH

Caption Answer

Figure 18.9 Middle adults are generally healthier than they used to be.

AL Active Learning

Exercise During Middle Adulthood Have students research health benefits of exercise during middle adulthood (e.g., reduced body fat, lowered risk of Alzheimer's disease). Then have them create an exercise plan to fit the schedule and physical ability level of a middle-aged person they know, such as a parent. **AL**

U Universal Access

Using Examples Ask students to think of people they know—such as family members, neighbors, or school personnel—who are either about age 40 or about age 65. Then ask students to think of ways the older people differ from the younger people. (Sample answers: The older people have wrinkles and gray hair; the older people are no longer working.) **BL**

Go Online

Have students explore **glencoe.com** and complete the Student Web Activity on Alzheimer's disease.

Reading Strategy

Creating Graphic Organizers Have pairs of students create a concept map to organize information in the text on the transitions of middle adulthood. Organizers should show the types of transitions that middle adults experience, including physical, mental, emotional, and social transitions. Tell students to add examples of each type of transition to their graphic organizer.

 **Cultural Awareness**

Extended Families People in some cultures are more likely to live in extended families, in which parents live not only with their children but also with other close relatives, such as their own parents and siblings. Ask students how living in an extended family might make it easier to deal with the social transitions of middle adulthood. **OL** **EL**

VIDEO BusinessWeek **HEALTH NEWS**

After students have watched the video, *Memory Loss and Technology,* have them choose partners and discuss with their partners whether memory pills would be a valuable medical contribution. Ask partners to think of examples of how better memory might affect the lives of older adults. Give partners a chance to share their ideas with the class.

Main Idea

Late Adulthood During late adulthood, people look back on their lives and accomplishments.
Ask Students: *What is an achievement you would like to look back on during late adulthood?*
(Sample answers: Graduating from college, having grandchildren, serving in the military)

■ **Figure 18.10** Middle adults still play an active role in the workplace. *Why is it healthful to make learning a lifelong pursuit?*

 **READING CHECK**

Explain How can skills developed in adolescence help you in middle adulthood?

 BusinessWeek **HEALTH NEWS**

Memory Loss and Technology

Analyze. Go to glencoe.com and watch the video *Memory Loss and Technology.* Medical advancements have changed the length and quality of life. With a partner, decide whether you think memory pills would be a useful medical contribution. Support your ideas with examples.

The use of computers gives older adults opportunities to broaden their access to information. People reach middle adulthood with a great deal of knowledge and experience, which they can use to pursue new interests.

Emotional Transitions

The emotional transitions people experience during middle adulthood can be similar to those experienced during puberty. By this time in life, a person may take pride in personal accomplishments. A middle adult may also experience some disappointments. Adults at this stage are said to be having a midlife crisis when they have questions and concerns about whether they have met their goals, feel loved and valued, and have made a positive difference in the lives of others.

Social Transitions

Most social transitions during middle adulthood focus on family. Often people are faced with the death of a parent or need to adjust to children growing up and leaving home. *The feelings of sadness or loneliness that accompany seeing children leave home and enter adulthood* are called **empty-nest syndrome**. Those who maintain healthy relationships with family and friends have less difficulty adjusting to these changes. For many, this is a time to apply their talents and life experiences to community programs. They may pursue new interests and make new friends. Developing good social skills earlier in life can help ease these transitions.

Late Adulthood

Main Idea People in late adulthood may reflect on their lives and accomplishments.

Late adulthood begins after age 65. One of the goals at this stage is to look back with satisfaction and a sense of fulfillment. Older adults may review the events of their lives and their achievements. If they have lived their lives with **integrity**, meaning they have made decisions with *a firm adherence to a moral code,* then they may feel fulfilled. A person who considers family a high priority may have succeeded in a career while providing for the family. People who remain committed to a system of values throughout life will have a sense of satisfaction. Many older adults are able to look back without regret and feel proud of their accomplishments.

CA

Health Literacy

Obesity and Life Expectancy For the first time in American history, current cohorts of teens and young adults are expected to have a shorter late adulthood than their parents. The reason? The rising epidemic of obesity and its associated health problems are lowering the life expectancy of today's young people. They are likely to die at earlier ages than their parents from diabetes, cardiovascular diseases, and other obesity-related conditions. However, the current trend can be halted if teens and young adults take steps now to adopt a healthful lifestyle and keep their weight under control.

Public Health Policies and Programs

The Social Security system, created in 1935, provides benefits to older adults as well as to people with disabilities. To assist with health care needs, the government offers Medicare to those over 65 and Medicaid to those with low incomes and limited resources. Advances in disease detection, prevention, and treatment have allowed older adults to maintain independent and satisfying lives.

Because better health care is available today, people can expect to live longer after retirement. For this reason, financial planning is essential. Some companies provide retirement benefits, but many workers still must plan ahead with personal or company-provided long-term savings plans. With the addition of these savings funds, in conjunction with Social Security benefits, the poverty rate for older adults has been reduced. Many are finding that, because of a lifetime of practicing healthful behaviors, the years after retirement are fulfilling and rewarding.

■ **Figure 18.12** Many older adults enjoy active lives. *Why is older adulthood such a rewarding time for many?*

 **READING CHECK**

Identify What programs help people in late adulthood?

 READING CHECK

Answer Social Security benefits, Medicare, Medicaid, retirement benefits, and long-term savings plans

③ ASSESS/ CLOSE

Assessment Resources

📁 *FAST FILE* **ACTIVITIES**
Lesson 3 Quiz

💿 *ExamView Assessment Suite* CD-ROM

Visit glencoe.com for:
Online Quizzes
Online Learning Center

LESSON 3 **ASSESSMENT**

After You Read

Reviewing Facts and Vocabulary

1. What is *empty-nest syndrome*?
2. What are some examples of activities older adults can participate in to remain mentally active?
3. What sort of physical changes do females in middle adulthood experience?

Thinking Critically

4. **Infer.** Why is it so important today for adults to plan financially for retirement?
5. **Identify.** How have changes in nutrition and health care changed the lives of older adults?

Applying Health Skills

6. **Accessing Information.** Research library or Internet resources to learn about the Social Security system. Identify problems that may arise with this system in the not-so-distant future. Share what you learn in the form of an informational poster or pamphlet.

Writing Critically

7. **Descriptive.** Write a short essay explaining the emotional transitions one may have in middle adulthood.

 Online

Visit **glencoe.com** and complete the Interactive Study Guide for this lesson.

Progress Monitoring

Reteaching

Write the terms Middle Adulthood and Late Adulthood on the board. Call on students to come to the board and list goals and transitions associated with these stages of adulthood.

Enrichment

Have students interview a trusted older adult, such as a grandparent or retired teacher, about the person's life and achievements. Afterward, ask students what they learned about late adulthood from the interview.

 Online

Have students visit **glencoe.com** and complete the Interactive Study Guide for this lesson.

LESSON 3 ASSESSMENT ANSWERS

1. Feelings of sadness or loneliness due to children leaving home and entering adulthood
2. Solve puzzles, read, play board games, return to school, learn new hobbies
3. Females enter menopause, or the end of ovulation and menstruation.
4. Because people can now expect to live for many years after they retire
5. Older adults are living longer, fuller lives.
6. Posters or pamphlets will vary.
7. Essays will vary.

Skills for a Happy Marriage

NHES Standard 4 Students will demonstrate the ability to use interpersonal communication skills to enhance health and avoid or reduce health risks.

Teaching Objectives

- Demonstrate communication skills in building and maintaining a healthy marriage relationship.
- Identify strategies for communicating needs, wants, and emotions.

Teaching Strategies

- Have students work in groups of two or three that include both genders. Direct them to follow the steps in the activity.
- Encourage teams to share their questions and answers on communication and conflict resolution with the class.
- Be sure resource packets include tips and information gathered from the chapter on good communication, emotional maturity, and values and interests shared in a strong, successful marriage.

Assessment

Using a rubric, student work should provide comprehensive evidence of the following criteria to achieve the highest score:

✓ Takes turns explaining each side without interruptions

✓ Uses "I" messages

✓ Employs listening skills

✓ Brainstorms solutions and resolves conflict in a way that benefits both parties

Hands-On
HEALTH

Activity ## Skills for a Happy Marriage

Many couples find marriage to be an exciting and challenging experience. Your task is to identify the skills needed for a successful partnership. You will develop a list of ten questions couples might have about how to communicate in a marriage and resolve conflicts in a healthful way. Then you will create a resource packet of information couples might find helpful.

What You'll Need

- paper and pencils
- computer with Internet access

What You'll Do

Step 1

Work in groups of two or three to review Chapter 18. Conduct research on the Internet for additional skills needed for a healthy marriage.

Step 2

List ten questions covering communication and conflict-resolution skills for a successful partnership.

Step 3

Review the chapter again and write answers to each of the questions you listed in step 2.

Apply and Conclude

Develop a resource packet or pamphlet to help couples identify strategies to resolve conflicts in healthy ways.

Checklist: Conflict-Resolution Skills

✓ Taking turns explaining each side without interruptions

✓ "I" messages

✓ Listening skills

✓ Brainstorming solutions

✓ Solutions that benefit both sides

Health Literacy

Mandatory Marriage Education High divorce rates—and the costs of divorce to individuals, families, and society—have led some legislators to pass laws encouraging or requiring couples to attend premarital education classes before marrying. Such classes generally focus on improving couples' communication skills. Communities in which such laws have been passed report declines in their divorce rates. Nonetheless, many people think that governments are overstepping their bounds when they make such classes mandatory.

To download quizzes and eFlashcards to your PDA, go to glencoe.com and click on the Study to Go icon.

LESSON 1

Changes During Adolescence

Key Concepts

▸ Adolescents begin moving toward adulthood during puberty.
▸ During adolescence, the brain develops important pathways.
▸ Adolescents will develop independence, find their identity, and establish their personal values.

Vocabulary

▸ adolescence (p. 496)
▸ hormones (p. 496)
▸ puberty (p. 496)
▸ cognition (p. 498)

LESSON 2

Adulthood, Marriage, and Parenthood

Key Concepts

▸ Adulthood is reached when physical and emotional maturity are achieved.
▸ There are three major stages during the adult years.
▸ Marriage is a commitment to share your life with another person.
▸ A married couple may have several different options when they decide to start a family.

Vocabulary

▸ physical maturity (p. 502)
▸ emotional maturity (p. 502)
▸ commitment (p. 504)
▸ adoption (p. 505)
▸ self-directed (p. 506)
▸ unconditional love (p. 507)

LESSON 3

Health Through the Life Cycle

Key Concepts

▸ Physical, mental/emotional, and social changes occur during middle adulthood.
▸ Developing lifelong healthful habits that include healthy nutrition and physical activity help promote health throughout the life span.
▸ People in late adulthood have the opportunity to reflect on their lives and accomplishments.

Vocabulary

▸ transitions (p. 508)
▸ empty-nest syndrome (p. 510)
▸ integrity (p. 510)

 **Online**

Students can visit **glencoe.com** to

- review content online with the Online Student Edition.
- test their knowledge of chapter content with Online Quizzes.
- access Interactive Health Tutor for more practice with vocabulary.

Assessment Resources

FAST FILE ACTIVITIES
Chapter 18 Test

ExamView
Assessment Suite CD-ROM

Visit glencoe.com for:
Audio Chapter Summaries
Online Quizzes

STUDY TO GO Tell students to visit **glencoe.com** where they can download quizzes and eFlashcards.

Chapter 18   Review   **513**

Study Tips

Using Visuals Encourage students to create and utilize visual study aids, such as graphic organizers and diagrams, when they are learning new material or reviewing material they have just learned. When students visualize what they are learning or studying, they use a different part of the brain than when they read or listen. Creating additional neural connections through visualization increases the chances that students will remember what they learn.

Assessment

Chapter 18 Assessment Answers

LESSON 1

Vocabulary Review

1. adolescence
2. puberty
3. cognition
4. hormones

Understanding Key Concepts

5. c
6. a
7. d
8. c

Thinking Critically

9. Sample answer: A good friend won't ask you to do something that goes against your personal values. Good friends usually share similar goals, experiences, and values.

10. Each teen goes through puberty at his or her own pace. Therefore, some teens develop the physical characteristics of adults before their friends do.

11. Parents or guardians can provide advice and feedback about the decisions teens need to make. They can also model decision making for their children. This support and guidance can help teens become more emotionally independent.

12. Answers may vary. Potentially risky situations might include those involving alcohol, sexual activity, excessive dieting, or reckless driving.

13. Practicing and learning decision-making skills and other values can help teens throughout their lives.

514

LESSON 1

Vocabulary Review

Use the vocabulary terms listed on page 513 to complete the following statements.

1. The period of time between childhood and adulthood is called _____.

2. The time when a person begins to develop certain traits of adults is called _____.

3. The ability to reason and think out abstract solutions is called _____.

4. Chemical substances called _____ help regulate the body's many functions.

Understanding Key Concepts

After reading the question or statement, select the correct answer.

5. Which will you most likely *not* learn to do during adolescence?
   a. Anticipate consequences
   b. Think logically
   c. Reflect on past accomplishments
   d. Understand different points of view

6. Assessing your own values when they might be different than the values of your peers shows that you are developing which of the following?
   a. Personal value system
   b. Emotional independence
   c. Vocational goals
   d. Self-control

7. Which is *not* an example of a vocational goal?
   a. Entering trade school
   b. Entering college
   c. Learning to repair automobiles
   d. Passing the science test tomorrow

---

8. Which is the term for the development of certain traits of adults of your gender?
   a. Adolescence
   b. Emotional maturity
   c. Puberty
   d. Physical maturity

Thinking Critically

After reading the question or statement, write a short answer using complete sentences.

9. **Describe.** Describe the characteristics of a good friend.

10. **Extend.** Not everyone develops at the same rate. What does this mean?

11. **Analyze.** How can parents or guardians make the transition to emotional independence easier for teens?

12. **Infer.** What sort of decisions might you make that could be potentially risky?

13. **Synthesize.** How will the values you developed earlier in life impact you as you go through the stages of development?

LESSON 2

Vocabulary Review

Correct the sentences below by replacing the italicized term with the correct vocabulary term.

14. *Emotional maturity* is the point at which the body and its organs are developed.

15. Children learn to make decisions about behavior when adults aren't present as they become more *physically mature*.

16. Giving love to a child without question in all situations is called *commitment*.

Health eSpotlight VIDEO Wrap-Up

Have students reread the Health eSpotlight question at the beginning of the chapter (page 495) and look at their original answer. **Ask Students:** *Now that you have read the chapter and watched the video, how would* *you respond differently if you were designing a fitness program for an elderly person?* Call on volunteers to describe how their responses would change.

17. Legally taking someone else's child to raise as your own is known as *integrity*.

Understanding Key Concepts
After reading the question or statement, select the correct answer.

18. Which is a responsibility of parenthood?
    a. Instilling values
    b. Setting limits
    c. Giving unconditional love
    d. All of the above

19. In a marriage, the partners don't always think of themselves first. Rather, they consider what is best for the relationship. What is this known as?
    a. Communication
    b. Emotional maturity
    c. Physical maturity
    d. Values and interests

20. Setting limits can help children become which of the following?
    a. Self-directed
    b. Physically mature
    c. Emotionally mature
    d. Committed

21. Which is the stage at which the physical body and all its organs are fully developed?
    a. Physical maturity
    b. Emotional maturity
    c. Marital adjustment
    d. Commitment

Thinking Critically
After reading the question or statement, write a short answer using complete sentences.

22. **Describe.** What happens in the three stages of development during the adult years?

23. **Analyze.** What should a couple consider before entering into marriage?

24. **Describe.** What particular challenges do teens who get married face?

25. **Analyze.** What are the different ways a couple may start a family?

LESSON 3

Vocabulary Review
Use the vocabulary terms listed on page 513 to complete the following statements.

26. The middle adult years are often full of _____, critical changes that occur at all stages of life.

27. When their children grow up and leave home, middle adults may suffer from _____.

28. People in late adulthood may reflect on whether they lived their lives according to their moral code, or with _____.

Understanding Key Concepts
After reading the question or statement, select the correct answer.

29. Which provides financial assistance to older adults, as well as disabled individuals?
    a. Social Security
    b. Medicare
    c. Medicaid
    d. None of the above

30. What is a social and mental/emotional change that middle and older adults experience?
    a. Sadness and loneliness when their children move away
    b. Pride in having met personal goals
    c. The opportunity to pursue talents and interests
    d. All of the above

LESSON 2
Vocabulary Review
14. Physical maturity
15. self-directed
16. unconditional love
17. adoption

Understanding Key Concepts
18. b
19. b
20. a
21. a

Thinking Critically
22. In young adulthood, people try to develop close personal relationships. In middle adulthood, they look outside themselves and care for others. In late adulthood, they try to understand the meaning and purpose of their life.
23. They should consider the long-term consequences of the decision to marry. Any doubts or questions about marrying should be explored and resolved before the marriage takes place.
24. Teens who get married may have increased responsibilities that interfere with their personal freedoms and their educational or career goals. They may also have financial pressures.
25. A couple may start a family in three different ways: adoption, foster parenting, or having a child of their own.

LESSON 3
Vocabulary Review
26. transitions
27. empty-nest syndrome
28. integrity

ExamView
Assessment Suite

Create and customize tests in minutes with this convenient digital platform.

- Create differentiated tests quickly and easily.
- All questions correlated to National/State Standards.
- Enhance tests with Document Based Questions (DBQ) and add your own photos or graphics.
- Build tests in both English and Spanish.
- Generate progress reports.

To order, go to glencoe.com and search for ISBN 0-07-888173-0.

Assessment

Understanding Key Concepts

29. a
30. d
31. d
32. a

Thinking Critically

33. The use of computers gives older adults opportunities to broaden their access to information. It also helps them remain mentally active, which strengthens the brain.

34. A midlife crisis occurs when middle adults have questions and concerns about whether they have met their goals, feel loved and valued, and have made a positive difference in the lives of others.

35. Someone might deal with empty-nest syndrome by maintaining healthy relationships with family and friends for help through the transition. The person also might pursue new interests or make new friends.

31. Arthritis may affect which of the following during late adulthood?
    a. Heart
    b. Eyesight and hearing
    c. Teeth and gums
    d. Joints

32. What is a potential benefit of strength training in later life?
    a. Preserving bone density
    b. Improving sleep habits
    c. Improving mental sharpness
    d. Maintaining a healthy weight

Thinking Critically

After reading the question or statement, write a short answer using complete sentences.

33. **Assess.** What role have computers played in changing the lives of people in late adulthood?

34. **Synthesize.** What is a midlife crisis?

35. **Predict.** How might a person deal with empty-nest syndrome?

Project-Based ASSESSMENT

The Journey Ahead

Background

During adolescence, many changes and transitions occur. Many teens feel the need to begin expressing more independence from their parents. They also begin showing more interest in developing close relationships with other teens. They also begin defining future goals and plans. The teens years can be difficult because of these changes and uncertainties.

Task

Groups of four or five students will develop a podcast aimed at middle school students. Each student will play the role of an expert and discuss one developmental task. The goal is to reassure younger students about the changes they will soon experience.

Audience

Middle school students

Purpose

Analyze the changes that teens experience. Reassure younger students that these feelings are normal.

Procedure

1. Review the section in the text describing developmental changes experienced by teens.

2. Select one developmental change that teens commonly experience.

3. Conduct research on that developmental task using reliable sources.

4. Discuss your findings with the group. Decide on a theme for the podcast. One student will play the role of moderator, and the other students will provide information on a developmental task.

5. Practice presenting the podcast. If possible, make an audio tape of your podcast to play for middle school students. Play the podcast, or perform it live for a group of middle school students.

6. Conduct a survey to determine if middle school students found the information reassuring and helpful.

Project-Based ASSESSMENT

Step 1 Review Students should reread the section in the text describing developmental changes teens go through.

Step 2 Research Have students get into groups and select one developmental change to research. Make sure students use reliable sources of information.

Step 3 Create Have students create their podcast. Encourage that they divide up specific tasks and also suggest they write a dialogue before they record their podcast.

Visit **glencoe.com** for Project-Based Assessment rubrics.

Math Practice

Interpret Graphs. From information she gathered at the public library, Marsha made the following bar graph that shows the number of people of each age group in her town last year. Use the graph to answer Questions 1–3.

Town Population by Age Last Year

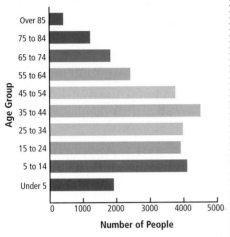

1. Which age group made up the greatest percentage of Marsha's town population last year?
   A. Under 5   C. 35 to 44
   B. 5 to 14   D. Over 85

2. Approximately how many people were below the age of 35?
   A. 4,000   C. 14,000
   B. 4,500   D. 18,500

3. If the town's total population was approximately 28,100, what percentage of the population was 15 to 24 years of age?
   A. 14%   C. 40%
   B. 24%   D. 50%

For more test practice, visit glencoe.com and complete the Online Quizzes for Chapter 18.

Reading/Writing Practice

Understand and Apply. Read the passage below, and then answer the questions.

> (1) Teenagers are working in greater numbers than ever before. (2) Some choose jobs in fields they feel strongly about, like conservation or recycling. (3) They might join the parks department to plant trees. (4) Teenagers interested in working with younger children can work in community centers, or tutor students after school. (5) Many teens work in their own neighborhoods, doing yard work.
>
> (6) Studies show that teens are successful workers. (7) They relate well to other teens, as well as to older adults. (8) Most teenage workers find a pleasant surprise—they like their jobs more than they expected to. (9) Many teens make lasting friendships on the job. (10) They also learn new skills related to their future career and educational choices.

1. Which detail below supports the idea that teenagers are successful in the workforce?
   A. Many teen have entered the workforce.
   B. Many join the parks department.
   C. Some teens work in conservation jobs.
   D. They relate well to other teens and to older adults.

2. The writer wants to add the following detail to this passage:
   Some teenagers—girls and boys—babysit neighborhood children.

   Based on the organization of this piece, after which number should this detail be added?
   A. Sentence 1   C. Sentence 6
   B. Sentence 4   D. Sentence 7

3. Write an essay giving examples of why you think teens can contribute in the workplace.

National Education Standards
Math: Operations, Data Analysis, Statistics
Language Arts: NCTE 1, NCTE 3, NCTE 4

Standardized Test Practice Answers

Math Practice
1. C
2. C
3. A

Reading/Writing Practice
1. D
2. B
3. Answers will vary but should include specific reasons how teens can contribute.

National Education Standards

Math: Number and Operations, Data Analysis, Statistics

Language Arts: NCTE 1, NCTE 3, NCTE 4

For the complete Math and Language Arts standards, visit glencoe.com.

Go Online

Online Study Tools
For more test practice, visit glencoe.com and complete the Online Quizzes for Chapter 18.

Test-Taking Tip

What to Ask Before Your Test Before taking a test, students should try to learn what type of exam will be given. For example, if they know that they will be taking a multiple-choice exam, a good way to prepare is by creating flashcards. They can use the flashcards to quiz themselves on the material and help memorize facts. On the other hand, if students know they will be taking an essay exam, a better way to prepare is by creating outlines. They can use the outlines to review the information and help identify relationships in the material.

Medical Specialists
Group Activity

- Divide the class into three groups, and assign each group one of the three careers described on this page.

- Ask groups to research their assigned career. Students should learn more about the educational requirements, future job potential, and any other aspects of the career that interest them.

- Arrange for one member of each group to interview a person who works in the assigned career. Suggest that they ask questions that will elicit information useful to students deciding on a career.

- If possible, arrange for another member of each group to shadow a person in the assigned career by following the person throughout the day on the job. These students should relate their experiences to other group members.

- Give groups a chance to share what they learned with the class.

Respiratory Therapist

Respiratory therapists help people who have trouble breathing due to a number of lung conditions, such as emphysema or asthma. They usually work as part of a team with physicians, nurses, and other medical professionals.

If a career as a respiratory therapist interests you, take communications, biology, and other science classes in high school. Educational requirements for respiratory therapists vary from state to state. Some states require a two-year college degree, and others require a four-year college degree.

Substance Abuse Counselor

Substance abuse counselors assess and treat people who have substance abuse problems. They often work closely with doctors, social workers, psychologists, and other health professionals to address the physical, social, and psychological needs of the user and the user's friends and family. If you're interested in a career as a substance abuse counselor, take communications, psychology, and sociology classes in high school. Substance abuse counselors need an undergraduate degree and a master's degree in psychology or counseling. Most states also require certification and licensing.

Medical Records Technician

Medical records technicians maintain patients' health information. Medical records management is a rapidly changing field. Until recently, medical information was recorded on paper and then filed. Medical records are now often kept on computers.

Medical records technicians need to be detail oriented and well organized. Taking computer classes in high school can help you decide if a career as a medical records technician is right for you. After high school, you may need an associate's degree in information management from a community college or vocational school.

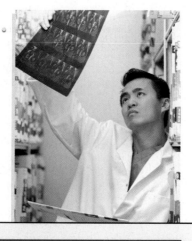

Skills for the 21st Century

Adaptability of Workers The one-job career that many adults experienced in the twentieth century is now a thing of the past. The next generation of workers can expect to switch jobs several times during their working years. The jobs themselves will also undergo radical shifts. According to one study, almost two-thirds of today's young children will work in jobs and careers that do not yet exist. All of these workplace changes will require workers to be adaptable. In fact, adaptability is likely to be viewed as one of the most important worker assets when today's students are adults. Helping students master such skills as problem-solving, communication, and accessing-information skills will help prepare them to be adaptable workers in the future.

CAREER SPOTLIGHT

HIV/AIDS Educator

Livia Phillips was a freshman in college when she became an HIV/AIDS educator for Students Teaching AIDS to Youth (STAY). She volunteered thousands of hours of her time and received scholarships that paid for her undergraduate studies. Livia is now pursuing a nursing degree.

Q. Why did you want to become a health educator?

A. *I wanted to be a resource person for health information. In school, I was the girl that anyone could talk to about their health problems and I loved helping my friends.*

Q. What is the highlight of your career?

A. *The last two years I worked as an educator in the HIV division of a substance abuse treatment facility. I educated residents about HIV/AIDS and offered testing and counseling services. It was very satisfying work and I hope to do it again.*

Q. What makes you successful at your career?

A. *I don't judge. I help people realize the risks they take with certain behaviors. I try to empower them to make good choices.*

HIV/AIDS Educator

- Invite a HIV/AIDS Educator from a local or state health department to speak to the class about careers in health education.

- Suggest that the speaker address topics such as educational requirements of the career, work environment, and pros and cons of the career.

- Ask each student to prepare a question in advance for the speaker. After the talk, call on students to ask the speaker any of the questions that remain unanswered.

- Help students relate the career of HIV/AIDS educator to another health education career they are likely to know more about, such as a high school health teacher. With the speaker, discuss similarities and differences between the two careers.

Encourage interested students to visit **glencoe.com** for more information on this career.

Activity **Beyond the Classroom**

Writing **Drug Prevention Careers.** Use print and online resources to learn more about substance prevention organizations. Many of these groups are nonprofit organizations that obtain funding from government and other sources. What types of careers might be available through one of these organizations? Research one nonprofit organization that aims to prevent substance abuse.

Make a list of at least five different careers within this organization that teens might consider. Develop a one-page informational flyer for two of the careers. Provide facts on the job responsibilities and education needed for these careers.

G Online

For more information, go to the Career Corner link at **glencoe.com**.

Activity **Beyond the Classroom**

Writing Keep students involved in the community and encourage parent participation by assigning the activities on this page for students to work on outside of class. Substance-abuse prevention organizations that students might learn about include the Gateway Foundation and Youth-to-Youth International. Careers available with these and similar organizations include case manager, chemical dependency technician, prevention assistant, and registered nurse. Students should research two of the careers and create a one-page flyer providing information on the education and job responsibilities required for the careers. Post the flyers in the classroom.

UNIT 7 Drugs

Flexible Technology Solutions
Focus

Health eSpotlight Video Series

By Chapter

Chapter 19 Medicines and Drugs
Video 19: Medicines and the Body

Chapter 20 Tobacco
Video 20: The Truth and the Lies

Chapter 21 Alcohol
Video 21: The Risks of Use and Abuse

Chapter 22 Illegal Drugs
Video 22: Staying Drug-Free

By Lesson

Chapter 19 *Video 19* For Use With
Segment 19.1 The Role of Medicines .... Lesson 1
Segment 19.2 Using Medicines Safely.............................. Lesson 2

Chapter 20 *Video 20* For Use With
Segment 20.1 The Health Risks of Tobacco Use .... Lesson 1
Segment 20.2 Choosing to Live Tobacco-Free .... Lesson 2
Segment 20.3 Promoting a Smoke-Free Environment........ Lesson 3

Chapter 21 *Video 21* For Use With
Segment 21.1 The Health Risks of Alcohol Use .... Lesson 1
Segment 21.2 Choosing to Live Alcohol-Free.................... Lesson 2
Segment 21.3 The Impact of Alcohol Abuse...................... Lesson 3

Chapter 22 *Video 22* For Use With
Segment 22.1 The Health Risks of Drug Use .... Lesson 1
Segment 22.2 Marijuana, Inhalants, and Steroids .... Lesson 2
Segment 22.3 Psychoactive Drugs .... Lesson 3
Segment 22.4 Living Drug-Free....................................... Lesson 4

By Skill

Practicing Healthful Behaviors .... Videos 3   13   17 **19** 23
Advocacy..Videos 16 **20** 28
Refusal Skills ....Videos 8 **21** 24
Decision Making ....Videos 15 **22** 26

■ Indicates videos featured in the unit that teach the corresponding skill. Other videos listed can also be used to teach that skill.

520A

Teach

Direct lesson plans beyond the classroom with multi-media fitness activities that students can do online, in class, or as a group.

PowerPoint® Presentation

- *Health eSpotlight* videos
- Audio and image bank

FITNESS ZONE Online

Fitness Zone Online is a multi-media resource that helps students find ways to be physically active each day.

- Clipboard Energizer Activities
- Fitness Zone Videos
- Polar Heart Rate Monitor Activities
- Nutrition, Physical Activity, and Injury Prevention Tips
- Links to Nutrition and Physical Activity Resources

Go Online

Online Learning Center

- Student Web Activities
- PuzzleMaker
- Interactive Health Tutor

Podcast Audio Chapter Summaries

Use the audio Podcast Audio Chapter Summaries to teach and review key concepts, and engage students with health content that they can download to a computer or portable MP3 player.

Assess/Close

Help students master chapter and lesson concepts with an integrated technology solution for assessment and performance evaluation.

Go Online

Online Learning Center

- Interactive Study Guides
- Online Quizzes

ExamView® Assessment Suite CD-ROM

Create and customize tests in minutes with this convenient digital platform.

- Create differentiated tests quickly and easily.
- All questions correlated to National/State Standards.
- Enhance tests with Document Based Questions (DBQ) and add your own photos and graphics.
- Build tests in both English and Spanish.
- Generate progress reports.

Enrich

Use these additional digital and online media resources to promote hands-on exploration of health topics covered in the lesson.

BusinessWeek HEALTH NEWS Online

Business Week Health Video Series

- *Drug Check*
- *Drugs Get Smart*
- *Quit Smoking: New Year's Resolution*

Study-to-Go

Download a portable version of eFlashcards and Self-Check Quizzes onto your Palm or Pocket PC.

Health Podcasts Activities

Glencoe's "It's Your Health" Podcast Activities provide students with a unique listening and learning experience that takes health education beyond the classroom. Download the audio files and print activities covering a range of current health topics that matter most to teens!

Drugs

Students will learn about medicines, tobacco, alcohol, and illegal drugs, including the health risks of each.

Health eSpotlight Video Series

At the beginning of each chapter, visit glencoe.com and have students watch the video and do the accompanying print activity.

 Chapter 19
Medicines and the Body

It's important to follow the directions when taking medication.

 Chapter 20
The Truth and the Lies

Friends and family can make an impact on a person's tobacco use.

 Chapter 21
The Risks of Use and Abuse

Using alcohol can cause serious problems in a user's life.

 Chapter 22
Staying Drug Free

Understanding the effects of drug abuse on the body can help a teen resist pressure.

Unit 7 Resources

- Career Corner
- 📁 FAST FILE RESOURCES
- Health Career Research Activity
- Family Involvement Activity
- Community Involvement Activity
- Unit Test

UNIT 7 Drugs

Chapter 19
Medicines and Drugs

 Medicines and the Body

Chapter 20
Tobacco

 The Truth and the Lies

Chapter 21
Alcohol

 The Risks of Use and Abuse

Chapter 22
Illegal Drugs

 Staying Drug Free

UNIT PROJECT

Improving Your Community

Using Visuals Students Against Destructive Decisions, also known as SADD, is a national organization that helps teens be positive role models. Their goal is to empower teens to abstain from destructive behaviors, such as drinking, drug use, and driving while impaired. Members educate their peers about the dangers of alcohol and drug use and provide prevention strategies.

 To learn more about SADD, go to the Unit Web Project at glencoe.com.

Get Involved. Locate other organizations that discourage alcohol and drug use. Find out how teens in your community can volunteer to help their peers.

520

UNIT PROJECT

SADD SADD was originally founded as Students Against Drunk Driving. It changed its name because its mission expanded beyond underage drinking to include preventing destructive behaviors associated with drug use, teen violence, and teen depression.
Get Involved Suggest that interested students use the telephone book and online search engines to find out about other organizations in their community. National organizations that may have a presence in the community include Mothers Against Drunk Driving (MADD), The Partnership for a Drug-Free America, the National Council on Alcoholism and Drug Dependence (NCADD), and Community Anti-Drug Coalitions of America (DADCA).

> *"It is our choices . . . that show what we truly are, far more than our abilities."*
> —J. K. Rowling, author

Activate Prior Knowledge

Ask students these questions before they read the chapter to build on what they already know.

Chapter 19
What are some different kinds of medicines?

(Sample answer: Pain killers, antibiotics, antihistamines)

Chapter 20
What are some health risks of using tobacco?

(Sample answer: Heart disease, lung cancer, emphysema)

Chapter 21
What impact does alcohol abuse have on society?

(Sample answer: Physical abuse in families, fatalities caused by drunk driving, peoples' lives ruined through alcoholism)

Chapter 22
What are some illegal drugs that are used by some teens and adults?

(Sample answer: Marijuana, LSD, cocaine, ecstasy)

TeacherWorks Plus provides:

- interactive Teacher Wraparound Edition
- click, drag, and drop to plan lessons
- instant access to many print program resources

How to Get Involved Provide students with these step-by-step instructions about how they can get involved in discouraging alcohol and drug use in their community.

1. Choose one of the organizations they find through their research.
2. Call the organization and find out if they are looking for volunteers.
3. Ask if there are any requirements to be a volunteer, such as age requirements. Find out if the organization has guidelines that volunteers must follow.
4. Find out some details of volunteer opportunities, such as if the organization needs help in the office or help in preparing for an event.

521

Chapter 19 pages 522–539	Standards		Features
	National	**State/Local**	*Hands-On* **HEALTH**
	1.12.6, 2.12.10, 3.12.1–3.12.3, 4.12.2, 5.12.1, 5.12.6, 6.12.1, 7.12.1, 7.12.3, 8.12.1, 8.12.4		• Stay Informed *(Advocacy)*, page 534
Lesson 1 **The Role of Medicines** pages 524–529 **BIG Idea** *Medicines are divided into classes and have different effects on different people.*	1.12.5, 3.12.1, 4.12.1, 7.12.1, 7.12.2		VIDEO **BusinessWeek** HEALTH NEWS • Drug Check, page 526 Out of Time
Lesson 2 **Using Medicines Safely** pages 530–533 **BIG Idea** *Medicines are only safe if they are used for the intended purpose and according to the directions on the label.*	2.12.10, 3.12.2, 3.12.3, 4.12.2, 5.12.6, 7.12.1, 7.12.3, 8.12.1, 8.12.4		VIDEO **BusinessWeek** HEALTH NEWS • Drugs Get Smart, page 532

(30 Min — Lesson 1)
(30 Min — Lesson 2)

Key to Ability Levels

Teaching Strategies and activities have been coded for ability level and appropriateness.

AL Activities for students working above grade level

OL Activities for students working on grade level

BL Activities for students working below grade level

EL Activities for English Learners

Glencoe Exclusive!
TeacherWorks™ Plus
All-In-One Planner and Resource Center

Resources	Lesson Assessment	Technology
Student Activity Workbook TEACH **FAST FILE** RESOURCES Vocabulary Practice TEACH Health Labs EXTEND	Chapter 19 Review Chapter 19 Assessment Standardized Test Practice ⊙ *ExamView® Assessment Suite* CD-ROM	**Teaching Tools:** ⊙ *TeacherWorks™* Plus DVD ⊙ *StudentWorks™* Plus DVD ⊙ *ExamView® Assessment Suite* CD-ROM 🕹 Transparency ⊙ Fitness DVD ⊙ PowerPoint® DVD ⊙ Health eSpotlight Video Series DVD
FAST FILE RESOURCES Reading Strategies Activity TEACH Reteaching Activity REVIEW Enrichment Activity EXTEND Health Skills Practice TEACH	Lesson 1 Assessment, page 529 📁 Lesson 1 Quiz *Fast File* ⊙ *ExamView® Assessment Suite* CD-ROM	**Web-Based Resources:** **Go Online** glencoe.com • Health Podcast Activities • Audio Chapter Summaries (English/Spanish) • Interactive Health Tutor • Health Skills Activities • Vocabulary PuzzleMaker • Parent Letters (English/Spanish) • Lesson Plans • Health Inventories • Online Quizzes • Study-to-Go • Unit Web Projects • Student Web Activities • Fitness Zone Activities
FAST FILE RESOURCES Reading Strategies Activity TEACH Reteaching Activity REVIEW Enrichment Activity EXTEND Health Skills Practice TEACH	Lesson 2 Assessment, page 533 📁 Lesson 2 Quiz *Fast File* ⊙ *ExamView® Assessment Suite* CD-ROM	

StudentWorks™ Plus

This is the student's backpack solution.

Includes:
- complete Interactive Student Edition
- full audio of English text and Spanish chapter summaries
- allows students to record assignments and track grades.
- links to online activities and additional student resources
- access to all student worksheets and workbooks

FOLDABLES® Study Organizer

Dinah Zike Foldables® Chapter Activity
Refer to the *Dinah Zike Reading and Study Skills for Glencoe Health.* Ask students to make a four-door book Foldable to record and organize the chapter's information. As students learn about medicines, they can use this Foldable to record key vocabulary and concepts.

Key to Symbols

 Transparencies   REVIEW activities to review or reinforce content

 CD-ROM   TEACH activities to teach basic concepts

 glencoe.com   EXTEND activities to extend or enrich lesson content

 Print Resources

Medicines and Drugs

Chapter Overview

Chapter 19 focuses on the different types of medicines, reactions to medicines, and using medicines safely.

Lesson 1

Medicines used to treat or prevent illness are classified based on how they work in the body. A medicine's effect on the body depends on many factors.

Lesson 2

Medicines are regulated by the government to make them safe to use. Taking medicines is safe when they are used for the intended purpose and according to the label's directions.

▶ **Activating Prior Knowledge**

Have students write their plans. **Ask Students:** *Which source of information about using medicine properly do you think is the most reliable? How can you access that source of information?* (Sample answer: Pharmacist)

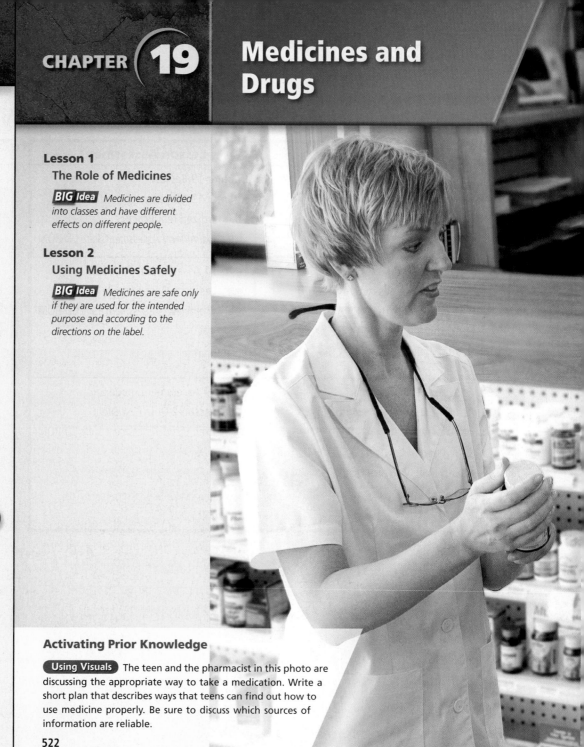

Lesson 1

The Role of Medicines

BIG Idea *Medicines are divided into classes and have different effects on different people.*

Lesson 2

Using Medicines Safely

BIG Idea *Medicines are safe only if they are used for the intended purpose and according to the directions on the label.*

Activating Prior Knowledge

Using Visuals The teen and the pharmacist in this photo are discussing the appropriate way to take a medication. Write a short plan that describes ways that teens can find out how to use medicine properly. Be sure to discuss which sources of information are reliable.

522

Universal Access

Differentiated Learning Glencoe provides teacher support and student materials for all learners in the health classroom.

- Chapter Summaries in English and Spanish are available online at **glencoe.com**.

- *Fast Files* and related worksheets support reluctant readers.

- Universal Access strategies throughout the Teacher Wraparound Edition and *Fast Files* help you present materials for gifted students, at-risk students, physically impaired students, and those with behavior disorders or learning disabilities.

Chapter Launchers

Health in Action

Discuss the **BIG** Ideas

Before beginning this chapter, think about how you would answer these questions:

▸ What are reasons people take medicines?

▸ What are possible consequences of not following the instructions on a medicine label?

Watch the *Health* **eSpotlight** Video Series

Medicines and the Body

A drug prescribed by a doctor can hurt you. Why is it important to follow a doctor's advice when taking medication?

Assess Your Health

Go Online

Visit **glencoe.com** and complete the Health Inventory for Chapter 19.

Chapter 19   Medicines and Drugs   **523**

Chapter Launchers

Health in Action

Discuss the **BIG** Ideas

Assign this activity before students read the chapter. Explain that the purpose of the questions is to help students assess their current knowledge of medicines.

Health **eSpotlight** Video Series

Medicines and the Body

Before Viewing the Video

Ask Students: *What problems might happen if a person doesn't follow the doctor's instructions when taking a medicine?* (Sample answer: The person may not get well or may have a bad reaction to the medicine.)

Go Online

Have students go to **glencoe.com** and take the Health Inventory for Chapter 19.

Chapter Skills

Reading Skills
- Reviewing Facts and Vocabulary, pp. 529, 533
- Reading/Writing Practice, p. 539

BIG Idea

Students will learn about types of medicines and how to use medicines safely.

Health Skills
- Applying Health Skills, pp. 529, 533

Vocabulary
- New Vocabulary, pp. 524, 530
- Reviewing Facts and Vocabulary, pp. 529, 533

Writing Skills
- Writing Critically, pp. 529, 533
- Reading/Writing Practice, p. 539

The Role of Medicines

1 FOCUS

GUIDE TO READING

BIG Idea Students will learn about the classification of medicines and the different effects that medicines have on different people. **Ask Students:** *Why would medicines have different effects on different people?* (Sample answer: Each person's body is unique. As a result, a medicine may work for one person and not another.)

Before You Read

Cluster Chart Students' cluster charts will vary.

Main Idea

Types of Medicines Medicines are classified into categories according to the way they work in the body. **Ask Students:** *What is a medicine that fights a pathogen, and what is a medicine that relieves pain?* (Sample answer: Antibiotics fight pathogens, and aspirin relieves pain.)

Real Life Issues

Ask volunteers to share their paragraphs with the class. **Ask Students:** *What symptoms would you want to relieve if you were Grant?* (Congestion, sneezing, coughing, headache)

GUIDE TO READING

BIG Idea *Medicines are divided into classes and have different effects on different people.*

Before You Read

Create a Cluster Chart. Draw a circle and label it "Medicines." Create four surrounding circles labeled "Prevent Disease," "Fight Pathogens," "Relieve Pain," and "Promote Health." As you read, fill in the chart with more circles and details about the kinds of medicines discussed in the lesson.

New Vocabulary

▶ medicines (p. 524)
▶ drugs (p. 524)
▶ vaccine (p. 525)
▶ side effects (p. 528)
▶ additive interaction (p. 528)
▶ synergistic effect (p. 528)
▶ antagonistic interaction (p. 529)

The Role of Medicines

Real Life Issues

Choosing Medicines Wisely. Grant has a cold with a cough and runny nose. He checks the medicine cabinet for any cold medications that will help him feel better. He finds more than one type of cold medicine in the cabinet. Grant is not sure which one he should take.

Writing *Write a paragraph that explains what Grant should look for in a cold medicine. For example, what symptoms he wants to relieve, how much he should take, and how many hours a dose will last.*

Types of Medicines

Main Idea Medicines are classified based on how they work in your body.

People use medicines to help restore their health when they are ill. **Medicines** are *drugs that are used to treat or prevent diseases or other conditions.* **Drugs** are *substances other than food that change the structure or function of the body or mind.* All medicines are drugs, but not all drugs are medicines. Drugs are effective in treating illness when taken as directed by a physician or according to the label instructions. Medicines that treat or prevent illness can be classified into four broad categories:

- Medicines that help prevent disease
- Medicines that fight pathogens
- Medicines that relieve pain and other symptoms
- Medicines that manage chronic conditions, help maintain or restore health, and regulate body's systems

---

More About...

Science Antibiotics kill bacteria in several ways, depending on the antibiotic. Some antibiotics damage the cell wall of bacteria, which interferes with bacterial reproduction. Other antibiotics interfere with bacterial DNA or prevent a cell process from making a necessary chemical. Ask students who are taking or have taken biology to make a presentation about the structure of bacteria and how antibiotics affect bacteria. This may require library or online research. Have students show images of bacteria and viruses, and explain why antibiotics work against bacteria but not against viruses.

■ **Figure 19.1** Many types of medications are available. *What was the last medication that you used, and for what purpose did you use it?*

CHAPTER 19

LESSON 1

Preventing Disease

Today, we have medicines that prevent disease. About 95 percent of children receive **vaccines**, *a preparation that prevents a person from contracting a specific disease.*

Vaccines Vaccines contain weakened or dead *pathogens* that cause the disease. When injected into your body, the vaccine produces antibodies that fight those pathogens. Your body also produces memory cells that recall how to make these antibodies. This provides you with long-lasting protection against these specific pathogens.

The protection from some vaccines, however, fades over time. The vaccines for tetanus must be given periodically. For other vaccines, like those that prevent the flu, a new vaccine is required every year.

Antitoxins Antitoxins, like vaccines, prevent disease. They can also help **neutralize** the effects of toxins. Antitoxins fight the bacteria that produce substances toxic to the body. Antitoxins are usually produced by injecting animals with safe amounts of a specific toxin. This stimulates the animal's immune system to produce antibodies. These antibodies are then used to make an antitoxin.

Fighting Pathogens

Medicines can also help your body fight the pathogens that cause illness.

Antibiotics *Antibiotics* are a class of drug that destroy disease-causing microorganisms, called *bacteria*. Antibiotics such as penicillin work either by killing harmful bacteria in the body or by preventing bacteria from reproducing.

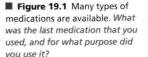

Go Online

Visit glencoe.com and complete the Student Web Activity on programs to vaccinate all children.

Academic Vocabulary

neutralize *(verb):* to counteract the effect of

② TEACH

R **Reading Strategy**

Flowchart Call on volunteers to make a flowchart on the board about how vaccines work. Steps should include making a vaccine with weakened or dead pathogens, introducing the vaccine into the body, the body producing antibodies, the body easily destroying the pathogens, and the body producing memory cells to recall how to produce antibodies for that pathogen. **BL**

Caption Answer

Figure 19.1 Sample answer: Ibuprofen, acetaminophen, a cold medication, an antibiotic

Academic Vocabulary

Neutralize Read the definition aloud, and call on a volunteer to describe how an antitoxin *neutralizes* the effects of a toxin. Then, explain that this verb is often used in contexts other than health or science. Ask students how one football team could neutralize the effects of an opposing team's good passing game. (With a good pass defense) Ask how someone running for political office could neutralize the effects of an opponent's television ads. (With television ads of his or her own)

Cooperative Learning

Guide to Pain Killers Americans often have more than one type of over-the-counter analgesic in the home for relief of headaches and various other minor aches and pains. The active ingredient in most common over-the-counter analgesics is aspirin, ibuprofen, or acetaminophen. Have students work in groups to investigate these three types of analgesics and write a guide to their use. Students should find out how each type works in the body, the side effects of each, warnings about the use of each, and the brand names associated with each. Ask students to organize what they learn into a guide that people could use when buying analgesics.

After students have watched the video, *Drug Check,* have them work in pairs to make a list of things to be aware of concerning drugs in the medicine cabinet and another list of resources where they could find information on the items in their first list. Call on a volunteer to read an item aloud from the first list, and then call on another volunteer to identify a possible resource where someone could find information about that topic.

C Critical Thinking

Comparing and Contrasting
After students have read about antibiotics and antivirals, have them compare the two types of medicines. Explain that antibiotics are used for such common illnesses as strep throat and ear infections, while antivirals are used for the common cold and the flu. Ask volunteers to explain how these medicines are similar. (They both relieve the symptoms of an illness.) Then, ask volunteers to explain how the two types are different. (Antibiotics are able to kill the pathogens, while antivirals are not.) **OL**

READING CHECK

Answer Vaccines produce anti-bodies that fight pathogens.

Drug Check

Analyze. Go to glencoe.com and watch the video *Drug Check.* How much do you really know about the drugs in your medicine cabinet? Make a list of things you should be aware of and a list of possible resources where you can find the information you need.

READING CHECK

Describe Explain how vaccines prevent a person from getting a disease.

When antibiotics were first introduced, they were considered a miracle drug because they saved so many lives. Some antibiotics, however, can cause nausea or stomach pain. Allergies are another side effect of antibiotic use. Tell your doctor if you experience any negative side effects of antibiotics, or if you know you are allergic to an antibiotic. Antibiotics can also lose their effectiveness. The bacteria that antibiotics kill have adapted to the drug over time.

Bacteria can develop a resistance in two ways: when antibiotics are overused, and when the patient does not finish taking the full prescription. If you do not finish taking all of a prescription, you may not kill all of the bacteria. The remaining bacteria may develop a resistance, or immunity, to treatment.

Antivirals and Antifungals Antibiotics are effective only against bacteria. They do not cure illnesses caused by viruses. Antiviral drugs are available to treat some viral illnesses, such as the flu. These medicines suppress the virus, but do not kill it. A person who takes antiviral medication for cold sores or fever blisters, which are caused by viruses, will still haves the virus in his or her body. As a result, the person often has symptom-free periods followed by flare-ups when symptoms reappear. Like bacteria, viruses can develop a resistance to medications. Fungi are another type of pathogen that can infect the body. Antifungals can suppress or kill fungus cells, such as athlete's foot and ringworm.

C

Relieving Pain

The most commonly used medicines are *analgesics,* or pain relievers. Analgesics range from relatively mild medicines, such as aspirin, to strong narcotics, such as opium-based morphine and codeine. Aspirin is used to relieve pain and reduce fever. Other analgesics fight *inflammation,* or redness, swelling, and pain.

Even though aspirin is a widely used drug, it can cause stomach upset, dizziness, and ringing in the ears. Children who take aspirin when they have a fever are at risk of developing Reye's syndrome, a potentially life-threatening illness of the brain and liver. For that reason, aspirin should not be given to anyone under the age of 20 unless directed by a health care professional. Some people who are sensitive to aspirin take acetaminophen or ibuprofen. Acetaminophen is the recommended analgesic for children.

Pain Reliever Dependence Certain types of medicines that relieve pain can be addictive. These medicines, usually called narcotics, require a doctor's prescription. Patients who use these drugs can become physically or psychologically dependent on them.

526 **Chapter 19** Medicines and Drugs

Promoting School Wellness

Medicine at School A good school health program has a medical professional in charge of providing necessary medicine in emergency situations, such as for a severe asthma attack. In addition, the school may be able to provide medicines through a health professional for certain students who have special needs. In contrast, a school nurse is not usually permitted to provide even OTC pain killers to students without parental permission. Ask the school nurse or other health professional to speak to the class about medicines at school, including what the nurse has on hand and what medicines students are allowed to bring and take at school. Make sure students have prepared relevant questions to ask.

Managing Chronic Conditions

R Some medicines are used to treat chronic conditions. These medicines maintain or restore health, and offer people with chronic diseases a higher level of wellness.

Allergy Medicines Antihistamines reduce allergy symptoms such as sneezing, itchy or watery eyes, and a runny nose. They block the chemicals released by the immune system that cause an allergic response. For people with allergies such as those to peanuts or bee stings, severe symptoms can appear suddenly. An allergic reaction can lead to death. Individuals who know they are allergic to substances that cause severe reactions can ask a doctor to prescribe a single-dose shot of epinephrine. The medication will doctor can prescribe a single-dose medicine called epinephrine. The patient is taught to self-administer a shot with a single-dose injector.

Body-Regulating Medicines Some medicines regulate body chemistry. Insulin used by people with diabetes regulates the amount of sugar in their blood. Asthma sufferers may take medicines every day to control symptoms and prevent attacks. They may also use inhalers during an asthma attack. Cardiovascular medicines are taken to regulate blood pressure, normalize irregular heartbeats, or regulate other functions of the cardiovascular system.

AL **Antidepressant and Antipsychotic Medicines** Medications can also help people suffering from mental illnesses. These medicines can help regulate brain chemistry, or stabilize moods. For example, mood stabilizers are often used in the treatment of mood disorders, depression, and schizophrenia. Proper medication can help people with these diseases live healthy lives. As with other prescribed medications, it is important to talk to your doctor before you stop taking the medication, even if you feel better.

Cancer Treatment Medicines Some cancers can be treated and even cured. Some medicines can be used to treat cancer. These medicines can reduce rapid cell growth and help stop the spread of cancer cells. One drug, chemotherapy, uses chemicals to kill fast-growing cancer cells. Immunotherapy, or biological therapy, uses the body's immune system to fight the cancer cells. Because these medications can also destroy healthy cells, serious side effects may occur as part of the treatment. Other medications can help treat the side effects.

■ **Figure 19.2** Strep throat is a bacterial infection that is treated with antibiotics prescribed by a doctor. *Why is it important to take all of the antibiotics a doctor prescribes, even if you are feeling better?*

READING CHECK

Describe Give two reasons that a person would take a body-regulating medicine.

Caption Answer

Figure 19.2 When you don't finish the full prescription, all the bacteria in your system might not be killed. The remaining bacteria are likely to be the most resistant, or immune to treatment.

R **Reading Strategy**

Analyzing Content Some medicines are used to treat chronic conditions. **Ask Students:** *What are some chronic diseases that people live with and take medicine for daily or periodically?* (Sample answer: Allergies, asthma, some types of cancer)

AL **Active Learning**

Antidepressants In recent decades, antidepressants have become a commonly prescribed medicine for adults, and they are also prescribed for many children and teens. Ask interested students to investigate the risks and benefits of teens using antidepressants, including the conditions these medicines are prescribed for and the side effects that are important to watch for when teens take these drugs. Have students write a report about what they learn. **AL**

READING CHECK

Answer Sample answer: A person with diabetes can use insulin to regulate the amount of sugar in the blood. A person with cardiovascular disease can take medicines to regulate blood pressure, normalize irregular heartbeats, or regulate other functions of the cardiovascular system.

ELL Support

Name and Repeat Write the following terms on the board: *synergistic effect, antagonistic interaction.* Define each word aloud.

Beginning Say aloud a sentence such as "The synergistic effect of the two medicines gave the patient great relief from the symptoms of the illness." Ask students to repeat the sentence. Use the other term in a sentence, and ask students to repeat.

Intermediate Ask students for sentence examples of each term.

Advanced Ask students to use a dictionary to define these forms of the words: *synergy, antagonism, interact.* Have students write sentences with those words using the definitions they found.

■ **Figure 19.3** Medications help many people with conditions such as asthma and diabetes live active, normal lives. *How do medicines work to control these diseases?*

Taking Medications

Main Idea Medicines enter the body in a variety of ways.

Medicines can be delivered to the body in many ways. Factors that determine how a medicine is taken include what the medicine is used for, and how it will most quickly and effectively help a person.

- **Oral medicines** are taken by mouth in the form of tablets, capsules, or liquids. These medicines pass from the digestive system into the bloodstream.
- **Topical medicines** are applied to the skin. Transdermal skin patches also deliver a medicine through the skin.
- **Inhaled medicines,** such as asthma medicines, are delivered in a fine mist or powder.
- **Injected medicines** are delivered through a shot, and go directly into the bloodstream.

However you take a medicine, it is always important to follow the directions on the medicine label.

Reactions to Medications

Main Idea The effect of medicine depends on many factors.

Medicines can have a variety of effects. They can cause **side effects**, *reactions to medicine other than the one intended.* Some side effects may be mild, such as drowsiness, but others may be more severe, and can even cause death.

Medicine Interactions

When two or more medicines are taken together, or when a medication is taken with certain foods, the combination may have a different effect than when the medicine is taken alone. Types of medicine interactions include the following:

- **Additive interaction** occurs when *medicines work together in a positive way.* For example, an anti-inflammatory and a muscle relaxant may be prescribed to treat joint pain.
- **Synergistic effect**—*the interaction of two or more medicines that results in a greater effect than when each medicine is taken alone*—occurs when one medicine increases the strength of another.

528 **Chapter 19** Medicines and Drugs

Myths & Reality

Medicines

Myth: A person with a serious illness should put off taking pain killers for as long as possible.

Fact: A person does not build up a tolerance to pain killers, and pain killers rarely become addictive for someone with a medical need. Therefore, there is no reason that someone with pain should suffer. Putting off taking a pain killer until pain is almost unbearable could make managing the pain more difficult.

Myth: Modern medicines have conquered many communicable diseases.

Fact: The only modern medicines that can kill pathogens and cure a disease are antibiotics, and bacteria can become resistant to antibiotics. Most other medicines simply suppress the symptoms of a disease.

- **Antagonistic interaction** occurs when *the effect of one medicine is canceled or reduced when taken with another medicine.* For example, someone who receives an organ transplant must take anti-rejection medicines. If the person is diabetic and takes insulin, the anti-rejection medicine may decrease the effectiveness of the insulin.

Tolerance and Withdrawal

When a person takes a medication for a long period of time, the body can become used to the medication. Problems that may occur include:

- **Tolerance** is a condition in which the body becomes used to the effect of a medicine. The body requires increasingly larger doses to produce the same effect. Sometimes a person will experience "reverse tolerance." In this condition, the body requires less medicine.

- **Withdrawal** occurs when a person stops using a medicine on which he or she has become physiologically dependent. Symptoms of withdrawal can include nervousness, insomnia, severe headaches, vomiting, chills, and cramps which gradually ease in time. Talk to your health care provider if you experience withdrawal.

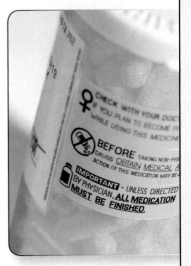

■ **Figure 19.4** Medicine labels include important information about possible side effects and interactions. *Why is it important to read this information before you take the medicine?*

LESSON 1 **ASSESSMENT**

After You Read

Reviewing Facts and Vocabulary

1. Define the term *medicine* and the term *drugs*.
2. What types of medicines fight pathogens? What types of medicines prevent disease?
3. Compare a *synergistic effect* with an *antagonistic interaction*.

Thinking Critically

4. **Analyze.** Why are vaccines given to children at a young age?
5. **Evaluate.** Explain why people should not stop taking prescribed medications without talking to their doctor.

Applying Health Skills

6. **Accessing Information.** Use reliable online resources to find information on new and experimental drugs. Write a paragraph evaluating one of the drugs, and list the reasons why you think the information is reliable.

Writing Critically

7. **Descriptive.** Write a paragraph describing why it's important to take a medicine as your doctor prescribed.

Go Online

Visit glencoe.com and complete the Interactive Study Guide for this lesson.

---

3 ASSESS/ CLOSE

Assessment Resources

📁 **FAST FILE ACTIVITIES**
Lesson 1 Quiz

💿 *ExamView Assessment Suite* CD-ROM

Visit glencoe.com for:
Online Quizzes
Online Learning Center

Progress Monitoring

Reteaching

Have pairs of students work together to make a two-column table entitled Types of Medicines. The first column should be labeled Type, and the second column should be labeled Description/Effects. Students should list the types of medicines discussed in the lesson and write details of each type.

Enrichment

Have students further investigate tolerance and withdrawal. Ask them to report on which kinds of medicines or which specific widely used medicines are associated with these conditions.

Go Online

Have students visit glencoe.com and complete the Interactive Study Guide for this lesson.

LESSON 1 ASSESSMENT ANSWERS

1. *Medicines* are drugs that are used to treat or prevent diseases or other conditions. *Drugs* are substances other than food that change the structure or function of the body or mind.
2. Antibiotics, antitoxins, antivirals, and antifungals
3. A *synergistic effect* causes the effect of one medicine to be greater, while an *antagonistic interaction* reduces or cancels the effect of one medicine.
4. The sooner vaccines are given, the sooner the risk of diseases is reduced.
5. Sample answer: If people stop, their symptoms may return. In the case of antibiotics, the bacteria may become resistant.
6. Research results will vary. Students should cite a reliable source for information.
7. Paragraphs will vary. Students should describe side effects, tolerance, and withdrawal.

529

Using Medicines Safely

1 FOCUS

GUIDE TO READING

BIG Idea Students will learn that medicines are safe if they are used for the intended purpose and according to directions. **Ask Students:** *What problems do you think could occur if you take more than the recommended dose of a medicine?* (Sample answer: The medicine itself could make you sick.)

Before You Read

T-Chart Students' T-charts will vary, though each should include the concept that prescription medicines need a written approval to buy while OTC medicines do not.

Main Idea

Standards for Medicines
The federal government tests and approves new medicines. **Ask Students:** *What does a drug company need to do to get permission to sell a new medicine?* (Sample answer: It needs to test the medicine to make sure it's safe and effective.)

Real Life Issues

Ask volunteers to read their dialogues aloud. Students may explain that two people may have different conditions or need a different amount of medicine to be safe.

LESSON **2**

GUIDE TO READING

BIG Idea *Medicines are safe only if they are used for the intended purpose and according to the directions on the label.*

Before You Read

Make a T-Chart. Make a two-column chart like the one below. Label one column "Prescriptions" and the other column "OTCs." As you read, fill in the first column with information about prescription medicines. Fill in the second column with information about over-the-counter (OTC) medicines.

Prescriptions	OTCs

New Vocabulary

- prescription medicines (p. 531)
- over-the-counter (OTC) medicines (p. 531)
- medicine misuse (p. 532)
- medicine abuse (p. 533)
- drug overdose (p. 533)

Using Medicines Safely

Real Life Issues

Safety First. Monica is on the swim team and has an earache. She visits her doctor, who prescribes an antibiotic. Monica is supposed to take the medicine for ten days. Her friend Amy, who is also on the swim team, thinks she may have an ear infection, too. Amy doesn't want to go to the doctor, though, so she asks Monica if she can share her medicine.

Writing *Write a dialogue in which Monica explains to Amy why she doesn't think she should share her medication.*

Standards for Medicines

Main Idea Medicines are regulated to make them safe.

All new medicines in the United States must meet standards set by the Food and Drug Administration (FDA). Before approving a drug for use, the FDA receives information about a medicine's chemical composition, intended use, effects, and possible side effects. Drug manufacturers test new medicines according to FDA guidelines. That includes completing at least three clinical trials for a drug. During a clinical trial, the drug is tested on human volunteers. They are monitored to determine the drug's effectiveness and to identify any harmful side effects.

Sometimes, if a drug hasn't yet completed clinical trials but is thought to be effective, people with life-threatening illnesses are allowed to use the drug. This usage is referred to as *experimental*. Patients are given experimental drugs only after clinical trials show that the drugs are safe and may be effective in treating their illness.

Home and Community

Pharmacists Perhaps the people in the community who know the most about medicines are the pharmacists who work in drugstores and the pharmacies of grocery and department stores. A pharmacist has at least a college degree in pharmacy, and some are doctors of pharmacy (PharmD). Although a physician needs to know about medicines in order to prescribe them, a pharmacist has to know about every medicine prescribed, including drug interactions and side effects. Pharmacists advise the public about medicines, including over-the-counter medicines. Divide the class into small groups. Ask each group to collaborate on a list of questions to ask a pharmacist and then make an appointment to interview a local pharmacist about medicines.

The FDA does not regulate herbal and dietary supplements. These supplements do not go through the same testing procedures or meet the same strict requirements for safety and proven effectiveness. Many people believe that herbal supplements are safe because some are advertised as "natural." Even supplements made from natural compounds can have harmful side effects or interactions. Never take any supplement without telling you health care provider first.

Prescription Medicines

Prescription medicines are *medicines that are dispensed only with the written approval of a licensed physician or nurse-practitioner.* A licensed pharmacist dispenses these medicines. Prescription medicines provide only the amount of medicine that is needed to treat your condition. If more medicine is needed, your health care provider must approve a refill. A prescription medicine should be taken *only* by the person whose name appears on the label.

Over-the-Counter (OTC) Medicines

Over-the-counter (OTC) medicines, or *medicines you can buy without a doctor's prescription* are available without a prescription. The FDA considers these medicines to be safe if they are used as the label directs. However, all medicines can harm you if not used according to the directions.

While all OTC medicines are available without a prescription, the distribution of some OTC medicines is controlled. For example, cold medications that contain pseudoephedrine must be kept behind the pharmacy counter. These medications can be used to make highly addictive, illegal drugs.

Medicine Labels

When the FDA approves a medicine, it is considered safe when used as directed. The FDA requires that all prescription and OTC medicine labels contain information telling consumers how to use the medicine safely and effectively. The requirements for prescription and OTC medicine labels differ. Prescription medicine labels must also include any special instructions for taking the medicine, the prescribing doctor's name, the patient's name, the pharmacy's name and address, the date the prescription was filled, the prescription number, and whether refills are allowed. **Figure 19.7** on page 532 shows the information that must appear on all OTC medicine labels.

■ **Figure 19.6** Medicines are regulated by the FDA, but herbal supplements are not. *Explain whether herbal supplements are safer than medicines.*

READING CHECK

Describe How would you obtain a prescription medicine?

---

2 TEACH

U Universal Access

Understanding Abbreviations
Explain to students who are learning English that it's common to abbreviate multiple-word nouns and adjectives by using the initial letters in each word. An over-the-counter medicine becomes an *OTC* medicine. This is especially true for government agencies, such as the *Food and Drug Administration,* or *FDA.* Once the abbreviation is established, the full name often is rarely used. **EL**

Caption Answer

Figure 19.6 Sample answer: Herbal supplements are not safer than medicines because they are not regulated by the FDA and may have harmful side effects.

AL Active Learning

Researching FDA Approval
Ask students to research the process a new medicine goes through, from the initial research at a drug company to the final approval by the FDA. Ask students to collaborate on a large flowchart of the process that can be displayed on a classroom wall. **AL**

READING CHECK

Answer With the written approval of a licensed physician or nurse practitioner

---

Teacher to Teacher

Kathy Marlowe • C. Reynolds High School, Asheville, NC

Peer-to-Peer Teaching I have learned the importance of peers teaching peers. To prepare for this activity, I make up seven packets with information on the drug categories along with a drug chart. In groups of three or four, the students will select a drug category to research. They will answer the following questions: (1) drugs in that category, (2) how they affect the body, (3) short-term effects, (4) long-term effects, and (5) one interesting fact that they learned about their drug category. When students have finished their research, I have them come up and present to the class their information. As the information is being presented on the overhead, each student in the class is filling in his or her chart.

LESSON 2

BusinessWeek HEALTH NEWS

After students have watched the video, *Drugs Get Smart*, have them meet in small groups to discuss the benefits of personalized drug treatments. Then, ask each student to write a paragraph expressing an opinion about whether tailored drugs are an advancement or not. Call on volunteers to read their paragraphs aloud. Encourage informal debate on the issue.

Main Idea

Medicine Misuse It is dangerous to take medicines when there is no need for them or without following the label's directions. **Ask Students:** *Why do people sometimes take a medicine when there's no need for it?* (Sample answer: They do it to get some other effect, such as getting "high.")

C Critical Thinking

Identifying Cause and Effect
Describe a teen who is using an OTC topical medicine for acne, taking an herbal supplement for weight loss, and chewing on antacids every day for indigestion. The teen comes down with strep throat, and the doctor prescribes an antibiotic. Ask students what the teen should do before filling the prescription and taking the antibiotic. (The teen should let the doctor know about all medicines he or she is taking in order to avoid an antagonistic interaction.) **OL**

Figure 19.7 Over-The-Counter Medicine

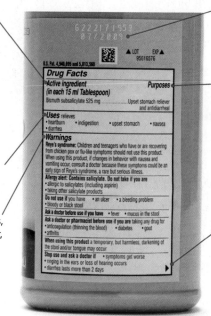

Active Ingredient: Ingredient that treats condition, including amount per unit

Inactive Ingredients: Substances added to the product that do not help treat the condition, such as flavor and color

Uses: Conditions or symptoms treated by the product

Warnings: Side effects, interactions, when to talk to a doctor, when not to take the product, keep out of reach of children

Expiration Date: The date you should no longer use the medicine

Purpose: Product category and what the product is supposed to do, such as antacid

Other Information and Directions: Some information may be printed on the opposite side of the label. This information may include how to take the medicine, how to store the product, and required information about certain ingredients, such as sodium

Medicine Misuse

Main Idea Taking medicines unnecessarily or without following the label instructions is dangerous.

BusinessWeek HEALTH NEWS

Drugs Get Smart

Analyze. Go to glencoe.com and watch the video *Drugs Get Smart*. In a group, discuss the benefits connected to personalized drug treatments. Write a paragraph explaining why you think the tailored drugs may or may not be an advancement in the treatment of medicine.

Medicine misuse can prevent the user from getting the full benefit of the medicine and can have serious health consequences. **Medicine misuse** involves *using a medicine in ways other than the intended use.* Examples of medicine misuse are:

- Failing to follow the instructions on or in the package
- Giving a prescription medicine to a person for whom it was not prescribed, or taking another person's medicine
- Taking too much or too little of a medicine
- Taking a medicine for a longer or shorter period than prescribed or recommended
- Discontinuing use of a medicine without informing your health care provider
- Mixing medicines without the knowledge or approval of your health care provider

532 Chapter 19 Medicines and Drugs

Teens Want to Know

Are OTC Diet Pills Safe to Take? Most are safe in that the FDA makes sure OTC medicines are safe to use. OTC diet pills, though, contain ingredients that you probably should not be taking unless your doctor thinks it necessary. Most OTC diet pills contain stimulants, such as caffeine and a chemical called PPA, that suppress the appetite somewhat. A stimulant also decreases drowsiness, and taking stimulants regularly may cause insomnia. Many diet pills that contain stimulants can also cause dizziness, anxiety, headaches, depression, and even irregular heartbeat. These side effects make taking OTC diet pills more of a problem than they're worth.

Medicine Abuse

Intentionally taking medications for nonmedical reasons is **medicine abuse**. Most teens—96 percent—use medicines correctly. Some, however, think that medicines requiring a prescription and OTC medicines are safer than illegal drugs. Abusing any medicine is dangerous and illegal. Teens should avoid using drugs to:

- To lose weight or stay awake while studying. A healthy diet and exercise are the safest way to maintain a healthy weight. Getting plenty of sleep and managing your time wisely will help you study effectively.

- To fit in with peers. A dangerous trend is the emergence of "pill parties," where teens mix whatever OTC and prescription medicines are available. Mixing medicines, drugs, or alcohol is extremely dangerous.

- Avoid taking any medicine that was prescribed to someone else. Medicines are prescribed to treat a specific illness. It's illegal and unsafe to use a drug not prescribed to you.

One danger of medicine misuse is **drug overdose**—*a strong, sometimes fatal reaction to taking a large amount of a drug.* Misusing medicines can also lead to addiction. Never use a medicine other than how it is prescribed or intended.

READING CHECK

List What are some ways that teens might abuse medicines?

Explore **glencoe.com** and complete the Student Web Activity describing how dietary supplements are regulated.

LESSON 2 ASSESSMENT

After You Read

Reviewing Facts and Vocabulary

1. How do *prescription medicines* differ from *OTC medicines*?

2. List four pieces of information that must be on an OTC medicine label. Describe the purpose of each piece of information.

3. What is *medicine misuse*? How does it differ from *medicine abuse*?

Thinking Critically

4. **Analyze.** Why does the FDA regulate medicines and the information on medicine labels?

5. **Evaluate.** What are three ways you can avoid medicine abuse?

Applying Health Skills

6. **Advocacy.** Create a bookmark that gives information on the importance of correct medicine use.

Writing Critically

7. **Expository.** Create a script for a commercial or PSA that explains how people can use their health care providers, pharmacists, and medicine labels to ensure that they are using their medicines properly.

Visit **glencoe.com** and complete the Interactive Study Guide for this lesson.

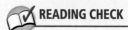 **READING CHECK**

Answer Sample answer: Teens may think stimulants will help them lose weight.

(3) ASSESS/ CLOSE

Assessment Resources

📁 **FAST FILE ACTIVITIES**
Lesson 2 Quiz

💿 *ExamView Assessment Suite* CD-ROM

Visit glencoe.com for:
Online Quizzes
Online Learning Center

Progress Monitoring

Reteaching
Divide the class into small groups, and ask each group to write ten questions related to information discussed in Lesson 2. Then, have groups exchange and answer each other's questions.

Enrichment
Assign a common OTC medicine and ask students to examine the medicine label at a store and take notes on the information provided. Have them write a report that includes the active ingredient, inactive ingredients, uses, purpose, directions for use, warnings, and other information.

Go Online

Have students visit **glencoe.com** and complete the Interactive Study Guide for this lesson.

LESSON 2 ASSESSMENT ANSWERS

1. *Prescription medicines* are dispensed only with the approval of a licensed physician or nurse practitioner. An *OTC* can be bought without a prescription.

2. Sample answers: Active ingredient, uses, directions, and warnings

3. Using a medicine in ways other than the intended use; medicine abuse is taking medication for nonmedical reasons.

4. Sample answer: To ensure that they work as intended and that consumers have the information to use medicines safely

5. Sample answers: Avoid using drugs to lose weight and to fit in. Avoid taking medicine that was prescribed for a family member.

6. Bookmarks will vary but should contain accurate information.

7. Scripts will vary.

533

Stay Informed

NHES Standard 8 Students will demonstrate the ability to advocate for personal, family, and community health.

Teaching Objectives

- Demonstrate the ability to understand the health risks and benefits of medicines.
- Advocate for proper use of medicines by developing an informative pamphlet or poster.

Teaching Strategies

- Divide students into teams of four or five and supply them with index cards and paper bags.
- When all cards are completed, have teams exchange bags. Have teams compete in matching terms with definitions until one team matches all cards in their bag correctly.
- Discuss with the class their ideas for creating a pamphlet or poster. Ask volunteers to suggest ways to focus their resource for a specific audience. For example, a poster might be more appropriate for younger audiences, a pamphlet for more mature groups.

Assessment

Using a rubric, student work should provide comprehensive evidence of the following criteria to achieve the highest score:

✓ Clear, health-enhancing stand

✓ Support for the position with relevant information

✓ Awareness of the audience

✓ Encouragement of others to make healthful choices

Activity **Stay Informed**

Medicines can treat many health problems. If they're taken improperly, however, the same medicines can cause health problems. Working in teams of four or five, compete to determine which team can better define medicine terms. Then, create an informative pamphlet or poster on how to use medicines wisely.

What You'll Need

- textbook for each student
- six index cards per student
- pens or pencils
- small paper bag, one per team
- markers, paints, and poster board

What You'll Do

Step 1

Form teams of four or five. Write each vocabulary term on an index card and the definition of each term on a different index card.

Step 2

Place all the cards into a bag.

Step 3

At your teacher's signal, exchange bags with another team and match each term with the correct definition.

Apply and Conclude

Create a poster or pamphlet listing medicine facts. Persuade others to make positive health choices regarding the use of medicines.

Checklist: Advocacy

✓ Clear, health-enhancing message

✓ Support for the position with relevant information

✓ Awareness of the audience

✓ Encouragement of others to make healthful choices

Health Literacy

Medicine Safety Some students may want to include safety tips about taking medicines on their posters. Here are several tips for using medicines safely:

- When you buy a medicine, make sure the package is tightly sealed and has never been opened.

- When you pick up a prescription, make sure it's the right medicine. For example, if you've taken a pill before, check to see that the prescription contains pills of the same size, shape, and color.

- Ask your doctor or pharmacist whether taking a medicine will affect everyday activities, such as concentrating at school or driving a car.

To download quizzes and eFlashcards to your PDA, go to glencoe.com and click on the Study to Go icon.

LESSON 1

The Role of Medicines

Key Concepts

▸ Medicines can help manage chronic conditions, including allergies, diabetes, asthma, and depression, and can treat cancer.

▸ Medicines can be taken orally or topically. They can be inhaled or taken by injection.

▸ When taking medicines, some people may experience side effects or allergies.

▸ When medicines interact, they may have a different effect than intended.

Vocabulary

▸ medicines (p. 524)
▸ drugs (p. 524)
▸ side effects (p. 528)
▸ additive interaction (p. 528)
▸ synergistic effect (p. 528)
▸ antagonistic interaction (p. 529)

LESSON 2

Using Medicines Safely

Key Concepts

▸ The FDA regulates medicines and their distribution to make sure that medicines are safe and effective.

▸ Written approval in the form of a prescription is needed for some medicines, but OTC medicines can be bought without a prescription.

▸ Medicines can be dangerous if they are not used as directed.

Vocabulary

▸ prescription medicines (p. 531)
▸ over-the-counter (OTC) medicines (p. 531)
▸ medicine misuse (p. 532)
▸ medicine abuse (p. 533)
▸ drug overdose (p. 533)

 Online

Students can visit glencoe.com to

• review content online with the Online Student Edition.

• test their knowledge of chapter content with Online Quizzes.

• access Interactive Health Tutor for more practice with vocabulary.

Assessment Resources

📁 **FAST FILE ACTIVITIES**
Chapter 19 Test

💿 *ExamView*
Assessment Suite CD-ROM

Visit glencoe.com **for:**
Audio Chapter Summaries
Online Quizzes

STUDY TO GO Tell students to visit glencoe.com where they can download quizzes and eFlashcards.

Chapter 19 Review **535**

Study Tips

Missed Classes Explain to students that everyone misses class occasionally. Even when a class is missed for a legitimate reason, students are still responsible for knowing the material discussed in class that day. One way to solve this problem is to form a partnership with another student at the beginning of the course. Each agrees to provide notes to the other when circumstances cause one student to miss class. If an agreement hasn't been made with a partner, a student who has missed class should ask other students if they would share their notes. A last resort is the teacher. Most teachers will find a way to provide notes for a class that has been legitimately missed.

Chapter 19 Assessment Answers

CHAPTER 19   Assessment

LESSON 1

Vocabulary Review

1. synergistic effect
2. side effects
3. Medicines
4. additive interaction
5. drug

Understanding Key Concepts

6. a
7. d
8. c
9. b
10. b
11. a
12. c

Thinking Critically

13. Sample answer: When a patient does not finish the full prescription of an antibiotic, not all the bacteria in a person's system are killed. The remaining bacteria are likely to be the most resistant.

LESSON 1

Vocabulary Review

Correct the sentences below by replacing the italicized term with the correct vocabulary term.

1. A(n) *drug* is the interaction of two or more medications that results in a greater effect than when each medicine is taken alone.

2. People may experience *synergistic effects* while taking a medicine, which are effects that are not intended.

3. *Antagonistic interactions* are used to treat or prevent disease, and are dangerous when mixed with alcohol.

4. A(n) *side effect* occurs when medicines work together in a positive way.

5. A(n) *additive interaction* is a substance other than food that changes the structure or function of the body or mind.

Understanding Key Concepts

After reading the question or statement, select the correct answer.

6. A vaccine for polio will do which of the following?
   a. Causes the body to make antibodies to fight polio
   b. Causes people to develop the polio disease
   c. Protects the body against the measles virus
   d. Protects people against polio for a short time

7. What type of medicine might your doctor prescribe if you have an ear infection caused by bacteria?
   a. Antifungal
   b. Antitoxin
   c. Antiviral
   d. Antibiotic

8. What type of medicine might your doctor prescribe if you have the flu?
   a. Antitoxin
   b. Antibiotic
   c. Antiviral
   d. Antifungal

9. Why would you take an antihistamine?
   a. To cure an allergy
   b. To relieve allergy symptoms
   c. To slow an allergic reaction
   d. To build immunity

10. If a person takes two medicines at the same time and one is less effective than when taken alone, what is this called?
    a. Additive interaction
    b. Antagonistic interaction
    c. Side effect
    d. Synergistic effect

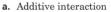

11. What type of medication is aspirin?
    a. Analgesic
    b. Antiviral
    c. Antihistamine
    d. Antibiotic

12. A body-regulating medication would not be used for which of the following?
    a. Diabetes
    b. Asthma
    c. Headache
    d. High blood pressure

Thinking Critically

After reading the question or statement, write a short answer using complete sentences.

13. **Analyze.** How do bacteria become resistant to certain types of antibiotics?

Health eSpotlight VIDEO Wrap-Up

Medicines and the Body Have students reread the Health eSpotlight questions at the beginning of the chapter (page 523) and look at their original answers. **Ask Students:** *What do you now know about the importance of following a doctor's instructions that you didn't know before reading the chapter?* Call on volunteers to describe what they have learned and how they would change their responses.

14. **Evaluate.** Why do narcotic pain relievers require a doctor's prescription?

15. **Describe.** How can medication help people with mental illness?

16. **Compare.** What might taking a medicine orally rather than taking a medicine topically help a person?

17. **Explain.** What can result if a person takes a medication for a long period of time?

18. **Evaluate.** Anne does not like the side effects of the prescription medicine she is taking. Why should she talk to her doctor before she stops taking the medicine?

19. **Describe.** How does a vaccine work? Can a vaccine help cure disease? If so, how?

20. **Explain.** What is the difference between a synergistic effect and an antagonistic effect when taking medicines?

LESSON 2

Vocabulary Review

Use the vocabulary terms listed on page 535 to complete the following statements.

21. Medicines that you can buy without a doctor's prescription are called _____.

22. If you take a large amount of a medicine, you could have a life-threatening reaction known as a(n) _____.

23. Intentionally taking medicines for nonmedical reasons it is known as _____.

24. Medicines that are available only with the recommendation of a doctor, and are dispensed only by a licensed pharmacist are called _____.

25. Failing to follow the instructions on or included with a medicine package is an example of _____.

Understanding Key Concepts

After reading the question or statement, select the correct answer.

26. Which does *not* describe a prescription medication?
   a. Only a specified amount is distributed.
   b. Written approval is required.
   c. It should be taken only by the person it is prescribed to.
   d. It can be purchased without a doctor's recommendation.

27. Which must have proven safety and effectiveness before being sold?
   a. Prescription medicines
   b. Herb-based diet pills
   c. Protein shake drink mix
   d. Vitamins

28. Which of the following information is *not* on an OTC medicine label?
   a. The directions for taking the medicine
   b. The expiration date
   c. The inactive ingredients in the medicine
   d. The name of the pharmacy

29. Which of the following is a way a person could misuse a medicine?
   a. Taking only half of the prescription with your doctor's approval
   b. Saving half of an antibiotic prescription in case you get sick later
   c. Following the instructions on the medicine label
   d. Taking two medicines at the same time, as directed by a doctor

30. Why might teens abuse medicines?
   a. They take medicine only as prescribed by a doctor.
   b. They do not like the side effects of a certain medicine.
   c. They believe the medicine may help them study longer.
   d. They think the medicine is hard to obtain.

Chapter 19 Assessment **537**

14. Sample answer: Narcotic pain relievers can be addictive.

15. Sample answer: Certain drugs can affect the way the brain works by regulating brain chemistry.

16. Medicines taken orally are taken by mouth in the form of tablets, capsules, or liquids, and the medicine reaches the circulatory system through the digestive system. Topical medicines are applied to the skin.

17. Sample answer: The person could develop a tolerance for the medicine or become dependent on the medicine.

18. Sample answer: She may not get well if she stops, and going off a medicine can have worse effects than the side effects. Her doctor may be able to help reduce the side effects or prescribe another medicine.

19. Sample answer: Most vaccines contain weakened or dead pathogens. When the vaccine is injected, the body produces antibodies that can easily destroy those weakened or dead pathogens. The body also produces memory cells that recall how to make antibodies for that pathogen.

20. Synergistic effect is when one medicine increases the effect of another. Antagonistic effect is when one medicine cancels or reduces the effect of another.

LESSON 2

Vocabulary Review

21. over-the-counter (OTC) medicines
22. drug overdose
23. medicine abuse
24. prescription medicines
25. medicine misuse

ExamView®
Assessment Suite

Create and customize tests in minutes with this convenient digital platform.

- Create differentiated tests quickly and easily.
- All questions correlated to National/State Standards.
- Enhance tests with Document Based Questions (DBQ) and add your own photos or graphics.
- Build tests in both English and Spanish.
- Generate progress reports.

To order, go to **glencoe.com** and search for ISBN 0-07-888173-0.

Assessment

Understanding Key Concepts

26. d
27. a
28. d
29. b
30. c
31. d
32. c

Thinking Critically

33. Sample answer: Herbal supplements are not regulated by the FDA and could have adverse effects.

34. Sample answer: Certain medicines contain chemicals that can be used to make illegal drugs.

35. Sample answer: The label tells you how to use the medicine safely.

36. Sample answer: Before a drug can be approved, it must be tested to make sure that it is safe and effective.

37. Sample answer: If you take a medicine not prescribed for you, you don't know how your body will react. If you don't know your proper dosage, you could have a drug overdose. If you mix medicines, you risk harmful interactions.

---

31. Which is *not* a risk of abusing medicines?
    a. Addiction
    b. Death from heart failure
    c. Paranoia
    d. Taking too little medicine

32. Which of the following organizations tests and approves all prescription medicines before they are sold to the public?
    a. the Centers for Disease Control and Prevention
    b. the U.S. Department of Agriculture
    c. the Food and Drug Administration
    d. the Consumer Product Safety Commission

Thinking Critically

After reading the question or statement, write a short answer using complete sentences.

33. **Explain.** Why should you talk to your doctor before taking herbal supplements?

34. **Analyze.** Why does the FDA limit the distribution of certain OTC medicines?

35. **Explain.** Why should you always read the label before taking a medicine?

36. **Evaluate.** How do the FDA guidelines for approving medicines protect the health of the public?

37. **Discuss.** How can taking medicines not prescribed to you, or mixing medicines, harm your health?

Project-Based ASSESSMENT

Explaining Vaccines

Background

Your body's immune system has the ability to recognize foreign material, such as bacteria and viruses, and destroy them. Your body remembers features of these pathogens so that if they reappear, you will fight them easily and effectively. Vaccines use this principle to help protect you. By exposing your immune system to parts of a pathogen, or a pathogen that has been altered so it cannot hurt you, a vaccine allows your body to prepare for that pathogen if you become infected with it later.

Task

Create a cartoon or comic book that explains to young children how vaccines work.

Audience

Students in grades 1 through 3

Purpose

Explain why vaccines work, and how important they are in maintaining your health.

Procedure

1. Review the text and write notes describing some basic facts about vaccines.

2. Conduct research to learn how the body's immune system works. Find answers to these questions: How do vaccines help prepare the body to fight pathogens? How do antitoxins work? Can vaccines and antitoxins fight disease?

3. Collect various cartoons or comic books to see the different styles and formats that you might use.

4. Create and draw your cartoon or comic book. Be sure your facts are accurate. Use words and pictures that clearly show how vaccines work.

5. Read your cartoon or comic book to younger students. Let them study the illustrations.

6. Ask the younger students follow-up questions to assess whether they learned how vaccines work.

Project-Based ASSESSMENT

Step 1 Research Have students use library and online resources to find out more about how vaccines work.

Step 2 Create a Cartoon or Comic Book Have students create cartoons or comic books. Students should also prepare three to five questions to assess whether younger students learned how vaccines work from the cartoon or comic book.

Step 3 Evaluate Make sure students include accurate information about how vaccines work in their cartoons or comic books. The information should be presented on a level that can be understood by young children. Have students write a self-evaluation of their work.

Visit glencoe.com for Project-Based Assessment rubrics.

Math Practice

Interpret Graphs. The table below shows the percentages of nonmedical use of psychotherapeutics among 12- to 17-year-olds. Use the table to answer Questions 1–3.

Non-Medical Use of Psychotherapeutics Among 12- to 17-Year-Olds

	Past Year		Past Month	
	1999	2000	1999	2000
Any Psycho-therapeutic*	7.1%	7.1%	2.9%	3.0%
Pain Relivers	5.5%	5.4%	2.1%	2.3%
Tranquilizers	1.6%	1.6%	0.5%	0.5%
Sedatives	0.5%	0.5%	0.2%	0.2%
Stimulants**	2.1%	2.4%	0.7%	0.8%

* Denotes the non-medical use of any prescription-type pain reliver, tranquilizer, stimulant, or sedative; does not include over-the-counter drugs.
** Includes methamphetamine

Source: U.S. Department of Health and Human Services, Substance Abuse and Mental Health Services Administration, NHSDA

1. If the 12,000 students surveyed in 1999 were all ninth graders, how many of them have never used any psychotherapeutic drugs in the past year?
   A. 10,000
   B. 11,148
   C. 852
   D. 967

2. After reviewing the chart above, determine the mean, median, and mode of the 2000 data.

3. On one line graph, show the trend, both annually and monthly, of prescription drug abuse in 1999.

G⊙ Online

For more test practice, visit **glencoe.com** and complete the Online Quizzes for Chapter 19.

Reading/Writing Practice

Understand and Apply. Read the passage below, and then answer the questions.

> Aspirin was first introduced by a German company in 1899. Centuries earlier, people used similar chemicals to ease pain and reduce fever. The ancient Greeks used a bitter powder extracted from the bark of willow trees to treat pain. In the 1700s, physicians treated patients with another willow-derived substance that was later discovered to be the chemical salicin.
>
> By the mid-1800s, European pharmacists used an acid form of salicin to treat arthritis. However, patients who took salicylic acid would often suffer from a painful side effect, a severe upset stomach. With the introduction of the milder aspirin, many patients experienced pain relief with fewer stomach problems.

1. What was the author's purpose in writing this piece?
   A. To list the dosages of aspirin
   B. To describe the types of pain relievers
   C. To explain how aspirin works
   D. To tell how aspirin products are used

2. Which sentence best represents the main idea of the second paragraph?
   A. Arthritis causes pain and swelling.
   B. Salicylic acid relieves pain, but can irritate the digestive tract.
   C. European pharmacists tend to prescribe painkillers other than aspirin.
   D. Older aspirin-like products caused stomach irritation.

3. Write a pamphlet that outlines the importance of following a doctor's instructions when taking medicines.

National Education Standards
Math: Number and Operations
Language Arts: NCTE 3, NCTE 4

Standardized Test Practice

Standardized Test Practice Answers

Math Practice
1. B
2. Mean, 3.4; median, 2.4, mode, none (no number occurs more than once)
3. Students' graphs should have the type of drug plotted on the y-axis and the number of students plotted on the x-axis. The graph line should reflect the values given in the table.

Reading/Writing Practice
1. D
2. D
3. Pamphlets will vary. Students should include the idea that following doctors' instructions is the only safe way to use medicines. Students should support main points in the pamphlet with relevant information from the passage.

National Education Standards

Math: Number and Operations

Language Arts: NCTE 3, NCTE 4

For the complete Math and Language Arts standards, visit **glencoe.com**.

G⊙ Online

Online Study Tools
For more test practice, visit **glencoe.com** and complete the Online Quizzes for Chapter 19.

Test-Taking Tip

Mean, Median, and Mode Tell students that some math questions on standardized tests give a list of numbers and ask them to determine the mean, median, and mode. Point out that these are all types of averages. Explain that to determine the mean of a list of numbers, you divide the sum of the numbers by the total number of numbers in the list. To determine the median, you put all the numbers in order from the smallest to the largest and then choose the middle number in the list. If the list has an even number of numbers, then the median is the sum of the two middle numbers divided by 2. To determine the mode, you find the number that appears most often in the list. If no number appears more than once, then the list has no mode.

Chapter 20 pages 540–563	Standards		Features
	National	**State/Local**	**TIME** HEALTH
	1.12.3, 1.12.5, 2.12.5, 2.12.9, 2.12.10, 4.12.1, 5.12.6, 8.12.1, 8.12.2		• Clearing the Air, page 558
Lesson 1 **The Health Risks of Tobacco Use** pages 542–547 **BIG Idea** The chemicals in all tobacco products harm the body.	1.12.5, 1.12.7, 1.12.8, 2.12.7, 2.12.9, 3.12.2, 4.12.1, 5.12.1, 5.12.4, 5.12.6, 8.12.1, 8.12.4		**Real World CONNECTION** • Health Risk of Tobacco, page 547 🕐 Out of Time
Lesson 2 **Choosing to Live Tobacco-Free** pages 548–552 **BIG Idea** Avoiding tobacco use will bring lifelong health benefits.	1.12.1, 1.12.5, 2.12.7, 2.12.9, 2.12.10, 3.12.2, 4.12.2–4.12.4, 7.12.1		VIDEO **BusinessWeek HEALTH NEWS** • Quit Smoking: New Year's Resolution, page 550 **Health Skills Activity** • Helping Teens Stay Tobacco-Free (Advocacy), page 552 🕐 Out of Time
Lesson 3 **Promoting a Smoke-Free Environment** pages 553–557 **BIG Idea** Secondhand smoke is harmful, but there are ways to reduce exposure.	1.12.1, 1.12.3, 2.12.5, 2.12.9, 2.12.10, 4.12.1, 5.12.6, 8.12.1, 8.12.2		**TEENS Making a Difference** • A Voice for Change, page 556

30 Min (Lesson 1) · *30 Min* (Lesson 2) · *30 Min* (Lesson 3)

Key to Ability Levels

Teaching Strategies and activities have been coded for ability level and appropriateness.

AL Activities for students working above grade level   **BL** Activities for students working below grade level

OL Activities for students working on grade level   **EL** Activities for English Learners

Glencoe Exclusive!
TeacherWorks Plus
All-In-One Planner and Resource Center

Resources	Lesson Assessment	Technology
Student Activity Workbook **TEACH** **FAST FILE RESOURCES** Vocabulary Practice **TEACH** Health Labs **EXTEND**	Chapter 20 Review Chapter 20 Assessment Standardized Test Practice ⊙ *ExamView® Assessment Suite* CD-ROM	**Teaching Tools:** ⊙ *TeacherWorks*™ Plus DVD ⊙ *StudentWorks*™ Plus DVD ⊙ *ExamView® Assessment Suite* CD-ROM 🖳 Transparency ⊙ Fitness DVD ⊙ PowerPoint® DVD ⊙ Health eSpotlight Video Series DVD
FAST FILE RESOURCES Reading Strategies Activity **TEACH** Reteaching Activity **REVIEW** Enrichment Activity **EXTEND** Health Skills Practice **TEACH**	Lesson 1 Assessment, page 547 📁 Lesson 1 Quiz *Fast File* ⊙ *ExamView® Assessment Suite* CD-ROM	**Web-Based Resources:** **Go Online** glencoe.com • Health Podcast Activities • Audio Chapter Summaries (English/Spanish) • Interactive Health Tutor
FAST FILE RESOURCES Reading Strategies Activity **TEACH** Reteaching Activity **REVIEW** Enrichment Activity **EXTEND** Health Skills Practice **TEACH**	Lesson 2 Assessment, page 552 📁 Lesson 2 Quiz *Fast File* ⊙ *ExamView® Assessment Suite* CD-ROM	• Health Skills Activities • Vocabulary PuzzleMaker • Parent Letters (English/Spanish) • Lesson Plans • Health Inventories • Online Quizzes
FAST FILE RESOURCES Reading Strategies Activity **TEACH** Reteaching Activity **REVIEW** Enrichment Activity **EXTEND** Health Skills Practice **TEACH**	Lesson 3 Assessment, page 557 📁 Lesson 3 Quiz *Fast File* ⊙ *ExamView® Assessment Suite* CD-ROM	• Study-to-Go • Unit Web Projects • Student Web Activities • Fitness Zone Activities

StudentWorks Plus

This is the student's backpack solution.

Includes:
• complete Interactive Student Edition
• full audio of English text and Spanish chapter summaries
• allows students to record assignments and track grades.
• links to online activities and additional student resources
• access to all student worksheets and workbooks

Dinah Zike Foldables® **FOLDABLES® Study Organizer**
Chapter Activity
Refer to the *Dinah Zike Reading and Study Skills for Glencoe Health*. Have students make a vocabulary book Foldable to record and define new vocabulary and concepts related to tobacco use. Students can label the tabs with vocabulary terms and concepts and give definitions and examples under the tabs.

Key to Symbols

 Transparencies   **REVIEW** activities to review or reinforce content

 CD-ROM   **TEACH** activities to teach basic concepts

 glencoe.com   **EXTEND** activities to extend or enrich lesson content

 Print Resources

Tobacco

Chapter Overview

Chapter 20 focuses on the health risks of using tobacco and ways of avoiding tobacco.

Lesson 1

All forms of tobacco contain substances that harm the body and cause disease.

Lesson 2

Living tobacco-free has many health, emotional, and social benefits.

Lesson 3

Environmental tobacco smoke causes health problems in smokers and nonsmokers. Efforts to create a smoke-free society are gaining ground in the United States.

▶ **Activating Prior Knowledge**

After students have finished writing, call on volunteers to read their paragraphs aloud. As students describe various messages they've seen, discuss whether students think the anti-tobacco messages have helped reduce tobacco use among teens.

CHAPTER **20** **Tobacco**

Lesson 1

The Health Risks of Tobacco Use

BIG Idea *The chemicals in all tobacco products harm your body.*

Lesson 2

Choosing to Live Tobacco-Free

BIG Idea *Avoiding tobacco use will bring lifelong health benefits.*

Lesson 3

Promoting a Smoke-Free Environment

BIG Idea *Secondhand smoke is harmful, but there are ways you can reduce your exposure.*

Activating Prior Knowledge

Using Visuals As this billboard shows, people are getting the message out about the dangers of tobacco use. Write a short paragraph comparing and contrasting the anti-tobacco and pro-tobacco messages you have seen in advertisements.

540

Universal Access

Differentiated Learning Glencoe provides teacher support and student materials for all learners in the health classroom.

- Chapter Summaries in English and Spanish are available online at **glencoe.com**.

- *Fast Files* and related worksheets support reluctant readers.

- Universal Access strategies throughout the Teacher Wraparound Edition and *Fast Files* help you present materials for gifted students, at-risk students, physically impaired students, and those with behavior disorders or learning disabilities.

Chapter *Launchers*

Health in Action

Discuss the **BIG** Ideas

Before beginning this chapter, think about how you would answer these questions:

- ▶ In what ways does tobacco harm your body?
- ▶ What are the consequences of tobacco use?
- ▶ Why should you avoid secondhand smoke?

Watch the *Health eSpotlight* Video Series

VIDEO

The Truth and the Lies

What would you say to encourage a friend to avoid tobacco use? How do tobacco ads lie to the public?

Assess Your Health

Go Online

Visit **glencoe.com** and complete the Health Inventory for Chapter 20.

Chapter 20 Tobacco **541**

Chapter *Launchers*

Health in Action

Discuss the **BIG** Ideas

Assign this activity before students read the chapter. Explain that the purpose of the questions is to help students assess their current knowledge of the consequences of tobacco use to both smokers and non smokers.

Health eSpotlight
Video Series

VIDEO *The Truth and the Lies*

Before Viewing the Video

Ask Students: *What do you think is most important for a person to know before starting to use tobacco?* (Sample answer: Using tobacco can cause lung cancer and other serious illnesses.) After students have watched the video, discuss how understanding long-term consequences can affect a person's decision-making process.

Go Online

Have students go to **glencoe.com** and take the Health Inventory for Chapter 20.

Chapter Skills

Reading Skills
- Reviewing Facts and Vocabulary, pp. 547, 552, 557
- Reading/Writing Practice, p. 563

BIG Idea

Students will learn about the health risks of tobacco use and about living tobacco-free.

Vocabulary
- New Vocabulary, pp. 542, 548, 553
- Reviewing Facts and Vocabulary, pp. 547, 552, 557

Health Skills
- Health Skills Activity, p. 551
- Applying Health Skills, pp. 547, 552, 557

Writing Skills
- Real World Connection, p. 547
- Writing Critically, pp. 547, 552, 557
- Reading/Writing Practice, p. 563

LESSON 1

The Health Risks of Tobacco Use

1 FOCUS

📖 **GUIDE TO READING**

BIG Idea Students will learn about the substances in tobacco and the harmful effects of tobacco use. **Ask Students:** *What are some harmful effects of smoking tobacco products?* (Sample answer: Being out of breath during physical activity, getting lung cancer and other diseases)

Before You Read

Venn Diagram Students' Venn diagrams will vary.

Main Idea

Health Risks of Tobacco Use
All tobacco products contain chemicals that can cause serious health problems. **Ask Students:** *What substance in tobacco causes a person to become addicted?* (Nicotine)

Real Life Issues

Pair students to work on a dialogue together. Ask volunteers to share their dialogues with the class. Most students will have Elena telling Victor that smoking will hurt his performance on the soccer field and may have worse long-term effects. Students should also describe effective ways that Victor can reduce stress.

542

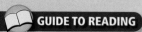

LESSON 1

📖 **GUIDE TO READING**

BIG Idea *The chemicals in all tobacco products harm your body.*

Before You Read

Create a Venn Diagram. Draw a Venn diagram that has two overlapping circles. Label one circle "Tobacco Smoke" and the other circle "Smokeless Tobacco." Write the risks of each in the circles. Put the risks shared by both in the area where the circles overlap.

Tobacco Smoke — Smokeless Tobacco

New Vocabulary

- addictive drug (p. 543)
- nicotine (p. 543)
- stimulant (p. 543)
- carcinogen (p. 543)
- tar (p. 543)
- carbon monoxide (p. 543)
- smokeless tobacco (p. 544)
- leukoplakia (p. 544)

The Health Risks of Tobacco Use

Real Life Issues ....

Dealing with Stress. Elena's older brother, Victor, attends high school, has a part-time job, and is on the soccer team. He feels stressed because he does not have enough time to work, play soccer, and study. Victor has started smoking because he thinks it will help him deal with his stress.

Writing *Write a dialogue having Elena tell Victor what she has learned in health class about the dangers of tobacco use. Have Elena suggest other ways that Victor can deal with his stress.*

Health Risks of Tobacco Use

Main Idea All forms of tobacco contain chemicals that are dangerous to your health.

Advertisements for tobacco products often feature healthy, attractive people, sending the message that using tobacco has no health consequences. So what's the truth about tobacco? All tobacco products display warning labels stating that using tobacco products can be harmful to an individual's health.

Medical studies have shown that tobacco use is the leading cause of preventable death and disability in the United States. Any form of tobacco use, such as smoking, chewing, or dipping tobacco, can cause health problems. Smoking has been linked to lung disease, cancers, and heart disease. About 90 percent of adult smokers began the habit as teenagers. Most teens think that they can just quit whenever they choose. The reality is that quitting is difficult. It's easier to avoid tobacco use rather than quit later.

More About...

Teens and Tobacco Use Although teen tobacco use has fallen in recent years, too many teens are still using tobacco products. Here are a few statistics about teen tobacco use:

- About 23 percent of high school students and 10 percent of middle school students are current smokers.

- About a third of children and teens who try cigarettes become regular smokers.

- About 9.9 percent of high school boys and 1.2 percent of high school girls use smokeless tobacco.

■ **Figure 20.1** All tobacco products must carry warning labels showing they are harmful to your health. *Why do people who use tobacco ignore these warnings?*

Nicotine

Tobacco users have difficulty quitting because tobacco contains an **addictive drug**, *a substance that causes physiological or psychological dependence.* All tobacco products contain **nicotine**, *the addictive drug found in tobacco leaves.* Nicotine is a **stimulant**, *a drug that increases the action of the central nervous system, the heart, and other organs.* Using nicotine raises blood pressure, and increases the heart rate. You will learn more about the effects of addictive drugs in Chapter 22.

Poisonous Substances in Tobacco Smoke

HS Tobacco is an addictive and toxic drug. It's a **carcinogen**, *a cancer-causing substance.* Tobacco smoke contains tar and carbon monoxide. It also contains the same poisonious compounds found in products such as paint, rat poison, and toilet cleaner.

Tar Cigarette smoke contains **tar**, *a thick, sticky, dark fluid produced when tobacco burns.* The tar damages a smoker's respiratory system by paralyzing and destroying cilia, the tiny hairlike structures that line the upper airways and protect the body against infection. Tar also destroys the alveoli, or air sacs, which absorb oxygen and rid the body of carbon dioxide. Lung tissue is also damaged, reducing lung function. Smokers are susceptible to diseases such as bronchitis, pneumonia, emphysema, heart disease, and cancer. As many as 87 percent of cancer deaths result from smoking.

Carbon Monoxide **Carbon monoxide**, *a colorless, odorless, and poisonous gas,* is another compound found in cigarette smoke. It is absorbed more easily than oxygen. Carbon monoxide deprives the body's tissues and cells of oxygen. It also increases the risk of high blood pressure, heart disease, hardening of the arteries, and other circulatory problems.

Go Online

Go to glencoe.com and complete the Student Web Activity on the efforts tobacco companies make to market their products to teens.

READING CHECK

Identify List three harmful substances in tobacco smoke.

---

2 TEACH

Caption Answer

Figure 20.1 People who use tobacco ignore the warnings because they are addicted to the nicotine.

HS Health Skills Practice

Poster Divide the class into small groups, and ask each group to make a poster that shows the harmful substances in tobacco products. A poster might have an illustration of a burning cigarette with callouts that identify and explain nicotine, carcinogens, tar, and carbon monoxide. Encourage groups to be creative in their approaches. Display the posters in the classroom. **BL** **OL** **EL**

Go Online

Have students visit glencoe.com and complete the Student Web Activity on the efforts tobacco companies make to market their products to teens.

READING CHECK

Answer Tar, nicotine, and carbon monoxide

ELL Support

Name and Repeat Write the following terms on the board: *nicotine, stimulant, carcinogen.* Define each term aloud.

Beginning Use each word in a sentence, such as "Both nicotine in tobacco and caffeine in coffee are stimulants." Ask students to repeat each sentence.

Intermediate Ask students for sentence examples for each word.

Advanced Have students do research to make a list of 1) common stimulants and 2) other substances in which carcinogens are found.

Pipes, Cigars, and Smokeless Tobacco

Main Idea No tobacco product is safe to use.

The dangers of tobacco use are not limited to smoking cigarettes. The smoke from pipes and cigars also causes serious health consequences. Cigars contain significantly more nicotine and produce more tar and carbon monoxide than cigarettes. One cigar can contain as much nicotine as an entire pack of 20 cigarettes. Pipe and cigar smokers also increase the risk of developing cancers of the lips, mouth, throat, larynx, lungs, and esophagus.

Another form of tobacco that some believe to be safer to use than cigarettes is **smokeless tobacco**, *tobacco that is sniffed through the nose, held in the mouth, or chewed.* Smokeless (sometimes called "spit") tobacco products are *not* a safe alternative to smoking. The nicotine and carcinogens in these products are absorbed into the blood through the mucous membranes in the mouth or the digestive tract.

The harmful chemicals of smokeless tobacco are absorbed into the body at levels up to three times the amount of a single cigarette. That's because the exposure to harmful chemicals in smokeless tobacco is often three times longer than that of a smoked cigarette. Using smokeless tobacco also irritates the sensitive tissues of the mouth, causing **leukoplakia** (loo-koh-PLAY-kee-uh), or *thickened, white, leathery-looking spots on the inside of the mouth that can develop into oral cancer.* Smokeless tobacco causes cancers of the mouth, throat, larynx, esophagus, stomach, and pancreas. People who chew eight to ten plugs of tobacco each day take in the same amount of nicotine as a smoker who smokes two packs of cigarettes a day. Smokeless tobacco is as addictive as smoked tobacco, making quitting just as difficult as it is for someone who uses smoked tobacco.

R

Harmful Effects of Tobacco Use

Main Idea Tobacco use causes both short-term and long-term damage to your body.

Health officials have warned the public about the dangers of tobacco use for several **decades**. **Figure 20.3** shows how smoking can damage one body system, the lungs. If a pregnant female smokes, she risks the health of her fetus, as well as her own health. Pregnant women who smoke during pregnancy risk giving birth to an infant with a low birth weight and other health problems.

Academic Vocabulary

decade *(noun):* a group or set of ten

Sidebar (left column)

Main Idea

Pipes, Cigars, and Smokeless Tobacco It is not safe to use any tobacco product. **Ask Students:** *What are some smokeless tobacco products?* (Sample answers: Chewing tobacco and snuff)

Caption Answer

Figure 20.2 Sample answer: Talk to friends and family, participate in anti smoking campaigns

---

Main Idea

Harmful Effects of Tobacco Use Using tobacco has negative short-term and long-term effects on the body. **Ask Students:** *How can smoking tobacco hurt you in the short term?* (Sample answer: Smoking reduces cardiorespiratory endurance, making you out of breath when you play sports.)

R **Reading Strategy**

Cause and Effect Ask students what happens when smokeless tobacco is absorbed into the body. (It's absorbed at levels of up to three times the amount of a single cigarette.) Why? (Because the exposure to the harmful chemicals is often three times longer than a smoked cigarette) **BL OL**

■ **Figure 20.2** Cigarette filters do not protect smokers from the more than 50 carcinogens, including cyanide and arsenic, which are in tobacco products. The filters themselves contain poisonous chemicals such as those used in insecticides, paint, toilet cleaner, antifreeze, and explosives. *How can you warn others about the risks of using tobacco products?*

Myths & Reality

Smoking

Myth: Air pollution outside is much more harmful than environmental tobacco smoke (ETS) indoors.

Fact: The risk a person has for developing cancer from carcinogens in ETS is 100 times greater than the risk of developing cancer from carcinogens in the air outside.

Myth: It's safe to smoke in the home when children are away.

Fact: Even if the smoke is gone, dust, surfaces, and furniture in the home can become contaminated with carcinogens and other toxins that can be inhaled and ingested by children.

Short-Term Effects

Some effects of tobacco use occur immediately. These short-term effects include the following:

- **Brain chemistry changes.** The addictive properties of nicotine cause the body to crave more of the drug. The user may experience withdrawal symptoms, such as headaches, nervousness, and trembling as soon as 30 minutes after the last tobacco use.

- **Respiration and heart rate increase.** Breathing during physical activity becomes difficult and endurance is decreased. Nicotine may cause an irregular heart rate.

- **Taste buds are dulled and appetite is reduced.** Tobacco users often lose much of their ability to enjoy food.

- **Users have bad breath, yellowed teeth, and smelly hair, skin, and clothes.** If tobacco use continues for any length of time, these unattractive effects can become permanent.

Long-Term Effects

Over time, tobacco use can cause damage to many body systems, as shown in **Figure 20.4** on page 546. People who are exposed to others who smoke can also suffer many health problems. Here are some of those health problems:

- **Chronic bronchitis** can occur when the cilia in the bronchi become so damaged that they are useless. This leads to a buildup of tar in the lungs, causing chronic coughing and excessive mucus secretion.

- **Emphysema** is a disease that destroys the tiny air sacs in the lungs. The air sacs become less elastic, making it more difficult for the lungs to absorb oxygen. A person with advanced emphysema uses up to 80 percent of his or her energy just to breathe.

- **Lung cancer** can develop when the cilia in the bronchi are destroyed, and extra mucus cannot be expelled. Cancerous cells can multiply, block the bronchi, and move to the lungs. Nearly 90 percent of lung cancer deaths are caused by smoking.

- **Coronary heart disease and stroke** can be caused by nicotine. Nicotine constricts blood vessels, which cuts down blood flow to the body's limbs. Nicotine also contributes to plaque buildup in the blood vessels, which can lead to hardened arteries, a condition called *arteriosclerosis*. Arteries may become clogged, increasing the risk of heart attack and stroke. The risk of developing heart disease is greater for smokers than for nonsmokers.

- **A weakened immune system** from long-term tobacco use makes the body more vulnerable to disease.

■ **Figure 20.3** Smokers cause severe damage to their lungs. Compare the healthy lung (top) with the one damaged by tobacco smoke (bottom). *How do tar and the other substances in tobacco smoke affect the respiratory system and its ability to function?*

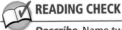 **READING CHECK**

Describe Name two ways in which the health of long-term tobacco users will suffer.

Lesson 1 The Health Risks of Tobacco Use **545**

CHAPTER 20

LESSON 1

W Writing Support

Children's Book Divide the class into small groups, and ask each group to write and illustrate a children's book that could be used to teach young students about the short-term effects of tobacco use. Groups might draw cartoons, produce labeled illustrations, or use images printed from the Internet. Tell students that the information the book contains should be accurate but also understandable to elementary-school students. **AL**

C Critical Thinking

Compare and Contrast Have students work in pairs. Pairs should write a two-paragraph summary comparing and contrasting short-term and long-term effects of smoking. Encourage students to divide the work so that one partner writes and the other partner verbalizes the similarities and differences. **BL OL**

Caption Answer

Figure 20.3 Breathing during physical activity becomes more difficult; long-term effects include chronic bronchitis, emphysema, and lung cancer

READING CHECK

Answer Sample answer: Users' lungs will become damaged, and they may develop lung cancer or emphysema.

Teacher to Teacher

Raymond Farmer, Morristown-Hamblen High School West, Morristown, TN

Negative Effects of Tobacco Use In an effort to make a more permanent impact on the negatives of tobacco use, I have the students research some of the various chemicals found in tobacco (example: nicotine, cyanide, formaldehyde, etc.). They then discuss the harmful effects of each chemical and then the effect of all as a whole. They also list both short and long-term effects (as many as possible) and what these effects may lead to. After this, we look at recovery of smokers and smokeless tobacco users after they quit and the time it takes to get the damage repaired to the body based on findings of the USDA and American Heart Association.

R Reading Strategy

Analyzing a Graphic Direct students' attention to **Figure 20.4**. For each body system identified as affected by tobacco use, call on a volunteer to briefly explain the function of that system. Call on another volunteer to explain how each of the health problems listed beneath a system would affect that system's ability to function and thus affect a person's overall health. **OL**

W Writing Support

Personal Writing Have students write a letter to a fictitious friend who is addicted to a tobacco product. Students should include health risks as well as other consequences, such as the cost to the individual. Have volunteers share their letters with the class. **OL**

Main Idea

Other Consequences of Tobacco Use Using tobacco has serious costs beyond the health risks. **Ask Students:** *How does tobacco use by individuals cost society as a whole?* (Sample answer: Tobacco use costs society a great deal in medical expenses.)

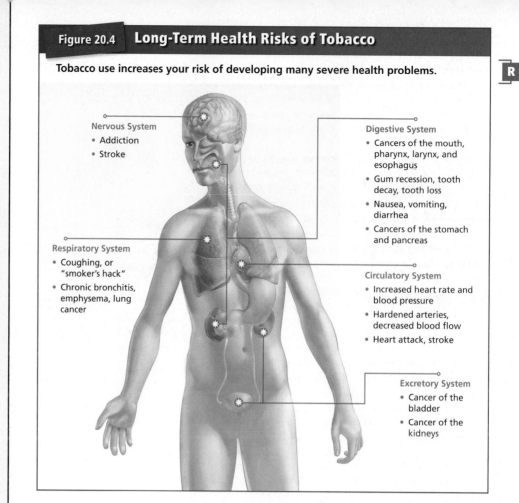

Figure 20.4 Long-Term Health Risks of Tobacco

Tobacco use increases your risk of developing many severe health problems.

Nervous System
• Addiction
• Stroke

Digestive System
• Cancers of the mouth, pharynx, larynx, and esophagus
• Gum recession, tooth decay, tooth loss
• Nausea, vomiting, diarrhea
• Cancers of the stomach and pancreas

Respiratory System
• Coughing, or "smoker's hack"
• Chronic bronchitis, emphysema, lung cancer

Circulatory System
• Increased heart rate and blood pressure
• Hardened arteries, decreased blood flow
• Heart attack, stroke

Excretory System
• Cancer of the bladder
• Cancer of the kidneys

Other Consequences of Tobacco Use

Main Idea As well as health risks, tobacco use is costly.

Making the decision to avoid the use of tobacco products will safeguard your health.

- **Costs to society.** Tobacco-related illnesses cost the United States about $165 billion each year. Productivity suffers when smokers call in sick due to tobacco-related illnesses.
- **Cost to individuals.** A person smoking one pack of cigarettes a day will spend about $1,500 a year on the habit.
- **Legal consequences.** Selling tobacco products to individuals under the age of 18 is illegal. Using tobacco products on school property may lead to suspension or expulsion.

W

Teens Want to Know

Will Quitting Smoking Make a Person Gain Weight? In the short term, yes. The average weight gain is 5 to 10 pounds. The reasons? Smoking burns calories; nicotine is an appetite suppressant; and a person who quits smoking tends to eat more as a replacement for smoking. However, a person who quits smoking can counteract this tendency by increasing daily physical activity or eating fewer high-fat, high-calorie foods. The person who quits smoking is much healthier with a few extra pounds and no more harmful effects from tobacco.

Real World CONNECTION

Health Risks of Tobacco

Latoya knows that tobacco use causes serious health problems. She wants to encourage her friends to avoid tobacco use. She does Internet research to learn more about the health effects of tobacco use.

Latoya researches statistics on tobacco-related deaths. She finds figures from the CDC listing the estimated annual number of smoking-related deaths in the United States:

- ▶ Lung cancer .... 123,800 deaths
- ▶ Other cancers .... 34,700 deaths
- ▶ Chronic lung disease .... 90,600 deaths
- ▶ Coronary heart disease ...... 86,800 deaths
- ▶ Stroke................................. 17,400 deaths
- ▶ Other diagnoses .... 84,600 deaths

Activity Reading / Writing

Using reliable resources, conduct research to learn more about tobacco use among teens. Search for the following information:

1. How many teens begin smoking each year?

2. How can tobacco use affect a teen's physical health?

3. What impact can tobacco use have on a teen's mental/emotional and social health?

After completing your research, write a persuasive essay urging teens who use tobacco to quit. Include information urging teens who have never smoked not to start the habit.

Real World CONNECTION

Have students meet in small groups to conduct the research.

 ASSESS/ CLOSE

Assessment Resources

📁 **FAST FILE ACTIVITIES**
Lesson 1 Quiz

💿 *ExamView*
Assessment Suite CD-ROM

Visit glencoe.com for:
Online Quizzes
Online Learning Center

LESSON **1** ASSESSMENT

After You Read

Reviewing Facts and Vocabulary

1. What is an *addictive drug*? What is the addictive drug in tobacco?

2. List three types of toxic substances found in cigarette smoke. Why are these substances harmful?

3. Explain four ways using tobacco immediately affects your body.

Thinking Critically

4. **Identify.** What are three ways in which tobacco use affects the respiratory system?

5. **Analyze.** In addition to protecting your health, explain reasons you should not use any form of tobacco.

Applying Health Skills

6. **Advocacy.** Write an editorial for a newspaper that encourages people to quit using tobacco products, and explain the long-term effects of tobacco use on the body.

Writing Critically

7. **Persuasive.** Create a pamphlet raising awareness of the health risks of tobacco use. Include information on the long-term effects of tobacco use.

G⊕ Online

Visit glencoe.com and complete the Interactive Study Guide for this lesson.

Progress Monitoring

Reteaching

Have students work in pairs to list the short- and long-term effects on health of using tobacco, and the serious consequences of using tobacco beyond the harmful health effects.

Enrichment

Have students investigate further the effects of using smokeless tobacco and make a poster warning teens about the dangers.

G⊕ Online

Have students visit **glencoe.com** and complete the Interactive Study Guide for this lesson.

LESSON **1** ASSESSMENT ANSWERS

1. A substance that causes physiological or psychological dependence; nicotine

2. Nicotine, tar, carbon monoxide; nicotine causes addiction, tar causes such diseases as emphysema and lung cancer, carbon monoxide deprives the body of oxygen.

3. *Any four:* Brain chemistry changes; respiration and heart rates increase; taste buds are dulled; appetite is reduced; users have bad breath, yellowed teeth, and smelly clothes

4. Sample answer: Breathing during physical activity becomes difficult, tar destroys cilia and alveoli, and lung cancer may develop.

5. Sample answer: Tobacco products cost too much, and I could become addicted.

6. Editorials will vary, but should demonstrate an understanding of the long-term effects of using tobacco.

7. Pamphlets will vary.

LESSON 2

Choosing to Live Tobacco-Free

1 FOCUS

GUIDE TO READING

BIG Idea Students will learn that not using tobacco has lifelong benefits. **Ask Students:** *What is the worst thing you'll avoid by avoiding the use of tobacco?* (Sample answer: Getting a terrible disease when I get older)

Before You Read

T-Chart Students' T-charts will vary.

Main Idea

Teens and Tobacco Fewer teens are starting to use tobacco. **Ask Students:** *What do you think is the main reason some teens begin to smoke?* (Sample answer: Their older friends or parents smoke, and so they think smoking will make them look mature.)

Real Life Issues ··············

Have students meet in small groups to discuss the questions and collaborate on answers. Then, lead a class discussion on how a friend could encourage Juan to quit and support his efforts.

LESSON 2

GUIDE TO READING

BIG Idea *Avoiding tobacco use will bring lifelong health benefits.*

Before You Read

Make a T-Chart. Make a two-column chart like the one below. Label one column "Start" and the other column "Quit." Fill in the first column with reasons why teens start using tobacco. Fill in the second column with reasons why tobacco users want to quit using tobacco.

Start	Quit

New Vocabulary

▸ nicotine withdrawal (p. 551)
▸ nicotine substitutes (p. 551)
▸ tobacco cessation program (p. 551)

Choosing to Live Tobacco-Free

Real Life Issues ···························

Quitting Smoking. Juan started smoking a year ago. Juan does not like the hold that tobacco has on him, so he has decided to quit. It's been harder than he thought it would be. His friends Joe and Pamela want to help Juan become tobacco-free, but they aren't sure how.

Writing *Write a short essay explaining how Juan's friends can encourage him to quit and support his efforts.*

Teens and Tobacco

Main Idea Fewer teens are starting to use tobacco.

The number of nonsmokers in the United States, including teens, is on the rise. Knowing the health risks of tobacco use helps teens make the healthful decision to stay tobacco-free. However, some teens are influenced by tobacco company advertisements and other pressures. These teens may begin to use tobacco.

Why Some Teens Use Tobacco

Teens start smoking for many reasons. Some teens falsely believe that smoking will help control their weight or cope with stress. Others believe that smoking will make them seem mature and independent. The truth is that smoking reduces the body's capacity for physical activity, so it actually may lead to weight gain. Health problems caused by tobacco use and nicotine dependency may increase the tobacco user's stress level. Many times, teens are influenced to try tobacco products by movies, TV, and advertisements. Media images may convince teens that tobacco use is glamorous.

Home and Community

Helping Smokers Quit Many smokers want to quit, but find quitting difficult. Most communities have tobacco cessation programs to help smokers quit. Ask interested students to research a smoking cessation program for teens in North Carolina called NOT (No On Tobacco). Have students compare their strategies with another organization's to find out if the strategies are the same for adults and teens. Students should prepare a report.

■ **Figure 20.5** Teens who choose a tobacco-free lifestyle will feel mentally and physically better than teens who use tobacco. *What are some healthful ways to control weight and relieve stress?*

Reduced Tobacco Use Among Teens

AL

More teens recognize the health risks of tobacco use and are avoiding the use of tobacco products. The CDC reports that 77 percent of high school students nationwide do not smoke. This number is up from 65 percent just a few years ago, as shown in **Figure 20.6**. Several factors contribute to this trend:

HS

- **Tobacco legislation.** In 1998, tobacco companies and 46 states reached a legal settlement that restricts tobacco advertising aimed at young people. Tobacco companies are required to fund ads that discourage young people from smoking. It is illegal for anyone under the age of 18 to purchase tobacco products in the United States.

- **No-smoking policies.** Legislation has limited smoking in public places and businesses.

- **Family values.** Teens whose parents avoid tobacco use are more likely to avoid tobacco use themselves.

- **Positive peer pressure.** Teens who do not smoke act as healthy role models for other teens.

- **Health risks.** More teens understand that tobacco use can lead to diseases, such as health disease, cancer, and respiratory problems.

READING CHECK

Explain Why has tobacco use among teens decreased?

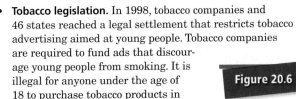

Figure 20.6 **Teens Smoking Less**

High school students who reported smoking a cigarette in the last 30 days

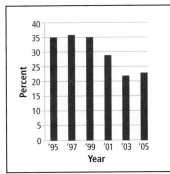

Source: Center for Disease Control and Prevention, 2005

Lesson 2 Choosing to Live Tobacco-Free **549**

2 TEACH

AL Active Learning

Survey Have students generate questions for a survey of teen tobacco use, such as, *Are you currently a smoker? Do you use smokeless tobacco? Do you object to the smell of smoke on others?* Then ask volunteers to develop a ten-question questionnaire to be used to survey area teens. The questionnaire should include a statement that ensures the participants' anonymity. Have students tabulate the data, and discuss the results as a class. **OL**

HS Health Skills Practice

Communication Have interested students write a report on the history of tobacco legislation and/or new nonsmoking policies in various states. Students should be sure to include reliable sources of information in their reports. When completed, have volunteers share what they've found with the class. **AL**

Reading Strategy

Organizing Information Begin an outline of Lesson 2 on the board by using the section headings as the outline's first level: "Teens and Tobacco," "Benefits of Living Tobacco-Free," and "Quitting Tobacco Use." Call on a volunteer to provide the second level of headings under "Teens and Tobacco": "Why Some Teens Use Tobacco" and "Reduced Tobacco Use Among Teens." Write these second level headings on the board. Ask students to complete the outline. Remind them to include highlighted, boldface terms and the important concepts under the second level heads.

Main Idea

Benefits of Living Tobacco-Free Choosing not to use tobacco brings many benefits. **Ask Students:** *What is a benefit of not using tobacco other than having better physical health?* (Sample answer: Not smelling like smoke)

VIDEO BusinessWeek
HEALTH NEWS

After students have watched the video, *Quit Smoking: New Year's Resolution,* have them write their paragraph. Then, call on volunteers to describe one of the methods for discouraging nicotine use and state an opinion about whether the method would be effective. Ask if anyone has a different opinion about that method. Encourage informal debate about the effectiveness of each method described.

Main Idea

Quitting Tobacco Use There are good reasons to quit tobacco use. **Ask Students:** *What do you think the hardest thing about quitting tobacco would be?* (Sample answer: Overcoming the cravings)

R Reading Strategy

Reasons to Quit Write "Reasons to Quit Tobacco Use" on the board. Ask volunteers to identify reasons why a teen would decide to quit. Students can draw on the list in their text and add other reasons of their own. Then, ask why quitting tobacco can be very difficult to do despite all these reasons to quit. (Symptoms of nicotine withdrawal) **BL**

550

VIDEO BusinessWeek
HEALTH NEWS

Quit Smoking: New Year's Resolution

Analyze. Go to glencoe.com and watch the video *Quit Smoking: New Year's Resolution.* Consider the new approaches that companies and health care providers are taking to discourage nicotine use. In a paragraph, explain whether you think these methods will be effective.

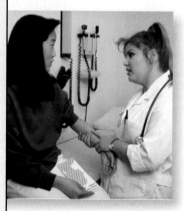

■ **Figure 20.7** Health care professionals can help tobacco users find the resources they need to successfully quit using tobacco. *Why is it difficult for people to quit?*

Benefits of Living Tobacco-Free

Main Idea A tobacco-free lifestyle has many benefits.

If you do not use tobacco, you have better cardiovascular endurance and lung function. You can improve your fitness level and athletic performance. When you avoid tobacco, you reduce your risk of lung cancer, heart disease, and stroke.

Living tobacco-free has mental/emotional and social benefits, too. You will have a sense of freedom because you know that you are not dependent on an addictive substance. You will have less stress because you do not have to worry about tobacco-related health problems. You will have more confidence in social situations because you look and feel better.

Strategies for Avoiding Tobacco

The best way to avoid the negative consequences of tobacco use is never to start using tobacco products. With these strategies, you can stick to your decision to live tobacco-free:

- **Surround yourself with positive influences.** Being around people who share your healthy-living values and beliefs will strengthen your commitment to lead a tobacco-free life. Choose friends who do not use tobacco.

- **Reduce peer pressure.** By staying away from situations where tobacco products may be used, you reduce the chance of being pressured to use tobacco.

- **Be prepared with refusal skills.** Practice in advance what you will say if someone offers you tobacco. Be assertive, and leave the situation if the pressure continues. Be confident and stand up for your healthy choices.

Quitting Tobacco Use

Main Idea There are good reasons for quitting tobacco use.

Teens who use tobacco give these reasons for quitting:
- They begin to have health problems, such as asthma, coughing, or respiratory infections.
- They realize the high cost of tobacco or find it difficult to purchase tobacco products if they are under 18.
- They realize that using tobacco can lead to other risky behaviors, such as the use of alcohol and other drugs.
- They understand the damaging effects of secondhand smoke and do not want to harm others.
- They feel more powerful because they are not controlled by an addiction to nicotine.

R

Health Literacy

Nicotine Replacement Therapy Both over-the-counter and prescription medicines are used to help tobacco users quit. The method employed by most medicines is nicotine replacement therapy, which involves providing a substitute source of nicotine while the tobacco user quits smoking or using smokeless tobacco. The amount of nicotine is gradually reduced to limit withdrawal symptoms. Over-the-counter medicines come in three main forms—patches, gum, and lozenges. Some prescription medicines come as inhalers or nasal sprays. When used with behavioral counseling, nicotine replacement therapy has about a 35–40 percent success rate.

Ending the Addiction Cycle

Overcoming nicotine addiction can be difficult, but millions of people have succeeded. It is not impossible. It is common to experience symptoms of **nicotine withdrawal**, *the process that occurs in the body when nicotine, an addictive drug, is no longer used.* Symptoms can include irritability, difficulty concentrating, anxiety, sleep disturbances, and cravings for tobacco. To relieve the symptoms, some people use **nicotine substitutes**, *products that deliver small amounts of nicotine into the user's system while he or she is trying to give up the tobacco habit.* These include gum, patches, nasal sprays, and inhalers. Some are over-the-counter products; others require a doctor's prescription. Smoking while using nicotine substitutes is dangerous due to increased nicotine exposure.

Getting Help to Quit Tobacco Use

People who want to quit can try the following strategies:

- **Prepare for the quit day.** Set a target date, and stick to it. Prepare your environment and avoid tobacco triggers.

- **Get support and encouragement.** Tell everyone you know about your plan to quit. Support from family and friends will increase a person's chance of success.

- **Access professional health services.** Seek advice from a doctor, enroll in a **tobacco cessation program**—*a course that provides information and help to people who want to stop using tobacco*—or join a support group. Other helpful resources include the American Lung Association, the American Cancer Society, the Centers for Disease Control and Prevention (CDC), and local hospitals. Many high schools also sponsor tobacco cessation programs.

- **Replace tobacco use with healthy behaviors.** Try sugarless gum or carrots until cravings pass. Physical activity, good nutrition, avoiding drugs and alcohol, and using stress-management techniques can help you succeed.

READING CHECK

Describe What are the symptoms of nicotine withdrawal?

Go Online

Explore **glencoe.com** and complete the Student Web Activity on the American Lung Association's recommendations for quitting smoking.

Lesson 2 Choosing to Live Tobacco-Free **551**

Advocacy: Helping Teens Stay Tobacco-Free

NHES Standard 8 Students will demonstrate the ability to advocate for personal, family, and community health.

Objectives

- Advocate for increased awareness of why tobacco products should not be on display.
- Influence peers to stay tobacco-free.

Teaching Strategies

- Review with students reasons why some teens start smoking.
- If possible, use a camera to take photos of a few local supermarket tobacco displays to show students before they write their letters.

Assessment

Using this list, student work should provide comprehensive evidence of the following criteria to achieve the highest score:

√ Takes a clear, health-enhancing stand
√ Completes a respect-ful, well-written letter with relevant supporting information
√ Creates a well-constructed petition that could be circulated in the community
√ Encourages others to make healthful choices

Cooperative Learning

Teen Tobacco Cessation Program
After students have read about strategies for quitting tobacco use, divide the class into small groups. Ask each group to design a tobacco cessation program for teen tobacco users. Students should keep in mind such questions as, *Where should those in the program meet? How long would each session last? What should occur at each session? How should adults be involved?* Ask each group to explain its program to the class. Discuss the elements of each group's program that students think would be particularly effective.

③ ASSESS/ CLOSE

Assessment Resources

📁 **FAST FILE ACTIVITIES**
Lesson 2 Quiz

💿 *ExamView*
Assessment Suite CD-ROM

Visit glencoe.com for:
Online Quizzes
Online Learning Center

Progress Monitoring

Reteaching
Call on students at random to list factors that contributed to reduced teen tobacco use, strategies teens can use for avoiding tobacco use, and strategies for getting help in quitting tobacco use.

Enrichment
Have students research and report on the various over-the-counter products sold at local pharmacies to help people quit smoking. Ask students to find out how the products help in the cessation of tobacco use.

G⊘ Online
Have students visit **glencoe.com** and complete the Interactive Study Guide for this lesson.

552

Health Skills Activity
Advocacy

Helping Teens Stay Tobacco-Free

Isabella recently quit smoking with the help of her friend, Anthony. Isabella told Anthony that she started smoking after giving in to the peer pressure. She also believed that tobacco products were not harmful to her health. She felt that tobacco products in a locked case at her local supermarket looked appealing. Anthony and Isabella want to discourage other teens from using tobacco by asking store managers to use less prominent product displays.

Writing Write a persuasive letter to a store manager asking that tobacco products be removed from open display areas. Include the following information in your letter:

1. Health problems caused by tobacco use.
2. The number of deaths each year from tobacco use.
3. The financial cost of tobacco-related health issues.

LESSON 2 ASSESSMENT

After You Read

Reviewing Facts and Vocabulary
1. What are four reasons that smoking among teens is on a downward trend?
2. List three reasons that you might use to convince a friend to quit using tobacco products.
3. Why might some people use nicotine substitutes when quitting smoking?

Thinking Critically
4. **Evaluate.** How will staying tobacco-free benefit your physical, mental/emotional, and social health?
5. **Synthesize.** Explain how the media influences teens to use and not to use tobacco products.

Applying Health Skills
6. **Refusal Skills.** Write a scenario describing a teen being pressured to use tobacco. Develop three refusal statements that the teen can use to avoid tobacco use.

Writing Critically
7. **Narrative.** Write a short story from the point of view of someone who is trying to quit smoking. Include at least three reasons for quitting and why it might be difficult to quit.

G⊘ Online

Visit **glencoe.com** and complete the Interactive Study Guide for this lesson.

LESSON 2 ASSESSMENT ANSWERS

1. Sample answer: Anti-tobacco messages, expense, no smoking policies, positive peer pressure
2. Sample answer: Cost, health problems, hard to buy
3. A nicotine substitute delivers small amounts of nicotine into the user's system while the user is trying to quit a tobacco habit.
4. Sample answer: I will reduce my risk of having severe health problems, I will look healthier, and I will not waste my money on tobacco.
5. Sample answer: Ads and movies make smoking look cool; antismoking media campaigns encourage people to stop using tobacco products.
6. Scenarios will vary. Have students role-play their scenarios and practice their refusal statements.
7. Short stories will vary.

Promoting a Smoke-Free Environment

Real Life Issues

Avoiding Secondhand Smoke.
Ken visits his aunt and uncle once a week. Ken's uncle smokes and often lights up a cigarette while Ken is in the room. Ken doesn't like breathing secondhand smoke, but he doesn't want to offend his uncle. He is not sure what he can do to convince his uncle not to smoke.

Writing *Write a paragraph about what you would do in this situation if you were Ken.*

Health Risks of Tobacco Smoke

Main Idea Tobacco smoke can harm nonsmokers.

The health effects of tobacco smoke affect smokers and nonsmokers alike. Nonsmokers who breathe air containing tobacco smoke are also at risk for health problems. **Environmental tobacco smoke (ETS)**, or secondhand smoke, is *air that has been contaminated by tobacco smoke.* ETS is composed of **mainstream smoke**, *the smoke exhaled from the lungs of a smoker,* and **sidestream smoke**, *the smoke from the burning end of a cigarette, pipe, or cigar.* Because mainstream smoke has been exhaled by a smoker, it contains lower concentrations of carcinogens, nicotine, and tar. For this reason, sidestream smoke is more dangerous than mainstream smoke. ETS from cigarettes, cigars, and pipes contains more than 4,000 chemical compounds. More than 50 of those chemicals are cancer-causing carcinogens. Some studies show that infants and young children who are exposed to ETS are more likely to develop asthma than their peers who are not exposed to ETS. Inhaling ETS is a serious health risk.

BIG Idea *Secondhand smoke is harmful, but there are ways you can reduce your exposure.*

Before You Read
Make an Outline. Use the headings of this lesson to make an outline of what you will learn about the risks of smoking. Use a format like this to help you organize your notes.

```
    I.
        A.
            1.
            2.
        B.
    II.
```

New Vocabulary
- environmental tobacco smoke (ETS) (p. 553)
- mainstream smoke (p. 553)
- sidestream smoke (p. 553)

Review Vocabulary
- *Healthy People* (Ch.1, L.4)

Promoting a Smoke-Free Environment

① FOCUS

GUIDE TO READING

BIG Idea Students will learn that environmental tobacco smoke (ETS) is harmful but there are ways to reduce its effects. **Ask Students:** *What do you think you might learn in this lesson?* (Sample answer: How to handle situations in which people are smoking and putting others at risk)

Before You Read

Outline Students' outlines will vary.

Main Idea

Health Risks of Tobacco Smoke Even if you do not smoke, you can be harmed by tobacco smoke. **Ask Students:** *How can a nonsmoker be harmed by someone smoking nearby?* (Sample answer: By breathing in some of the tobacco smoke that is in the air)

Real Life Issues

Ask volunteers to share ideas with the class. Students might suggest that Ken could respectfully ask his uncle not to smoke.

English Language Coach

Extend Vocabulary Write *mainstream smoke* and *sidestream smoke* on the board. Explain to English language learners that in this context, the adjectives *mainstream* and *sidestream* can be taken almost literally. The "main stream" of the tobacco smoke is from the burning tobacco into the lungs and then out into the air. The "side stream" is another flow or stream of tobacco smoke coming directly from the burning tobacco itself. Point out that *mainstream* also has a much wider use in English, meaning "in the prevailing current of thought or influence."

② TEACH

Caption Answer

Figure 20.9 Patrons and employees are not exposed to environmental tobacco smoke.

HS Health Skills Practice

Advocacy Have students work in small groups to find out about health risks to nonsmokers. Then, ask each group to make a poster that informs teens about these risks. Display posters in the classroom. **OL** **BL**

✔ READING CHECK

Answer Mainstream smoke is exhaled from the lungs of a smoker, while sidestream smoke comes from the burning end of a cigarette, pipe, or cigar.

W Writing Strategy

Letter to a Young Mother Ask students to imagine that they have a cousin who is a few years older and married and has just found out that she is pregnant. This cousin, though, is a smoker. Have students compose a respectful but informative letter to the young mother-to-be about the harmful effects her smoking can have on the unborn baby, on the infant after birth, and on the child as it gets older. **OL**

■ **Figure 20.9** Smoking is prohibited in many restaurants, and some restaurants are required to have a nonsmoking section. *How does this rule protect the health of restaurant customers and employees?*

✔ READING CHECK

Analyze How do mainstream smoke and sidestream smoke differ?

Health Risks to Nonsmokers

Secondhand smoke causes about 3,000 deaths from lung cancer every year. ETS causes eye irritation, headaches, ear infections, and coughing in people of all ages. It worsens asthma and other respiratory problems, and it increases the risk of coronary heart disease. **HS**

Health Risks to Unborn Children and Infants

Choosing to live tobacco-free is one of the healthiest choices a pregnant female can make for her baby. Smoking during pregnancy can seriously harm the developing fetus. Nicotine passes through the placenta, constricting the blood vessels of the fetus. Carbon monoxide reduces the oxygen levels in the blood of the mother and fetus. This increases the risk of impaired fetal growth, spontaneous miscarriage and prenatal death, premature delivery, low birth weight, deformities, and stillbirths. The infant may also suffer from growth and developmental problems during early childhood. **W**

Babies of mothers who smoked during pregnancy or who are exposed to ETS are more likely to die of sudden infant death syndrome (SIDS). Infants exposed to ETS after birth are twice as likely to die of SIDS. They may have severe asthma attacks, ear infections, or respiratory tract infections.

◆ Promoting School Wellness

School Tobacco Policies Most schools have had no smoking on school grounds at least since the 1994 Federal Pro Children Act, which prohibited smoking in facilities that provide various federally funded children's services. Each school, though, has its own policies about the consequences that students face when caught smoking or with tobacco products at school. Ask a school administrator to briefly address the class about the school's tobacco policies, including specific punishments for violation of those policies. Have students make posters to inform other students about these policies.

■ **Figure 20.10** Parents protect the health and development of their children by staying tobacco-free. *How can tobacco use harm young children?*

Caption Answer

Figure 20.10 Children of smokers tend to have health problems, and second-hand smoke can slow lung development.

Health Risks to Young Children

Young children are particularly sensitive to ETS. Children of smokers are more likely to be in poor health than children of nonsmokers. Consider these facts:

- Children of smokers tend to have a higher incidence of sore throats, ear infections, and upper respiratory problems than children of nonsmokers.
- Secondhand smoke can slow lung development. Children who live with smokers are more likely to have weaker lungs than children of nonsmokers.

Also, children learn by example. The children of smokers are more than twice as likely to smoke themselves.

Reducing Your Risks

Main Idea You can take action to reduce the effects of ETS.

Since you spend so much time in your home, you can make an effort to minimize the health effects of ETS. If a family member smokes, encourage that person to quit by telling him or her the health effects of tobacco smoke. Try to establish smoke-free areas in the house, or make a rule that smokers go outside. If a smoker cannot always smoke outside, air cleaners can help remove some contaminants from the air. Open windows to allow fresh air in.

If you have a visitor who smokes, politely request that he or she does not smoke inside your home. If you are visiting a home in which someone smokes, try to stay outside or in a different room as much as possible. Ask to open the windows to provide fresh air. Suggest meeting elsewhere, such as in your home or at a library. In restaurants and other public places, request seating in a nonsmoking area. Express your preference wherever you can for a smoke-free environment.

FITNESS ZONE

I hate the smell of cigarette smoke. It reminds me that my grandfather has emphysema. He coughs and struggles to breathe all the time. When he was my age, he ran track and played football. Smoking made it hard for him to breathe, and so he stopped being active. I don't ever plan to smoke because I've seen what it did to my grandfather's health. For more fitness tips, visit the Online Fitness Zone at **glencoe.com**.

G Online

For more vocabulary practice, go to the Interactive Health Tutor at **glencoe.com**.

FITNESS ZONE

Posture and balance are important. Try this:

- Have students place an object on their heads such as a pencil.
- Students should mimic whatever action the teacher takes. If teacher lifts a hand, students should lift a hand.
- Students will try and keep an object balanced on their heads.
- Try balancing on one leg!

Main Idea

Reducing Your Risks Using certain strategies will help reduce the effects of ETS. **Ask Students:** *What could a teen do to reduce his or her risk when living in a home where an adult smokes?* (Sample answer: The teen could ask the adult not to smoke in the room where the teen is.)

Lesson 3   Promoting a Smoke-Free Environment   **555**

Writing Strategy

Antismoking Short Story Despite laws against selling cigarettes to teens, studies have shown that most teens who smoke get their cigarettes by purchasing them, either from a store or a vending machine. Ask students to write a short story about a campaign by teens to stop local stores from selling tobacco products to the underaged. Explain that a short story usually begins with an incident that provides the motivation for the action in the rest of the story. Ask volunteers to read their completed short stories to the class.

TEENS Making a Difference

Answers to Activity Questions

1. Students might suggest forming a group or joining a group similar to the group in which Elizabeth was a member.

2. Answers will vary depending on the state. If students don't know the answer, ask them to find out.

3. The group conducted a survey to find out what owners of bowling alleys thought, and then group members spoke with Idaho legislators. These teens helped move the legislature to remove the exemption from the law.

Main Idea

Creating a Smoke-Free Society
Selling tobacco to teens under 18 is illegal in most states, and smoking in public places is prohibited in many states. **Ask Students:** *Can teens buy cigarettes in stores in this area?* (Answers will vary. Students might suggest that even though it is illegal, some stores do take the chance of selling cigarettes to teens.)

AL Active Learning

State and Local Laws Ask students to find out exactly what the state and local laws are concerning smoking in public places. Have them call the local health department or use online resources. Students should find out in what public places smoking is prohibited, what businesses are exempt, what the penalties are for violations, and how citizens can make complaints about violations they see. Have students write a report about their findings. **AL**

TEENS Making a Difference

"Teens really do have a voice!"

A Voice for Change

Elizabeth W., of Idaho, is a member of the Magic Valley Tobacco-Free Coalition. The group challenged part of the Idaho Clean Indoor Air Act requiring all public buildings accessible to youth—except bowling alleys—to be tobacco-free. Elizabeth's group surveyed owners of bowling alleys. "Most owners actually wanted to be smoke-free," explains Elizabeth. "They said they didn't lose revenue by going tobacco-free."

On Lobby Day, when a bill was being presented, the teens met with representatives in favor of the exemption, presenting them with facts on the dangers of tobacco. Their hard work paid off. The vote passed to remove the exemption. Elizabeth says, "Young people think they don't have a voice, but when something like this happens, you find out you really do."

Activity Write your answers to the following questions in your personal health journal.

1. What can you do to make your community healthier for teens?

2. Does your state have a Clean Indoor Air Act? Is it similar to the Idaho law? If so, what businesses are exempt?

3. What actions did Elizabeth's group take to change the law? What impact did these teens have?

Creating a Smoke-Free Society

Main Idea In most states, it is illegal to sell tobacco to teens under the age of 18, and it is illegal to smoke in public places.

 READING CHECK

List What are three ways you can reduce your exposure to ETS?

Medical research shows that any exposure to secondhand smoke can cause health problems. When a smoker chooses to smoke, that person makes a decision that affects his or her health, and the health of others. In the United States, efforts to create a smoke-free society continue to grow. The health effects of tobacco use, and the cost of health-related illnesses are just some of the reasons for this movement. **AL**

According to the U.S. Surgeon General, the only way to fully protect people from the damaging health effects of ETS is to prohibit smoking in public places. Many states now prohibit smoking in any workplace. Advertisements aimed at young people encourage them not to smoke, and public service announcements encourage parents not to smoke near their children.

556 Chapter 20 Tobacco

Skills for the 21st Century

Smoking Policies at Work Company policies regarding smoking vary. Many companies prohibit smoking on the job, while others have designated smoking areas. A few companies will not even hire new employees who smoke and give current employees a certain period of time to quit. Have small groups of students discuss what smoking policies they think are fair and appropriate for a company to adopt. Then have groups explain their ideas to the class. Ask interested students to inquire with local companies about their smoking policies and report their findings to the class.

Supporting National Health Goals

One of the goals of *Healthy People 2010* is to reduce tobacco use and the number of tobacco-related deaths. States and local communities are also supporting the efforts to create a smoke-free society. Laws prohibiting the sale of tobacco to minors have been enacted. Some states have successfully sued tobacco companies to recover the costs of treating tobacco-related illnesses. The money awarded in these cases may be used to fund anti-smoking campaigns or to offset the medical costs related to tobacco use. Community activities that promote a healthy lifestyle provide everyone with the opportunity to practice healthful behaviors. These activities allow anyone to become a role model encouraging others to avoid tobacco use.

■ **Figure 20.11** Laws restrict where people may smoke, as well as who can buy tobacco products. *What are the benefits of having smoke-free public places?*

LESSON 3 ASSESSMENT

After You Read

Reviewing Vocabulary and Facts

1. What is *environmental tobacco smoke,* and what chemical does it contain?

2. List three ways that ETS affects children.

3. What are two public policies aimed at reducing ETS?

Thinking Critically

4. **Analyze.** How can smoking during pregnancy have long-term effects on the child?

5. **Explain.** Why should you try to avoid ETS, and how can you reduce your exposure to ETS?

Applying Health Skills

6. **Analyzing Influences.** Keep a log of how many tobacco ads you see in one week. Note what type of media was used (print, audio, video), where you saw the ad, and who was targeted. List steps you could take to eliminate these influences in your community.

Writing Critically

7. **Personal.** Describe a situation in which you were exposed to ETS. Include how you felt afterward physically and mentally. Then write about how you could have prevented being exposed to ETS in that situation.

G͜e Online

Visit **glencoe.com** and complete the Interactive Study Guide for this lesson.

Caption Answer

Figure 20.11 Smoke-free public places limit people's exposure to ETS.

❸ ASSESS/ CLOSE

Assessment Resources

📁 *FAST FILE* **ACTIVITIES**
Lesson 3 Quiz

💿 *ExamView Assessment Suite* CD-ROM

Visit glencoe.com for:
Online Quizzes
Online Learning Center

Progress Monitoring

Reteaching
Have students write a brief summary of each section of the lesson.

Enrichment
Have interested students find out about the federal program Healthy People 2010 by doing an online search to find the program's Web site. Ask students to report to the class about the program's goals and any tobacco-related activities by affiliated organizations in the area.

G͜e Online

Have students visit **glencoe.com** and complete the Interactive Study Guide for this lesson.

LESSON 3 ASSESSMENT ANSWERS

1. Air that has been contaminated with tobacco smoke; mainstream smoke and sidestream smoke

2. Sample answer: It increases a child's risk of ear infections, respiratory problems, and sore throats.

3. Sample answer: Prohibiting smoking in public places and banning smoking on flights

4. Sample answer: The child is more likely to die of SIDS; the infant may suffer from growth and developmental problems during early childhood.

5. Sample answer: ETS can cause lung cancer and other health problems. To reduce exposure, I can ask people not to smoke around me.

6. The number of ads seen will vary.

7. Responses will vary.

557

Clearing the Air

Focus

Motivator

Ask students to identify the short-term effects and the long-term effects of tobacco use they learned about in Lesson 1. List their responses on the board.

Teach

Global Issue As tobacco companies have come under increasing pressure in the United States, many have turned to aggressively marketing their products in other parts of the world, especially in developing nations. Ask students to do research online about tobacco sales and advertising outside the United States and about tobacco laws in other countries compared to those in this country. Discuss their findings in class. Also have students explain why they should be concerned about how tobacco is marketed and used in other parts of the world. (Problems in other countries might have effects on this country in the future.)

Accessing Information Some tobacco companies have tried to develop what they call "healthier" cigarettes. The claim is that these tobacco products produce less secondhand smoke, leave no lingering odor, and present less of a cancer risk than other cigarettes. Ask students whether they believe these claims. Then, have students do online research to find out whether these claims have merit.

Antismoking Ad Provide a number of examples of magazine advertisements for tobacco products for students to examine. Tell them they should make their antismoking ads just as attractive to the magazine reader but with information in the ad about the short-term and long-term effects of tobacco use.

558

TIME HEALTH
CULTURE & COMMUNITY

Clearing the Air

A growing number of teen activists has declared a media war on big tobacco companies.

"**D**o you want to be deceived?" yells the speaker at the podium, 17-year-old Andy Berndt. "No!" roar the more than 700 teenage antismoking activists who have packed New Jersey's Liberty Science Center. The shout seems loud enough to be heard all the way across the Hudson River—at Philip Morris's Manhattan headquarters. That's where this protest is aimed: at the giant cigarette companies that, the activists believe, target teen smokers.

A Stand Against Smoking

Each of the teens in the auditorium wears a white T-shirt declaring "Not for Sale." This means that they can't be bought by the millions of dollars tobacco companies spend every day advertising cigarettes. They've come here to declare something else—the creation of a statewide teen antitobacco group called REBEL (Reaching Everyone by Exposing Lies). It's the newest in a pack of teen-led antismoking organizations starting up nationwide. Their mission: to teach teens not just about the health risks of smoking, but about the tactics tobacco companies use to hook young people on their products.

Recently "Not for Sale" commercials began airing on MTV and Nickelodeon.

Over the last decade, the audience meant to benefit from that message has been growing. Every day, 6,000 teenagers try smoking for the first time and 1,200 Americans die from tobacco-related disease. Studies show that nearly 80 percent of regular smokers light up their first cigarette by their 18th birthday.

Andy Berndt doesn't think that lectures about health risks that can occur years down the road will convince teens to stop smoking. "No adult can make kids understand the issues like another kid," he says. "If we educate other kids about all the ways the tobacco industry is trying to deceive them, we'll win the war." ■

TIME to THINK... About Smoking

By yourself or in a small group, create your own antismoking advertisement for a magazine or a newspaper. Pay careful attention to the message you want to send by your choice of words and images. Share your ad with the class.

Academic Integration

Math Using the average cost of $4 per pack of cigarettes, have students determine the following for a pack-a-day smoker:

- The cost of buying cigarettes each week ($4 $\times$ 7 = $28)
- The cost of buying cigarettes each month ($4 $\times$ 30 = $120)
- The cost of buying cigarettes each year ($4 $\times$ 365 = $1,580)

Then, ask students how much a pack-a-day smoker would spend in a lifetime, assuming the smoker started smoking at age 15 and smoked for 60 years. ($1,580 per year $\times$ 60 years = $94,800)

STUDY TO GO To download quizzes and eFlashcards to your PDA, go to glencoe.com and click on the Study to Go icon.

LESSON 1

The Health Risks of Tobacco Use

Key Concepts

▸ All tobacco products contain harmful chemicals, including carcinogens and nicotine, an addictive drug.

▸ In addition to carcinogens and other toxic substances, tobacco smoke contains tar and carbon monoxide.

▸ Tobacco use causes both short-term and long-term damage to your body, such as lung cancer and heart disease.

▸ Tobacco use can also cause legal, social, and financial problems.

Vocabulary

▸ addictive drug (p. 543)
▸ nicotine (p. 543)
▸ stimulant (p. 543)
▸ carcinogen (p. 543)
▸ tar (p. 543)
▸ carbon monoxide (p. 543)
▸ smokeless tobacco (p. 544)
▸ leukoplakia (p. 544)

LESSON 2

Choosing to Live Tobacco-Free

Key Concepts

▸ Some teens are influenced by peers or the media to use tobacco, but many who start want to quit.

▸ The number of tobacco-free teens is steadily increasing.

▸ You can avoid using tobacco by carefully choosing your friends, avoiding places where tobacco is present, and having a refusal plan.

▸ Tobacco users often find it difficult to quit using tobacco because they experience nicotine withdrawal.

Vocabulary

▸ nicotine withdrawal (p. 551)
▸ nicotine substitutes (p. 551)
▸ tobacco cessation program (p. 551)

LESSON 3

Promoting a Smoke-Free Environment

Key Concepts

▸ Environmental tobacco smoke (ETS) is harmful to nonsmokers and smokers because it contains toxic substances.

▸ A pregnant mother should avoid tobacco to protect the fetus.

▸ ETS is especially harmful to infants and young children.

▸ Laws and public policies are reducing ETS in public places.

Vocabulary

▸ environmental tobacco smoke (ETS) (p. 553)
▸ mainstream smoke (p. 553)
▸ sidestream smoke (p. 553)
▸ Healthy People (p. 557)

Go Online

Students can visit glencoe.com to

● review content online with the Online Student Edition.

● test their knowledge of chapter content with Online Quizzes.

● access Interactive Health Tutor for more practice with vocabulary.

Assessment Resources

📁 **FAST FILE ACTIVITIES**
Chapter 20 Test

💿 *ExamView Assessment Suite* CD-ROM

Visit glencoe.com **for:**
Audio Chapter Summaries
Online Quizzes

 Tell students to visit glencoe.com where they can download quizzes and eFlashcards.

Study Tips

Study Groups Tell students that one effective way to keep pace with material they have to learn is to form a study group. A study group usually includes three to five students, all of whom should be friendly with one another and motivated to learn. Explain that study groups often meet two or three times a week for an hour to an hour and a half each session. At a study session, group members compare notes, talk over difficult concepts, and work together to understand the course material.

Assessment

Chapter 20 Assessment Answers

LESSON 1

Vocabulary Review

1. carcinogen
2. nicotine
3. tar

Understanding Key Concepts

4. c
5. b
6. b
7. d

Thinking Critically

8. No. Smokeless tobacco contains nicotine and carcinogens. Chewing tobacco can irritate the mouth and cause cancers.
9. Yes. I would have a higher risk of developing cancers of the mouth, pharynx, larynx, esophagus, stomach, pancreas, lungs, bladder, and kidneys.
10. Nicotine constricts blood vessels, reduces blood flow, and causes plaque to build up in the arteries, which will cause them to harden, thus increasing the risk of heart attack and stroke.
11. Her employer will lose money because she is likely to be less productive at work and miss work as a result of illness. She may not be able to pay her medical bills, which will then have to be paid by taxpayers.
12. Sample answer: Tobacco users smell like smoke and so people will avoid them.

LESSON 2

Vocabulary Review

13. nicotine withdrawal
14. nicotine substitute
15. tobacco cessation program

560

LESSON 1

Vocabulary Review
Correct the sentences below by replacing the italicized term with the correct vocabulary term.

1. A(n) *stimulant* is a cancer-causing substance.

2. Tobacco users can become addicted to the *carbon monoxide* in tobacco.

3. When tobacco burns, it produces a thick, sticky, dark fluid known as *leukoplakia*.

Understanding Key Concepts
After reading the question or statement, select the correct answer.

4. Which physical response is *not* caused by nicotine?
   a. Increased heart rate
   b. Physiological addiction
   c. Reduced oxygen in the blood
   d. Higher blood pressure

5. Leukoplakia can develop into which condition?
   a. Emphysema   c. Heart disease
   b. Oral cancer   d. Bad breath

6. Which of the following are ways that tobacco harms the cardiovascular system?
   a. Increased heart rate, hardened arteries, chronic bronchitis
   b. Increased heart rate, hardened arteries, increased risk of heart attack
   c. Increased heart rate, chronic bronchitis, emphysema
   d. Chronic bronchitis, emphysema, lung cancer

7. Which of the following is a way that tobacco use immediately affects the body?
   a. Chronic bronchitis
   b. Increased risk of cancer
   c. Leukoplakia
   d. Increased heart rate

Thinking Critically
After reading the question or statement, write a short answer using complete sentences.

8. **Explain.** Is smokeless tobacco less harmful than cigarettes? Why or why not?

9. **Analyze.** If you started smoking today and continued to smoke until you are 30 years old, would you have a higher risk of developing cancer? If so, why?

10. **Explain.** How does nicotine cause an increased risk of stroke?

11. **Discuss.** Kate says that it is her choice to smoke, and that she is the only one who has to worry about her health. How does her decision to smoke affect other people?

12. **Identify.** How can using tobacco impact the social life of a tobacco user?

LESSON 2

Vocabulary Review
Use the vocabulary terms listed on page 559 to complete the following statements.

13. When a tobacco user no longer uses tobacco, the body no longer gets nicotine, and the user experiences _____.

14. A(n) _____ can be used to deliver small amounts of nicotine to the body while a tobacco user is quitting tobacco.

15. A person who wants to successfully quit tobacco could join a(n) _____ that will help the person learn how to quit.

Health eSpotlight VIDEO Wrap-Up

The Truth and the Lies Have students reread the Health eSpotlight questions at the beginning of the chapter (page 541) and look at their original answers. **Ask Students:** *What do you now know about what you* *would tell a younger sibling or friend that you didn't know before reading the chapter?* Call on volunteers to describe what they have learned and how they would change their responses.

Understanding Key Concepts

After reading the question or statement, select the correct answer.

16. Which is a strategy to keep you from becoming a tobacco user?
 a. Practicing refusal statements
 b. Saving money
 c. Trying a cigarette
 d. Using nicotine gum

17. Which of the following is a reason that a teen tobacco user should quit the habit?
 a. Tobacco use looks sophisticated.
 b. Their friends also smoke.
 c. They can quit as adults.
 d. They will experience health problems.

18. Why do people who are trying to quit tobacco experience physical symptoms such as irritability and anxiety?
 a. They are not committed to quitting.
 b. They are experiencing nicotine withdrawal.
 c. They are upset that other people want them to quit.
 d. They are not engaged in healthier behaviors.

19. Which is *not* a strategy that can help people give up tobacco?
 a. Develop a new daily routine.
 b. Take up a physical activity.
 c. Model adults who smoke.
 d. Join a support group.

20. People gain which health benefit by *not* using tobacco?
 a. Good refusal skills
 b. Friends who do not use tobacco
 c. Lower risk of many diseases
 d. Less money to spend on other interests

Thinking Critically

After reading the question or statement, write a short answer using complete sentences.

21. **Describe.** Why do tobacco users try to quit the habit?

22. **Infer.** Why did tobacco use among teens begin to decrease after 1998?

23. **Identify.** Why do some teens choose to use tobacco and other teens do not?

24. **Predict.** What are two reasons that teen tobacco users find quitting tobacco difficult?

25. **Describe.** What can a person do to quit using tobacco successfully?

LESSON 3

Vocabulary Review

Choose the correct term in the sentences below.

26. Environmental tobacco smoke is another name for *secondhand smoke / sidestream smoke.*

27. *Mainstream smoke / Sidestream smoke* comes from a smoker's lungs.

28. Higher concentrations of toxic substances are in *mainstream smoke / sidestream smoke.*

Understanding Key Concepts

After reading the question or statement, select the correct answer.

29. Which is *not* a way that smoking during pregnancy affects the fetus?
 a. Prenatal death
 b. High birth weight
 c. Premature delivery
 d. Developmental problems

30. How can you reduce your risk from ETS?
 a. Become a smoker.
 b. Take vitamins.
 c. Allow visitors to smoke in your house.
 d. Visit places that are smoke-free.

Chapter 20 Assessment **561**

Understanding Key Concepts

16. a
17. d
18. b
19. c
20. c

Thinking Critically

21. Sample answer: They have health problems, the cost is high, and they want to avoid serious health problems in the future.

22. Since 1998, tobacco companies have been required to fund antitobacco messages.

23. Sample answer: Teens who use tobacco may have felt peer pressure or have been influenced by the media. Teens who choose not to use tobacco may want to avoid health risks and do not want to smell of tobacco.

24. Sample answer: Nicotine is addictive, and they may experience peer pressure to keep smoking.

25. Prepare for the quit day, get support and encouragement, access professional health services, replace tobacco use with healthier alternatives, change daily behavior, engage in healthful behaviors, and prepare for difficult situations.

Vocabulary Review

26. secondhand smoke
27. Mainstream smoke
28. sidestream smoke

ExamView®
Assessment Suite

Create and customize tests in minutes with this convenient digital platform.

- Create differentiated tests quickly and easily.
- All questions correlated to National/State Standards.
- Enhance tests with Document Based Questions (DBQ) and add your own photos or graphics.
- Build tests in both English and Spanish.
- Generate progress reports.

To order, go to **glencoe.com** and search for ISBN 0-07-888173-0.

Assessment

LESSON 3

Understanding Key Concepts

29. b
30. d
31. a
32. d

Thinking Critically

33. Sample answer: If the parents stop, the child's risk for health problems is reduced. Also, if the parents do not smoke, then the child will be less likely to start smoking.

34. Sample answer: I'd suggest going out to a restaurant to eat.

35. Sample answer: I can help make people aware of the health risks of ETS so they will support laws against ETS.

36. Sample answer: The program involves adults and teens in ways to reduce tobacco use and the number of tobacco-related deaths.

37. Sample answer: No. The mainstream smoke and sidestream smoke from Jim's tobacco use can harm his friends' health.

---

31. Which is a way that the government is reducing ETS exposure?
    a. Banning smoking in public places
    b. Distributing more tobacco licenses
    c. Forming youth antismoking groups
    d. Giving away air cleaners

32. ETS can cause which of these conditions?
    a. Headache
    b. Lung cancer
    c. Sudden infant death syndrome
    d. All of the above

Thinking Critically

After reading the question or statement, write a short answer using complete sentences.

33. **Identify.** If parents stop smoking, how will that decision help their children's health?

34. **Apply.** Your friend invites you over for dinner, but you know that your friend's parent smokes. What can you do?

35. **Infer.** What can you do to promote public policies that support a smoke-free environment?

36. **Explain.** How does the *Healthy People 2010* program promote health?

37. **Analyze.** Jim smokes around his friends, who do not smoke. Jim's friends say that they're not worried about the health effects of breathing the ETS created by Jim's tobacco smoke. Are they right *not* to be worried about their health? Explain your answer.

Project-Based ASSESSMENT

Smoking in the Movies

Background

Smoking tobacco is discouraged or forbidden in many places. Restaurants, public buildings, schools, offices, airplanes, and even some outdoor parks are smoke-free zones. Yet, many movies continue to show people using tobacco products. In this activity, you will encourage filmmakers to stop showing people smoking in film.

Task

Compose a letter to the editor opposing smoking in movies, especially in movies aimed at teens.

Audience

Students in your school

Purpose

Take a public position on the dangers of media that influence teens to smoke tobacco.

Procedure

1 Review your text for information on the health effects of tobacco use.

2 Conduct research to determine why people start smoking and what influences teens to smoke.

3 Learn the position of health advocacy organizations on smoking in movies and on television.

4 Read various letters to the editor in your local newspaper to study the structure and language.

5 Write a letter to the editor, making a clear argument opposing smoking in movies.

6 Follow-up by reading the letters to the editor section of the paper to see if your letter is published. Collect your letter and any responses in a file.

Project-Based ASSESSMENT

Step 1 Research Ask students to find out more about what influences teens to smoke and what the position is of health advocacy organizations on smoking in the media.

Step 2 Compose a Letter Have students write their letter to the editor opposing smoking in the movies. Review the letters for grammar and clarity before students send them to newspapers.

Step 3 Evaluate Make sure the information in student letters is accurate. A well-written letter will make a strong case against smoking in movies, with supporting facts about the effects of smoking and the role that movies play in influencing teens to smoke.

Visit **glencoe.com** for Project-Based Assessment rubrics.

Standardized Test Practice

Math Practice

Interpret Graphs. Fred has decided to conduct a survey over the school year to find out what percentage of students in 8th, 10th, and 12th grades at his school reported cigarette use each month. Use the information Fred gathered in the graph to answer Questions 1–3.

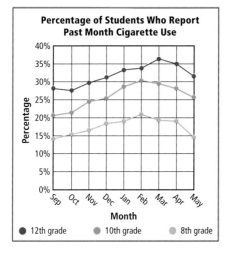

Percentage of Students Who Report Past Month Cigarette Use

● 12th grade ● 10th grade ● 8th grade

1. Which grade level had the highest percentage of smokers from September to May?
   A. 8th grade
   B. 10th grade
   C. 12th grade
   D. All grade levels were the same.

2. During which time span was smoking the most common for 8th, 10th, and 12th graders?
   A. Sep.–Oct.   C. Jan.–Mar.
   B. Nov.–Jan.   D. Mar.–May

3. In general, what trend is common to all three grade levels from September to May, according to the chart shown here? What influences do you think contributed to this trend?

Go Online

For more test practice, visit glencoe.com and complete the Online Quizzes for Chapter 20.

Reading/Writing Practice

Understand and Apply. Read the passage below, and then answer the questions.

> Today you will make a number of decisions. These decisions may or may not have a lasting effect on your life. One decision that will have a lasting effect is the decision not to start smoking. As you know, smoking is dangerous to your health. Smokers have a greater chance than nonsmokers of dying of lung and heart diseases. Cigarette smoke is also dangerous to others: secondhand smoke harms the health of nonsmokers, including the smoker's friends and family.
>
> Smoking is also addictive. Tobacco poisons the user, but the nicotine in tobacco smoke makes the user want—and need—more. Many smokers admit that they would like to quit, but they think they can't. Starting is easy; quitting is hard. If you start smoking now, you may be starting a habit that is dangerous to you, your friends, and your family.

1. Which sentence best summarizes the writer's view of smoking?
   A. Many smokers have difficulty quitting.
   B. Smoking is a harmful habit.
   C. Starting is easy, quitting is hard.
   D. Smokers will get lung cancer.

2. How does the writer support the statement that nicotine is addictive?
   A. By explaining that nicotine makes users want more
   B. By stating how easy it is to quit smoking
   C. By telling how easy it is to start smoking
   D. By describing the dangers to nonsmokers

3. Create a podcast to encourage teens not to start smoking.

National Education Standards
Math: Data Analysis, Reasoning
Language Arts: NCTE 1, NCTE 3, NCTE 4

Standardized Test Practice Answers

Math Practice
1. C
2. C
3. The percentage of students who smoked increased from September to February and March and then decreased.

Reading/Writing Practice
1. B
2. A
3. Podcasts will vary but should include a script with accurate supporting details about the dangers of smoking.

National Education Standards

Math: Data Analysis, Reasoning

Language Arts: NCTE 1, NCTE 3, NCTE 4

For the complete Math and Language Arts standards, visit glencoe.com.

Go Online

Online Study Tools
For more test practice, visit glencoe.com and complete the Online Quizzes for Chapter 20.

Test-Taking Tip

Answering Multiple-Choice Questions
Explain to students that standardized tests often rely on multiple-choice questions for many parts of the test. Here are some tips for approaching multiple-choice questions.

- Read all the possible choices before marking the correct answer.

- Cross out choices that you know are incorrect.

- When two of the answer choices are direct opposites, often one of the opposites is the right choice.

- Try to find an answer choice that contains language used by the teacher or from the textbook. This is often the correct answer.

563

Chapter 21 pages 564–589	Standards		Features
	National	**State/Local**	
	1.12.1, 1.12.5, 1.12.8, 2.12.5, 2.12.9, 3.12.2, 7.12.1, 8.12.1–8.12.4		**TIME** HEALTH • Keeping the Lid on the Bottle, page 584
Lesson 1 **The Health Risks of Alcohol Use** pages 566–571 **BIG Idea** *Alcohol use can harm the body and the brain and cause a person to make poor decisions.*	1.12.5, 1.12.8, 2.12.9, 4.12.1, 4.12.4, 5.12.6, 8.12.2, 8.12.4		*Health Skills* Activity • A Drink at Home *(Refusal Skills)*, page 571 Ⓥ Out of Time
Lesson 2 **Choosing to Live Alcohol-Free** pages 572–577 **BIG Idea** *Choosing not to use alcohol protects a person from dangerous health consequences.*	1.12.5, 2.12.1, 2.12.3, 2.12.5, 2.12.9, 2.12.10, 3.12.1, 4.12.2, 5.12.6, 7.12.1		*Real World* CONNECTION • Analyzing the Media, page 575 Ⓥ Out of Time
Lesson 3 **The Impact of Alcohol Abuse** pages 578–583 **BIG Idea** *Problem drinking and alcoholism harm both the drinkers and the people around them.*	1.12.2, 2.12.1, 2.12.2, 2.12.3, 2.12.10, 3.12.3, 4.12.1, 8.12.3		**TEENS** Making a Difference • Advocating for Change, page 581

Key to Ability Levels

Teaching Strategies and activities have been coded for ability level and appropriateness.

AL Activities for students working above grade level

OL Activities for students working on grade level

BL Activities for students working below grade level

EL Activities for English Learners

Chapter 21 Planning Guide

Glencoe Exclusive!
TeacherWorks Plus
All-In-One Planner and Resource Center

Resources	Lesson Assessment	Technology
Student Activity Workbook TEACH **FAST FILE RESOURCES** Vocabulary Practice TEACH Health Labs EXTEND	Chapter 21 Review Chapter 21 Assessment Standardized Test Practice ⊙ *ExamView® Assessment Suite* CD-ROM	**Teaching Tools:** ⊙ *TeacherWorks™* Plus DVD ⊙ *StudentWorks™* Plus DVD ⊙ *ExamView® Assessment Suite* CD-ROM ⬚ Transparency ⊙ Fitness DVD ⊙ PowerPoint® DVD ⊙ Health eSpotlight Video Series DVD
FAST FILE RESOURCES Reading Strategies Activity TEACH Reteaching Activity REVIEW Enrichment Activity EXTEND Health Skills Practice TEACH	Lesson 1 Assessment, page 571 📁 Lesson 1 Quiz *Fast File* ⊙ *ExamView® Assessment Suite* CD-ROM	**Web-Based Resources:** **Go Online** glencoe.com • Health Podcast Activities • Audio Chapter Summaries (English/Spanish) • Interactive Health Tutor
FAST FILE RESOURCES Reading Strategies Activity TEACH Reteaching Activity REVIEW Enrichment Activity EXTEND Health Skills Practice TEACH	Lesson 2 Assessment, page 577 📁 Lesson 2 Quiz *Fast File* ⊙ *ExamView® Assessment Suite* CD-ROM	• Health Skills Activities • Vocabulary PuzzleMaker • Parent Letters (English/Spanish) • Lesson Plans • Health Inventories • Online Quizzes
FAST FILE RESOURCES Reading Strategies Activity TEACH Reteaching Activity REVIEW Enrichment Activity EXTEND Health Skills Practice TEACH	Lesson 3 Assessment, page 583 📁 Lesson 3 Quiz *Fast File* ⊙ *ExamView® Assessment Suite* CD-ROM	• Study-to-Go • Unit Web Projects • Student Web Activities • Fitness Zone Activities

StudentWorks Plus

This is the student's backpack solution.

Includes:
- complete Interactive Student Edition
- full audio of English text and Spanish chapter summaries
- allows students to record assignments and track grades.
- links to online activities and additional student resources
- access to all student worksheets and workbooks

FOLDABLES
Study Organizer

Dinah Zike Foldables®
Chapter Activity
Refer to the *Dinah Zike Reading and Study Skills for Glencoe Health.* Ask students to make a folded book Foldable to record what they learn about alcohol. Under the four tabs, students can define terms and record information from the chapter.

Key to Symbols

 Transparencies

 CD-ROM

 glencoe.com

 Print Resources

REVIEW activities to review or reinforce content

TEACH activities to teach basic concepts

EXTEND activities to extend or enrich lesson content

Alcohol

Chapter Overview

Chapter 21 focuses on how alcohol use can harm the body and the benefits of living alcohol-free. Problems of alcohol abuse and alcoholism are also discussed.

Lesson 1

Alcohol is an addictive drug that has harmful short-term and long-term effects. Binge drinking can lead to alcohol poisoning, which can be fatal.

Lesson 2

Many factors influence some teens to use alcohol. Many teens make the commitment to stay alcohol-free—a choice that has many benefits.

Lesson 3

Problem drinking and alcoholism harm both the drinkers and the people around them.

▶ Activating Prior Knowledge

Have teens work in small groups to write a summary that explains how choosing to stay alcohol free can help a teen avoid risky behaviors. Then, ask each group to read its summary aloud. Lead a discussion on why teens are more likely to take risks when using alcohol.

Lesson 1
The Health Risks of Alcohol Use

BIG Idea *Alcohol use can harm your body and your brain and cause you to make poor decisions.*

Lesson 2
Choosing to Live Alcohol-Free

BIG Idea *Choosing not to use alcohol protects you from dangerous health consequences.*

Lesson 3
The Impact of Alcohol Abuse

BIG Idea *Problem drinking and alcoholism harm both the drinkers and the people around them.*

Activating Prior Knowledge

Using Visuals The teens in this photo are looking at a car that was crashed as a result of a drunk-driving accident. Summarize how choosing to stay alcohol-free can help teens avoid risky behaviors such as drunk driving.

564

Universal Access

Differentiated Learning Glencoe provides teacher support and student materials for all learners in the health classroom.

- Chapter Summaries in English and Spanish are available online at **glencoe.com**.
- *Fast Files* and related worksheets support reluctant readers.

- Universal Access strategies throughout the Teacher Wraparound Edition and *Fast Files* help you present materials for gifted students, at-risk students, physically impaired students, and those with behavior disorders or learning disabilities.

Health in Action

Discuss the **BIG** Ideas

Before beginning this chapter, think about how you would answer these questions:

▶ How does alcohol use contribute to risky behaviors?

▶ In what ways does problem drinking harm people?

▶ How can you encourage others to stay alcohol-free?

Watch the *Health* eSpotlight Video Series

The Risks of Use and Abuse

How does alcohol abuse impact your health triangle? How does the media impact alcohol use?

Assess Your Health

Go Online

Visit glencoe.com and complete the Health Inventory for Chapter 21.

Chapter 21   Alcohol   **565**

Chapter Launchers

Health in Action

Discuss the **BIG** Ideas

Assign this activity before students read the chapter. Explain that the purpose of the questions is to help students assess their current knowledge of problems associated with using alcohol.

Health eSpotlight
Video Series

The Risks of Use and Abuse

Before Viewing the Video

Ask Students: *What is one problem a teen who uses alcohol regularly would have?* (Sample answer: The teen would probably not do well in school, and may get suspended for alcohol use.)

Go Online

Have students go to **glencoe.com** and take the Health Inventory for Chapter 21.

Chapter Skills

Reading Skills

- Reviewing Facts and Vocabulary, pp. 571, 577, 583
- Reading/Writing Practice, p. 589

Vocabulary

- New Vocabulary, pp. 566, 572, 578
- Reviewing Facts and Vocabulary, pp. 571, 577, 583

BIG Idea

Students will learn about the effects that alcohol has on a user and about choosing to live alcohol free.

Health Skills

- Health Skills Activity, p. 571
- Applying Health Skills, pp. 571, 577, 583

Writing Skills

- Real World Connection, p. 575
- Writing Critically, pp. 571, 577, 583
- Reading/Writing Practice, p. 589

The Health Risks of Alcohol Use

1 FOCUS

GUIDE TO READING

BIG Idea Alcohol can harm the body and brain, causing an individual to make poor decisions. **Ask Students:** *What is one health risk related to alcohol use that you anticipate learning in this lesson?* (Sample answer: Why some alcohol users don't think straight when they're drinking.)

Before You Read

Outline Students' outlines will vary in details, though the first two levels should reflect the headings and subheadings of Lesson 1.

Main Idea

Alcohol Alcohol is a drug that is addictive. **Ask Students:** *What do you think are some health consequences of alcohol addiction?* (Sample answer: Liver damage, heart disease)

Real Life Issues ....

Have partners write dialogues together. Then ask partners at random to role-play their dialogues for the class. After each role-play, ask students whether they think Sarah's facts and way of communicating in the dialogue would convince Jamie to change her behavior.

566

 GUIDE TO READING

BIG Idea Alcohol use can harm your body and your brain and cause you to make poor decisions.

Before You Read

Make an Outline.
Use the headings of this lesson to make an outline of what you'll learn about the harmful effects of alcohol use. Use a format like this to help you organize your notes.

New Vocabulary

▸ ethanol (p. 566)
▸ fermentation (p. 566)
▸ depressant (p. 567)
▸ intoxication (p. 567)
▸ binge drinking (p. 569)
▸ alcohol poisoning (p. 569)

The Health Risks of Alcohol Use

Real Life Issues ....

Knowing the Risks. Sarah is worried because she has seen her younger sister, Jamie, experiment with alcohol. Jamie is only in high school, and Sarah feels that her sister does not fully understand the risks of her behavior. Jamie doesn't think there is a problem because she has had alcohol only a few times with her friends. Sarah is concerned that her sister is putting herself at risk, and she knows it's against the law to drink if you're under 21.

Writing *Write a dialogue in which Sarah tries to convince Jamie to change her behavior. Sarah should communicate her concern to Jamie.*

Alcohol

Main Idea Alcohol is an addictive drug.

Alcohol advertisements show images of happy, healthy-looking young adults to promote and sell a drug that is addictive, physically damaging, and often an entry into other drug use. Alcohol, or more accurately, **ethanol**—*the type of alcohol in alcoholic beverages*—is a powerful and addictive drug. It's a drug that can have serious consequences for teens who use alcohol. Using alcohol during the teen years can affect brain development. Ethanol can be produced synthetically, or naturally by fermenting fruits, vegetables, and grains. **Fermentation** is *the chemical action of yeast on sugars.* Water, flavoring, and minerals are mixed with ethanol to produce beverages such as beer, wine, and flavored malt-liquor drinks. Alcohol also can be processed to create spirits, or liquors, such as whiskey and vodka.

More About...

Teens and Alcohol Teen drinking is a problem of great concern in the United States. Emphasize this point with these facts:

• About 41 percent of students have consumed alcohol by 8th grade.

• About 75 percent of students have consumed alcohol by the time they graduate from high school.

• More than 50 percent of 12th graders say they have been drunk at least once.

• About 6 percent of youth ages 12 to 20 are heavy drinkers.

Have interested students research more statistics about drinking among teens.

Short-Term Effects of Alcohol

Main Idea Alcohol impairs the central nervous system.

Alcohol is a **depressant**, *a drug that slows the central nervous system.* Using alcohol slows reaction time, impairs vision, and diminishes judgment. If a person consumes too much alcohol, he or she will become intoxicated. **Intoxication** is *the state in which the body is poisoned by alcohol or another substance, and the person's physical and mental control is significantly reduced.* Alcohol stays in a person's system until the liver can metabolize it, or break it down. The amount of alcohol that can cause intoxication varies from person to person. **Figure 21.2** on page 568 describes many of alcohol's effects.

Factors that Influence Alcohol's Effects

Some factors that influence the onset and intensity of alcohol's effects include:

- **Body size.** A smaller person feels the effect of the same amount of alcohol faster than a larger person does.
- **Gender.** Alcohol generally moves into the bloodstream faster in females than in males, because females tend to have smaller bodies than males.
- **Food.** Food in the stomach slows down the passage of alcohol into the bloodstream.
- **Rate of intake.** If a person drinks alcohol faster than the liver can break it down, the person becomes intoxicated.
- **Amount.** As the amount of alcohol consumed increases, the level of alcohol in the bloodstream rises.
- **Medicine.** Alcohol can interfere with the effects of medicines, and medicines can heighten the effects of alcohol.

■ **Figure 21.1** Alcohol impairs both physical and mental abilities. *How can alcohol use decrease your performance in activities that you enjoy?*

---

② TEACH

Main Idea

Short-Term Effects of Alcohol
Alcohol impairs the central nervous system. **Ask Students:** *What effects have you seen in people who have been drinking alcohol?* (Sample answer: Slurred speech, poor balance, poor judgment)

R Reading Strategy

Organizing Information Have students read the section, *Factors that Influence Alcohol's Effects.* Using a graphic organizer of their choice, have students organize the information presented in this section. **OL AL**

Caption Answer

Figure 21.1 Sample answer: Alcohol slows reaction time, impairs vision, and diminishes clear thinking and good judgment.

ELL Support

Name and Repeat Write the following words on the board: *depressant, intoxication, interaction.* Define each word aloud.

Beginning Use sentences such as "Alcohol acts as a depressant on the central nervous system." Ask students to repeat the sentence. Use the other two words in a sentence, and ask students to repeat.

Intermediate Ask students for sentence examples using each word.

Advanced Have students compare and contrast the use of the word *depressant* in this context with the words *depression* and *depressed* as used in a psychological context.

567

C **Critical Thinking**

C **Critical Thinking**

Identifying Cause and Effect
Ask students which teen in each of the following pairs would feel alcohol's effects more quickly: A male teen and a female teen, each weighing about 135 pounds (The female, because alcohol moves into the bloodstream faster in females); A male teen weighing 140 pounds and a male teen weighing 195 pounds (The male teen weighing 140 pounds, because a smaller-sized person feels the effects faster). **OL**

U **Universal Access**

Analyzing a Graphic Ask volunteers to read aloud the first effect listed under "Changes to the Brain" in **Figure 21.2**. Make sure all students understand the words and concepts in this short-term effect of alcohol. Continue the same process with the next effect listed. For effects such as "Memory" and "Stomach," ask volunteers how these effects might be seen by an observer of someone who is drinking alcohol. **BL** **EL**

 **READING CHECK**

Answer It may increase the risk of harmful side effects from the drug; it may decrease the effectiveness of the medicine; it may cause the change of some medications into chemicals that can damage the liver or other organs; it may increase the effects of some drugs.

Figure 21.2 **Short-Term Effects of Alcohol**

Physical and mental impairment begin with the first drink of alcohol and increase as more alcohol is consumed.

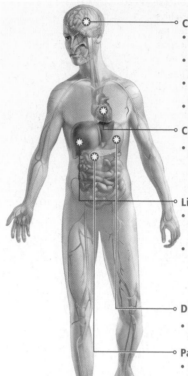

C

U

Changes to the Brain
- **Development.** Pathways and connections necessary for learning may be permanently damaged.
- **Memory.** Thought processes are disorganized, and memory and concentration are dulled.
- **Judgment and control.** Judgment is altered and coordination is impaired. Movement, speech, and vision may be affected.
- **Risk of stroke.** Alcohol use may increase risk of stroke in young people.

Cardiovascular Changes
- **Heart.** Small amounts of alcohol can increase the heart rate and blood pressure. High levels of alcohol have the opposite effect, decreasing heart rate and blood pressure. Heart rhythm becomes irregular. Body temperature drops.

Liver and Kidney Problems
- **Liver.** Toxic chemicals are released as the liver metabolizes alcohol. These chemicals cause inflammation and scarring of the liver tissue.
- **Kidneys.** Alcohol causes the kidneys to increase urine output, which can lead to dehydration.

Digestive System Problems
- **Stomach.** Alcohol increases stomach acid production and can cause nausea and vomiting.

Pancreas Problems
- **Pancreas.** Consuming large amounts of alcohol quickly can cause pancreatitis, which is accompanied by acute, severe pain. The pancreas produces enzymes that break down nutrients in foods. Alcohol use can disrupt the absorption of these nutrients.

Alcohol and Drug Interactions

Alcohol can change the effect of medicines. These interactions can lead to illness or death. Medicines that may cause reactions have warning labels that advise people not to use alcohol. Note these typical alcohol-drug interactions:

- The body may absorb the drug or alcohol more slowly, increasing the length of time that alcohol or the drug is in the body.
- Alcohol use can decrease the effectiveness of some medications, and increase the effectiveness of others.
- Enzymes in the body can change some medications into chemicals that can damage the liver or other organs.

READING CHECK

Describe How can alcohol change the way a medicine affects your body?

Health Literacy

Alcohol's Effects on Teens Drinking alcohol has different and more damaging effects on the teen brain than on the adult brain. The reason is that a teen's brain is still growing and developing. Recent research suggests that drinking during adolescence may do damage to brain cells that affects the ability of teens to learn and remember. Have students do online research to find out about the most recent research on how drinking affects teen brain development. Ask students to write a report about what they learn.

Long-Term Effects of Alcohol

Main Idea Alcohol use can have negative effects on a person's health.

AL

Alcohol use can have long-term effects on a user's physical, mental/emotional, and social health. The effects of alcohol use may also be felt by the people who are close to someone who uses alcohol. Excessive alcohol use over a long period of time can damage many of the body systems, such as:

HS

- damage to brain cells and a reduction in brain size,
- increase in blood pressure, which may lead to a heart attack or stroke,
- buildup of fat cells in the liver, which can lead to cell death,
- damage to the digestive lining of the stomach causing ulcers and cancer of the stomach, and
- destruction of the pancreas.

If a person stops using alcohol, some of the physical effects of long-term alcohol use can be reversed over time. The negative effects of alcohol use can also include damage to relationships with family, friends, and others. Excessive alcohol use over a prolonged period of time can damage most body systems. **Figure 21.4** on page 570 shows more of the long-term effects of alcohol abuse.

Binge Drinking and Alcohol Poisoning

Main Idea Consuming a large amount of alcohol over a short period of time can be fatal.

Some people choose to drink large amounts of alcohol during one session. **Binge drinking**, *drinking five or more alcoholic drinks at one sitting,* is a serious problem. Rapid binge drinking is sometimes done on a bet or a dare. Whatever the reason for binge drinking, it can have dangerous consequences. Drinking any alcohol can impair a drinker's physical and mental abilities.

Binge drinking can severely impair the drinker's body systems. It can lead to **alcohol poisoning**—*a severe and potentially fatal physical reaction to an alcohol overdose.* Alcohol acts as a depressant on body organs. Involuntary actions, such as breathing and the gag reflex that prevents choking may be impaired. Alcohol is also a stomach irritant.

Lesson 1 The Health Risks of Alcohol Use **569**

READING CHECK

Explain How does long-term alcohol use affect the liver?

■ **Figure 21.3** The effects of alcohol depend on many factors, including gender and body size. *Why might women be affected more by alcohol use than men?*

Main Idea

Long-Term Effects of Alcohol
Alcohol use can have negative effects on a person's health. **Ask Students:** *What is one long-term effect of drinking alcohol too much and too often?* (Sample answer: The brain is damaged, and there's a loss of memory.)

AL Active Learning

Posters Have small groups of students make a poster about the short-term and long-term effects of alcohol. Have each group concentrate on one body system of these three: nervous system, cardiovascular system, and digestive system. Ask groups to use illustrations and text to show information about both the short-term and long-term effects of alcohol on its body system. Display the posters in the classroom. **OL**

HS Health Skills Practice

Accessing Information Ask students to search online to find Web sites that provide reliable information about the short-term and long-term effects of alcohol consumption. Have them make a table of their results that includes the name of the Web site, the organization that sponsors the site, the Internet address, and the type of information provided. **AL**

READING CHECK

Answer It can cause fatty liver, alcoholic hepatitis, or cirrhosis.

Teacher to Teacher

Kathy Marlowe • C. Reynolds High School, Asheville, NC

I have found that one of the most effective ways to get across to teenagers the effects of drinking and driving is to have them put on the "drunk goggles." I place a piece of tape on the ground in a straight line. I ask each student to try to walk the line heel-to-toe with a pair of goggles on. As the student walks the line, his or her classmates are to act as if they are the police checking a drunk driver. Not only are they looking at the performance, but they are listening to what the goggled student is saying. I ask: "In your opinion, should he or she be taken to jail?"

Health Skills Activity

Refusal Skills:
A Drink at Home

NHES Standard 4 Students will demonstrate the ability to use interpersonal communication skills to enhance health and avoid or reduce health risks.

Objectives

- Identify reasons to avoid using alcohol.
- Apply refusal skills to resist peer pressure to drink alcohol.

Teaching Strategies

- Review examples of effective refusal skills.
- Have students work in small groups to develop possible responses Zach could use to refuse Karen's offer.

Assessment

Using this list, student work should provide comprehensive evidence of the following criteria to achieve the highest score:

√ Includes the word no in the response

√ Explains why he is refusing to drink

√ Suggests reasonable alternatives to drinking

√ Describes the body language used to back up the refusal

√ Includes description of walking away from the situation if necessary

Figure 21.4 **Long-Term Effects of Alcohol**

Alcohol has a negative effect on many of the body organs, and excessive long-term alcohol use can cause death.

The Brain	The Cardiovascular System	The Digestive System	The Pancreas
Addiction Physical dependence can lead to the inability to control the frequency and amount of drinking. **Loss of brain functions** Loss of verbal skills, visual and spatial skills, and memory. **Brain damage** Excessive use of alcohol can lead to brain damage and to a reduction of brain size. The learning ability and memory of adolescents who drink even small amounts can be impaired.	**Heart damage** The heart muscles become weakened and the heart becomes enlarged, reducing its ability to pump blood. This damage can lead to heart failure. Reduced blood flow can also damage other body systems. **High blood pressure** Damages the heart and can cause heart attack and stroke.	**Irritation of digestive lining** Can lead to stomach ulcers and cancer of the stomach and esophagus. **Fatty liver** Fats build up in the liver and cannot be broken down, leading to cell death. **Alcoholic hepatitis** Inflammation or infection of the liver. **Cirrhosis of the liver** Liver tissue is replaced with useless scar tissue. Cirrhosis can lead to liver failure and death.	**Swelling of the pancreas lining** The passageway from the pancreas to the small intestine can become blocked, and chemicals needed for digestion cannot pass to the small intestine. The chemicals begin to destroy the pancreas itself, causing pain and vomiting. A severe case of pancreatic swelling can lead to death.

Effects of Alcohol Poisoning

A person who drinks too much alcohol may eventually pass out. Even though the person is unconscious, alcohol that is in the stomach continues to enter the bloodstream. So, even if someone is unconscious, that person's blood alcohol level will continue to rise. This increases the risk of alcohol poisoning. It is dangerous to assume that a person who has passed out after consuming a lot of alcohol will be fine if left to "sleep it off." Some of the symptoms of alcohol poisoning include:

- mental confusion and stupor.
- coma and an inability to be roused.
- vomiting and seizures.
- slow respiration—ten seconds between breaths or fewer than eight breaths per minute.
- irregular heartbeat.
- hypothermia or low body temperature—pale or bluish skin color.

If you suspect that a person has alcohol poisoning, call 911 immediately.

Myths & Reality

Alcohol

Myth: Beer or wine won't get you drunk as fast as hard liquor.

Fact: The amount of alcohol consumed, not the type of drink, makes a person drunk. A can of beer, a 4-ounce glass of wine, or a mixed drink all contain about the same amount of alcohol.

Myth: Drinking alcohol warms the body.

Fact: While drinking alcohol can make the drinker's skin feel warm, blood vessels in the skin expand and actually cause the body to lose heat. Outside on a cold day, this can result in hypothermia.

Health Skills Activity

Refusal Skills

A Drink at Home

Zach is going to Karen's house on Saturday to watch a couple of movies with friends. When Zach arrives at Karen's house, he is surprised to find that many of the teens there are drinking beer.

Karen sees him. "Hi, Zach. Do you want a beer?"

"Where did you get those?" asks Zach. "Aren't your parents home?"

"No, they're not home. What they don't know won't hurt them," says Karen. "Come on, I'll get you a beer. It's no big deal."

Zach has an agreement with his parents that he won't drink alcohol. He knows his parents would not approve of him drinking. He doesn't want his friends to think he's not part of the crowd, but he knows he needs to make it clear that he is not going to drink.

Writing Write a script completing the dialogue between Zach and Karen. How can Zach refuse alcohol and still remain friends with Karen? When writing your dialogue, use the following refusal skills:

1. Say no in a firm voice.
2. Explain why you are refusing.
3. Suggest alternatives to the proposed activity.
4. Back up your words with body language.
5. Leave the situation if necessary.

LESSON 1 ASSESSMENT

After You Read

Reviewing Facts and Vocabulary

1. What is *intoxication*? What influences how fast a person becomes intoxicated?
2. Explain how alcohol acts as a *depressant* on the central nervous system.
3. What is *binge drinking*? What can happen as a result of binge drinking?

Thinking Critically

4. **Analyze.** Is it safe to take an over-the-counter medicine after drinking alcohol? Explain your reasoning.
5. **Describe.** How can drinking even moderate amounts of alcohol permanently affect teens?

Applying Health Skills

6. **Advocacy.** Write a PSA script that advises other teens of the dangers of binge drinking. Include the health risks and what to do if someone drinks too much alcohol.

Writing Critically

7. **Persuasive.** Write a letter to your city council member asking that police prosecute stores that sell alcohol to anyone who is underage.

Go Online

Visit glencoe.com and complete the Interactive Study Guide for this lesson.

---

③ ASSESS/CLOSE

Assessment Resources

📁 **FAST FILE ACTIVITIES**
Lesson 1 Quiz

💿 *ExamView Assessment Suite* CD-ROM

Visit glencoe.com for:
Online Quizzes
Online Learning Center

Progress Monitoring

Reteaching

Ask students to work in teams to write five quiz questions and answers about the main concepts of this lesson. Have teams exchange questions. When each team finishes answering the questions, have teams compare answers.

Enrichment

Ask students to do research to find out more about how alcohol affects the nervous system. Have them use the information they find to write a report that includes real-world examples of how alcohol changes reaction times, memory, and other aspects of nervous-system functions.

Go Online

Have students visit glencoe.com and complete the Interactive Study Guide for this lesson.

LESSON 1 ASSESSMENT ANSWERS

1. The state in which the body is poisoned by alcohol or another substance, and mental and physical control is reduced; factors include body size, gender, food, rate of intake, amount, and medicine
2. Slows reaction time, impairs vision, and diminishes clear thinking and good judgment
3. Drinking five or more alcoholic drinks at one sitting; impaired physical and mental abilities, alcohol poisoning
4. No, because interactions can lead to illness, injury, or death
5. Alcohol can damage brain development, and teens who drink can have impaired learning ability and memory.
6. Scripts will vary.
7. Responses will vary.

LESSON 2

Choosing to Live Alcohol-Free

1 FOCUS

BIG Idea Students will learn about how choosing not to use alcohol protects them from dangerous health consequences. **Ask Students:** *What is one benefit of living without drinking alcohol?* (Sample answers: Having a healthier body; probably living longer)

Before You Read

Concept Map Students' concept maps will vary.

Main Idea

Alcohol Use Several factors influence teen alcohol use. **Ask Students:** *Why do you think drinking alcohol even once can have dangerous consequences?* (Sample answer: It can lead to risky behavior that may result in arrest, injury, or even death)

Real Life Issues

Ask volunteers to share their paragraphs with the class. Students might mention staying away from situations where alcohol is available in order to avoid using alcohol.

LESSON 2

📖 **GUIDE TO READING**

BIG Idea *Choosing not to use alcohol protects you from dangerous health consequences.*

Before You Read

Make a Cause-and-Effect Concept Map. Draw a box around the phrase "Teen Alcohol Use," as shown here. Write at least three consequences of alcohol use, each in its own box. Connect the consequence boxes to the Teen Alcohol Use box as shown.

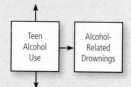

New Vocabulary

▸ psychological dependence (p. 572)
▸ physiological dependence (p. 572)
▸ alcohol abuse (p. 575)
▸ alcoholism (p. 575)

Choosing to Live Alcohol-Free

Real Life Issues

Avoiding Alcohol. Kyle's friend Andrew says he will start drinking because his other friends drink, and he wants to fit in. Andrew also wants to buy alcohol even though he is underage. He wants Kyle to ask his older brother to buy alcohol for an upcoming party. Kyle wants to avoid using alcohol, and he does not want to do anything illegal.

Writing *Write a paragraph describing what you would do if you were Kyle. Explain your decision to Andrew.*

Alcohol Use

Main Idea Several factors influence teen alcohol use.

Alcohol use by responsible adults is legal. Anyone who drinks alcohol, however, increases the risk of the negative consequences. One consequence of alcohol use is **psychological dependence**, *a condition in which a person believes that a drug is needed in order to feel good or to function normally.* Overuse of alcohol can lead to a **physiological dependence**, *a condition in which the user has a chemical need for a drug.*

Factors that Influence Alcohol Use

A teen's choices about alcohol use are influenced by

- **peer pressure.** When alcohol use is not an accepted activity in a group, a teen will not feel pressure to drink.

- **family.** When a teen's parents discourage and avoid the use of alcohol, the teen is more likely to do the same.

- **media messages.** Media messages may make alcohol use seem glamorous and fun.

R

🏔️👥 Home and Community

Advertising Alcohol A major goal of public health advocates has been to limit exposure by children and teens to alcohol advertising. Yet the alcohol industry spends more than $4.5 billion a year on advertising alcohol products, and there are relatively few laws and regulations about such advertising.

Some states regulate outdoor advertising by prohibiting alcohol ads near schools and playgrounds, and ads that target teens. Ask students to call their state's Alcohol Beverage Control agency to find out what restrictions their state has on outdoor alcohol advertisements.

■ **Figure 21.5** Exercise, eating a balanced diet, and avoiding alcohol can help teens stay healthy. *Why should teens avoid alcohol?*

[handwritten notes: Good Time 41 / Celebrate 30 / Get Drunk 28 / Feel Good 24 / Relax 21]

Advertising Techniques

Companies that produce alcohol spend billions of dollars each year to associate their product with youthful, healthy people who seem to be having fun. These companies advertise in ways that are visible to teens and children, on billboards, TV, and radio, and in magazines and newspapers. Alcohol companies also sponsor sporting events, music concerts, art festivals, exhibits, and college events. Manufacturers and advertisers, however, never show consumers the negative side of alcohol use.

Alcohol companies target teens and young adults by marketing beverages that appear safer than other alcoholic beverages. These drinks are sweet and look similar to non-alcoholic carbonated beverages. In reality, these beverages contain alcohol.

Health Risks of Alcohol Use

Main Idea Alcohol can harm more than just your health.

In the United States, nearly 50 people die each day as a result of alcohol-related traffic collisions. Alcohol use is linked to deaths from drowning, fire, suicide, and homicide. A nondrinker's risk of being injured increases if the friends that person is with are drinking.

Alcohol and the Law

It is illegal for anyone under the age of 21 to buy, possess, or consume alcohol. For teens who break the law, the consequences can be very serious. Teens who use alcohol can be arrested and sentenced to a youth detention center.

READING CHECK

Explain How do advertisements try to encourage teens to start drinking?

[handwritten notes: Why? / Where? / Who Has the most Inf / Why Don't Kids Drink]

 Online

Visit **glencoe.com** and complete the Student Web Activity on reducing alcohol use among teens.

② TEACH

Caption Answer

Figure 21.5 Alcohol is addictive, is illegal for teens to possess, can lead to risky behaviors, and may permanently affect brain development.

R Reading Strategy

Real World Connections Make a heading on the board titled "Reasons Why Teens Use or Don't Use Alcohol." Ask volunteers to identify three factors that influence alcohol use. They should identify peer pressure, family, and media messages. Write those on the board. Then, ask for examples of each factor influencing a teen to use alcohol and not to use alcohol. **BL**

Main Idea

Health Risks of Alcohol Alcohol can harm more than just health.
Ask Students: *What are some consequences if a teen is arrested for using alcohol?* (Sample answers: Going to court, having to get treatment or go to jail, disappointing parents)

READING CHECK

Answer Ads associate alcohol with youthful, healthy people who are having fun.

English Language Coach

Extend Vocabulary Help students learning English to differentiate between *psychological dependence* and *physiological dependence* by examining the meanings of the adjectives in the two terms. Explain that *psychological* is the adjective form of the word *psychology,* which is the study of the mind and behavior. *Physiological* is the adjective form of the word *physiology,* which is the study of the functions and activities of living things. To put it simply, psychological dependence has to do with mental health, and physiological dependence has to do with physical health.

573

CA Cultural Awareness

Legal Drinking Age Explain that the United States has a relatively high drinking age. For example, China and Nigeria have no minimum age to purchase alcohol. The drinking age is 16 in Germany and France; 18 in Mexico, Israel, and Great Britain; and 20 in Japan. Ask interested students to research the drinking age and attitudes toward alcohol use in various countries around the world. **AL**

AL Active Learning

Questionnaire Have students develop five to ten questions to use in a survey of teens in their community about alcohol use. They might include such questions as: *Do you think there is a connection between alcohol and teen violence? What do you think influences some teens to avoid drinking?* Have students survey teens they know. Discuss the results in class. **OL**

FITNESSZONE

Have students do this N, S, W, E jump activity:

- Teacher faces the front of the room and calls it north.
- Teacher calls a direction and students jump in that direction.

■ **Figure 21.6** Your decision to avoid alcohol is influenced by the people around you. *How can having friends who do not use alcohol help you to stay alcohol-free?*

FITNESSZONE

We learned about alcohol use at a school assembly. The speaker said that people who start drinking before the age of 15 are five times more likely to have alcohol-related problems later in life. They also said that new research shows that alcohol use by teens can harm our brains and that our brains are still developing. After hearing that, I have even more reason to refuse alcohol. For more fitness tips, visit the Online Fitness Zone at glencoe.com.

Any arrest and conviction can affect a teen's future. An arrest can limit college and employment options. Breaking the law can also damage a teen's reputation and cause that teen to lose the trust of friends and family members. **CA**

Alcohol and Violence

Teens can protect their health by avoiding situations where alcohol is present. Fights are more likely to break out at parties where alcohol is used. Teens who are involved in fights face school or police disciplinary action. Teens who drink are also more likely to be victims or perpetrators of violent crimes, such as rape, aggravated assault, and robbery. It is estimated that alcohol use is a factor in one-third to two-thirds of sexual assaults or date-rape cases. **AL**

Alcohol and Sexual Activity

Alcohol impairs judgment and lowers inhibitions, and can cause a person to compromise his or her values. Teens who use alcohol are more likely to become sexually active at an earlier age, and to engage in unprotected sexual activity. Approximately 25 percent of sexually active teens use alcohol or drugs before engaging in sexual activity. Teens who drink often are twice as likely to contract an STD as teens who do not drink. **C**

Teens Want to Know

Can Teens Become Alcoholics? Yes, teens can become addicted to alcohol. One recent study of adults found that almost half of adult alcoholics became addicted to alcohol before the age of 21. A teen's alcoholism is often not recognized as such by parents or peers. Teen drinking has often been excused as a phase that youth go through. Yet, alcohol is addictive, and some teens become addicted as easily as some adults do. Indications of alcoholism in a teen include drinking alone, when upset, or to cope with emotional problems.

Real World CONNECTION

Analyzing the Media

What media images come to mind when you think of advertisements for alcohol? Many ads feature attractive young people whose message seems to be, "You can be like us if you use this product." When you see ads like this, ask yourself the following:

▶ **What is really being advertised?** Is it alcohol or the desire to be viewed as someone who is attractive and fits into a large group of friends?

▶ **What is the hidden message?** Are the advertisers trying to say you need alcohol to have fun?

▶ **What is the truth?** What are some other reasons that the people in the ad may be enjoying themselves?

Activity Reading / Writing

Use a critical eye when examining alcohol ads in magazines, newspapers, television, and billboards. Select three alcohol ads and ask yourself the following questions.

1. What is really being advertised?
2. What is the hidden message?
3. What is the truth?
4. How do the advertisers distort the truth about alcohol?

After analyzing the ads, select one and create a poster showing how the ad distorts the truth. Use your creativity to show how the ad, or even just elements of the ad, can be misleading.

Alcohol and the Family

It is estimated that 25 percent of all youth are exposed to **alcohol abuse**—*the excessive use of alcohol*—within their families. Young people who live in a household in which a family member abuses alcohol are at a high risk for

- neglect, abuse, or social **isolation**.
- economic hardship.
- personal use of alcohol themselves.
- mental illness or physical problems.

Studies show that a person who begins drinking alcohol as a teen is four times more likely to develop alcohol dependence than someone who waits until adulthood to use alcohol. This dependence, called **alcoholism**, is *a disease in which a person has a physical or psychological dependence on drinks that contain alcohol.*

Academic Vocabulary

isolation *(noun):* the state of being withdrawn or separated

Alcohol and School

Most schools have adopted a zero-tolerance policy for students found using alcohol on school property. Students who use alcohol may become ineligible for or be suspended from school activities or graduation, or expelled from school. These students could also be placed in an alternate education program. Ultimately, a student may find that his or her options for choosing a college or job may be limited.

 **READING CHECK**

List Name three risky behaviors that can be caused by alcohol use.

Lesson 2 Choosing to Live Alcohol-Free **575**

Writing Strategy

Writing a Reflective Paper A reflective paper is used to describe a personal or hypothetical experience, evaluate that experience, and then reflect on how the experience can be applied in the future. Have students write a reflective paper that includes:

- A scenario in which a teen is affected by alcohol abuse in the family and finds a

way to get help for the situation without turning to alcohol.

- An evaluation of how the effects of alcohol caused serious problems in the home.
- How the teen can use those experiences to commit to living alcohol free.

Avoiding Alcohol

Main Idea You will experience many benefits if you choose to live alcohol-free.

Living alcohol-free is a choice that some adults make. Many other adults choose to drink alcohol occasionally and responsibly. Alcohol is addictive, and once you start drinking, it may be difficult to stop. Teens who start drinking by age 15 are five times more likely to become dependent on alcohol than people who do not start drinking until age 21.

Benefits of Living Alcohol-Free

Many teens make the commitment to stay alcohol-free. Avoiding alcohol will help you with the following:

- **Maintaining a healthy body.** You will avoid the damage alcohol can do to the brain and body organs and decrease the likelihood of being injured in an accident.
- **Establishing healthy relationships.** You can be open and honest with your family about your activities and habits.
- **Making healthy decisions.** Avoiding intoxication will allow you to make decisions that protect your health.
- **Avoiding risky behaviors.** You will reduce the risk of making unhealthy choices, such as drinking and driving.
- **Avoiding illegal activities.** You can avoid arrest and legal problems by being alcohol-free. Purchasing or possessing alcohol is against the law for anyone under 21.
- **Avoiding violence.** Avoiding alcohol reduces your risk of being a victim of or participating in a violent crime.
- **Achieving your goals.** Being alcohol-free allows you to stay focused on your short-term and long-term goals.

W

■ **Figure 21.7** Avoiding alcohol use can help you avoid risky behaviors. *How can teen alcohol use put your future at risk?*

Promoting School Wellness

Alcohol Policies at School Most schools have policies regarding alcohol use by students, as well as by faculty and staff. For students, there are consequences for being caught with alcoholic beverages or for being under the influence of alcohol. Suspension, or even expulsion, may be mandated for some offenses. A good coordinated school health program also has established procedures for helping students with alcohol problems. Ask a school administrator to make a brief presentation to the class about the school's alcohol policies. Have students prepare relevant questions beforehand.

Refusing Alcohol

HS

At times, it may be difficult to avoid situations in which you are pressured to use alcohol. Saying no is much easier when you know how you will respond *before* you are faced with the situation. If you find yourself in a situation where alcohol is present, be assertive and use refusal skills. Call your parents or another trusted adult for a ride home, if needed. Here are some examples of refusal statements:

- "I don't like the taste."
- "No, thanks. I need to be in top shape for the game this week."
- "I don't drink alcohol—besides, I'm heading home."
- "I really can't, my parents would be angry. We have an agreement."
- "I don't want to risk getting kicked off the team."

Another strategy to avoid alcohol use is to plan alcohol-free activities with friends. Avoid parties or social gatherings where alcohol is served. Practice your refusal skills to build confidence when you are with peers who may use alcohol.

■ **Figure 21.8** Having a strategy to stay alcohol-free will help you avoid the risks of alcohol use. *What are some ways to avoid using alcohol?*

 READING CHECK

Explain How can staying alcohol-free help you stay physically and mentally healthy?

LESSON 2 ASSESSMENT

After You Read

Reviewing Facts and Vocabulary

1. What is *alcohol abuse,* and how are teens likely to be affected if it occurs in their family?
2. How does *alcohol abuse* differ from *alcoholism*?
3. Explain whether teens are at risk of alcohol dependence.

Thinking Critically

4. **Evaluate.** What are four possible consequences of poor decisions made while under the influence of alcohol?
5. **Analyze.** Explain how teens can stay alcohol-free.

Applying Health Skills

6. **Refusal Skills.** You arrive at a party and see that other teens are drinking alcohol. Write a dialogue describing how you use refusal skills effectively to stay alcohol-free.

Writing Critically

7. **Descriptive.** Write a scenario between a teen and a parent. The teen is providing reasons for remaining alcohol-free.

 Online

Visit **glencoe.com** and complete the Interactive Study Guide for this lesson.

Caption Answer

Figure 21.8 Sample answer: Avoid situations where alcohol is present.

③ ASSESS/CLOSE

Assessment Resources

📁 *FAST FILE* **ACTIVITIES**
Lesson 2 Quiz

💿 *ExamView Assessment Suite* CD-ROM

Visit glencoe.com for:
Online Quizzes
Online Learning Center

Progress Monitoring

Reteaching
Call on students to identify factors that influence teens to use or not use alcohol, and to name benefits of living alcohol-free.

Enrichment
Ask students to find out what the laws are in their state about the responsibility adults have for teens under their supervision who drink or drink in their house when they are not there. Can the adults be charged with a crime? Ask students to write a report about what they learn.

 Online

Have students visit **glencoe.com** and complete the Interactive Study Guide for this lesson.

LESSON 2 ASSESSMENT ANSWERS

1. The excessive use of alcohol; they may experience neglect, abuse, social isolation, economic hardship, personal use of alcohol, and mental illness or physical problems
2. *Alcohol abuse* is the excessive use of alcohol, while *alcoholism* is a disease in which a person has a physical or psychological dependence on drinks that contain alcohol.
3. Yes, teens who drink are more likely to develop alcohol dependence than someone who waits until adulthood to use alcohol.
4. Sample answer: Legal trouble, violence, suspension from school, getting an STD
5. Sample answer: Teens can avoid situations where alcohol is present.
6. Dialogues will vary.
7. Scenarios will vary.

The Impact of Alcohol Abuse

① FOCUS

GUIDE TO READING

BIG Idea Students will learn how drinking and alcoholism harm both the drinkers and the people around them. **Ask Students:** *What is one way that problem drinkers affect society?* (Sample answer: Problem drinkers cause deaths in automobile accidents.)

Before You Read

Note Cards Students' note cards will vary.

Main Idea

Alcohol and Driving It is very dangerous to drink and drive. **Ask Students:** *Why would driving after drinking alcohol be an unsafe behavior?* (Alcohol slows reaction time and diminishes good judgment.)

Real Life Issues ··············

Students should demonstrate their communication skills in writing the letter, including using "I" messages to express feelings and using a respectful tone. Ask volunteers to share their letters with the class. Discuss the difficulties that Lily faces in having an alcoholic parent and what actions Lily could take to help her mother and herself.

 LESSON **3**

 **GUIDE TO READING**

BIG Idea *Problem drinking and alcoholism harm both the drinkers and the people around them.*

Before You Read

Make Note Cards. Label one note card "Alcohol Abuse." Then, make a note card for each vocabulary term in this lesson. On each note card, write what you already know about each term. As you read the lesson, add information to each card about each term.

Alcohol Abuse

New Vocabulary

▸ blood alcohol concentration (BAC) (p. 578)
▸ fetal alcohol syndrome (FAS) (p. 580)
▸ alcoholic (p. 581)
▸ recovery (p. 582)
▸ sobriety (p. 582)

The Impact of Alcohol Abuse

Real Life Issues ·····························

Living with Alcohol Abuse. Lily's mother drinks alcohol every day. She is always drunk and out of control. Lily thinks her mother may be an alcoholic. Her mother says that drinking helps her unwind at the end of the day. Recently, Lily's mother lost her job because she was drunk at work. Lily often finds herself taking care of her mother whenever she is drunk.

Writing *Write a letter to Lily's mother as if you were Lily. In your letter, explain how her mother's drinking is affecting Lily's life.*

Alcohol and Driving

Main Idea Drinking and driving is very dangerous.

Driving after drinking can have disastrous and even deadly results. One-fifth of all teen drivers involved in fatal car accidents have a blood alcohol concentration of 0.01 percent. A person's **blood alcohol concentration (BAC)** is *the amount of alcohol in a person's blood, expressed as a percentage.* BAC depends on the quantity and type of alcohol that was consumed, the rate of consumption, and body size and gender. **Figure 21.9** illustrates how the alcohol content varies in common alcoholic beverages. Any amount of alcohol in the blood can cause the following:

- Slow reflexes
- Reduced ability to judge distances and speeds
- Increase in risk-taking behaviors
- Reduced concentration and increased forgetfulness

 Home and Community

Dealing with Sensitive Issues
Alcoholism in the family and driving under the influence may be emotional topics for students who have been directly affected by either of these issues. Allow students to take the lead in whether or not they want to talk about a particular episode. Do not single out particular students by asking if they have had experience with drunk driving or alcoholism in the family. Remind students that there are counseling options available at school and in the community, in organizations such as Alateen.

Figure 21.9 Comparing Beer, Wine, and Spirits

Each of these beverages contains the same amount of pure alcohol.

Drink	Alcohol by Volume	Alcohol Content
Beer (12 oz.)	4%	0.5 oz.
Wine (5 oz.)	10%	0.5 oz.
Vodka or Whiskey (1.25 oz.)	40%	0.5 oz.

Driving While Intoxicated

Driving while intoxicated (DWI), or driving under the influence (DUI), is illegal. Adult drivers who have a BAC of 0.08 percent can be charged with drunk driving. For those under 21, there is no acceptable BAC, since it's illegal to use alcohol. The consequences for DWI or DUI include

- injuries to or death of the driver and others.
- arrest, jail time, court appearance and fine or bail, a police record, and possible lawsuits.
- severely restricted driving privileges and/or immediate confiscation of driver's license.
- higher auto insurance rates or a canceled insurance policy.

Riding in a vehicle with a driver who has been drinking is just as dangerous as if you were the one drinking and driving. If someone you're with has been drinking, find a ride with someone who has not been drinking, or call home for a ride.

Go Online

Explore **glencoe.com** and complete the Student Web Activity to learn more about alcoholism and how it can be treated.

☑ READING CHECK

Explain Why is it dangerous to drive after drinking alcohol?

■ **Figure 21.10** Approximately 17,000 people die in alcohol-related crashes each year. *What are other consequences of drinking and driving?*

Lesson 3   The Impact of Alcohol Abuse   **579**

Academic Integration

Math Bring home the problem of drinking and driving by relating national statistics to your school's student population. According to the Centers for Disease Control and Prevention (CDC), a survey found that about 30 percent of teens reported riding in a motor vehicle with a driver who had been drinking in the past month. Ask students to relate that statistic to the number of students in their school. (If there are 1,000 students, the answer is 300 students; 1,000 $\times$ 0.3 = 300.)

Main Idea

Alcohol and Pregnancy A female who drinks during pregnancy can harm her fetus. **Ask Students:** *How can alcohol that a pregnant woman drinks affect the fetus?* (The bloodstream of the fetus is connected to the pregnant woman's bloodstream.)

HS Health Skills Practice

Advocacy Tell students to assume an older neighbor is pregnant and drinking alcohol. Ask them to write a letter to the neighbor explaining the risks of alcohol to the fetus and advocating against drinking alcohol during pregnancy. OL

W Writing Support

Expository Writing Ask students to research and write reports on the effects of *Fetal Alcohol Syndrome.* Students should be sure to include statistics and long-term effects. AL

Main Idea

Alcoholism The disease of alcoholism affects both alcoholics and the people around them. **Ask Students:** *In what ways could an alcoholic affect members of his or her family?* (Sample answer: The alcoholic might abuse family members when drinking.)

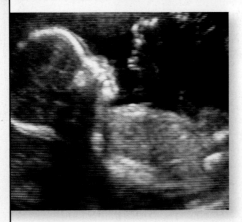

■ **Figure 21.11** When a pregnant female drinks, so does her fetus. *What effect can alcohol have on a fetus?*

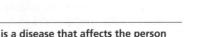

READING CHECK

List Name four problems that a baby born to a mother who drank alcohol during pregnancy may have.

Alcohol and Pregnancy

Main Idea A female who drinks during pregnancy can harm her fetus.

When a pregnant female drinks, alcohol passes directly from her body into the bloodstream of the fetus. A fetus processes alcohol much more slowly than the mother does. As a result, there is more alcohol in the fetus's system for a longer period of time. Infants born to mothers who drink during pregnancy are at risk of **fetal alcohol syndrome (FAS),** *a group of alcohol-related birth defects that include physical and mental problems.*

Effects of Fetal Alcohol Syndrome (FAS)

The effects of FAS are both severe and lasting. Infants born with FAS may have the following problems:

- Small head and deformities of face, hands, or feet
- Heart, liver, and kidney defects
- Vision and hearing problems
- Central nervous system problems, developmental disabilities, and poor coordination
- Difficulties learning and short attention span
- Hyperactivity, anxiety, and social withdrawal

FAS is one of the leading preventable causes of mental retardation. Females who are trying to become pregnant or may be pregnant should not drink *any* alcohol.

Alcoholism

Main Idea Alcoholism is a disease that affects the person who drinks and others around him or her.

Alcoholics are physically or psychologically dependent on alcohol. The symptoms of alcoholism include the following:

- **Craving**—Feeling a strong need for alcohol to manage tension or stress, and a preoccupation with alcohol
- **Loss of control**—Inability to limit alcohol consumption
- **Physical dependence**—Withdrawal symptoms, such as nausea, sweating, shakiness, and anxiety
- **Tolerance**—A need to drink increasingly more alcohol in order to feel its effects

Health Literacy

Fetal Alcohol Syndrome Each year, as many as 40,000 babies in the United States are born with some kind of alcohol-related damage. There is no kind or amount of alcohol that is safe to drink while pregnant. Therefore, a woman who thinks she may be or may become pregnant should avoid alcohol. Sometimes, a pregnant woman can drink during pregnancy without seeming to affect the fetus. This is no indication that drinking during the next pregnancy will not cause FAS.

TEENS Making a Difference

Advocating for Change

Elianna Y., of California, joined the substance-free group Friday Night Live as a freshman. Three years later, Elianna is one of the leaders of the group.

Under Elianna's leadership, Friday Night Live is targeting alcopops, sweet, malt-flavored beverages that contain distilled spirits. "They're popular with teens, even though it's illegal for teens to drink alcohol. Currently alcopops are taxed the same as beer," says Elianna. Friday Night Live has petitioned California legislators to raise the tax.

"I feel like I am making a difference in people's lives not only with the policy changes, but also as a role model," said Elianna. "Being young doesn't mean you can't do anything. A young person can make a difference in the community."

"A young person can make a difference."

Activity Write your answers to the following questions in your personal health journal:

1. What issues in your community would motivate you to become a leader?
2. Describe two benefits that might result from the change in this tax law.
3. How can you make a difference in your community regarding alcohol and teens?

Alcoholics

An **alcoholic** is *an addict who is dependent on alcohol.* The behavior of alcoholics varies—some are aggressive and violent, while others may become withdrawn. Alcoholism is not limited to any age, race, or ethnic or socioeconomic group.

Growing scientific evidence suggests that alcoholism is partially due to genetics. One study shows that children of alcoholics are four times more likely to become alcoholics. Environmental factors such as family, friends, culture, peer pressure, availability of alcohol, and stress also contribute to alcoholism. The age at which a person starts drinking also influences the risk of alcoholism. Teens who start drinking are at a higher risk of becoming alcoholics during their lifetime than people who begin drinking as adults.

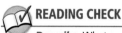 **READING CHECK**

Describe What are the symptoms of alcoholism?

Lesson 3 The Impact of Alcohol Abuse **581**

TEENS Making a Difference

Answers to Activity Questions

1. Answers will vary. Students may mention issues related to alcohol use.
2. Sample answer: Fewer teens would buy or drink the product, and the company that makes alcopops may pull it from the market.
3. Answers will vary. Students may suggest getting involved in advocating against teen alcohol use.

C Critical Thinking

Analyzing Describe for students two teens: One has an alcoholic parent. The other's parents are not alcoholics, but the teen has a best friend who drinks heavily and always has alcohol available. Ask students which teen is more likely to become an alcoholic. After listening to students' ideas, point out that both teens are at risk but neither is certain to become an alcoholic, as genetics and environment are simply factors, not absolutes. **OL**

READING CHECK

Answer Craving alcohol, loss of control, physical dependence, tolerance

---

Cooperative Learning

Write a Skit Review with students the material in the text on alcoholism. Divide the class into small groups, and have each group write a skit that could be used to teach teens about alcoholism. The skit could focus on a teen struggling with alcoholism or a group of friends who work together to help a teen find help for an alcohol problem. Each skit should include dialogue and stage directions that demonstrate what students have learned about alcoholism. Ask groups to perform their skits for the class.

Main Idea

Effects on Family and Society
Alcohol abuse plays a role in crimes and has negative effects on people who are around problem drinkers. **Ask Students:** *Why would alcohol abuse be a factor in crime?* (Sample answer: Impaired judgment and lowered inhibitions caused by alcohol abuse could make a person more likely to commit or be a victim of crime.)

W **Writing Support**

Summarize Ask students to summarize the stages of alcoholism in three paragraphs. Remind students to write in sentence form. **OL**

HS **Health Skills Practice**

Accessing Information Have students contact or visit offices of organizations in their community that have programs to help alcoholics, such as Alateen and Students Against Destructive Decisions (SADD). Ask students to pick up brochures that provide information about alcoholism or the organization's programs. Display the brochures in the classroom. **OL**

■ **Figure 21.12** Alcohol causes serious damage to the liver. Compare the healthy liver (top) with the liver that has been damaged by alcohol abuse. *What effect does alcohol have on the liver?*

Figure 21.13

Steps to Recovery

Step 1—Admission
• The person admits to having a drinking problem and asks for help.

Step 2—Detoxification
• The person goes through detoxification, a process in which the body adjusts to functioning without alcohol.

Step 3—Counseling
• The person receives counseling to help him or her learn to change behaviors and live without alcohol.

Step 4—Recovery
• The person takes responsibility for his or her own life.

582   Chapter 21   Alcohol

Stages of Alcoholism

Alcoholism develops in three stages: abuse, dependence, and addiction. All alcoholics do not, however, experience each stage equally.

• **Stage 1—Abuse.** Alcoholism may begin with social drinking. A physical and psychological dependence develops. The person may experience memory loss and blackouts, and may begin to lie or make excuses to justify his or her drinking.

• **Stage 2—Dependence.** The person cannot stop drinking and is physically dependent on alcohol. The drinker tries to hide the problem, but performance on the job, at school, and at home suffers.

• **Stage 3—Addiction.** In the final stage of alcoholism, the person is addicted. At this stage, the liver may be already damaged, and so less alcohol may be required to cause drunkenness. If the alcoholic stopped drinking, he or she would experience severe withdrawal symptoms.

W

Effects on Family and Society

Main Idea Alcohol abuse plays a role in crimes and has negative effects on people who are around problem drinkers.

The United States is home to an estimated 15 million alcoholics and problem drinkers. Alcohol abuse affects more than just the drinker. It is a major factor in the four leading causes of accidental death: car accidents, falls, drowning, and house fires. Alcohol also plays a major role in violent crimes, such as homicide, forcible rape, and robbery. About 40 percent of violent crimes are alcohol related.

Often, people close to alcoholics develop mentally unhealthy behaviors, such as *codependency*. Codependents ignore their own emotional and physical needs and instead focus their energy and emotions on the needs of the alcoholic. In the process, codependents lose their self-esteem and their trust in others, and their own physical health suffers.

Treatment for Alcohol Abuse

Main Idea Alcoholics can recover if they get treatment.

Alcoholism cannot be cured, but it *can* be treated. **Recovery** is *the process of learning to live an alcohol-free life.* Recovering alcoholics must make a lifelong commitment to **sobriety**,

Skills for the 21st Century

Problem Solving in the Workplace At one time, if an employee was found to have an alcohol problem, the employee was usually fired. Now, with a better understanding of alcoholism as a disease that can be treated, employers have other options for employees who abuse alcohol. Divide

the class into groups, and ask each group to devise a company policy for handling employees who show signs of alcoholism. Ask groups to share their policies with the class. Interested students can contact local companies about their policies and report their findings to the class.

which is *living without alcohol.* The steps to recovery outlined in **Figure 21.13**, include admitting that alcohol use is a problem; detoxification, or adjusting to functioning without alcohol; receiving counseling to change behaviors; and recovery, or taking responsibility for one's own life. Here are a few of the resources and programs available to help alcoholics and problem drinkers, as well as their families and friends:

HS

- **Al-Anon/Alateen** helps families and friends learn to deal with the effects of living with an alcoholic.
- **Alcoholics Anonymous** provides help for alcoholics.
- **Mothers Against Drunk Driving (MADD)** provides education to prevent underage drinking.
- **National Association for Children of Alcoholics** provides help for children of alcoholics.
- **National Drug and Alcohol Treatment Referral Routing Service** provides treatment referral and information about treatment facilities.
- **Students Against Destructive Decisions (SADD)** provides peer-led education about avoiding alcohol use.
- **SAMSHA's National Clearinghouse for Alcohol and Drug Information** provides information about alcohol and other drugs.

 READING CHECK

Explain Describe what an alcoholic must do in order to recover.

 **LESSON 3** 📖 **ASSESSMENT**

After You Read

Reviewing Vocabulary and Facts

1. What is *blood alcohol concentration (BAC),* and what is the legal BAC for teen drivers?
2. What is *fetal alcohol syndrome (FAS),* and what causes it?
3. Why does an alcoholic go through detoxification when trying to become sober?

Thinking Critically

4. **Analyze.** How does a moderate amount of alcohol, which otherwise might not be harmful to a female, have the potential to harm her fetus?
5. **Discuss.** What are two possible outcomes of drinking and driving?

Applying Health Skills

6. **Accessing Information.** Use reliable sources to identify community and other resources that help alcoholics and their families. Then, design a webpage that lists these resources.

Writing Critically

7. **Narrative.** Write a one-page story showing how a teen can use refusal skills to avoid getting into a car with a driver who has been drinking.

Go Online

Visit **glencoe.com** and complete the Interactive Study Guide for this lesson.

LESSON 3 ASSESSMENT ANSWERS

1. The amount of alcohol in a person's blood expressed as a percentage; no legal BAC
2. A group of alcohol-related birth defects that include physical and mental problems; caused by mothers who drink alcohol during pregnancy
3. Alcoholics are physically dependent on alcohol.
4. The fetus processes alcohol much slower than the mother, so there is more alcohol in the fetus' system for a longer period of time.
5. Sample answer: injuring or killing yourself or others; getting arrested and serving jail time
6. Web pages will vary. Students may do an online search to find organizations and services.
7. Stories will vary.

 ASSESS/ CLOSE

Assessment Resources

📁 *FAST FILE* ACTIVITIES
Lesson 3 Quiz

💿 *ExamView Assessment Suite* CD-ROM

Visit glencoe.com for:
Online Quizzes
Online Learning Center

Progress Monitoring

Reteaching
Have students work with partners to list the possible consequences for a teen who drives after drinking, the problems that babies with FAS have, and the stages of alcoholism.

Enrichment
Have students investigate further the causes of alcoholism with an emphasis on how both genetics and environmental factors play a role in whether an alcohol user becomes addicted. Ask students to prepare a written report on what they learn.

Go Online

Have students visit **glencoe.com** and complete the Interactive Study Guide for this lesson.

Keeping the Lid on the Bottle

Focus

Motivator

Ask students whether they think that parents who serve alcohol to minors on their own property should be legally responsible if police trace a keg of beer to them. Should the parents be prosecuted? Why or why not?

Teach

Effective Strategies Review with students the potential consequences for driving while intoxicated (DWI) or driving under the influence (DUI) listed in Lesson 3.

Ask Students: *Given these consequences, why do you think people still drink and drive? What influences might be affecting their behavior?* (Sample answer: Peer pressure, thrill seeking, desire to be accepted, alcohol dependency, diminished judgment from drinking) List students' responses on the board. Discuss ways for teens to overcome these influences and avoid risky behaviors. Ask students whether the ideas in the article—peer group talks, registration tags for beer kegs, a lower BAC—would make a difference in these behaviors.

Creating Slogans After students identify three powerful reasons why people should not drink and drive, ask them to turn that information into a creative slogan. Their slogan should be based on fact, take a clear stand for a healthy choice, and use memorable language to express a point. Slogans might include: "Stay Alive—Don't Drink and Drive" and "Are You Dying for a Drink?"

584

TIME HEALTH
MEDIA & ADVOCACY

Keeping the Lid on the Bottle

Teens can make a difference when it comes to preventing underage drinking.

Kasey Folse, 16, is a member of the Louisiana Alliance to Prevent Underage Drinking. He works to enact laws that make it harder for those who are underage to buy alcohol, such as registration tags for beer kegs. These tags would allow police to trace kegs back to whomever purchased them and punish that person if the beer was being served to underage drinkers. Kasey is also working to offer teens a place to talk about alcohol issues. "Kids don't really have anywhere to turn at my school," says Kasey. "It would definitely help if we had someone to talk one on one with students to deal with alcohol and drug questions."

Things weren't all that different at Andrew Araiza's Mary Carroll High School in Corpus Christi, Texas. Andrew says that many teens "don't consider all the problems associated with alcohol, like poisoning, accidents, and suicide."

Andrew is executive vice president of Texans Standing Tall, a coalition of youths and adults against underage drinking. He has successfully lobbied to remove liquor ads from the state's hunting license handbook and helped lower the legal blood alcohol limit from .1 to .08. Andrew says, "Having peer-group talks, where a teen with a problem describes what happened to him or her—that would get the message across."

Thanks to Ann Miller, 18, that message is coming through loud and clear at Oregon's Canby High. She educates teens about drinking, counsels those with problems, and encourages them to attend a local youth-oriented Alcoholics Anonymous meeting. The result is a greater awareness of the drawbacks of alcohol use and a population of teens who aren't afraid to ask for help. "People with a drinking problem have got to have good treatment available and good support from the adults around them," says Miller. ∎

TIME to THINK... About Blood Alcohol Level

On the Internet or your school's media center, look up government statistics about alcohol-related traffic accidents. Use those statistics to come up with three powerful reasons why people should not drink and drive.

More About...

Drinking and Driving Alcohol-related traffic deaths remain a serious problem in the United States. The following are 2005 statistics from the Centers for Disease Control and Prevention (CDC):

- 16,885 people died in alcohol-related traffic deaths, about 40 percent of all traffic deaths.

- 23 percent of drivers ages 15–20 who were killed in motor vehicle crashes had a BAC of 0.08 or higher.

- Almost 1.4 million drivers were arrested for driving under the influence of alcohol or drugs.

To download quizzes and eFlashcards to your PDA, go to glencoe.com and click on the Study to Go icon.

LESSON 1

The Health Risks of Alcohol Use

Key Concepts

▶ Alcohol is an addictive drug that slows the central nervous system (CNS) and impairs physical abilities and judgment.

▶ Mixing alcohol with medicines or other drugs is extremely dangerous.

▶ Long-term excessive alcohol use harms many of the body systems, and can possibly damage adolescent brain development processes.

▶ People who binge drink put themselves at serious risk of alcohol poisoning.

Vocabulary

▶ ethanol (p. 566)
▶ fermentation (p. 566)
▶ depressant (p. 567)
▶ intoxication (p. 567)
▶ binge drinking (p. 569)
▶ alcohol poisoning (p. 569)

LESSON 2

Choosing to Live Alcohol-Free

Key Concepts

▶ Peer pressure, advertising, and family can influence a teen's choice to use or not to use alcohol.

▶ Alcohol use leads to risky behaviors that have serious consequences.

▶ Teens who do not use alcohol are more likely to make healthy decisions that maintain their health.

▶ In order to stay alcohol-free, teens should try to avoid situations where alcohol will be present, and they should have a refusal plan.

Vocabulary

▶ psychological dependence (p. 572)
▶ physiological dependence (p. 572)
▶ alcohol abuse (p. 575)
▶ alcoholism (p. 575)

LESSON 3

The Impact of Alcohol Abuse

Key Concepts

▶ No one should drive after drinking alcohol because it impairs mental and physical abilities.

▶ If a female drinks while she is pregnant, her baby may be born with mental and physical birth defects.

▶ Dependence on alcohol causes alcoholics to harm themselves and the people around them.

▶ Alcoholics can recover if they seek help.

Vocabulary

▶ blood alcohol concentration (BAC) (p. 578)
▶ fetal alcohol syndrome (FAS) (p. 580)
▶ alcoholic (p. 581)
▶ recovery (p. 582)
▶ sobriety (p. 582)

Go Online

Students can visit **glencoe.com** to

- review content online with the Online Student Edition.
- test their knowledge of chapter content with Online Quizzes.
- access Interactive Health Tutor for more practice with vocabulary.

Assessment Resources

📁 **FAST FILE ACTIVITIES**
Chapter 21 Test

💿 *ExamView*
Assessment Suite CD-ROM

Visit glencoe.com for:
Audio Chapter Summaries
Online Quizzes

 Tell students to visit **glencoe.com** where they can download quizzes and eFlashcards.

Study Tips

Using Sticky Notes Tell students that a good way to help them remember what they read in the textbook or other books is to flag important information with small sticky notes. When they come to a statement that states a main idea or sums up a section, they can place a sticky note at that position for quick reference. Periodically, students can review the flagged information and even make notes about these important passages in a notebook or on note cards. This practice makes reviewing for tests much more efficient.

Assessment

Chapter 21 Assessment Answers

LESSON 1

Vocabulary Review

1. intoxication
2. Binge drinking
3. Alcohol poisoning

Understanding Key Concepts

4. b
5. a
6. b
7. d

Thinking Critically

8. Alcohol slows the central nervous system, which diminishes clear thinking and good judgment.
9. Interactions between medications and alcohol can lead to illness, injury, or death.
10. Sample answer: The brain becomes dependent on alcohol. The brain can become damaged, causing loss of memory and verbal and visual skills. The brain may decrease in size.
11. Sample answer: He does have a drinking problem because when he drinks he cannot control his actions.
12. Answers will vary. Students should describe the dangers of alcohol poisoning and suggest calling 9-1-1 immediately.

LESSON 2

Vocabulary Review

13. alcohol abuse
14. physiological dependence
15. alcoholism
16. psychological dependence

LESSON 1

Vocabulary Review

Correct the sentences below by replacing the italicized term with the correct vocabulary term.

1. Drinking alcohol can lead to *fermentation*, a state of reduced physical and mental control.

2. *Intoxication* is when a person drinks five or more alcoholic drinks at one sitting.

3. *Binge drinking* is a potentially fatal reaction to an alcohol overdose.

Understanding Key Concepts

After reading the question or statement, select the correct answer.

4. Which is *not* a short-term effect of alcohol?
    a. Coordination is impaired.
    b. Vision is impaired.
    c. More stomach acid is produced.
    d. Judgment is altered.

5. Which type of person is most likely to be quickly affected by alcohol?
    a. A small female who has not eaten
    b. A large female who just ate dinner
    c. A small male who just ate dinner
    d. A large male who has not eaten

6. Which is a potential consequence of long-term excessive alcohol use?
    a. A heart attack
    b. The need for a liver transplant
    c. Swelling of the brain
    d. An increased ability to control drinking

7. Which person is most likely to be at risk for alcohol poisoning?
    a. A person who has two drinks a week
    b. A person who has two drinks per day
    c. A person who binge drinks
    d. A person who drinks until he or she is drunk

Thinking Critically

After reading the question or statement, write a short answer using complete sentences.

8. **Describe.** Why are teens who drink more likely to put themselves in risky situations?

9. **Evaluate.** Terry takes a 12-hour allergy medication, and then drinks alcohol after waiting an hour. Explain why this is not a safe behavior.

10. **Explain.** How does long-term excessive drinking affect the brain?

11. **Analyze.** Dana drinks only occasionally, but when he drinks he does things that he later regrets. His friends assure him that he is fun when he drinks, and that he should not worry about his actions. Does Dana have a drinking problem? Explain.

12. **Evaluate.** A person passes out after drinking. Explain the dangers of leaving the person alone, and what action should be taken.

LESSON 2

Vocabulary Review

Use the vocabulary terms listed on page 585 to complete the following statements.

13. Teens are likely to experience neglect or abuse if there is _____ in their family.

14. People who have a chemical need for alcohol have a _____.

15. A dependence on drinks with alcohol is called _____.

16. When a person believes that alcohol use is needed to feel good or function normally, that person has a _____.

Health eSpotlight VIDEO Wrap-Up

The Risks of Use and Abuse Have students reread the Health eSpotlight questions at the beginning of the chapter (page 565) and look at their original answers. **Ask Students:** *What do you now know about how alcohol abuse affects a user's family, school,* *and social life that you didn't know before watching the video and reading the chapter?* Call on volunteers to describe what they have learned and how they would change their responses.

Understanding Key Concepts

After reading the question or statement, select the correct answer.

17. Which of the following influences teens to stay alcohol-free?
    a. Having peers who drink alcohol
    b. Seeing alcohol ads on TV
    c. Having parents who disapprove of alcohol use
    d. Attending alcohol-sponsored sporting events

18. Which is *not* a result of the high-risk behaviors associated with alcohol use?
    a. Increased deaths in traffic accidents
    b. Increased frequency of date rape
    c. Suspension from sports teams
    d. Improved job prospects

19. If you stay alcohol-free, which is a likely benefit?
    a. Decreased likelihood of getting a sexually transmitted disease
    b. Increased likelihood of being injured in an accident
    c. Decreased likelihood of making responsible decisions
    d. Increased likelihood of being a victim of violent crime

20. Which is *not* a strategy to remain alcohol-free?
    a. Planning an alcohol-free party
    b. Practicing refusal statements
    c. Attending parties with people who use alcohol
    d. Calling for a ride home if alcohol is present

Thinking Critically

After reading the question or statement, write a short answer using complete sentences.

21. **Explain.** What are the dangers of adult alcohol use? What are the dangers for teens?

22. **Analyze.** How does sponsoring community events and music concerts help alcohol companies sell their products?

23. **Discuss.** How does teen alcohol use impact the community?

24. **Evaluate.** Why are alcohol-free teens more likely to achieve their long-term goals than teens who use alcohol?

25. **Examine.** Why is avoiding gatherings where alcohol is present the best way to stay alcohol-free?

LESSON 3

Vocabulary Review

Choose the correct term in the sentences below.

26. *Blood alcohol concentration (BAC)/Fetal alcohol syndrome (FAS)* is a condition that babies can be born with if a female drinks while pregnant.

27. The amount of alcohol in a person's blood that is expressed as a percentage is *blood alcohol concentration/fetal alcohol syndrome*.

28. An addict who is dependent on alcohol is in/an *sobriety/alcoholic*.

Understanding Key Concepts

After reading the question or statement, select the correct answer.

29. It is illegal for adults to drive when they have what BAC level?
    a. 0.01   c. 0.05
    b. 0.02   d. 0.08

Understanding Key Concepts

17. c
18. d
19. a
20. c

Thinking Critically

21. Adults are at risk for health problems and becoming alcoholics. Teens are at risk of getting suspended from school and engaging in unprotected sexual activity that can lead to sexually transmitted diseases.
22. Consumers, including teens, associate good feelings with alcohol products.
23. Teens who use alcohol are more likely to engage in risky behavior and illegal activities.
24. Teens who avoid alcohol are less likely to be involved in accidents, violent crimes, and illegal activities. They are more likely to stay focused on their goals and make healthy decisions that help them reach their goals.
25. At gatherings where alcohol is present, there is peer pressure on teens to drink alcohol.

LESSON 3

Vocabulary Review

26. Fetal alcohol syndrome (FAS)
27. detoxification
28. recovery

Understanding Key Concepts

29. d

ExamView®
Assessment Suite

Create and customize tests in minutes with this convenient digital platform.

- Create differentiated tests quickly and easily.
- All questions correlated to National/State Standards.
- Enhance tests with Document Based Questions (DBQ) and add your own photos or graphics.
- Build tests in both English and Spanish.
- Generate progress reports.

To order, go to **glencoe.com** and search for ISBN 0-07-888173-0.

Assessment

Understanding Key Concepts

30. d
31. d
32. b

Thinking Critically

33. Alcohol slows reflexes, reduces ability to judge distances and speeds, increases risk-taking behaviors, reduces concentration, and increases forgetfulness.

34. Answers will vary but should demonstrate the understanding that any amount of alcohol can harm a fetus and cause FAS.

35. Genetics and environmental factors such as family, friends, culture, peer pressure, availability of alcohol, stress, and the age at which a person starts drinking

36. Sample answer: She can contact organizations such as Alcoholics Anonymous, or she can find counseling services in the community.

---

30. Which is *not* likely to occur if a person is caught drinking and driving?
    a. A field sobriety test will be conducted.
    b. The person loses driving privileges.
    c. The person loses insurance coverage.
    d. There will be no penalty.

31. A baby born with FAS may have which of the following?
    a. Anxiety
    b. Facial deformities
    c. Kidney problems
    d. All of the above

32. Which of the following is *not* part of the stages of alcoholism?
    a. Becoming intoxicated regularly
    b. Going through detoxification
    c. Making excuses for alcohol-related problems
    d. Alcohol taking control of the drinker's life

Thinking Critically

After reading the question or statement, write a short answer using complete sentences.

33. **Identify.** What effects of alcohol make it risky to drive after drinking?

34. **Apply.** Jacob's mother is seven months pregnant. She thinks it is alright to start having an occasional glass of wine with dinner because the fetus is mostly developed. What should Jacob tell her?

35. **Analyze.** What factors increase one's likelihood of becoming an alcoholic?

36. **Synthesize.** Jesse knows she has a drinking problem and wants help. Explain what she can do to find help.

Project-Based ASSESSMENT

The Power of Persuasion

Background
Companies that sell alcohol often use television advertising to convince people to buy and use their products. Alcohol commercials use powerful combinations of video and audio to sell their product. Anti-alcohol ads may also appear on television. These ads aim to reduce alcohol use among teens.

Task
Write a script for a 30-second TV ad demonstrating how saying no to alcohol is an attractive and practical option for teens.

Audience
Students in your class

Purpose
Persuade teens to say no to alcohol use.

Procedure

1 Working with a small group, create a list of situations in which teens may be pressured by other teens to use alcohol.

2 Select one situation that teens in your school may encounter. Conduct research using reliable sources to learn ways that advertisers might try to persuade teens to use their products.

3 Write a script that includes dialogue for a narrator and two teens. Include a list of images and sounds that might be used in the ad.

4 With your group, rehearse the ad. Make any necessary revisions.

5 Perform the commercial for the whole class. Discuss the results.

Project-Based ASSESSMENT

Step 1 View Ads Have students work in small groups to make a list of situations in which teens are pressured to use alcohol. Students in each group can collaborate on a script and the performance of the commercial. Provide access to recordings of 30-second television ads.

Step 2 Create the Ad Have groups choose a situation from their list and write a script. After teacher review of the script, give groups time to practice.

Step 3 Evaluate Have groups perform their commercials for the class. Commercials should present an attractive and realistic situation in which teens refuse alcohol.

Visit **glencoe.com** for Project-Based Assessment rubrics.

Math Practice

Interpreting Graphs. The graph below shows the relationship between blood alcohol level and breath alcohol level. After reviewing the graph, answer the questions that follow.

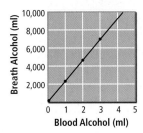

Blood Alcohol (ml)

1. Based on the graph, how many milliliters of blood are equivalent to 3150 ml of air?
   A. 1 ml
   B. 1.5 ml
   C. 3 ml
   D. 2100 ml

2. What type of function is shown on the graph?
   A. Exponential
   B. Higher degree
   C. Linear
   D. Quadratic

3. An increase in body temperature of 1.8 degrees F results in an increase of 7 percent in the test results. If a graph similar to the one shown were drawn for a person with a temperature of 97 degrees F, would the slope be greater than or less than the slope of this graph?

G⊙ Online

For more test practice, visit glencoe.com and complete the Online Quizzes for Chapter 21.

Reading/Writing Practice

Understand and Apply. Read the passage below, and then answer the questions.

Having a natural mentor can help teens make positive choices, according to a study by Students Against Destructive Decisions (SADD). Natural mentors can include parents, other family members, teachers, coaches, members of the clergy, and other trusted adults.

In the study, 46% of teens who have a natural mentor reported having a higher sense of self. Only 25% of teens who did not have a natural mentor agreed that they have a higher sense of self.

More than half of the students surveyed also said that having a natural mentor impacted them in a positive way. Teens are willing to talk to their natural mentors about avoiding alcohol, drugs, and sexual activity.

1. The study's findings show that
   A. a mentor has no influence on teens.
   B. a mentor can help teens make positive choices.
   C. a natural mentor is always a parent.
   D. teens with a natural mentor have a higher sense of self.

2. Based on this article, a natural mentor is
   A. another teen who may be one or two years older.
   B. a parent or other trusted adult.
   C. an adult the teen is paired with through a matching program.
   D. a teacher or school counselor who has had training as a mentor.

3. Write a one-page, persuasive essay describing the importance of having a natural mentor. Describe how mentors can help teens.

National Education Standards

Math: Number and Operations, Problem Solving
Language Arts: NCTE 3, NCTE 4

Standardized Test Practice

Standardized Test Practice Answers

Math Practice
1. B
2. C
3. Because 97°F is a below-normal body temperature, a larger volume of air would represent the amount of alcohol in 1 mL of blood. Therefore, the slope of the graph line would be greater.

Reading/Writing Practice
1. D
2. B
3. Essays will vary.

National Education Standards

Math: Number and Operations, Problem Solving

Language Arts: NCTE 3, NCTE 4

For the complete Math and Language Arts standards, visit glencoe.com.

G⊙ Online

Online Study Tools
For more test practice, visit glencoe.com and complete the Online Quizzes for Chapter 21.

Test-Taking Tip

Predicting Changes in Graphs Tell students that some questions on standardized tests ask how a graph would change if a factor that influences graph values were to change. To answer, students should analyze closely any example given about a change in a factor. In question 3 of the Math Practice test on this page, the example indicates that an increase in body temperature would result in an increase in the test results, which would translate into a slope less than the slope of the graph shown. Therefore, a decrease in body temperature would increase the slope of the graph.

589

Chapter 22 pages 590–621	Standards		Features
	National	**State/Local**	
	1.12.5, 1.12.8, 2.12.9, 3.12.4, 3.12.5, 5.12.4, 7.12.3, 8.12.4		*Hands-On* **HEALTH** • Saying No *(Refusal Skills)*, page 616
30 Min **Lesson 1** **The Health Risks of Drug Use** pages 592–597 **BIG Idea** *Drug misuse and substance abuse are life-threatening behaviors.*	1.12.8, 3.12.2, 4.12.1, 4.12.2, 8.12.4		*Real World* **CONNECTION** • Trends in Illegal Drug Use, page 597 ⏱ Out of Time
30 Min **Lesson 2** **Marijuana, Inhalants, and Steroids** pages 598–602 **BIG Idea** *Three often-abused drugs that can have serious physical and mental side effects are marijuana, inhalants, and anabolic steroids.*	1.12.8, 2.12.9, 3.12.2, 5.12.2, 5.12.6, 5.12.7, 7.12.3, 8.12.1		*Health Skills* **Activity** • Making Choices About Drugs *(Decision Making)*, page 602
30 Min **Lesson 3** **Psychoactive Drugs** pages 603–610 **BIG Idea** *Psychoactive drugs affect the central nervous system and can be especially damaging to the developing brain and body of a teen.*	1.12.5, 1.12.8, 2.12.9, 3.12.2, 7.12.3, 8.12.1, 8.12.4		
30 Min **Lesson 4** **Living Drug-Free** pages 611–615 **BIG Idea** *By deciding not to use drugs, you promote your own health and influence others to do the same.*	1.12.5, 1.12.8, 2.12.3, 3.12.4, 3.12.5, 4.12.4, 5.12.4, 5.12.6, 7.12.1, 7.12.2, 7.12.3		**TEENS Making a Difference** • Staying Drug-Free, page 615

Key to Ability Levels

Teaching Strategies and activities have been coded for ability level and appropriateness.

AL Activities for students working above grade level

OL Activities for students working on grade level

BL Activities for students working below grade level

EL Activities for English Learners

Chapter 22 Planning Guide

Resources	Lesson Assessment	Technology
Student Activity Workbook TEACH FAST FILE RESOURCES Vocabulary Practice TEACH Health Labs EXTEND	Chapter 22 Review Chapter 22 Assessment Standardized Test Practice 🔘 ExamView® Assessment Suite CD-ROM	**Teaching Tools:** 🔘 TeacherWorks™ Plus DVD 🔘 StudentWorks™ Plus DVD 🔘 ExamView® Assessment Suite CD-ROM ⎍ Transparency 🔘 Fitness DVD 🔘 PowerPoint® DVD 🔘 Health eSpotlight Video Series DVD
FAST FILE RESOURCES Reading Strategies Activity TEACH Reteaching Activity REVIEW Enrichment Activity EXTEND Health Skills Practice TEACH	Lesson 1 Assessment, page 597 📁 Lesson 1 Quiz Fast File 🔘 ExamView® Assessment Suite CD-ROM	**Web-Based Resources:** Go Online glencoe.com • Health Podcast Activities • Audio Chapter Summaries (English/Spanish) • Interactive Health Tutor • Health Skills Activities • Vocabulary PuzzleMaker • Parent Letters (English/Spanish) • Lesson Plans • Health Inventories • Online Quizzes • Study-to-Go • Unit Web Projects • Student Web Activities • Fitness Zone Activities
FAST FILE RESOURCES Reading Strategies Activity TEACH Reteaching Activity REVIEW Enrichment Activity EXTEND Health Skills Practice TEACH	Lesson 2 Assessment, page 602 📁 Lesson 2 Quiz Fast File 🔘 ExamView® Assessment Suite CD-ROM	
FAST FILE RESOURCES Reading Strategies Activity TEACH Reteaching Activity REVIEW Enrichment Activity EXTEND Health Skills Practice TEACH	Lesson 3 Assessment, page 609 📁 Lesson 3 Quiz Fast File 🔘 ExamView® Assessment Suite CD-ROM	
FAST FILE RESOURCES Reading Strategies Activity TEACH Reteaching Activity REVIEW Enrichment Activity EXTEND Health Skills Practice TEACH	Lesson 4 Assessment, page 615 📁 Lesson 4 Quiz Fast File 🔘 ExamView® Assessment Suite CD-ROM	

StudentWorks Plus

This is the student's backpack solution.

Includes:
• complete Interactive Student Edition
• full audio of English text and Spanish chapter summaries
• allows students to record assignments and track grades.
• links to online activities and additional student resources
• access to all student worksheets and workbooks

FOLDABLES® Study Organizer

Dinah Zike Foldables® Chapter Activity
Refer to the *Dinah Zike Reading and Study Skills for Glencoe Health*. Ask students to make a four-door book Foldable with the tabs "Marijuana," "Inhalants," "Steroids," and "Psychoactive Drugs." As students study the chapter, they can take notes about the different types of drugs.

Key to Symbols

⎍ Transparencies
🔘 CD-ROM
 glencoe.com
📁 Print Resources

REVIEW activities to review or reinforce content
TEACH activities to teach basic concepts
EXTEND activities to extend or enrich lesson content

CHAPTER **22** **Illegal Drugs**

Illegal Drugs

Chapter Overview

Chapter 22 discusses how illegal drugs affect the body and provides strategies for avoiding the use of illegal drugs.

Lesson 1

Using illegal drugs is a high-risk behavior. Drug abuse poses risks to physical, mental/emotional, and social health.

Lesson 2

Marijuana is a gateway drug that itself is dangerous and illegal. Inhalants are sniffed or inhaled for mind-altering effects. Steroids pose serious risks when misused.

Lesson 3

Psychoactive drugs—which include stimulants, depressants, opiates, and hallucinogens—affect the central nervous system and alter activity in the brain.

Lesson 4

Teens can make a commitment to a drug-free life and use refusal skills to avoid drug use.

▶ **Activating Prior Knowledge**

Call on volunteers to share responses. Students might mention peer pressure, stress, and problems at home or school as reasons someone might take illegal drugs. Healthful activities might include taking up a sport or hobby and discussing problems with a caring adult.

Lesson 1

The Health Risks of Drug Use

BIG Idea *Drug misuse and substance abuse are life-threatening behaviors.*

Lesson 2

Marijuana, Inhalants, and Steroids

BIG Idea *Three often-abused drugs that can have serious physical and mental side effects are marijuana, inhalants, and anabolic steroids.*

Lesson 3

Psychoactive Drugs

BIG Idea *Psychoactive drugs affect the central nervous system and can be especially damaging to the developing brain and body of a teen.*

Lesson 4

Living Drug-Free

BIG Idea *By deciding not to use drugs, you promote your own health and influence others to do the same.*

Activating Prior Knowledge

Using Visuals While looking at this photo, think of reasons why someone might take illegal drugs. List healthful activities that could take the place of drug use. Explain why these kinds of activities are safer than using illegal drugs.

590

Universal Access

Differentiated Learning Glencoe provides teacher support and student materials for all learners in the health classroom.

- Chapter Summaries in English and Spanish are available online at **glencoe.com**.

- *Fast Files* and related worksheets support reluctant readers.

- Universal Access strategies throughout the Teacher Wraparound Edition and *Fast Files* help you present materials for gifted students, at-risk students, physically impaired students, and those with behavior disorders or learning disabilities.

Chapter Launchers

Health in Action

Discuss the **BIG** Ideas

Before beginning this chapter, think about how you would answer these questions:

▸ Why do some people use illegal drugs?

▸ How can you respond to peer pressure to use drugs?

▸ How has peer pressure influenced you to do something safe and healthy?

Watch the *Health eSpotlight* Video Series

Staying Drug-Free

What are some of the short- and long-term effects of drug use?

Assess Your Health

Go Online

Visit glencoe.com and complete the Health Inventory for Chapter 22.

Chapter 22 Illegal Drugs **591**

Chapter Launchers

Health in Action

Discuss the **BIG** Ideas

Ask students to respond to the questions aloud. Explain that the purpose of the questions is to help them assess their knowledge of influences on drug use and how they would resist pressure to use drugs.

Health eSpotlight
Video Series

Staying Drug-Free

Before Viewing the Video

Ask Students: *What are some of the consequences of drug use?* (Overdose, loss of friends, addiction) After students have watched the video, ask volunteers to describe ways to resist pressure to use drugs. Invite students to identify healthful activities as alternatives to drug use.

Go Online

Have students go to glencoe.com and take the Health Inventory for Chapter 22.

Chapter Skills

Reading Skills
- Reviewing Facts and Vocabulary, pp. 597, 602, 610, 615
- Reading/Writing Practice, p. 621

BIG Idea

Students will learn the harmful effects of using illegal drugs and abusing legal drugs and strategies to avoid drug use.

Vocabulary
- New Vocabulary, pp. 592, 598, 603, 611
- Reviewing Facts and Vocabulary, pp. 597, 602, 610, 615

Health Skills
- Health Skills Activity, p. 602
- Applying Health Skills, pp. 597, 602, 610, 615

Writing Skills
- Real World Connection, p. 597
- Writing Critically, pp. 597, 602, 610, 615
- Reading/Writing Practice, p. 621

591

LESSON 1

Health Risks of Drug Use

① FOCUS

GUIDE TO READING

BIG Idea Students will learn that drug misuse and substance abuse can pose serious risks to health. **Ask Students:** *What are some health risks of drug misuse and substance abuse?* (Sample answer: Damage to organs, overdose leading to death)

Before You Read

K-W-L Chart Students' charts will vary.

Main Idea

Substance Abuse Substance abuse includes the use of illegal substances, as well as the misuse of legal substances. **Ask Students:** *What are examples of misusing a legal drug?* (Sample answer: Taking someone else's medicine, mixing medicines, an adult drinking too much alcohol)

Real Life Issues ....

Ask volunteers to share their paragraphs with the class. Students might mention walking away, suggesting a healthful activity, or saying no.

LESSON 1

 **GUIDE TO READING**

BIG Idea *Drug misuse and substance abuse are life-threatening behaviors.*

Before You Read

Create a K-W-L Chart. Make a three-column chart. In the first column, list what you **k**now about the negative effects of illegal drugs. In the second column, list what you **w**ant to know about this topic. As you read, use the third column to summarize what you **l**earned.

K	W	L

New Vocabulary

▶ substance abuse (p. 592)
▶ illegal drugs (p. 592)
▶ illicit drug use (p. 592)
▶ overdose (p. 593)
▶ addiction (p. 595)

Review Vocabulary

▶ psychological dependence (Ch.21, L.2)
▶ physiological dependence (Ch.21, L.2)

Health Risks of Drug Use

Real Life Issues ....

Don't Dally in the Alley. Chris is very excited for the weekend to begin. The new sequel to his favorite video game is being released today. As he walks down the block toward the video game store, he hears someone call his name. His new friend, Eric, is hanging out in the alley with some students from school that Chris has heard are into drugs. "You want to try something new?" asks Eric. Chris isn't sure what to say. He likes Eric, but he doesn't want to get pressured into doing drugs.

Writing *Write a paragraph that describes three ways Chris could avoid getting involved with drugs in this situation.*

Substance Abuse

Main Idea Substance abuse includes the use of illegal substances, as well as the misuse of legal substances.

Medicines cure and prevent disease. Sometimes medicines are accidentally used in an improper way. At other times, medicines are intentionally abused. **Substance abuse** is *any unnecessary or improper use of chemical substances for non-medical purposes.* It includes the overuse, or multiple use of a drug, use of an illegal drug, or use of a drug with alcohol.

Some abused substances are **illegal drugs**, *chemical substances that people of any age may not lawfully manufacture, possess, buy, or sell.* Using illegal drugs is a crime called **illicit drug use**, *the use or sale of any substance that is illegal or otherwise not permitted.* This includes the sale of prescription drugs to those for whom the drugs are not intended.

Health Literacy

Abuse of Prescription Drugs The National Institute on Drug Abuse (NIDA) reports that in one recent year, 6.4 million people age 12 or older had used prescription medicines for nonmedical purposes. These medicines included pain relievers, tranquilizers, stimulants, and sedatives. Sixty percent reported that they got the drug from a friend or a relative. OxyContin® was the only prescription drug whose use increased among 8th-, 10th-, and 12th-graders combined. Vicodin® was the second most prevalent illicit drug reported by 12th-graders.

Factors That Influence Teens

 Teens are faced with many choices, including the use of drugs. Many factors influence the choices a teen makes about drug use. Some influences can include:

- **Peer pressure**, or the influence of your friends or social group. Peers can influence teens to avoid illegal drug use. Teens whose friends avoid drug use are more likely to say no to drugs themselves.
- **Family members** can help teens resist drug use. Parents and other family members can encourage teens to abstain from drug use.
- **Role models** such as coaches, athletes, actors, and professionals who speak about the benefits of being drug-free.
- **Media messages** on TV, radio, Web sites, movies, and music can influence how you feel about drug use.
- **Perceptions of drug behavior** that may lead teens to believe that drug use is higher than it is in reality. According to the CDC, more than 70 percent of ninth-graders have never used marijuana.
- **Misleading information** about some drugs can lead teens to think that certain drug use can be beneficial. Some teens believe that steroid use boosts sports performance.

How Drugs Affect Your Health

Main Idea Illegal drug use can lead to death.

AL Unlike medicines, illegal drugs are not monitored for quality, purity, or strength. They don't come with labels that list safety guidelines or suggested dosage. Drug abuse affects your physical, mental/emotional, and social health.

- **Physical health.** A serious danger of drug abuse is the risk of an **overdose**, or *a strong, sometimes fatal reaction to taking a large amount of a drug.* For some illegal drugs, users inject the substances with a needle. This increases the risk of contracting diseases such as hepatitis B and HIV.
- **Mental health.** Drug use may impair a teens ability to reason and think. The illegal drug Ecstasy **alters** the brain's structure and function. The influence of illegal drug use may cause teens to behave in ways that go against their values. **Figure 22.3**, on page 595, shows how drug use affects the brain.

 READING CHECK

Describe How could having a prescription for a legal drug lead to illicit drug use?

■ **Figure 22.1** Role models can influence you to avoid drugs. *How would having drug-free role models give you an advantage in resisting drugs?*

Academic Vocabulary

alter *(verb):* to make different

Lesson 1   Health Risks of Drug Use   **593**

English Language Coach

Distinguish Vocabulary To help students understand the difference between *illegal* and *illicit,* draw a Venn diagram on the board. Label the left circle *Illegal.* Label the right circle *Legal.* Label the middle section *Illicit.* Explain that both *illegal* and *illicit* mean unlawful. *Illicit* includes the unlawful sale of illegal *and* legal drugs, the use of illegal drugs, and the abuse of legal drugs. Ask students to copy the Venn diagram and write in examples in each section. Have volunteers share their examples with the class.

---

② TEACH

HS Health Skills Practice

Analyzing Influences Have students draw a line in the middle of a sheet of paper. Ask them to write in the left column an example of a negative influence for each of the influences discussed in the text. They should write a positive influence in the right column, except for "misleading information." Discuss the influences as a class and how to overcome the negative influences. **OL**

READING CHECK

Answer Illicit drug use includes selling prescription drugs on the street to make money.

AL Active Learning

Discussion Divide students into small groups. Have them discuss the question: Do you think teens should be responsible for preventing drug use by their friends? Ask them to consider how far a friend should go in preventing drug use. Appoint a spokesperson in each group to summarize the group's conclusions. **BL**

Main Idea

How Drugs Affect Your Health The serious side effects of illegal drugs can be deadly. **Ask Students:** *What might be some serious side effects of using illegal drugs?* (Sample answer: Overdosing, addiction, damage to body organs)

Caption Answer

Figure 22.1 Role models are people you admire and want to imitate. If you admire someone who avoids drugs, you are likely to imitate their decision to avoid drugs.

LESSON 1

R Reading Strategy

Research Information Have students use online, community, and government resources to research statistics on the psychological dependence on drugs among teens. Students also should search for the statistics from five years ago. Ask students to compare the statistics with national ones. Have students organize the information in a graphical display. **AL**

READING CHECK

Answer The user needs more and more of the drug to get the same effect.

U Universal Access

Word Meanings Write the words *psychological* and *physiological* on the board. Ask students to use a dictionary to look up the meanings of the word parts *psycho* (of the mind) and *physio* (of the physical and chemical functioning of the body). Have them think of words with the same parts and their meanings. (Examples: physical, psychic) Then ask students to use the words to write a sentence that distinguishes their meanings. **BL EL**

Caption Answer

Figure 22.2 Drugs cloud reasoning and thinking, and users can lose control of their behavior.

READING CHECK

Explain How does tolerance affect a drug user?

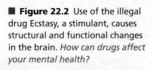

■ **Figure 22.2** Use of the illegal drug Ecstasy, a stimulant, causes structural and functional changes in the brain. *How can drugs affect your mental health?*

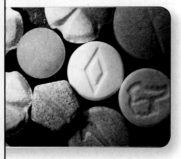

• **Social health.** Teens who use drugs may lose friendships with teens who choose to live drug-free. Relationships with family members may also suffer. Some teens may have to accept the legal consequences of drug use. Substance abuse is a leading cause of crime, suicide, and unintentional injuries.

Other Effects of Drug Use

Teens who use illegal drugs may also experience unwanted physical reactions that may result in death. These reactions can occur with a teen's first drug use or even if a teen has used a drug in the past and believes that he or she can tolerate the drug. The manufacture of some illegal drugs is not regulated, so the compounds in each batch of a drug may be different. Other consequences are:

• **Tolerance.** This is a condition in which the body becomes accustomed to the drug and causes the user to experience a need for more and more of the drug to achieve the desired effect.

• **Psychological dependence.** *Psychological dependence is a condition that develops over time and causes a person to believe that a drug is needed in order to feel good or to function normally.* **R**

• **Physiological dependence.** A user develops a chemical need for a drug. Symptoms of withdrawal occur when the effects of the drug wear off. Symptoms can include nervousness, insomnia, headaches, vomiting, chills, and cramps. In some cases, withdrawal symptoms are severe and can result in death. **U**

• **Addiction.** Another serious consequence is **addiction,** *a physiological or psychological dependence on a drug.* An addict is someone who requires persistent, compulsive use of a substance known by the user to be harmful. Because addiction always involves both psychological and physiological dependence, people who are addicted to a substance have great difficulty in stopping its use on their own. Professional intervention to stop using illegal drugs is often necessary.

Trying a drug just once or using a drug only a few times can quickly lead to a serious cycle of addiction. In the addiction cycle, a user takes a drug to experience short-term pleasure. As the effects of the drug wear off, the user then experiences the physical and psychological consequences of withdrawal. In order to relieve these symptoms, the user takes the drug again to to relieve the pain and to repeat the feelings of short-term pleasure once again. The cycle continues until a person gets medical help to stop using the drug.

Teens Want to Know

Does Everyone Who Takes Illegal Drugs Get Addicted? Not everyone gets addicted, but there is no way to predict who will and who will not. The more risk factors a person has, the greater the chance. Genetics accounts for 40–60 percent of the chance of addiction. People with mental disorders are also at higher risk. The risk increases with negative factors in the environment, such as peers and parents who use drugs. Protective factors reduce the risk. Have students brainstorm protective factors in a person's environment.

Figure 22.3 Drug Use and the Brain

R Drug use leads to changes in thinking and the lowering of inhibitions. *What effect could a lowering of inhibitions have on a teen's physical health?*

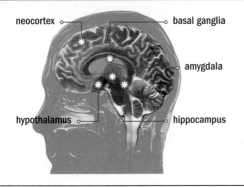

neocortex — basal ganglia

amygdala

hypothalamus — hippocampus

Drugs Take a Heavy Toll

Main Idea In addition to the physical risks to a person's health, substance abuse can damage all aspects of your life.

Some people believe that drugs can help them escape from their problems. Drug use, however, can actually create problems that affect a user's physical, mental/emotional, and social health.

Consequences for the Individual

C Teens who use illegal drugs may stop pursuing their interests and goals, and the goals their parents, teachers, and other adults set for them. Taking drugs lowers inhibitions, which may lead teens to engage in behaviors that can harm their physical health. These behaviors may include engaging in sexual activity, which increases the risk of acquiring sexually transmitted infections, or acting recklessly.

Drug use is also a leading factor in teen depression and suicide. Teens who are involved in drug use are more likely to be arrested. Teens who are convicted of a drug offense can be sent to jail. Teen drug use can also lead to increased violence, crime, and accidental death.

Consequences for Friends and Family

When a teen abuses drugs, it affects everyone in his or her life. Teens who use illegal drugs may lose interest in healthy activities. They may stop spending time with friends who value a drug-free lifestyle. Family members who feel responsible for their loved ones feel the burden of the emotional and financial costs of drug abuse.

Lesson 1   Health Risks of Drug Use   **595**

Teacher to Teacher

Jia Oliver Jordan • Booker T. Washington Magnet High School, Montgomery, AL

Illegal Drugs When teaching illegal drugs, I have students create a substance abuse pamphlet. Students use technology to access websites and gather fact-based information on the mental, physical, and social consequences of substance abuse. They are required to design the pamphlet using their personal creativity and include information that supports the avoidance of illegal substances. After the assignment is complete, students are required to present their pamphlets and findings to their classmates and myself.

Caption Answer

Figure 22.3 Teens may engage in sexual activity, putting themselves at risk for STDs and pregnancy.

Main Idea

Drugs Take a Heavy Toll Substance abuse can harm more than just your physical health; it can damage all aspects of your life. **Ask Students:** *How might a person's life change if he or she used drugs?* (Sample answer: The person might lose interest in hobbies or sports or in achieving goals. The person might lose friends and cause distress to family members.)

R **Reading Strategy**

Analyzing an Illustration Have students examine **Figure 22.3**. **Ask Students:** *What body functions are the different areas of the brain responsible for?* (Sample answer: neocortex—thinking; hypothalamus—emotion; hippocampus—memory; amygdala—emotion and memory; basal ganglia—movement) **OL**

C **Critical Thinking**

Drawing Conclusions Explain that people under the influence of drugs may act on impulse. Their reasoning is clouded, or they feel "high," so they do not consider the consequences of their actions. Ask: What is the connection between drug use and the risk of getting HIV or hepatitis B? (Sample answer: When people are using drugs, they are less likely to be concerned about the risk from contaminated needles or sexual activity.) **OL**

READING CHECK

Answer They can hurt other people through violence, neglect, worry, and causing health problems in their children.

AL Active Learning

Debate Divide the class into small groups. Ask them to debate whether pregnant women should be prosecuted for child abuse for using illegal drugs while pregnant. **OL**

W Writing Support

Personal Writing Ask students to write an entry in their journal about what they would stand to lose if they engaged in substance abuse. Ask volunteers to share their entries, but allow students to keep entries private if they wish. Discuss as a class strategies students would use or have used to avoid drug use. **OL**

CA Cultural Awareness

Global Laws Have each student choose a different country and use current online or print resources to investigate penalties for drug use in that country. Ask students to share their findings with the class. Students might be surprised at the leniency or harshness of laws in other countries. **OL**

Caption Answer

Figure 22.4 Sample answer: Illicit drug use can lead to arrest, conviction, court fines, legal fees, suspension from school, jail time, and probation.

Consequences for Others

A developing fetus receives nutrients through the mother's placenta. If a pregnant female takes drugs, those drugs are passed to the fetus. These drugs have a greater effect on the fetus than the mother. The fetus may be born with birth defects, behavioral problems, or a drug addiction. After birth, a nursing mother's breast milk may contain traces of drugs that are passed to the baby. **AL**

Consequences for Society

People who abuse drugs cause harm to society. Illegal drug use can result of a rise in drug-related crime and violence. Driving while intoxicated (DWI) or driving under the influence (DUI) can result in collisions that cause injuries and deaths. Drug abuse also affects our nation's economy. Research by the Office of National Drug Control Policy shows that drug abuse costs the U.S. economy $180 billion per year. These costs result from **W**

- lost work hours and productivity due to drug-related illnesses, jail time, accidents, and deaths.
- health care costs and legal fees.
- law enforcement costs and insurance costs due to drug-related damages, injuries, and deaths.

The consequences of drug abuse—mental, emotional, physical, legal, and social—are 100 percent preventable. By choosing a drug-free lifestyle, you avoid these consequences. **CA**

READING CHECK

Infer How can illicit drug use by one person affect people who do not use drugs?

■ **Figure 22.4** Some states automatically suspend the driving privileges of minors convicted of a drug offense. *What are other legal consequences of illicit drug use?*

596   Chapter 22   Illegal Drugs

Skills for the 21st Century

Visual Literacy Employers are increasingly looking for visualization skills—interpreting visuals and communicating using a digital format. Students should be familiar with computer graphics and digital cameras and how to use them creatively. Have small groups start a chapter project to make a CD or DVD to advocate a drug-free lifestyle for teens. They can film fun activities or interesting places in the community to show healthful alternatives. Enlist the help of the media specialist, other school personnel, or community/business groups for equipment needs.

Real World CONNECTION

Trends in Illegal Drug Use

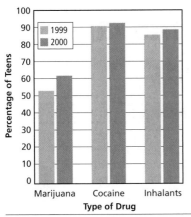

Percentage of Teens (y-axis, 0–100)

Legend: 1999, 2000

Type of Drug (x-axis): Marijuana, Cocaine, Inhalants

Source: Centers for Disease Control and Prevention, National Youth Risk Behavior Survey: 1991–2005

 Activity Reading / Writing

Analyze the table to determine whether the number of teens who have never used drugs is increasing or decreasing. Is there a trend in teen drug use? After analyzing the table, complete the following activity:

1. Write a newspaper article describing the factors that are influencing teens' choices not to use drugs.

2. Include information on the impact of drug use on the individual, family, friends, and the community.

3. Include information on the the physical, mental/emotional, social, and legal consequences of drug use.

4. Read your article to the class or submit it to the school newspaper.

LESSON 1 ASSESSMENT

After You Read

Reviewing Facts and Vocabulary

1. What is an *overdose*?

2. How can an addiction affect your health?

3. How does drug abuse affect society?

Thinking Critically

4. **Infer.** Why might an addiction to a drug become more expensive as the body develops a tolerance to the drug?

5. **Analyze.** Distinguish between *substance abuse* and *illicit drug use*. How are these terms similar? How are they different?

Applying Health Skills

6. **Accessing Information.** Conduct a survey of teens. Ask: What percentage of teens do you think use drugs? Compare your information to statistics from reliable sources. Create a poster presenting your information.

Writing Critically

7. **Persuasive.** Write a dialogue between you and a friend who is thinking about trying an illegal drug. Tell your friend the consequences of drug use.

Go Online

Visit glencoe.com and complete the Interactive Study Guide for this lesson.

LESSON 1 ASSESSMENT ANSWERS

1. A strong, sometimes fatal reaction to taking a large amount of a drug

2. A person who is addicted cannot stop taking the drug, regardless of the harm it is causing his or her health.

3. It can lead to crime and violence, as well as injury and death from vehicle collisions. These effects also have an economic cost to society.

4. The user needs a greater quantity of the drug to feel the same effect. More drugs cost more money, and more damage to health leads to medical expenses.

5. Similar: Both can involve using illegal drugs or abusing legal drugs. They are both life-threatening. Different: Illicit drug use involves the unlawful sale of legal or illegal drugs. Substance abuse refers to personal use, not sale.

6. Surveys will vary.

7. Dialogues will vary.

Real World CONNECTION

Advise students to prepare an outline first, then decide on the details to include.

3 ASSESS/ CLOSE

Assessment Resources

📁 **FAST FILE ACTIVITIES**
Lesson 1 Quiz

💿 *ExamView Assessment Suite* CD-ROM

Visit glencoe.com **for:**
Online Quizzes
Online Learning Center

Progress Monitoring

Reteaching

Call on students to identify effects of drugs on users and on people around them. Then discuss how these effects can be avoided by not using drugs.

Enrichment

Have students research drug testing by employers. For example, how widespread it is, what they test for, and the reasons they give for testing. Ask students to write a paragraph explaining and defending their point of view on whether employers should test employees for drugs.

Go Online

Have students visit **glencoe.com** and complete the Interactive Study Guide for this lesson.

597

Marijuana, Inhalants, and Steroids

1 FOCUS

GUIDE TO READING

BIG Idea Marijuana, inhalants, and steroids are often abused and pose serious risks to health. **Ask Students:** *What do you know about the side effects of these drugs?* (Sample answer: Marijuana can cause lung cancer, inhalants can cause instant death, and steroids can lead to violent behavior.)

Before You Read

Chart Students' charts may vary.

Main Idea

Marijuana Serious physical, mental, social, and legal consequences can result from using marijuana. **Ask Students:** *How might marijuana affect school performance?* (Sample answer: It would likely lead to poor performance because it affects short-term memory, thinking, and problem solving.)

Real Life Issues

Students should include refusal skills as part of the dialogue. Call on volunteers to share their dialogues with the class. Students might mention that they would not risk taking an unknown substance into their body.

598

LESSON 2

GUIDE TO READING

BIG Idea *Three often-abused drugs that can have serious physical and mental side effects are marijuana, inhalants, and anabolic steroids.*

Before You Read

Create a Chart. Create a chart with three columns. Label the columns "Marijuana," "Inhalants," and "Steroids." As you read, list the physical, mental, and legal consequences of each.

Marijuana	Inhalants	Steroids

New Vocabulary

▶ marijuana (p. 599)
▶ paranoia (p. 600)
▶ inhalants (p. 601)
▶ anabolic-androgenic steroids (p. 601)

Marijuana, Inhalants, and Steroids

Real Life Issues

I Dare You. Darnell usually meets his friends a few minutes early each morning at the bus stop. Today, his friend Vince has a marijuana cigarette he found in his older brother's car. To Darnell, it looks like a bunch of dirt rolled up in toilet paper. "Hey, Darnell," says Vince, "I dare you to light this thing and smoke it." Darnell hesitates, then asks, "Why would I smoke some trash you got out of your brother's car?" Vince laughs. "Who knows?" he says. "It could get you high. Give it a try. What are you, chicken?"

Writing *Write a paragraph describing some of the reasons why Darnell should not accept this dare.*

Marijuana

Main Idea Using marijuana has serious physical, mental, social, and legal consequences.

Every day, you make choices based on information that's available to you. Before deciding to see a particular movie, you may read a review. Before deciding what to eat, you might browse the list of ingredients. Illegal drugs don't come with warning labels that help you make smart decisions. Drugs like marijuana can be mixed with unknown chemicals and have unexpected effects on your health. Even when you are certain of the source of a drug, using it illegally may cause serious harm to your health. Misusing any drugs can have serious consequences to your health.

598 **Chapter 22** Illegal Drugs

Myths & Reality

Marijuana Use

Myth: Marijuana is not addictive.

Fact: Marijuana can lead to addiction. Heavy users develop withdrawal symptoms when they try to stop.

Myth: Marijuana makes you mellow.

Fact: Some people may feel relaxed, but research has shown a link between violent behavior and frequency of use.

Myth: The effects of marijuana on memory are temporary.

Fact: People normally lose neurons in the hippocampus over time. Chronic marijuana use may speed up that process.

C Marijuana is *a plant whose leaves, buds, and flowers are usually smoked for their intoxicating effects.* Marijuana may also be included in some foods and eaten to gain it's intoxicating effects. The drug is also known as grass, weed, or pot. Marijuana is one of the most widely used illegal drugs. Hashish, or hash, is a stronger form of marijuana.

HS Marijuana is considered a possible *gateway drug,* a drug that may lead to the user to try other, more dangerous drugs. Studies have shown that a teen who uses marijuana is 15 times more likely to use cocaine than a teen who has never used marijuana. All forms of marijuana are mind-altering and can damage the user's health. Some forms of marijuana may be combined with other drugs during processing, making the effects of marijuana even more unpredictable. Marijuana use can lead to risky behavior and even death.

U
Figure 22.5 | Health Risks of Marijuana

The effects of marijuana use varies from person to person, and can be influenced by a person's mood and surroundings.

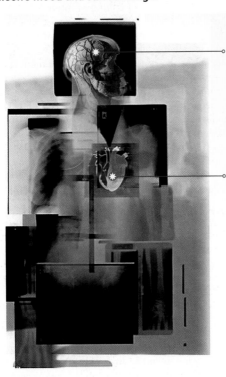

- Hallucinations and paranoia
- Impaired short-term memory, reaction time, concentration, and coordination
- Decreased initiative and ambition
- Bloodshot eyes, dry mouth

- Lung irritation, coughing
- Heart and lung damage
- Increased risk of lung cancer
- Weakened immunity to infection

- Increased appetite
- Increased risk of stillbirth and birth defects
- Changed hormone levels
- In females, risk of infertility
- In males, lowered sperm count and testosterone levels

Lesson 2   Marijuana, Inhalants, and Steroids   **599**

2 TEACH

C Critical Thinking
Making Inferences Ask students how they think marijuana affects an athlete's performance and why. (Sample answer: The athlete would not play well because reaction time, concentration, and coordination are impaired.) **OL**

HS Health Skills Practice
Refusal Skills Divide the class into groups, and have group members brainstorm a list of ways someone might pressure them to use marijuana. Then ask groups to generate a list of ways to refuse each kind of pressure. Ask each group to share its lists with the class. Then have students write an entry in their journal describing which refusal method would work best for them. **OL**

U Universal Access
Vocabulary Pair English learners and reluctant readers with a reading proficient partner. Students should read the material in this lesson together. The reading partner should explain unfamiliar terms, for example, that a hallucination means seeing or hearing something that is not real. **EL** **BL**

Academic Integration

Science THC, the main active ingredient in marijuana, binds to cannabinoid receptors on brain cells. Parts of the brain with high concentrations of receptors are the cerebellum, hippocampus, cerebral cortex, and basal ganglia. The hypothalamus, amygdala, spinal cord, and brain stem have moderate concentrations. When THC attaches to a neuron, it interferes with normal communication between neurons. Ask small groups of students to use their textbook to draw a cross-section diagram of the brain. Have them label the parts affected by THC and include brief captions of how the functions are affected.

LESSON 2

C Critical Thinking

Identifying Cause and Effect
Have students state the mental effects of marijuana use. Ask them to explain how personality problems and marijuana can be a vicious cycle. (Sample answer: A person who already has problems in school or with making friends may make the problems worse by using marijuana in response to that.) Ask students to brainstorm actions to help break this cycle. **OL**

Academic Vocabulary

Intense Explain that feelings can vary in intensity, or strength. Have students compare the intensity of the feeling of hunger they have after just eating to how they feel after going several hours without eating. Ask them to identify which feeling is intense. Point out that the feeling of well-being users get from marijuana is very strong.

AL Active Learning

Advertisements Pair English learners with a writing proficient partner to design an advertisement for a teen magazine on the dangers of driving and marijuana use. Ask each pair to display and explain its ad to the class. **OL EL**

Physical Consequences of Marijuana Use

Because marijuana is often smoked, users face the same health risks as tobacco smokers. Marijuana smoke contains more cancer-causing chemicals than tobacco smoke, which can result in serious health consequences. Marijuana users often inhale the unfiltered smoke, which can cause damage to the respiratory system. Smoking marijuana may also damage the immune system, making the user more susceptible to infections. Many of the physical effects of marijuana use are summarized in **Figure 22.5** on page 599.

Marijuana also poses risks to the reproductive system. In males, it interferes with sperm production and *lowers* levels of the male hormone testosterone. In females, marijuana *raises* testosterone levels which may lead to *infertility*, or the inability to bear children.

Mental and Emotional Consequences

Marijuana raises levels of a brain chemical called *dopamine*. This chemical produces a pleasurable feeling. In some users, marijuana triggers the release of so much dopamine that the user reaches a feeling of **intense** well-being or elation, called a "high." When the drug wears off, however, the pleasure sensation stops, often dramatically. This abrupt letdown is called a "crash."

Marijuana users can experience slow mental reflexes and may suffer from sudden feelings of anxiety and **paranoia**, *an irrational suspiciousness or distrust of others*. The user might feel dizzy, have trouble walking, and have a hard time remembering things that just happened. Short-term memory is affected, which can lead to problems at school and at work. Users often experience distorted perception, loss of coordination, and trouble with thinking and problem solving. A few hours after use, the person can become very sleepy. These consequences can be deadly if the user is driving a vehicle.

Academic Vocabulary

intense *(adjective):*
existing in an extreme degree

C

Driving and Marijuana Use

The National Highway Traffic Safety Administration (NHTSA) estimates that 10 to 22 percent of drivers involved in car crashes were on drugs. Driving under the influence of marijuana can be dangerous because marijuana interferes with depth perception, increases reaction time, causes sleepiness, impairs judgment, and slows reflexes. The penalties and legal consequences of driving under the influence of any drug—including marijuana—include suspension of a driver's license, fines, loss of eligibility for federal college loans, and possibly a jail term. If injury or death of another person results, the driver may face serious legal prosecution as well as devastating emotional consequences.

AL

600 **Chapter 22** Illegal Drugs

Home and Community

Drugged Driving Laws Drugged driving is driving with prohibited drugs in the blood. Only a minority of states have laws prohibiting driving with any detectable level of an illegal drug in the bloodstream. Other states define the term more loosely, for example, "causes the driver to be impaired." Ask students to research their state's drugged driving laws. They may wish to contact the state department in charge of traffic safety or motor vehicles for this information. Have students share their findings with other teens in the school.

Inhalants

Main Idea Inhalants can cause the death of brain cells.

Inhalants are *substances whose fumes are sniffed or inhaled to give effect*. Some inhalants are prescribed by doctors to treat allergies, asthma, and other medical conditions. However, some substances are inhaled to achieve a high. Solvents, aerosols, glues, paints, varnishes, and gasoline can cause brain damage.

Most inhalants depress the central nervous system. Immediate effects include a glassy stare, slurred speech, impaired judgment, nausea, coughing, nosebleeds, fatigue, and lack of coordination. Using inhalants can lead to permanent loss of brain cells. Long-term use can cause liver and kidney damage, blindness, brain damage, paralysis, cardiac arrest, and death.

All inhalants are extremely dangerous, and many are labeled as poisons. Inhalants can be harmful even if you are not trying to abuse them. They can be accidentally inhaled when doing household chores. When using inhalants, work in a well-ventilated room and wear a mask if a project requires long exposure to the fumes.

Consequences of Steroid Use

Main Idea Steroids can cause severe health problems.

Anabolic-androgenic steroids are *synthetic substances similar to male sex hormones. Anabolic* refers to muscle building, and *androgenic* refers to increased male characteristics. Steroids may be prescribed for some medical conditions, but using steroids without medical supervision is dangerous.

Steroid use can result in unnatural muscle growth. When combined with physical conditioning, steroids can increase muscle strength, but the tendons and ligaments do not get stronger which can lead to injury. Other side effects include weight gain, acne, high blood pressure, and liver and kidney tumors. Steroid users who inject the drug may contract HIV or hepatitis B. These drugs may also cause violent behavior, extreme mood swings, depression, and paranoia. The effects on males include shrinking testicles, reduced sperm count, baldness, development of breasts, and an increased risk for prostate cancer. The effects on females include facial hair, baldness, menstrual cycle changes, and a deepened voice.

Any nonmedical use of steroids is illegal. Athletes who use steroids can face expulsion from a team or event, monetary fines, tarnished reputation, and jail time.

■ **Figure 22.6** Marijuana contains 421 different chemicals. The main psychoactive ingredient, THC (delta-9-tetrahydrocannabinol), is stored in body fat, and traces of it can be present in the blood for as long as a month. *Why could a marijuana user fail a drug test weeks after using the drug?*

 READING CHECK

Explain Where does the term *anabolic-androgenic steroids* come from?

Health Skills Activity

Decision Making: Making Choices About Drugs

NHES Standard 5 Students will demonstrate the ability to use decision-making skills to enhance health.

Teaching Objectives
- Identify options and values that promote individual health.
- Apply decision-making skills to make a health-promoting decision.

Teaching Strategies
- Review with students the six steps in the decision-making process.
- Pair students, have them write a dialogue that incorporates the steps, and invite students to share their dialogues with the class.

Assessment

Using this list, student work should provide comprehensive evidence of the following criteria to achieve the highest score:

√ States the situation
√ Identifies and lists several options
√ Considers values
√ Selects a healthful decision
√ Evaluates the decision

Reading Strategy

Researching and Summarizing Ask students to search for recent articles about steroid use in a well-known athlete. They can use online sources, newspapers, or sports magazines. Have students read and summarize the article in their own words. Ask them to include why the athlete started using steroids, how they affected the athlete's performance, and the consequences of steroid use for that individual. Have volunteers share their summaries with the class.

LESSON 2

 ASSESS/ CLOSE

Assessment Resources

 FAST FILE ACTIVITIES
Lesson 2 Quiz

ExamView
Assessment Suite CD-ROM

Visit glencoe.com for:
Online Quizzes
Online Learning Center

Progress Monitoring

Reteaching
Ask students to list four important facts about each drug in the lesson. Collect and read the facts aloud without naming the drug. Call on students to identify the drug or drugs.

Enrichment
Have students work in groups to prepare a lesson to teach elementary students about the dangers of marijuana and inhalant use. Encourage groups to use props and skits. Arrange with elementary teachers for students to present their lessons.

Go Online

Have students visit **glencoe.com** and complete the Interactive Study Guide for this lesson.

Health Skills Activity
Decision Making

Making Choices About Drugs

Naomi and her best friend, Jill, and two new friends, Gwen and Miriam, are driving together to a concert by their favorite band. Gwen, stops at a nearby park.

"My brother told me about this," says Gwen as she pulls out a paper bag. "You can get high by sniffing this stuff."

"I heard the same thing!" says Miriam. "Do you guys want to try?"

Jill turns to Naomi. "I'm not so sure, I don't want to do drugs?" whispers Jill.

Naomi learned in her health class how dangerous inhalants can be. Gwen and Miriam are fun to hang out with, though, and Naomi doesn't want to disappoint her two new friends.

Writing Apply the six steps of the decision-making model to Naomi's situation.
1. State the situation.
2. List the options.
3. Weigh the possible outcomes.
4. Consider your values.
5. Make a decision and act.
6. Evaluate the decision.

LESSON 2 ASSESSMENT

After You Read

Reviewing Facts and Vocabulary
1. What body systems are harmed by smoking marijuana?
2. What are *inhalants*?
3. Why does using steroids for increasing muscle strength often result in injury?

Thinking Critically
4. **Infer.** Marijuana users often inhale the smoke very deeply and hold it in their lungs longer than cigarette smokers do. How might this practice make marijuana more dangerous than smoking tobacco?
5. **Compare.** How do the effects of steroids differ in males and females?

Applying Health Skills
6. **Accessing Information.** Research reliable sources to learn more about the dangers of accidentally or purposefully inhaling chemicals. Create a poster showing how inhalants can affect your physical health.

Writing Critically
7. **Persuasive.** Write a public service announcement describing the dangers of driving while under the influence of marijuana.

Go Online

Visit **glencoe.com** and complete the Interactive Study Guide for this lesson.

LESSON 2 ASSESSMENT ANSWERS

1. The respiratory, immune, nervous, and reproductive systems
2. Substances whose fumes are sniffed or inhaled to give a mind-altering effect
3. Although steroids can increase muscle strength, the associated tendons and ligaments do not get stronger.
4. The smoke is held in the lungs for a longer amount of time, so there is more time for the chemicals to be absorbed by the lungs and cause damage.
5. Having more than the normal amount of male sex hormones in males causes abnormal effects on the body. Having too many male sex hormones in females causes their bodies to develop male characteristics.
6. Posters will vary.
7. Public service announcements will vary.

Psychoactive Drugs

Real Life Issues

Skip this "Trip." It's early fall, and school has just started. Alex and his friends are at a party hosted by some college kids down the street. The party is a little wilder than they anticipated. At one point, a guy offers Alex a "hit" of LSD. "It's awesome," says the young man, who looks a little out of it. "No thanks," says Alex. "I'm not into drugs."

Writing *Write a paragraph that describes at least three safe activities that can give your body a physical adrenaline rush or stimulate the senses without the use of illegal drugs.*

Effects of Psychoactive Drugs

Main Idea Psychoactive drugs change the functioning of the central nervous system.

The central nervous system (CNS) is amazingly complex. Every human activity, from bending a finger to solving complicated problems, involves the CNS. **Psychoactive drugs,** *chemicals that affect the central nervous system and alter activity in the brain,* change the functioning of the CNS. The four main groups of psychoactive drugs are stimulants, depressants, opiates, and hallucinogens.

Some psychoactive drugs have medicinal value. When psychoactive drugs are misused or abused, a person's health and the functioning of all the body systems are seriously affected. The effects on a teen's developing brain and body can be especially damaging.

GUIDE TO READING

BIG Idea *Psychoactive drugs affect the central nervous system and can be especially damaging to the developing brain and body of a teen.*

Before You Read

Make Flash Cards. As you read the lesson, write each vocabulary term on the front of an index card. Write the definition on the back of each card. Use the cards to quiz a partner on the terms and their meanings.

| Euphoria |
| Stimulants |
| |
| |
| |
| |

New Vocabulary

▸ psychoactive drugs (p. 603)
▸ designer drugs (p. 605)
▸ hallucinogens (p. 605)
▸ euphoria (p. 605)
▸ depressants (p. 605)
▸ stimulants (p. 606)
▸ opiates (p. 609)

Psychoactive Drugs

① FOCUS

GUIDE TO READING

BIG Idea Students will learn about different kinds of psychoactive drugs and that they are especially harmful to teens. **Ask Students:** *What questions do you think this lesson will answer?* (Sample answer: What effects do psychoactive drugs have on the mind? Why are they so harmful to teens?)

Before You Read

Flash Cards Encourage students to include examples of each term.

Main Idea

Effects of Psychoactive Drugs
Psychoactive drugs change the functioning of the central nervous system. **Ask Students:** *Why do you think psychoactive drugs are classified into groups?* (Sample answer: The drugs in one group may have similar effects, which are different from drugs in the other groups.)

ELL Support

Forming Nouns from Verbs Help students recognize that in science content, nouns are often formed from verbs.

Beginning Write *stimulate* and *depress* on the board. Modify the endings to form the nouns. (stimulant, depressant) Underline the suffixes. Discuss the meanings of the words.

Intermediate Provide simple sentences to check for understanding, for example,

"Games _____ me." (stimulate) "Games are a _____." (stimulant)

Advanced Have students use the verbs and noun forms of the verbs presented above to write simple sentences. Add the words *hallucinogen* and *designer* to the task.

Real Life Issues

Ask volunteers to share their paragraphs. Students might suggest movies, video games, and listening to music with friends. Advise students to consider all the activities that were discussed, then list three activities they have not done but think they might enjoy.

②TEACH

R Reading Strategy

Compare and Contrast Have students make a five-column chart. They should list each consequence from **Figure 22.7** in the first column and label columns 2–5 with each type of drug. Ask them to place a check beside each consequence that applies to the drug in each column. Have students use the information in their charts to write a summary on each type of drug to show how it compares with the others. **BL** **OL**

C Critical Thinking

Making Inferences Have students read about the effects of stimulants on brain cells. Ask students to infer why these effects might be more severe in teens, whose brains are still developing, than in adults. (Sample answer: The drugs might prevent normal growth and development.) **BL**

U Universal Access

Locating Information Tell students that people who abuse drugs often take several different ones. They might take amphetamines to get going and opiates to sleep. Have students locate these two drugs in **Figure 22.7** and read their effects. Then ask them to explain what they think happens when someone gets in the habit of taking stimulants and depressants. (Sample answer: They put a great strain on the heart function.) **BL**

604

Figure 22.7 **Health Risks of Psychoactive Drugs** **R**

Type of Drug	Consequences to Your Health
Stimulants	
Amphetamines	• Decreased appetite, weight loss, malnutrition • High blood pressure, rapid heartbeat, heart failure, death • Aggressiveness, increased tolerance, addiction
Cocaine	• Nausea, abdominal pain, malnutrition, headache, stroke, seizure, heart attack, death • Exposure to HIV through contaminated needles, addiction
Crack	• Extreme addiction with the same consequences as cocaine • Rapid increase in heart rate and blood pressure, death
Methamphetamine (Meth)	• Memory loss, heart and nerve damage • Increased tolerance, addiction
Depressants	
Barbiturates	• Fatigue, confusion, impaired muscle coordination • Reduced heart rate, blood pressure, respiratory function, death
GHB	• Drowsiness, nausea, vomiting, loss of consciousness • Impaired breathing, coma, death
Rohypnol (roofies)	• Decreased blood pressure, drowsiness, memory loss, gastrointestinal disturbances
Tranquilizers	• Depression, fever, irritability, loss of judgment, dizziness
Opiates	
Codeine	• Reduced respiratory function, respiratory arrest, death • Exposure to HIV through contaminated needles, addiction
Heroin	• Confusion, sedation, unconsciousness, coma, addiction
Morphine	• Rapid onset of tolerance, addiction
Opium	• Nausea, constipation, addiction
Oxycodone (OxyContin®)	• Drowsiness, nausea, constipation, addiction • Reduced respiratory function, respiratory arrest, death
Hallucinogens	
DXM (tussin)	• Nausea, dizziness, lack of coordination, rashes • Hallucinations, disorientation, paranoia, panic attacks, seizures
Ecstasy (MDMA)	• Confusion, depression, paranoia, muscle breakdown
Ketamine	• Kidney and cardiovascular system failure, death • Memory loss, numbness, impaired motor function
LSD	• Delusions, illusions, hallucinations, flashbacks, numbness, tremors
Mescaline (peyote)	• Delusions, illusions, hallucinations, flashbacks, numbness, tremors
PCP	• Loss of appetite, depression, panic, aggression, violent actions
Psilocybin (mushrooms)	• Delusions, illusions, hallucinations, paranoia, extreme anxiety, nausea

C

U

More About...

How Drugs Produce Pleasure Drugs of abuse flood the brain with dopamine, which helps to regulate feelings of pleasure. This over stimulation causes feelings of euphoria. The effects are felt immediately, are much stronger, and last longer than those from natural rewards. These powerful effects motivate people to continue taking the drugs. The brain gradually adjusts by producing less dopamine or reducing the number of receptors for it. The abuser eventually needs to take more of the drug just to get normal levels of dopamine. Long-term drug use leads to serious changes in neurons and brain circuits.

Consequences of Psychoactive Drug Use

Psychoactive drug use can result in health problems and addiction. Using psychoactive drugs often leads to poor judgment and behaviors, which may put teens at risk for unintentional injuries, violence, STDs, unintended pregnancy, and suicide. Choosing a drug-free life can protect your health.

Club Drugs, Stimulants, and Depressants

Main Idea Club drugs, stimulants, and depressants can cause irreversible health damage.

Certain drugs are classified by their effects. They may speed up or slow down the senses, or affect judgment.

Club Drugs

The term *club drug* describes drugs found at concerts, dance clubs, and drug parties, called raves. These drugs are sometimes disguised in foods, or slipped into drinks and taken without a person's knowledge. Many club drugs are **designer drugs**, *synthetic drugs that are made to imitate the effects of other drugs.* Designer drugs can be several hundred times stronger than the drugs they imitate.

Ecstasy (MDMA) Ecstasy, or MDMA, has both stimulant and hallucinogenic effects. **Hallucinogens** are *drugs that alter moods, thoughts, and sense perceptions, including vision, hearing, smell, and touch.* Ecstasy may cause short-term **euphoria**, *a feeling of intense well-being or elation.*

HS

Rohypnol Rohypnol, or "roofies," are **depressants**, or sedatives that are colorless, odorless, and tasteless. These are *drugs that tend to slow the central nervous system.* It is called the "date-rape" drug. Unwanted physical contact, unplanned pregnancies, and exposure to HIV and STDs can result. It's illegal to give someone a drug without his or her knowledge. Engaging in sexual activity with a person under the influence of a date-rape drug is a criminal offense.

AL

GHB GHB, or gamma hydroxybutyric acid, is another CNS depressant. It is **available** as a clear liquid, a white powder, and in a variety of tablets and capsules. Like Rohypnol, it can be used as a date-rape drug.

Ketamine Ketamine is an anesthetic used to treat animals. It causes hallucinations and may result in respiratory failure.

READING CHECK

Apply What should you do if you are at a party where people are taking psychoactive drugs?

■ **Figure 22.8** Never allow a stranger to handle your drink at a social event. *Why are Rohypnol and GHB often known as date-rape drugs?*

Academic Vocabulary

available *(adjective):* present or ready for immediate use

Lesson 3 Psychoactive Drugs **605**

Main Idea

Club Drugs, Stimulants, and Depressants Club drugs, stimulants, and depressants can cause irreversible health damage. **Ask Students:** *Why would someone slip a drug into another person's drink without his or her knowledge?* (Sample answer: The perpetrator wants to take advantage of the victim through rape.)

HS Health Skills Practice

Practicing Healthful Behaviors Invite students to generate preventive measures they can take at a social event to reduce the risk of being a victim of date rape. (Sample answers: Do not get a drink from a punch bowl. Accept unopened drinks only, and open them yourself. When you go to the bathroom, leave the drink with a trusted friend or get a new drink when you come back. Keep your hand over your drink at all times.) **OL**

AL Active Learning

Bumper Sticker Point out that most teens do not abuse drugs. Tell students that in a recent government survey, the percentage of 10th graders who used Ecstasy, GHB, and Rohypnol in the previous year was 2.8, 0.7, and 0.5, respectively. Ask students to use these statistics to design a bumper sticker to advocate against using club drugs. **OL AL**

Caption Answer

Figure 22.8 Because they are often colorless, tasteless, and odorless, they can be added to beverages without a victim knowing about it.

Writing Strategy

Expository Writing Point out the connection between drug use and the high risk of contracting an STD—including HIV—or becoming pregnant. Have students use club drugs as examples to write a paragraph that explains this connection. They should include specific effects of the drugs that alter behavior. Ask them to write another paragraph that describes healthful behaviors to avoid drug use.

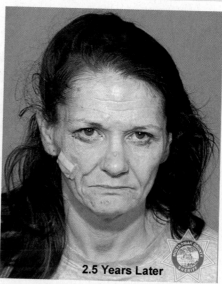

05© "Faces of Meth"

2.5 Years Later

■ **Figure 22.9** One common effect of meth use is delusions of bugs crawling on the user's skin. As a result, many meth users scratch and pick at their skin until they develop unsightly sores. *What other physical effects can meth use cause?*

■ **Figure 22.10** "Energy drinks" often have so much caffeine that their labels must warn pregnant women and people with high blood pressure not to drink them. *Why is the small serving size of a typical energy drink misleading?*

606

Meth Methamphetamine, or meth, is a stimulant. **Stimulants** are *drugs that speed up the central nervous system.* Meth is a white, odorless powder that easily dissolves in alcohol or water. Because its nonmedical form is produced in makeshift labs, the drug is readily available but its quality is uncertain. Meth may provide a short-term feeling of euphoria, but often its use also causes depression, paranoia, and delusions. Meth use can cause death.

HS

LSD (Acid) Acid, or lysergic acid diethylamide (LSD), can cause hallucinations and severely distorted perceptions of sound and color. Flashbacks—states in which a drug user experiences the emotional effects of a drug long after its actual use—can also occur. Users may experience emotions ranging from extreme euphoria, to panic, to terror or deep depression. The resulting behaviors can lead to serious injury or death.

Other Stimulants

Stimulants speed up the CNS. The nicotine in tobacco products is a highly effective stimulant. You can learn more about nicotine in Chapter 20. The caffeine in coffee, tea, cola, and power drinks are all stimulants. "Energy" or "power" drinks often contain four to ten times the amount of caffeine as a regular-sized cola. Other dangerous stimulants include cocaine, amphetamines, and methamphetamines.

AL

Teens Want to Know

Is It Still Drug Abuse If a Person Is Trying to Reach a Worthwhile Goal? Students sometimes use prescription stimulants to help them stay awake to study, to improve athletic performance, or to lose weight. While these goals may be worthwhile, this type of intentional misuse of a drug is still substance abuse and has harmful effects on the body. Assign students to research the abuse of stimulants for staying awake. Have them include how this strategy usually backfires and produces side effects that harm health and interfere with studying.

Cocaine Cocaine is a rapidly acting, powerful and highly addictive stimulant. Cocaine is a white powder extracted from the leaves of the coca plant. Using cocaine is illegal. Users may experience a surge of self-confidence and euphoria. The feelings of confidence induced by cocaine are followed by an emotional letdown. Regular use can lead to depression, fatigue, paranoia, and physiological dependence. Cocaine use can cause malnutrition and, especially among teens, may result in cardiac problems. When cocaine is injected, users risk contracting HIV or hepatitis B from infected needles. Overdosing can result in death.

Crack An even more dangerous form of cocaine is crack, also called rock or freebase rock. Crack reaches the brain seconds after being smoked or injected. Once in the blood, it causes the heart rate and blood pressure to soar to dangerous levels. Death may result from cardiac or respiratory failure. Mixing crack (or any drug) with alcohol can be fatal. Both substances combine in the liver, increasing the risk of death from liver failure.

Amphetamines Amphetamines are highly addictive. Some people use amphetamines to stay alert, to improve athletic performance, or to lose weight. It is easy to develop a tolerance to amphetamines, causing the user to ingest more and more of the substance. Regular use can result in an irregular heartbeat, paranoia, aggressive behavior, and heart failure.

Other Depressants

Depressants are drugs that tend to slow the central nervous system and can have negative, sometimes deadly effects on your health. Depressants are dangerous because they can slow heart and respiration rates and lower blood pressure. Alcohol is a commonly used depressant. Combining small amounts of depressants can cause shallow breathing, weak or rapid pulse, coma, and death.

Barbiturates Barbiturates are sedatives that are rarely used for medical purposes. Using barbiturates can cause mood changes, excessive sleepiness, and coma. Users may feel intoxicated. Combining barbiturates with alcohol can be fatal.

Tranquilizers Tranquilizers are depressants that relieve anxiety, muscle spasms, sleeplessness, and nervousness. When tranquilizers are overused, they can cause physiological and psychological dependence, coma, and death.

■ **Figure 22.11** Both cocaine and crack are dangerous illegal stimulants. *How are cocaine and crack related?*

 READING CHECK

Compare Name two legal stimulants that are commonly used.

 READING CHECK

Explain Why can combining depressants be dangerous?

Caption Answer

Figure 22.11 Crack is a more dangerous form of cocaine.

 Writing Support

Compare and Contrast Have students read the various stimulants listed on pages 606 and 607. Students should write an essay comparing and contrasting cocaine and crack. **AL**

READING CHECK

Answer Caffeine in coffee, tea, and soda, and nicotine in cigarettes

HS **Health Skills Practice**

Accessing Information Have students access online resources to research and write a report on the problem of amphetamine abuse. Include information on laws and how your state laws address the problem. **AL**

English Language Coach

Cause and Effect Write clue words found in this lesson that indicate a cause-and-effect relationship on the board: *cause, because, induced by, lead to.* Explain that to identify a relationship, students can ask themselves questions. To find an effect, they can ask, "What happened?" To find a cause, they can ask, "Why did it happen?" Pair reluctant readers and English learners with more proficient readers. Ask them to look through this lesson, identify cause-and-effect sentences, and rewrite them in a way that still conveys the cause-and-effect relationship.

LESSON 3

Hallucinogens and Opiates
Hallucinogens and opiates seriously alter the sensory controls in the brain. **Ask Students:** *How might hallucinations be dangerous?* (Sample answer: They might lead a person to think he or she can do impossible things, such as fly.)

FITNESS ZONE

Weight-bearing activities are important to do to help prevent osteoporosis. Try the following combination:

- Straddle jump
- Jump feet together
- Scissor jump
- Have students create their own combination.

READING CHECK

Answer Users sometimes harm themselves physically, behave violently, or overdose.

W Writing Support

Personal Writing Have students write an entry in their journal on why they think a teen might try a hallucinogen. What might they say to a friend who is experimenting with them? Ask volunteers to share their entries, but allow them to keep their responses private if they wish. **OL**

FITNESS ZONE

My "drug" is my favorite sport: running. I don't need to get high on any illegal substance, because when I go for a run, I get all the benefits of a good workout and it makes me feel great. I challenge myself to improve every day, and in the end I have something to be proud of. Keeping my body and my brain in top condition for running is the best thing I can do to stay healthy. For more physical activity ideas, visit the Online Fitness Zone at **glencoe.com**.

READING CHECK

Apply Why are hallucinogens sometimes fatal?

Hallucinogens and Opiates

Main Idea Hallucinogens and opiates seriously alter the sensory controls in the brain.

The sections of the brain that interpret sensory input can be permanently damaged by the effects of psychoactive drugs. Hallucinogens overload the brain's sensory controls. Opiates, which are highly addictive, cause confusion and dull the senses.

Hallucinogens

Hallucinogens can cause serious mental/emotional and physical consequences for users. These drugs alter mood, and impair judgement, thoughts, and sense perception. Users may behave in ways that they normally would not. A person who uses hallucinogens may believe that he or she is invincible. Using these drugs can also cause increases in heart and respiratory rates, which can lead to heart and respiratory failure. Using these drugs can cause coma. Hallucinogens have no medical use. **W**

Ecstasy, ketamine, acid (LSD), phencyclidine (PCP or angel dust), dextromethorphan (DXM), psilocybin (mushrooms), and mescaline (peyote) are examples of powerful and dangerous hallucinogens. Hallucinogens overload the sensory controls in the brain, causing confusion, intensified sensations, and hallucinations. The altered mental states caused by hallucinogens can last for several hours or several days. Users can also experience flashbacks, or states in which they feel emotional effects of a drug long after its actual use. The effects of using these drugs are extremely unpredictable. Users sometimes harm themselves physically, or behave violently and harm others.

PCP PCP, or angel dust, is one of the most dangerous of all drugs, and its effects vary greatly from user to user. The drug creates a distorted sense of time, increased muscle strength, increased feelings of violence, and the inability to feel pain. Overdoses can cause death, but most PCP-related deaths are caused by the destructive behavior or disorientation that the drug produces. For example, PCP users have died in fires because they became disoriented and had no sensitivity to the pain of burning. Flashbacks can occur at any time, causing pain, confusion, and lack of control.

DXM DXM, or "tussin," is a cough suppressant sold as an over-the-counter medicine. When used in the recommended dosage, DXM is not dangerous. When misused, it can cause hallucinations, paranoia, panic attacks, nausea, increased heart rate and blood pressure, seizures, and addiction.

Skills for the 21st Century

Information Literacy Information literacy involves accessing information efficiently, assessing it critically, and using it accurately and creatively. Students should learn to deconstruct media messages—analyze their accuracy, interpret the message, and identify what the creators of the message have to gain. Have students search the Internet for information on drug abuse. They will likely discover information that refutes information from reliable sources, such as government, universities, and this text. Have them print out information from several different kinds of sources and assess whether the sources are reliable.

■ **Figure 22.12** Talk to your doctor or pharmacist about any prescription medications that you are given. *Why is it important for pharmacists to keep records of all sales of opiates?*

U **Mushrooms and Peyote** Psilocybin (mushrooms) and mescaline (peyote cactus) are hallucinogens found in nature as a fungus and a plant. When eaten, they cause hallucinations, nausea, and flashbacks. Use of these drugs can also lead to poisoning and death when dealers harvest toxic species.

Opiates

CA **Opiates**, or narcotics, are *drugs such as those derived from the opium plant that are obtainable only by prescription and are used to relieve pain.* Morphine, oxycodone, and codeine are common examples of opiates. When opiates are used according to the directions provided by a health care professional, they are an effective pain reliever. Abusing opiates dulls the senses, causes drowsiness, constipation, slow and shallow breathing, convulsions, coma, and death. Pharmacists record all sales of opiates because the drug is addictive.

Codeine Codeine is a highly addictive ingredient in some prescription cough medicines. Even if a user takes codeine as prescribed, drowsiness can occur. The drug should not be used before driving a vehicle. Codeine use can cause dizziness, labored breathing, low blood pressure, seizures, and respiratory arrest.

Some people may be allergic to codeine. These people may experience difficulty breathing or mood changes. Codeine use has also been linked to death in infants. The CDC has issued a warning against giving any medications containing codeine to infants or small children. If you or someone you know experiences a problem after taking codeine, call 911 immediately.

G⊙ Online

Go to glencoe.com and complete the Student Web Activity on psychoactive drugs and the health risks of stimulants, depressants, and hallucinogens.

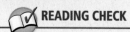

Answer They are both opiates.

❸ ASSESS/ CLOSE

Assessment Resources

📁 **FAST FILE ACTIVITIES**
Lesson 3 Quiz

💿 *ExamView*
Assessment Suite CD-ROM

Visit glencoe.com for:
Online Quizzes
Online Learning Center

Progress Monitoring

Reteaching
Have each student write a question about a drug with the answer being the name of a drug or drugs. Divide the class into two teams, and play a game in which you call out the questions and each team attempts to answer them.

Enrichment
Have each student choose a drug and research additional information on it. Ask students to present their findings in a report, chart, poster, or other method of their choice.

 Go Online

Have students visit glencoe.com and complete the Interactive Study Guide for this lesson.

Morphine Morphine is a much stronger drug than codeine. It is sometimes prescribed to treat severe pain, but is generally used for only a short time. Side effects include fast or slow heartbeat, seizures, hallucinations, blurred vision, rashes, and difficulty swallowing.

Heroin Heroin is a processed form of morphine that is injected, snorted, or smoked. Heroin comes in many forms, including a white or brownish powder and a black, sticky tar. Dealers may mix heroin with medicines or household substances to create other forms, such as "cheese" or "cheese heroin."

Heroin slows breathing and pulse rate. It can also cause infection of the heart lining and valves, as well as liver disease. Infectious diseases such as HIV and hepatitis B can also result from the use of infected needles. Large doses can cause coma or death, and Fetal death if the user is pregnant.

Oxycodone When used properly under the supervision of a doctor, Oxycodone is a prescription drug that helps to relieve moderate to severe chronic pain. Oxycodone contains a strong opiate. It is often referred to by the brand name OxyContin®. A side effect of this drug is supression of the respiratory system, which cause death from respiratory failure.

LESSON 3 📖 ASSESSMENT

After You Read

Reviewing Facts and Vocabulary
1. On what body system do *psychoactive drugs* act?
2. Name the four types of drugs described in this lesson and give an example of each.
3. What are *opiates*?

Thinking Critically
4. **Evaluate.** An acquaintance offers you a drug that she says is natural. Does this mean it is safe to take? Why or why not?
5. **Apply.** Why is it important to follow directions from your doctor or pharmacist when taking a prescription drug such as codeine?

Applying Health Skills
6. **Advocacy.** Research the different types of designer drugs, the forms they take, and how they affect health. Use what you have learned to design a Web site that warns about the dangers of these drugs.

Writing Critically
7. **Narrative.** Write a script convincing a friend not to try drugs. Include information on the harmful effects and health consequences drug use.

Go Online

Visit glencoe.com and complete the Interactive Study Guide for this lesson.

LESSON 3 ASSESSMENT ANSWERS

1. The central nervous system
2. Sample answers: Stimulants: cocaine; depressants: GHB; opiates: morphine; hallucinogens: PCP
3. Drugs such as those derived from the opium plant that are obtainable only by prescription and are used to relieve pain
4. No. Many drugs that come from natural sources, such as opium, psilocybin, and mescaline, can have harmful effects.
5. Codeine is addictive, and when taken in the wrong dosage, it can cause dizziness, labored breathing, respiratory arrest, low blood pressure, twitching, and seizures.
6. Check students' sources for reliability. Enlist the help of the media specialist if needed.
7. Students' scripts will vary.

Living Drug-Free

Real Life Issues

A Sister's Advice. When Penny arrives home, her younger sister is on her bed, crying. "Lisa, what happened?" asks Penny. "A girl at the recreation center offered me drugs," Lisa says. "I didn't know what to do, so I just ran off." Penny gives Lisa a comforting hug. "Sounds to me like you did the right thing," she assures her. Lisa looks up, her eyes red. "But they're going to make fun of me at school on Monday," she says. "Maybe so," replies Penny, "but would they make fun of you for eating right and working out? I always tell people who offer me drugs that I'm an athlete, and I'm not into that."

Writing *Make a list of reasons to say no to drug use.*

Resisting Pressure to Use Drugs

Main Idea Most teens never experiment with illegal drugs.

By deciding not to use drugs, you protect your health, and become a role model to others. Peer pressure can be intense during the teen years. When the subject of drug use comes up, you may be told that "everybody's doing it." This claim is not true. Most teens never experiment with illegal drugs. Almost 62 percent of high school students have never tried marijuana, and more than 90 percent have never tried cocaine.

Committing to Be Drug-Free

It is sometimes difficult to make decisions quickly. You may not have time to consider all of the consequences until after a dangerous situation has passed. You may feel unsure about saying no to drug use. If your friends put pressure on you to use drugs, you may need to decide whether you want to continue to remain friends with someone who uses drugs.

GUIDE TO READING

BIG Idea *By deciding not to use drugs, you promote your own health and influence others to do the same.*

Before You Read

Create an Outline. Preview this lesson by scanning the pages. Then, organize the headings and subheadings into an outline. As you read, fill in the outline with important details.

```
I.
   A.
      1.
      2.
   B.
II.
```

New Vocabulary

▶ drug-free school zones (p. 613)
▶ drug watches (p. 613)
▶ rehabilitation (p. 614)

Living Drug-Free

① FOCUS

GUIDE TO READING

BIG Idea People who avoid drugs promote their health and are a positive influence on others. **Ask Students:** *How can a person positively influence others not to use drugs?* (Sample answers: Being a role model, talking about the dangers of drugs, helping users get help)

Before You Read

Outline Students' details will vary, but all should use the same headings.

Main Idea

Resisting Pressure to Use Drugs Most teens never experiment with illegal drugs. **Ask Students:** *What are ways you can resist peer pressure to use drugs?* (Sample answer: Use refusal skills, avoid people who use drugs)

Real Life Issues

Remind students to think of the different kinds of consequences of drug use—legal, to others, to personal health and goals. When they have finished, ask volunteers to share one or two items from their lists.

Academic Integration

Math Write these years and percentages on the board: 2001–19.4; 2002–18.2; 2003–17.3; 2004–16.1; 2005–15.7; 2006–14.9. Explain that these percents represent students reporting past month use of any illicit drug. They were obtained from national surveys of 8th-, 10th-, and 12th-graders. Ask students to construct a bar graph to display this information. Percent should be the y-axis, and Year should be the x-axis. After students have drawn the graph, have them explain the trend. *(Drug use has consistently declined every year.)*

2 TEACH

C Critical Thinking

Evaluating Ask students how resisting drugs is part of being a responsible individual. Ask volunteers to name protective factors and alternative activities that help them resist drugs. Then discuss as a class what responsibilities a person has to help others resist drugs. **OL**

W Writing Support

Narrative Writing Present the following scenario: Kaylee and Kim have been close friends since grade school. Kim has started using drugs and is trying to talk Kaylee into using them. Have students work with a partner to write a dialogue between the girls in which Kim is pressuring Kaylee, who uses refusal skills to resist. Ask volunteers to perform their dialogues for the class. **OL**

U Universal Access

Being a Buddy Tell students that the risk of drug abuse for students increases with stress, especially when their lives change, for example, moving to a new school or a divorce in the family. The risk of drug abuse can be decreased by having friends who avoid drugs. Ask students to think of ways they could be a buddy to a new student or a student who is stressed out. **BL OL**

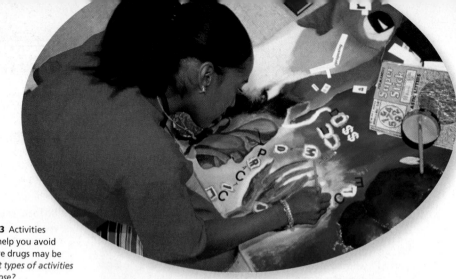

■ **Figure 22.13** Activities you enjoy can help you avoid situations where drugs may be available. *What types of activities would you choose?*

Caption Answer

Figure 22.13 Sample answers: Playing a sport, doing volunteer work

---

 READING CHECK

Answer Sample answer: Most teens are not doing it, including me.

612

To commit to remaining drug-free, choose friends who share your attitude about drug use, and avoid places where drugs may be available. **C**

Even a teen who has used drugs in the past can choose not to use drugs in the future. Refusal skills can help you say no to drugs. Thinking of and practicing refusal statements ahead of time will help you feel comfortable using them. Examples of refusal statements include: **W**

• "No thanks, I don't do drugs."
• "I can't. I'm on medication."
• "I'm not interested. That stuff makes me sick."
• "No. I have to be in great shape for tomorrow's game."

Healthy Alternatives

Choosing friends who value a drug-free lifestyle and participating in activities that do not involve drugs can help you avoid drug use. It can also help to build self-esteem, provide role models, reinforce values, and help you make new friends. The following activities are just a few healthy alternatives to drug use. **U**

• **Hobbies.** Enjoy hobbies such as photography, cooking, art, or music.
• **Sports.** Get physical activity through outdoor recreation, team, and individual sports.
• **Community activities.** Participate in neighborhood events, political movements, community service, religious activities, and local clubs.
• **School organizations.** Get involved in service groups, honor societies, and advocacy groups at school.

READING CHECK

Apply What can you say to someone who pressures you to use drugs by telling you that "everybody's doing it"?

Promoting School Wellness

Integrated Approach to Drug Prevention A coordinated school health program involves parents and community members in its drug prevention efforts. A council or committee might also include administrators, teachers, and students. Members identify health issues, prioritize them, and plan actions to address them. If your school has such a committee, have interested students volunteer to serve as representatives. A helpful resource describing model programs is the brochure "Preventing Drug Use Among Children and Adolescents," found on the NIDA Web site.

Drug Prevention Efforts

Main Idea Schools and communities are working together to support students in their efforts to be drug-free.

Everyone can help reduce substance abuse by committing to remain drug-free. Schools and communities also provide ways to help young people avoid drugs.

School Efforts

Near schools, **drug-free school zones**, *areas within 1,000 to 1,500 feet of schools and designated by signs, within which people caught selling drugs receive especially severe penalties,* have been established. Penalties are often double what they might be for the same drug offense committed elsewhere. Other efforts at schools to eliminate drug use include drug education classes, zero-tolerance policies, and the expulsion of students found using drugs. Some schools conduct locker searches and maintain police patrol on campus.

Community Efforts

Communities across the nation are taking action to prevent drug abuse. **Drug watches** are *organized community efforts by neighborhood residents to patrol, monitor, report, and otherwise try to stop drug deals and drug abuse.* Anti-drug programs in your community can help protect your family and friends from drug abuse.

Becoming Drug-Free

Main Idea Many types of counseling are available for those who want to become drug-free.

Once someone begins using drugs, addiction can occur rapidly. **Figure 22.15** on page 614 lists some warning signs of drug abuse. The following steps can guide you in helping a friend or family member.

- Identify sources of help in your community.
- Talk to the person when he or she is sober. Express your affection and concern, and describe the person's behavior without being judgmental.
- Listen to the person's response. Be prepared for anger and denial.
- Offer to go with your friend or family member to a counselor or support group.

 Go Online

Go to glencoe.com and complete the Student Web Activity on the benefits of living a drug-free life.

READING CHECK

Contrast How are some of the penalties for illicit drug use in a drug-free school zone more severe than in other areas?

■ **Figure 22.14** The penalties for using, selling, or possessing drugs in a drug-free school zone are more severe than in other areas. *How far from a school is the border of a typical drug-free school zone?*

Main Idea

Drug Prevention Efforts Schools and communities are working together to help students avoid drugs. **Ask Students:** *What is our school doing or could it do to prevent drug use among students?* (Sample answer: Teach refusal skills and how to deal with stress.)

HS Health Skills Practice

Goal Setting Review the steps in a goal-setting action plan. Ask students to choose a goal they want to reach in the next five years. Point out that being drug-free can be a goal in itself. Ask students to write an action plan to achieve their goal. Discuss as a class how any use of drugs would make those goals difficult or impossible to reach. **OL**

Main Idea

Becoming Drug-Free It is never too late to get help, even for teens who are already using drugs. **Ask Students:** *What kinds of help might students who are using drugs need?* (Sample answer: Counseling and medical treatment)

Caption Answer

Figure 22.14 Within 1,000 to 1,500 feet of schools

Cooperative Learning

Presentation Ask students to work together to research the most important drug-related facts and attitudes to share with other students in your school. Divide the class into small groups to plan an entertaining presentation, such as a skit or a rap or other song. Students might choose to work together as a class to plan a short play. Encourage students to include alternative activities to drug use in a fun, interesting way. Arrange to have the class make its presentations at a school assembly.

AL Active Learning

Role-Play Divide the class into groups of four. Have groups write and role-play a situation in which two students try to persuade two other students to get treatment for drug abuse. Ask students to include in their role-play specific people whom they can ask for help. Make sure that English learners are placed with English proficient students. Tell students to allow everyone a chance to speak. **EL** **OL**

C Critical Thinking

Inferring Have students read about getting help for drug abuse. Ask them to explain why enabling does not help a drug user but actually promotes drug use. Have them include examples of enabling behavior. Invite students to share their findings in a short oral report. **AL**

Academic Vocabulary

Adjust Have students provide examples of situations to which they have adjusted. For example, they might have moved to a new school and adjusted by making new friends. Point out that in the same way, former drug users can adjust by developing new ways of coping with problems, such as joining a support group.

Figure 22.15 **Warning Signs of Drug Use**

The following behaviors may indicate that a person has a drug problem.

- Lies about the drugs he or she is using, constantly talks about drugs
- Stops participating in activities that once were an important part of his or her life
- Changes eating or sleeping habits, shows rapid weight loss
- Takes unnecessary risks, participates in unsafe behaviors
- Gets in trouble with authorities, such as school administrators or police
- Seems withdrawn, depressed, tired, and cares less about appearance
- Has red-rimmed eyes and runny nose not related to colds or allergies
- Has blackouts and forgets what he or she did under the influence
- Has difficulty concentrating

AL

Getting Help

Drug abuse is a treatable condition. **Rehabilitation** is *the process of medical and psychological treatment for physiological or psychological dependence on a drug or alcohol.* Most drug users need the help family, friends, and counseling to end their addiction. **C**

Drug treatment centers offer a safe place to withdraw from drug use. Many of these centers provide medications to help with the physical and psychological effects of withdrawal. Types of drug treatment centers include:

- **Outpatient drug-free treatment.** These programs usually do not include medications and often use individual or group counseling.
- **Short-term treatment.** These centers can include residential therapy, medication therapy, and outpatient therapy.
- **Maintenance therapy.** Intended for heroin addicts, this treatment usually includes medication therapy.
- **Therapeutic communities.** These are residences for drug abusers. The centers include highly structured programs that may last from six to 12 months.

Academic Vocabulary

adjust *(verb):* to bring to a more satisfactory state

Drug counselors can also help people **adjust** to a life without drugs. Some counselors use behavioral change strategies to help a person become drug-free. These strategies include avoiding the people who supply or do the drug, recalling negative consequences of doing the drug, practicing refusal skills, and filling free time with planned, healthy activities.

Former drug users may also attend support groups. These meetings are gatherings of people who share a common problem. Support groups provide the long-term support that the recovering user needs to remain drug-free, in addition to family support.

614 Chapter 22 Illegal Drugs

 Home and Community

Community Resources for Drug Problems Have students work in small groups to access phone directories and online resources to collect information on local drug hotlines, treatment centers, and support groups. Ask students to find out the services, costs, hours of operation, and contact information for each agency and support group. They can make a poster with this information and distribute copies of it in the school and other places in the community with permission. Some agencies might provide brochures that students can hand out at school.

TEENS Making a Difference

"We don't have time to consider using drugs."

Staying Drug-Free

Sandra L., of Florida, is president of her school's chapter of Drug Free Youth in Town (DFYIT). "Every weekend thirty to fifty of our 300 members do community service. The purpose is to have fun and not have time to think about drugs," says Sandra.

DFYIT teens pledge to be drug-free and agree to random drug tests. "We wear T-shirts with the words 'Drug-free and willing to prove it,'" Sandra says.

Through Sandra's leadership, DYFIT members have volunteered at a number of events, including an arts festival, an AIDS walk, a food and toy drive, and haunted houses on Halloween.

The 300-plus members of DFYIT rely on Sandra to organize their volunteer work. "Knowing that I am helping them stay away from drugs is rewarding."

Activity Write your answers to the following questions in your personal health journal:

1 What fun activities could teens volunteer for in your community?

2 How would you organize a similar club at your school?

3 List at least six reasons why it's important to stay drug-free.

LESSON 4 ASSESSMENT

After You Read

Reviewing Facts and Vocabulary

1. What are three healthy alternatives to using drugs?
2. What is a *drug-free school zone*?
3. Describe *rehabilitation*.

Thinking Critically

4. **Analyze.** Why is it important to commit to being drug-free before drugs are offered to you?
5. **Apply.** Former drug users try to fill their free time with healthy activities. What kinds of healthy activities could a former user try in order to remain drug-free?

Applying Health Skills

6. **Practicing Healthful Behaviors.** List five healthy alternatives to drug use, and share your ideas with the class.

Writing Critically

7. **Narrative.** Write a short story about someone who has stopped using drugs. Describe the types of community resources that provide help.

 Go Online

Visit glencoe.com and complete the Interactive Study Guide for this lesson.

Lesson 4 Living Drug Free **615**

TEENS Making a Difference

Answers will vary for all questions.

❸ ASSESS/CLOSE

Assessment Resources

📁 **FAST FILE ACTIVITIES**
Lesson 4 Quiz

 ExamView Assessment Suite CD-ROM

Visit glencoe.com **for:**
Online Quizzes
Online Learning Center

Progress Monitoring

Reteaching
Have students work in pairs and use the outlines they constructed at the beginning of the chapter to identify the main idea in each section. One person reads each main idea in his or her outline, and the partner gives a supporting detail. Then they switch and repeat the exercise.

Enrichment
Encourage students to get involved with state or local anti-drug groups. They might participate in a marathon or help distribute anti-drug information.

LESSON 4 ASSESSMENT ANSWERS

1. Sample answer: Starting a hobby, participating in a sport, and joining a school organization
2. An area within 1,000 to 1,500 feet of a school, designated by signs, within which people caught selling drugs receive especially severe penalties
3. The process of medical and psychological treatment for physiological or psychological dependence on a drug or alcohol
4. Sample answer: Peer pressure can be persuasive. The best way to combat it is to be prepared with strong refusal strategies.
5. Sample answer: The person could join a support group, make a weekly date with friends, join an athletic facility, or volunteer for a community organization.
6. You might wish to have students work in pairs or small groups and pool their ideas.
7. Stories will vary.

Saying No

NHES Standard 4 Students will demonstrate the ability to use interpersonal communication skills to enhance health and avoid or reduce health risks.

Teaching Objectives

- Identify a minimum of ten different illegal drugs and their effect on a person's health and wellness.
- Encourage others to make healthful choices related to being drug-free.

Teaching Strategies

- Have students follow steps in activity and use their textbooks and reliable print and online resources in their research.
- Be certain students include specific information in their presentations, explaining ways drugs affect physical, mental/emotional, and social health.
- As students develop their presentations, encourage them to incorporate strategies to demonstrate effective ways to practice refusal skills. Remind them of the audience and suggest they use creativity to engage younger students.

Assessment

Using a rubric, student work should provide comprehensive evidence of the following criteria to achieve the highest score.

✓ Includes the word "no" in their response
✓ Explains why they are refusing
✓ Proposes alternatives

Hands-On HEALTH

Activity Saying No

Illegal drug use can harm your physical, mental/emotional, and social health. You will create a presentation for younger students, providing information about illegal drugs and advice on how to use refusal skills to avoid drug use.

What You'll Need

- a computer with Internet access
- one large sheet of white paper and colored markers

What You'll Do

Step 1

Working with a partner, review the text for information on the risks of drug use. On the large sheet of paper, list the names of ten illegal drugs, and the effects of each drug.

Step 2

Create a computer presentation that helps younger students understand the risks of using illegal drugs. Show them how to use refusal skills.

Step 3

Show your presentation to a class of middle school students, and demonstrate refusal skills.

Apply and Conclude

Ask the middle school students for feedback. Write a short reflective paper on the effectiveness of your presentation, including what you would do differently.

Checklist: Refusal Skills

- ✓ Say no, and explain why you are refusing
- ✓ Propose alternative activities to the group
- ✓ Use body language to back up your words
- ✓ Walk away from the situation if necessary

Anti-Drug Rally!
- Practice Refusal Skills
- Learn how to get help
Today at 4:00 pm
Main Auditorium

More About...

Stress and Drug Abuse Post-traumatic stress disorder (PTSD) is a known risk factor for drug abuse. It can occur in people who witness or become victims in a violent attack, natural disaster, or accident. Children exposed to severe stress are more likely to abuse drugs than adults. Children and teens who have suffered trauma and may be experiencing PTSD should be identified and treated to reduce the risk of later problems with drugs and alcohol. Teachers and other adults should be attentive to how children and teens are responding to a stressful event and take action as needed to get professional help for them.

STUDY TO GO To download quizzes and eFlashcards to your PDA, go to glencoe.com and click on the Study to Go icon.

LESSON 1

The Health Risks of Drug Use

Key Concepts

▶ It is illegal to use, sell, or possess illegal drugs, or to sell or use prescription medications for nonmedical purposes.

▶ Misusing medicines and drugs can lead to addiction.

▶ Drug abuse can have negative consequences for the user, friends, family, and society.

Vocabulary

▶ substance abuse (p. 592)
▶ illegal drugs (p. 592)
▶ illicit drug use (p. 592)
▶ overdose (p. 593)
▶ addiction (p. 595)

LESSON 2

Marijuana, Inhalants, and Steroids

Key Concepts

▶ Using Marijuana can damage a user's health.

▶ Sniffing inhalants can permanently damage or kill brain cells.

▶ The nonmedical use of anabolic-androgenic steroids is illegal and can pose serious health risks.

Vocabulary

▶ marijuana (p. 599)
▶ paranoia (p. 600)
▶ inhalants (p. 601)
▶ anabolic-androgenic steroids (p. 601)

LESSON 3

Psychoactive Drugs

Key Concepts

▶ Many illegal drugs often contain unknown ingredients.

▶ Stimulants include legal drugs, such as nicotine, caffeine, and many medicines, and illegal drugs, such as cocaine and crack.

▶ Hallucinogens can result in flashbacks that often cause mental and emotional problems that can occur long after use.

Vocabulary

▶ psychoactive drugs (p. 603)
▶ designer drugs (p. 605)
▶ hallucinogens (p. 605)
▶ euphoria (p. 605)
▶ depressants (p. 605)
▶ stimulants (p. 606)
▶ opiates (p. 609)

LESSON 4

Living Drug-Free

Key Concepts

▶ Choosing to remain drug-free will protect your health.

▶ You can use refusal skills to maintain your commitment to remaining drug-free.

▶ Drug-free school zones and drug watches are two ways that communities help young people avoid drugs.

Vocabulary

▶ drug-free school zones (p. 613)
▶ drug watches (p. 613)
▶ rehabilitation (p. 614)

Chapter 22   Review   **617**

 Go Online

Students can visit **glencoe.com** to

• review content online with the Online Student Edition.

• test their knowledge of chapter content with Online Quizzes.

• access Interactive Health Tutor for more practice with vocabulary.

Assessment Resources

📁 **FAST FILE ACTIVITIES**
Chapter 22 Test

💿 **ExamView**
Assessment Suite CD-ROM

Visit glencoe.com for:
Audio Chapter Summaries
Online Quizzes

 STUDY TO GO Tell students to visit **glencoe.com** where they can download quizzes and eFlashcards.

Study Tips

Rewarding Study Time Some students have difficulty motivating themselves to study. One effective strategy is to treat one-self for studying. Advise students to reward themselves for even small goals, such as studying for 45 minutes. During a break, they can eat a healthful snack or e-mail a friend, for example. Have students make a list of short activities they like to do that can serve as rewards. They may also want to plan big rewards, such as attending a concert, after they perform well on a test or after so many weeks of sticking with their study schedule.

Assessment

Chapter 22 Assessment Answers

LESSON 1

Vocabulary Review
1. addiction
2. Substance abuse
3. overdose

Understanding Key Concepts
4. b
5. c
6. c

Thinking Critically
7. Sample answer: Suspension from school, jail time and probation, denial of federal student loans, court fines, and legal fees can make getting into and paying for college or getting a job more difficult.
8. Sample answer: Even if you or anyone you know does not use drugs, you are still at risk of injury or death from an accident caused by someone driving under the influence. Also, taxes that pay law enforcement costs, insurance costs, and health care costs for society are affected by illegal drug use.

LESSON 2

Vocabulary Review
9. Paranoia
10. inhalants
11. Anabolic-androgenic steroids

Understanding Key Concepts
12. d
13. b
14. b

LESSON 1

Vocabulary Review
Use the vocabulary terms listed on page 617 to complete the following statements.

1. Drug users often find it difficult to stop using drugs without help because _____ involves both psychological and physiological dependence.

2. _____ is any unnecessary or improper use of chemical substances for nonmedical purposes.

3. Taking more than the recommended amount of a prescription drug can lead to serious health problems or even death from a(n) _____.

Understanding Key Concepts
After reading the question or statement, select the correct answer.

4. Which of the following is *not* usually a factor in deciding to use an illegal drug?
   a. Peer pressure at school
   b. The original source of the drug
   c. How role models live their lives
   d. Messages on television and in movies

5. Which of the following can be a negative consequence of drug use?
   a. Temporary euphoria
   b. Decrease in tolerance
   c. Contraction of an STD
   d. Strengthened refusal skills

6. Many people perceive the level of drug use by teens as
   a. much lower than it is in reality.
   b. much lower than in other countries.
   c. much higher than it is in reality.
   d. much higher than in other countries.

Thinking Critically
After reading the question or statement, write a short answer using complete sentences.

7. **Infer.** How might the legal consequences of drug use interfere with a teen's future educational and career goals?

8. **Analyze.** How can illicit drug use affect you if you and your friends do not use drugs?

LESSON 2

Vocabulary Review
Choose the correct term in the sentences below.

9. *Paranoia / Marijuana* is an irrational suspiciousness or distrust of others.

10. Using *anabolic-androgenic steroids / inhalants* leads to loss of brain cells.

11. *Anabolic-androgenic steroids / Inhalants* can increase muscle strength but not tendon and ligament strength, and causes injuries.

Understanding Key Concepts
After reading the question or statement, select the correct answer.

12. Which consequence of using marijuana can lead to reproductive system problems?
   a. Increased appetite
   b. Feelings of paranoia
   c. Heart and lung damage
   d. Changes in testosterone level

13. Which substance has a legal medical use when used as an inhalant?
   a. Gasoline   c. Solvent
   b. Nitrous oxide   d. Varnish

14. Which drugs are *not* usually taken in through the respiratory system?
   a. Aerosols
   b. Anabolic-androgenic steroids
   c. Marijuana
   d. Nitrous oxide

Health eSpotlight VIDEO Wrap-Up

Staying Drug-Free Have students reread the Health eSpotlight questions at the beginning of the chapter (page 591) and look at their original answers. **Ask Students:** *What do you now know about the consequences of drug use and resisting pressure to use drugs that you didn't know before reading the chapter?* Call on volunteers to describe what they have learned and how they would change their responses.

Thinking Critically

After reading the question or statement, write a short answer using complete sentences.

15. Analyze. How could using marijuana harm your social interactions with friends?

16. Infer. Why might it be difficult for law enforcement officials to discover and prevent illegal inhalant use?

17. Extend. If an athlete chooses to use steroids to increase muscle mass, how does this perceived benefit actually turn out to be a negative consequence?

LESSON 3

Vocabulary Review

Choose the correct word in the sentences below.

18. *Stimulants/Depressants* speed up the central nervous system.

19. Drugs that cause *euphoria/hallucinations* give users a temporary feeling of intense well-being.

20. *Opiates/Hallucinogens* are often obtainable by prescription, but are heavily monitored because they can cause serious addiction.

Understanding Key Concepts

After reading the question or statement, select the correct answer.

21. Which type of psychoactive drug is best known for altering sense perceptions?
   a. Depressants
   b. Hallucinogens
   c. Opiates
   d. Stimulants

22. Which type of psychoactive drug is used medically to block pain messages to the brain?
   a. Depressants   **c.** Opiates
   b. Hallucinogens   **d.** Stimulants

23. Which hallucinogen is classified as a designer drug?
   a. DXM   **c.** MDMA
   b. LSD   **d.** PCP

24. Why are Rohypnol and GHB linked to exposure to STDs?
   a. They are highly addictive.
   b. They can be used as date-rape drugs.
   c. They are usually taken intravenously.
   d. They affect the body's immune response.

Thinking Critically

After reading the question or statement, write a short answer using complete sentences.

25. Infer. Dangerous drugs are often even more dangerous when mixed together. Why might a drug user take a depressant after taking a stimulant?

26. Evaluate. Why could driving under the influence of a psychoactive drug contribute to an accident?

27. Analyze. Why is it important for doctors and pharmacists to monitor the legal medical use of opiates?

LESSON 4

Vocabulary Review

Use the vocabulary terms listed on page 617 to complete the following statements.

28. _____ is a way to help drug users fight addiction.

29. A community effort to monitor and report illicit drug use is called a(n) _____.

Thinking Critically

15. Sample answer: Marijuana often causes feelings of paranoia in users, which can cause hurt feelings or misunderstandings between friends.

16. Many inhalants, such as solvents and spray paints, are readily available at stores for legal use in household projects.

17. Steroids can increase muscle strength, which seems like a benefit for athletes. However, the associated tendons and ligaments don't get stronger. This difference in strength can result in injuries that can end an athlete's career.

LESSON 3

Vocabulary Review

18. Stimulants
19. euphoria
20. Opiates

Understanding Key Concepts

21. b
22. c
23. c
24. b

Thinking Critically

25. A stimulant speeds up the central nervous system, while a depressant slows it down. A drug abuser might take a depressant after taking a stimulant to counteract the effects of the stimulant.

26. Psychoactive drugs alter activity in the brain and affect the central nervous system. Hallucinations could cause a driver to brake or speed up dangerously. An altered CNS could affect reaction times and awareness of nearby dangers.

Assessment

27. Opiates are highly addictive and dangerous if used improperly. Doctors and pharmacists must make sure that patients are taking them as directed and not abusing them.

LESSON 4

Vocabulary Review

28. Rehabilitation
29. drug watch
30. drug-free school zone

Understanding Key Concepts

31. d
32. a
33. a

Thinking Critically

34. Peers can urge each other to try illegal drugs, or they can encourage each other to avoid drugs.
35. Many of the warning signs of drug use are often signs of other problems, such as allergies, eating disorders, or emotional problems.
36. Many addictions can be treated through medication, drug counseling, treatment centers, or support groups.

---

30. Penalties for drug use are often double what they might be for the same drug offense committed outside of a(n) _____.

Understanding Key Concepts

After reading the question or statement, select the correct answer.

31. Which is *not* a way that communities and schools are helping to prevent drug use?
    a. Organizing drug watches
    b. Providing drug treatment centers
    c. Establishing drug-free school zones
    d. Making it illegal to prescribe addictive medicines

32. Which is *not* a warning sign of drug use?
    a. Allergic reactions
    b. Regular hangovers
    c. Difficulty concentrating
    d. Change in sleeping habits

33. Which type of drug treatment strategy involves a meeting of people who share a common problem?
    a. Support group
    b. Outpatient therapy
    c. Medication therapy
    d. Individual counseling

Thinking Critically

After reading the question or statement, write a short answer using complete sentences.

34. **Connect.** How is peer pressure related to a teen's decision to use or avoid drugs?

35. **Analyze.** Why might it be difficult to determine whether a person has a problem with illegal drugs?

36. **Evaluate.** Why is it important to recognize when someone has an addiction to drugs and to discuss the problem with him or her?

Project-Based ASSESSMENT

Drugs: Truth and Consequences

Background
Abstaining from illegal drug use is a health factor you can control. Being knowledgeable of the types of illegal drugs and the dangers associated with using them will help reinforce your decision to lead a drug-free life.

Task
Create a pamphlet that provides information about drugs and the consequences of drug abuse on teens.

Audience
Students and adults in your community.

Purpose
Educate others about the kinds of illegal drugs that are available. Present information about the effects of illegal drugs and the problems related to teen substance abuse.

Procedure

1. Research information about the types of illegal drugs and the health consequences of drug use.
2. Use statistics from reliable sources to prove the information you find.
3. Look at other pamphlets for ideas, and write a draft of your pamphlet. Make sure to include all the elements you want to cover. Make any necessary revisions.
4. Use a computer desktop publishing system or construction paper and colored pencils to create the final version of your pamphlet.
5. Distribute the finished pamphlets in your school library and other appropriate places in your community.

Project-Based ASSESSMENT

Step 1 Research Information Have students use reliable online and print resources, as well as this text, to collect information. Advise them to confine their research to drug use in teens.

Step 2 Create Pamphlet Ask the class to collect and bring in brochures from various sources or print them off the Internet. Remind students to make their pamphlets appealing to their audience. Enlist the aid of the school media specialist if needed.

Step 3 Evaluate Evaluate the pamphlets based on clarity, appeal, and accuracy. Topics should focus on drug abuse in teens.

Visit **glencoe.com** for Project-Based Assessment rubrics.

Math Practice

Reading Tables. Nonmedical use of substances known as *anabolic steroids* is considered substance abuse. The consequences of misusing steroids involves more than health risks. There are also legal consequences. The table shows the abuse of anabolic steroids in a 2004 study that involved students from both public and private schools.

Percentage of Teens in Grades 8, 10, and 12 Who Use or Have Used Steroids			
Grade	8th	10th	12th
Ever used	1.9%	2.4%	3.4%
Used in past year	1.1%	1.5%	2.5%
Used in past month	0.5%	0.8%	1.6%

1. If 12,000 of the students studied were tenth graders, how many of them have not used anabolic steroids in the past month?
   A. 96
   B. 180
   C. 11,820
   D. 11,904

2. If 20,000 of the students were eighth graders, how many of them have not ever used anabolic steroids?
   A. 380
   B. 3800
   C. 16,200
   D. 19,620

3. Examine the values in the table. Provide a logical explanation as to why the percentages are higher for older students.

Go Online

For more test practice, visit glencoe.com and complete the Online Quizzes for Chapter 22.

Reading/Writing Practice

Understand and Apply. Read the passage below, and then answer the questions.

> It was New Year's Eve, and Carrie was anxious to go to a friend's party. Carrie and her friend, Camille, decided to drive over together. They picked up Camille's new boyfriend, Carl, on the way.
> "Hey, let's have some fun tonight," said Carl. "I bought this new drug that everyone's talking about. It'll make the party more fun. What do you say?"
> Carrie put her hand up. "I don't want to take drugs. I can have fun without them."
> "Aw, come on, everyone's trying it," said Carl. Camille looked at Carrie, then shrugged and looked only slightly apologetic. She really liked this new guy.
> "No. It's not for me," Carrie said. "I don't want to use drugs."

1. What is the author's purpose in this piece?
   A. To show how refusal skills work
   B. To illustrate the dangers of drug use
   C. To illustrate the dangers of driving while under the influence of drugs
   D. To tell about the importance of supporting peers through a difficult time

2. What else can Carrie do to avoid drug use?
   A. Describe the physical effects of drug use..
   B. Leave the party and go home.
   C. Tell Camille that Carl's a bad influence.
   D. All of the above

3. Create a pamphlet with pictures or graphics and strong refusal statements showing middle school students how to use refusal skills when offered illegal drugs.

National Education Standards
Mathematics: Number and Operations
Language Arts: NCTE 2, NCTE 3

Standardized Test Practice Answers

Math Practice
1. D
2. D
3. Answers will vary, but might include that a certain number of students started using steroids at an early age. Every year, more students use steroids and are included in the totals, raising the percentages.

Reading/Writing Practice
1. A
2. B
3. Pamphlets will vary but should include strong refusal statements.

National Education Standards

Math: Number and Operations

Language Arts: NCTE 2, NCTE 3

For the complete Math and Language Arts standards, visit glencoe.com.

Go Online

Online Study Tools
For more test practice, visit glencoe.com and complete the Online Quizzes for Chapter 22.

Test-Taking Tip

Get to the Root Tell students that if they do not know the definition of a word, they might be able to infer its meaning by examining its roots, prefixes, and suffixes. For instance, words that start with *non-*, *un-*, *a-*, *dis-*, and *in-* generally reverse what the rest of the word means. Words that end in *-ly* are usually adverbs, and thus, are descriptive terms.

Drugs

Why Limit Where People Can Smoke?

All 50 states and the District of Columbia have laws or regulations restricting smoking in certain places. Restrictions can be mandated by laws or regulations implemented at the state or local level. State restaurant associations and state and local chambers of commerce are increasingly supporting such laws. Some private employers and businesses voluntarily ban or limit smoking in the workplace.

Benefits of a Smoke-Free Environment

Leading health advisors maintain that smoke-free environments for nonsmokers are the best way to reduce their exposure to second-hand smoke. A recent Surgeon General's report concludes that there is no level of secondhand smoke that is safe. Separate areas for smokers and ventilating buildings are not effective. The report also states that smoking restrictions result in reduced smoking by smokers.

Legal Issues

Some smokers assert that smoking is a fundamental right and that their freedom is being restricted. Non-smokers counter that their rights are violated when they cannot enter an establishment because of the presence of secondhand smoke. Health authorities claim that they are not telling smokers they cannot smoke at all, but that the public has reasonable expectations of being protected from health hazards in public places.

Why Limit Where People Can Smoke?

Most people know that smoking is hazardous to your health. Smoking causes cancer, heart disease, high blood pressure, and many other health problems. However, people still debate the hazards of secondhand smoke. People also debate whether the rights of nonsmokers should be considered over the rights of smokers. There are laws in place to limit where people can smoke. For example, federal law prohibits smoking on airplanes, and many cities and towns do not allow smoking in restaurants and public buildings. Is it fair to restrict smoking?

There are two sides to this issue. Read the viewpoints and consider both positions. How do they compare to your own thoughts on this topic?

Outdoor Smoking

622 Unit 7 Real-World Health

More About...

Effects of Secondhand Smoke on Children Infants and young children are more susceptible to the effects of second-hand smoke than adults because their bodies are still developing. They may experience slowed lung growth due to exposure. They are more likely to suffer from bronchitis and respiratory symptoms such as cough-ing, wheezing, and breathlessness. Exposed children are also more at risk for ear infections. Those with asthma have more frequent and severe attacks. A recent study revealed that tobacco smoke affected artery function in exposed children by restricting blood flow. About 22 million children aged 3 to 11 are exposed annually to secondhand smoke.

Benefits of Restricting Smoking

There is no debate. The National Institutes of Health reports that secondhand smoke contains more than 50 chemicals that can cause cancer. Restricting where people smoke limits the exposure of nonsmokers to these harmful substances. Nonsmokers should not have to breathe secondhand smoke. It's a health risk that should not be forced on others. Smokers may decide to expose themselves to the dangers of smoking, but they should not have the right to decide to expose nonsmokers to those health dangers too.

" I don't want to smell someone else's smoke, and that's my choice. Besides, secondhand smoke kills people."

—Tashauna J., age 15

Benefits of Unrestricted Smoking

Many people dislike the smell of tobacco smoke, but the rights of smokers should be balanced against the rights of nonsmokers. Some studies show there are dangers linked to secondhand smoke, but other studies have shown no danger. If a smoker is not hurting others, he should be able to smoke wherever he wants. Smokers who are trying to quit need time to adjust to a nonsmoking lifestyle. In several states, restaurants restrict smoking. So do airports, and many businesses. As long as smokers are polite and don't blow their smoke toward nonsmokers, they should be able to smoke wherever they want.

" If the jury is still out on the harm caused by secondhand smoke, why should I or anyone else care where people smoke?"

—Kevin C., age 16

Activity ▶ Beyond the Classroom

1. **Summarize** what you learned about the impact of secondhand smoke after reading Chapter 20. Write a one-page letter to the editor persuading others of your point of view. What other issues besides health risks should be considered when determining where people should be able to smoke?

2. **Analyze** laws in your city and state that restrict smoking. Where is smoking prohibited? What laws govern the size and location of areas where smoking is permitted? What age limits apply to people in your state who want to purchase cigarettes or other tobacco products?

Go Online

For more information, go to the Health Careers link at **glencoe.com**.

Teaching Strategies

- **Evaluating Restrictions** Explain that restrictions can be grouped into three main levels: designated smoking areas, smoking allowed if separately ventilated, and no smoking allowed. Divide students into small groups, and have them discuss these questions: What kinds of places should have smoking restrictions? What level should they be? Tell students to consider restaurants, bars, childcare centers, hospitals, malls, grocery stores, retail stores, city buses, and enclosed sporting events. Should private business owners be subject to business restrictions? Have each group summarize its discussion and share it with the class.

- **Synthesizing Solutions** Ask students to work in groups to generate a list of options for the issue of smoking restrictions. Options can include possible compromises. For example, should smokers have their own bars and restaurants that cater to their preferences? Do students agree with smokers who argue that people do not have to work there if they do not like the smoke? Have students share their options with the class. Then lead a class discussion on the pros and cons of each option.

Activity ▶ Beyond the Classroom

Writing

1. Have students use their summaries to craft their letters. Remind students that a persuasive letter should contain facts and a clearly stated position, as well as any action the writer wants the reader to take.

2. Answers will vary. Suggest that students search online for this information or contact local and state authorities. State or regional chapters of lung or cancer associations can most likely provide this information, too.

Flexible Technology Solutions

Focus

Health eSpotlight Video Series

By Chapter

Chapter 23 Communicable Diseases
Video 23: Communicable Diseases

Chapter 24 Sexually Transmitted Diseases and HIV/AIDS
Video 24: No One is Immune

Chapter 25 Noncommunicable Diseases and Disabilities
Video 25: Straight Facts on Disease and Disabilities

By Lesson

Chapter 23 *Video 23*   For Use With

Segment 23.1 Understanding Communicable Diseases...... Lesson 1
Segment 23.2 Common Communicable Diseases............... Lesson 2
Segment 23.3 Fighting Communicable Diseases................ Lesson 3
Segment 23.4 Emerging Diseases and Pandemics.............. Lesson 4

Chapter 24 *Video 24*   For Use With

Segment 24.1 Sexually Transmitted Diseases .... Lesson 1
Segment 24.2 Preventing and Treating STDs .... Lesson 2
Segment 24.3 HIV/AIDS.. Lesson 3
Segment 24.4 Preventing and Treating HIV/AIDS .... Lesson 4

Chapter 25 *Video 25*   For Use With

Segment 25.1 Cardiovascular Disease.............................. Lesson 1
Segment 25.2 Cancer .... Lesson 2
Segment 25.3 Allergies, Asthma, Diabetes, and Arthritis.... Lesson 3
Segment 25.4 Physical and Mental
                         Challenges.. Lesson 4

By Skill

Practicing Healthful Behaviors ....Videos 3   13   17   19   **23**
Refusal Skills ....Videos 8   21   **24**
Accessing Information ....Videos 2   10   14   **25**

▪ Indicates videos featured in the unit that teach the corresponding skill. Other videos listed can also be used to teach that skill.

Teach

Direct lesson plans beyond the classroom with multi-media fitness activities that students can do online, in class, or as a group.

PowerPoint® Presentation

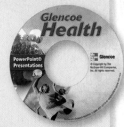

- *Health eSpotlight* videos
- Audio and image bank

Online

Fitness Zone Online is a multi-media resource that helps students find ways to be physically active each day.

- Clipboard Energizer Activities
- Fitness Zone Videos
- Polar Heart Rate Monitor Activities
- Nutrition, Physical Activity, and Injury Prevention Tips
- Links to Nutrition and Physical Activity Resources

Go Online

Online Learning Center

- Student Web Activities
- PuzzleMaker
- Interactive Health Tutor

Podcast Audio Chapter Summaries

Use the audio Podcast Audio Chapter Summaries to teach and review key concepts, and engage students with health content that they can download to a computer or portable MP3 player.

Assess/Close

Help students master chapter and lesson concepts with an integrated technology solution for assessment and performance evaluation.

Go Online

Online Learning Center

- Interactive Study Guides
- Online Quizzes

ExamView® Assessment Suite CD-ROM

Create and customize tests in minutes with this convenient digital platform.

- Create differentiated tests quickly and easily.
- All questions correlated to National/State Standards.
- Enhance tests with Document Based Questions (DBQ) and add your own photos and graphics.
- Build tests in both English and Spanish.
- Generate progress reports.

Enrich

Use these additional digital and online media resources to promote hands-on exploration of health topics covered in the lesson.

Business Week Health Video Series

- *HIV Combo Drugs*
- *Cancer Vaccine*

Study-to-Go

Download a portable version of eFlashcards and Self-Check Quizzes onto your Palm or Pocket PC.

Health Podcasts Activities

Glencoe's "It's Your Health" Podcast Activities provide students with a unique listening and learning experience that takes health education beyond the classroom. Download the audio files and print activities covering a range of current health topics that matter most to teens!

Diseases and Disorders

In this unit, students will learn about the causes and prevention of communicable diseases, including sexually transmitted diseases, and the causes and management of noncommunicable diseases.

Health eSpotlight
Video Series

At the beginning of each chapter, visit glencoe.com and have students watch the video and do the accompanying print activity.

 Chapter 23
Communicable Diseases

There are some simple ways to stop the spread of communicable diseases.

 Chapter 24
No One Is Immune

Staying educated on STDs and HIV/AIDS can help avoid them.

 Chapter 25
Straight Facts on Diseases and Disabilities

Heart disease and type 2 diabetes may be preventable by choosing healthful behaviors.

Unit 8 Resources

- Career Corner
- 📁 FAST FILE RESOURCES
- Health Career Research Activity
- Family Involvement Activity
- Community Involvement Activity
- Unit Test

Chapter 23
Communicable Diseases

 Communicable Diseases

Chapter 24
Sexually Transmitted Diseases and HIV/AIDS

 No One Is Immune

Chapter 25
Noncommunicable Diseases and Disabilities

 Straight Facts on Diseases and Disabilities

UNIT PROJECT

Building Healthy Communities

Using Visuals Special Olympics provides year-round sports training and athletic competition to over 2.25 million people with intellectual disabilities. The nonprofit organization relies on the time, energy, and enthusiasm of its volunteers.

 Go Online To learn more about the goals of Special Olympics, go to the Unit Web Project at glencoe.com.

Get Involved. Conduct research on other organizations in your community that help people affected by disease or disability. Contact one organization and find out how teens can volunteer to help.

624

UNIT PROJECT

Building Healthy Communities Special Olympics was founded in 1968 by Eunice Kennedy Shriver and has grown to become a global community serving more than 160 countries. Special Olympics World Games are held every four years and are hosted by countries around the world. The Special Olympics Athlete Oath is "Let me win. But if I cannot win, let me be brave in the attempt."

Get Involved Suggest that interested students assemble information about volunteer opportunities in their community. On a school-wide community bulletin board, have student coordinators post up-to-date information about local volunteer opportunities and the training that these organizations offer. For example, babysitting, CPR, or other classes offered by the Red Cross could be featured.

"The future depends on what we do in the present."
— *Mahatma Gandhi, early 20th-century philosopher and peace activist*

Unit 8   Diseases and Disorderss   **625**

Activate Prior Knowledge

Ask students these questions before they read the chapter to build on what they already know.

Chapter 23
What are some ways that certain diseases can be spread from one person to another?

(Answers will vary. Students might mention touching, sneezing, and sharing the same glass.)

Chapter 24
What is the relationship between HIV and AIDS?

(HIV is the cause of the disease called AIDS.)

Chapter 25
What are two different types of cancer?

(Sample answer: Lung cancer and breast cancer)

TeacherWorks Plus provides:

- interactive Teacher Wrap-around Edition
- click, drag, and drop to plan lessons
- instant access to many print program resources

How to Get Involved Provide students with these step-by-step instructions about how they can assemble information about volunteer opportunities.

1. Choose an organization, such as the American Red Cross.
2. Call the organization and find out if they are looking for volunteers.
3. Are there any requirements to be a volunteer? Find out if the organization has any guidelines that volunteers must follow.
4. Some ways students can help out are by participating in walkathons, staffing help lines, doing light office work, making phone calls, and distributing flyers.

Chapter 23 pages 626–655	Standards		Features
	National	**State/Local**	TIME HEALTH
	1.12.1, 1.12.3, 1.12.5, 1.12.6, 1.12.8, 2.12.10, 5.12.2, 5.12.6, 6.12.1, 7.12.1		• Vaccine: The Battle Within, page 650
Lesson 1 **Understanding Communicable Diseases** pages 628–632 BIG Idea *Learning about communicable diseases and how they spread can help you prevent them.*	1.12.1, 1.12.5, 5.12.2, 7.12.1, 7.12.2, 7.12.3, 8.12.3		
Lesson 2 **Common Communicable Diseases** pages 633–637 BIG Idea *You can lower your chances of catching a communicable disease by learning about the causes and symptoms of these diseases, and how to avoid them.*	1.12.1, 1.12.5, 3.12.2, 8.12.2, 8.12.4		*Health Skills* Activity • Caring for Your Immune System *(Decision Making)*, page 637 (Y) Out of Time
Lesson 3 **Fighting Communicable Diseases** pages 638–644 BIG Idea *By learning about and practicing prevention strategies, you can help your body stay healthy.*	1.12.5, 1.12.6, 1.12.7, 2.12.10, 3.12.2, 4.12.1, 7.12.1, 7.12.3		
Lesson 4 **Emerging Diseases and Pandemics** pages 645–649 BIG Idea *Today, infectious diseases have the potential to spread quickly throughout the world.*	1.12.1, 3.12.2, 4.12.1, 7.12.1, 7.12.3		

Key to Ability Levels

Teaching Strategies and activities have been coded for ability level and appropriateness.

AL Activities for students working above grade level

OL Activities for students working on grade level

BL Activities for students working below grade level

EL Activities for English Learners

Chapter 23 Planning Guide

TeacherWorks™ Plus
All-In-One Planner and Resource Center

Resources	Lesson Assessment	Technology
Student Activity Workbook TEACH **FAST FILE RESOURCES** Vocabulary Practice TEACH Health Labs EXTEND	Chapter 23 Review Chapter 23 Assessment Standardized Test Practice *ExamView® Assessment Suite* CD-ROM	**Teaching Tools:** *TeacherWorks™* Plus DVD *StudentWorks™* Plus DVD *ExamView® Assessment Suite* CD-ROM Transparency Fitness DVD PowerPoint® DVD Health eSpotlight Video Series DVD
FAST FILE RESOURCES Reading Strategies Activity TEACH Reteaching Activity REVIEW Enrichment Activity EXTEND Health Skills Practice TEACH	Lesson 1 Assessment, page 632 Lesson 1 Quiz *Fast File* *ExamView® Assessment Suite* CD-ROM	
FAST FILE RESOURCES Reading Strategies Activity TEACH Reteaching Activity REVIEW Enrichment Activity EXTEND Health Skills Practice TEACH	Lesson 2 Assessment, page 637 Lesson 2 Quiz *Fast File* *ExamView® Assessment Suite* CD-ROM	**Web-Based Resources:** Go Online glencoe.com • Health Podcast Activities • Audio Chapter Summaries (English/Spanish) • Interactive Health Tutor • Health Skills Activities • Vocabulary PuzzleMaker
FAST FILE RESOURCES Reading Strategies Activity TEACH Reteaching Activity REVIEW Enrichment Activity EXTEND Health Skills Practice TEACH	Lesson 3 Assessment, page 644 Lesson 3 Quiz *Fast File* *ExamView® Assessment Suite* CD-ROM	• Parent Letters (English/Spanish) • Lesson Plans • Health Inventories • Online Quizzes • Study-to-Go
FAST FILE RESOURCES Reading Strategies Activity TEACH Reteaching Activity REVIEW Enrichment Activity EXTEND Health Skills Practice TEACH	Lesson 4 Assessment, page 649 Lesson 4 Quiz *Fast File* *ExamView® Assessment Suite* CD-ROM	• Unit Web Projects • Student Web Activities • Fitness Zone Activities

 StudentWorks Plus

This is the student's backpack solution.

Includes:
- complete Interactive Student Edition
- full audio of English text and Spanish chapter summaries
- allows students to record assignments and track grades.
- links to online activities and additional student resources
- access to all student worksheets and workbooks

FOLDABLES Study Organizer

Dinah Zike Foldables®
Chapter Activity
Refer to the *Dinah Zike Reading and Study Skills for Glencoe Health*. Ask students to make a layered-look book Foldable to record and organize information about communicable diseases. As students read and discuss the chapter, they can label the tabs and record important points under appropriate tabs.

Key to Symbols

 Transparencies   REVIEW activities to review or reinforce content

 CD-ROM   TEACH activities to teach basic concepts

 glencoe.com   EXTEND activities to extend or enrich lesson content

Print Resources

Communicable Diseases

Chapter Overview

Chapter 23 focuses on learning about communicable diseases, including how they spread, how to prevent their spread, and how the body responds to infection. Diseases that are spreading globally are also discussed.

Lesson 1

Learning about the causes of communicable diseases and how they spread can help a person prevent becoming infected with the disease.

Lesson 2

Learning about the causes and symptoms of communicable diseases and about how to avoid them can lower a person's chances of catching a communicable disease.

Lesson 3

Learning about the immune system and practicing prevention strategies can help a person remain healthy.

Lesson 4

In the modern world, dangerous communicable diseases can spread globally with amazing speed.

▶ Activating Prior Knowledge

After students have written their paragraphs, call on volunteers to share their thoughts about the teen with the class and ask other students to respond to the ideas expressed. In class discussion, have students discuss times they have been ill.

Lesson 1

Understanding Communicable Diseases

BIG Idea *Learning about communicable diseases and how they spread can help you prevent them.*

Lesson 2

Common Communicable Diseases

BIG Idea *You can lower your chances of catching a communicable disease by learning about the causes and symptoms of these diseases, and how to avoid them.*

Lesson 3

Fighting Communicable Diseases

BIG Idea *By learning about and practicing prevention strategies, you can help your body stay healthy.*

Lesson 4

Emerging Diseases and Pandemics

BIG Idea *Today, infectious diseases have the potential to spread quickly throughout the world.*

Activating Prior Knowledge

Using Visuals Take a look at the photo on this page. Why do you think this teen is at a doctor's office? Have you ever felt the way she does? What did you do to get better? Explain your thoughts in a short paragraph.

626

 Universal Access

Differentiated Learning Glencoe provides teacher support and student materials for all learners in the health classroom.

- Chapter Summaries in English and Spanish are available online at glencoe.com.
- *Fast Files* and related worksheets support reluctant readers.

- Universal Access strategies throughout the Teacher Wraparound Edition and *Fast Files* help you present materials for gifted students, at-risk students, physically impaired students, and those with behavior disorders or learning disabilities.

Chapter Launchers

Health in Action

Discuss the **BIG** Ideas

Before beginning this chapter, think about how you would answer these questions:

- How often do you get a cold or the flu?
- How do you think you get these illnesses?
- What do you do to recover from them?

Watch the *Health* eSpotlight Video Series

Communicable Diseases
What are some ways to stop the spread of infectious diseases?

Assess Your Health

G⊙ Online

Visit glencoe.com and complete the Health Inventory for Chapter 23.

Chapter Launchers

Health in Action

Discuss the **BIG** Ideas

Ask students to respond to these questions aloud. Explain that the purpose of the questions is to help students assess their current knowledge of the causes and treatments of communicable diseases.

Health eSpotlight
Video Series

 Communicable Diseases

Before Viewing the Video

Ask Students: *What is the most important measure a person can take to avoid becoming ill with a disease that spreads from person to person?* (Answers will vary. Some students might suggest staying away from sick people is the most important measure.)

G⊙ Online

Have students go to **glencoe.com** and take the Health Inventory for Chapter 23.

Chapter Skills

Reading Skills
- Reviewing Facts and Vocabulary, pp. 632, 637, 644, 649
- Reading/Writing Practice, p. 655

BIG Idea

Students will learn about diseases that spread from one organism to another and through the environment.

Health Skills
- Health Skills Activity, p. 637
- Applying Health Skills, pp. 632, 637, 644, 649

Vocabulary
- New Vocabulary, pp. 628, 633, 638, 645
- Reviewing Facts and Vocabulary, pp. 632, 637, 644, 649

Writing Skills
- Writing Critically, pp. 632, 637, 644, 649
- Reading/Writing Practice, p. 655

LESSON 1

Understanding Communicable Diseases

1 FOCUS

GUIDE TO READING

BIG Idea Students will learn what communicable diseases are and how they spread. **Ask Students:** *What is a common disease that spreads from person to person, and what causes that disease?* (Sample answer: The common cold spreads from person to person, and it is caused by a virus.)

Before You Read

T-Chart Students' T-charts will vary, though the information in the two columns should include main differences between how communicable diseases are spread versus caused.

Main Idea

Communicable Diseases
Several different kinds of microorganisms cause communicable diseases. **Ask Students:** *What are three kinds of microorganisms?* (Answers will vary but may include viruses, bacteria, and protozoa.)

Real Life Issues ••••••••••••

After students have written their paragraphs, ask volunteers to share their ideas. Students might suggest that Nolan get vaccinations and do research online to prepare.

LESSON 1

GUIDE TO READING

BIG Idea *Learning about communicable diseases and how they spread can help you prevent them.*

Before You Read

Create a T-Chart. Make a T-chart and label the columns "How communicable diseases are caused" and "How communicable diseases are spread." As you read, fill in the chart with information about both topics.

Causes	Ways Spread

New Vocabulary

▶ communicable disease (p. 628)
▶ infection (p. 628)
▶ virus (p. 629)
▶ bacteria (p. 629)
▶ toxins (p. 629)
▶ vector (p. 630)

Review Vocabulary

▶ pathogens (Ch.15, L.1)

Understanding Communicable Diseases

Real Life Issues ••••••••••••••••••••••••

Taking Precautions. Nolan is very excited about his family's upcoming vacation in Central America because it will be his first time outside the United States. His friends warn him to be careful about drinking unbottled water while in Central America. They say the water might not be safe to drink. Nolan wonders what precautions he can take.

Writing *Write a paragraph explaining how Nolan might prepare for the trip. Suggest places where he could find information about potential health risks and how to avoid them.*

Understanding the Causes of Communicable Diseases

Main Idea Communicable diseases are caused by several kinds of microorganisms.

You've probably "caught" an illness from someone before. The illness you contracted was a **communicable disease**, *a disease that is spread from one living organism to another or through the environment.* Such illnesses are also known as *contagious* and *infectious* diseases.

Communicable diseases can occur when pathogens, microorganisms that cause disease, enter your body. If your body does not fight off the invaders quickly and successfully, you develop an **infection**, *a condition that occurs when pathogens in the body multiply and damage body cells.* **Figure 23.1** lists diseases caused by common pathogens, which include viruses, bacteria, fungi, protozoa, and rickettsias.

C

More About...

Bacteria Bacteria are single-celled organisms. Unlike the nonliving viruses, bacteria are living things. A defining difference between bacteria and most other cells is that bacterial cells lack a nucleus. Each bacterial cell contains the genetic material DNA and is surrounded by a cell wall. A huge community of bacteria live in and on the human body, and most are not harmful. In fact, there are about 10 times the number of bacteria in the human gastrointestinal tract as there are human cells in the whole body—about 100 trillion bacterial cells to 10 trillion human cells. About 1 trillion bacteria live on a normal human's skin. On a square centimeter of skin, there are 100–1,000 bacteria.

Viruses

Two of the most common communicable diseases—the cold and the flu—are caused by viruses. A **virus** is *a piece of genetic material surrounded by a protein coat.* In order to reproduce, viruses invade the cells of living organisms.

Once a virus has penetrated a cell, it begins to multiply. The new viruses burst out of the cell and start taking over other cells. As the virus multiplies and spreads, disease sets in, and the body's immune system jumps into action. Usually, the virus runs its course and is killed by the immune system. Antibiotics do not work against viruses, but can sometimes treat the symptoms of a virus.

Bacteria

Bacteria are *single-celled microorganisms* that live almost everywhere on earth. Most bacteria are harmless. Some are even helpful, like the ones that help you digest food. Unfortunately, some bacteria do cause diseases.

Disease-causing bacteria can produce **toxins**, *substances that kill cells or interfere with their functions.* Unlike diseases caused by viruses, a bacterial disease can often be treated with antibiotics. However, because of the overuse of these drugs, some bacteria have become resistant to antibiotics as they have evolved.

✓ READING CHECK

Describe How does a virus affect the body?

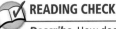 **Online**

Visit **glencoe.com** and complete the Student Web Activity on drug-resistant bacteria.

R

Figure 23.1	**Diseases by Type of Pathogen**

Every common communicable disease can be traced to a particular type of pathogen. *Which of the diseases listed here have you experienced?*

Viruses	Bacteria	Fungi	Protozoa	Rickettsias
• common cold • influenza (flu) • viral pneumonia • viral hepatitis • polio • mononucleosis • measles • AIDS • viral meningitis • chicken pox • herpes • rabies • smallpox • West Nile virus	• bacterial foodborne illness • strep throat • tuberculosis • diphtheria • gonorrhea • Lyme disease • bacterial pinkeye • bacterial pneumonia • bacterial meningitis	• athlete's foot • ringworm • vaginal yeast infection	• malaria • amoebic dysentery • sleeping sickness	• typhus • Rocky Mountain spotted fever

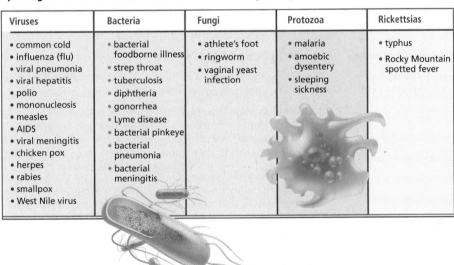

Lesson 1 Understanding Communicable Diseases **629**

---

② TEACH

C Critical Thinking

Pathogens and Infections Call on students to read aloud the definitions of *pathogen* (from Chapter 15) and *infection*. Emphasize that pathogens enter the body all the time. If the body is healthy and its immune system is working well, then the pathogens are destroyed before they can do harm. Ask students what must occur for a pathogen to cause an infection. **OL**

Caption Answer

Figure 23.1 Answers will vary. Most students will have experienced the common cold and influenza.

R Reading Strategy

Analyzing a Chart After students have read about the different kinds of pathogens, direct their attention to **Figure 23.1**. **Ask Students:** *Of these diseases, can you name one that can be treated with an antibiotic and explain why?* (Sample answer: Strep throat, because it is a disease caused by bacteria) *Can you name a disease caused by a microorganism that is more complex than bacteria are?* (Sample answer: Malaria; it is caused by a protozoan) **BL**

✓ READING CHECK

Answer A virus invades the body, penetrates cells, multiplies, bursts out of cells, spreads through the body, and causes disease.

How Diseases Spread Diseases can be transmitted in a variety of ways. **Ask Students:** *What are three ways that diseases can be spread from person to person?* (Answers will vary but may include descriptions of an infected person touching another person or sneezing and coughing to spread a disease.)

W Writing Support

Making a Chart Have students make a table to record information about how communicable diseases are transmitted. On the board, write the title *Methods of Transmission.* Make the beginnings of a three-column table below the title with these column headings: *Method, Description,* and *Examples.* Ask students to use this form to organize the information about ways diseases spread. **OL**

AL Active Learning

Modeling Transmission Without letting most students know, cover the right hand of three or four students with talcum powder. Ask those students to circulate throughout the classroom, shaking hands, touching friends' arms, picking up objects, and grabbing doorknobs. After about 10 minutes, lead a class discussion about how the talcum powder was transmitted, similar to the way pathogens are transmitted by direct contact and indirect contact. **OL EL**

Other Pathogens

Other types of organisms that can cause communicable diseases include the following:

- **Fungi** are plantlike organisms that can cause diseases of the lungs, the mucous membranes, and the skin. Athlete's foot is a common fungal disease.

- **Protozoa** are single-celled microorganisms that are larger and more complex than bacteria. Malaria is an example of a disease caused by protozoa.

- **Rickettsias**, which resemble bacteria, often enter the body through insect bites. Typhus is caused by rickettsias.

How Diseases Spread

Diseases can be transmitted in a variety of ways.

Pathogens infect humans and other living things in a variety of ways. Knowing how diseases are transmitted is your first line of defense against them.

Direct Contact

Many pathogens are transmitted through direct contact with an infected person. This includes touching, biting, kissing, and sexual contact. Other transmission methods include

- **puncture wounds.** A person can get tetanus from stepping on a rusty nail.

- **childbirth.** A pregnant woman may transmit an infection to her unborn child through the placenta.

- **contact with infected animals.** Animal bites and scratches can sometimes transmit disease.

Academic Vocabulary

contact *(noun):* union or touching of surfaces

Indirect Contact

You don't have to be in direct **contact** with a person to become infected. Indirect contact can be just as dangerous.

Contaminated Objects If you touch a contaminated object (for example, a doorknob), you could pick up pathogens. The pathogens can enter your body if you then rub your eyes. To protect yourself, keep your hands away from your mouth, nose, and eyes, and wash your hands regularly.

Vectors Pathogens are often spread by a **vector**, *an organism that carries and transmits pathogens to humans or other animals.* Common vectors include flies, mosquitoes, and ticks. Diseases that spread this way, such as malaria, West Nile virus, and Lyme disease, are called *vector-borne* diseases.

Promoting School Wellness

Preventing the Spread of Diseases A coordinated school health program includes health services that provide optimum sanitary conditions for the school facility and environment. Steps are taken by school staff members to clean surfaces and prevent the spread of disease in all parts of a school. Special attention may be directed to rest-rooms, locker rooms, kitchens and cafeterias, and drinking fountains. Ask a supervisor in charge of maintaining a healthy facility to make a brief presentation to the class, with an emphasis on products and procedures used to prevent the spread of diseases in the school. Make sure students are prepared to ask relevant questions.

Contaminated Food and Water When food is improperly handled or stored, harmful bacteria can develop. This is true not only for meat and fish but for fruits and vegetables as well. Water supplies that become contaminated with human or animal feces can also cause illnesses such as hepatitis A.

Airborne Transmission

When an infected person sneezes or coughs, pathogens are released into the air as tiny droplets that can travel as far as 10 feet. Even when the droplets evaporate, the pathogens may float on dust particles until they are inhaled. Other pathogens such as fungal spores are also small enough to spread this way. Diseases spread by airborne transmission include chicken pox, tuberculosis, influenza, and inhalation anthrax.

Taking Precautions

Main Idea You can take steps to prevent infection.

There is no guaranteed way to avoid communicable diseases completely, but a few simple practices can dramatically reduce your risk. As you learn about these practices, think about how you can include them in your daily life.

Wash Your Hands

HS

Washing your hands regularly with soap and warm water is the single most effective way to protect yourself from catching or spreading disease. Always wash your hands

- before you eat.
- after you use the bathroom.
- after handling pets.
- before and after inserting contact lenses or applying makeup.
- after touching an object handled by an infected person.

Identify List three ways communicable diseases can be spread.

■ **Figure 23.2** Japan is known for being a very polite society. People who have colds or the flu often wear masks when they go outdoors. *Why do you think people in some cultures wear masks when they are ill?*

631

READING CHECK

Answer Sample answer: Direct contact, indirect contact, and airborne transmission

HS Health Skills Practice

Practicing Healthful Behaviors
Ask interested students to experiment to find the most effective hand washing method. To simulate hard-to-remove bacteria, students can "contaminate" their hands with a tablespoon of cooking oil and a teaspoon of cinnamon, rubbed all over. Then, over a sink, students can wash their hands with various combinations of these variables: warm or cold water, soap or no soap, and rubbing for 10 seconds or 20 seconds. Ask students to report their results to the class. (Most students will discover that using soap and warm water and rubbing for 20 seconds is most effective in removing the "contamination.") **AL**

Caption Answer

Figure 23.2 To avoid spreading communicable diseases to other people

Teacher to Teacher

Tom Williams • Fayetteville High School, Fayetteville, AR

How Did I Catch That? Purchase some germ powder or ultraviolet black light powder and put some on your hands. When students are entering into the class shake some students' hands, or pat them on the back. Try to do this in a natural manner not to alert the students. Then start teaching the communicable disease section on how it is transmitted. Use the black light to expose those particular students you touched and relate how direct and nondirect contact spreads disease unknowingly.

 READING CHECK

Answer Your body works best when you get all the nutrients your body needs and stay fit. This will help you fight an infection.

③ ASSESS/ CLOSE

Assessment Resources

📁 **FAST FILE ACTIVITIES**
Lesson 1 Quiz

💿 *ExamView*
Assessment Suite CD-ROM

Visit glencoe.com for:
Online Quizzes
Online Learning Center

Progress Monitoring

Reteaching
Have students make sketches in their notebooks to represent each way a communicable disease can be transmitted.

Enrichment
Ask students to investigate the fungal disease known as athlete's foot. Have them find out the cause, symptoms, and treatment of the disease. Ask students to explain why the pathogen often spreads in the damp, dark conditions common to locker rooms.

 Online

Have students visit **glencoe.com** and complete the Interactive Study Guide for this lesson.

Protect Yourself from Vectors

Some vector-borne diseases, such as West Nile virus and bird flu, are on the rise. To protect yourself, follow these steps:

- Limit the time you spend outdoors at dawn and dusk, when mosquitoes are most active.
- Wear pants and long-sleeved shirts to avoid insect bites.
- Use insect repellent, and avoid contact with dead birds.

Other Prevention Strategies

 READING CHECK

Explain How do a healthful diet and regular physical activity help you avoid communicable diseases?

These additional strategies will also help reduce your risk of getting or spreading communicable diseases:

- Avoid sharing personal items, such as eating utensils.
- Handle food properly. (See Chapter 10, Lesson 4.)
- Eat well and exercise. Getting the nutrients your body needs and staying fit will help you fight against infection.
- Avoid tobacco, alcohol, and other drugs.
- Abstain from sexual contact.
- Cover your mouth when you cough or sneeze, and wash your hands after using a tissue.

LESSON 1 ASSESSMENT

After You Read

Reviewing Facts and Vocabulary

1. Define the word *communicable*.
2. List three ways that communicable diseases are spread through indirect contact.
3. How is a virus different from bacteria?

Thinking Critically

4. **Analyze.** The fungus that causes athlete's foot lives in warm, moist places. What can you do to reduce your risk of infection when you are in gym locker rooms or other public places?
5. **Synthesize.** If you had a cold, what actions would you take to prevent spreading the illness to other people?

Applying Health Skills

6. **Practicing Healthful Behaviors.** Create an e-mail announcement that your school could send to parents at the beginning of the school year. In your e-mail, give strategies for avoiding communicable diseases such as the flu or the common cold.

Writing Critically

7. **Narrative.** Write a short story from the point of view of bacteria or a virus. Describe how the bacteria or virus finds its way into someone's body, and what happens when it gets there.

Go Online

Visit **glencoe.com** and complete the Interactive Study Guide for this lesson.

632   **Chapter 23**   Communicable Diseases

LESSON 1 ASSESSMENT ANSWERS

1. Something that can be spread from person to person or through the environment
2. Through contaminated objects, vectors, and contaminated food and water
3. A *virus* is a piece of genetic material surrounded by a protein coat, while *bacteria* are single-celled microorganisms that live almost everywhere on Earth.
4. Sample answer: You could keep shoes on in the locker room and wear flip-flops in the shower.
5. Sample answer: Cover your mouth and nose when coughing and sneezing.
6. E-mails will vary. Information in the announcements should reflect an understanding of what causes communicable diseases and how they are spread.
7. Stories will vary, but should relate how bacteria and viruses enter the body and cause disease.

Common Communicable Diseases

Real Life Issues

Passing It On. It's the day before the big exam, and Morgan plans to meet up with her friends at the library to study. Unfortunately, she's been sneezing and has a sore throat. Morgan is concerned about giving her cold to her friends, but she needs this study session to get ready for the exam.

Writing *Write a paragraph explaining how you think Morgan can prevent passing on her illness to her friends.*

Respiratory Infections

Main Idea Many diseases begin as respiratory infections.

Many communicable diseases occur in the **respiratory tract**, *the passageway that makes breathing possible.* This passageway includes the nose, throat, and lungs. The respiratory tract connects the outside world to the inside of your body, so it's no wonder that this system is at risk for infection. However, a few habits can help you avoid getting sick:

- Avoid close contact with sick people. If you're ill, stay home.
- Wash your hands often.
- Avoid touching your mouth, eyes, and nose.
- Eat right and get physical activity to strengthen your immune system.
- Abstain from smoking.

Colds, influenza, pneumonia, strep throat, and tuberculosis are the most common respiratory infections.

BIG Idea *You can lower your chances of catching a communicable disease by learning about the causes and symptoms of these diseases, and how to avoid them.*

Before You Read

Create a K-W-L Chart. Make a three-column chart. In the left column, write what you **k**now about common communicable diseases. In the middle column, write what you **w**ant to know about these diseases. As you read, use the third column to summarize what you **l**earned.

K	W	L

New Vocabulary

▶ respiratory tract (p. 633)
▶ mucous membrane (p. 634)
▶ pneumonia (p. 634)
▶ jaundice (p. 635)
▶ cirrhosis (p. 635)

Common Communicable Diseases

1 FOCUS

 **GUIDE TO READING**

BIG Idea Students will learn about the causes, symptoms, and prevention of common communicable diseases. **Ask Students:** *What are three communicable diseases common among friends and family?* (Answers will vary but may include the common cold, influenza, and strep throat.)

Before You Read

K-W-L Chart Students' charts will vary. The information in the third column should reflect a knowledge of the diseases from the lesson.

Main Idea

Respiratory Infections Many common communicable diseases begin in the respiratory tract. **Ask Students:** *What are three parts of the respiratory tract?* (nose, throat, and lungs)

Reading Strategy

Organizing Information Have students make a concept map to organize and record the most important information in Lesson 2. To help them begin, make a circle on the board and write inside the circle *Common Communicable Diseases.* Draw lines diagonally and below the first circle to three circles. In those circles, write the headings of the lesson's three subsections, *Respiratory Infections, Hepatitis,* and *Other Communicable Diseases.* Ask students to copy this beginning concept map into their notebooks and then expand the concept map by adding vocabulary terms, names of diseases, and important information about the diseases.

Real Life Issues

Ask students to share how they think Morgan could prevent passing on her illness. (Methods might include staying home and studying alone; sharing information with friends by phone, e-mail, or instant messaging; and trading notes with friends and studying independently.)

2 TEACH

AL Active Learning

The Best Treatment Have students work in small groups to create a puppet show that could be used to teach younger students how to treat the common cold, influenza, and pneumonia. Allow 20 minutes of planning time for groups to write their puppet show. Provide markers, paper bags, and other materials for puppet making. Have groups perform their puppet shows for the class and, if possible, for classes of younger students. **OL**

FITNESSZONE

Have students perform this mirroring activity:

- Students should get into pairs with each student holding one paper plate.

- Teacher holds a paper plate and does large body movements.

- Students mirror teacher's movement.

- Students can also work in pairs with one person acting as the leader.

U Universal Access

Silent P Write the word *pneumonia* on the board. Explain that this term derives from a Greek word meaning "lung," and point out that the initial letter in this term is silent—not pronounced. Pronounce the term correctly, and ask students to say the word aloud. **EL BL**

634

FITNESSZONE

I'm always on the go . . . even when I'm sick. I had a bad cold two weeks ago, but I didn't let that stop me from working out. Unfortunately, it made me feel worse. My doctor says that when you're sick, exercise puts extra stress on the body and the immune system. This may drag out illnesses. Next time I get sick, I'm going to rest until I feel better. For more fitness tips, visit the Online Fitness Zone at **glencoe.com**.

READING CHECK

Identify Name at least three respiratory infections.

Common Cold

The common cold is a viral infection that causes inflammation of the **mucous membrane**, *the lining of various body cavities, including the nose, ears, and mouth*. Sneezing, a sore throat, and a runny nose are the most common symptoms. Cold germs spread through direct contact with an infected person, indirect contact with contaminated objects, or airborne transmission.

Because a cold is caused by a virus, there is no cure. Your body has to fight off the infection. The best treatment is to get plenty of rest and drink liquids.

AL

Influenza

Influenza, or the flu, is a viral infection of the respiratory tract. Symptoms include high fever, fatigue, headache, muscle aches, and coughing. Like the common cold, the flu can spread through the air or through direct or indirect contact.

Because the flu is a viral infection, antibiotics can't cure it. Antiviral drugs may be effective in treating flu symptoms if taken early enough. Usually, though, most people treat the flu with proper nutrition, plenty of rest, and lots of liquids. Many people choose to get a flu vaccination once a year. This shot protects you from one type of flu virus that may be common that year. Getting a yearly flu vaccine is especially important for older adults and people with chronic health problems.

Pneumonia

In severe cases, the flu can lead to **pneumonia**, *an infection of the lungs in which the air sacs fill with pus and other liquids*. Its symptoms are similar to those of the flu, which means that sometimes people can have pneumonia without realizing it. People who are vulnerable to pneumonia include older adults and those who already have the flu.

Pneumonia can be caused by a virus or by bacteria. Viral pneumonia is sometimes treated with antiviral drugs. Bacterial pneumonia, if diagnosed early enough, can be treated with antibiotics. Pneumonia can be fatal, especially when it strikes older adults and people with lung or heart problems.

U

Strep Throat

Strep throat is a bacterial infection spread by direct contact with an infected person or through airborne transmission. Symptoms include sore throat, fever, and enlarged lymph nodes in the neck. Left untreated, strep throat can lead to serious conditions, including heart damage. Strep throat can be treated with antibiotics.

Health Literacy

Teens and Aspirin Aspirin, or acetylsalicylic acid, has long been a popular pain reliever. Teens, though, should not take aspirin or any related products (salicylates) when they have chicken pox, influenza, or any illness that has symptoms that might be influenza. In such cases, the teen is at risk for getting Reye syndrome, whose symptoms include disorientation, severe headache, coma, and even death. Because of this connection, cold and flu medicines that contain a combination of drugs usually do not contain aspirin as the medicine's pain reliever. Ask interested students to conduct a study of such medicines sold in a local pharmacy to make a list of medicines teens should avoid because they contain a salicylate.

■ **Figure 23.3** There are many methods of spreading communicable diseases. *What can you do every day to reduce your risk of infection?*

Tuberculosis

Tuberculosis, or TB, is a bacterial disease that usually attacks the lungs. It spreads through the air and typically affects people with weak immune systems. Symptoms include fatigue, coughing, fever, weight loss, and night sweats.

TB is treated with antibiotics. Because some strains have become resistant, doctors sometimes have to prescribe several antibiotics at one time to see which kind will work for an individual. TB infections have dropped significantly in the United States during the last 60 years due to the development of antibiotics. Most people who are infected with TB bacteria never actually develop the disease because their immune systems prevent the bacteria from multiplying and spreading. However, the disease continues to be a serious health problem worldwide, especially among people with other viral infections such as HIV.

Hepatitis

Main Idea There are three common types of hepatitis.

Hepatitis is a viral infection that causes inflammation of the liver. There are at least five different kinds of hepatitis, but the most common are types A, B, and C. Symptoms include **jaundice**, *a yellowing of the skin and eyes*. Some people also develop **cirrhosis**, or *scarring of the liver*. Vaccines are available for hepatitis A and B, but because the disease comes from a virus, there is no cure.

- **Hepatitis A** usually attacks the digestive system through contact with the feces of an infected person. Common symptoms include fever, vomiting, fatigue, abdominal pain, and jaundice. The best ways to avoid hepatitis are to stay away from people already infected and to wash your hands thoroughly after using any public restroom.

G⊘ Online

Explore **glencoe.com** and complete the Student Web Activity on germ transmission and prevention strategies.

Lesson 2   Common Communicable Diseases   **635**

Main Idea

Hepatitis There are three common types of hepatitis. **Ask Students:** *If a disease is spread through contact with human feces, what is probably the best way to prevent the spread of that disease to others?* (Sample answer: The person who has the disease should always wash his or her hands thoroughly when leaving a restroom.)

HS **Health Skills Practice**

Accessing Information Today, someone who becomes ill often turns to the Internet to find information that can identify the illness and recommend treatment. Not all Web sites provide reliable information, however. Divide the class into small groups, and ask each group to find a Web site that provides accurate and trustworthy information about tuberculosis. Ask each group to find information on the Web site about this communicable disease and write a paragraph about any recent occurrences. Groups should cite the source of the information by writing the title of the Web site and the Web address. **AL**

G⊘ Online

Have students visit **glencoe.com** and complete the Student Web Activity on germ transmission and prevention strategies.

ELL Support

Name and Repeat Write the following words on the board: *influenza, pneumonia, jaundice, cirrhosis.* Define each word aloud.

Beginning Use sentences such as "Olivia missed school because of a severe case of influenza." Ask students to repeat the sentence. Use the other three words in sentences, and ask students to repeat them.

Intermediate Ask students for sentence examples for each word.

Advanced Ask students to research the derivation of the names of these diseases.

Health Skills Activity

Decision Making: Caring for Your Immune System

NHES Standard 5 Students will demonstrate the ability to use decision-making skills to enhance health.

Objectives

- Apply decision-making skills to make a health-promoting decision.
- Analyze the role of individual responsibility for enhancing health.

Teaching Strategies

- Discuss with students the responsibility a person with a communicable disease has to others and to the wider community.
- After students have written their paragraphs, have them work in small groups to analyze the consequences of various options and reach a consensus decision about what Zoë should do. Ask groups to share their results with the class.

Assessment

Using this list, student work should provide comprehensive evidence of the following criteria to achieve the highest score:

√ Clearly states the situation
√ Evaluates options
√ Considers values
√ Reflects clear decision

READING CHECK

Identify Which of the body's organs is affected by hepatitis?

- **Hepatitis B** has symptoms similar to those of hepatitis A, but it can cause liver failure and cirrhosis. This virus can be spread through sexual contact or contact with an infected person's blood. You can avoid getting hepatitis B by not sharing personal care items such as razors and toothbrushes, by abstaining from sexual activity and use of illegal drugs, and by not getting tattoos and body piercings.
- **Hepatitis C** is the most common blood-borne infection in the United States. Symptoms include jaundice, dark urine, fatigue, abdominal pain, and loss of appetite. Hepatitis C can lead to chronic liver disease, liver cancer, and liver failure. The disease is most often spread by direct contact with needles that are contaminated with infected blood. You can lower your chances of infection by not sharing personal care items and abstaining from illegal drug use and sexual activity.

Other Communicable Diseases

Main Idea Stay informed about communicable diseases.

Respiratory infections and hepatitis are the most common communicable diseases, but there are many more. The more you know about these diseases and how they are transmitted, the better your chances of not getting them. **Figure 23.4** provides information about additional communicable diseases.

Figure 23.4 Common Communicable Diseases

	Mononucleosis	Measles	Encephalitis	Meningitis	Chicken pox
Type/ Transmission	Virus; spread by direct contact, including sharing eating utensils and kissing	Virus; spread by coughs, sneezes, or a person talking	Virus; carried by mosquitoes	Virus or bacteria; spread by direct or indirect contact	Virus; spread through air or contact with fluid from blisters
Symptoms	Chills, fever, sore throat, fatigue, swollen lymph nodes	High fever, red eyes, runny nose, cough, bumpy red rash	Headache; fever; hallucinations; confusion; paralysis; disturbances of speech, memory, behavior, and eye movement	Fever, severe headache, nausea, vomiting, sensitivity to light, stiff neck	Rash, itching, fever, fatigue
Treatment/ Prevention	Rest if tired	No definite treatment; vaccine for prevention	If caused by herpes simplex virus, antiviral medicine; if caused by another virus, no known treatment	Viral meningitis: antiviral medicine if severe; bacterial meningitis: antibiotics; vaccine available	Rest, stay home so others aren't infected; vaccine available

Teens Want to Know

Do Body Piercings Really Put Me at Risk for Hepatitis? Getting body piercings does put a person at risk for getting hepatitis as well as other blood-borne diseases, which are communicable diseases spread by contact with blood. If the equipment used to do the piercing is contaminated with blood, then the person getting the piercing is at risk for getting hepatitis B, hepatitis C, tetanus, tuberculosis, and HIV, the virus that causes AIDS. Another risk associated with body piercing is the sharing of jewelry among friends. Researchers have documented at least one case of hepatitis C transmitted when friends shared a belly-button ring.

Health Skills Activity

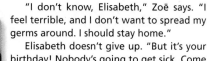

Decision Making

Caring for Your Immune System

It's Friday night, and Zoë is at home trying to rest. She's had the flu all week, and she still feels feverish and fatigued. Her phone rings. She blows her nose and answers it.

"Hey, Zoë! It's Elisabeth. Your birthday's tomorrow—are we all still going to the Ice Cream Company for one of those 12-person sundaes? That was so fun last year!"

"I don't know, Elisabeth," Zoë says. "I feel terrible, and I don't want to spread my germs around. I should stay home."

Elisabeth doesn't give up. "But it's your birthday! Nobody's going to get sick. Come on, we're counting on you!"

"I'll think about it," Zoë replies. "Let me call you back later."

 Writing Write a paragraph in which Zoë explains her decision to Elisabeth. Use the six steps of decision making as a guideline:

1. State the situation.
2. List the available options.
3. Weigh the possible outcomes of each option.
4. Consider your values.
5. Make a decision, and act on it.
6. Evaluate the decision.

LESSON 2 ASSESSMENT

After You Read

Reviewing Facts and Vocabulary

1. How is a common cold different from the flu?

2. What are three ways to prevent a respiratory tract infection?

3. Can hepatitis be treated successfully with antibiotics? Explain.

Thinking Critically

4. **Explain.** Why do you think the respiratory tract is where most infections from communicable diseases occur?

5. **Cause and Effect.** How does hepatitis spread from one illegal drug user to another?

Applying Health Skills

6. **Accessing Information.** Research the Web site for your state's Health Department. Write a brief summary of the information you find about communicable diseases in your state.

Writing Critically

7. **Persuasive.** Create a handout for elementary school students about the importance of washing your hands regularly. The handout should convince young people that hand washing is one of the best ways to avoid catching communicable diseases.

Go Online

Visit glencoe.com and complete the Interactive Study Guide for this lesson.

Lesson 2 Common Communicable Diseases **637**

---

③ ASSESS/CLOSE

Assessment Resources

📁 *FAST FILE* **ACTIVITIES**
Lesson 2 Quiz

💿 *ExamView*
Assessment Suite CD-ROM

Visit glencoe.com **for:**
Online Quizzes
Online Learning Center

Progress Monitoring

Reteaching

Write the name of each common communicable disease discussed in Lesson 2 on a piece of paper, and place the pieces in a hat. Have a student draw a piece of paper out of the hat and describe the cause of the disease on the paper. Call on other students to provide the symptoms, prevention, and treatment of the disease.

Enrichment

Have students choose one of the common communicable diseases discussed in Lesson 2 and find out more about it, using library and online resources. Ask students to prepare a report of what they find.

Have students visit **glencoe.com** and complete the Interactive Study Guide for this lesson.

LESSON 2 ASSESSMENT ANSWERS

1. The symptoms of the flu, which include high fever and fatigue, are more serious than the symptoms of the common cold.
2. Sample answer: Avoid close contact with sick people. Wash your hands often. Avoid touching your mouth, eyes, and nose.
3. Hepatitis cannot be treated with antibiotics because it is caused by a virus.
4. Sample answer: The respiratory tract exposes the inside of the body to bacteria and viruses outside.
5. It spreads when one drug user shares a needle with another drug user.
6. Students' responses should include the name of the state health agency, the Web site address, and information about communicable diseases in the state.
7. Handouts will vary but should include how handwashing prevents the spread of disease.

Fighting Communicable Diseases

① FOCUS

GUIDE TO READING

BIG Idea Students will learn about prevention strategies to help stay healthy. **Ask Students:** *What defenses does the body have against attacking pathogens?* (Answers will vary but may include mention of the skin and the immune system.)

Before You Read

Vocabulary Cards
Students' first definition on the note cards will vary. The second definition on each card should closely match the definition given for the term in Lesson 3.

Main Idea

Physical and Chemical Barriers The body's first line of defense against pathogens includes physical and chemical barriers. **Ask Students:** *What is in your mouth that prevents pathogens from easily gaining access to your insides?* (Sample answer: Saliva contains chemicals that destroy pathogens.)

Real Life Issues ············

Discuss the changes students think Ashley could take to avoid catching colds. (Ideas might include: cut back on volunteering, eat a good lunch, and get more sleep.)

638

LESSON **3**

GUIDE TO READING

BIG Idea *By learning about and practicing prevention strategies, you can help your body stay healthy.*

Before You Read

Create Vocabulary Cards. Write each new vocabulary term on a separate note card. For each term, write a definition based on your current knowledge. As you read, fill in additional information related to each term.

Immune System

New Vocabulary

▸ immune system (p. 639)
▸ inflammatory response (p. 639)
▸ phagocytes (p. 640)
▸ antigens (p. 640)
▸ immunity (p. 640)
▸ lymphocyte (p. 640)
▸ antibody (p. 641)
▸ vaccine (p. 641)

Fighting Communicable Diseases

Real Life Issues ························

Too Busy to Stay Healthy. Sang's friend Ashley always seems to have a cold. Ashley complains that she's tired all the time because her schedule is so busy. In addition to school, Ashley has a part-time job and also volunteers at a local animal shelter. Sang has also noticed that Ashley frequently skips lunch.

Writing *Write a dialogue between Sang and Ashley in which they discuss how Ashley's behavior may be contributing to her colds. The girls should come up with ideas for Ashley that will help her avoid catching colds so often.*

Physical and Chemical Barriers

Main Idea Physical and chemical barriers make up your body's first line of defense against pathogens.

You wear a coat or sweater to stay warm, a hat to keep the sun off your head and face, and a helmet during many sports activities. Your coat, sweater, hat, and helmet are all barriers that protect your body, but have you ever stopped to think about how your body deals with invasion from microscopic pathogens? Your body has its own built-in barriers to handle these tiny invaders.

There are two kinds of barriers that help protect you: physical and chemical. Physical barriers, such as the skin, block pathogens from invading your body. Chemical barriers, such as the enzymes in tears, destroy those invaders. See **Figure 23.5** for more examples of physical and chemical barriers that defend you against pathogens.

More About...

Barriers to Pathogens Here are a few facts about the physical and chemical barriers that prevent pathogens from infecting the body.

- Skin secretions are acidic (less than 7.0 pH), which prevents growth of bacteria.
- Hair follicle secretions contain lactic acid and fatty acids, which inhibit growth of some bacteria and fungi. This is why

fungal growths, such as athlete's foot, occur in areas not covered by hair.

- An enzyme in saliva, tears, and perspiration called lysozyme damages the cell walls of some bacteria, causing the bacterial cells to disintegrate.
- Both skin and mucous membranes constantly shed cells, removing the microorganisms attached to the cells.

Figure 23.5 Physical and Chemical Barriers

Your body uses physical and chemical barriers to fight pathogens. *Which barriers are physical? Which are chemical?*

Tears and saliva contain enzymes that disable and even destroy pathogens.

Mucous membranes form a protective lining for your mouth, nose, and many other parts of your body. These membranes produce mucus, a sticky substance that traps pathogens before they can cause infection, then carries the trapped pathogens to other parts of the body for disposal.

Skin is like a personal coat of armor, stopping most pathogens in their tracks as they try to enter the body.

Cilia are small hairs that line parts of your respiratory system. Cilia sweep mucus and pathogens to the throat, where they can be swallowed or coughed out.

Gastric juice in the stomach destroys many pathogens that enter your body through the nose or mouth.

The Immune System

Main Idea Your body's immune system is your best ally in the fight against communicable diseases.

Although your body's physical and chemical barriers stop many pathogens before they can cause infection or disease, pathogens can—and do—sneak past these defenses. That's when your **immune system**, *a network of cells, tissues, organs, and chemicals that fights off pathogens,* goes to work. The immune system fights pathogens using two major strategies: the inflammatory response and specific defenses.

The Inflammatory Response

Have you ever gotten a splinter or a cut? If so, you probably remember that the affected area became red and swollen. These are symptoms of the **inflammatory response**, *a reaction to tissue damage caused by injury or infection.* This response prevents further injury to the tissue and stops the invading pathogens. Your immune system knows a foreign object such as a wood splinter might have pathogens on it. It also knows that a cut could allow pathogens to get into your body. That's why it triggers the inflammatory response.

Lesson 3 Fighting Communicable Diseases **639**

② TEACH

R Reading Strategy

Connecting to the Real World
After students have examined the physical and chemical barriers in **Figure 23.5**, use the example below to show how the body stops pathogens from entering. Describe someone using a pencil that an infected person just used. The skin, a physical barrier, stopped the spread of pathogens by indirect contact. Similarly, mucous membranes in the nose stop pathogens in the air, and saliva stops pathogens in food. Ask students to identify which barrier was responsible. **BL**

Caption Answer

Figure 23.5 Skin, mucous membranes, and cilia are physical barriers. Tears, saliva, and gastric juice are chemical barriers.

Main Idea

Immune System The body's immune system is the best ally in the fight against communicable diseases. **Ask Students:** *When pathogens get past the body's physical and chemical barriers, how does the body fight against infection and the development of a disease?* (Specialized cells attack and destroy the invading pathogens.)

Writing Strategy

Glossary of Terms The terminology in this lesson is complex and perhaps new to most students. To help them understand the function of the immune system, have students work in groups to write entries for a glossary of terms associated with the immune system. Each group could be assigned one of the lesson's subsections, and students in a group could work together to write a glossary-type entry for every specialized term in that subsection. The entry for each term might include both a pronunciation guide and a definition. Have groups put together all the terms in a glossary of terms that students can use for review.

W Writing Support

Narrative Writing After students have read about the inflammatory response, ask them to write a story with a phagocyte as the main character. Tell students that this story should be an imaginative description of a phagocyte joining the inflammatory response to stop invading pathogens after some kind of injury to the body. Students' stories may be comic or tragic, but all should accurately describe this strategy against disease. **OL** **AL**

U Universal Access

Analogy To reinforce students' understanding of the difference between the inflammatory response and specific defenses, use the analogy of a gardener keeping a garden clean. At first, the gardener removes every plant that is unwanted in the garden, such as grasses and various weeds. This is a general response to weeds, similar to the inflammatory response. After that work is done, some weeds may persist. The gardener might then try more specific measures, such as using chemicals to eliminate the specific kinds of weeds. **BL**

Academic Vocabulary

Enable Call on a volunteer to use the word enable as a verb in a sentence. Ask other students whether it was used correctly as a verb. If not, ask for another volunteer to give a sentence.

The inflammatory response, which works against all types of pathogens, includes the following actions.

1. In response to tissue damage and invading microorganisms, blood vessels near the injury expand. This allows more blood to flow to the area and begin fighting the invading pathogens.
2. Fluid and cells from the bloodstream cause swelling and pain because of pressure on the nerve endings.
3. **Phagocytes,** *white blood cells that attack invading pathogens,* surround the pathogens and destroy them with special chemicals. Pus, a mass of dead white blood cells and damaged tissue, may build up at the site of inflammation as a response to bacteria.
4. With the pathogens killed and tissue damage under control, the body begins to repair the tissue.

Go Online

Visit glencoe.com and complete the Interactive Study Guide for this lesson.

Academic Vocabulary

enable *(verb):* to make possible

Specific Defenses

Although the inflammatory response kills many pathogens, some may survive. So, in addition to the inflammatory response, the immune system triggers specific defenses in reaction to certain pathogens. This process is called the *immune response.* When the immune system recognizes a particular pathogen, it activates specific defenses in an attempt to prevent this type of infection from occurring again.

Figure 23.6 describes the immune response. During this process, your immune system reacts quickly to **antigens,** *substances that can trigger an immune response.* Antigens are found in toxins and on the surfaces of pathogens. Macrophages, a type of phagocyte, make antigens recognizable to white blood cells. This **enables** the white blood cells to destroy the pathogens. The result of this type of immune response is known as **immunity,** *the state of being protected against a particular disease.*

Lymphocytes

The **lymphocyte,** *a specialized white blood cell that coordinates and performs many functions of specific immunity,* plays an important role in the immune response. There are two types of lymphocytes: T cells and B cells.

T Cells This type of lymphocyte has a variety of functions:
- **Helper T cells** trigger the production of B cells and killer T cells.
- **Killer T cells** attack and destroy infected body cells. These cells don't attack the pathogens, only the infected cells.
- **Suppressor T cells** coordinate the actions of other T cells. They suppress, or "turn off," helper T cells when the infection has been cleared.

640 Chapter 23 Communicable Diseases

Health Literacy

Boosting Immunity with Gentle Exercise Tai chi, which was developed in China long ago, is a form of gentle physical exercise involving slow, graceful movements. This form of exercise is common in China and has been growing in popularity in the United States. In a recent study, researchers tested older adults to see if practicing tai chi could help in preventing these adults from getting shingles, a painful condition caused by a virus. The results showed doing tai chi greatly boosted the adults' immunity to the illness. The reason for the results was not clear. Perhaps immunity was boosted because doing tai chi reduces stress and increases the flow of blood and oxygen to the brain.

Figure 23.6 The Immune Response

1. Pathogens invade the body.
2. Macrophages engulf the pathogen.
3. Macrophages digest the pathogen, and T cells recognize antigens of the pathogen as invaders.
4. T cells bind to the antigens.
5. B cells bind to antigens and helper T cells.
6. B cells divide to produce plasma cells.
7. Plasma cells release antibodies into the bloodstream.
8. Antibodies bind to antigens to help other cells identify and destroy the pathogens.

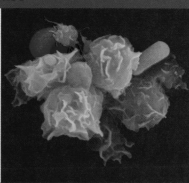

R

B Cells These lymphocytes have just one job: producing antibodies. An **antibody** is *a protein that acts against a specific antigen*. Each B cell is programmed to make one type of antibody that is specific to a certain pathogen. The different purposes of antibodies include

- attaching to antigens to mark them for destruction.
- destroying invading pathogens.
- blocking viruses from entering body cells.

AL

Immune System Memory

Your immune system also "remembers" the antigens it has dealt with in the past. When antigens activate certain T cells and B cells, the cells become *memory lymphocytes*. These special memory cells circulate in your bloodstream and through the lymphatic system, shown in **Figure 23.7** on page 642. When memory cells recognize a former invader, the immune system sends antibodies and killer T cells to stop the invasion. For example, if you've had measles or been vaccinated against it, your immune system remembers and will attack the antigens for the measles virus.

Your immune system's memory not only identifies invading pathogens. It also helps you develop immunity from certain diseases. There are two types of immunity: active and passive.

C

Active Immunity This type of immunity develops from natural or artificial processes. Your body develops naturally acquired active immunity when it is exposed to antigens from invading pathogens. Artificially acquired active immunity is developed from a **vaccine**, *a preparation of dead or weakened pathogens that are introduced into the body to stimulate an immune response*.

READING CHECK

Identify Name three ways that your immune system helps protect you against pathogens.

Lesson 3 Fighting Communicable Diseases **641**

R Reading Strategy

Analyzing a Graphic To reinforce students' understanding of the immune response, illustrated in **Figure 23.6**, ask a student to read aloud the first stage. Then ask a volunteer to define the term *pathogen*. Ask another student to read aloud the second stage, and ask a volunteer to explain what a macrophage is. Continue this process through the eight stages of the immune response, making sure students understand the terminology used at each stage. **AL**

AL Active Learning

Skit Divide the class into groups, and ask each group to create a skit in which students can act out what the B cells do. Each group should have enough students to play the many roles. Give groups 20 minutes to write and rehearse a skit. Then invite groups to perform their skits for the class. **OL**

C Critical Thinking

Using Analogies Explain that the use of the words *remember* and *memory* for a function of the immune system is using an analogy to help the reader understand the process. An analogy is a resemblance between things that are otherwise unalike. Point out that the immune system does not have a brain and so does not remember like a person remembers. Ask students to explain why this analogy works. **OL EL**

READING CHECK

Answer The inflammatory response, specific defenses, and creation of lymphocytes

---

Reading Strategy

The Immune Response To reinforce students' understanding of the immune response, help them make a flowchart, using **Figure 23.6** as a reference. Write the first step in a square on the board, "Pathogens invade the body," and ask students to copy that step into their notebooks. Ask if students think anything should be added to this step for clarification. Continue this process through the eight steps listed in the figure. For each step, have students review the information in the lesson about the different types of cells, adding any information to the flowchart that would help them remember the process. Students can use their completed flowcharts for study and review.

641

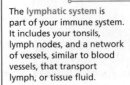 **Reading Strategy**

Making Connections To reinforce students' understanding of immune system memory, have them review how lymph circulation works as described in Chapter 15, Lesson 1. **Ask Students:** *Where is lymph found, and what does it consist of?* (Lymph fills the spaces around body cells. It consists of water, proteins, fats, and lymphocytes.) Then, have students examine **Figure 23.7**, including the caption, and ask them to name a protein that lymph contains. (antibodies) **OL**

C Critical Thinking

Classifying Discuss the meaning of *active* and *passive* with students, and ask them to describe behaviors that are either active or passive. Then, describe different ways that immunity is produced and have students classify each as either active immunity or passive immunity. For example, describe getting a flu vaccine (active immunity) and a baby being fed by its mother's milk (passive immunity). **OL** **EL**

Caption Answer

Figure 23.7 There are two types of lymphocytes: T cells and B cells. Killer T cells attack and destroy infected body cells.

Figure 23.7   Immunity and the Lymphatic System

The lymphatic system circulates antibodies to give you protection against many diseases. This protection can last throughout your life. *What role do lymphocytes play in fighting disease?*

R

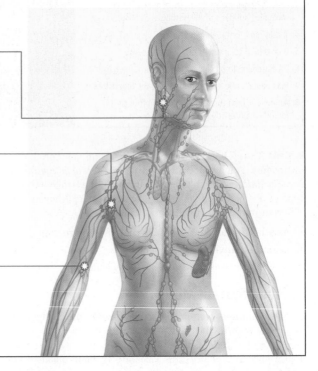

The **lymphatic system** is part of your immune system. It includes your tonsils, lymph nodes, and a network of vessels, similar to blood vessels, that transport lymph, or tissue fluid.

Lymph nodes can become enlarged when your body is fighting an infection because of the increased number of lymphocytes. If swelling lasts for three days, see your health care professional.

Lymphocytes are produced by lymph nodes. These nodes occur in groups and are concentrated in the head and neck, armpits, chest, abdomen, and groin.

Vaccines cause your immune system to produce disease-fighting antibodies without causing the disease itself. Today, more than 20 serious human diseases can be prevented by vaccination. For some diseases, you need to be vaccinated only once in your life. For other diseases, such as measles, tetanus, and influenza, you may need to be vaccinated at regular intervals.

Passive Immunity You acquire passive immunity when your body receives antibodies from another person or an animal. This type of immunity is temporary, usually lasting only a few weeks or months. Like active immunity, passive immunity can be either natural or artificial.

Natural passive immunity occurs when antibodies pass from mother to child during pregnancy or while nursing. Artificial passive immunity happens when you receive an injection prepared with antibodies that are produced by an animal or a human immune to the disease.

C

Myths & Reality

Influenza Immunization

Myth: There is no need to get a flu vaccine because the flu is not a serious disease.

Fact: Every year in the United States, about 36,000 people die from influenza and about 200,000 people are hospitalized because of the disease.

Myth: The side effects of a flu shot are worse than getting the flu.

Fact: For the vast majority of people, the worst side effect of a flu shot is a sore arm. The nasal mist flu vaccine can cause nasal congestion, a sore throat, and a cough in some people.

Prevention Strategies

C

> **Main Idea** Strategies for preventing the spread of disease include practicing healthful behaviors, tracking diseases, and getting vaccinations.

The immune system is a powerful fighter against infection, and you can keep it tuned up and in good working order by eating a nutritious, well-balanced diet and getting regular physical activity. In addition, you can take preventive measures to avoid disease and stay healthy. These include frequent hand washing, handling food properly, avoiding insect bites, and abstaining from sexual contact.

Tracking Reportable Diseases

AL

Community, national, and global efforts also play a crucial role in fighting communicable diseases. Agencies such as the Centers for Disease Control and Prevention (CDC) and the World Health Organization (WHO) keep a constant watch on the spread of diseases around the world. By tracking infections such as hepatitis, influenza, and yellow fever, they can often predict where the diseases might strike next. This information helps countries prepare and develop their own prevention strategies.

Vaccinations

In the past, smallpox killed hundreds of millions of people. Today, thanks to the smallpox vaccine, the disease has been essentially wiped out. Scientists and health care workers are always trying to stay one step ahead of communicable diseases and develop new vaccines. Vaccines fall into four categories:

- **Live-virus vaccines** are made from pathogens grown in laboratories. This process removes most of the pathogens' disease-causing characteristics. The pathogens are weak, but they can still stimulate the immune system to produce antibodies. The vaccine for measles, mumps, and rubella (MMR) and the vaccine for chicken pox are produced this way.
- **Killed-virus vaccines** use dead pathogens. Even though the pathogens are no longer active, they still stimulate an immune response. Flu shots, the Salk vaccine for polio, and the vaccines for hepatitis A, rabies, cholera, and plague are all killed-virus vaccines.
- **Toxoids** are inactivated toxins from pathogens. They are used to stimulate the production of antibodies. Tetanus and diphtheria immunizations use toxoids.

READING CHECK

Explain Why is it important to track communicable diseases?

Lesson 3 Fighting Communicable Diseases **643**

Main Idea

Prevention Strategies Strategies for preventing the spread of disease include practicing healthful behaviors. **Ask Students:** *What can a person do to avoid disease?* (wash hands, handle food properly)

C Critical Thinking

Making Inferences Ask for a volunteer to read aloud the Main Idea about preventing the spread of disease. Ask students how they can help prevent the spread of disease. (Taking care of oneself, such as washing hands contributes to a healthy immune system.) **OL**

AL Active Learning

Smallpox Vaccine Success Ask interested students to research the methods used in the worldwide public health campaign by the World Health Organization and other agencies that resulted in the eradication of the smallpox virus. This success was primarily due to the immunization of people around the world. The last reported case of smallpox occurred in 1977. Ask students to write a report of what they find. **AL**

READING CHECK

Answer By tracking infections, agencies such as the CDC and WHO can often predict where diseases might strike next. This information helps countries prepare and develop their own prevention strategies.

Cooperative Learning

Develop a Film Pitch After students have read about agencies that track reportable diseases, divide the class into small groups. Ask the students of each group to work together to develop a "pitch" to movie-studio executives for a film about a scientist in the WHO or CDC who discovers that a disease is spreading fast and then works to stop the spread. Tell students that this film will be a thriller, with a Hollywood star in the lead role. Tell students that the pitch they develop should include accurate information about how diseases spread as well as an enthusiastic description of the film's plot. Have groups make their pitches to the class.

③ ASSESS/ CLOSE

Assessment Resources

📁 *FAST FILE* Activities
Lesson 3 Quiz

💿 *ExamView*
Assessment Suite CD-ROM

Visit glencoe.com for:
Online Quizzes
Online Learning Center

Progress Monitoring

Reteaching
Ask students to write a paragraph describing the events that occur during the immune response, using **Figure 23.6** as a guide.

Enrichment
Have students write ten true-or-false quiz questions about the main concepts and vocabulary terms in Lesson 3. Have students quiz one another using their prepared questions.

 **Online**

Have students visit **glencoe.com** and complete the Interactive Study Guide for this lesson.

- **New and second-generation viruses** are on the cutting edge of disease-fighting technology. One example is the vaccine for hepatitis B, which is made from genetically altered yeast cells.

Immunization for All When you receive a vaccine, you are not only keeping yourself healthy, but you are also helping to protect everyone around you. Vaccination reduces the number of people who are at risk for a communicable disease. That's why it's important to keep your immunizations up-to-date.

To find out which immunizations you need, ask your family physician or local health department. Maintaining a record of your vaccinations will help you keep track of when you need "booster" shots.

Most schools and preschools require students to show proof of current immunizations before admission. Each state also has its own laws about immunization and school attendance. Make sure you know and follow the public health policies and government regulations in your community. Remember, everyone can play an active role in preventing the spread of communicable diseases.

LESSON 3 ASSESSMENT

After You Read

Reviewing Facts and Vocabulary
1. What is the purpose of the inflammatory response?
2. What is the difference between *active immunity* and *passive immunity*?
3. What is a *phagocyte*?

Thinking Critically
4. **Analyze.** Discuss the meaning of *memory* as it applies to the immune system. How is it similar to your brain's memory?
5. **Synthesize.** You could say that your good health is the result of a successful partnership between you and your body. Support this statement using facts from the lesson.

Applying Health Skills
6. **Analyzing Influences.** A healthy immune system depends on a healthful diet and regular physical activity. Consider the influences that might affect your ability to practice these habits. In what ways do these influences make it easier for you to stay healthy? In what ways do they make it more difficult?

Writing Critically
7. **Expository.** Write a paragraph explaining why keeping your own vaccinations up to date is a duty not only to yourself but also to the people around you.

G⊙ Online

Visit **glencoe.com** and complete the Interactive Study Guide for this lesson.

LESSON 3 ASSESSMENT ANSWERS

1. To prevent further injury to tissue and to stop invading pathogens
2. *Active immunity* is produced by the immune system. *Passive immunity* is when the body receives antibodies from another person or animal.
3. A substance that is capable of triggering an immune response
4. Sample answer: The immune system "remembers" antigens much like the brain remembers previous experiences.
5. Sample answer: My immune system works automatically, but I need to support it by practicing healthful behaviors.
6. Answers will vary. Student responses should mention both positive and negative influences of media, family, and peers.
7. Answers will vary but should include how immunization reduces risks.

Emerging Diseases and Pandemics

CHAPTER 23

LESSON 4

Real Life Issues ....

Expressing Concerns. It's the last weekend before the new school year starts, and Noah is at a barbecue with some friends. He sees that the hamburgers are still pink inside after they are taken off the grill. Noah remembers hearing that under-cooked hamburger meat can make people sick. The burgers look delicious, though, and he's really hungry. He wants to say something to the adult who is cooking the hamburgers, but he's not sure how to express his concerns.

Writing *Write a paragraph explaining Noah's concerns. Suggest a way he can politely share what he knows with the person who is cooking the food.*

Emerging Infections

Main Idea Some diseases are becoming more dangerous and widespread.

Vaccines and modern technology have saved millions of lives, but communicable diseases continue to be the top cause of deaths worldwide. Health experts label some communicable diseases as **emerging infections**, *communicable diseases whose occurrence in humans has increased within the past two decades or threatens to increase in the near future.*

Scientists now believe that some diseases once thought to be noncommunicable may, in fact, be caused by infectious pathogens. Such diseases include Alzheimer's, diabetes, and coronary artery disease. Many factors are involved in the development and spread of these diseases. See **Figure 23.8** on page 646 to learn more about how emerging infections spread.

GUIDE TO READING

BIG Idea Today, *infectious diseases have the potential to spread quickly throughout the world.*

Before You Read

Organize Information. Make a table and label the columns "Disease," "How It's Spread," and "Prevention Strategies." As you read, fill in the chart with information about the emerging infections discussed in this lesson.

Disease	How It's Spread	Prevention Strategies

New Vocabulary

▶ emerging infections (p. 645)
▶ giardia (p. 647)
▶ epidemic (p. 648)
▶ pandemic (p. 648)

Emerging Diseases and Pandemics

❶ FOCUS

GUIDE TO READING

BIG Idea Students will learn that infectious diseases have the potential to spread around the world quickly. **Ask Students:** *What is different today compared to a hundred years ago that allows a disease to spread more quickly around the world?* (Sample answer: Air travel allows for more international travel.)

Before You Read

Organize Information Tables will vary but should include the basic information about the emerging diseases discussed in the lesson.

Main Idea

Emerging Infections The occurrence of some dangerous communicable diseases have increased greatly in the past two decades. **Ask Students:** *What communicable disease from another part of the world has recently become a threat to the people of North America?* (Sample answers: Avian influenza, West Nile virus)

English Language Coach

Emerge Explain to students that the word *emerge* consists of two parts. The prefix *e-* means "out," and the base word *–merge* means "plunge." The word *emerge*, then, means "to plunge out." The word *emerging* is the form of *emerge* used as an adjective. An *emerging disease* is a disease that is "plunging out," or suddenly appearing. Point out that there is another common word derived from *emerge*, and that is *emergency*. An emergency is a situation that calls for immediate action. Similarly, an emerging disease can be thought of as a disease that may become an emergency.

Real Life Issues ....

Noah could politely but assertively tell the adult cook that the food may be contaminated and needs to be well cooked to be safe to eat.

2 TEACH

R Reading Strategy

Analyzing a Chart Write this title on the board: *How Emerging Infections Are Spread.* Underneath the heading, write the first factor listed in **Figure 23.8**, *Transport Across Borders.* Ask a student to read aloud the description of How It Happens in the second column. Then have students find and read the description of West Nile Virus in their text. Discuss how birds carrying this disease move across borders. Continue this process for each of the five factors listed in the chart. **BL** **EL**

Caption Answer

Figure 23.8 As residential areas expand, people move closer to wooded areas.

C Critical Thinking

Making Inferences Ask students to recall what they learned in Lesson 2 about the ways by which influenza spreads. (Through the air or through direct or indirect contact) Then ask students which of those ways of transmission has not been present in cases of avian flu in Asia. (airborne transmission) Have students infer from this information what would have to occur for avian flu to become a pandemic. Explain that this change could occur if the virus mutates, and that is what many scientists fear could happen. **OL**

☑ READING CHECK

Answer There is no vaccine and humans have little or no resistance to the virus.

Figure 23.8 | Factors Behind Emerging Infections

R

Emerging infections spread in several ways. *Why is Lyme disease increasing today?*

The Factor	How It Happens	Examples
Transport across borders	Infected people and animals carry pathogens from one area to another; sometimes spread by insect carriers such as mosquitoes.	Dengue fever, found mostly in South and Central America and Asia, has now appeared in the southwestern United States. West Nile encephalitis has spread from Asia and Africa to Europe and the Americas. Both diseases are carried by mosquitoes.
Population movement	As residential areas expand, people move closer to wooded areas.	Lyme disease in the United States
Resistance to antibiotics	Widespread use of anti-biotics gives rise to drug-resistant pathogens.	The pathogens that cause tuberculosis, gonorrhea, and a type of pneumonia are resistant to one or more antibiotics.
Changes in food technology	Mass production and distribution of food mean that a small amount of pathogens can infect a great number of people.	*E. coli* and *Salmonella* have been responsible for widespread outbreaks of illness.
Agents of bioterrorism	Some pathogens are deadly even in tiny amounts, and they can be dispersed over a large area.	In 2001, envelopes containing anthrax spores were sent to government and media figures in the United States.

☑ READING CHECK

Explain Why are health organizations so worried about avian influenza?

Avian Influenza

Avian influenza is caused by a virus that occurs naturally among birds. Wild birds carry the virus in their intestines and usually do not get sick from it. However, the virus has spread to domesticated birds, such as chickens, ducks, and turkeys, through contact with water, feed, cages, or dirt infected by wild birds. Avian flu is passed to humans if there is direct contact with infected birds or contaminated surfaces. In rare cases, mostly in Asia, people have died from avian influenza. Because there is no vaccine and no cure, and because humans have little or no resistance to the virus, health authorities are watching this disease very carefully.

C

West Nile Virus

Mosquitoes sometimes feed on birds carrying the West Nile virus, a pathogen commonly found in Africa, the Middle East, and West Asia. When infected mosquitoes bite humans, they often transfer the virus. About 20 percent—one out of five—of those bitten will develop West Nile fever, a potentially severe illness. The best preventive measure is to protect yourself from mosquito bites.

Skills for the 21st Century

Personal Responsibility in the Workplace After students have read about the spread of resistant diseases, explain that people who work in health-care settings must always keep in mind that such diseases can be spread by staff members if they don't follow certain precautions. Point out that doctors, nurses, and medical technicians often work without immediate supervision, and they must each take personal responsibility for following these precautions at all times. Have students brainstorm a list of precautions for hospital or clinic staff to prevent the spread of disease. (Students might list hand washing between patients, wearing disposable gloves, wearing gowns and face masks, and properly disposing of needles.) Then have students research online to find the CDC's Standard Precautions, designed to reduce the risk of transmission of pathogens.

Salmonella and *E. coli*

W

Salmonella and *E. coli* are bacteria that sometimes live in animals' intestinal tracts. If people come in contact with these bacteria by eating contaminated food produced by these animals, they may become ill. Illnesses can spread quickly to large areas if contamination occurs in central agricultural or food-processing facilities and contaminated food products are distributed to cities and towns all over the world. Storing foods carefully and cooking meat to proper temperatures will kill *Salmonella* and *E. coli* bacteria. For more tips on avoiding foodborne illness, see Chapter 10, Lesson 4.

Recreational Water Illnesses

AL

Swimming is a fun activity, but if the water is not regularly treated with disinfectants, chlorine, or other chemicals, you run the risk of getting a *recreational water illness,* or RWI. RWIs can occur when water is contaminated by harmful strains of bacteria such as *E. coli* or by **giardia**, *a microorganism that infects the digestive system.*

RWIs are most commonly spread through swallowing or having contact with water contaminated with untreated sewage or feces from humans or animals. RWIs are on the rise throughout the world, particularly in areas where raw sewage is dumped in untreated waterways. To help prevent RWIs, don't swim when you have diarrhea. Try not to let water in your mouth, and definitely try not to swallow it. Also, remember to practice good hygiene: take a shower before swimming, and wash your hands after using the bathroom.

Other Emerging Infections

W

Other emerging infections with serious health concerns include HIV/AIDS, lyme disease, SARS, and mad cow disease. As with other highly communicable diseases, awareness is the first step toward prevention.

HIV/AIDS is not a new disease, but it is spreading quickly and has become a global health threat. You will learn more about HIV and AIDS in Chapter 24.

■ **Figure 23.9** Swimming is a fun way to stay fit, but it can pose a risk of getting an RWI. *What actions can you take to avoid RWIs?*

Writing Strategy

Narrative Writing Ask students to write a short story about a scientist, doctor, or health department official who performs heroically during a pandemic that occurs in the students' region. Explain that in their stories they might project that any of the diseases discussed in Lesson 4 may become a pandemic. They should write about the disease creatively but accurately as they tell the story of how the main character saves lives or prevents tragedy from occurring.

W **Writing Support**

Expository Writing Have students write a letter to a fictional cousin explaining that he or she just got sick from *Salmonella* poisoning. The letter should explain what *Salmonella* is, how it is transmitted, and what precautions should be taken to avoid getting the disease. Have volunteers share their finished letters with the class. **OL**

AL **Active Learning**

Posters Divide the class into small groups, and ask each group to design and make a poster that incorporates tips to help prevent recreational water illnesses. Ask groups to think of ways to get the message across in a tasteful way. Students might draw humorous cartoons to show behaviors that are necessary to avoid spreading RWIs. Display the finished posters in the classroom. **OL**

W **Writing Support**

Report on Disease Ask students who need a challenge to choose one of the diseases discussed in Lesson 4 and do further research. Ask them to find more information about what causes the disease, how it spreads, and how at risk people in their local area are for getting the disease. Ask students to write a report about what they find. **AL**

Caption Answer

Figure 23.9 Try not to let water in your mouth, and definitely try not to swallow it. Practice good hygiene.

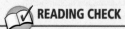
Academic Vocabulary

community *(noun):* a population of individuals in a common location

Lyme Disease This disease is transmitted to humans through tick bites. Lyme disease is on the rise because, as suburban **communities** grow, people build their homes ever closer to heavily wooded areas, where ticks thrive. To protect yourself, avoid bushy areas with high grass and a lot of leaf litter. When you go hiking, use insect repellent and wear pants with long legs and shirts with long sleeves.

SARS Severe Acute Respiratory Syndrome, or SARS, is a viral illness first reported in Asia in 2003. The illness spread to more than two dozen countries, causing more than 8,000 people to fall ill and killing almost 800. Health and government agencies were able to contain the virus and stop the spread of illness, but it is possible that SARS could strike again.

Mad Cow Disease This is also known as *bovine spongiform encephalopathy,* or BSE. This disease, which affects the brain functions of cattle, has reached epidemic proportions in Great Britain. An **epidemic** is *a disease outbreak that affects many people in the same place and at the same time.* Scientists are worried that BSE could spread to humans.

How Diseases Affect the World

Main Idea Diseases can spread with amazing speed.

The world's countries are connected through trade and travel. These connections make it easy for infectious diseases to travel faster and farther than ever before. Sometimes a disease becomes a **pandemic**—*a global outbreak of an infectious disease.* An outbreak of avian flu or *E. coli* in a small area of the globe can quickly spread and threaten the health of entire countries, even continents.

Medical treatment and prevention requires constant research to find the causes and the cures for emerging diseases. There is always the possibility that one of these illnesses could become a pandemic. In fact, scientists predict that a new flu pandemic is likely to happen soon. The U.S. government has already launched programs that will educate the public about flu pandemics. Health agencies plan for pandemics and develop rapid-response strategies to reduce their impact.

READING CHECK

Explain Why can pandemics spread so quickly throughout the world?

The Impact of Travel

The mobility of people in our globalized world contributes to the spread of disease. For example, an American tourist can pick up an infection in another country, return home, and spread it to his family, friends, and coworkers.

 **Home and Community**

Planning for Pandemics Health agencies plan for the outbreak of a pandemic because a pandemic could be devastating. For example, the flu pandemic of 1918 resulted in about 675,000 deaths in the United States and perhaps 50 million deaths worldwide. In the United States, the federal government, under the leadership of the Department of Health and Human Services, coordinates planning throughout the country for the possibility of a pandemic occurring. Every state and many cities have plans of action in the case of a pandemic. Have interested students contact the local health department to find out about plans in their state and city.

Figure 23.10 Travel is exciting, but it can also pose health risks. *How does air travel contribute to the spread of infection?*

Mutation of Pathogens

The increased development of antibiotics has saved countless lives. However, because antibiotics are so widely used, some pathogens have mutated into new forms that are resistant to antibiotics. Pathogens become drug-resistant in a three-step process:

- Pathogens invade the body and cause illness.
- Antibiotics attack the pathogens.
- The pathogens that survive the antibiotics reproduce, creating a new generation of drug-resistant pathogens.

LESSON 4 ASSESSMENT

After You Read

Reviewing Facts and Vocabulary

1. What is an *emerging infection*?
2. How are recreational water illnesses most commonly spread?
3. How is a *pandemic* different from an *epidemic*?

Thinking Critically

4. **Evaluate.** If a friend told you that you don't need to worry about infectious diseases because you can always take antibiotics, what would you say?
5. **Analyze.** In a Colorado meatpacking plant, a vat of hamburger meat has been infected with *E. coli* bacteria. Weeks later, people in a dozen American states get sick. How might the contamination have occurred over such a large area?

Applying Health Skills

6. **Accessing Information.** Choose one emerging disease from this lesson that you want to know more about. Research how the disease spreads, and find as many tips for avoiding the disease as you can.

Writing Critically

7. **Expository.** You have been asked to write a column for an airline magazine that explains emerging diseases to travelers. Think about what air travelers in particular need to know about how diseases spread, and what they can do to stop a disease from becoming a pandemic.

Go Online

Visit **glencoe.com** and complete the Interactive Study Guide for this lesson.

Assessment Resources

📁 **FAST FILE ACTIVITIES**
Lesson 4 Quiz

💿 *ExamView Assessment Suite* CD-ROM

Visit glencoe.com for:
Online Quizzes
Online Learning Center

Progress Monitoring

Reteaching
Name an emerging disease discussed in the lesson and call on a student to describe its symptoms. Then, call on a second student to explain the way that disease is spreading.

Enrichment
Have students research the development of resistant diseases in hospital settings and what measures hospitals are taking to stop the spread of these diseases.

Go Online

Have students visit **glencoe.com** and complete the Interactive Study Guide for this lesson.

LESSON 4 ASSESSMENT ANSWERS

1. A communicable disease whose occurrence in humans has increased within the past two decades or threatens to increase in the near future
2. Through swallowing or contact with water contaminated with untreated sewage
3. A *pandemic* is a global outbreak of an infection, while an *epidemic* is an outbreak in which many people in the same place at the same time are affected.
4. Sample answer: Antibiotics are not effective against all types of pathogens, some pathogens become resistant to antibiotics.
5. The plant shipped the infected meat to stores across the country.
6. Responses will vary depending on the disease chosen to research.
7. Responses will vary but should explain emerging diseases and prevention.

649

Vaccine: The Battle Within

Focus

Motivator

Ask students, "What vaccines are recommended for teenagers?" (Sample answers: Varicella: Chickenpox, Hepatitis B, MMR: Measles-Mumps-Rubella, and Tetanus-Diphtheria) Discuss with the class how these vaccines prevent disease.

Teach

Booster Shots Certain vaccines require what is known as a "booster shot" a couple of years after the initial vaccination. Ask students, "What is a booster? Why do you need one? What are some examples of vaccines that require booster shots?" (Sample answers: Tetanus, diphtheria) Explain that the body creates immunity to viruses with some vaccines, such as measles, mumps, or varicella. Yet the immunity to inactivated bacterial toxins, such as tetanus and diphtheria, fades over time. For these toxins, people should receive a booster shot every 10 years, starting at the age of 11 or 12.

About Vaccines Using online or library resources, have students research what disease causes the most deaths among unvaccinated children in the United States. Ask students, "Why are some children not being vaccinated?" Write their responses on the board. (Sample answers: Price of vaccines, fear of negative side effects, poor access to health care, lack of information about vaccines) Ask, "What can be done to overcome these barriers? What steps are being taken in our community to overcome them?"

TIME HEALTH
SCIENCE & TECHNOLOGY

Vaccine: The Battle Within

To create better vaccines, scientists must study the immune system's complex network of cellular guards.

Pathogen

1. B lymphocytes seek specific pathogens.

Identifies target pathogen.

Pathogen is exposed.

2. Antigen-presenting cell uncovers pathogens.

3. Helper T cell sounds alarm.

Pathogen is exposed.

4. B lymphocyte plasma cell releases antibody designed to kill specific pathogen.

5. Killer T cell binds and destroys its target pathogen.

6. Natural killer cell kills any invading bug in its path.

Searching for the Bad Bugs...

1. Spotting the Enemy
Formed in bone marrow, B lymphocytes are the only immune cells that can make antibodies—the first line of immune defense. Antibodies are proteins that detect and bind themselves to pathogens in the blood to neutralize them.

2. Exposing the Bad Guys
Often pathogens camouflage themselves against detection by antibodies with proteins called antigens. Antigen-presenting cells (APCs) chop up the proteins. This exposes the pathogens to destruction.

3. Sounding the Alarm
Helper T cells recognize and bind to bugs exposed by APCs. Once activated, helper Ts secrete hormones called cytokines. These signal the immune system to send more macrophages, B cells, and T cells to destroy the invaders, as well as more white blood cells containing enzymes that digest antigens.

...And Then Destroying Them

4. Building the Bombs
After they encounter antigens in the blood, some B cells retreat to the lymph nodes, where they become plasma cells and churn out antibodies that can bind to the antigens.

5. Going in for the Kill
Killer T cells must recognize antigens. Then they mature quickly to perform their second function—destroying pathogens. Killer T cells attach to a pathogen and douse it with a lethal toxin. Then they detach and go off to kill again, leaving the infected cell to die.

6. Bringing in the Big Guns
Natural killer cells are unspecialized fighters. They flood infected cells with toxins and destructive enzymes, but don't need to have the antigens exposed by APCs.

TIME to THINK... | About Vaccines

Every year nearly 2 million children worldwide die from diseases that vaccination could have prevented. Use the Internet or your school's media center to learn what diseases cause the most deaths among unvaccinated children. Why are these children not being vaccinated? Report your findings to the class.

Health Literacy

What Washing Does When you wash your hands with soap and water, the rubbing of the hands scrapes off dirt, oils, and other particles, including pathogens. Some soaps contain antibacterial agents designed to kill bacteria, but such chemicals do nothing to eliminate viruses. Studies have shown that a vigorous washing with soap and water washes away many viruses, including cold viruses. The amount of rubbing one does is the key to washing thoroughly, and that is why rubbing the hands for 30 seconds or more is essential.

To download quizzes and eFlashcards to your PDA, go to glencoe.com and click on the Study to Go icon.

LESSON 1

Understanding Communicable Diseases

Key Concepts
▶ Communicable diseases are caused by pathogens.
▶ Communicable diseases can spread through direct contact, indirect contact, and airborne transmissions.
▶ To reduce your risk of disease, wash your hands regularly, eat properly, exercise, and avoid contact with vectors.

Vocabulary
▶ communicable disease (p. 628)
▶ pathogens (p. 628)
▶ infection (p. 628)
▶ virus (p. 629)
▶ bacteria (p. 629)
▶ toxins (p. 629)
▶ vector (p. 630)

LESSON 2

Common Communicable Diseases

Key Concepts
▶ Many communicable diseases start in the respiratory tract.
▶ Hepatitis, a widespread viral disease, attacks the liver.
▶ Practicing good hygiene and avoiding risk behaviors can help protect you from some communicable diseases.

Vocabulary
▶ respiratory tract (p. 633)
▶ mucous membrane (p. 634)
▶ pneumonia (p. 634)
▶ jaundice (p. 635)
▶ cirrhosis (p. 635)

LESSON 3

Fighting Communicable Diseases

Key Concepts
▶ Physical and chemical barriers stop or destroy many pathogens before they can cause disease.
▶ Your body's immune system fights pathogens with the inflammatory response and specific defenses.
▶ Vaccinations protect you from specific communicable diseases.

Vocabulary
▶ immune system (p. 639)
▶ inflammatory response (p. 639)
▶ phagocytes (p. 640)
▶ antigens (p. 640)
▶ immunity (p. 640)
▶ lymphocyte (p. 640)
▶ antibody (p. 641)
▶ vaccine (p. 641)

LESSON 4

Emerging Diseases and Pandemics

Key Concepts
▶ Emerging infections, such as avian influenza, are on the rise.
▶ Infections spread more easily and quickly than in the past.
▶ Pathogens can mutate and become resistant to antibiotics.

Vocabulary
▶ emerging infections (p. 645)
▶ giardia (p. 647)
▶ epidemic (p. 648)
▶ pandemic (p. 648)

Chapter 23 Review **651**

G⊙ Online

Students can visit **glencoe.com** to

• review content online with the Online Student Edition.
• test their knowledge of chapter content with Online Quizzes.
• access Interactive Health Tutor for more practice with vocabulary.

Assessment Resources

 FAST FILE ACTIVITIES
Chapter 23 Test

ExamView Assessment Suite CD-ROM

Visit glencoe.com for:
Audio Chapter Summaries
Online Quizzes

 Tell students to visit glencoe.com where they can download quizzes and eFlashcards.

Study Tips

Using Search Engines Doing research to complete homework assignments and for writing reports often involves finding good online sources. Explain that using a search engine is the first step in finding Web sites that contain needed information. Point out that a search engine searches through pages on the Web to find specific words on those pages for which the search engine has been instructed to search. Explain that different search engines employ different methods in searching and may yield different results when searching for the same words and phrases. For that reason, it is often useful to do the same search with two or more search engines to find the best results.

Assessment

Chapter 23 Assessment Answers

Vocabulary Review

1. pathogen
2. toxin
3. infection

Understanding Key Concepts

4. c
5. b
6. a

Thinking Critically

7. A disease can develop.
8. Cell division
9. Sample answer: Washing your hands regularly, handling food properly, and protecting yourself from vectors
10. Answers will vary but should demonstrate an understanding of how taking responsibility for preventing the spread of disease contributes to both personal and community health.

Vocabulary Review

11. mucous
12. respiratory tract
13. pneumonia

Understanding Key Concepts

14. a
15. d
16. b

Vocabulary Review

Correct the sentences below by replacing the italicized term with the correct vocabulary term.

1. A(n) *infection* is an organism that causes disease.

2. A substance that kills cells or interferes with their functions is called a(n) *vector*.

3. When pathogens in the body multiply and damage body cells, a(n) *virus* results.

Understanding Key Concepts

After reading the question or statement, select the correct answer.

4. Another word for *communicable* is
   a. harmless.
   b. sudden.
   c. contagious.
   d. painful.

5. The common cold and influenza are caused by
   a. overeating.
   b. viruses.
   c. bacterial infection.
   d. exposure to toxins.

6. Malaria, West Nile virus, and Lyme disease are examples of diseases that are spread by
   a. vectors.
   b. contaminated utensils.
   c. sexual contact.
   d. contaminated water.

Thinking Critically

After reading the question or statement, write a short answer using complete sentences.

7. **Explain.** If the body's immune system cannot fight off an infection, what happens?

8. **Identify.** Name the process by which bacteria multiply themselves.

---

9. **Synthesize.** Describe at least three strategies for reducing your risk of getting or spreading communicable diseases.

10. **Evaluate.** Consider your role in preventing disease. How do your behaviors affect the health of your community as well as your own health?

Vocabulary Review

Use the vocabulary terms listed on page 651 to complete the following statements.

11. The lining of body cavities (such as the mouth) is made of _____.

12. The passageway that makes breathing possible is the _____.

13. Influenza can lead to _____, a potentially fatal infection of the lungs.

Understanding Key Concepts

After reading the question or statement, select the correct answer.

14. Which of the following habits probably will *not* help you avoid respiratory tract infections?
   a. Rinsing with mouthwash
   b. Frequent hand washing
   c. Avoiding close contact with ill people
   d. Abstaining from smoking

15. Some strains of tuberculosis have become resistant to which form of treatment?
   a. Bed rest   c. Dietary changes
   b. Surgery   d. Antibiotics

16. What is the most common blood-borne infection in the United States?
   a. Hepatitis A   c. Hepatitis C
   b. Hepatitis B   d. None of the above

Health eSpotlight VIDEO Wrap-Up

Communicable Diseases Have students reread the Health eSpotlight questions at the beginning of the chapter (page 627) and look at their original answers. **Ask Students:** *What do you now know about stopping communicable diseases and supporting your immune system that you didn't know before watching the video and reading the chapter?* Call on volunteers to describe what they have learned and how they would change their responses.

Thinking Critically

After reading the question or statement, write a short answer using complete sentences.

17. Evaluate. What is the best treatment for the common cold?

18. Identify. Receiving a flu vaccine once a year is especially important for which groups of people?

19. Explain. Why do doctors sometimes have to prescribe several antibiotics for a person in order to treat one disease?

20. Synthesize. Explain how peer pressure might contribute to the spread of hepatitis B.

LESSON **3**

Vocabulary Review

Choose the correct word in the sentences below.

21. *Antigens / Lymphocytes* are substances that are capable of triggering an immune response.

22. *Inflammation / Immunity* is the state of being protected against a particular disease.

23. A preparation of dead or weakened pathogens used to stimulate an immune response is called a(n) *vaccine / antibody*.

Understanding Key Concepts

After reading the question or statement, select the correct answer.

24. What is the role of phagocytes in the inflammatory response?
   a. They prevent pus from building up.
   b. They surround and destroy pathogens.
   c. They trigger the production of T cells.
   d. They cause blood vessels to expand.

25. If you receive antibodies from another person or an animal instead of producing them in your own body, it is called
   a. communicable disease.
   b. specific defense.
   c. active immunity.
   d. passive immunity.

26. Live-virus, killed-virus, toxoid, and second-generation virus are all categories of
   a. vaccines.
   b. antigens.
   c. preventive strategies.
   d. antibiotics.

27. To remain effective, some vaccinations
   a. must have passive immunity.
   b. contain amateur pathogens.
   c. must be repeated at regular intervals.
   d. are most successful if given when a person is young.

Thinking Critically

After reading the question or statement, write a short answer using complete sentences.

28. Identify. What two major strategies does the immune system use to fight pathogens?

29. Explain. Why do health agencies like the CDC and WHO track and monitor the spread of diseases?

30. Synthesize. If you do not receive up-to-date immunizations, how might your future be affected?

LESSON **4**

Vocabulary Review

Correct the sentences below by replacing the italicized term with the correct vocabulary term.

31. West Nile encephalitis is an example of a(n) *acute infection*.

Chapter 23 Assessment **653**

Thinking Critically

17. Getting plenty of rest and drinking liquids
18. Older adults and people with chronic health problems
19. Some pathogens have become resistant to certain antibiotics.
20. Sample answer: Peer pressure could lead to sexual contact, illegal drug use, or tattooing and piercing, all of which can spread hepatitis B.

LESSON **3**

Vocabulary Review

21. Antigens
22. Immunity
23. vaccine

Understanding Key Concepts

24. b
25. d
26. a
27. c

Thinking Critically

28. The inflammatory response and specific defenses
29. To predict where diseases might strike next, information that is important in prevention strategies
30. Sample answer: I might be infected with a serious disease.

Create and customize tests in minutes with this convenient digital platform.

- Create differentiated tests quickly and easily.
- All questions correlated to National/State Standards.
- Enhance tests with Document Based Questions (DBQ) and add your own photos or graphics.
- Build tests in both English and Spanish.
- Generate progress reports.

To order, go to **glencoe.com** and search for ISBN 0-07-888173-0.

Assessment

Assessment

LESSON 4

Vocabulary Review

31. emerging infection
32. pandemic
33. Giardia

Understanding Key Concepts

34. b
35. c
36. a

Thinking Critically

37. Sample answer: Transport across borders, population movement, and changes in food technology
38. Pathogens invade the body and cause illness. Antibodies attack the pathogens. Some pathogens survive and reproduce.
39. Answers will vary but should include mention of how travel increases the rate at which diseases spread.
40. Sample answer: There is no vaccine and no cure for avian flu, and humans have little or no resistance to the virus. An outbreak of avian flu could spread quickly around the world and kill millions.

32. A global outbreak of an infectious disease is called a(n) *mutation*.

33. *Antibody* is a microorganism that infects the digestive system.

Understanding Key Concepts

After reading the question or statement, select the correct answer.

34. The incidence of emerging infections is
    a. decreasing.
    b. increasing.
    c. holding steady.
    d. virtually nonexistent, thanks to modern medicine.

35. The most effective way to prevent infection from *Salmonella* and *E. coli* is to
    a. visually inspect food before eating.
    b. avoid eating salmon.
    c. cook meat thoroughly.
    d. wash your hands after you eat.

36. Which of the following is *not* a strategy for preventing the spread of RWI?
    a. Relying on chlorine treatments
    b. Staying out of the water when you have diarrhea
    c. Keeping water from entering your mouth when you are swimming
    d. Taking a shower before swimming

Thinking Critically

After reading the question or statement, write a short answer using complete sentences.

37. **Explain.** How do emerging infections happen?

38. **Describe.** What are the three steps of pathogen mutation?

39. **Evaluate.** What is the impact of travel on the spread of diseases?

40. **Analyze.** Why are health officials around the world concerned about avian flu?

Project-Based ASSESSMENT

Victory for Vaccines

Background
Polio is a communicable disease caused by a virus. The disease can affect the central nervous system—the brain and spinal cord—and cause paralysis. In the early 1950s, there was a polio epidemic in the United States. Many people, mostly children, died. Since 1954, there have been fewer and fewer cases of polio in the United States. In fact, by 1975 the disease was almost completely eliminated in the United States.

Task
Your task is to research two scientists, Dr. Jonas Salk and Dr. Albert Sabin, and their role in the near eradication of polio in the United States. You will present your findings in an oral report.

Audience
Students in your class

Purpose
Make people aware of the importance of vaccinations in controlling disease.

Procedure
1. Use reliable print and online resources to find articles about polio.
2. Learn how the vaccines for polio were discovered.
3. Tell how the two vaccines differ from each other.
4. Explain why there are still some cases of polio in the United States.
5. Describe the efforts that are being made to eliminate polio in the rest of the world. What health groups are involved in the effort?
6. Prepare a written report of your research, and make an oral presentation to your class.

Project-Based ASSESSMENT

Step 1 Finding Resources Students should easily find information about polio and how devastating the disease was before vaccines were developed. In addition to library resources, students can use search engines to investigate the disease on the Web.

Step 2 Discovery of Vaccines Students should find that Jonas Salk was the first to develop a vaccine in 1952. Albert Sabin developed another polio vaccine in 1957.

Step 3 Vaccines Differ The Salk polio vaccine is a killed-virus vaccine. Today, the Salk vaccine is given in two injections a month apart, with boosters needed every 5 years. The Sabin vaccine is a live-virus vaccine, which is given in three doses in the first two years of a child's life, with a booster given before the child starts school.

Visit **glencoe.com** for Project-Based Assessment rubrics.

Math Practice

Solve Problems. Use the passage below to answer Questions 1–3.

> If you have ever had a bacterial infection, you have seen how quickly bacteria can multiply in your body. Bacteria reproduce by dividing in two in a process known as binary fission. Under ideal conditions, binary fission takes about 15 minutes. However, this time can vary from 10 minutes to 24 hours.
>
> Starting with a single bacterium, how can you find out how many bacteria exist after a certain length of time? After one reproductive cycle, you have two bacteria, or 2^1. After two cycles, you have four, or 2^2. You can summarize this pattern with the formula $B = 2^n$, where B is the number of bacteria, and n is the number of reproductive cycles.

1. One bacterium has a reproductive cycle of 30 minutes. How many bacteria will there be at the end of four hours?
   A. 16
   B. 120
   C. 256
   D. 512

2. How many bacteria exist after seven reproductive cycles?
   A. 14
   B. 64
   C. 128
   D. It depends on the length of the reproductive cycle.

3. What would be the shape of a graph on which time is plotted on the x-axis and number of bacteria is plotted on the y-axis? Where is the slope of the line the steepest?

Gê Online

For more test practice, visit glencoe.com and complete the Online Quizzes for Chapter 23.

Reading/Writing Practice

Understand and Apply. Read the passage below, and then answer the questions.

> I can't wait to go camping again with my family this summer. We always have a great time. Last year my best friend, Randy, came with us. I'm hoping he wants to go again, even after the argument we had last time.
>
> It was late in the afternoon at the campsite, and we were walking along the river. I knew the mosquitoes would be coming out soon, so I took a bottle of insect repellent out of my backpack and sprayed it on my exposed skin. I told Randy he should do the same, but he just laughed. "You worry too much," he said.
>
> I told him mosquitoes carry diseases that can spread to people, and that it's important to prevent insect bites. He put on the insect repellant, but he was annoyed. Things were tense between us for a while, but we got over it. Still, I wonder if it will happen again this year.

1. When did the author decide it was time to apply insect repellent?
   A. Noon   C. Sunset
   B. Late afternoon D. Before going to bed

2. What reason did the author give Randy as to why it's important to put on insect repellent?
   A. Insect bites can be painful.
   B. Mosquitoes are annoying.
   C. Mosquitoes carry diseases that can spread to people.
   D. Insect bites are the leading cause of infection among teens.

3. How do you think the author felt during this encounter? Do you think he handled the situation appropriately? Explain.

Standardized Test Practice Answers

Math Practice
1. C
2. C
3. The line on the graph would curve up as it goes to the right from the zero point. The line would have its steepest slope the farthest to the right.

Reading/Writing Practice
1. B
2. C
3. Answers will vary. Students should recognize that the author was concerned for Randy's safety though intimidated by Randy's hostile response. Opinions will vary about whether the author handled the situation appropriately. Accept all reasonable responses.

Gê Online

Online Study Tools
For more test practice, visit glencoe.com and complete the Online Quizzes for Chapter 23.

Test-Taking Tip

Identifying Trends in Graphs Explain to students that graphs are powerful tools for seeing trends in data. Point out that some questions on standardized tests require students to identify trends by projecting what a graph would look like with given data and then identifying what trend the graph would show. This is the case in question 3 of the Math Practice. Tell students that to answer this question, they should sketch a rough graph with the answers to questions 1 and 2. They might also calculate a few other values that would appear on the graph, such as the number of bacteria after two and four reproductive cycles. With these results in mind, students can project what a completed graph would look like and identify a trend in the graph line.

Sexually Transmitted Diseases and HIV/AIDS

Chapter 24 pages 656–685	Standards		Features
	National	**State/Local**	
	1.12.1, 1.12.5, 1.12.6, 2.12.9, 4.12.2, 6.12.4, 7.12.1, 7.12.3, 8.12.4		*Hands-On* **HEALTH** • STDs: A Game of Risks (*Practicing Healthful Behaviors*), page 680
Lesson 1 **Sexually Transmitted Diseases** pages 658–663 **BIG Idea** *Sexually transmitted diseases (STDs) are highly communicable infections that are contracted through sexual contact.*	2.12.9, 3.12.2, 7.12.1, 8.12.4		
Lesson 2 **Preventing and Treating STDs** pages 664–668 **BIG Idea** *All STDs are preventable and most can be treated, but some are incurable.*	1.12.5, 1.12.8, 2.12.9, 4.12.1, 7.12.1		*Health Skills* **Activity** • The Lines of Defense (*Refusal Skills*), page 666 Out of Time
Lesson 3 **HIV/AIDS** pages 669–673 **BIG Idea** *HIV is the virus that causes AIDS, a disease that weakens the body's immune system and may have fatal consequences.*	1.12.1, 1.12.8, 1.12.9, 3.12.4, 8.12.4		**TEENS** Making a Difference • Promoting AIDS Education, page 673
Lesson 4 **Preventing and Treating HIV/AIDS** pages 674–679 **BIG Idea** *HIV/AIDS is preventable and treatable, but is incurable.*	1.12.1, 1.12.5, 1.12.8, 2.12.9, 3.12.2, 7.12.2, 7.12.3, 8.12.4		VIDEO **BusinessWeek** **HEALTH NEWS** • HIV Combo Drugs, page 678 *Real World* **CONNECTION** • AIDS Awareness Campaign, page 679 Out of Time

Each lesson marked **30 Min**.

Key to Ability Levels

Teaching Strategies and activities have been coded for ability level and appropriateness.

AL Activities for students working above grade level

OL Activities for students working on grade level

BL Activities for students working below grade level

EL Activities for English Learners

Chapter 24 Planning Guide

Glencoe Exclusive!
TeacherWorks Plus™
All-In-One Planner and Resource Center

Resources	Lesson Assessment	Technology
Student Activity Workbook TEACH FAST FILE RESOURCES Vocabulary Practice TEACH Health Labs EXTEND	Chapter 24 Review Chapter 24 Assessment Standardized Test Practice ⊙ ExamView® Assessment Suite CD-ROM	**Teaching Tools:** ⊙ TeacherWorks™ Plus DVD ⊙ StudentWorks™ Plus DVD ⊙ ExamView® Assessment Suite CD-ROM 🖳 Transparency ⊙ Fitness DVD ⊙ PowerPoint® DVD ⊙ Health eSpotlight Video Series DVD
FAST FILE RESOURCES Reading Strategies Activity TEACH Reteaching Activity REVIEW Enrichment Activity EXTEND Health Skills Practice TEACH	Lesson 1 Assessment, page 663 📁 Lesson 1 Quiz Fast File ⊙ ExamView® Assessment Suite CD-ROM	**Web-Based Resources:** Go Online glencoe.com • Health Podcast Activities • Audio Chapter Summaries (English/Spanish) • Interactive Health Tutor
FAST FILE RESOURCES Reading Strategies Activity TEACH Reteaching Activity REVIEW Enrichment Activity EXTEND Health Skills Practice TEACH	Lesson 2 Assessment, page 668 📁 Lesson 2 Quiz Fast File ⊙ ExamView® Assessment Suite CD-ROM	• Health Skills Activities • Vocabulary PuzzleMaker • Parent Letters (English/Spanish) • Lesson Plans
FAST FILE RESOURCES Reading Strategies Activity TEACH Reteaching Activity REVIEW Enrichment Activity EXTEND Health Skills Practice TEACH	Lesson 3 Assessment, page 673 📁 Lesson 3 Quiz Fast File ⊙ ExamView® Assessment Suite CD-ROM	• Health Inventories • Online Quizzes • Study-to-Go • Unit Web Projects
FAST FILE RESOURCES Reading Strategies Activity TEACH Reteaching Activity REVIEW Enrichment Activity EXTEND Health Skills Practice TEACH	Lesson 4 Assessment, page 679 📁 Lesson 4 Quiz Fast File ⊙ ExamView® Assessment Suite CD-ROM	• Student Web Activities • Fitness Zone Activities

StudentWorks Plus

This is the student's backpack solution.

Includes:
- complete Interactive Student Edition
- full audio of English text and Spanish chapter summaries
- allows students to record assignments and track grades.
- links to online activities and additional student resources
- access to all student worksheets and workbooks

FOLDABLES®
Study Organizer

Dinah Zike Foldables®
Chapter Activity
Refer to the *Dinah Zike Reading and Study Skills for Glencoe Health.* Ask students to make a concept-map book Foldable to organize information about the risks of STDs. As students study the chapter, they can make notes under the tab for behaviors, consequences, or prevention.

Key to Symbols

 Transparencies

 CD-ROM

 glencoe.com

 Print Resources

REVIEW activities to review or reinforce content

TEACH activities to teach basic concepts

EXTEND activities to extend or enrich lesson content

Sexually Transmitted Diseases and HIV/AIDS

Chapter Overview

Chapter 24 presents the symptoms, diagnoses, and treatments for common STDs, including HIV/AIDS.

Lesson 1

STDs are highly communicable infections. Common STDs may be present with symptoms or no symptoms. All have possible long-term effects if not treated.

Lesson 2

STDs can be diagnosed and treated, and most can be cured. Infected persons are responsible for notifying contacts. Practicing abstinence is the best way to avoid high-risk behavior.

Lesson 3

HIV/AIDS is an incurable disease that attacks the immune system. Infection can be avoided by practicing behaviors to reduce the risk.

Lesson 4

HIV/AIDS is diagnosed through antibody tests. Treatment can slow the progress but not cure the disease. Early diagnosis is essential to prevent the spread of the disease and prolong life through treatment.

▶ **Activating Prior Knowledge**

Ask volunteers to share their paragraphs. Students may mention that scientists might learn more about how HIV is spread and how to stop it from spreading. **Ask Students:** *How might this knowledge affect your behavior?* (Sample answer: I would use the information to reduce my risk of HIV infection.)

Lesson 1
Sexually Transmitted Diseases

BIG Idea *Sexually transmitted diseases (STDs) are highly communicable infections that are contracted through sexual contact.*

Lesson 2
Preventing and Treating STDs

BIG Idea *All STDs are preventable and most can be treated, but some are incurable.*

Lesson 3
HIV/AIDS

BIG Idea *HIV is the virus that causes AIDS, a disease that weakens the body's immune system and may have fatal consequences.*

Lesson 4
Preventing and Treating HIV/AIDS

BIG Idea *HIV/AIDS is preventable and treatable, but it is incurable.*

Activating Prior Knowledge

Using Visuals Take a look at the photo on this page. What effect can the work of this scientist and others have on the knowledge and behaviors of teens? Explain your thoughts in a short paragraph.

656

Universal Access

Differentiated Learning Glencoe provides teacher support and student materials for all learners in the health classroom.

- Chapter Summaries in English and Spanish are available online at **glencoe.com**.
- *Fast Files* and related worksheets support reluctant readers.

- Universal Access strategies throughout the Teacher Wraparound Edition and *Fast Files* help you present materials for gifted students, at-risk students, physically impaired students, and those with behavior disorders or learning disabilities.

Chapter Launchers

Health in Action

Discuss the **BIG** Ideas

Before beginning this chapter, think about how you would answer these questions:

▶ What do you know about infections that are spread through sexual contact?

▶ Why is it important for you to know about these infections?

Watch the *Health* eSpotlight Video Series

VIDEO

No One Is Immune

Being educated about STDs can help you avoid them. How would you inform other teens about the risks of STDs?

Assess Your Health

Go Online

Visit **glencoe.com** and complete the Health Inventory for Chapter 24.

Chapter Launchers

Health in Action

Discuss the **BIG** Ideas

Ask students to respond aloud to the questions. Explain that the purpose of the questions is to help them assess their knowledge of infections spread through sexual contact.

Health eSpotlight
Video Series

VIDEO

No One Is Immune

Before Viewing the Video

Explain that staying educated on the types and causes of STDs can help a person avoid them.
Ask Students: *How would you inform other teens of the dangers and risks of STDs?* (Sample answers: Discussing the issue, making pamphlets, PSAs) *What is the best way to avoid getting an STD?* (Sample answer: Practicing abstinence is the best way to avoid getting an STD.)

Go Online

Have students go to **glencoe.com** and take the Health Inventory for Chapter 24.

Chapter Skills

Reading Skills
- Reviewing Facts and Vocabulary, pp. 663, 668, 673, 679
- Reading/Writing Practice, p. 685

BIG Idea

Students will learn about STDs, including HIV/AIDS.

Health Skills
- Health Skills Activity, p. 666
- Applying Health Skills, pp. 663, 668, 673, 679

Writing Skills
- Writing Critically, pp. 663, 668, 673, 679
- Reading/Writing Practice, p. 685

Vocabulary
- New Vocabulary, pp. 658, 664, 669, 674
- Reviewing Facts and Vocabulary, pp. 663, 668, 673, 679

657

Sexually Transmitted Diseases

1 FOCUS

BIG Idea Students will learn that STDs are communicable infections that are spread through sexual contact. **Ask Students:** *What different types of STDs have you heard about?* (Answers will vary.)

Before You Read

Cluster Chart Students' charts may vary, though each should closely reflect the material in the lesson about the symptoms and long-term effects of STDs.

Main Idea

What Are STDs? Anyone who has sexual contact with another person risks contracting an STD. **Ask Students:** *What do all STDs have in common?* (They are transmitted through sexual contact)

Real Life Issues

Ask volunteers to share their reasons with the class. Have students write an entry in their journal describing a personal reason for learning about STDs. Students can share their reasons or keep them confidential.

LESSON 1

GUIDE TO READING

BIG Idea *Sexually transmitted diseases (STDs) are highly communicable infections that are contracted through sexual contact.*

Before You Read

Create a Cluster Chart. Draw a circle and label it "STDs." Use surrounding circles to identify common STDs. As you read, continue filling the chart with more details about each type of infection.

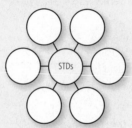

New Vocabulary

▸ sexually transmitted diseases (STDs) (p. 658)
▸ sexually transmitted infections (STIs) (p. 658)
▸ asymptomatic (p. 659)

Review Vocabulary

▸ communicable disease (Ch.23, L.1)
▸ epidemic (Ch.23, L.4)

Sexually Transmitted Diseases

Real Life Issues

Developing Awareness. Today is the third session of the juniors' human sexuality class, and the topic is diseases and infections that are spread through sexual contact. Tricia and her friends do not want to go to class. They say they've heard it all before, and besides, it's embarrassing to talk about. Joe and his friends think they should attend because the more they know, the safer they'll be.

Writing *Write reasons for going to the class that Joe's group might suggest to Tricia's group. Include reasons why teens are at risk for STDs.*

What Are STDs?

Main Idea Anyone who has sexual contact with another person risks contracting a sexually transmitted disease.

Sexually transmitted diseases (STDs) are *infections spread from person to person through sexual contact*. Also known as **sexually transmitted infections (STIs)**, STDs are communicable diseases that can be easily transmitted from one person to another. For an infection to occur, a person must engage in sexual activity that involves direct genital contact or the exchange of semen or other body fluids with someone infected with an STD.

Some STDs are caused by a bacterial infection and can be cured with medication. Other STDs are caused by viruses and are incurable. Early diagnosis and treatment are crucial to controlling or curing an STD.

Health Literacy

Effectiveness Rates of Contraceptive Methods in Preventing Pregnancy and STDs		
Method	**Pregnancy Prevention**	**STD Prevention**
Abstinence	100%	100%
Hormonal (pill, patch, ring)	98–99%	None
Condom	89%	Reduction in risk of some STDs
Diaphragm	83%	None
Fertility Awareness	80%	None
Cervical Cap	77%	None
Sponge	72–86%	None
Spermicide	50–80%	None

Source: FDA

However, several of the most common STDs are often **asymptomatic**, meaning that *individuals show no symptoms, or the symptoms are mild and disappear after the onset of the infection.* This lack of symptoms makes STDs particularly dangerous. A person may not realize that he or she is infected. Therefore, he or she may not seek treatment. An individual with an undiagnosed STD may unknowingly pass the infection on to future sexual partners.

Any person who has sexual contact with another person risks contracting an STD. The risk of contracting an STD also increases as the number of sexual partners increases. It is estimated that approximately 9 million young people between the ages of 15 and 24 will become infected with an STD each year. As **Figure 24.1** shows, many of these cases will not be diagnosed, treated, or reported, creating a serious health crisis.

Females are more likely to suffer complications from STDs, and the effects are more serious in females than in males. Both the physical and psychological effects on people infected with STDs are significant, and so the consequences for health care in the United States are serious as well. The Centers for Disease Control and Prevention (CDC) estimates that direct medical costs connected to STDs are now at more than $14.1 billion a year.

READING CHECK

Explain What makes STDs particularly dangerous for teens?

| Figure 24.1 | **STDs in the United States** |

This chart shows the discrepancy between the estimated number of new STD cases in the United States and the number of reported cases. *Why do you think such a large percentage of STDs are undiagnosed and unreported?*

STD	Estimated Number of New Cases Each Year	Reported Cases (2004–2005)
Human Papillomavirus (HPV)	6.2 million	5.5 million
Chlamydia	3 million	976,445
Genital Herpes	1 million	269,000
Gonorrhea	700,000	339,593
Trichomoniasis	7.4 million	221,000
Syphilis	70,000	33,278
Hepatitis B	120,000	60,000

Source: CDC, Division of STD Prevention, 2000, 2004, 2005

② TEACH

W Writing Support

Summarize Ask students to write a one- or two-paragraph dialogue in which one teen is using refusal skills to avoid being pressured by his or her partner to engage in sexual activity. Students should be sure to have the teen state the position clearly, suggest an alternative, and stand his or her ground. OL

AL Active Learning

Debate Divide the class into small groups. Ask each group to debate whether tests for STDs should be a standard part of an examination by a physician. Have a spokesperson from each group share the pros and cons with the class. OL

READING CHECK

Answer Because many STDs produce few or no symptoms, many will not be diagnosed, treated, or reported.

Caption Answer

Figure 24.1 There is still much misinformation and bias concerning HIV-positive people; the confidential name method protects people's privacy.

English Language Coach

Prefixes Help students recognize prefixes that change the meaning of a root word. Write the words *symptomatic* and *asymptomatic* on the board. Point out that *a-* in *asymptomatic* means "without." So the word means "without symptoms." Ask volunteers to think of words they have studied in science classes with the prefix *a-*, or write these words on the board: *biotic, abiotic, sexual reproduction, asexual reproduction.* Ask students to define these terms or to look them up in a dictionary. Other science terms for practice include *symmetry, asymmetry, photic, aphotic.*

Main Idea

Common STDs Six STDs are the most common. **Ask Students:** *What are the six most common STDs?* (Genital HPV infections, chlamydia, genital herpes, gonorrhea, trichomoniasis, syphilis)

AL **Active Learning**

Public Service Announcement Divide the class into six groups, and assign each group one of the STDs discussed in the lesson. Ask groups to prepare a 30-second public service announcement (PSA) to educate the public about the STD. Advise students to write the PSA in their own words. Have groups present their PSAs to the class. **OL**

C **Critical Thinking**

Making Inferences Ask students why some people might find out they have chlamydia only when they try to conceive or father a child. (If they had no symptoms after they were first infected, they might not have known to get tested and treated. They would know they were infected only when they discovered the effects of chlamydia on their fertility.) **BL** **OL**

W **Writing Support**

Persuasive Writing Point out that STDs are dealt with by health agencies differently from most other communicable diseases, for example, contact tracing. Ask students to write a paragraph about the complications of chlamydia. Paragraphs should reflect students' knowledge of the infection and long-term effects. **AL**

Academic Vocabulary

transmit *(verb):* to send from one person or place to another

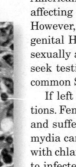

■ **Figure 24.2** This photo shows the bacteria that causes chlamydia. *What health complications can chlamydia cause?*

Common STDs

Main Idea There are approximately 25 different STDs, six of which are considered the most common.

Of the approximately 25 STDs worldwide, the following six are considered the most common: genital HPV infections, chlamydia, genital herpes, gonorrhea, trichomoniasis, and syphilis. **Figure 24.3** shows the symptoms and possible long-term effects of these STDs. **AL**

Genital HPV Infections

Genital HPV infections are caused by human papillomavirus (HPV), a group of more than 100 kinds of viruses. More than 30 of these viruses are transmitted through sexual contact. Close to 6 million people in the United States are infected with HPV each year.

HPV infections can cause genital warts, which appear as bumps or growths near or on the genitals. Most genital HPV infections do not have symptoms and will disappear without medical treatment. However, some HPV infections, if not diagnosed and treated, may cause abnormal Pap tests or, more seriously, may result in certain types of cervical cancer. A vaccine treatment is now available for protection against HPV. It is not a cure, but is recommended to reduce the number of cases of cervical cancer.

Chlamydia

Chlamydia is a bacterial infection that affects the reproductive organs of both males and females. About 2.8 million Americans contract chlamydia each year, with the disease affecting young females three times more often than males. However, less than half of all cases are reported. As with genital HPV, chlamydia often produces no symptoms. Thus, sexually active teens may not know they are infected, do not seek testing, and go untreated. Chlamydia is still the most common STD among teens. **C**

If left untreated, chlamydia can cause serious complications. Females can develop pelvic inflammatory disease (PID) and suffer chronic pelvic pain or infertility. Untreated chlamydia can also lead to infertility in males. Pregnant females with chlamydia can deliver prematurely, and the infants born to infected mothers may develop eye disease or pneumonia, as well as fatal complications. Females with chlamydia are up to five times more likely to become infected with HIV if exposed to the virus. You will learn more about HIV and AIDS in Lesson 3. **W**

More About...

HPV Vaccine Every year, about 10,000 to 11,000 women in the U.S. are diagnosed with cervical cancer, and about 3,700 die from it. HPV is the major cause of cervical cancer. The HPV vaccine confers almost 100% protection against four types of HPV, which together cause 70% of cervical cancers and 90% of genital warts in women. The vaccine does not prevent all cancer-causing types of HPV. About 30% of cervical cancers and 10% of genital warts will not be prevented by the vaccine. Barrier protection does not completely protect against HPV because areas that are not covered can be exposed. The virus can be spread by contact with the skin around the genital area. The only sure way to prevent HPV is to abstain from sexual activity.

Figure 24.3 STD Symptoms

This chart shows the symptoms and possible long-term effects of common STDs.
Why is delayed treatment for STDs never a healthy choice?

STD	Symptoms in Males	Symptoms in Females	Possible Long-Term Effects
Genital HPV Infection	Genital warts on the penis, scrotum, groin, anus, or thigh	Genital warts in or around the vagina, vulva, cervix, or anus	Development of cervical cancer in females
Chlamydia	Penis discharge; burning during urination; itching or burning sensations around penis	Lower abdominal or back pain; nausea; fever; bleeding between periods; pain during intercourse; muscle ache; headache; abnormal vaginal discharge; burning sensation when urinating	In males, inflammation of urethra In females, inflammation of cervix, damage to fallopian tubes, chronic pelvic pain, infertility
Genital Herpes	Blisters on or around genitals or rectum; sores that can take weeks to heal; flu-like symptoms, including fever and swollen glands	Blisters on or near vagina or rectum; sores that can take weeks to heal; flu-like symptoms, including fever and swollen glands	Psychological distress; can cause life-threatening infection in baby born to mother with the disease
Gonorrhea	Burning sensation when urinating; green, yellow, or white discharge from penis; painful, swollen testicles	Pain or burning when urinating; increased vaginal discharge; vaginal bleeding between periods	In males, painful condition of testicles leading to infertility if untreated (epididymitis) In females, chronic pelvic pain and infertility
Trichomoniasis	Temporary irritation inside penis; mild burning after urination or ejaculation	Thick, gray or yellowish green vaginal discharge with strong odor; painful urination; vaginal itching	Discomfort; higher susceptibility to other STDs; premature or low-birth-weight babies born to infected pregnant females
Syphilis	Single sore on the genitals (sores disappear but infection remains); skin rash	Single sore on the vagina (sores disappear but infection remains); skin rash	Serious damage to internal organs, including brain, heart, and nerves

Genital Herpes

Genital herpes is caused by the herpes simplex virus. Herpes simplex 1 usually causes cold sores in or near the mouth. Herpes simplex 2 typically causes genital sores. Both types, however, can infect the mouth and the genitals. In the United States, about 45 million people ages 12 and older have contracted genital herpes.

Many people infected with genital herpes are asymptomatic and are not aware they have the infection. If symptoms do occur, the first outbreak will usually appear as blisters on the genitals or rectum within two weeks of the virus being transmitted. The blisters break, leaving sores that can take several weeks to heal. Usually the first sores are followed by shorter, less severe outbreaks that can occur on and off for years. Antiviral treatments can lessen the frequency of outbreaks, but there is no cure for genital herpes.

Lesson 1   Sexually Transmitted Diseases   **661**

R Reading Strategy

Comparing and Contrasting
Have students compare and contrast symptoms of STDs in males and females. Ask students why a female with symptoms of chlamydia might be less likely than a male to seek medical treatment. (Sample answer: Many of the symptoms in females could be signs of other diseases.)
OL

C Critical Thinking

Synthesize Ask students which STDs discussed in the text can be asymptomatic. (All of them) Why should a person who is asymptomatic seek testing after being exposed to an STD? (Sample answer: Most people infected with an STD are asymptomatic, and consequences of infection can be serious.) **OL**

U Universal Access

Vocabulary Explain that medical treatment is any procedure or medicine that relieves illness or injury. A cure for a communicable disease rids the body of the pathogens that cause it. A cure can be part of a treatment. **Ask Students:** Is there is a cure for the common cold? (No) What treatments have you used when you have had a cold? (Answers will vary but may include over-the-counter medicines, fluids, and rest.) **BL** **EL**

Academic Integration

Math Explain that incidence of STDs is the number of new cases each year. Prevalence is the number of cases present at any one time. Draw three columns with three rows on the board. Label the first row *STD, Incidence, Prevalence.* Fill in the second row *HPV, 6,200,000, 20,000,000.* Fill in the third row *Herpes, 1,000,000, 45,000,000.* Ask: What do you notice about the incidence and prevalence of these diseases? (The prevalence is greater than the incidence.) What are the reasons for this? (These infections cannot be cured. Herpes persists for life. HPV may persist for life or a long time.) Have students calculate the incidence and prevalence rates of these two STDs based on the U.S. estimated population of 302 million. (HPV: 2.1% and 6.6%; HSV: 0.3% and 14.9%)

READING CHECK

Answer If left undiagnosed and untreated, STDs can have serious or long-lasting health effects.

C Critical Thinking

Drawing Conclusions Have students identify the type of pathogen that causes gonorrhea. (bacteria) Remind students that bacterial infections can be cured with antibiotics; viral infections cannot. Discuss with students which long-term effects can be prevented if treated early. **OL**

HS Health Skills Practice

Accessing Information Have students access your state's health department online. Ask them to list the STDs that are reportable by law. **AL**

Go Online

Have students visit **glencoe.com** and complete the Student Web Activity on how common STDs affect American teens.

READING CHECK

Explain Why is it important that STDs are diagnosed as soon as possible?

Go Online

Visit **glencoe.com** and complete the Student Web Activity on how common STDs affect American teens.

Gonorrhea

Gonorrhea is a bacterial STD that usually affects mucous membranes. Gonorrhea is the second most commonly reported infectious disease in the United States. The CDC estimates that more than 700,000 Americans are infected with gonorrhea each year, but only half of these are reported. **C**

Many males with gonorrhea are asymptomatic, and infected females show only mild symptoms. Left untreated, gonorrhea can cause severe health problems, such as infertility. The bacteria can also spread to the bloodstream and cause permanent damage to the body's joints. Females can pass the infection to their babies during childbirth. These babies may contract eye infections that cause blindness.

Trichomoniasis

Trichomoniasis is caused by a microscopic protozoan that results in infections of the vagina, urethra, and bladder. About 7.4 million new cases of trichomoniasis occur every year in the United States.

Although the disease may not produce symptoms, some males have a temporary irritation inside the penis, mild discharge, or slight burning during and after urination or ejaculation. Many infected females often experience *vaginitis,* an inflammation of the vagina characterized by discharge, odor, irritation, and itching. Females with trichomoniasis are also more likely to contract HIV if they are exposed to it. Babies born to females with trichomoniasis are often premature and have low birth weights.

Syphilis

Syphilis, an infection caused by a small bacterium called a spirochete, attacks many parts of the body. People with syphilis develop sores in the genital area lasting a couple of weeks. The disease is passed from one person to another by direct contact with the sores during sexual activity.

Syphilis progresses through three stages. During the primary stage, a sore appears on the external genitals or the vagina. At this stage, the disease can be easily treated. If the infection goes untreated, the sore heals, but the infection remains. In the second stage, the infection produces a skin rash. As in the first stage, the untreated rash will disappear, but the infection remains and progresses to the third stage. During this stage, syphilis can damage internal organs, cause brain dementia, and may cause death.

Teacher to Teacher

Jia Oliver Jordan • Booker T. Washington Magnet High School, Montgomery, AL

Helping Students Overcome STD Anxiety When teaching the chapter on sexually transmitted diseases, I find that students are sometimes uncomfortable with the subject. In order to help them relax, I allow them to speak openly about what they think they know about various STDs. I use the information they provide to begin a fact-based discussion on the topic. I also have students repeat the various ways STDs can be transmitted.

The STD Epidemic

HS

Main Idea Accurate health information and responsible behavior will help fight the STD epidemic.

The United States currently faces an STD epidemic. The CDC estimates that each year, 19 million people are infected with an STD. Almost half are under the age of 24. Many STD cases go undiagnosed and untreated because of

- **embarrassment or fear.** Some people are too embarrassed or afraid to seek medical help.
- **lack of symptoms.** Many people infected with STDs are asymptomatic, and are unaware they have a disease.
- **misinformation.** If STD symptoms disappear without treatment, the infected person may mistakenly believe the disease has been cured. People may not have all the facts and may receive wrong information from friends.
- **notification policies.** State laws require health care providers to report certain but not all STDs. People who have contracted HPV infections or genital herpes are not required to report their infections or inform any partners of their condition. Infected individuals may unknowingly transmit the disease to others.

■ **Figure 24.4** The CDC provides important updated information about STDs at their Web site. *Where else might you find reliable information about STDs?*

LESSON 1 ASSESSMENT

After You Read

Reviewing Facts and Vocabulary

1. What is a *sexually transmitted disease*?
2. Name four common STDs.
3. In the United States, approximately how many people are infected with an STD each year?

Thinking Critically

4. **Synthesize.** How can you communicate the danger of STDs to other teens?
5. **Analyze.** Why is it important to learn about the reasons STDs go undiagnosed and untreated?

Applying Health Skills

6. **Accessing Information.** Create a directory identifying resources in your community where teens can find accurate information about the diagnosis and treatment of STDs.

Writing Critically

7. **Expository.** Describe the cause-and-effect relationship between the reasons many STDs go unreported and undiagnosed and the current STD epidemic in the United States.

 Online

Visit **glencoe.com** and complete the Interactive Study Guide for this lesson.

LESSON 1 ASSESSMENT ANSWERS

1. An infection spread from person to person through sexual contact
2. Answers should include any four: genital HPV infections, chlamydia, genital herpes, gonorrhea, trichomoniasis, syphilis
3. About 19 million people
4. Sample answer: You could inform them of the numbers of people infected by STDs, the reasons for the epidemic, and the long-lasting effects of the diseases.
5. Sample answer: Teens may not make those mistakes if they suspect an infection. An increase in number of people treated will help curb the epidemic.
6. Students can use telephone directories and online resources.
7. Encourage students to include the four reasons listed in the text on this page.

Caption Answer

Figure 24.4 Parents, guardians, teachers; local or state health department; reliable online Web sites of medical facilities, hospitals, doctors' offices

③ ASSESS/ CLOSE

Assessment Resources

📁 **FAST FILE** ACTIVITIES
Lesson 1 Quiz

💿 *ExamView Assessment Suite* CD-ROM

Visit glencoe.com for:
Online Quizzes
Online Learning Center

Progress Monitoring

Reteaching
Have students make a chart that lists three facts about each of the most common STDs, and call on students to share their lists. Then ask students to identify the reasons for the STD epidemic.

Enrichment
Ask students to compare and contrast the symptoms of chlamydia in males and in females. Have them list reasons a female with chlamydia is less likely than a male to exhibit signs of the disease until it is in an advanced stage.

Online

Have students visit **glencoe.com** and complete the Interactive Study Guide for this lesson.

Preventing and Treating STDs

❶ FOCUS

📖 GUIDE TO READING

BIG Idea Students will learn that all STDs can be prevented and most can be treated, but some are incurable. **Ask Students:** *Which STDs that you have studied cannot be cured with antibiotics?* (HPV and genital herpes)

Before You Read

Outline Students' outlines may vary. Abstinence should be included for all STDs in the first column. Treatments should include vaccines, antibiotics, and other medicines.

Main Idea

Prevention Through Abstinence Practicing abstinence is the most effective way to avoid STDs. **Ask Students:** *What long-term effects of STDs might you avoid when you practice abstinence?* (Sample answer: Cancer, infertility, damage to internal organs)

Real Life Issues

Call on volunteers to share their dialogues with the class. Students might suggest that Maria mention that she wants to stay healthy. She wants to avoid having to take medicines, possibly for life, and she wants to have children someday.

LESSON **2**

Preventing and Treating STDs

📖 GUIDE TO READING

BIG Idea *All STDs are preventable and most can be treated, but some are incurable.*

Before You Read
Create an Outline. Preview this lesson by scanning the pages. Then organize the headings and subheadings into an outline. As you read, fill in your outline with important details.

```
I.
   A.
      1.
      2.
   B.
II.
```

New Vocabulary
▸ antibiotics (p. 664)
▸ HPV vaccine (p. 667)

Review Vocabulary
▸ abstinence (Ch.1, L.3)
▸ refusal skills (Ch.2, L.1)

Real Life Issues ⋯⋯⋯⋯⋯⋯⋯⋯⋯⋯⋯⋯

Making Personal Decisions. Maria and Jake have been dating for six months. Together, they work on the school newspaper, play tennis, and enjoy eating out. Lately, though, Jake has been more and more insistent that they take their relationship "to the next level." Maria has had two previous sexual relationships, but she has now decided to practice abstinence. She made her decision based partly on what she learned about STDs. "It's not worth all the risks," Maria tells Jake. She is committed to her decision to practice abstinence.

Writing *Write a dialogue between Maria and Jake. Include an explanation of the risks that you think Maria is talking about, and show how Jake might respond in a healthful way.*

Prevention Through Abstinence

Main Idea The most successful method to prevent the spread of STDs is abstinence.

About 9 million American teens contract STDs annually. Some are bacterial infections, such as chlamydia or gonorrhea, that can be treated and cured with antibiotics. **Antibiotics** are *a class of chemical agents that destroy disease-causing microorganisms while leaving the patient unharmed.* Others, such as genital herpes and HPV, are incurable viral infections. Any STDs that are not diagnosed early and treated can result in serious permanent or long-term health consequences.

The only method that is 100 percent successful in preventing the contraction and spread of STDs is abstinence. Abstinence before marriage is the best way to avoid STDs.

664 Chapter 24 Sexually Transmitted Diseases and HIV/AIDS

Skills for the 21st Century

Communication Skills Students need to be able to stand up assertively for their values. Throughout a person's life, other people in social and work situations will make requests or demands. Some of these will be unreasonable, and some will go against the person's values. Have students write a brief account of an incident in which a peer, co-worker, or boss made such a request. They should include how they responded and the outcome. Ask volunteers to share their paragraphs and analyze whether they could have responded more appropriately. Point out that many employers provide assertiveness training; they want employees to maintain honest and assertive communication with co-workers and bosses.

■ **Figure 24.5** Group outings are one way to enjoy the company of friends and avoid pressure to engage in sexual activity. *Why might you want to discuss your commitment to abstinence with your friends?*

② TEACH

AL Active Learning

Bulletin Board Have students call out reasons for abstinence as you write them on the board. Ask volunteers to use markers to copy them in large letters on construction paper. Have small groups sketch or cut out pictures from discarded magazines to show teen activities that do not involve physical intimacy. Have volunteers arrange the reasons and pictures in a bulletin board display. **BL**

HS Health Skills Practice

Refusal Skills Have students brainstorm words and body language they could use if pressured to have sex or engage in other high-risk behavior. Explain that knowing several stock phrases can help them be prepared and confident if this situation arises. **OL**

Academic Vocabulary

Guideline Call on a volunteer to use the word *guideline* in a sentence. Ask other students whether it was used correctly. If not, ask for another volunteer to give a sentence.

 To help you protect your health and stay committed to abstinence, follow these **guidelines**:

- Set personal limits on physical affection.
- Avoid dating someone who is sexually active or who pressures you to go beyond your limits.
- Avoid situations where you may feel pressured to engage in sexual activity.
- Avoid people who make fun of your decisions or urge high-risk behaviors, including use of alcohol or drugs.
- Choose group outings where you can enjoy the company of friends and avoid pressure to engage in sexual activity.
- Be clear about your decision to practice abstinence, and discuss it with others who are close to you.
- Practice refusal skills. Use words and body language to resist the pressure to engage in sexual activity.

Academic Vocabulary

guideline *(noun):* an outline of conduct

Understanding the Risks

Each month, about 750,000 teens are diagnosed with an STD. This age group is at high risk partly because many teens are unaware of a partner's past behavior. It's impossible to look at someone and tell if that person has an STD. Because many STDs go undiagnosed, it is not enough for a partner simply to say that he or she is uninfected. Abstinence is the only sure method of preventing STDs.

Writing Strategy

Writing About Abstinence Tell students to imagine that a good friend has been unusually quiet lately. When asked what is wrong, the friend responds that he or she is being pressured to engage in sexual activity. Ask students to write a letter to the friend describing the reasons to practice abstinence until marriage. They should include refusal skills for dealing with the partner. They also should point out the consequences of engaging in high-risk behavior. Encourage students to keep in mind the audience for their writing and use a tone that is caring and concerned for the friend's future.

Health Skills Activity

Refusal Skills: The Lines of Defense

NHES Standard 4 Students will demonstrate the ability to use interpersonal communication skills to enhance health and avoid or reduce health risks.

Objectives

- Analyze the relationship between the use of refusal skills and the avoidance of unsafe situations such as sexual activity.
- Apply refusal skills to resist peer pressure to engage in sexual activity.

Teaching Strategies

- Review examples of refusal skills.
- Allow students to work in small groups to develop possible responses Mark and Alyssa could use to refuse Emma's request. Have groups share their responses.

Assessment

Using this list, student work should provide comprehensive evidence of the following criteria to achieve the highest score:

√ Includes "no" in response
√ Explains why they are refusing
√ Proposes alternatives
√ Demonstrates effective body language that backs up words
√ Describes walking away if necessary

Health Skills Activity

Refusal Skills

The Lines of Defense

Mark and Alyssa have been dating for a year. Both are committed to practicing abstinence. It hasn't always been easy, but they believe firmly that it is the safest and most caring method of avoiding STDs and unintended pregnancy.

One afternoon, Alyssa's friend Emma says, "Hey, guys, I'm having a party tonight. For once, my parents won't be there. The new guy I'm dating is bringing his band. It's going to be great. "

Mark and Alyssa glance at each other, and then Alyssa shakes her head. "Sounds like fun," she replies, "but things could get out of hand."

Mark agrees, "Yeah, thanks for the invitation, but I think we'll pass."

"Oh, give me a break!" says Emma, annoyed. "What are you afraid of?"

Writing Write a dialogue in which Mark and Alyssa use refusal skills to respond to Emma. Follow these steps:

1. Say no in a firm voice.
2. Explain why you are refusing.
3. Suggest alternatives to the proposed activity.
4. Back up your words with body language.
5. Leave if necessary.

Avoiding High-Risk Behaviors and STDs

Avoiding high-risk behaviors can help prevent people from contracting STDs. High-risk behaviors include

- **being sexually active with more than one person.** This includes having a series of sexual relationships with one person at a time. However, being sexually active with even one partner puts a person at risk.
- **engaging in unprotected sex.** Even protected sex, or barrier protection, is not 100 percent effective in preventing the transmission of STDs. Abstaining from sexual activity is the only method that is 100 percent effective in avoiding STDs.
- **engaging in sexual activity with high-risk partners.** Such partners include those with a history of being sexually active with more than one person and those who have injected illegal drugs. Taking a person's word about past behaviors is not wise. Sexual activity with just one infected person puts you at risk.
- **using alcohol and other drugs.** Alcohol can lower inhibitions and cause teens to engage in sexual activity when they might ordinarily choose not to. To safeguard your health, it's important to be in control of your decisions.

✓ READING CHECK

Explain How can the use of alcohol or other drugs increase a person's risk of contracting an STD?

Teens Want to Know

If I Seek Treatment for an STD, Will My Parents Find Out? In all 50 states, adolescents can legally consent to testing and treatment of STDs. Medical care can be provided without parental consent or knowledge. The laws for consent to vaccination differ by state. Some states provide vaccinations without parental consent. Ask students to discuss whether they agree with these policies. Point out that while health care providers cannot notify the parents, the teen can. Then ask students to imagine how they would feel if they were a parent and their child received testing and treatment without their knowledge. Have them analyze the benefits of communicating this information to parents or guardians.

Figure 24.6 Diagnosis Methods and Treatments for STDs

CA Diagnosis methods and successful treatments for common STDs vary.

STD	Diagnosis Method	Treatment/Cure
Genital HPV Infection	Pap test in females; genital warts diagnosed by a physical examination	No cure; warts may clear up without medication or by using medications applied by patient; or may clear up with treatments performed by a health care provider
Chlamydia	Urine tests; tests on specimen collected from the infected site	Treated and cured with antibiotics
Genital Herpes	Visual inspection by a health care professional; testing of infected sore; blood tests	No cure; antiviral medication can shorten and prevent outbreaks
Gonorrhea	Laboratory test (Gram's stain); urine test	Treated and cured with antibiotics; successful treatment becoming difficult due to increase of drug-resistant strains; medication stops infection but cannot repair damage done by disease
Trichomoniasis	Physical examination and laboratory test	Prescription drug, metronidazole, given by mouth in a single dose; both partners should receive treatment at same time
Syphilis	Physical examination; blood test	Curable with penicillin or other antibiotics; treatment will not repair damage already done

HPV Vaccine

The Food and Drug Administration (FDA) has approved the **HPV vaccine**, *a vaccine that can prevent cervical cancer, pre-cancerous genital lesions (or sores), and genital warts caused by genital HPV infection.* This vaccine protects against four types of HPV infections. Health officials recommend the vaccine for females 9 to 26 years old. Studies are under way to learn if the vaccine has health benefits for males. At this time, no vaccines are available for any other types of STDs.

Diagnosing and Treating STDs

Main Idea Only a health care professional can accurately diagnose and treat an STD.

If STDs are not diagnosed and treated early, serious long-term consequences can result. Teens who believe they might be infected with an STD should talk to a health care professional. Many public health clinics provide information and treatment free of charge. **Figure 24.6** summarizes diagnosis and treatment methods for common STDs.

Main Idea

Diagnosing and Treating STDs Only a health care professional can accurately diagnose and treat an STD. **Ask Students:** *Why is it still important for people to seek medical care if they suspect they have a viral STD?* (People need to confirm whether they have an STD and have the type identified to determine the treatment.)

CA Cultural Awareness

Seeking Treatment Explain that people of various ethnic backgrounds may feel particularly uncomfortable discussing intimate topics, such as symptoms of an STD. Healthcare facilities frequently lack providers who speak the language of non-native speakers of English. Discuss the influence these and other cultural differences might have on an individual's decision to seek medical treatment for a possible STD. OL

C Critical Thinking

Making Inferences Ask students what might happen if a person used a home remedy to treat an STD and the symptoms disappeared. (Sample answer: The person might think he or she is cured though the infection might still be present.) Why is it important for people who have an STD not to try to treat it themselves? (The treatments will not be effective; curable STDs must be treated with specific antibiotics.) OL

Cooperative Learning

STD Pamphlets Have small groups create a pamphlet for teens about the six most common STDs. They should describe symptoms, diagnosis, and treatment. They should include information about asymptomatic infection and the importance of getting tested and notifying partners. Have them list telephone numbers, addresses, and Web sites for local and state health agencies and clinics that offer treatment for STDs. Encourage students to make the pamphlets visually appealing and easy to read and understand.

READING CHECK

Answer Antibiotics can cure chlamydia, gonorrhea, trichomoniasis, and syphilis. STDs caused by HPV and herpes are incurable.

③ ASSESS/ CLOSE

Assessment Resources

📁 *FAST FILE* **ACTIVITIES**
Lesson 2 Quiz

💿 *ExamView*
Assessment Suite CD-ROM

Visit glencoe.com **for:**
Online Quizzes
Online Learning Center

Progress Monitoring

Reteaching
Have students outline the lesson, detailing important facts. Direct students to list reasons for practicing abstinence as the only reliable means of avoiding infection with an STD.

Enrichment
Have students research and analyze influences on the incidence of STDs during the past century. Influences include changes in social attitudes and in health care, such as antibiotics and contraceptive methods. Ask students to synthesize their findings in a short paper.

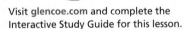

Have students visit **glencoe.com** and complete the Interactive Study Guide for this lesson.

Keep in mind that not all genital infections are STDs; some are localized skin infections or rashes. Only a trained professional can determine which test will most effectively screen for a particular STD. When an STD has been diagnosed, a health care professional will prescribe the most effective medication and monitor the patient's treatment. STDs cannot be cured using common household products, homemade remedies, or over-the-counter treatments. Also, remember that taking medicines prescribed to others is risky.

Antibiotics can effectively treat bacterial STDs, but viral STDs are incurable. However, medications can lessen the discomfort from sores and skin irritations caused by STDs.

READING CHECK

Explain Which types of STDs can be treated and possibly cured? Which cannot?

Act Responsibly

Everyone has an obligation to prevent the spread of STDs. One way to help control this epidemic is to practice abstinence. A second way is to report any known infections. Public health clinics can sometimes help locate past partners to make sure they get medical treatment. Ultimately, however, it is the responsibility of any person infected with an STD to notify everyone with whom he or she has had sexual contact. Informing someone else about a possible STD infection could save a life.

LESSON **2** 📖 **ASSESSMENT**

After You Read

Reviewing Facts and Vocabulary
1. What is the only 100 percent effective method for preventing the spread of STDs?
2. Identify two high-risk behaviors that can lead to contracting an STD.
3. What is the *HPV vaccine*?

Thinking Critically
4. **Synthesize.** Predict situations that could lead to pressures to engage in sexual activity, and identify ways to avoid these situations.
5. **Analyze.** Explain the causes and consequences of teen health risk behaviors that could result in STD infection, and describe prevention strategies.

Applying Health Skills
6. **Refusal Skills.** Write a scenario in which one teen is pressuring another to engage in behavior that puts both at high risk for contracting an STD. The second teen should use refusal skills to respond to the pressure.

Writing Critically
7. **Persuasive.** Write a public service announcement urging teens to get medical help for all health problems, including suspected STDs. Include local resources for medical care.

G⊙ Online

Visit **glencoe.com** and complete the Interactive Study Guide for this lesson.

LESSON **2** ASSESSMENT ANSWERS

1. Practicing abstinence
2. *Any two:* Sexual activity with more than one person; unprotected sex; sexual activity with high-risk partners; using alcohol and other drugs
3. A vaccine that prevents infection by four types of human papilloma viruses and therefore prevents cervical cancer and genital warts
4. Answers will vary.

5. High-risk behaviors such as drug or alcohol use can often lead to sexual activity and increase the risk for contracting an STD. Prevention includes practicing abstinence and avoiding high-risk situations and people.
6. Students should include the five steps of refusal skills.
7. PSAs will vary.

HIV/AIDS

Real Life Issues

Finding Out the Facts. Mariano, Cal, and Janine heard a rumor at school that one of the seniors tested positive for HIV. "I'm not going to play ball with the seniors. I don't want to come into contact with their sweat," says Janine.

Cal laughs. "Get real. You can't get HIV from sweat!"

"Well, sweat's a bodily fluid, isn't it?" Janine shoots back.

"I'm not sure exactly how HIV/AIDS is passed around," says Mariano slowly. "Let's figure out where we can go or who we can ask to find out."

Writing *Write a list of true/false questions about HIV/AIDS that Mariano and his friends might have about how HIV is transmitted. After reading the lesson, return to your list and answer each question.*

What Is HIV/AIDS?

Main Idea HIV/AIDS weakens the body's immune system.

Human immunodeficiency virus (HIV) is *a virus that attacks the immune system.* Once HIV enters the body, it finds and destroys the white blood cells that fight disease. The final stage of an HIV infection is **acquired immunodeficiency syndrome (AIDS)**, *a disease in which the immune system is weakened.*

AIDS has become one of the deadliest diseases in human history. More than 25 million people around the world have died of this disease, including more than 500,000 Americans. Health care officials estimate that currently 40 million people worldwide have HIV/AIDS. The statistics are alarming:

- Approximately 12 million of the people who have HIV/AIDS are in the 15 to 24 age group.
- Half of all new HIV infections are among young people. Every day, about 7,000 young people become infected.

GUIDE TO READING

BIG Idea *HIV is the virus that causes AIDS, a disease that weakens the body's immune system and may have fatal consequences.*

Before You Read

Create a K-W-L Chart. Make a three-column chart. In the first column, list what you <u>k</u>now about HIV/AIDS. In the second column, list what you <u>w</u>ant to know about this topic. As you read, use the third column to summarize what you <u>l</u>earned.

K	W	L

New Vocabulary

- human immunodeficiency virus (HIV) (p. 669)
- acquired immunodeficiency syndrome (AIDS) (p. 669)

Review Vocabulary

- pandemic (Ch.23, L.4)
- mucous membranes (Ch.23, L.2)
- lymphocytes (Ch.23, L.3)
- antibodies (Ch.23, L.3)

HIV/AIDS

1 FOCUS

GUIDE TO READING

BIG Idea HIV is the virus that causes AIDS, a disease that weakens the body's immune system. **Ask Students:** *What questions do you think this lesson will answer?* (Sample answer: What is the difference between HIV and AIDS?)

Before You Read
K-W-L Chart Students' charts will vary.

Main Idea

HIV/AIDS HIV/AIDS is a disease of the immune system. **Ask Students:** *What is the function of the immune system, and why is it important?* (The immune system works against pathogens. It is important in helping fight off communicable diseases, which can be serious or even fatal.)

Real Life Issues

Encourage students to include questions they have heard repeated or to which they do not know the answer. After students have written their questions, ask volunteers to read their lists.

ELL Support

Making a Glossary Help students create a personal HIV/AIDS glossary. They can record the vocabulary terms and any other terms with which they are unfamiliar.

Beginning Have students copy and break down the definition in their own words. For example, they may need help with the meaning of "specialized" in the definition of *lymphocytes.*

Intermediate Ask students to write each definition in their own words. Pro-vide sentences reworded from the text to check for understanding, for example, "B cells and T cells are two types of _____." (lymphocytes)

Advanced Ask students to write each definition in their own words. Then have them write sentences that use each term.

② TEACH

 READING CHECK

Answer HIV is the virus that causes AIDS. AIDS is the final stage of an HIV infection. HIV is always present in an infected person.

C Critical Thinking

Comparing and Contrasting Ask students in what ways is HIV/AIDS similar to the six most common STDs. (Sample answers: It is spread through sexual contact. People may not know they are infected.) *How is it different?* (Sample answers: It attacks the immune system. It is a fatal disease with no cure.) OL

Main Idea

Understanding HIV/AIDS HIV/AIDS is transmitted in a variety of ways. **Ask Students:** *What behaviors can you think of in which blood might be passed from one person to another?* (Sample answers: Sharing razors, getting body piercing or tattoos with contaminated instruments)

AL Active Learning

Poetry/Rap Have small groups use the material on these pages to develop a poem about how HIV is and is not transmitted. Ask them to include abstinence as the best way to avoid HIV. Allow students to set their poems to a rap beat, if they wish. Ask groups to read or perform their poem for the class. OL AL

670

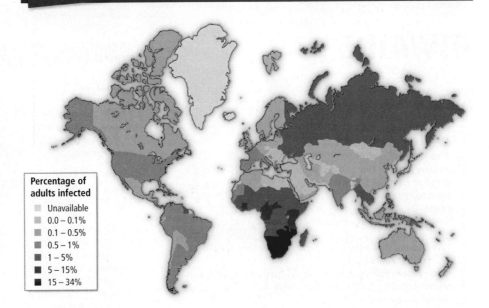

Figure 24.7 **Worldwide HIV Infection Rates for Adults**

Percentage of adults infected
- Unavailable
- 0.0 – 0.1%
- 0.1 – 0.5%
- 0.5 – 1%
- 1 – 5%
- 5 – 15%
- 15 – 34%

 READING CHECK

Explain How are HIV and AIDS related?

As **Figure 24.7** shows, HIV infection is a worldwide concern. Health care officials consider HIV/AIDS a *pandemic,* a global outbreak of infectious disease. Many experts and scientists consider HIV/AIDS to be the most serious public health problem facing the world. The seriousness of the HIV/AIDS pandemic is greatly increased because many of the young people who are infected do not know it.

Understanding HIV/AIDS

Main Idea HIV/AIDS is transmitted in a variety of ways.

HIV is a fragile virus and cannot live outside the human body. Exposure to air at room temperature kills the virus. HIV cannot be spread through airborne transmission, through casual contact such as shaking hands or hugging, or from insect bites. Although the virus has been found in sweat, tears, and saliva of infected persons, the amount is too small to be considered dangerous. **C**

HIV is transmitted among humans only when one person's infected blood, semen, or vaginal secretions comes in contact with another person's broken skin or mucous membranes. **AL**

670 Chapter 24 Sexually Transmitted Diseases and HIV/AIDS

Myths & Reality

HIV Transmission

Myth: You can get HIV from eating after an infected person or sharing their utensils.

Fact: HIV is not transmitted through food or eating utensils.

Myth: You cannot get HIV from having sex just one time.

Fact: A single exposure to HIV can result in infection.

Myth: You can get HIV from being in a pool or hot tub with an infected person.

Fact: This is true only if you are having sexual contact with the person. Infection requires direct contact with mucous membranes. Just being in the same pool or hot tub will not result in infection.

Mucous membranes can be found in the mouth, eyes, nose, vagina, rectum, and the opening in the penis.

HIV is spread in three ways:

- **During sexual intercourse.** HIV can enter the bloodstream through microscopic openings in tissues of the vagina, anus, mouth, or the opening in the penis. People with STDs are more vulnerable to HIV infection because STDs cause changes in the body's membranes that increase the likelihood of HIV transmission.

- **By sharing needles.** Anyone who uses needles contaminated with HIV allows the virus to enter directly into his or her bloodstream. Needles used for body piercings and tattoos also can come in contact with contaminated blood. If those needles are not properly cleaned or sterilized, other customers can become infected.

- **From mother to baby.** A pregnant female infected with HIV can pass the virus to her unborn baby through the umbilical cord, during childbirth, or through breastfeeding. If an expectant mother knows she's infected, she can take medication that might prevent her child from contracting HIV. During childbirth, the doctor and nurses will work to prevent the newborn from coming into contact with the mother's blood, and the mother will be asked not to breastfeed her infant. The number of infected infants has declined in the United States now that pregnant females are routinely tested for HIV.

How HIV/AIDS Affects the Immune System

W
HIV attacks the body's immune system by destroying *lymphocytes*. These are specialized white blood cells that perform many immune functions, such as fighting pathogens. As you learned in Chapter 23, there are two types of lymphocytes: B cells and T cells. Helper T cells stimulate B cells to produce antibodies, which help destroy pathogens that enter the body. When HIV enters certain cells, including lymphocytes, it reproduces itself and eventually destroys the cell. **Figure 24.8** on page 672 shows how HIV attacks cells. As more cells are destroyed, the immune system becomes weaker and weaker. The body then becomes vulnerable to *AIDS-opportunistic illnesses,* infections the body could fight off if the immune system were healthy.

HIV infection usually goes through identifiable stages before progressing to AIDS:

C
- **Asymptomatic stage.** This stage can last for ten years or more. The virus is largely **confined** to the lymph nodes, where it invades and takes over helper T cells. There are no outward signs of infection.

READING CHECK

List What are the three ways that HIV is spread?

Academic Vocabulary

confine *(verb):* to keep within limits

READING CHECK

Answer During sexual activity, through contaminated needles, and from infected mother to baby

W Writing Support

Expository Writing Ask students to summarize in a paragraph in their own words how HIV weakens the immune system. Have them include a clear main idea, supporting details, and present the information in a logical order. **BL OL**

C Critical Thinking

Drawing Conclusions Point that the asymptomatic stage of HIV/AIDS can last as long as ten years. Ask: How does this make the control of HIV/AIDS difficult? (If people are unaware they are infected and have no symptoms, they can spread the virus for many years before they have symptoms and are diagnosed.) **OL**

Reading Strategy

Making Inferences Refer students to the map of the world. Ask them to identify the parts of the world with the highest HIV infection rates. (sub-Saharan Africa, followed by most of Africa and parts of Asia) Ask students to use what they know about this part of the world and what they have read in this lesson to infer what accounts for the high rates.

(Sample answers: These areas may not have many testing facilities, or people may not have access to them, so people do not know they are infected. People may not be educated on how the disease is spread.) Have students research the countries with the highest number of HIV/AIDS cases and write a paragraph describing the reasons.

U Universal Access

Interpreting Diagrams
Describe what is happening in each step in **Figure 24.8** on page 672 as students follow the diagram. Then pair students with more proficient learners and ask them to draw a picture of each step in the diagram and write a caption in their own words. BL EL

HS Health Skills Practice

Decision Making Skills Provide a scenario in which two teens are deciding whether to give blood or not. One teen is okay with it and the other is afraid of contracting HIV. OL

Figure 24.8 **How HIV Attacks Cells**

Once inside the cell, HIV is safe from attack by the immune system's antibodies. *How does this make HIV particulary dangerous?* U

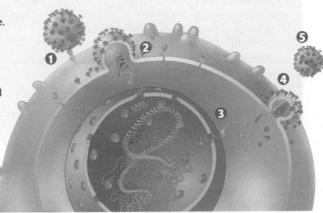

1. HIV attaches to cell surface.
2. Virus core enters cell and goes to nucleus.
3. Virus makes a copy of its genetic material.
4. New virus assembles at cell surface.
5. New virus breaks away from host cell.

- **Middle stage.** This stage occurs in about 40 to 70 percent of infected patients. Patients experience fever, headache, sore throat, rash, diarrhea, and enlarged lymph nodes.
- **Symptomatic stage.** Helper T cells fall to 200 to 400 per milliliter of blood. The patient experiences flu-like symptoms, such as headache, fever, body aches, swollen glands, diminished appetite, weight loss, and skin rashes.
- **AIDS stage.** Helper T cells drop to less than 200, or one or more AIDS-opportunistic illnesses are present.

When the virus has destroyed or impaired most of the immune system's white blood cells, the patient is in the final stage of HIV and is said to have AIDS. People with AIDS have immune systems that are so weakened that they may die from illnesses from which they would ordinarily recover.

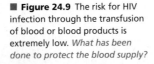

■ **Figure 24.9** The risk for HIV infection through the transfusion of blood or blood products is extremely low. *What has been done to protect the blood supply?*

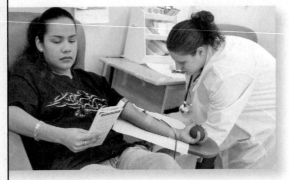

Giving or Receiving Blood: Is It Safe?

Some people fear that they might be infected with HIV when donating or receiving blood. In the United States, health care professionals always use sterile needles to draw blood. In addition, all donated blood has been tested for HIV since 1985. According to the CDC, "The U.S. blood supply is among the safest in the world." HS

🏔️👫 Home and Community

Blood Donations Ask students to use telephone directories and online resources to find locations in your community where blood can be donated. Have them find the criteria for donating blood in your state. Donors generally must weigh at least 110 pounds and be at least 17 years old. Some states allow donations at age 16. Then have students contact the donor sites or print out information from their Web sites on the criteria, location, and times a person can donate. Ask students to make signs or posters encouraging students to donate blood. Tell them to include information about the safety of blood donation.

TEENS Making a Difference

Promoting AIDS Education

Hoonie K., of Pennsylvania, decided to take a stand by becoming a Student AIDS Educator (SAE). "There's a lot of misinformation and prejudices about HIV/AIDS. My goal is to educate my peers so they take action to prevent it."

SAEs meet with an adult adviser each week to obtain the latest information about HIV. They also help students who need more information or want to be tested. "We direct them to the appropriate places," Hoonie explains. "Everything is anonymous."

Hoonie hopes to expand the group's efforts by hosting a concert to raise money for HIV/AIDS research. "We want more opportunities to educate our peers."

Activity Write your answers to the following questions in your personal health journal.

1 Write three questions you would ask a Student AIDS Educator.

2 Where can you find accurate HIV/AIDS information in your community?

3 Why is it important to educate people about HIV/AIDS?

LESSON 3 ASSESSMENT

After You Read

Reviewing Facts and Vocabulary

1. How does HIV affect the human immune system?
2. How can you protect yourself from contracting HIV/AIDS?
3. Why do the body's antibodies fail to protect people from HIV?

Thinking Critically

4. **Analyze.** Why has the CDC implemented mandatory testing for all donated blood?
5. **Synthesize.** How does the immune system respond to the presence of HIV in the body?

Applying Health Skills

6. **Advocacy.** Create a poster or public service announcement that warns teens about the risks of contracting HIV/AIDS.

Writing Critically

7. **Expository.** Write an essay that explains the relationship between HIV and AIDS. Discuss why the infection is considered one of the world's deadliest diseases.

Go Online

Visit glencoe.com and complete the Interactive Study Guide for this lesson.

Lesson 3   HIV/AIDS   **673**

CHAPTER 24
LESSON 3

3 ASSESS/ CLOSE

Assessment Resources

 FAST FILE ACTIVITIES
Lesson 3 Quiz

 ExamView
Assessment Suite CD-ROM

Visit glencoe.com **for:**
Online Quizzes
Online Learning Center

Progress Monitoring

Reteaching
Write on the board several ways HIV is and is not transmitted. Read each one aloud, and have the class respond "yes" or "no" to the question "Is HIV spread this way?" Cross out or circle the ways as appropriate.

Enrichment
Have students use the map in this lesson to choose a country with a high HIV infection rate. The students should research information about how HIV is affecting family and social structures in that country and how the government is responding to the epidemic.

Go Online

Have students visit glencoe.com and complete the Interactive Study Guide for this lesson.

LESSON 3 ASSESSMENT ANSWERS

1. HIV invades and destroys white blood cells, so that the immune system is weakened.
2. By practicing abstinence from high-risk behaviors such as sexual activity, illegal drug use, and sharing contaminated tattoo/piercing instruments
3. HIV enters the cells too quickly for the antibodies to destroy them; *antibodies* work in the bloodstream, not in cells; and HIV can mutate so the *antibodies* do not recognize it.

4. To prevent donated blood containing HIV to be given to another person
5. Helper T cells cause B cells to produce antibodies to HIV. HIV destroys more and more T cells, and the immune system is weakened. Opportunistic illnesses then overcome the immune system.
6. Posters or PSAs will vary.
7. Essays will vary.

673

LESSON 4

Preventing and Treating HIV/AIDS

① FOCUS

GUIDE TO READING

BIG Idea Students will learn that HIV/AIDS can be prevented and treated, but cannot be cured. **Ask Students:** *Why can't HIV/AIDS be treated with antibiotics?* (It is a virus, which cannot be treated with antibiotics.)

Before You Read

Chart Students' charts will vary but should closely reflect the material in the lesson. Encourage students to take notes in their own words.

Main Idea

Preventing HIV/AIDS A person can practice responsible behaviors to avoid HIV/AIDS. **Ask Students:** *What is the best way to prevent HIV/AIDS?* (By practicing abstinence to avoid sexual activity and other high-risk behavior)

Real Life Issues

Before students write, suggest that they first try to imagine how they might feel if they were in Kari's situation. Have them jot down their thoughts. Then ask students to imagine how Tony feels and write from his point of view.

LESSON 4

GUIDE TO READING

BIG Idea *HIV/AIDS is preventable and treatable, but it is incurable.*

Before You Read

Organize Information. Make a three-column chart. Label the columns "Prevention," "Diagnosis," and "Treatment." As you read, fill in the chart with information about how HIV/AIDS can be prevented, diagnosed, and treated.

Prevention	Diagnosis	Treatment

New Vocabulary

▶ EIA (p. 677)
▶ Western blot (p. 677)
▶ rapid test (p. 677)

Academic Vocabulary

estimate *(verb):* to determine roughly the size or extent of

---

Preventing and Treating HIV/AIDS

Real Life Issues ·····················

Worried About HIV. Tony is concerned about his older sister, Kari. She confided that she enjoys college life, but she and her friends are under a lot of pressure to have sex and to experiment with alcohol and other drugs. Kari is committed to abstinence, so she's chosen to hang out with people who respect her decision. Yesterday, however, one of her closest friends called to tell her that he tested positive for HIV. Kari was shocked and upset by the news that someone she cares about deeply is infected with HIV.

Writing *Write a dialogue between Tony and Kari. How might Tony express his concern and support for his sister?*

Preventing HIV/AIDS

Main Idea There are many actions you can take to avoid contracting HIV/AIDS.

The Centers for Disease Control and Prevention (CDC) estimates that more than one million Americans live with HIV, and 40,000 are infected each year. About 5,000 of those will be young people between the ages of 13 and 24. Teens who are sexually active or who use intravenous drugs have a particularly high risk for contracting HIV/AIDS. Take a look at **Figure 24.10**. The graph shows the number of HIV/AIDS cases reported among teens between 1995 and 2005.

There is no way to tell just by looking whether a person is infected with HIV. The CDC **estimates** that about 25 percent of the people in the United States who are infected with HIV do not know they are infected. Because they are unaware

674 Chapter 24 Sexually Transmitted Diseases and HIV/AIDS

Promoting School Wellness

Counseling About HIV A successful school program has one or more professionals such as certified school counselors, psychologists, or social workers to counsel and support students who need help with problems. In particular, students who think they might have been infected with HIV or other STDs may be reluctant to talk about it with anyone or to seek testing. If your school has these types of professionals, let students know that they are available. A counselor can help students work through their emotions and attitudes and refer them to medical providers for testing and treatment if needed.

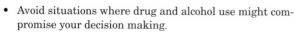

Figure 24.10 HIV/AIDS Among Teens

Female Male

Number of Cases

Year	Total	Female	Male
1995	390	160	230
1996	400	180	220
1997	356	156	200
1998	290	130	160
1999	305	150	155
2000	322	162	160
2001	351	151	200
2002	385	175	210
2003	471	221	250
2004	421	181	240
2005	510	219	291

Source: CDC, *HIV/AIDS Surveillance in Adolescents,* 2006

that they are HIV-positive, they may unknowingly spread the virus to others.Fortunately, you can take action to prevent the spread of HIV/AIDS. The following healthful behaviors will help protect you from infection:

U

- Practice abstinence.
- Do not share needles.
- Avoid situations where drug and alcohol use might compromise your decision making.
- Use refusal skills when you feel pressured to engage in risky behaviors.

For more information on HIV prevention strategies, see **Figure 24.11** on page 676. Notice that the listed behaviors all involve relationships. For example, sharing a needle always involves another person. Ask yourself:

CA

- What do I know about the people in my life and their behaviors?
- Will they put me at risk for getting HIV/AIDS?
- How can I be sure another person is not HIV-positive?

AL

Knowing as much as you can about the people around you and their behaviors can help you make responsible and informed decisions. It's also a good idea to practice refusal skills so you are prepared when pressured to engage in high-risk behaviors.

READING CHECK

Identify What are successful methods to avoid contracting HIV/AIDS?

Lesson 4   Preventing and Treating HIV/AIDS   **675**

Cooperative Learning

Learning Center Tell students they are going to put together a learning center to inform other students about HIV/AIDS. Divide the class into small groups. Have groups brainstorm activities, such as puzzles, "Test Your HIV IQ" quiz, and a video. Help each group choose one activity to create.

As a class, decide how and where you want to display the learning center. Provide art materials and resources for students. Encourage creativity and initiative. Get permission from the appropriate school personnel to set up the learning center in the school library, auditorium, or cafeteria.

② TEACH

U Universal Access

Benefits of Abstinence Ask students to draw two columns on a sheet of paper. Have them use the chart to list the ways to prevent HIV/AIDS on the left side. Have them list goals they want to achieve within the next ten years in the right column. Ask volunteers to share their goals. Then discuss how HIV infection might prevent them from reaching their goals. **BL**

CA Cultural Awareness

Celebrities with HIV Ask students to name actors, athletes, or other celebrities who have made public that they are HIV-positive. Have students discuss what influence these celebrities have had on the public's attitudes about people with HIV/AIDS. Ask volunteers to share any influences on their personal feelings, but do not pressure students to do so. **OL**

AL Active Learning

Guest Speaker Invite the nurse or a health professional from a hospital to come and talk about his or her HIV-related interactions with patients. Under what circumstances does he or she suggest HIV testing? How often does he or she raise the issue of HIV infection and/or HIV risk behaviors with patients? Allow students to ask questions. **OL**

READING CHECK

Answer Practice abstinence, do not share needles, avoid drug and alcohol use, and use refusal skills when you are pressured to engage in risky behaviors.

Diagnosing HIV/AIDS Several tests are used to diagnose HIV/AIDS.
Ask Students: *Why is it important for a person who thinks he or she might be infected to get tested if there is no cure?* (Sample answer: The person would know not to spread the infection to others and would be able to get the proper medical treatment.)

R Reading Strategy

Preventing HIV and AIDS
After students have examined **Figure 24.11**, ask: *How is HIV spread?* (Through semen and vaginal secretions.) *What are two ways to prevent HIV and AIDS?* (Avoid situations where pressured to engage in sexual activity or drug use, and avoid sharing needles.) **OL**

AL Active Learning

Timeline Encourage students to use information from the text and outside sources to construct a timeline of the history of HIV/AIDS. They might start with the year the first case was recognized. Have them include research milestones, such as drug treatments and tests, and periodically state the number of cases in the U.S. and worldwide. Have students display the timeline on a classroom wall. **AL**

Figure 24.11 Ways to Prevent HIV and AIDS

Practice abstinence. HIV is spread through semen and vaginal secretions. Wait to be sexually active until you are ready for a monogamous, lifelong relationship.

Avoid sharing needles or syringes used to inject drugs, including steroids.

Avoid sharing needles, knives, and razors used for cutting, tattoos, body art, or body piercing.

Avoid situations and events where you might feel pressured to engage in sexual activity or drug and alcohol use.

R

Diagnosing HIV/AIDS

Main Idea Several tests are used to diagnose HIV/AIDS.

If someone believes he or she may have been exposed to HIV, the person needs to be tested. Testing is available in a doctor's office, local health department or hospital, and sites that specialize in HIV testing. Some places, such as the health department, will do the test for free. **AL**

Typically, a blood sample or an oral specimen from between the inside of the cheek and the gum is collected and sent to a laboratory for analysis. Results are usually available within two weeks. At most testing sites, qualified personnel are available to answer questions, make referrals, and explain results.

Types of Laboratory HIV Tests

After collected samples are sent to a laboratory, technicians screen them for HIV antibodies. A person's body does not naturally have HIV antibodies: they are produced only in the presence of an infection. The most common laboratory tests used to screen, diagnose, and confirm HIV antibodies are the EIA and Western blot tests. **U**

More About...

Antibody Testing for HIV Most tests for HIV measure antibodies against HIV. The infected person must have enough antibodies for these tests to detect, and producing antibodies after exposure to HIV takes time. Most people develop detectable levels of antibodies within two to eight weeks. The average is 25 days. At three months following exposure, 97% of infected persons test positive. Rarely, detectable antibodies take up to six months to develop. If an antibody test is negative within the first three months following exposure, it should be repeated after at least another three months.

EIA Test The first test technicians run on a sample is an enzyme immunoassay, or **EIA**, *a test that screens for the presence of HIV antibodies in the blood.* If the results are positive, that means HIV antibodies are present, and the EIA test is repeated. If the second test is also positive, then the Western blot test is run. Both tests are more than 98 percent accurate.

Western Blot Test The **Western blot** is *a test that detects HIV antibodies and confirms the results of earlier EIA tests.* The Western blot test is used only after EIA tests produce positive results. If the results of the two EIA tests and the Western blot test are all positive, a person is diagnosed with HIV/AIDS. The combined EIA and Western blot tests are expsnsive. However, many health departments and HIV/AIDS information and counseling centers will pay for the costs of these tests.

Additional Tests Two other tests—the RNA and the CD4—may be run when a Western blot test comes back positive. The RNA, or viral load test, shows how many copies of the virus are circulating in the blood. The CD4 test looks at the number of white blood cells in a sample of blood. These two tests give a more complete picture of an HIV-infected person's condition. They can also help doctors monitor the disease and determine how much medicine, if any, a patient needs.

A **rapid test** is *an HIV test that produces results in only 20 minutes.* It can be used in situations where the infected person might not come back to learn the results of the test. A blood sample is collected and analyzed immediately on site. Although the results are fairly accurate, they are considered preliminary. If the result is positive, a Western blot test is done to confirm HIV antibodies.

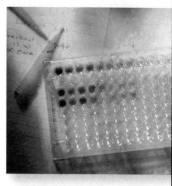

■ **Figure 24.12** In a positive EIA test, HIV antibodies bind to the HIV antigens on a plastic bead coated with HIV proteins. *Under what circumstances would HIV antibodies appear in a tissue or blood sample?*

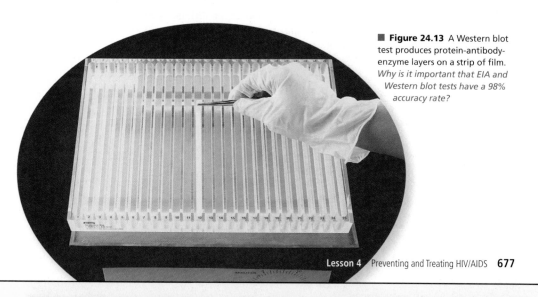

■ **Figure 24.13** A Western blot test produces protein-antibody-enzyme layers on a strip of film. *Why is it important that EIA and Western blot tests have a 98% accuracy rate?*

Lesson 4   Preventing and Treating HIV/AIDS   **677**

U Universal Access

Antibodies and Antigens Review the terms *antibody* and *antigen.* Point out that antibodies are used as markers for the presence of antigens. Students may be confused about how the immune system produces antibodies if HIV attacks the immune system. Explain that it takes time for HIV to destroy large numbers of the cells that direct antibody production. Have students write sentences using the terms *antibody* and *antigen.* **EL BL**

R Reading Strategy

Outlining Have students make an outline of the different types of HIV tests. Use the types (antibody, virus, white blood cells) as the major heads. You may wish to provide copies of the outline structure with some parts filled in for less proficient readers and those learning English. Pair English learners with proficient speakers. **OL BL EL**

HS Health Skills Practice

Advocacy Have students use telephone directories or online sources to identify community organizations and health care facilities that provide support for people with HIV/AIDS and their families. Ask students to identify volunteer opportunities, such as delivering flyers, answering telephones, or participating in fundraising events. Encourage students to become volunteers. **OL**

Caption Answer

Figure 24.13 Sample answer: When a person is being tested for a serious or fatal disease, it is very important that the results be accurate.

Academic Integration

English Have students write a research report on a topic related to HIV/AIDS. Review the following steps in writing a report:

- Select a topic that interests you. (Brainstorm topics with the class.)
- Access information from encyclopedias, Web sites, and newspaper articles. (Review with students the types of sources that are reliable, particularly online.)

- Use index cards to make notes and organize the information into an outline.
- Include a main idea and supporting details in each paragraph.
- Include an introduction, a body, and a conclusion for the overall report.
- Cite the sources used.

677

READING CHECK

Answer If the results are positive, a person can begin proper medical care so that progress of the virus can be slowed and avoid behaviors that spread HIV. If the results are negative, the person has peace of mind.

Main Idea

Treating HIV/AIDS Medicines are available to slow the progress of HIV, but the infection cannot be eliminated. **Ask Students:** *Can a person who is taking medications for HIV transmit the virus?* (Yes, because medicines do not cure the virus)

VIDEO BusinessWeek

HEALTH NEWS

Have students watch the video **HIV Combo Drugs,** and take notes. Briefly discuss the video after viewing. Before students write their paragraphs, ask them to think about the costs and availability of HIV treatment in developing nations and to consider whether drug treatment should be the priority in dealing with the HIV/AIDS pandemic.

AL Active Learning

Debate Tell students that an estimated 200,000 people in the U.S. are infected with HIV but do not know it. Have students debate whether mandatory HIV testing should be implemented in certain situations, such as applying for a marriage license or as part of a routine physical examination. **AL OL**

678

READING CHECK

Explain. Why is testing necessary for those who suspect they have contracted HIV/AIDS?

VIDEO BusinessWeek

HEALTH NEWS

HIV Combo Drugs

Analyze. Go to glencoe.com and watch the video *HIV Combo Drugs.* Consider the potential benefits of these drugs. Write a paragraph explaining whether it is important to make these benefits available to patients around the world.

G Online

Explore glencoe.com and complete the Student Web Activity on treatments for HIV/AIDS.

■ **Figure 24.14** Medical research has developed drugs that protect the immune systems of people with HIV. *How can early diagnosis aid the treatment of HIV?*

Home Testing Kits Home testing kits are marketed on the Internet and in newspapers and magazines. However, most are not trustworthy, particularly if they claim to provide results in a short time in your own home. Check to make sure that any home test is approved by the FDA. An FDA-approved test requires providing a spot of dried blood, which is then mailed to an approved lab for analysis. The results are more than 99 percent accurate and are available within two weeks. Appropriate counseling and referrals are provided for negative and positive test results.

Benefits of Early Diagnosis

There are several benefits to early testing and diagnosis of HIV/AIDS. Early detection allows a person to

- begin proper medical care early to slow the progress of the virus.
- avoid behaviors that could spread HIV to others.
- gain peace of mind when the results are negative.

AL

Treating HIV/AIDS

Main Idea Medications can slow the growth of HIV/AIDS, but there is no cure.

Since the early 1980s, drugs have been developed that slow the growth of the human immunodeficiency virus and treat some of the symptoms. No drug yet exists to cure HIV/AIDS. Many of the drugs available are also used to treat opportunistic infections. As you learned in Lesson 3, these infections occur in individuals who do not have healthy immune systems. AIDS-opportunistic illnesses include pneumonia and some types of cancers that can ultimately cause death.

To slow the growth of the AIDS virus, people take a combination of drugs, a treatment known as highly active antiretroviral therapy (HAART). In 2006, the FDA approved a once-daily, single-pill treatment for HIV/AIDS.

Health Literacy

HIV Vaccines The development of a vaccine to prevent HIV continues to prove challenging for several reasons. First, HIV targets the very cells that direct the activities of other immune cells. A vaccine would need to activate those cells, which is difficult because they are being destroyed. Second, researchers do not know how to induce the appropriate immune response to HIV because no one has ever recovered from the disease. Third, HIV continually mutates, so vaccines would have to work against several strains and constantly be modified. These are only some of the reasons. Nevertheless, clinical trials to test vaccines are ongoing at several medical schools and universities throughout the United States and the world.

Real World CONNECTION

AIDS Awareness Campaign

 Activity Reading / Writing

HIV/AIDS affects everyone. The table below shows the age of people diagnosed with AIDS in 2004.

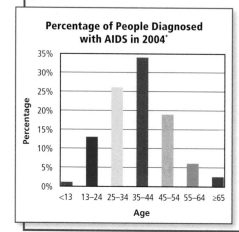

Percentage of People Diagnosed with AIDS in 2004*

Age: <13, 13–24, 25–34, 35–44, 45–54, 55–64, ≥65

Work in groups of 3 or 4 to create a campaign to raise awareness of HIV/AIDS prevention. Each member of your team will be responsible for completing one item for the campaign. Campaign materials can include the following:

- poster
- public service announcement script
- brochure
- opinion article for a newspaper

The materials should encourage teens to avoid behaviors that can put them at risk for HIV/AIDS.

*Based on data from 35 areas with long-term, confidential. name-based HIV reporting. Source: Centers for Disease Control and Prevention, *HIV/AIDS Among Youth* factsheet.

LESSON 4 ASSESSMENT

After You Read

Reviewing Facts and Vocabulary

1. How is HIV detected?
2. What test is used to confirm a diagnosis of HIV?
3. HIV/AIDS home testing kits may not be trustworthy. What should you do to make sure the results are accurate?

Thinking Critically

4. **Synthesize.** What are the benefits of getting tested for HIV when an infection is suspected?
5. **Analyze.** When and for what reasons are blood or tissue samples tested more than once for HIV?

Applying Health Skills

6. **Advocacy.** Working in small groups, plan a classroom, school, or community project to help support AIDS research.

Writing Critically

7. **Expository.** Write an essay discussing how a teen's health and social life might be affected if the teen tested positive for HIV.

Go Online

Visit **glencoe.com** and complete the Interactive Study Guide for this lesson.

Lesson 4 Preventing and Treating HIV/AIDS **679**

LESSON 4 ASSESSMENT ANSWERS

1. An EIA and Western blot test detect the presence of antibodies; an RNA test detects the virus.
2. The Western blot test
3. Check that it is approved by the FDA and requires a spot of dried blood to be mailed to an approved lab for analysis.
4. The person will know for certain whether he or she has HIV. If positive, treatment can begin early, and people can practice behaviors to reduce the spread of infection to others. If negative, the person has peace of mind.
5. Samples are tested again if the first test is positive for HIV. A third test confirms the findings of the first two tests. An accurate diagnosis is important because HIV/AIDS is a fatal disease that can be spread.
6. Students might access Web sites of health departments and schools to get ideas.
7. Essays will vary.

STDs: A Game of Risks

NHES Standard 7 Students will demonstrate the ability to practice health-enhancing behaviors and avoid or reduce risks.

Teacher Objectives

- Identify and describe symptoms, effects, and treatment for at least five different STDs.
- Create a plan to avoid the risks of contracting an STD.

Teaching Strategies

- To prepare students for this activity, choose one STD from the chapter and ask students to briefly describe the symptoms, long-term effects, and treatment for that STD. Write their answers on the board.
- After students have completed the game, discuss the consequences of contracting an STD. Ask students to identify ways to avoid these consequences. Then ask them to create individual self-management plans to avoid the risks associated with STDs.

Assessment

Using a rubric, student work should provide comprehensive evidence of the following criteria to achieve the highest score:

✓ Demonstrates health knowledge about STDs

✓ Identifies protective behaviors to avoid STDs

✓ Develops a plan to avoid the risk of contracting STDs

Hands-On
HEALTH

Activity ## STDs: A Game of Risks

You'll play a game called "STDs: A Game of Risks" and create a plan for reducing your risk of contracting an STD.

What You'll Need

- 32 index cards
- black marker

What You'll Do

Step 1

Work in teams of five or six. Write "STD," "Symptoms," "Long-Term Effects," and "Treatment" on four index cards. Spread these category cards in a row on a table or desk.

Step 2

Take five more index cards and write the name of one STD on each. For each STD you choose, write the symptoms, long-term effects, and treatment on three more cards. When finished, shuffle the cards and place them upside down in a stack.

Step 3

At your teacher's signal, turn over one card at a time and place the card under the correct category card. Arrange the cards to align them with the correct STD.

Apply and Conclude

Create a plan to avoid STDs. Include specific steps you can take.

Checklist: Practicing Healthful Behaviors

✓ Demonstration of health knowledge about STDs

✓ Identification of protective behaviors to avoid STDs

✓ Step-by-step plan to avoid risks of contracting STDs

✓ Implementation of plan

Home and Community

Parent Involvement Ask students to talk with their parents or guardian about ways to help their teens avoid behaviors that put them at risk for STDs. Some suggestions are talking with the teens, helping to plan safe activities, and giving advice on how to handle negative pressure from peers. Parents and students might also access library or online resources for ideas. They should work together to create guidelines. In the classroom, encourage students to pool their ideas and make a pamphlet that they can deliver to common locations in the community, such as libraries, grocery stores, and other places of business. Remind students to get permission to distribute the pamphlets.

To download quizzes and eFlashcards to your PDA, go to glencoe.com and click on the Study to Go icon.

LESSON **1**

Sexually Transmitted Diseases

Key Concepts
▶ STDS are transmitted through sexual contact.
▶ The risk of being infected with an STD increases as the number of sexual partners increases.
▶ STDs sometimes produce no symptoms. People may not realize they are infected, and therefore do not seek treatment.

Vocabulary
▶ sexually transmitted diseases (p. 658)
▶ sexually transmitted infections (p. 658)
▶ asymptomatic (p. 659)
▶ epidemic (p. 663)

LESSON **2**

Preventing and Treating STDs

Key Concepts
▶ Practicing abstinence is the only 100 percent successful method for preventing the transmission of STDs.
▶ It is crucial for people to seek diagnosis and treatment if they think they are infected with an STD.
▶ Bacterial STDs can be treated and cured with antibiotics, but viral STDs have no cure.

Vocabulary
▶ antibiotics (p. 664)
▶ abstinence (p. 664)
▶ refusal skills (p. 665)
▶ HPV vaccine (p. 667)

LESSON **3**

HIV/AIDS

Key Concepts
▶ HIV is the virus that causes AIDS.
▶ HIV destroys white blood cells, weakening the body's immune system.
▶ HIV is transmitted from one person to another through sexual intercourse, by sharing contaminated needles, or from mother to infant.

Vocabulary
▶ human immunodeficiency virus (HIV) (p. 669)
▶ acquired immunodeficiency syndrome (AIDS) (p. 669)
▶ pandemic (p. 670)
▶ mucous membranes (p. 670)
▶ lymphocytes (p. 671)
▶ antibodies (p. 671)

LESSON **4**

Preventing and Treating HIV/AIDS

Key Concepts
▶ HIV/AIDS has no cure at present.
▶ Medication can slow the progression of HIV, but cannot completely stop it.

Vocabulary
▶ EIA (p. 677)
▶ Western blot (p. 677)
▶ rapid test (p. 677)

Chapter 24 Review **681**

Go Online

Students can visit glencoe.com to

- review content online with the Online Student Edition.
- test their knowledge of chapter content with Online Quizzes.
- access Interactive Health Tutor for more practice with vocabulary.

Assessment Resources

📁 *FAST FILE* ACTIVITIES
Chapter 24 Test

💿 *ExamView*
Assessment Suite CD-ROM

Visit glencoe.com **for:**
Audio Chapter Summaries
Online Quizzes

 Tell students to visit glencoe.com where they can download quizzes and eFlashcards.

Study Tips

Control Distractions Advise students to take steps to minimize distractions when they study at home. Let family members know they are studying. Set cell phones to vibrate, and let the phone take messages. Turn off the e-mail alert sound on computers.

Have paper, highlighters, and other supplies handy. Advise students to take care of necessities, such as using the bathroom or getting something to drink, before they begin studying. They should take a 5-minute break about every 40 minutes to refresh the mind.

Assessment

Chapter 24 Assessment Answers

LESSON 1

Vocabulary Review

Use the vocabulary terms listed on page 681 to complete the following statements.

1. People infected with STDs often do not realize they have an infection because many STDs can be _____.

2. Health experts say that the United States currently faces an STD _____.

Understanding Key Concepts

After reading the question or statement, select the correct answer.

3. STDs can be passed from person to person through
   a. casual contact such as shaking hands.
   b. the air by coughing or sneezing.
   c. sexual contact.
   d. all of the above.

4. Females infected with trichomoniasis
   a. never experience symptoms.
   b. cannot be cured.
   c. are at higher risk of infection from HIV.
   d. are not endangering their health.

5. If left untreated, all STDs
   a. can lead to serious health problems.
   b. will eventually cure itself.
   c. will become asymptomatic.
   d. lead to infection by HIV/AIDS.

Thinking Critically

After reading the question or statement, write a short answer using complete sentences.

6. **Describe.** Give one reason why STDs go undiagnosed and untreated.

7. **Compare and Contrast.** What are the differences in the ways that STDs affect males and females?

LESSON 2

Vocabulary Review

Correct the sentences below by replacing the italicized term with the correct vocabulary term.

8. Many STDs can be treated and some cured with medications called *HPV vaccines.*

9. *A refusal skill* is the deliberate decision to avoid sexual activity.

Understanding Key Concepts

After reading the question or statement, select the correct answer.

10. Which is *not* a high-risk behavior?
    a. Engaging in sexual activity with multiple partners
    b. Engaging in unprotected sexual activity
    c. Using alcohol and other drugs
    d. Abstaining from sexual activity

11. Getting a diagnosis and treatment is
    a. acting responsibly.
    b. crucial for those infected with STDs.
    c. a healthful behavior.
    d. all of the above.

12. Treatment of an STD
    a. does not prevent reinfection.
    b. isn't always necessary.
    c. can be postponed.
    d. always cures the infection.

Thinking Critically

After reading the question or statement, write a short answer using complete sentences.

13. **Compare and Contrast.** Identify the differences and similarities between viral and bacterial STDs.

14. **Discuss.** Which STD can be treated with the HPV vaccine? What are its limitations? Who is eligible to receive this vaccination?

Health eSpotlight *Wrap-Up*

No One Is Immune Have students reread the Health eSpotlight questions at the beginning of the chapter (page 657) and look at their original answers. **Ask Students:** *What do you now know about avoiding STDs that you didn't know before reading the chapter?* Call on volunteers to describe what they have learned and how they would change their responses.

15. **Evaluate.** Why is preventing STD transmission more effective than treating STDs?

16. **Explain.** What are antibiotics? How are they used to treat STDs?

LESSON 3

Vocabulary Review
Choose the correct term in the sentences below.

17. *HIV / Mucous membrane* is transmitted through the bloodstream.

18. *Lymphocyte / AIDS* is the final stage of HIV infection.

19. Health care officials consider AIDS to be a(n) *antibody / pandemic*.

Understanding Key Concepts
After reading the question or statement, select the correct answer.

20. During the course of HIV/AIDS, the infected person
    a. gets stronger.
    b. should not hug anyone or shake hands.
    c. needs less and less medication.
    d. becomes vulnerable to opportunistic illnesses.

21. Which of the following is *not* a way that HIV attacks cells?
    a. The virus attaches itself to the cell's surface.
    b. The virus makes a copy of its genetic material.
    c. The virus shrinks cells.
    d. The new virus assembles at cell surface.

22. It is difficult for antibodies to fight AIDS because
    a. HIV weakens antibodies.
    b. HIV destroys white blood cells.
    c. HIV is protected once it enters cells.
    d. HIV mutates rapidly.

Thinking Critically
After reading the question or statement, write a short answer using complete sentences.

23. **Explain.** Describe how HIV infection progresses in the body.

24. **Identify.** Name three ways HIV is transmitted.

25. **Evaluate.** What misinformation causes some people to stay away from those infected with HIV?
    Why is this information wrong?

LESSON 4

Vocabulary Review
Use the vocabulary terms listed on page 681 to complete the following statements.

26. The _____ test is the first test that technicians use to screen for HIV.

27. If the initial test produces positive results twice, a(n) _____ test is run.

28. The _____ allows samples to be tested on site rather than sending them to labs.

Understanding Key Concepts
After reading the question or statement, select the correct answer.

29. A person who thinks he or she is infected with HIV/AIDS should
    a. use a home testing kit.
    b. hide the condition from others.
    c. get a medical diagnosis right away.
    d. hope that symptoms do not appear.

Chapter 24 Assessment **683**

Thinking Critically

14. Human papilloma virus; it is effective for the four common types of sexually transmitted HPV but not all of them; it is recommended for females 9 to 26 years old.

15. Preventing STDs means that a person never gets an infection, so there are no health consequences. The infection is not passed to others, so fewer people get infected.

16. Antibiotics are chemical agents that destroy disease-causing bacteria but do not harm the patient. They can eliminate several STDs caused by bacteria or protozoa.

LESSON 3

Vocabulary Review

17. HIV
18. AIDS
19. pandemic

Understanding Key Concepts

20. d
21. c
22. b

Thinking Critically

23. HIV enters white blood cells, reproduces, and destroys the cells. Over time, the immune system is weakened. By the last stage of AIDS, infected persons get opportunistic infections or cancer and die.

24. Sexual activity, sharing contaminated needles, and mother to baby

25. Many people think that HIV/AIDS can be transmitted through casual contact such as holding hands, hugging, coughing, breathing out, sneezing, or crying. HIV/AIDS is not spread through casual contact.

Assessment

Assessment

LESSON 4

Vocabulary Review

26. EIA
27. Western blot
28. rapid test

Understanding Key Concepts

29. c
30. c
31. d

Thinking Critically

32. Sample answer: Citizens in developing countries do not have the same access to health information and medical treatment as citizens in developed countries.

33. Getting proper medical care early, stopping the spread of HIV to others, returning to abstinence, gaining peace of mind if the results are negative

30. About one-fourth of the people infected with HIV/AIDS
    a. are males.
    b. are females.
    c. don't know they are infected.
    d. will never develop symptoms.

31. People who are infected with HIV/AIDS, but don't know it,
    a. won't become as ill as those who know they have the virus.
    b. don't need to change their high-risk behaviors.
    c. don't need to practice abstinence.
    d. can unknowingly spread the virus to others.

Thinking Critically

After reading the question or statement, write a short answer using complete sentences.

32. **Explain.** The number of HIV/AIDS infections is much higher in developing nations than in developed countries. Why might this number be higher in some countries?

33. **Identify.** What are some benefits of early diagnosis of HIV/AIDS?

Project-Based ASSESSMENT

Knowledge Is Power

Background

The starting point in preventing the spread of STDs is accurate information. Making sure that teens are well informed about STDs is especially important, because they are one of the age groups at highest risk of infection. How much do the teens in your school know about STDs? What information do they need to protect themselves from infection?

Task

Take an anonymous survey of 20 or more students in your school to determine areas in which they are uninformed or misinformed about STDs. Prepare a questionnaire based on the information in the chapter, and use it to assess students' knowledge of STDs and their transmission. Then, make a poster that provides students with information about STDs, including the fact that abstinence is the only 100 percent effective way to prevent infection.

Audience

Teens in your school

Purpose

Determine what information students need to protect themselves from STDs. Educate students by providing accurate information.

Procedure

1. Use the information in the chapter to make up the questions for the survey.

2. Select 20 or more students in your school and ask them to take the survey.

3. Analyze the answers to determine areas in which students are uninformed or misinformed.

4. Prepare a poster that provides the needed information.

5. The most informative and eye-catching posters will be displayed in your school.

Project-Based ASSESSMENT

Step 1 Questionnaire Have students brainstorm misinformation teens might have about STDs. Work with students to devise a consistent, anonymous method to administer the questionnaires.

Step 2 Create Poster Have students review their questionnaires and calculate the frequency of incorrect answers for each question. Students then choose one or more areas of misinformation and create their poster to address these.

Step 3 Evaluate Evaluate the posters based on how clearly they present the information, their appeal to a teen audience, and the accuracy of the information. Choice of topics should reflect findings from the questionnaire. Reasons for selecting the topics should be logical.

Visit **glencoe.com** for Project-Based Assessment rubrics.

Math Practice

Interpret Graphs. The bar graph below shows the number of new cases of different STDs reported in the United States. Study the bar graph, and then answer the questions.

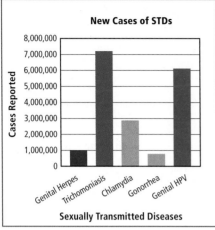

New Cases of STDs

Source: Centers for Disease Control and Prevention, 2004

1. If the population of the United States is about 296 million, what is the ratio of infection for trichomoniasis this year?
   A. 1 in 4   C. 1 in 400
   B. 1 in 40   D. 1 in 4,000

2. How much more common is genital HPV infection than genital herpes?
   A. Twice as common
   B. Three times more common
   C. Four times more common
   D. Six times more common

3. Using the bar graph, explain how you would predict the rates of STD infection for people in your state.

Go Online

For more test practice, visit glencoe.com and complete the Online Quizzes for Chapter 24.

Reading/Writing Practice

Understand and Apply. Read the passage below, and then answer the questions.

> During the late 1980s, Ryan White was the face of AIDS for many Americans. Ryan contracted AIDS through a blood transfusion. Many members of his community mistankenly believed that AIDS could spread through casual contact. They pressured the school board to ban Ryan from attending school. Ryan's family took his case to court, and he was eventually allowed to return to school.
>
> Ryan became an AIDS educator. He spoke of the need for everyone to learn about AIDS and to treat affected people with compassion and dignity. Ryan lived for six years following his AIDS diagnosis. He died in 1990 at age 18. Later that year, Congress passed the Ryan White Comprehensive AIDS Resources Emergency (CARE) Act. Today, the act provides about $1.5 billion annually to care for people living with HIV/AIDS.

1. What is the purpose of this passage?
   A. To describe an early case of AIDS
   B. To describe the fear of HIV/AIDS
   C. To show how Ryan fought AIDS
   D. To blame public officials

2. What was the result of the publicity surrounding Ryan's case?
   A. It helped Ryan live longer.
   B. It allowed Ryan to return to school.
   C. It provided the public with factual information about HIV/AIDS.
   D. It increased the hostility against Ryan.

3. Write a paragraph explaining how HIV can and cannot be spread. Explain why the virus can be spread only in certain ways.

National Education Standards

Math: Number and Operations, Problem Solving
Language Arts: NCTE 1, NCTE 3, NCTE 4

Chapter 24   Standardized Test Practice   **685**

Standardized Test Practice Answers

Math Practice
1. B
2. D
3. Sample answer: Because the rates for trichomoniasis and HPV infection are so much higher than the rates for the other diseases, those two STDs will probably be highest in my state.

Reading/Writing Practice
1. B
2. C
3. Answers will vary, but should reflect an understanding of how HIV is transmitted.

National Education Standards

Math: Number and Operations, Problem Solving

Language Arts: NCTE 1, NCTE 3, NCTE 4

For the complete Math and Language Arts standards, visit glencoe.com.

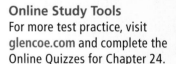

Online Study Tools
For more test practice, visit glencoe.com and complete the Online Quizzes for Chapter 24.

Test-Taking Tip

Obvious Answer Choices Tell students not to hastily choose an answer on a multiple-choice test that seems obvious or to choose an answer without reading all of the choices. Advise students to read each answer carefully before finally selecting one. Remember that only one answer choice of the several that is offered for each question is correct.

Noncommunicable Diseases and Disabilities

Chapter 25 pages 686–719	Standards		Features
	National	State/Local	
	1.12.1, 3.12.2, 4.12.1, 6.12.4, 7.12.1, 8.12.2, 8.12.4		Hands-On HEALTH • A Family Letter *(Practicing Healthful Behaviors)*, page 714
30 Min **Lesson 1** Cardiovascular Disease pages 688–694 **BIG Idea** *Preventive behaviors can reduce the risk for cardio-vascular disease and stroke.*	1.12.1, 1.12.4, 1.12.5, 3.12.3, 4.12.1, 5.12.6, 7.12.1, 7.12.2, 7.12.3		Real World CONNECTION • An Exercise Campaign, page 694 Out of Time
30 Min **Lesson 2** Cancer pages 695–701 **BIG Idea** *Cancer takes many different forms and can affect people of all ages.*	1.12.1, 2.12.9, 3.12.3, 4.12.2, 5.12.6, 7.12.1, 7.12.3		VIDEO BusinessWeek HEALTH NEWS • Cancer Vaccine, page 700
30 Min **Lesson 3** Allergies, Asthma, Diabetes, and Arthritis pages 702–708 **BIG Idea** *Practicing self-management strategies can help reduce the severity of allergies, asthma, diabetes, and arthritis.*	1.12.1, 3.12.3, 4.12.1, 5.12.6, 7.12.1, 7.12.3, 8.12.3		Health Skills Activity • Campaigning for Health *(Advocacy)*, page 706 Out of Time
30 Min **Lesson 4** Physical and Mental Challenges pages 709–713 **BIG Idea** *People with physical and mental challenges deserve to be treated with dignity and respect.*	1.12.2, 2.12.6, 2.12.10, 4.12.1, 4.12.4		

Key to Ability Levels

Teaching Strategies and activities have been coded for ability level and appropriateness.

- AL Activities for students working above grade level
- BL Activities for students working below grade level
- OL Activities for students working on grade level
- EL Activities for English Learners

Chapter 25 Planning Guide

Glencoe Exclusive!
TeacherWorks *Plus*
All-In-One Planner and Resource Center

Resources	Lesson Assessment	Technology
Student Activity Workbook TEACH *FAST FILE* RESOURCES Vocabulary Practice TEACH Health Labs EXTEND	Chapter 25 Review Chapter 25 Assessment Standardized Test Practice ⊙ *ExamView® Assessment Suite* CD-ROM	**Teaching Tools:** ⊙ *TeacherWorks™* Plus DVD ⊙ *StudentWorks™* Plus DVD ⊙ *ExamView® Assessment Suite* CD-ROM 🕹 Transparency ⊙ Fitness DVD ⊙ PowerPoint® DVD ⊙ Health eSpotlight Video Series DVD
FAST FILE RESOURCES Reading Strategies Activity TEACH Reteaching Activity REVIEW Enrichment Activity EXTEND Health Skills Practice TEACH	Lesson 1 Assessment, page 694 📁 Lesson 1 Quiz *Fast File* ⊙ *ExamView® Assessment Suite* CD-ROM	**Web-Based Resources:** Go Online glencoe.com • Health Podcast Activities • Audio Chapter Summaries (English/Spanish) • Interactive Health Tutor
FAST FILE RESOURCES Reading Strategies Activity TEACH Reteaching Activity REVIEW Enrichment Activity EXTEND Health Skills Practice TEACH	Lesson 2 Assessment, page 701 📁 Lesson 2 Quiz *Fast File* ⊙ *ExamView® Assessment Suite* CD-ROM	• Health Skills Activities • Vocabulary PuzzleMaker • Parent Letters (English/Spanish) • Lesson Plans
FAST FILE RESOURCES Reading Strategies Activity TEACH Reteaching Activity REVIEW Enrichment Activity EXTEND Health Skills Practice	Lesson 3 Assessment, page 708 📁 Lesson 3 Quiz *Fast File* ⊙ *ExamView® Assessment Suite* CD-ROM	• Health Inventories • Online Quizzes • Study-to-Go • Unit Web Projects
FAST FILE RESOURCES Reading Strategies Activity TEACH Reteaching Activity REVIEW Enrichment Activity EXTEND Health Skills Practice TEACH	Lesson 4 Assessment, page 713 📁 Lesson 4 Quiz *Fast File* ⊙ *ExamView® Assessment Suite* CD-ROM	• Student Web Activities • Fitness Zone Activities

StudentWorks *Plus*

This is the student's backpack solution.

Includes:
• complete Interactive Student Edition
• full audio of English text and Spanish chapter summaries
• allows students to record assignments and track grades.
• links to online activities and additional student resources
• access to all student worksheets and workbooks

FOLDABLES®
Study Organizer

Dinah Zike Foldables® Chapter Activity
Refer to the *Dinah Zike Reading and Study Skills for Glencoe Health.* Have students complete the foldable titled "Before You Read." As students read the chapter, have them record main ideas, new terms, and personal experiences on the appropriate pages of their Foldables.

Key to Symbols
🕹 Transparencies
⊙ CD-ROM
glencoe.com
📁 Print Resources

REVIEW activities to review or reinforce content
TEACH activities to teach basic concepts
EXTEND activities to extend or enrich lesson content

Noncommuni-cable Diseases and Disabilities

Chapter Overview

Chapter 25 focuses on various noncommunicable diseases, such as cardiovascular disease, cancer, and diabetes. Physical and mental disabilities are also discussed.

Lesson 1

Teens can take preventive measures to reduce the risks of diseases that affect the heart and blood vessels.

Lesson 2

Cancer takes different forms and can develop in almost any part of the body.

Lesson 3

Noncommunicable diseases, such as allergies, asthma, diabetes, and arthritis, can be managed with medications and behaviors.

Lesson 4

People with physical and mental disabilities have many of the same abilities as the rest of the population.

▶ **Activating Prior Knowledge**

Before students write their paragraphs, discuss what an adaptive device is and what devices are being used by the teens in the photo. (An adaptive device is any device that helps people with disabilities perform everyday tasks.)

CHAPTER 25

Noncommunicable Diseases and Disabilities

Lesson 1
Cardiovascular Disease

BIG Idea *Preventive behaviors can reduce your risk for cardiovascular disease and stroke.*

Lesson 2
Cancer

BIG Idea *Cancer takes many different forms and can affect people of all ages.*

Lesson 3
Allergies, Asthma, Diabetes, and Arthritis

BIG Idea *Practicing self-management strategies can help reduce the severity of allergies, asthma, diabetes, and arthritis.*

Lesson 4
Physical and Mental Challenges

BIG Idea *People with physical and mental challenges deserve to be treated with dignity and respect.*

Activating Prior Knowledge

Using Visuals Look at the photo on this page. Write a short paragraph describing how these teens are actively promoting their health. What technologies and devices can help people with disabilities lead full and active lives?

Universal Access

Differentiated Learning Glencoe provides teacher support and student materials for all learners in the health classroom.

- Chapter Summaries in English and Spanish are available online at glencoe.com.

- *Fast Files* and related worksheets support reluctant readers.

- Universal Access strategies throughout the Teacher Wraparound Edition and *Fast Files* help you present materials for gifted students, at-risk students, physically impaired students, and those with behavior disorders or learning disabilities.

Chapter Launchers

Health in Action

Discuss the **BIG** Ideas

Before beginning this chapter, think about how you would answer these questions:

▶ Why should you learn about heart disease and cancer?

▶ What do you know about asthma or allergies?

▶ Why is it important to be educated about physical and mental challenges?

Watch the *Health eSpotlight* Video Series

Straight Facts on Diseases and Disabilities

What can you do to reduce your risk of lifestyle diseases?

Assess Your Health

G⊕ Online

Visit **glencoe.com** and complete the Health Inventory for Chapter 25.

Chapter 25 Noncommunicable Diseases and Disabilities **687**

Chapter Launchers

Health in Action
Discuss the **BIG** Ideas

Have students write a response for each question in their journal. Encourage students to review their responses after completing each lesson. Suggest they rewrite their responses to reflect what they have learned.

Health eSpotlight
Video Series

Straight Facts on Diseases and Disabilities

Before Viewing the Video

Ask Students: *What do you think you can do to make your heart healthy?* After students have watched the video, call on a few volunteers to revisit the question.

G⊕ Online

Have students go to **glencoe.com** and take the Health Inventory for Chapter 25.

Chapter Skills

Reading Skills
- Reviewing Facts and Vocabulary, pp. 694, 701, 708, 713
- Reading/Writing Practice, p. 719

BIG Idea

Noncommunicable diseases can be prevented and managed with healthful behaviors.

Health Skills
- Health Skills Activity, p. 706
- Applying Health Skills, pp. 694, 701, 708, 713

Vocabulary
- New Vocabulary, pp. 688, 695, 702, 709
- Reviewing Facts and Vocabulary, pp. 694, 701, 708, 713

Writing Skills
- Real World Connection, p. 694
- Writing Critically, pp. 694, 701, 708, 713
- Reading/Writing Practice, p. 719

Cardiovascular Disease

1 FOCUS

GUIDE TO READING

BIG Idea Preventive behaviors can reduce the risk for cardiovascular disease and stroke. **Ask Students:** *Why should teens know the risks of cardiovascular disease?* (Sample answer: Cardiovascular disease can begin to develop in teens who practice unhealthful behaviors.)

Before You Read

Cluster Chart Students' cluster charts will vary. (Sample answers: Tobacco use, high blood pressure)

Main Idea

Cardiovascular Disease The cardiovascular system is at risk for many different serious diseases. **Ask Students:** *What is cardiovascular disease?* (A disease that affects the heart or blood vessels)

Real Life Issues

Have students recall what they have already learned about how food choices affect health. **Ask Students:** *How do poor food choices affect body weight?* (Eating foods high in fat and sugar can cause an increase in body weight as well as a buildup of plaque in the arteries.)

LESSON **1**

GUIDE TO READING

BIG Idea *Preventive behaviors can reduce your risk for cardiovascular disease and stroke.*

Before You Read

Create a Cluster Chart. Draw a circle and label it "Cardiovascular Disease," or CVD. Use surrounding circles to identify factors that contribute to this disease. As you read, continue filling in the chart with more details.

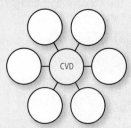

New Vocabulary

▶ noncommunicable disease (p. 688)
▶ cardiovascular disease (p. 688)
▶ hypertension (p. 689)
▶ atherosclerosis (p. 689)
▶ arteriosclerosis (p. 689)
▶ angina pectoris (p. 690)
▶ arrhythmias (p. 690)
▶ stroke (p. 692)

Cardiovascular Disease

Real Life Issues

Caring for Friends. Eduardo and Keith are good friends. Keith tells Eduardo about his grandfather's recent heart attack. "He's really over-weight," Keith says. "Nobody can eat as much as Grandpa." Eduardo has noticed that Keith tends to eat a lot too. "Food helps me take my mind off things," Keith explains. Eduardo wonders if Keith might be increasing his own risk of heart disease.

Writing *Write a dialogue in which Eduardo tries to make Keith aware of how his food choices might affect his long-term health.*

Cardiovascular Disease

Main Idea The heart, blood, and blood vessels are at risk for a number of potentially serious diseases.

You've learned about communicable diseases and how to prevent them. Some illnesses, however, are not infectious. A **noncommunicable disease** is *a disease that is not transmitted by another person, a vector, or the environment.* One of the most common noncommunicable diseases is **cardiovascular disease**, or CVD, *a disease that affects the heart or blood vessels.* CVD is responsible for almost 40 percent of all U.S. deaths, killing more than a million Americans every year.

Cardio refers to the heart, and *vascular* refers to the blood vessels. As you learned in Chapter 15, the cardiovascular system works tirelessly to keep you alive and well. A problem in just one part of the system can jeopardize your health. That's why it's important to know about the variety of cardiovascular diseases and how to prevent them.

U

More About...

Noncommunicable Diseases The World Health Organization (WHO) has identified noncommunicable diseases, also called chronic diseases, as a major health problem. Of the 57 million deaths in the world in 2002, 35.5 million (60 percent) resulted from noncommunicable diseases. Other types of noncommunicable diseases not discussed in this chapter include mental disorders, such as depression, bipolar-affective disorder, and schizophrenia; genetic or inherited disorders such as Down syndrome, sickle cell anemia, Huntington disease, and cystic fibrosis; and chronic respiratory diseases such as chronic bronchitis and emphysema.

Types of Cardiovascular Disease

Main Idea There are many different types of CVDs.

There are quite a few different cardiovascular diseases. As you read about these diseases, think about how each one is caused and what you can do to reduce your risk.

Hypertension

High blood pressure, or **hypertension**, can damage the heart, blood vessels, and other body organs if it continues over a long period of time. It is also a major risk factor for other types of CVDs. Because hypertension often has no symptoms in its early stages, it is sometimes called a "silent killer."

Hypertension can occur at any age, but it is more common among people over the age of 35. It is estimated that about one-third of American adults have hypertension. To treat hypertension, patients should manage their weight, get adequate physical activity, and eat a nutritious diet. Medication for hypertension is also available.

Atherosclerosis

When you were born, the lining of your blood vessels were smooth and elastic. What is the condition of your blood vessels today? If you smoke, have high blood pressure, or have high cholesterol levels, fatty substances called *plaques* can build up on your artery walls. This condition is known as **atherosclerosis**, *a disease characterized by the accumulation of plaque on artery walls.* People with atherosclerosis have a condition called **arteriosclerosis**, *hardened arteries with reduced elasticity.* **Figure 25.1** compares a healthy artery with unhealthy ones.

Figure 25.1 Healthy and Unhealthy Arteries

The artery on the far left is healthy, while the other arteries show evidence of atherosclerosis. *What lifestyle choices can increase your risk for atherosclerosis?*

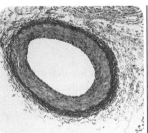 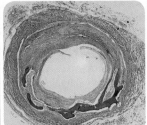 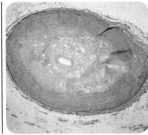

Lesson 1   Cardiovascular Disease   **689**

English Language Coach

Atherosclerosis vs. Arteriosclerosis Because these words are similar, students might confuse the meanings of atherosclerosis and arteriosclerosis. Show students that both words share the root *-sclerosis,* which means "a thickening or hardening of a body part." Then explain that the prefix *athero-* comes from a Greek word that means "gruel or formed with pus." The accumulation of plaque or pulpy fat in blood vessels is atherosclerosis. The prefix *arterio-* refers to an artery. When hardened arteries have lost their flexibility, it is called arteriosclerosis.

CHAPTER 25

LESSON 1

2 TEACH

U Universal Access

Reinforcing Vocabulary Break *noncommunicable* into syllables (non·com·mu·ni·ca·ble) and have students repeat it after you. Review the meaning of *communicable* from the previous chapter. Explain that the prefix *non-,* means "not," and when added to *communicable* changes its meaning to the opposite—"not transmitted from person to person." **BL EL**

Go Online

Assign students to go online and use the Student Web Activity at **glencoe.com** to learn more about maintaining heart health.

Main Idea

Types of Cardiovascular Disease There are many kinds of cardiovascular diseases. **Ask Students:** *What are some cardiovascular diseases that you have heard of?* (Answers will vary but may include high blood pressure and heart attack.)

AL Active Learning

Demonstration Cut off the end of a long, thin balloon. Attach it to a sink faucet and run water through it. Attach a similar balloon to the sink faucet and fill it with water. Point out how the sides of the balloon expand as it fills with water. Then prick a pin hole at the end of a third balloon. Attach it to the faucet and run water through it. Point out how the sides of the balloon expand even though water does flow out of the balloon. Explain that arteries act similarly when filled with plaque. The flow of blood slows down, which reduces the amount of oxygen reaching tissues and organs. **OL**

689

Go Online

Go to glencoe.com and complete the Student Web Activity on heart disease and maintaining healthy blood cholesterol levels.

LESSON 1

R Reading Strategy

Identifying Cause and Effect
As students read about the types of cardiovascular diseases, have them complete a three-column table in which they list the causes and effects of each disease. Then, when they read about the risk factors of cardiovascular diseases, instruct them to add to the table preventive measures for each disease. **BL**

HS Health Skills Practice

Accessing Information Many Internet sources are available with information about cardiovascular diseases. Have pairs of students find two Internet sites and compare their content. Students should devise a rating system to rate the reliability of the information on each site, its usefulness, the amount of information provided, and how accurate and detailed it is. **OL AL**

U Universal Access

Classifying Pair English language learners with English fluent students. Instruct pairs to work together to write a sentence that describes how a heart attack is similar to and different from cardiac arrest. Then have pairs classify angina pectoris and arrhythmias as diseases that can lead to either heart attack or cardiac arrest. **EL OL**

Academic Vocabulary

Regulate Demonstrate this usage of regulate by bouncing a ball slowly and then bouncing it quickly. Explain that you are "regulating" the speed at which the ball is bouncing. Ask students to give other examples. (Sample answer: Cruise control "regulates" a car's speed. A knob on a radio "regulates" its volume.)

690

☑ **READING CHECK**

Identify What are some healthful behaviors that can help prevent atherosclerosis?

Academic Vocabulary

regulate *(verb):* to fix the time, amount, degree, or rate of

---

The main cause of atherosclerosis is making unhealthful food choices—specifically, foods that have large amounts of saturated fat and cholesterol. Sometimes a blood clot forms near plaque buildup and blocks the artery. If this artery supplies blood to the heart or the brain, a heart attack or stroke may result.

Diseases of the Heart

Every day your heart pumps about 100,000 times, moving blood to all parts of your body. Like every other organ in your body, it needs oxygen from the blood in order to function. When the blood supply to the heart is restricted, the heart does not get the oxygen it needs. Under these conditions, a heart attack can occur. The result can be heart muscle damage or even sudden death due to cardiac arrest. **R**

Heart attack and cardiac arrest are not quite the same thing. *Heart attack* occurs due to insufficient blood supply to the heart. *Cardiac arrest,* in which the heart stops beating in a rhythmic way, occurs due to an electrical problem with the heart. To diagnose and treat heart disease, doctors use several techniques, shown in **Figure 25.2**. Commonly diagnosed heart diseases include angina pectoris, arrhythmias, heart attack, and congestive heart failure. **HS**

Angina Pectoris *Chest pain that results when the heart does not get enough oxygen* is called **angina pectoris** (an-JY-nuh PEK-tuh-ruhs). This pain, which usually lasts from a few seconds to minutes, is a warning sign that the heart is temporarily not getting enough blood. Angina is usually caused by atherosclerosis and should be taken seriously. It sometimes can be treated with medication.

Arrhythmias *Irregular heartbeats,* or **arrhythmias**, happen when the heart skips a beat or beats very fast or very slowly. Arrhythmias are quite common and usually don't cause problems. However, some types are serious, and should always be checked by a doctor. In one type of arrhythmia, called *ventricular fibrillation,* the electrical impulses that **regulate** heart rhythm become rapid or irregular. This is the most common cause of cardiac arrest. Cardiopulmonary resuscitation (CPR) and using an automated external defibrillator are the only ways to help someone suffering a cardiac arrest. You will learn more about these first-aid methods in Chapter 27.

Heart Attack A heart attack occurs when a reduced or blocked blood supply damages the heart muscle. Many heart attacks are sudden and cause intense chest pain, but about 25 percent produce no symptoms or produce unusual symptoms such as shortness of breath. Milder symptoms may be especially **U**

Home and Community

Blood Pressure Checks Many places in the community offer free blood pressure checks to the public. Some of these locations include drug stores, churches, community centers, and libraries. Have students make inquiries and observations to identify these locations within their community. Compile a class list of the locations and have students make a brochure that lists the locations and summarizes the benefits of blood pressure checks. Students can place the brochures throughout the community.

Figure 25.2 Diagnosing and Treating Heart Disease

As medical technology advances, more diagnostic tools and treatment options become available. *Which treatment option uses a small balloon to clear a blocked artery?*

Diagnostic Tools

Electrocardiogram (EKG)	Magnetic Resonance Imaging (MRI)	Angiography	CT Scan
Produces graph of heart's electrical activity. Shows heart function. 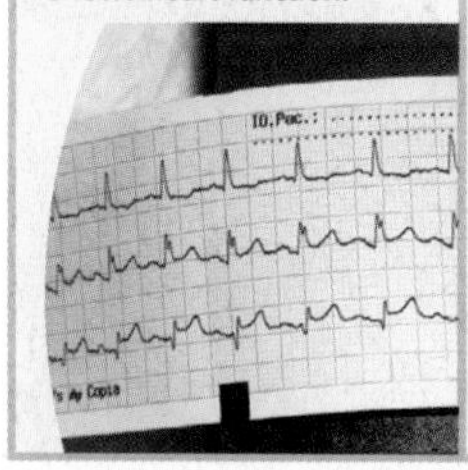	Uses powerful magnets to produce images. Shows heart damage and defects. 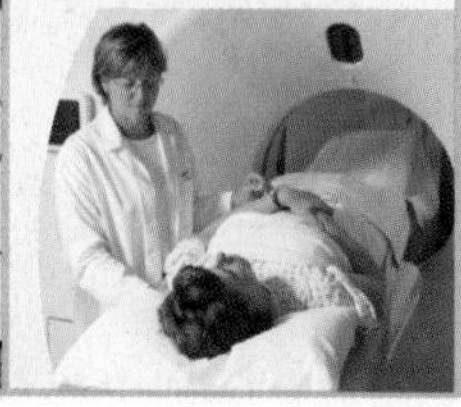	Thin, flexible tube guided through blood vessels to the heart. Dye is injected, and motion X-rays taken to look for heart obstructions. 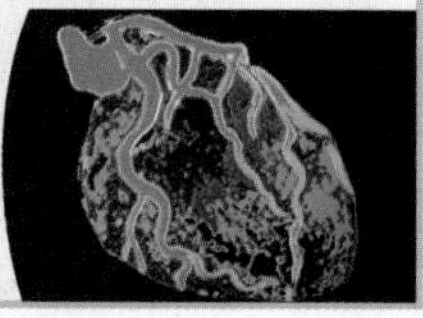	The patient lies on a table inside a doughnut-shaped machine. Scans create multiple images of the heart. Scans show calcium blockages in arteries and vessels. Scans show heart function.

Treatment Options

Coronary Bypass	Angioplasty	Pacemaker	Laser Intervention
Healthy vein removed from another area to create a detour around blocked artery. 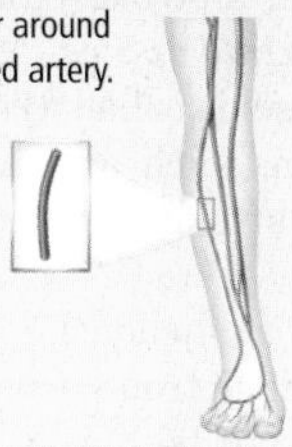	Tube with balloon inserted into blocked artery. Balloon inflated against artery walls, then deflated and removed. Metal structure may remain to keep artery open.	Implanted in chest. Sends electrical impulses to heart to make it beat regularly. 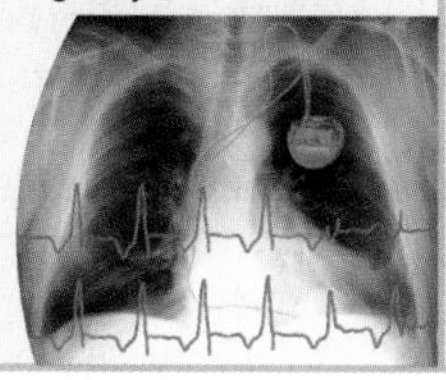	Laser fiber inserted into blocked artery. Laser vaporizes the blockage and restores the flow of blood. 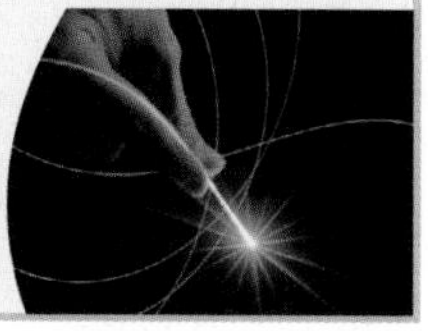

common among women. Anyone who experiences the following warning signs of heart attack should call 911 immediately:

- Pressure, fullness, squeezing, or aching in chest area
- Pain spreading to arms, neck, jaw, abdomen, or back
- Chest discomfort, with shortness of breath, lightheaded feeling, sweating, nausea, or vomiting

Congestive Heart Failure This occurs when the heart gradually weakens and can no longer maintain its regular pumping rate and force. It can be caused by a heart attack, high blood pressure, atherosclerosis, a heart valve defect, illegal drug use, or other factors. Congestive heart failure cannot be cured, but it can improve through continuous treatment, such as medication and practicing healthy lifestyle behaviors.

Caption Answer

Figure 25.2 Angioplasty

AL Active Learning

Guest Speaker Invite a heart surgeon, cardiologist, or a cardiac nurse to class to describe different treatments and diagnostic tests for cardiovascular diseases. Encourage the speaker to bring in visual results of diagnostic tests that show disease, as well as normal tissues to enable students to see the effects of the disease on the heart and blood vessels. OL

W Writing Support

Researching Have students use additional sources to find more detailed information about heart attacks. Students should use the information they learn to prepare a written presentation that describes the symptoms in detail. They should also explain what occurs during a heart attack. Encourage students to present their findings to the class. AL

C Critical Thinking

Making Inferences Discuss with students why heart failure occurs. (When the heart weakens and can no longer maintain its regular pumping rate.) Then ask students to infer why the heart is so sensitive to the lack of oxygen. (The heart is a large muscle that requires a lot of oxygen and other nutrients to work properly. When it does not get enough oxygen and nutrients, the heart muscle begins to die, resulting in a heart attack.) OL

ELL Support

Vocabulary Building List the types of heart disease on the board: *angina pectoris, arrhythmia, heart attack,* and *congestive heart failure.*

Beginning Pronounce each word for students and have them repeat after you. Use simple sentences to describe each condition. Have students draw a picture that describes each disease.

Intermediate Give descriptions of each disease and have students name the disease you are describing. Have them write a descriptive sentence for each.

Advanced Have students write a riddle that specifically identifies each disease.

Caption Answer

Figure 25.3 In case a person has a cardiac arrest

R Reading Strategy

Comparing and Contrasting
As students read about stroke, have them compare the causes, symptoms, and emergency response for strokes to those for heart attacks. Suggest that students make a Venn diagram to organize the information. **BL**

Main Idea

What Teens Need to Know
Cardiovascular disease can start to develop during the teen years. **Ask Students:** *What can you do to reduce the risk of cardiovascular disease?* (Sample answer: Avoid using tobacco, be physically active, and eat healthful foods)

C Critical Thinking

Applying Concepts Explain some of the warning signs of a stroke. Direct students to review all the warning signs discussed in this lesson. Have them identify other conditions they know about that have similar symptoms. (Sample answer: Influenza or indigestion) **OL**

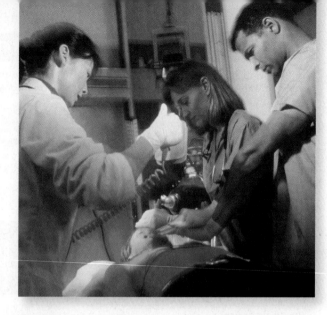

■ **Figure 25.3** In many cases sudden cardiac arrest can be reversed if CPR or electric shock using a defibrillator is applied. *Why is it important to have defibrillators available in many different public places?*

Stroke

Cardiovascular disease can affect the brain as well as the heart. Sometimes an artery supplying blood to the brain becomes blocked or bursts, resulting in a **stroke**—*an acute injury in which blood flow to the brain is interrupted*. A stroke that occurs because of a burst blood vessel is called a *cerebral hemorrhage*. Stroke can cause problems such as paralysis. The damage depends on the size of the stroke and what part of the brain is deprived of oxygen. **R**

Warning signs of stroke include severe headache, numbness on one side of the body, confusion, trouble walking, dizziness, and trouble seeing out of one or both eyes. Today, treatments exist that can stop a stroke as it is occurring. Drugs known as clot busters can break up a clot and restore the normal flow of blood to the brain. **C**

What Teens Need to Know

Main Idea CVD can begin during the teen years.

Did you know that CVD can start to develop during adolescence or even childhood? Autopsy results on adolescents who died from causes other than CVD have found that one in six already had evidence of CVD. Those who had a history of known risk factors, such as smoking or diabetes, were more likely to have blood vessel damage. A teen with damaged blood vessels may not experience any symptoms until later in adulthood, but the danger is already there.

Myths & Reality

Cardiovascular Disease

Myth: Most people with cardiovascular disease die suddenly.

Fact: Cardiovascular disease usually causes people to become progressively ill and debilitated, especially if it is not managed properly.

Myth: Cardiovascular disease affects only men.

Fact: According to the National Center for Health Statistics, 54 percent of the people identified with heart disease in 2004 were men and 46 percent were women.

Figure 25.4 CVD Risk Factors You Can Control

Risk Factor	Preventive Measure	Why It's Important
Tobacco Use	Avoid using tobacco.	About 20 percent of deaths from CVDs are smoking related. For teens, tobacco use is the biggest risk factor.
	Avoid secondhand smoke.	About 40,000 nonsmokers who are exposed to secondhand smoke die from CVDs each year.
High Blood Pressure	Have your blood pressure checked regularly.	High blood pressure strains your cardiovascular system.
	Eat healthfully, exercise regularly, and manage your weight.	
High Cholesterol	Eat fewer high-fat and high-cholesterol foods, and get regular physical activity.	High cholesterol can cause plaque to form in your arteries.
Physical Inactivity	Be sure you get at least 30 to 60 minutes of physical activity every day.	Physical activity strengthens your heart and helps you maintain a healthy weight.
Excess Weight	Maintain a healthy weight.	Excess weight puts a strain on the heart and raises blood pressure and blood cholesterol levels. It also increases your risk for type 2 diabetes (a risk factor for heart disease).
Stress	Use stress-management techniques.	Constant stress raises blood pressure.
Alcohol and Drug Use	Abstain from alcohol and other drugs.	Too much alcohol raises blood pressure and can cause irregular heartbeat or heart failure. Some illegal drugs increase heart rate and blood pressure and can result in heart failure.

Risk Factors

The American Heart Association has identified several factors that increase the risk of heart attack and stroke. **Figure 25.4** lists some actions you can take to reduce your risk of CVD. Unfortunately, there are also some risk factors that are unavoidable:

- **Heredity.** Children whose parents have CVD are more likely to develop CVD themselves.
- **Gender.** Men have a greater risk than women of developing CVD and having heart attacks. However, research shows that older women are less likely than men of the same age to survive a heart attack.
- **Age.** The risk of CVD increases with age. Approximately 80 percent of people who die of CVD are 65 or older.

Knowing about these risk factors can help you make healthful decisions to reduce your risk. For example, if CVD runs in your family, you can make a strong commitment to control your weight, exercise regularly, avoid tobacco use, and eat foods low in fat and cholesterol.

READING CHECK

Identify What are three decisions you could make today to reduce your risk of CVD?

Lesson 1 Cardiovascular Disease **693**

U Universal Access

Using Tables Give students pictures that illustrate each of the risk factors described in the table in **Figure 25.4**. Have them match the pictures to the risk factors. Then describe for students one preventive measure for each risk factor using simple sentences or phrases. To check their understanding, direct students to draw a picture for each preventive measure you describe. Finally, ask students to explain in their own words why the preventive measure is important. **EL**

HS Health Skills Practice

Advocacy Have students write a letter to the editor of their school or local newspaper in which they advocate the importance of making healthful lifestyle choices to reduce the risk of cardiovascular disease. Suggest that students focus their letters on one lifestyle choice and describe how this behavior reduces the risk of CVD. Review letters and encourage students to submit them for publication. **OL**

READING CHECK

Answer Avoid foods high in saturated fat and cholesterol, avoid tobacco, and control blood pressure.

Writing Strategy

Narrative Writing Have students write a narrative that tells the story of a young adult who learns that he or she has early symptoms of a cardiovascular disease such as hypertension or high cholesterol. Within their narratives, students should describe this person's lifestyle choices before and after the diagnosis and how this person feels about having to make the changes. Encourage students to fully develop the characters in the narrative and use dialogue to help move the story forward. Remind students to edit and proof their work before turning it in.

3 ASSESS/ CLOSE

Assessment Resources

📁 **FAST FILE ACTIVITIES**
Lesson 1 Quiz

💿 *ExamView*
Assessment Suite CD-ROM

Visit glencoe.com for:
Online Quizzes
Online Learning Center

Progress Monitoring

Reteaching

Have students make an outline of the lesson in which they include the types of cardiovascular disease with their descriptions, as well as the risk factors for CVD.

Enrichment

Encourage students to become involved with an organization such as the American Heart Association. Students could participate in or help organize a fundraiser like a walk-a-thon or bike-a-thon. Suggest that students involve other students in the class or student groups in the school.

Go Online

Have students visit **glencoe.com** and complete the Interactive Study Guide for this lesson.

Real World CONNECTION

An Exercise Campaign

Moderate exercise helps keep people healthy. Exercise burns calories, builds muscle, and helps the heart stay strong. Unfortunately, many people avoid exercise because they mistakenly think it has to be strenuous and time-consuming.

Activity Reading / Writing

Exercise can be as simple as a brisk walk, and most of the benefits are gained in the first half hour. More people should know that moderate exercise for just 30 minutes per day is a very efficient way to improve cardiovascular health.

Create a campaign to encourage teens to exercise for 30 minutes per day. The campaign should help teens understand why exercise is important, what kinds of exercises help their cardiovascular systems, and how much exercise people need. Design a poster with a catchy name and slogan that will inspire teens to begin a moderate exercise program.

LESSON 1 ASSESSMENT

After You Read

Reviewing Facts and Vocabulary

1. Define *cardiovascular disease*.
2. What can happen if hypertension continues over a long period?
3. What is a *stroke*?

Thinking Critically

4. **Compare and Contrast.** How is stroke similar to heart attack? How is it different?
5. **Synthesize.** How can practicing healthy lifestyle behaviors today help lower your risk for cardiovascular disease in the future?

Applying Health Skills

6. **Practicing Healthful Behaviors.** Evaluate your daily habits. What decisions can you make today to replace unhealthful choices with healthful ones?

Writing Critically

7. **Persuasive.** Imagine you have a friend who says that you don't need to worry about CVD until you are older. Write a letter convincing this friend that it's important to start taking preventive measures now.

Go Online

Visit **glencoe.com** and complete the Interactive Study Guide for this lesson.

LESSON 1 ASSESSMENT ANSWERS

1. A disease that affects the heart or blood vessels
2. It can damage the heart, blood vessels, and other body organs.
3. An acute injury in which blood flow to the brain is interrupted
4. Both are cardiovascular diseases that involve the blockage of blood flow. Heart attacks damage heart muscle, while strokes damage the brain.
5. Sample answer: By practicing healthy lifestyle behaviors, you are more likely to have normal blood pressure, healthy weight, and low cholesterol, which will reduce your risk for cardiovascular diseases.
6. Answers will vary.
7. Letters will vary, but should include facts from the lesson to support persuasive statements.

Cancer

Real Life Issues

Making a Healthful Choice. Amy wants her granddad to quit smoking. She learned in school that smoking can lead to health problems, such as heart disease and cancer. Amy's mom wants him to quit too. Amy and her mom have decided to write letters to Granddad telling him how they feel when they see him smoking. They want him to know how important he is to them, and why they want him to stay healthy.

Writing *What should Amy write to encourage her granddad to stop smoking? How can she use the letter to express her concern and support? Summarize your thoughts in a paragraph.*

What Is Cancer?

Main Idea Cancer has a variety of forms and affects different areas of the body.

Cells are the building blocks of your body. Approximately 100 trillion of these tiny structures make up who you are. The cells in your body are constantly growing, dividing, dying, and replacing themselves. Although most new cells are normal, some are not. When abnormal cells reproduce rapidly and uncontrollably, they can build up inside otherwise normal tissue. This *uncontrollable growth of abnormal cells* is called **cancer**.

How Cancer Harms the Body

When abnormal cells build up in the body, they can form a **tumor**. This is *an abnormal mass of tissue that has no natural role in the body.* Many people equate tumors with cancer. However, the presence of a tumor does not necessarily mean that a person has cancer. In fact, there are two kinds of tumors: benign and malignant.

GUIDE TO READING

***BIG* Idea** *Cancer takes many different forms and can affect people of all ages.*

Before You Read

Create a K-W-L Chart. Make a three-column chart. In the first column, write what you **k**now about the behaviors or lifestyle choices that can lead to cancer. In the second column, write what you **w**ant to know about cancer risk factors. As you read, use the third column to summarize what you **l**earned.

K	W	L

New Vocabulary

▸ cancer (p. 695)
▸ tumor (p. 695)
▸ benign (p. 696)
▸ malignant (p. 696)
▸ metastasis (p. 696)
▸ carcinogen (p. 697)
▸ biopsy (p. 700)
▸ remission (p. 701)

Lesson 2 Cancer **695**

Cancer

① FOCUS

GUIDE TO READING

***BIG* Idea** Cancer takes many forms and can affect people of all ages. **Ask Students:** *What kinds of cancer do you know about?* (Sample answer: skin, breast, prostate, lung, colon cancer)

Before You Read

K-W-L Chart Student's charts will vary. Sample answer: Know—Tobacco use causes cancer; Want to Know—Are only smokers at risk?; Learned—Nonsmokers exposed to secondhand smoke are also at risk.

Main Idea

What Is Cancer? There are several different types of cancer that can develop in almost any part of the body. **Ask Students:** *What is a tumor?* (An abnormal mass of tissue that has no natural role in the body)

Real Life Issues

Before students write their paragraphs, discuss how smoking affects the body. **Ask Students:** *Are smokers putting only their own health at risk?* (No, secondhand smoke is unhealthy for all people.)

Reading Strategy

Finding the Main Idea In this textbook, the main idea for each lesson section is easy to find. Point out that the Main Idea headings are located under the section headings. Direct students to take notes as they read the lesson by writing the main idea and listing its supporting details. Remind students to include all the vocabulary terms and their definitions in their notes, as well as relevant information from all graphics, tables, and charts.

② TEACH

Active Learning

Newspaper Article Have students choose one of the cancers described in **Figure 25.5** and write a newspaper article about it. Students should use the information in the chart to describe the cancer with the purpose of informing readers about the number of people affected each year, risk factors, symptoms, and screening methods for early detection. Have students proofread and correct their articles before turning them in. **OL**

R **Reading Strategy**

Analyzing a Table Discuss each of the cancers listed in **Figure 25.5**. Have students identify behaviors that would reduce the risks of each type of cancer. For example, the risk of prostate cancer could be reduced by eating a low-fat diet. Then discuss the actions a person could take to detect the cancer early. **OL**

U **Universal Access**

Comparing and Contrasting Teach beginning English language learners the term *tumor*, differentiating between benign and malignant tumors by describing the tumor as being slow-growing or fast-growing and spreading. Use drawings of body organs with and without tumors to help convey meaning. Teach intermediate and advanced English language learners the terms *benign* and *malignant*. Again use drawings, but also have students write phrases or sentences to check their understanding. **EL**

Figure 25.5 Types of Cancer

Organ Affected (new cases/year)	Some Risk Factors	Symptoms	Screening and Early Detection Methods
Skin (1 million) Most common type of cancer in the United States	Exposure to ultra-violet (UV) radiation from the sun, tanning beds, sunlamps, and other sources	Change on the skin, especially a new growth, a mole or freckle that changes, or a sore that won't heal	Physical exam, biopsies
Breast (267,000) Second leading cause of cancer death for women	Genetic factors, obesity, alcohol use, physical inactivity	Unusual lump; nipple that thickens, changes shape, dimples, or has discharge	Self-exam, mammogram
Prostate (232,090) Found mostly in men over 55	Possible hereditary link, possible link to high-fat diet	Frequent or painful urination; inability to urinate; weak or interrupted flow of urine; blood in urine or semen; pain in lower back, hips, or upper thighs	Blood test
Lung (173,770) Leading cause of cancer deaths in the United States	Exposure to cigarette smoke, radon, or asbestos	No initial symptoms; later symptoms include cough, shortness of breath, wheezing, coughing up blood, hoarseness	Chest X-ray
Colon/Rectum (146,940) Second leading cause of cancer deaths in the United States	Risk increases with age	Often no initial symptoms; later, blood in feces; frequent pain, aches, or cramps in stomach; change in bowel habits; weight loss	Test for blood in the stool, rectal exam, colonoscopy
Mouth (30,000) Occurs mostly in people over 40	Use of tobacco, chewing tobacco, or alcohol	Sore or lump on mouth that doesn't heal; unusual bleeding; pain or numbness on lip, mouth, tongue, or throat; feeling that something is caught in the throat; pain with chewing or swallowing; change in voice	Dental/oral exam
Cervix (11,000)	History of infection with human papillomavirus (HPV)	Usually no symptoms in early stages; later, abnormal vaginal bleeding, increased vaginal discharge	Pap test
Testicle (7,000) Most common cancer in men ages 15 to 34	Undescended testicle; family history of testicular cancer	Small, hard, painless lump on testicle; sudden accumulation of fluid in scrotum; pain in region between scrotum and anus	Self-exam

A **benign**, or *noncancerous*, tumor grows slowly. It is surrounded by membranes that prevent it from spreading. Does this mean it is harmless? No. Even if a benign tumor does not spread, it could still interfere with normal body functions. For example, a benign tumor in the brain could block the brain's blood supply.

A **malignant**, or *cancerous*, tumor does not stay in one place. It spreads to neighboring tissues and enters the blood or lymph to travel to other parts of the body. This process, *the spread of cancer from the point where it originated to other parts of the body*, is called **metastasis**. As cancer cells spread throughout the body, they divide and form new tumors.

696 **Chapter 25** Noncommunicable Diseases and Disabilities

More About...

Cancer Cells Cancer cells do not respond to the normal signaling in the body that directs body cells to grow. Cancer cells reproduce quickly and haphazardly, with new cells slightly different from the old cells. They do not self-destruct like normal cells when they are damaged. Cancer cells are missing molecules on their surface that enable them to stick together and stay in place. Finally, cancer cells do not mature into a cell with a specific job. Instead, they are usually very primitive in structure and have no function.

Many cancers kill normal cells as they compete with them for nutrients in the body. Whether a tumor is benign or malignant, it can put pressure on your organs and tissues and interfere with body functions. It can also block arteries, veins, and other passages that work best when they are unobstructed.

Types of Cancer

Cancers can develop in almost any part of the body and are classified according to the tissues they affect:

- **Lymphomas** are cancers of the immune system.
- **Leukemias** are cancers of the blood-forming organs.
- **Carcinomas** are cancers of the glands and body linings, including the skin and the linings of the digestive tract and lungs.
- **Sarcomas** are cancers of connective tissue, such as bones, ligaments, and muscles.

Figure 25.5 lists common types of cancers, grouped according to the body organ in which they first develop.

Risk Factors for Cancer

Main Idea Risk factors for cancer include lifestyle behaviors.

Every day, your body produces countless numbers of healthy, normal cells—but it also produces some abnormal ones. Your immune system usually kills these abnormal cells before they become cancerous. However, when the immune system is weak or the abnormal cells multiply faster than the immune system can destroy them, cancer may develop.

Carcinogens

Many cancers develop because of exposure to a **carcinogen**, or a *cancer-causing substance*. Tobacco and UV light are two of the most common carcinogens that cause cancer.

Tobacco Use The number one cause of cancer deaths in the United States is tobacco use. At least 43 different carcinogens have been identified in tobacco and tobacco smoke. Consider these numbers:

- About 215,000 new cases of lung cancer related to smoking are diagnosed each year.
- About 87 percent of lung cancer deaths are caused by smoking.
- About 30 percent of all other cancers are linked to tobacco use.

READING CHECK

Explain Are benign tumors harmless? Why or why not?

FITNESS ZONE

When I told my doctor that some of my older relatives have gotten cancer, she told me that eating a healthy diet and making healthy lifestyle choices can reduce my risks. Making healthier choices could mean 375,000 fewer cancer diagnoses in the U.S. every year. That convinced me to make better choices to protect my health. For more fitness tips, visit the Online Fitness Zone at glencoe.com.

Academic Vocabulary

link *(verb)*: to connect

READING CHECK

Answer No. A benign tumor can interfere with normal body functions.

C Critical Thinking

Making Connections Have students identify which classification of cancer—lymphoma, leukemia, carcinoma, or sarcoma—is represented by the list of cancers in **Figure 25.5**. (All of the cancers in the table are carcinomas. The breast, prostate, and testicle are glands. The other cancers begin in body linings.) **OL**

Main Idea

Risk Factors for Cancer Life-style choices can cause cancer. **Ask Students:** *What kind of cancer might result from sun exposure?* (skin cancer)

FITNESS ZONE

Have teams of two toss and catch a small ball as many times as possible per 30-second action below. Have each team record their totals. Then have them identify which activities were more challenging and why.

- Toss and catch while standing
- Toss and catch while hopping on left foot
- Toss and catch while walking in place. Toss and catch while hopping on right foot
- Toss and catch while jumping with two feet in place
- Toss and catch while jogging in place

Cooperative Learning

Develop a Survey Have groups of four students work together to develop a household carcinogen survey. Students should first identify common household carcinogens using library or Internet sources or by contacting the local health department or Environmental Protection Agency (EPA)

office. Students should use what they find to develop a survey that assesses a household's possible exposure to carcinogens. After you have reviewed the surveys, have groups survey their own households. Then have them make recommendations that will reduce the exposure to carcinogens.

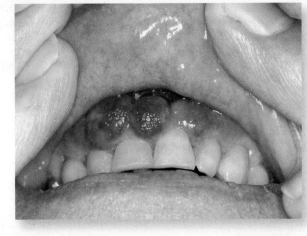

■ **Figure 25.6** This person's cancer may have been caused by using smokeless tobacco. *Smokeless tobacco is a major risk factor for what kind of cancer?*

Caption Answer

Figure 25.6 Mouth or oral cancer

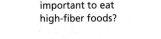 **Go Online**

Explore glencoe.com and complete the Student Web Activity on the cause and prevention of cancer.

W Writing Support

Writing a Summary Explain that a summary concisely describes the content of a piece of writing, such as an article, essay, or book. While a summary does not include the writer's opinions, it should be written in the writer's own words. Writing a summary helps to review and reinforce the content of a reading. Have students write a summary of carcinogens. **BL EL**

R Reading Strategy

Identifying Cause and Effect Call on students to explain why a diet high in fat and low in fiber can lead to cancer.

C Critical Thinking

Comparing and Contrasting Point out that certain healthful behaviors reduce the risks of both cancer and cardiovascular disease. (Maintaining a healthy weight, staying physically active, and eating nutritious foods) Have students research, using the library or online sources, to compare and contrast the effects of these behaviors on cardiovascular disease and cancer. Ask students to summarize their findings in a written report, poster, or PowerPoint presentation. **AL**

READING CHECK

Answer Fiber speeds the movement of waste through the intestines and out of the body, giving carcinogens less time to act on body cells.

The tobacco risk factor is not limited to smoking. Smokeless tobacco is a major risk factor for oral cancer, which affects the lips, mouth, and throat. Nonsmokers who are exposed to secondhand smoke are also at risk because they breathe in nicotine and other toxic chemicals.

Radiation Another carcinogen that commonly causes cancer is radiation. The glow of a suntan might look attractive, but a suntan is actually your skin's reaction to damage from the sun. UV radiation from the sun is the main cause of skin cancer. Tanning beds and sunlamps also emit UV radiation, which is just as damaging as the sun's rays. **W**

Sexually Transmitted Diseases

Some sexually transmitted viruses have the ability to cause cancer. For example, certain forms of human papillomavirus, or HPV, can cause cervical cancer. The hepatitis B virus, another sexually transmitted virus, can cause cancer in the liver.

Dietary Factors

About 30 percent of all cancer deaths are caused by dietary risk factors. A diet that is high in fat and low in fiber is often linked with colon, breast, and prostate cancers. Here's why: **R**

- **Fats** make colon cells more vulnerable to carcinogens. Colon cells divide faster if the diet is high in fat, increasing the risk that abnormal cells will form.

- **Dietary fiber** speeds the movement of waste through the intestines and out of the body. If a person's diet is low in fiber, the waste moves more slowly, giving carcinogens in the waste more time to act on the body's cells. **C**

 READING CHECK

Explain Why is it important to eat high-fiber foods?

Teens Want to Know

Can Tanning Beds Really Cause Cancer? Scientific studies show that people who use tanning beds have an increased risk of skin cancer. Even though some tanning salons advertise their tanning beds as using only "safe" UVA radiation, some also emit UVB radiation. UVA radiation stimulates the cells deeper in the skin to produce melanin, the brown pigment that causes tanning. UVB radiation burns the upper layers of skin, causing sunburn. Lamps used for tanning beds usually emit a larger concentration of UVA radiation than people receive from the sun.

Reducing Your Risk

Main Idea You can reduce your risk of cancer by practicing healthful behaviors.

Sometimes cancer seems to strike people at random. That is one of the most frightening aspects of the disease. Although some factors may be beyond your control, you can dramatically reduce your risk for cancer by practicing healthful behaviors. See **Figure 25.7** for steps you can start taking today.

READING CHECK

Identify What are three actions you could take to reduce your risk for cancer?

| Figure 25.7 | **How You Can Reduce Your Cancer Risk** |

There are many healthful behaviors you can practice to reduce your risk for cancer. *How many of these behaviors do you already practice?*

Protect your skin from UV radiation.

Avoid tobacco and alcohol. Tobacco is the single major cause of cancer death in the United States. Excess alcohol increases the risk of several types of cancer, including mouth and throat cancer.

Practice abstinence from sexual activity to reduce the risk of sexually transmitted diseases. Hepatitis B can cause liver cancer, and HPV can cause cancers of the reproductive organs.

Be physically active.

Maintain a healthy weight.

Eat nutritious foods. Include 2–4 servings of fruits and 3–5 servings of vegetables every day. These foods are good sources of fiber, and some contain compounds that act against carcinogens.

Follow an eating plan that is low in saturated fat and high in fiber.

Recognize the warning signs of cancer. Do regular self-exams to detect cancer early.

Main Idea

Reducing Your Risk It's possible to reduce the risk of cancer by practicing healthful behaviors. **Ask Students:** *What healthful behavior do you currently practice that will reduce your risk of cancer?* (Answers will vary but may include eating lots of vegetables.)

R Reading Strategy

Using Visuals Have students match the behaviors that reduce the risk of cancer with the risk factors for cancer described in the text. For each behavior listed in **Figure 25.7**, ask students to identify the cancer risk it will help reduce. Have students explain how the behavior will reduce the risk. **BL**

HS Health Skills Practice

Practicing Healthful Behaviors Have students identify one of the behaviors to reduce the risk of cancer described in **Figure 25.7** that they need to improve in their own lives. Direct them to write this behavior in their personal journal and write how they will implement this change. Encourage students to practice this behavior change for at least one week, making daily journal entries describing their progress and feelings. **OL**

READING CHECK

Answer Sample answer: Abstaining from sexual activity, protecting skin from UV radiation, avoiding high-fat foods

ELL Support

Reducing the Risks of Cancer Use the photographs in Figure 25.7 to discuss ways to reduce the risks of cancer.

Beginning Rewrite the behaviors that are pictured in **Figure 25.7** into simpler phrases. Have students match each phrase with the corresponding photograph.

Intermediate Find additional photographs for behaviors in **Figure 25.7** that do not have a photograph. Have students write a simple phrase that describes how the behavior reduces cancer risk.

Advanced Have students study the photographs and read the text in **Figure 25.7**. Have them write a summary of what they read.

Main Idea

Detecting and Treating Cancer
Early detection and the right type of treatment are critical for successfully treating cancer. **Ask Students:** *What is the importance of self-examinations?* (Sample answer: By checking your own body regularly for possible signs of cancer, you can detect the presence of cancer early.)

Cancer Vaccine After students have watched the video, *Cancer Vaccine,* divide the class into small groups. Have groups discuss the benefits of the cancer vaccine Provenge. Then ask them to describe the differences between the treatment with the vaccine and more traditional treatments. Invite volunteers from each group to summarize their discussions for the class.

W Writing Support
Persuasive Writing Have students write a letter to a friend or relative that persuades him or her to practice regular self-exams for early cancer detection. Letters should include logical reasons for doing self-exams, as well as statistics or facts that support self-exams. Students should use additional sources to find these statistics or facts. **OL**

Caption Answer

Figure 25.8 Change in the size or color of a wart or mole

Detecting and Treating Cancer

Main Idea Successful cancer treatment depends on early detection and the right kind of treatment.

Cancer Vaccine

Analyze. Go to glencoe.com and watch the video *Cancer Vaccine.* In a group, discuss the benefits associated with the cancer vaccine Provenge. What are some of the differences between this new treatment and more traditional cancer treatments, such as chemotherapy?

As medical technology continues to advance, doctors are able to detect cancer earlier than in past years. **Figure 25.8** shows the many warning signs for cancer. There have also been many advances in treatment options. The survival rate for people with cancer depends on two main factors: early detection and the type of cancer.

Early detection, the most critical factor in successful cancer treatment, depends on both self-examination and medical examination.

- **Self-examination** involves checking your own body for possible signs of cancer. Many types of cancer, including those of the breasts, testicles, and skin, are discovered early through self-examination.

- **Medical examination**, or medical screening, involves testing by a doctor for early signs of cancer. About half of all new cancer cases each year are detected during a routine medical screening.

If a doctor thinks cancer is a possibility, a **biopsy**—*the removal of a small piece of tissue for examination*—may be ordered. A biopsy is usually necessary to determine whether cancer is present. To help determine a tumor's location and size, doctors use X-rays and other imaging techniques.

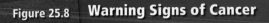

| Figure 25.8 | **Warning Signs of Cancer** |

The warning signs listed below do not necessarily indicate cancer, as there may be other causes. However, all are serious enough to bring to a doctor's attention right away. A person with any of these warning signs should see a doctor as soon as possible. *What is a warning sign of skin cancer?*

- **Fever, fatigue, pain, and discoloration of the skin.** These general signs can sometimes indicate cancer.
- **Change in bowel habits or bladder function.** This may suggest colon, bladder, or prostate cancer.
- **Sores that will not heal.** Persistent sores on skin, mouth, or genitalia should be examined promptly.
- **Unusual bleeding or discharge.** This could be present in phlegm, stool, urine, or discharge from vagina or nipples.

- **Thickening or lump in breast or other body part.** Many cancers can be felt through the skin.
- **Indigestion or trouble swallowing.** Though usually harmless, these symptoms can sometimes indicate cancer of the stomach, esophagus, or throat.
- **Change in wart or mole.** Change in color or size might indicate skin cancer.
- **Nagging cough or hoarseness.** This could indicate cancer of the lungs, larynx, or thyroid.

700   Chapter 25   Noncommunicable Diseases and Disabilities

Health Literacy

Robotic Surgery for Prostate Cancer
Prostate cancer is treated by surgically removing the entire prostate gland. Beginning in the 1990s, this surgery was done laparoscopically, which means that the surgeon makes several tiny incisions into the abdomen and views the tissues and surgical instruments with a microscopic camera

inserted into one of the incisions. Now surgeons use a robotic system that translates the surgeon's hand movements on a remote console into steady and accurate instrument movements. This results in more complete removal of cancerous tissue while avoiding extensive nerve and blood vessel damage.

Treatment Options

The methods used to treat cancer depend on several factors, such as the type of cancer and whether a tumor has spread from its original location. Treatment might include one or more of the methods listed below.

- **Surgery** removes some or all of the cancerous masses from the body.
- **Radiation therapy** uses radioactive substances to kill cancer cells and shrink cancerous masses.
- **Chemotherapy** uses chemicals to destroy cancer cells.
- **Immunotherapy** activates a person's immune system to recognize specific cancers and destroy them.
- **Hormone therapy** uses medicines to interfere with the production of certain hormones, such as estrogen, that help cancer cells grow. These treatments kill cancer cells or slow their growth.

When treatment works and the cancer is either gone or under control, the cancer is said to be in **remission**. This is *a period of time when symptoms disappear*. Today, more and more cancer survivors are able to lead full, active lives.

LESSON 2 ASSESSMENT

After You Read

Reviewing Facts and Vocabulary

1. What is *metastasis*?
2. What are the two important methods for early cancer detection?
3. Identify three cancer treatment options.

Thinking Critically

4. **Synthesize.** Based on what you know about your own lifestyle and what you now know about the risk factors for cancer, do you need to change any of your behaviors? Explain.
5. **Evaluate.** How does technology help in detecting and treating cancer?

Applying Health Skills

6. **Refusal Skills.** Based on what you have learned in this lesson, write down what you might say to someone trying to pressure you into using tobacco.

Writing Critically

7. **Expository.** Research the procedures used for early detection of cancer. Then write a short essay analyzing the benefits of health screenings, checkups, and early detection. Include information from your research to support your analysis.

Go Online

Visit **glencoe.com** and complete the Interactive Study Guide for this lesson.

READING CHECK

Identify Which cancer treatment option uses chemicals to destroy cancer cells?

CHAPTER 25

LESSON 2

 READING CHECK

Answer Chemotherapy

 3 ASSESS/ CLOSE

Assessment Resources

📁 *FAST FILE* ACTIVITIES
Lesson 2 Quiz

💿 *ExamView*
Assessment Suite CD-ROM

Visit glencoe.com for:
Online Quizzes
Online Learning Center

Progress Monitoring

Reteaching
Have students write one or two sentences that summarize each section of the lesson.

Enrichment
Treatment options for various cancers are improving every day. Invite students to choose one type of cancer and research the latest treatment options available.

Go Online

Have students visit **glencoe.com** and complete the Interactive Study Guide for this lesson.

LESSON 2 ASSESSMENT ANSWERS

1. The spread of cancer from the point where it originated to other parts of the body
2. Self-examination and medical examination
3. *Any three:* surgery, radiation therapy, chemotherapy, immunotherapy, hormone therapy
4. Answers will vary.
5. Sample answer: Doctors use biopsies and imaging techniques to detect cancer and various surgical techniques, therapies, and medications to treat it.
6. Answers will vary.
7. Answers will vary.

701

Allergies, Asthma, Diabetes, and Arthritis

 ① **FOCUS**

📖 **GUIDE TO READING**

BIG Idea Self-management strategies can help reduce the severity of allergies, asthma, diabetes, and arthritis. **Ask Students:** *What are your experiences with allergies?* (Answers will vary.)

Before You Read

Vocabulary Cards Definitions should reflect those given in the lesson.

Main Idea

Allergies Many different substances can cause allergies. **Ask Students:** *What are some symptoms of allergies?* (Sample answers: Sneezing, runny nose, itchy eyes, hives, difficulty swallowing)

Real Life Issues ·············

Have students use the decision-making process in their answers. **Ask Students:** *Why would it be important for Julie's coach to know that she has asthma?* (Sample answer: If Julie has an asthma attack, her coach will be prepared to help her.)

📖 **GUIDE TO READING**

BIG Idea *Practicing self-management strategies can help reduce the severity of allergies, asthma, diabetes, and arthritis.*

Before You Read

Create Vocabulary Cards. Write each new vocabulary term on a separate index card. For each term, write a definition based on your current knowledge. As you read, fill in additional information related to each term.

Allergy

New Vocabulary

▸ allergy (p. 702)
▸ histamines (p. 703)
▸ asthma (p. 704)
▸ diabetes (p. 705)
▸ autoimmune disease (p. 705)
▸ arthritis (p. 707)
▸ osteoarthritis (p. 707)
▸ rheumatoid arthritis (p. 708)

Allergies, Asthma, Diabetes, and Arthritis

Real Life Issues ························

Using Good Judgment. Julie has had asthma since she was little. She controls the condition with medication and prides herself on being able to keep up with her friends. This year she wants to join the track team. However, she is afraid that if she tells the coach that she has asthma, he might discourage her from trying out. She thinks her chances of making the team will improve if she doesn't tell the coach.

Writing *If you were Julie's friend, what would you say to her? Write your response in a paragraph.*

Allergies

Main Idea Allergies are caused by a variety of substances.

If you are sneezing and have a runny nose, you might not have a cold. Rather, you might have an **allergy**—*a specific reaction of the immune system to a foreign and frequently harmless substance.* These substances are present in your environment and make their way into your body. Have you noticed how many advertisements for allergy medications are on TV and in magazines? That's because allergies are a very common noncommunicable illness, affecting 40 million to 50 million Americans.

The substances that cause allergies are called *allergens.* Allergens include pollen, certain foods, dust, mold spores, chemicals, insect venom, dander from animals, and certain medicines. Allergens produce the allergic reactions of sneezing and a runny nose in a four-step process.

⧗ **Promoting School Wellness**

Healthy School Environments All school facilities should provide a healthy environment for the students and staff using them. Students with allergies and asthma should have an environment as free from allergens and asthmatic triggers as possible. Building supplies known to be toxic, such as asbestos and lead paint, should be removed or completely contained. Invite the school's maintenance supervisor into the classroom to describe how the school environment is monitored to protect students' and staff's health. Also have the supervisor describe procedures used to reduce indoor air pollution.

1. The allergen enters the body, which treats the allergen as a foreign invader.

2. Antigens on the surface of allergens attach to special immune cells in the linings of the nasal passage.

3. These immune cells release **histamines**, *chemicals that can stimulate mucus and fluid production.*

4. Histamines cause sneezing, itchy eyes, runny nose, and other allergy symptoms.

There are many kinds of allergic reactions. Some allergies produce hives—itchy raised bumps on the skin. More serious reactions that can be life threatening include the following:

- Severe hives
- Itching or swelling of an area stung by an insect
- Difficulty breathing or swallowing
- Swelling of the tongue, mouth, or eyes
- Sharp drop in blood pressure, which can cause dizziness

Diagnosing Allergies

Sometimes you can diagnose an allergy yourself. For example, you may notice that you break out in a rash after eating certain foods. In many cases, though, tests are needed to identify the source of an allergic reaction. Blood tests and skin tests are common methods. During a skin test, small amounts of possible allergens are applied to a scratched area of the skin. If a person is allergic to any of the allergens, the skin will swell and turn red.

Treating Allergies

The simplest way to treat an allergy is to avoid the allergen that causes it. Many people avoid peanuts, milk, or foods made with these items because they know they are allergic to them. When avoidance is not possible, people with allergies can take *antihistamines*. These medicines help control allergy symptoms. Talk to your doctor or pharmacist about which medication may be most helpful for you. Some antihistamines may aggravate other medical conditions, such as heart conditions or lung problems.

Allergies range from mild to life threatening. People with long-lasting or severe allergies should seek medical attention. If you suffer from severe allergies, your doctor may prescribe antihistamines or a single, injectable dose of medicine that you carry with you at all times. If someone you know experiences a severe allergic reaction, call 911 immediately.

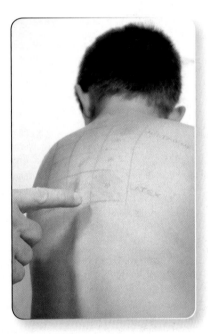

■ **Figure 25.9** Skin tests can determine which substances cause an individual to have allergic reactions. *Why are several different substances used when doing skin patch tests?*

Lesson 3   Allergies, Asthma, Diabetes, and Arthritis   **703**

READING CHECK

Describe How does the production of histamines affect the body?

CHAPTER 25

LESSON 3

READING CHECK

Answer Histamines cause sneezing, itchy eyes, runny nose, and other allergy symptoms.

2 TEACH

AL Active Learning

Poster Have pairs of students create a poster that diagrams the sequence of steps in an allergic reaction. You might suggest that some pairs show an alternative ending in which an antihistamine is used to control the allergic reaction. Encourage students to use symbols to represent the various components of the reaction, as well as informative labels. **BL OL**

R Reading Strategy

Concept Map Have students create a concept map to organize the information in the lesson about treating allergies. Students can title the concept map *Allergies*, and use *Causes, Diagnosis,* and *Treatment* as main headings. **BL EL**

Caption Answer

Figure 25.9 To determine which substances cause an allergic reaction

Academic Integration

Science Obtain prepared slides of various allergens, such as pollen, mold spores, dust, and animal dander. Have students examine these slides under the microscope and make observations. Discuss with students the size of these allergens and how they might be filtered from an indoor environment. Pro- vide examples or pictures of furnace filters. Explain that electrostatic air filters remove particles from the air by giving the particles an electric charge as they enter the filter. The particles stick to oppositely charged collection plates inside the filter, no matter how small they are.

Main Idea

Asthma Although asthma has no cure, it can be managed. **Ask Students:** *What are the warning signs of an asthma attack?* (Shortness of breath, chest tightness, coughing, or sneezing)

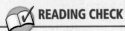

READING CHECK

Answer *Any three:* Air pollution, pet dander, tobacco smoke, mold, pollen, dust mites, exercise

W Writing Support

Personal Writing For students who do not have asthma, instruct them to write a letter to an imaginary friend who does. The letter should include the four strategies for managing asthma and identify the triggers of an asthma attack. Give students who have asthma the option to write a diary entry in which they describe how they manage their asthma based on the four strategies described in the lesson. **OL**

C Critical Thinking

Assessing Cause and Effect Explain that the incidence of asthma has increased dramatically over the last 25 years. Have interested students use additional sources to find out why more people are getting asthma. Students can summarize their findings with a written report, poster, or PowerPoint® presentation that they present to the class. **AL**

Caption Answer

Figure 25.10 By monitoring the condition, managing the environment, managing stress, and taking medication properly

---

Asthma

Main Idea Asthma has no cure, but it can be managed.

More than 15 million people in the United States have **asthma**—*an inflammatory condition in which the small airways in the lungs become narrowed, causing difficulty in breathing.* This disease can develop at any age, but about one-third of asthma sufferers are under the age of 18. Asthma can be life threatening, so those who have it must take the condition seriously and learn to manage it.

The bronchial tubes of people with asthma are highly sensitive to certain substances called *triggers.* Common asthma triggers include air pollution, pet dander, tobacco smoke, microscopic mold, pollen, and dust mites. Sometimes an asthma attack may be triggered by exercise. During an asthma attack, the muscles of the bronchial walls tighten and produce extra mucus. Symptoms may range from minor wheezing to severe difficulty in breathing. **W**

Managing Asthma

People with asthma are usually under a doctor's care and take prescribed medications. They also help themselves with these self-management strategies: **C**

- **Monitor the condition.** Learn to recognize the warning signs of an attack: shortness of breath, chest tightness or pain, coughing, or sneezing. Responding quickly can help prevent attacks or keep them from getting worse.

- **Manage your environment.** Avoid exposure to tobacco smoke, wash bedding frequently, and be aware of the air quality in your area.

- **Manage stress.** Stress can trigger an asthma attack. Learn relaxation and stress-management techniques to reduce your risk.

- **Take medication properly.** Medications help relieve symptoms, prevent flare-ups, and make air passages less sensitive to triggers. Many people with asthma use *bronchodilators,* or inhalers. These devices deliver medicine that relaxes and widens respiratory passages.

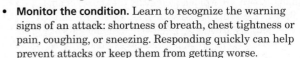

READING CHECK

Identify Name three triggers that can cause an asthma attack.

■ **Figure 25.10** These are some environmental conditions that trigger asthma. *What are some ways that people with asthma can manage their condition?*

Teacher to Teacher

Lisa Brewer • Scott High School, Taylor Mill, KY

Teaching Asthma When teaching about asthma, one strategy I like using in the lesson includes straws and clothes pins. This gives the students an idea of what it is like to live with asthma. I use a clothes pin with a spring and either a coffee stirrer or a narrow straw. The students place the clothes pin on their noses and the straw in their mouths. The students are only to breathe through the straw. We begin with sitting in class and then make our way to the hallways, including the stairs. The students love this and it really conveys what it's like to not be able to breathe clearly.

Diabetes

Main Idea Type 2 diabetes is on the rise.

It's likely you know someone with **diabetes**—*a chronic disease that affects the way body cells convert sugar into energy.* It is one of the fastest-growing diseases in the United States, with more than 1 million new cases diagnosed every year. Young people are especially at risk today. Symptoms of diabetes include the following:

- Frequent urination
- Excessive thirst
- Unexplained weight loss
- Sudden changes in vision
- Tingling in hands or feet
- Frequent fatigue
- Sores that are slow to heal
- More infections than usual

In a person with diabetes, the pancreas produces too little or no insulin, a hormone that helps glucose from food enter body cells and provide them with energy. Some diabetics do produce enough insulin, but their cells don't **respond** normally to it. As a result, glucose builds up in the blood instead of being delivered to cells.

HS The only way to diagnose diabetes is through a blood test. Diabetes can be successfully managed with medication, a healthful eating plan, and regular moderate exercise. If the disease is not treated, the long-term effects include blindness, kidney failure, limb amputations, heart disease, and stroke.

Type 1 Diabetes

Type 1 diabetes accounts for 5 to 10 percent of all diabetes cases. It appears suddenly and progresses quickly. The body fails to produce insulin, glucose builds up in the blood, and cells don't get the energy they need. Over time, the high blood sugar level can cause damage to the eyes, kidneys, nerves, and heart.

Scientists have not yet been able to determine what causes type 1 diabetes. Some suspect an environmental trigger—for example, an unidentified virus—that stimulates an immune response. The body begins attacking itself and destroys the cells of the pancreas that produce insulin. Type 1 diabetes is thus known as an **autoimmune disease**, *a condition in which the immune system mistakenly attacks itself, targeting the cells, tissues, and organs of a person's own body.* People with type 1 diabetes must take daily doses of insulin, either through injections or through a specially attached pump.

Academic Vocabulary

respond *(verb):* to react in response

Reading Strategy

Comparing and Contrasting Differentiating between type 1 and type 2 diabetes can be troubling to students. Suggest that students make a Venn diagram to compare and contrast the characteristics of the two types of diabetes. Some students might learn better by writing the characteristics of each type on slips of paper and physically arranging the slips of paper into categories. All students should devise some mnemonic phrase or word association to help them differentiate between type 1 and type 2 diabetes. For example, type 2 diabetes is often caused by getting 2 little exercise and eating 2 many fatty foods.

Main Idea

Diabetes Type 2 diabetes is one of today's fastest-growing diseases.
Ask Students: *How can you reduce the risk of type 2 diabetes?* (Choose low-fat, low-calorie foods and stay physically active)

AL Active Learning

Interview Have student pairs write and enact a mock interview about the symptoms, causes, and treatment of type 2 diabetes. One student might pose as a physician while the other poses as the interviewer. Ask selected pairs to perform their interview for physical education classes or for middle school and elementary school students. **OL**

Academic Vocabulary

Respond List on the board several different stimuli such as hearing a telephone ring, smelling pizza in the next room, or seeing heavy, dark storm clouds in the sky. Invite students to describe how they would respond to each stimulus. Then have students write a sentence for response that conveys its meaning.

HS Health Skills Practice

Goal Setting Have students record their level of physical activity and their food choices for one week. At the end of the week, students should assess their activity level and food choices. Then direct students to write a specific health goal that will improve either their activity level or food choices. Have them devise an action plan to meet this goal. After a week of implementing their plan, have students assess their progress and devise a plan to overcome obstacles or set a more challenging goal. **OL**

Health Skills Activity

Advocacy: Campaigning for Health

NHES Standard 8 Students will demonstrate the ability to advocate for personal, family, and community health.

Objectives

- Explain how healthful food choices reduce the risk of diabetes.
- Develop and implement a campaign to make teens aware of the risk of diabetes and the importance of healthy foods.

Teaching Strategies

- Review the causes of type 2 diabetes and how low-calorie, low-fat foods help reduce the risk. Encourage students to give reasons that would convince teens of the reasons for replacing the candy and soda machines.
- Have students work in small groups to create their brochures and petitions.

Assessment

Using this list, student work should provide comprehensive evidence of the following criteria to achieve the highest score:

√ Clear, health-enhancing stand
√ Support for the position with relevant information
√ Awareness of the audience
√ Encouragement of others to make healthful choices

✓ READING CHECK

Answer More young people are inactive and overweight.

Health Skills Activity

Advocacy

Campaigning for Health

Fiona and Bernard's health class just learned about the increase of type 2 diabetes among teens. "I don't want our generation to be known as the diabetes generation," Fiona says, concerned.

"What can we do?" asks Bernard.

"Let's start by asking that the sodas and candy in vending machines be replaced with healthier choices," Fiona suggests.

"Sounds great, but we also need to raise awareness of the issue," says Bernard. "We need to create some posters and information sheets, and maybe a petition."

Writing Write an ending to the scenario in which Fiona and Bernard organize their campaign. Use these guidelines:

1. List the reasons why healthier food items should be offered.
2. Create a brochure explaining the risk of diabetes and the importance of healthy foods.
3. Draft a petition to be signed by other students.

Type 2 Diabetes

Type 2 diabetes accounts for 90 to 95 percent of all cases of diabetes. It usually appears after age 40, but growing numbers of younger people—even children and teens—are developing this disease. In this form of diabetes, the body is unable to make enough insulin or to use insulin properly. Some scientists fear that type 2 diabetes will become an epidemic for two reasons: there are more older people in the population, and there are more obese and inactive young people. The increase in childhood obesity is directly linked to the increase in type 2 diabetes among children.

To help prevent type 2 diabetes, include these healthful behaviors in your life:

- **Choose low-fat, low-calorie foods.** People whose eating plans are high in fat, calories, and cholesterol have an increased risk of diabetes.
- **Participate in regular physical activity.** Being active helps control weight and lower blood cholesterol levels.

People with diabetes can live full, normal lives if they manage their condition. This includes monitoring their blood sugar levels, making healthful eating decisions, engaging in regular physical activity, and taking prescribed medications.

✓ READING CHECK

Explain What is one reason that type 2 diabetes is increasing among young people?

Myths & Reality

Diabetes

Myth: You can get diabetes from eating too much sugar.

Fact: Diabetes is caused by a combination of genetic and lifestyle factors. However, if you are overweight and physically inactive, you are at risk for developing type 2 diabetes.

Myth: I don't have a family history of diabetes, so I will not get it.

Fact: While some people inherit a greater risk of developing diabetes, many people without a family history of diabetes are diagnosed with it. Weight and physical activity are other factors that can determine whether you will develop diabetes.

Arthritis

Main Idea Arthritis is a major cause of disability.

Arthritis is *a group of more than 100 different diseases that cause pain and loss of movement in the joints.* Arthritis affects people of all ages, though it is more common in older adults. The two main forms of arthritis are osteoarthritis and rheumatoid arthritis. Both can be debilitating, limiting movement in the affected joints. There is currently no cure for either type, but self-management techniques can reduce pain and improve movement.

Osteoarthritis

Half of all arthritis cases involve **osteoarthritis**—*a disease of the joints in which cartilage breaks down.* Cartilage is the strong, flexible tissue that cushions your joints. Osteoarthritis causes the cartilage to become pitted and frayed. In time, it may wear away completely, causing the bones to rub painfully against each other.

People with osteoarthritis experience aches and soreness, especially when moving. Osteoarthritis mainly affects the large, weight-bearing joints, such as the knees and hips. However, the fingers, feet, lower back, and other joints are also at risk. Several strategies can reduce your risk:

- **Control your weight.** Maintaining a healthy weight reduces stress on your joints.
- **Stay active.** Physical activity strengthens your joints.
- **Prevent sports injuries.** Warm up before exercising, participate in strength training, and use protective equipment to avoid joint injuries.
- **Protect against Lyme disease.** If left untreated, Lyme disease can result in a rare form of osteoarthritis. When walking in wooded areas, use insect repellent and wear long-sleeved shirts and pants.

■ **Figure 25.11** Staying active will help keep your joints strong. *What other healthful behaviors can help prevent arthritis?*

707

U **Universal Access**

Modeling Pronounce both types of arthritis for students to repeat. Use a skeleton or diagram of the skeletal system to differentiate between the symptoms for each. Model how the tissue that cushions the joints wears away in osteoarthritis. Then model how the tissue swells, thickens, and becomes distorted in rheumatoid arthritis. Have students write a phrase or a sentence that defines each type of arthritis. **BL** **EL**

Main Idea

Arthritis Arthritis is a major cause of disability. **Ask Students:** *How can regular physical activity help prevent arthritis?* (Sample answer: Regular physical activity keeps joints strong and flexible.)

C **Critical Thinking**

Distinguishing Point out that treatment methods for osteoarthritis include exercise and controlling weight. Ask students to explain why these opposite activities are beneficial. **OL**

ELL Support

Reviewing Noncommunicable Diseases Make a chart on poster board with the headings *Allergies, Asthma, Diabetes,* and *Arthritis.*

Beginning Write single words or short phrases on slips of paper that describe each disease. Have students match the descriptions to the disease.

Intermediate Have students read each heading on the poster and the descriptions

on the slips of paper. Ask them to describe each disease's symptoms and treatment.

Advanced Have students use the completed chart as a prompt to write a brief paragraph for each disease that describes its symptoms and treatments.

LESSON 3

Answer It reduces stress on joints.

 ASSESS/ CLOSE

Assessment Resources

📁 *FAST FILE* ACTIVITIES
Lesson 3 Quiz

💿 *ExamView*
Assessment Suite CD-ROM

Visit glencoe.com for:
Online Quizzes
Online Learning Center

Progress Monitoring

Reteaching
Assign small groups one of the diseases discussed in the lesson. Instruct them to develop a five-minute class presentation in which they summarize the key points about the disease.

Enrichment
Encourage students to learn more about autoimmune diseases, such as type 1 diabetes and rheumatoid arthritis, and their effects on the body. Have them choose one autoimmune disease that is not discussed in the lesson and prepare a lesson to teach the class about it.

 Online

Have students visit **glencoe.com** and complete the Interactive Study Guide for this lesson.

☑ **READING CHECK**

Explain How does keeping a healthy weight affect arthritis?

Rheumatoid Arthritis

Rheumatoid arthritis is *a disease characterized by the debilitating destruction of the joints due to inflammation.* It is three times more common in women than in men. Symptoms usually first appear between the ages of 20 and 50, but the disease can also affect young children. Some of the symptoms and side effects include

- joint pain, inflammation, swelling, and stiffness.
- deformed joints that can't function normally.
- possible fever, fatigue, and swollen lymph glands.

Rheumatoid arthritis is caused by an autoimmune disorder. It affects mainly the joints in the hand, foot, elbow, shoulder, neck, knee, hip, and ankle. The effects are usually *symmetrical,* meaning that both sides of the body develop the same symptoms at the same time. Treatments focus on relieving pain, reducing inflammation, and keeping the joints flexible. Treatment methods include medication, exercise, rest, joint protection, and physical and occupational therapy.

LESSON 3 ASSESSMENT

After You Read

Reviewing Facts and Vocabulary

1. What are *histamines*? What role do they play in allergies?
2. Name three strategies for managing asthma.
3. What are the two main forms of arthritis?

Thinking Critically

4. **Synthesize.** If someone has allergies, is it safer to stay indoors or to get as much fresh air as possible? Explain.
5. **Evaluate.** Many people have diabetes but are not aware of it. What makes this lack of awareness dangerous?

Applying Health Skills

6. **Practicing Healthful Behaviors.** Make a three-column chart. In the first column, list the four diseases described in this lesson. In the second column, identify risk factors for each disease. In the third column, write down actions you can take to reduce your risk for each disease.

Writing Critically

7. **Narrative.** Write a story about a teen who has one of the diseases covered in this lesson. Describe how the condition affects the teen's daily life and how he or she manages the disease.

G⚛ Online

Visit **glencoe.com** and complete the Interactive Study Guide for this lesson.

LESSON 3 ASSESSMENT ANSWERS

1. *Histamines* are chemicals that can stimulate mucus and fluid production. They cause sneezing, itchy eyes, runny nose, and other allergy symptoms.
2. *Any three:* Monitor the condition, manage the environment, manage stress, and take medication properly
3. Osteoarthritis and rheumatoid arthritis
4. Sample answer: It depends on what the person is allergic to. In either case, taking appropriate medication can help relieve allergy symptoms.
5. Sample answer: If diabetes is not treated, the long-term effects include blindness, kidney failure, limb amputation, heart disease, and stroke.
6. Charts will vary.
7. Stories will vary.

Physical and Mental Challenges

Real Life Issues ....

Dealing with a Disability. Peter was born with a physical disability that affects the way he walks. He doesn't need a wheelchair or a cane, but when he walks, he looks very different from most people. It also takes him longer to get from one place to another. Because he moves more slowly, Peter is always the last one picked for team sports. He sometimes hears people laughing at him.

Writing *What would you say to someone who laughs at Peter? In a paragraph, explain why this behavior is wrong.*

Physical Challenges

Main Idea Most physical challenges affect sight, hearing, and motor ability.

Almost 20 percent of American adults have some type of **disability**—*any physical or mental impairment that limits normal activities, including seeing, hearing, walking, or speaking.* The range of physical challenges is quite broad. However, as **Figure 25.12** on page 710 shows, most physical challenges fall into one of three categories: sight impairment, hearing impairment, or motor impairment.

Sight Impairment

Worldwide, more than 40 million people are blind. In the United States, about 1.3 million people are legally blind, and at least 5 million more have some degree of sight impairment that cannot be corrected with glasses or contact lenses. Sight impairment is more common among older adults, but it can affect people of all ages.

GUIDE TO READING

BIG Idea *People with physical and mental challenges deserve to be treated with dignity and respect.*

Before You Read

Create a T-Chart. Make a two-column chart. Label one column "Physical Challenges" and the other "Mental Challenges." As you read, fill in the columns with examples and descriptions of each.

Physical Challenges	Mental Challenges

New Vocabulary

▶ disability (p. 709)
▶ profound deafness (p. 710)
▶ mental retardation (p. 712)
▶ Americans with Disabilities Act (p. 713)

Physical and Mental Challenges

① FOCUS

GUIDE TO READING

BIG Idea People with physical and mental challenges deserve to be treated with dignity and respect.
Ask Students: *What are some physical challenges that people experience?* (Sample answers: blindness, deafness, being wheelchair bound)

Before You Read

T-Chart Students' T-charts will vary.

Main Idea

Physical Challenges The most common physical disabilities affect sight, hearing, and movement. **Ask Students:** *What are some causes of physical disabilities?* (Answers will vary but may include disease, heredity, injury, or nerve damage.)

Real Life Issues ....

Before students write their paragraphs, discuss how Peter might feel about getting laughed at. **Ask Students:** *Why is it wrong to laugh at people like Peter?* (Accept all reasonable answers.)

Writing Strategy

Personal Writing Instruct students to write in their private journals any experiences they have had with a disabled person. Have disabled students in your class write about how they have felt in interactions with people without disabilities. Direct students to list feelings they had during the experience—comfortable, awkward, curious, pity, and so on—and identify why they had those emotions. Then have them develop and write strategies that they can implement on their next encounter to make it a better one.

② TEACH

AL Active Learning

Simulating Have students simulate sight impairment (blindfold), hearing impairment (ear plugs), and motor impairment (crutches or wheelchair). You can have students take part in a specific activity or spend the school day simulating the impairment. Afterward, have students summarize their experience. Have them include how their perceptions were different and how other people's perceptions of them might have changed. **BL OL**

W Writing Support

Writing Sentences Pair English language learners with English proficient students and have them work together to make a graphic organizer for the lesson section about hearing impairment. After checking the graphic organizer, have English language learners use the graphic organizer as a prompt to write phrases or sentences about physical challenges. Have students read their phrases or sentences aloud to you. **EL**

Figure 25.12 **Dealing with Physical Challenges**

Sight, hearing, and motor impairment are examples of physical disabilities. *How has technology affected people with disabilities?*

The common causes of blindness include

- **complications from diabetes,** in which high blood sugar levels lead to damage of the retina. Complications from diabetes are the leading cause of blindness.
- **macular degeneration,** a disease in which the retina degenerates. This is the main cause of blindness in people over 55.
- **glaucoma,** a disease that damages the eye's optic nerve.
- **cataracts,** a condition in which the eye's lens becomes clouded.

AL

Blindness can also result from an injury, but disease is a much more common cause. Regular eye exams can lead to early diagnosis of many conditions and help prevent blindness or slow its progress.

READING CHECK

Identify What is the number one cause of blindness?

Hearing Impairment

Almost 30 million Americans have disabilities that affect their ability to hear. Hearing problems range from mild to severe. The most acute form is **profound deafness,** *hearing loss so severe that a person affected cannot benefit from mechanical amplification, such as a hearing aid.*

A variety of factors cause hearing impairment, including the following:

W

 Home and Community

Special Olympics Explain that Special Olympics is a year-round sports program that provides training and competition to children and adults with mental disabilities. There are Special Olympics programs across the United States and in many countries around the world. Special Olympics depend on community volunteers to coach athletes, keep score during games, manage teams, and help at events. Encourage students to get involved. You might consider having your class volunteer at a Special Olympics event in your community.

- **Heredity.** If one or both parents have hearing impairment, their child is more likely to develop it as well.
- **Injury.** An injury to the ears or head, such as a skull fracture, can cause hearing loss.
- **Disease.** Ear infections, brain tumors, measles, and other conditions can lead to hearing loss.
- **Obstruction.** Hearing loss is sometimes caused by a buildup of wax or a bone blockage in the ear.
- **Nerve damage.** Nerve damage often occurs with age, but it can also be the result of repeated exposure to loud noises, such as stereos, traffic, video games, and concerts.

Hearing loss due to loud noises is easy to prevent: wear earplugs if you're exposed to loud noise, and turn down the volume if you're wearing earphones while listening to music. Anyone who works around loud machinery, airplanes, or other sources of high decibel levels should wear earplugs to protect their hearing. To learn more about how your ears work and ways you can protect your hearing, see Chapter 13, Lesson 3.

We live in a noisy world, and some experts think the increase in environmental noise is why hearing loss may be occurring earlier in people's lives than it did a few decades ago. Hearing impairment can be a gradual process. If you ever notice any change in your hearing, it may be time to visit an *audiologist,* a specialist in hearing problems.

Academic Vocabulary

volume *(noun):* the degree of loudness

Motor Impairment

Tasks that are simple for most people—tying a shoe, climbing the stairs, opening a jar, lifting a glass—can be a challenge for people with a motor impairment. Motor impairments result when the body's range of motion and coordination are affected by a brain injury or a nervous system disorder.

People with motor impairments cope with physical challenges in different ways, depending on their situation. The following treatments and devices have helped many people with motor impairment adapt to their situation and lead full, active lives:

- **Physical therapy** helps people keep their joints flexible and their muscles stretched, improving their ability to move around.
- **Occupational therapy** helps people learn how to perform everyday functions so that they can lead independent lives.
- **Assistive devices** include motorized wheelchairs and special computers, as well as artificial limbs for people with limb amputations. These devices help people perform everyday tasks. People who cannot use their hands and arms can also use mouth sticks or head sticks to operate a wheelchair or send instructions to a computer.

Lesson 4   Physical and Mental Challenges   **711**

Cooperative Learning

Campaign to Protect Hearing Have pairs of students develop an informational campaign to make teens aware of the dangers of listening to loud music. Students should research acceptable levels of noise (measured in decibels) and levels that cause hearing damage. Instruct pairs to use their findings to develop a campaign slogan and informational materials. Pairs might choose to create a brochure, poster, t-shirt, or banner to advertise their campaign. Pairs can present their campaign to the class, as well as to the rest of the school.

R Reading Strategy

Drawing Conclusions After students read about hearing impairment, have them write a conclusion about the causes of hearing impairment. A conclusion should be a short paragraph that does not summarize the reading. Explain that the conclusion should describe how the various points of the reading fit together into one picture. **OL**

CA Cultural Awareness

Interacting with People with Disabilities Although students with disabilities might be mainstreamed in students' classes, interacting comfortably with disabled people might require practice. Explain that it's often easier to focus on the person's abilities and strengths rather than the disability. Remind students to offer assistance, but wait until it is accepted before helping. **BL OL**

U Universal Access

Guest Speaker Invite an occupational therapist and/or a physical therapist to the classroom to describe how they help people with motor impairment. Have the speaker describe the differences between occupational and physical therapies and typical cases they see. Finally have the therapist describe how he or she helps a person learn to use an assistive device. **OL**

Academic Vocabulary

Volume Demonstrate this usage of volume by adjusting the volume knob of a radio. As you make the sound louder, describe it as increasing the volume. As you make the sound quieter, describe it as decreasing the volume. Assess students' understanding by asking them to increase and decrease the volume of the radio.

Main Idea

Mental Challenges Mental disabilities have been linked to several different causes. **Ask Students:** *What are some factors that cause mental disabilities?* (Sample answers: Injury, disease, brain abnormalities, genetic disorders)

READING CHECK

Answer Injury, disease, and brain abnormality

C Critical Thinking

Identifying Relationships Invite students to describe the relationship between a healthy lifestyle and a reduced risk of mental disability. Students might explain that making healthful choices can help prevent mental impairment. OL

Main Idea

Accommodating Differences People with physical and mental challenges deserve the same treatment and opportunities as everyone else. **Ask Students:** *What are some needs that people with disabilities might have?* (Sample answers: Access to buildings, public transportation)

HS Health Skills Practice

Advocacy Explain that groups who lobby for laws that protect the rights of people with disabilities use the same advocacy techniques that students are learning. Have students brainstorm needs that people with disabilities might experience in your school or community. Point out that these needs are not always physical barriers, but can also include prejudice or other emotional barriers. Have the class choose one need and divide the tasks of planning and implementing an advocacy campaign. OL AL

712

READING CHECK

List What are three factors that may cause mental retardation?

■ **Figure 25.13** Guide dogs are trained to assist the visually and hearing impaired. *How do you think guide dogs help people with visual and hearing impairments?*

Mental Challenges

Main Idea Mental disabilities have been linked to several different causes.

One challenge that affects a person's ability to live independently is **mental retardation**. This is *a below-average intellectual ability present from birth or early childhood and associated with difficulties in learning and social adaptation.* Several factors have been found to cause mental retardation, including injury, disease, and brain abnormality. Additional factors include the following:

- **Genetic disorders** such as Down syndrome, phenylketonuria (PKU), Tay-Sachs, and Fragile X syndrome result in babies born with mental retardation.
- **Behaviors during pregnancy** can have a serious impact. Pregnant women who use alcohol or other drugs greatly increase the risk that their babies will be born with mental retardation, low birth weight, or fetal alcohol syndrome.
- **Rubella infection** during pregnancy puts the baby at risk. Immunization against rubella either during childhood or in the first three months of pregnancy reduces this risk.
- **Restricted oxygen supply** can cause mental retardation during birth. Head injury, stroke, and certain infections such as meningitis can also limit oxygen supply, causing mental retardation in older individuals.

Accommodating Differences

Main Idea It is important to provide equal treatment and opportunities for people with physical and mental challenges.

In recent decades, the federal government has begun to address the difficulties of living in a society that may not meet the needs of people with disabilities. Advocacy efforts have resulted in laws and policies that address discrimination. These policies are based on the following principles:

- Public transportation vehicles and building entrances must be wheelchair accessible, so that people with motor impairments can readily participate in business and social activities.
- People should be evaluated on the basis of individual merit, not on assumptions about disabilities.
- People with disabilities, to the extent they are able, should have the same opportunities as everyone else.

712 Chapter 25 Noncommunicable Diseases and Disabilities

Skills for the 21st Century

Interpersonal and Self-Directional Skills Make students aware that they will encounter people with disabilities in the workplace and in public places. Give them the opportunity to practice interacting with disabled students in your school. Team up with special education teachers and plan activities or projects that students can work on together as equal team members. Be sure to give students tips for working successfully and appropriately with the students who are disabled. Special education teachers might give your students some helpful pointers as well.

In 1990, the U.S. government passed the **Americans with Disabilities Act** (ADA), *a law prohibiting discrimination against people with physical or mental disabilities in the workplace, transportation, public accommodations, and telecommunications.* The ADA includes the following provisions:

- **Employers** with 15 or more employees must give qualified individuals with disabilities an equal opportunity to benefit from employment-related opportunities.
- **State and local governments** must provide accessible entrances in buildings and communicate effectively with people who have hearing, vision, or speech disabilities.
- **Telephone companies** must set up telecommunications relay services (TRS) that allow callers with hearing and speech challenges to communicate through an assistant.

In 1998, the government passed another law, the Workforce Investment Act. This law ensures that any information posted to a Web site by a government agency must be accessible by those who are disabled.

■ **Figure 25.14** Federal law requires that accommodations be made for people with disabilities. *Can you name other ways that our society has helped people with disabilities?*

Caption Answer

Figure 25.14 Sample answer: Requiring employers to offer equal services to disabled employees

3 ASSESS/ CLOSE

Assessment Resources

📁 *FAST FILE* ACTIVITIES
Lesson 4 Quiz

💿 *ExamView Assessment Suite* CD-ROM

Visit glencoe.com **for:**
Online Quizzes
Online Learning Center

LESSON 4 ASSESSMENT

After You Read

Reviewing Facts and Vocabulary

1. What are three common causes of blindness?

2. What is an assistive device?

3. Is mental retardation preventable? Explain.

Thinking Critically

4. **Analyze.** What are some challenges that someone with a sight or hearing impairment might have commuting to work each day?

5. **Evaluate.** Why is it important to make buildings and services accessible to people with physical and mental challenges?

Applying Health Skills

6. **Advocacy.** Create a flyer that promotes better understanding of physical and mental challenges and empathy for people with these disabilities. Include appropriate information and statistics.

Writing Critically

7. **Expository.** Write about the accommodations your school has made to assist people with physical or mental challenges. Describe these accommodations and explain whether your school needs to make any additional accommodations.

 Go Online

Visit glencoe.com and complete the Interactive Study Guide for this lesson.

Progress Monitoring

Reteaching
Have students make a chart that lists factors that cause physical and mental disabilities.

Enrichment
Invite students to learn how the provisions of the Americans with Disabilities Act changed the way cities and buildings look. For example, before this law, public restrooms did not have wheelchair accessible stalls. Students can write a summary of their inferences.

Go Online

Have students visit **glencoe.com** and complete the Interactive Study Guide for this lesson.

LESSON 4 ASSESSMENT ANSWERS

1. *Any three:* Complications from diabetes, macular degeneration, glaucoma, cataracts

2. A device that helps a physically challenged person perform everyday tasks

3. Sometimes; certain behaviors during pregnancy and failure to get rubella immunizations can increase the risk of mental retardation.

4. Sample answer: A sight-impaired person might have trouble reading signs or boarding buses. A hearing-impaired person might not hear the bus driver or train conductor call out stops.

5. Sample answer: Because they have the same needs and interests as the rest of the population

6. Flyers will vary.

7. Answers will vary.

A Family Letter

NHES Standard 7 Students will demonstrate the ability to practice health-enhancing behaviors and avoid or reduce risks.

Teaching Objectives

- Comprehend health promotion and disease prevention.
- Research valid information about the prevention and intervention of this disease.
- Identify ways to practice health-enhancing behaviors.

Teaching Strategies

- Using a minimum of 25 index cards, write one disease from this chapter on each card. Place these cards in a container.
- Have students choose one card. Alternatively, they may select a disease identified in this chapter that is a relevant concern for them and their family.
- Have students follow the steps in the activity. They may work in groups of two or three if they wish, sharing resources and action plan ideas.
- Read and discuss the family letters.
- Invite students who used an existing family disease or concern to mail their letter to family members. *Be sure students understand they should keep personal information private.*

Assessment

Using a rubric, student work should provide comprehensive evidence of the following criteria to achieve the highest score:

✔ Identifies healthful behaviors to reduce risk of disease

✔ Creates a list to demonstrate healthful habits

✔ Incorporates a health-enhancing plan to reduce risk of disease

Activity **A Family Letter**

Your teacher will present a set of index cards with the names of noncommunicable diseases. You will conduct research on one of these diseases and develop a plan for reducing risks of getting the disease. Then, you will write a letter to your family persuading them to make healthy choices to prevent getting the disease.

What You'll Need

- print and online resources
- paper and pens or pencils
- envelopes (optional)

What You'll Do

Step 1

Select one card from your teacher and conduct research on the signs, symptoms, risk factors, and treatment for the disease printed on the card.

Step 2

Based on your findings, list at least four healthful behaviors that can reduce the risk of getting this disease.

Step 3

Create a health-enhancing action plan to reduce your risks for this disease.

Apply and Conclude

Write a letter to your family suggesting specific healthful behaviors all of you can adopt to reduce the risks associated with this disease.

Checklist: Practicing Healthful Behaviors

 Identification of protective behaviors

 Steps demonstrating healthful habits

 Knowledge of healthful behaviors, habits, and techniques

 **Home and Community**

Preventing Noncommunicable Diseases Many community health agencies hold classes or provide information about reducing the risks of noncommunicable diseases. Many of these health agencies also provide free screenings for such problems as various cancers, cholesterol levels, and hearing assessments. Have students find the kinds of classes and screenings available in your area. Students can compile the class findings into an informational pamphlet.

To download quizzes and eFlashcards to your PDA, go to glencoe.com and click on the Study to Go icon.

LESSON 1

Cardiovascular Disease

Key Concepts

▶ Cardiovascular disease can begin developing in your teens.
▶ You can reduce your risk for CVD by avoiding tobacco, alcohol, and other drugs; maintaining a healthy weight; and getting regular physical activity.
▶ Some risk factors for CVD, such as heredity, cannot be avoided.

Vocabulary

▶ noncommunicable disease, cardiovascular disease (p. 688)
▶ hypertension, atherosclerosis, arteriosclerosis (p. 689)
▶ angina pectoris (p. 690)
▶ arrhythmias (p. 690)
▶ stroke (p. 692)

LESSON 2

Cancer

Key Concepts

▶ Cancer is the uncontrollable growth of abnormal cells.
▶ Avoiding carcinogens like tobacco and ultraviolet radiation can reduce your risk for some kinds of cancers.
▶ Many cancers can be treated successfully if detected early.

Vocabulary

▶ cancer, tumor (p. 695)
▶ benign, malignant, metastasis (p. 696)
▶ carcinogen (p. 697)
▶ biopsy (p. 700)
▶ remission (p. 701)

LESSON 3

Allergies, Asthma, Diabetes, and Arthritis

Key Concepts

▶ Allergic reactions are caused by allergens.
▶ Taking proper medication and practicing management techniques can reduce the number and severity of asthma attacks.
▶ Type 2 diabetes is strongly associated with obesity.
▶ Arthritis causes pain and loss of movement in the joints.

Vocabulary

▶ allergy (p. 702)
▶ histamines (p. 703)
▶ asthma (p. 704)
▶ diabetes, autoimmune disease (p. 705)
▶ arthritis, osteoarthritis (p. 707)
▶ rheumatoid arthritis (p. 708)

LESSON 4

Physical and Mental Challenges

Key Concepts

▶ Sight, hearing, and motor impairments are common physical disabilities.
▶ The Americans with Disabilities Act provides accommodation for people with physical and mental disabilities.

Vocabulary

▶ disability (p. 709)
▶ profound deafness (p. 710)
▶ mental retardation (p. 712)
▶ Americans with Disabilities Act (p. 713)

Chapter 25 Review **715**

 Go Online

Students can visit **glencoe.com** to

• review content online with the Online Student Edition.
• test their knowledge of chapter content with Online Quizzes.
• access Interactive Health Tutor for more practice with vocabulary.

Assessment Resources

FAST FILE ACTIVITIES
Chapter 25 Test

 ExamView Assessment Suite CD-ROM

Visit glencoe.com for:
Audio Chapter Summaries
Online Quizzes

STUDY TO GO
Tell students to visit glencoe.com where they can download quizzes and eFlashcards.

Study Tips

Finding Relationships Among Facts
Explain that facts are easier to remember if they are related to other facts. Graphic organizers and web diagrams are useful tools to organize facts and show their relationship to other facts. Encourage students to look for relationships among facts while studying a chapter. Suggest they construct graphic organizers or web diagrams to organize the facts to make them more meaningful and easier to remember.

Assessment

Chapter 25 Assessment Answers

LESSON 1

Vocabulary Review

1. Stroke
2. hypertension
3. cardiovascular disease

Understanding Key Concepts

4. b
5. a
6. b

Thinking Critically

7. Communicable diseases spread from person to person. Noncommunicable diseases are not transmitted by another person, a vector, or the environment.
8. High cholesterol causes plaque to build up on artery walls.
9. The heart gradually weakens and can no longer maintain its regular pumping rate and force.
10. Sample answer: Cardiovascular disease often begins developing in teens, even if symptoms do not occur until many years later.

LESSON 2

Vocabulary Review

11. tumor
12. carcinogens
13. biopsy

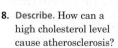

LESSON 1

Vocabulary Review

Correct the sentences below by replacing the italicized term with the correct vocabulary term.

1. *Heart attack* is an acute injury in which blood flow to the brain is interrupted.

2. High blood pressure is also known as *atherosclerosis.*

3. A disease that affects the heart or blood vessels is called a *noncommunicable disease.*

Understanding Key Concepts

After reading the question or statement, select the correct answer.

4. Which of the following behaviors is a preventive measure against cardiovascular disease?
   a. Avoiding exposure to loud noises
   b. Maintaining a healthy weight
   c. Waking up early every morning
   d. Taking vitamin supplements

5. Which of the following statements is true about stroke?
   a. A stroke can cause paralysis.
   b. A stroke is an acute injury that affects the liver.
   c. During a stroke, blood flow to the brain increases.
   d. During a stroke, the brain gets too much oxygen.

6. Which of the following statements is *not* true about tobacco use?
   a. About 20 percent of deaths from cardiovascular disease are smoking related.
   b. People who smoke less than a pack a day are generally safe from cardiovascular disease.
   c. Cardiovascular disease can be caused by exposure to secondhand smoke.
   d. For teens, tobacco use is the number one risk factor for cardiovascular disease.

Thinking Critically

After reading the question or statement, write a short answer using complete sentences.

7. **Explain.** What is the difference between a communicable disease and a noncommunicable disease?

8. **Describe.** How can a high cholesterol level cause atherosclerosis?

9. **Analyze.** What happens during congestive heart failure?

10. **Explain.** Why is it important to learn about cardiovascular disease as a teen, rather than waiting until you are older?

LESSON 2

Vocabulary Review

Use the vocabulary terms listed on page 715 to complete the following statements.

11. A(n) _____ is an abnormal mass of tissue that has no natural role in the body.

12. Cancer-causing substances are called _____.

13. During a(n) _____, a doctor removes a small piece of tissue for examination.

Understanding Key Concepts

After reading the question or statement, select the correct answer.

14. Which of the following is true about malignant tumors?
   a. They are inconvenient but harmless.
   b. They stay in their original location.
   c. They travel to other parts of the body via the blood or lymph.
   d. They occur only in older adults.

Health eSpotlight *Wrap-Up*

Straight Facts on Diseases and Disabilities List on the board the various groups of noncommunicable diseases discussed in the chapter. **Ask Students:** *What ways can you protect yourself against each* *of these diseases?* Then have them identify ways or behaviors that are common to more than one disease. Discuss how these behaviors fit into a healthful lifestyle.

15. Which of the following statements is true about cancer?
    a. Smoking is the leading cause of cancer deaths in the United States.
    b. Cancer is a hereditary disease.
    c. People who live in moderate or cool climates have a low risk for cancer.
    d. Metastasis can be stopped with a healthful diet.

16. What percentage of all cancer deaths are caused by dietary risk factors?
    a. 10   c. 30
    b. 20   d. 40

Thinking Critically

After reading the question or statement, write a short answer using complete sentences.

17. **Describe.** What happens during metastasis?

18. **Explain.** Why is it important to pay attention to the moles on your skin?

19. **Identify.** What are three cancers that can be detected through self-examination?

20. **Evaluate.** What is the connection between abstaining from sexual activity and reducing cancer risk?

LESSON 3

Vocabulary Review

Correct the sentences below by replacing the italicized term with the correct vocabulary term.

21. Chemicals that can stimulate mucus and fluid production are called *allergens*.

22. *Arthritis* affects the way body cells convert sugar into energy.

23. *Allergy* is a condition in which the airways in the lungs become narrowed.

Understanding Key Concepts

After reading the question or statement, select the correct answer.

24. Severe hives and difficulty swallowing are symptoms of a serious
    a. asthma attack.
    b. diabetic seizure.
    c. allergic reaction.
    d. arthritic condition.

25. The only way to diagnose diabetes is by
    a. watching for the key symptoms.
    b. undergoing a biopsy procedure.
    c. receiving an eye exam.
    d. getting a blood test.

26. The main areas affected by osteoarthritis are
    a. internal organs, such as the liver.
    b. weight-bearing joints, such as the knees.
    c. the neck and shoulders.
    d. the sinuses.

Thinking Critically

After reading the question or statement, write a short answer using complete sentences.

27. **Identify.** What are four strategies for managing asthma?

28. **Explain.** Why are some scientists concerned that type 2 diabetes will become an epidemic?

29. **Synthesize.** How can your family reduce asthma triggers in your home?

LESSON 4

Vocabulary Review

Use the vocabulary terms listed on page 715 to complete the following statements.

30. _____ is hearing loss so severe that hearing aids have no effect.

31. The _____ is a law that prohibits discrimination against people with disabilities.

Chapter 25   Assessment   717

Understanding Key Concepts

14. c
15. a
16. c

Thinking Critically

17. Cancer spreads to other parts of the body.
18. Changes in color or size could indicate cancer.
19. Breast, testicular, and skin cancer
20. Abstaining from sexual activity helps people avoid such infections as HPV and hepatitis B, which can cause cancer.

LESSON 3

Vocabulary Review

21. histamines
22. Diabetes
23. Asthma

Understanding Key Concepts

24. c
25. d
26. b

Thinking Critically

27. Monitor the condition, manage the environment, manage stress, take medication properly
28. The population has more older people and more obese and inactive young people. Both are risk factors for type 2 diabetes.
29. Sample answer: Keep pets outside. Do not allow smoking inside.

LESSON 4

Vocabulary Review

30. Profound deafness
31. Americans with Disabilities Act

ExamView®
Assessment Suite

Create and customize tests in minutes with this convenient digital platform.

- Create differentiated tests quickly and easily.
- All questions correlated to National/State Standards.
- Enhance tests with Document Based Questions (DBQ) and add your own photos or graphics.
- Build tests in both English and Spanish.
- Generate progress reports.

To order, go to **glencoe.com** and search for ISBN 0-07-888173-0.

Assessment

Understanding Key Concepts

32. c
33. c
34. d

Thinking Critically

35. Sight impairment, hearing impairment, motor impairment
36. If one or both parents have hearing impairment, their child is more likely to have it.
37. Sample answer: Artificial limbs enable people to walk; wheelchairs give people mobility; mouth sticks enable people to operate wheelchairs and computers.
38. Sample answer: The ADA gives people with physical and mental challenges greater access to public services.

Assessment

Understanding Key Concepts

After reading the question or statement, select the correct answer.

32. Glaucoma and diabetes complications are two common causes of
    a. deafness.   c. blindness.
    b. mental illness.   d. paralysis.

33. What percentage of Americans have some type of disability?
    a. 5   c. 20
    b. 10   d. 40

34. Advocates for people with physical and mental challenges believe that
    a. people are defined by their disabilities.
    b. people with disabilities should have different opportunities.
    c. everyone must learn to read braille.
    d. buses and building entrances should be wheelchair accessible.

Thinking Critically

After reading the question or statement, write a short answer using complete sentences.

35. **Identify.** What are the three main categories of physical challenges?

36. **Analyze.** What is the role of heredity in hearing impairment?

37. **Explain.** What are three ways that assistive devices help people with motor impairments?

38. **Evaluate.** Discuss the impact of the Americans with Disabilities Act. How does it affect the lives of people with physical and mental challenges?

Project-Based ASSESSMENT

Reducing Risk

Background
Scientists have identified behaviors and treatments that decrease the risk of noncommunicable diseases. While some risk factors for these diseases are related to heredity, gender, and age, many other factors can be modified to reduce disease risk.

Task
Choose one of the diseases discussed in the chapter, research it, and develop a poster illustrating the nature of the disease.

Audience
Students in your class and adults in the community

Purpose
Inform people about the nature, risk factors, and treatment of a particular noncommunicable disease.

Procedure
1. Choose a noncommunicable disease that you find interesting.
2. Collect information concerning all aspects of the disease.
3. Find or create illustrations showing the effect of the disease on the body.
4. Include information on positive, preventive measures that lower risks related to your chosen disease. Make sure you also include recent medical advances in the diagnosis and treatment of the disease.
5. Make a poster incorporating all these aspects.
6. Submit your poster to your teacher.
7. Insightful and compelling posters will be displayed in your school and in select community locations.

Project-Based ASSESSMENT

Step 1 Research Have students use reliable library and Internet sources to research their chosen disease.

Step 2 Make a Poster Explain that posters should summarize the information they learned about how the disease affects the body, its symptoms, its risk factors, as well as preventive measures, treatment options, and recent medical advances.

Step 3 Evaluate Students should create posters that are informative, visually interesting, and easy to read. Students can use their posters as visual aids in an oral presentation.

Visit **glencoe.com** for Project-Based Assessment rubrics.

Math Practice

Interpret Graphs. Frequent sunburns can lead to melanoma, a deadly type of skin cancer. The bar graph below shows the percentage of young people ages 11 to 18 who reported getting sunburned. Use the graph to answer the questions that follow.

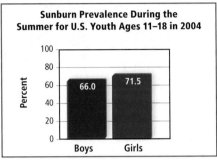

Sunburn Prevalence During the Summer for U.S. Youth Ages 11–18 in 2004

Adapted from "Cancer Statistics Presentation 2007," American Cancer Society, Inc., 2007.

1. Which group makes up the greatest percentage of all youth surveyed?
   A. Girls who got a sunburn that summer
   B. Girls who did not get a sunburn that summer
   C. Boys who got a sunburn that summer
   D. Boys who did not get a sunburn that summer

2. What percentage of boys did *not* get a sunburn that summer?
   A. 28.5%
   B. 34.0%
   C. 66.0%
   D. 71.5%

3. If you examined a representative sample that consisted of 500 boys, how many would have gotten a sunburn that summer?

Go Online

For more test practice, visit glencoe.com and complete the Online Quizzes for Chapter 25.

Reading/Writing Practice

Understand and Apply. Read the passage below and then answer the questions.

It's the last home game of the season, and Lincoln High School's basketball team is headed for another victory. The team has compiled its best-ever record this season. Some people attribute this success to Shawn, the assistant manager.

Shawn is mentally retarded. His impairment prevents him from being a regular player, but he loves helping manage the team and practicing with the players. He's so devoted to the team that players say he inspires them to play harder.

As the clock runs down, cheers fill the gymnasium. Lincoln wins! At the team's annual banquet, the coach presents Shawn with a special Most Valuable Player award for his contribution to the team.

1. How would you best describe Shawn's role on the basketball team?
   A. He helps organize the equipment.
   B. He is the team's point guard.
   C. His enthusiasm inspires the players to give their best effort on the court.
   D. He practices but doesn't play.

2. What message does Shawn's MVP award send to other students and faculty?
   A. Mental retardation is a barrier to athletic achievement.
   B. Teens with mental disabilities can make valuable contributions.
   C. It is important to treat Shawn differently.
   D. Other teams should ask Shawn to be their assistant manager.

3. Describe the effect that Shawn's success might have on other students with physical or mental challenges.

National Education Standards

Math: Number and Operations, Data Analysis
Language Arts: NCTE 1, NCTE 3, NCTE 4

Standardized Test Practice

Standardized Test Practice Answers

Math Practice
1. A
2. B
3. 330 boys

Reading/Writing Practice
1. C
2. B
3. Answers will vary. Students should incorporate information from Lesson 4 of this chapter and focus on the positive effects of recognizing the strengths of individuals with physical challenges.

National Education Standards

Math: Number and Operations, Data Analysis

Language Arts: NCTE 1, NCTE 3, NCTE 4

For the complete Math and Language Arts standards, visit glencoe.com.

Go Online

Online Study Tools
For more test practice, visit glencoe.com and complete the Online Quizzes for Chapter 25.

Test-Taking Tip

Using Outlines Suggest to students that they use an outline to help them answer essay questions on an exam. Explain that the outline will help them organize their thoughts into a coherent answer. The outline will also help them see if they have missed any important points before they begin writing the answer. Students can practice this skill by writing an outline for their answer in the margin of the test for all essay questions they answer throughout the year.

Health Careers
Group Activity

- Poll the class to determine which career interests each student. Divide the class into three groups based on their interests. For students without a preference, assign them to groups at your discretion.

- Have group members work together to determine the educational requirements for their career. Have students look up online course catalogs to determine the types of courses required for the degree. Also have students find community and state colleges and universities that offer the degree required for the career.

- Groups should find out what local companies, businesses, or agencies hire people with their assigned career. Suggest that they also find out typical salary ranges.

- Encourage students to interview someone with their assigned career. Students can find people with the career by networking with family and friends or by working with the guidance office. Before students interview a health professional, review their interview questions.

- Have groups present their findings about the career to the class. You might have them summarize their findings on a poster, PowerPoint® presentation, or video.

Public Health Specialist

Public health specialists help educate communities and organizations on how to reduce communicable diseases, occupational diseases, and foodborne illnesses. They also run wellness programs. Other responsibilities of a public health specialist include speaking to groups about disease prevention, monitoring disease trends, and attending professional meetings and conferences.

Most public health specialists need a master's degree to stay competitive in the field. By taking classes in biology, statistics, and economics, you can start acquiring the background and skills necessary for this career.

Dietitian and Nutritionist

Dietitians and nutritionists promote healthful eating habits and suggest dietary changes in order to prevent and treat illness. They supervise the preparation of meals and coordinate programs to educate people about nutrition. Dietitians and nutritionists need at least a bachelor's degree. Some states require additional licenses or certifications. A variety of classes, including nutrition, biology, and biochemistry, will help you prepare for this field.

Nurse

Nurses help treat ill or injured patients in a wide variety of settings. Although many nurses work in hospitals, many others work in clinics, private homes, and branches of the U.S. military. In the United States and many other countries, there is a rapidly growing demand for qualified nurses. More and more men are joining the nursing profession.

To legally practice nursing, an individual must become a registered nurse (RN). This process includes earning a two- or four-year college degree and then passing a licensing exam. To help prepare for a career in nursing, take classes in biology, psychology, algebra, and anatomy.

 Promoting School Wellness

School Nurse The school nurse plays an integral role in promoting the health and wellness of a school environment. Besides administering first aid, the school nurse is responsible for maintaining the immunization records of each student and the medication records of students who require medication during the school day. Invite your school nurse to the class to describe his or her responsibilities. Ask what he or she likes about the job and its educational requirements.

Pratibha Vakharia always knew that she was destined to be a doctor. In high school, she took biology and other science classes. During her medical training, Dr. Vakharia worked with children who had allergies and asthma—an experience that led her to open a private practice as an allergist.

Q. What are the things you love about your job?

A. *I get to treat patients of all ages. I treat everything from food allergies to drug reactions to insect stings. I love the process of finding the culprit behind an allergic reaction.*

Q. What surprised you the most about being an allergist?

A. *Many days, I'm treating things other than the allergy. An allergist develops a bond with the patients where they can discuss other concerns, like stress or family issues.*

Q. What are some advantages of being an allergist?

A. *The field has a lot of variety and flexibility compared to surgical branches. It is easier to set up a balance between family and professional life.*

Activity **Beyond the Classroom**

Writing Communicate with Health Professionals. Visit or call a health professional in your school or community. This professional could be a school nurse, a family doctor, an employee of your local health department, or another expert. Ask this person to describe the top three concerns about the health of teens in your area. Ask for specific details and examples. Based on what you learn, create a brochure, poster, or blog to share this information with your classmates. Feel free to do your own research on these health concerns, and add your findings to your report.

Go Online

For more information, go to the Career Corner link at glencoe.com.

Allergist

Invite a health professional to class to talk with students about his or her career.

- Invite students to prepare questions for the health professional. Have them write their questions on index cards. Choose appropriate and relevant questions to give the speaker before he or she comes to class.

- Suggest that the speaker describes the education required for the profession, as well as interests that indicate a health profession would be a good fit. The speaker should also describe a typical working day and what he or she likes most about the profession.

- Ask the speaker to describe his or her experiences with communicable and noncommunicable diseases as they relate to teen health. Tell the speaker what students have learned in this unit and suggest that he or she share any relevant or useful information.

Encourage interested students to visit **glencoe.com** for more information on this career.

Activity **Beyond the Classroom**

Writing Encourage students to work together in groups, especially if they plan to interview a health professional at school. Also suggest that students interview friends or family members who are health professionals or a health professional with whom they already have a relationship. Have students present their poster, brochure, or blog to the class. Discuss with students any similarities and differences among the findings.

Flexible Technology Solutions

Focus

Health eSpotlight Video Series

▶ By Chapter

Chapter 26 Safety and Injury Prevention
Video 26: Staying Safe

Chapter 27 First Aid and Emergencies
Video 27: Be Prepared

Chapter 28 Community and Environmental Health
Video 28: Taking Care of Everyone

▶ By Lesson

Chapter 26 *Video 26*   For Use With

Segment 26.1 Personal Safety and Protection .... Lesson 1
Segment 26.2 Safety at Home and in Your Community ...... Lesson 2
Segment 26.3 Outdoor Safety.. Lesson 3
Segment 26.4 Safety on the Road .... Lesson 4

Chapter 27 *Video 27*   For Use With

Segment 27.1 Providing First Aid .... Lesson 1
Segment 27.2 CPR and First Aid for Shock and Choking..... Lesson 2
Segment 27.3 Responding to Other Common
                      Emergencies .... Lesson 3
Segment 27.4 Emergency Preparedness........................... Lesson 4

Chapter 28 *Video 28*   For Use With

Segment 28.1 Community and Public Health.................... Lesson 1
Segment 28.2 Air Quality and Health............................... Lesson 2
Segment 28.3 Protecting Land and Water .... Lesson 3

▶ By Skill

Decision Making ....Videos 15   22   **26**
Communication Skills ....Videos 5   6   **27**
Advocacy...Videos 16   20   **28**

■ Indicates videos featured in the unit that teach the corresponding skill. Other videos listed can also be used to teach that skill.

Teach

Direct lesson plans beyond the classroom with multi-media fitness activities that students can do online, in class, or as a group.

PowerPoint® Presentation

- *Health* eSpotlight videos
- Audio and image bank

FITNESS ZONE Online

Fitness Zone Online is a multi-media resource that helps students find ways to be physically active each day.

- Clipboard Energizer Activities
- Fitness Zone Videos
- Polar Heart Rate Monitor Activities
- Nutrition, Physical Activity, and Injury Prevention Tips
- Links to Nutrition and Physical Activity Resources

Go Online

Online Learning Center

- Student Web Activities
- PuzzleMaker
- Interactive Health Tutor

Podcast Audio Chapter Summaries

Use the audio Podcast Audio Chapter Summaries to teach and review key concepts, and engage students with health content that they can download to a computer or portable MP3 player.

Assess/Close

Help students master chapter and lesson concepts with an integrated technology solution for assessment and performance evaluation.

Go Online

Online Learning Center

- Interactive Study Guides
- Online Quizzes

ExamView® Assessment Suite CD-ROM

Create and customize tests in minutes with this convenient digital platform.

- Create differentiated tests quickly and easily.
- All questions correlated to National/State Standards.
- Enhance tests with Document Based Questions (DBQ) and add your own photos and graphics.
- Build tests in both English and Spanish.
- Generate progress reports.

Enrich

Use these additional digital and online media resources to promote hands-on exploration of health topics covered in the lesson.

Business Week Health Video Series

- *Safer Driving Through Technology*
- *Fluorescent Light Bulbs*

Study-to-Go

Download a portable version of eFlashcards and Self-Check Quizzes onto your Palm or Pocket PC.

Health Podcasts Activities

Glencoe's "It's Your Health" Podcast Activities provide students with a unique listening and learning experience that takes health education beyond the classroom. Download the audio files and print activities covering a range of current health topics that matter most to teens!

UNIT 9

Safety and Environmental Health

In this unit, students will learn strategies to stay safe at home, in the outdoors, and on the road. They will also learn basic safety precautions and about the forms and consequences of pollution.

Health eSpotlight Video Series

At the beginning of each chapter, visit glencoe.com and have students watch the video and do the accompanying print activity.

 Chapter 26 *Staying Safe*

Safety plans can help prevent injury during a crisis.

 Chapter 27 *Be Prepared*

Knowing the basics of first aid can help save lives.

 Chapter 28 *Taking Care of Everyone*

It's important to keep the air and water clean.

Unit 9 Resources

- Career Corner
- 📁 FAST FILE RESOURCES
- Health Career Research Activity
- Family Involvement Activity
- Community Involvement Activity
- Unit Test

UNIT 9 Safety and Environmental Health

Chapter 26
Safety and Injury Prevention

 Staying Safe

Chapter 27
First Aid and Emergencies

 Be Prepared

Chapter 28
Community and Environmental Health

 Taking Care of Everyone

UNIT PROJECT

Lifesaving Services

Using Visuals **The American Red Cross** helps communities survive weather emergencies and natural disasters. Every year, the Red Cross responds to more than 70,000 disasters. It also offers classes in first aid, CPR, and water safety to about 11 million Americans. Blood drives conducted by the Red Cross provide about half the nation's blood supply, or 6 million pints per year.

 To learn more about the Red Cross, go to the Unit Web Project at glencoe.com.

Get Involved. Learn more about the Red Cross and the services this organization provides in your area. If possible, arrange to take one of the Red Cross classes for teens on subjects such as child care, first aid, CPR, aquatics, and water safety.

722

UNIT PROJECT

Lifesaving Services The American Red Cross was founded in 1881 by Clara Barton, who headed the organization through the twentieth century. Today, the American Red Cross provides relief to victims of disasters and helps people prepare for and respond to various kinds of emergencies.

Get Involved Suggest that interested students contact the local chapter of the American Red Cross about volunteer opportunities in their community. The American Red Cross includes a Youth Services division, through which teens can receive training in first aid, CPR, baby sitting, and various other skills. Teen volunteers are encouraged to help organize Red Cross clubs to help support international Red Cross programs.

"Diligence is a priceless treasure; prudence a protective charm."
— *Chinese proverb*

American Red Cross
Orange County Chapter

Help Can't Wait

Unit 9   Safety and Environmental Health   **723**

Activate Prior Knowledge

Ask students these questions before they read the chapter to build on what they already know.

Chapter 26
What are some accidents that commonly occur in homes?

(Answers will vary. Students might mention falls, fires, electrical shocks, and poisonings.)

Chapter 27
What is first aid, and for what type of illnesses and injuries is it provided?

(Answers will vary. Some students might know that first aid is immediate, temporary care given to an ill or injured person until professional medical care can be provided.)

Chapter 28
What are different forms of pollution that can affect the environment?

(Answers will vary. Students might mention air pollution, noise pollution, land pollution, and water pollution.)

Glencoe Exclusive!
TeacherWorks Plus
All-In-One Planner and Resource Center

***TeacherWorks Plus* provides:**

- interactive Teacher Wraparound edition
- click, drag, and drop to plan lessons
- instant access to many print program resources

How to Get Involved Provide students with these step-by-step instructions about how they can get involved with the American Red Cross.

1. Find out the address and phone number of the local chapter of the American Red Cross. A telephone book may provide this information. If not, visit the Web site of the American Red Cross and use its search function to find a local chapter.

2. Call the local chapter, and ask for information about teens' volunteering with the Red Cross.

3. Gather information about any requirements for teens to volunteer and about what roles teens play when they volunteer.

4. Make a class presentation about how teens can get involved with the Red Cross.

723

Chapter 26 pages 724–755	Standards		Features
	National	**State/Local**	
	1.12.5, 1.12.8, 1.12.9, 2.12.6, 6.12.1, 7.12.1, 7.12.3		**TIME** HEALTH • Cruise Control, page 750
Lesson 1 **Personal Safety and Protection** pages 726–730 **BIG Idea** *Learning basic safety precautions can help a person avoid threatening or harmful situations.*	1.12.5, 1.12.8, 1.12.9, 2.12.6, 4.12.1, 5.12.2, 7.12.1, 7.12.3, 8.12.1, 8.12.4		*Health Skills* **Activity** • Meeting a Friend Online *(Decision Making)*, page 729 Ⓨ Out of Time
Lesson 2 **Safety at Home and in Your Community** pages 731–738 **BIG Idea** *Reducing the potential for accidents can help a person stay safe at home and at work.*	1.12.5, 1.12.8, 1.12.9, 2.12.4, 7.12.1, 7.12.3,		*Real World* **CONNECTION** • Accidents and Unintentional Injuries, page 736 Ⓨ Out of Time
Lesson 3 **Outdoor Safety** pages 739–743 **BIG Idea** *Common sense and caution can minimize the risk of accidental injuries during outdoor activities.*	1.12.5, 1.12.8, 1.12.9, 7.12.1, 7.12.3		
Lesson 4 **Safety on the Road** pages 744–749 **BIG Idea** *Drivers, pedestrians, and others on the road need to follow rules to stay safe.*	1.12.5, 1.12.8, 1.12.9, 4.12.1, 5.12.2, 7.12.1, 7.12.3, 8.12.1, 8.12.4		**VIDEO** BusinessWeek HEALTH NEWS • Safer Driving Through Technology, page 745

Each lesson is marked **30 Min**.

Key to Ability Levels

Teaching Strategies and activities have been coded for ability level and appropriateness.

AL Activities for students working above grade level

OL Activities for students working on grade level

BL Activities for students working below grade level

EL Activities for English Learners

Chapter 26 Planning Guide

Resources	Lesson Assessment	Technology
Student Activity Workbook TEACH *FAST FILE* RESOURCES Vocabulary Practice TEACH Health Labs EXTEND	Chapter 26 Review Chapter 26 Assessment Standardized Test Practice 💿 *ExamView® Assessment Suite* CD-ROM	**Teaching Tools:** 💿 *TeacherWorks™* Plus DVD 💿 *StudentWorks™* Plus DVD 💿 *ExamView® Assessment Suite* CD-ROM 🕹 Transparency 💿 Fitness DVD 💿 PowerPoint® DVD 💿 Health eSpotlight Video Series DVD
FAST FILE RESOURCES Reading Strategies Activity TEACH Reteaching Activity REVIEW Enrichment Activity EXTEND Health Skills Practice TEACH	Lesson 1 Assessment, page 730 📁 Lesson 1 Quiz *Fast File* 💿 *ExamView® Assessment Suite* CD-ROM	
FAST FILE RESOURCES Reading Strategies Activity TEACH Reteaching Activity REVIEW Enrichment Activity EXTEND Health Skills Practice TEACH	Lesson 2 Assessment, page 738 📁 Lesson 2 Quiz *Fast File* 💿 *ExamView® Assessment Suite* CD-ROM	**Web-Based Resources:** **Go Online** glencoe.com • Health Podcast Activities • Audio Chapter Summaries (English/Spanish) • Interactive Health Tutor • Health Skills Activities • Vocabulary PuzzleMaker
FAST FILE RESOURCES Reading Strategies Activity TEACH Reteaching Activity REVIEW Enrichment Activity EXTEND Health Skills Practice TEACH	Lesson 3 Assessment, page 743 📁 Lesson 3 Quiz *Fast File* 💿 *ExamView® Assessment Suite* CD-ROM	• Parent Letters (English/Spanish) • Lesson Plans • Health Inventories • Online Quizzes • Study-to-Go
FAST FILE RESOURCES Reading Strategies Activity TEACH Reteaching Activity REVIEW Enrichment Activity EXTEND Health Skills Practice TEACH	Lesson 4 Assessment, page 749 📁 Lesson 4 Quiz *Fast File* 💿 *ExamView® Assessment Suite* CD-ROM	• Unit Web Projects • Student Web Activities • Fitness Zone Activities

StudentWorks *Plus*

This is the student's backpack solution.

Includes:
- complete Interactive Student Edition
- full audio of English text and Spanish chapter summaries
- allows students to record assignments and track grades.
- links to online activities and additional student resources
- access to all student worksheets and workbooks

FOLDABLES®
Study Organizer

Dinah Zike Foldables®
Chapter Activity
Refer to the *Dinah Zike Reading and Study Skills for Glencoe Health*. Ask students to make a half-book Foldable to record and organize information on home and outside safety. As students read, have them define terms, outline safety suggestions, and record points they consider important in the appropriate columns.

Key to Symbols

🕹 Transparencies	REVIEW activities to review or reinforce content
💿 CD-ROM	TEACH activities to teach basic concepts
🖱 glencoe.com	EXTEND activities to extend or enrich lesson content
📁 Print Resources	

Safety and Injury Prevention

Chapter Overview

Chapter 26 focuses on learning basic safety precautions as a way to avoid harmful situations, as well as how to stay safe at home, during outdoor activities, and when on the road.

Lesson 1

Learning essential safety precautions can help a person recognize and avoid threatening or harmful situations.

Lesson 2

Reducing the potential for accidents can help a person stay safe at home. Staying safe includes following basic safety precautions related to fires, electricity, falls, poisons, firearms, computers, and intruders.

Lesson 3

With common sense and caution, a person can minimize the risk of accidental injuries during such outdoor activities as camping and hiking, winter sports, swimming and diving, and boating.

Lesson 4

Following the rules of the road and being aware of others are basic ways to stay safe on the road. Drivers, pedestrians, school bus riders, bicyclists, skaters, and motorcycle and ATV riders can stay safe if they follow such basic precautions.

▶ **Activating Prior Knowledge**

After students have brainstormed their lists, call on volunteers to share one item on their lists with the class. Discuss the validity of each action mentioned. Tell students they should revise their lists when they read about safety on the road in Lesson 4.

Lesson 1
Personal Safety and Protection

BIG Idea *Learning basic safety precautions can help you avoid threatening or harmful situations.*

Lesson 2
Safety at Home and in Your Community

BIG Idea *Reducing the potential for accidents can help you stay safe at home and at work.*

Lesson 3
Outdoor Safety

BIG Idea *Common sense and caution can minimize the risk of accidental injuries during outdoor activities.*

Lesson 4
Safety on the Road

BIG Idea *Drivers, pedestrians, and others on the road need to follow rules to stay safe.*

Activating Prior Knowledge

Using Visuals Look at the photo on this page. What action do you see these teens taking to protect their health? On a sheet of paper, brainstorm a list of other actions you could take to protect your health and safety while participating in recreational activities.

724

Universal Access

Differentiated Learning Glencoe provides teacher support and student materials for all learners in the health classroom.

- Chapter Summaries in English and Spanish are available online at **glencoe.com**.
- *Fast Files* and related worksheets support reluctant readers.

- Universal Access strategies throughout the Teacher Wraparound Edition and *Fast Files* help you present materials for gifted students, at-risk students, physically impaired students, and those with behavior disorders or learning disabilities.

Chapter Launchers

Health in Action

Discuss the BIG Ideas

Before beginning this chapter, think about how you would answer these questions:

▶ What basic precautions do you take in your daily life?

▶ How do you protect your safety at home?

▶ How do you stay safe outdoors and on the road?

Watch the *Health eSpotlight* Video Series

VIDEO

Staying Safe

What safety habits do you practice on a daily basis?

Assess Your Health

Go Online

Visit **glencoe.com** and complete the Health Inventory for Chapter 26.

Chapter 26 Safety and Injury Prevention **725**

Chapter Launchers

Health in Action

Discuss the BIG Ideas

Ask students these questions aloud. Explain that the purpose of the questions is to help students assess their current knowledge of safety and injury prevention.

Health eSpotlight Video Series

 Staying Safe

VIDEO

Before Viewing the Video

Ask Students: *What is the most important precaution a person can take to prevent injury while doing any activity?* (Answers will vary. Some students might suggest that paying attention to what you're doing is the most important precaution.)

Go Online

Have students go to **glencoe.com** and take the Health Inventory for Chapter 26.

Chapter Skills

Reading Skills
- Reviewing Facts and Vocabulary, pp. 730, 738, 743, 749
- Reading/Writing Practice, p. 755

BIG Idea

You'll learn about safety and injury prevention in the home and in the community.

Vocabulary
- New Vocabulary, pp. 726, 731, 739, 744
- Reviewing Facts and Vocabulary, pp. 730, 738, 743, 749

Health Skills
- Health Skills Activity, p. 729
- Applying Health Skills, pp. 730, 738, 743, 749

Writing Skills
- Real World Connection, p. 736
- Writing Critically, pp. 730, 738, 743, 749
- Reading/Writing Practice, p. 755

725

Personal Safety and Protection

1 FOCUS

GUIDE TO READING

BIG Idea Students will understand that learning basic safety precautions can help them avoid threatening or harmful situations. **Ask Students:** *What basic safety precaution has helped you avoid a threatening or harmful situation in the past?* (Answers will vary.)

Before You Read

T-Chart Students' two-column charts will vary. The information about risks and how to avoid them should reflect the discussion in the lesson about learning to protect yourself and safety online.

Main Idea

Safety Strategies Learning how to recognize and avoid dangerous situations are keys to reducing the risk of becoming the victim of a crime. **Ask Students:** *What are three ways to avoid a dangerous situation?* (Accept any reasonable responses.)

Real Life Issues ....

After students have written their paragraphs, call on a few volunteers to share what they've written with the class. Discuss how Barry can best protect his safety.

726

LESSON 1

GUIDE TO READING

BIG Idea *Learning basic safety precautions can help you avoid threatening or harmful situations.*

Before You Read

Create a T-Chart. Make a chart with two columns labeled "Personal Safety" and "Internet Safety." As you read, fill in each column with information about types of risks and how to avoid them.

Personal Safety	Internet Safety

New Vocabulary

▸ personal safety (p. 726)
▸ self-defense (p. 727)
▸ cyberbullying (p. 729)

Personal Safety and Protection

Real Life Issues ....

The Quick Way or the Safe Way? Barry stayed after school to help build sets for the school play. It took longer than he expected, and now it's dark outside. If Barry walks home his usual way, sticking to busy and well-lit streets, he'll be late for dinner. He knows of a shortcut, but it involves cutting through dark alleyways. Barry realizes that might be dangerous, but he doesn't want to be late.

Writing *Write a paragraph explaining how Barry could deal with this situation in a way that protects his safety.*

Safety Strategies

Main Idea The key to personal safety is learning how to recognize and avoid dangerous situations.

Did you know that teens are the victims of more violent crimes than any other age group? Teens are more likely than children to go out at night, but they are less likely than adults to protect their **personal safety**—*the steps you take to prevent yourself from becoming the victim of crime.*

People living in urban areas report the highest rates of violent crime. However, crime can occur in any neighborhood and among any ethnic or socioeconomic group. About half of all violent crime occurs within one mile of a victim's home, and many victims know their attackers.

To reduce your risk of becoming a crime victim, always be aware of your surroundings and take precautions to protect yourself and your belongings. Whenever you leave your home, keep the following tips in mind.

🏔️👪 Home and Community

Self-Defense Classes In most communities, there are a variety of self-defense classes offered. These might include private businesses offering martial arts training, basic self-defense training at community centers or through organizations such as the YMCA. Ask interested students to phone or visit one or more businesses or organizations in their community that have these classes to find out what kind of training is offered, how much the classes cost, and how long the courses last. They might begin by looking in local phone books. They can also go online to look for classes in their area.

- If you carry a cell phone, make sure it's easy to get to. Remember that 911 will connect you with emergency services anywhere in the United States.
- Avoid walking alone at night or in isolated areas, such as alleys or parks. Stick to brightly lit, well-traveled streets.
- Walk briskly and confidently. Wear comfortable shoes so that you can move quickly.
- Carry your wallet or purse in a place that makes it difficult to grab. Avoid openly displaying expensive jewelry, electronics, or anything that would attract a thief.
- If you drive, park your car in a well-lit area and lock it. Before getting in, check to make sure no one is inside, and lock the doors as soon as you get in.
- Never hitchhike or give a ride to anyone you do not know well. Keep in mind that even someone you've met before could be dangerous.
- Get on and off public transportation in busy, well-lit areas. Sit near the driver or with a group of people.
- Know the locations of nearby public places where you can seek help if you need it.
- Let your family know where you're going and when you'll be back. Call them if your plans change.

Learning to Protect Yourself

One way that you can protect yourself from crime is to avoid the places where it is likely to occur. Be aware of what's happening around you, even when you are in familiar places. If you cannot avoid a dangerous situation, you can do the next best thing: know how to protect yourself. **Self-defense** includes *any strategy for protecting yourself from harm.* One self-defense strategy is to project a strong, confident image. Criminals are more likely to attack those who look vulnerable, confused, or inattentive. Show confidence by holding your head high and walking with a deliberate stride.

FITNESS ZONE

I'm really careful to avoid exercising outside after dark. When I go for a walk with my mom in the evenings, we wear reflective clothing so other people can see us, and we use flashlights to see where we're going. We also walk against traffic so we can see what is coming toward us. For more fitness tips, visit the Online Fitness Zone at glencoe.com.

■ **Figure 26.1** Parking in a well-lit area and keeping your car locked are two steps to avoiding crime. *What types of crimes could you prevent by taking these steps?*

English Language Coach

Health Glossary Have students create a health glossary for the vocabulary terms used in this chapter. This glossary can include both the new vocabulary terms highlighted in each lesson as well as the academic vocabulary and other new or difficult words used in the chapter. Students should write each term and a short definition in a notebook or on index cards. Encourage students to work in pairs with English-proficient students to review the meaning and pronunciation of each term in their glossaries. Advanced students can practice using the terms in spoken and written sentences.

2 TEACH

W Writing Strategy

Taking Precautions After students have read the tips to keep in mind when leaving home, ask them to pick two tips and write a paragraph on how they can use those precautions in their daily lives. Remind students to use specific examples. **BL**

FITNESS ZONE

Have students get into pairs.

- Each student holds a sheet of paper in one hand.
- Have one student be the leader. The leader will use the paper like a streamer.
- They should move the paper around while their partner mirrors what they do.

Caption Answer

Figure 26.1 Answers will vary but may include car theft or theft of items in the car.

CA Cultural Awareness

Self-Defense In class discussion, have students consider whether violent crimes are more or less common in the United States than in other industrialized countries around the world. Then have interested students research what kinds of self-defense classes are available in the United States and in Canada, England, or Japan. Ask students to report their findings to the class. **AL**

727

Health Skills Practice

Advocacy Divide the class into small groups, and ask each group to make a poster advocating actions to take that would reduce a person's risk of being the victim of a crime. Posters will vary depending on the particular precautions groups focus on. Hang the posters on the classroom walls. OL

 READING CHECK

Answer Avoid walking alone at night or in isolated areas. Avoid openly displaying expensive jewelry, electronics, or anything that would lure a thief.

Caption Answer

Figure 26.2 Answers will vary but may include avoiding places where crime is more likely to occur.

U **Universal Access**

Your Identity Emphasize that students should keep their identity private while online. Explain that a person's *identity* includes all the distinguishing characteristics of a person, beginning with the person's full name. Ask students what the verb form of identity is. (identify) OL EL

Academic Vocabulary

Encounter Call on volunteers to use the word in a sentence about unexpectedly meeting a friend at the mall or while on vacation. Ask other students whether the term was used correctly.

728

READING CHECK

Cause and Effect
Give two examples of behaviors that can help you avoid a dangerous situation.

Academic Vocabulary

encounter *(verb):* to experience

If you think you are being followed in a public place, let the stalker know that you are aware of his or her presence. Try changing directions or crossing the street. If necessary, seek help from someone nearby or enter a business that's open. If you are attacked or about to be attacked, do whatever is necessary to escape, such as running, yelling, or kicking. Shout "fire" instead of "help"—it's more likely to get a response.

Self-defense classes can teach you additional strategies for protecting yourself. When you hear "self-defense," you may think of martial arts fighting, and some classes do teach these skills. However, self-defense classes can also teach you how to size up a situation, figure out what to do, and catch your attacker off-guard. Most important, these classes can give you the confidence you need to defeat an attacker.

Staying Safe Online

Main Idea Teens need to protect themselves online.

The Internet is a useful resource, but it can also be a dangerous place. The hazards you can **encounter** range from upsetting situations, like being insulted in a chat room, to physical threats, such as Internet predators.

When you're online, you need to know how to protect yourself. Here are a few precautions to take when you're online:

- **Keep your identity private.** Avoid posting personal information in any public space. This includes your full name, address, phone number, financial information, passwords, the name of your school, and anything else a stranger could use to track you down in the real world.

- **Keep online relationships online.** Agreeing to meet in person with someone you've met online can be risky.

■ **Figure 26.2** Self-defense classes can boost your confidence and help you take charge of your own safety. *What other strategies can you use to protect yourself?*

Teens Want to Know

Should I Fight Back If I'm Ever Attacked? If you've been trained in martial arts, you may be able to fight back against an attacker. For most people, though, fighting back only increases the risk of making the situation worse. If you actually fight back, the attacker may become even more violent. In most situations, a good strategy is simply to get away from the attacker. This is where a self-defense class can help. Self-defense classes teach techniques to break an attacker's hold and run. Of course, the best defense against an attack is to avoid it or prevent it from occurring. To do that, you need to follow the tips in your text for reducing your risk of becoming a victim of a crime.

Health Skills Activity

Decision Making

Meeting a Friend Online

Lately, Marisa has been spending time in a chat room for teens who share her hobby, photography. She's also posted some of her nature photos online. Marisa has met some interesting people in the chat room. One is a guy named Craig, who loves her photos and says she's a talented pho-tographer. He's asked her to post photos of herself and any

she's taken at her school and in her neighborhood. Marisa enjoys Craig's compliments, but she's not sure if she should share photos that show personal details, such as what school she goes to or the area she lives in. What should she do?

> **Writing** Use the decision-making process to help Marisa decide how to respond to Craig in a way that protects her safety.
> 1. State the situation.
> 2. List the options.
> 3. Weigh the possible outcomes.
> 4. Consider values.
> 5. Make a decision and act.
> 6. Evaluate the decision.

- **Don't respond to inappropriate messages.** If anyone sends you a message that makes you feel uncomfortable for any reason, tell a parent or other trusted adult.

- **Let your parents or guardians know what you're doing online.** Tell them about the people you meet online, the same way you'd talk to them about your friends in the real world.

Coping with Cyberbullies

About 40 percent of teens say they have experienced *cruel or hurtful online contact*, or **cyberbullying**. Such contact can come from people you know or from strangers. It can range from immature and annoying to threatening and scary.

To avoid becoming a target of cyberbullying, be careful how you communicate online. When you use a Web site, learn and follow its rules for postings. Also, be careful how you word your messages. What may be a joke to you may come across as an attack or insult to someone else. Avoid getting into "flame wars," trading insults back and forth.

If you receive hurtful messages, don't respond to them. Cyberbullies are often looking for attention, and if you don't react, they'll go find someone who will. If the bullying contin-ues, however, seek help from a trusted adult. Save the mes-sages as evidence and contact your Internet service provider (ISP). It may be possible to block all future communications from the cyberbully. If any actual crime has been committed, such as making violent threats, contact the police.

READING CHECK

List What are three types of information you should keep private while online?

Health Skills Activity

Decision Making: Meeting a Friend Online

NHES Standard 5 Students will demonstrate the ability to use decision-making skills to enhance health.

Objectives
- Apply decision-making skills to make a personal safety decision.
- Demonstrate ways to avoid and reduce potentially harmful situations.

Teaching Strategies
- Before students write how Marisa should respond to Craig, advise them to review the four basic safety precautions in their text for when you're online.
- Ask volunteers to share how they used the decision-making process to help Marisa decide what to do.

Assessment
Using a rubric, student work should provide comprehensive evidence of the following crite-ria to achieve the highest score:

√ Clear description of the situation
√ Several options with pos-sible outcomes of each
√ Influence of values on pos-sible decisions
√ Health-enhancing decision and an evaluation of it

Writing Strategy

Cyberbullying by IM After students have read the description of cyberbullying, ask each student to write a dialogue of instant messages (IM) that begins as a friendly communication but quickly deteriorates into cyberbullying. In this dialogue, students should show a safe way of dealing with the bully. Ask volunteers to share their dialogues with the class. Using these examples, discuss safe strategies to deal with cyberbullying.

Caption Answer

Figure 26.3 Answers will vary but may include keeping your identity private and not responding to inappropriate messages.

3 **ASSESS/ CLOSE**

Assessment Resources

 ***FAST FILE* ACTIVITIES**
Lesson 1 Quiz

 ExamView
Assessment Suite CD-ROM

Visit glencoe.com for:
Online Quizzes
Online Learning Center

Progress Monitoring

Reteaching
Have students look at the photo in **Figure 26.1**. Then call on volunteers to describe ways that these teens can reduce their risk of becoming a victim of crime.

Enrichment
Have students contact their local police department to interview a police officer about personal safety precautions. Students should prepare a poster with safety tips from this lesson and any the police officer shared.

Have students visit **glencoe.com** and complete the Interactive Study Guide for this lesson.

■ **Figure 26.3** The Internet can be a useful tool for keeping in touch with your friends. *What precautions should you take to protect your safety online?*

Avoiding Internet Predators

Internet predators use online contact to build up trust so they can lure victims into a face-to-face meeting. To avoid falling victim to Internet predators, follow the general guidelines for online safety. Keep your identity private, and don't agree to meet in person with someone you've met online. If you ever find yourself in an online conversation that makes you feel uncomfortable or threatened—for any reason—log off and let a trusted adult know about the incident.

LESSON 1 **ASSESSMENT**

After You Read

Reviewing Facts and Vocabulary
1. What steps can you take to protect yourself from an attack when entering or leaving a car?
2. Name two threats you may encounter on the Internet.
3. How can you avoid becoming the target of a cyberbully?

Thinking Critically
4. **Evaluate.** Why is it important to avoid dangerous situations, even if you know how to defend yourself?
5. **Synthesize.** Gina is walking home from school when she notices someone is following her. What could she do to protect herself?

Applying Health Skills
6. **Communication Skills.** Suppose you have been posting on a message board about current events. The group is debating a political issue that you have strong opinions about. Write a message you could post that expresses your opinions in a way that is respectful toward those who disagree with you.

Writing Critically
7. **Creative.** Write lyrics for a pop song or rap about personal safety. Choose a topic in this lesson as the basis for your lyrics.

 Go Online

Visit **glencoe.com** and complete the Interactive Study Guide for this lesson.

LESSON 1 ASSESSMENT ANSWERS

1. Park in a well-lit area, lock your car, check the car for intruders before getting in, and lock the doors as soon as you get in.
2. Cyberbullying and Internet predators
3. Sample answer: Be careful how you communicate online.
4. Sample answer: It is easier to avoid getting into a dangerous situation than it is to try to get out of one.

5. Sample answer: She should try crossing the street or changing direction. If she still is followed, she could go into a store or other business and ask for help.
6. Answers will vary. Students may write on any topic, though the message should not be disrespectful to someone who would have another opinion.
7. Lyrics will vary but should reflect information discussed in the lesson.

Safety at Home and in Your Community

Real Life Issues

Fire Safety. Lucius and his family are moving into a new house. As he's examining his bedroom on the second floor, his dad comes in and looks out the window. "We'll need to find a place to store a ladder," he says. "This window's your emergency exit in case of fire. Come to think of it, we need to develop a fire safety plan for the whole house."

Writing *What do you think is involved in developing a fire safety plan? Why is it important to have such a plan?*

The Accident Chain

Main Idea Many accidental injuries are preventable.

Every year, more than 20 million children and teens require medical attention or face restricted activity due to unintentional injuries. These are *injuries resulting from an unexpected event*. You can prevent these injuries by breaking the **accident chain**, *a sequence of events that leads to an unintentional injury*. **Figure 26.4** on page 732 shows how stopping just one of the events in the chain can prevent the injury.

Keeping Your Home Safe

Main Idea Safety precautions can prevent injuries at home.

Accidents in the home are one of the top causes of injury and death in the United States. Common types of household accidents include fires, falls, and poisonings. You can reduce the risk of these accidents by taking safety precautions.

GUIDE TO READING

BIG Idea *Reducing the potential for accidents can help you stay safe at home and at work.*

Before You Read

Organize Information. Use a T-chart to organize the information in this lesson. On one side, list causes of accidental injuries. On the other side, list safety precautions that can prevent them.

Causes	Safety Precautions

New Vocabulary

▶ unintentional injuries (p. 731)
▶ accident chain (p. 731)
▶ fire extinguisher (p. 732)
▶ smoke alarm (p. 732)
▶ Occupational Safety and Health Administration (OSHA) (p. 738)

Review Vocabulary

▶ carbon monoxide (Ch.20, L.1)
▶ peer mediation (Ch.9, L.2)

Safety at Home and in Your Community

① FOCUS

GUIDE TO READING

BIG Idea Students will learn how to reduce the potential for accidents at home and at work. **Ask Students:** *What could you have done to avoid an accident you've had in the past?* (Answers will vary but might include paying more attention to what he or she was doing or making sure to follow rules about operating a piece of machinery.)

Before You Read

Organize Information
The information in students' T-charts may vary.

Main Idea

The Accident Chain By understanding the accident chain, it's possible to prevent many accidental injuries. **Ask Students:** *What are some steps your family has taken to make your home a safer place to live?* (Answers will vary. Students might describe baby-proofing a home, installing smoke alarms, or placing nonskid mats under rugs.)

Real Life Issues

Call on volunteers to share their ideas regarding their fire safety plan. Make a list of suggestions on the board, and discuss the importance of each.

English Language Coach

Using Analogies Write the word *chain* on the board. Explain to students who are fluent in languages other than English that a chain is a physical object that can be defined as "a series of usually metal links connected to or fitted into one another." If possible, show students a metal chain. Point out that if one of the links is broken, the chain falls apart. Because most people have an understanding of this physical object, its characteristics can be used in an analogy to explain an abstract concept. Explain that an analogy is resemblance in some particulars between things otherwise unlike. Write the term *accident chain* on the board. Ask students to explain how an accident chain is like a metal chain. (They are both a kind of series, and if one item in the series is missing, the series is interrupted.)

② TEACH

R Reading Strategy

Analyzing a Graphic Direct students' attention to **Figure 26.4** and call on volunteers to read aloud the caption to the first link in the chain, the Unsafe Situation. Ask students why this is an unsafe situation. (Because Stan's alarm didn't go off, he has to rush. His rushing makes the situation unsafe.) **BL OL**

U Universal Access

Word Meanings Review the meaning of the words *fire extinguisher*. Point out that to "extinguish" means to "cause something to stop burning." So, *fire extinguisher* means "to put out a fire." If possible, take the students into the hallway to point out what a fire extinguisher looks like. **EL**

AL Active Learning

Fire Safety Plan Have students create a fire safety plan for their home. As an example, make a drawing of the floor plan of a common house or apartment. Include the position of doors, hallways, windows, and stairs. Then, show with arrows the fastest way to escape from every room, and identify an alternative escape route if the first route is blocked by smoke or flames. Show students this example, and ask them to make one of their own home. **OL**

Figure 26.4	**The Accident Chain**

Breaking any of the links in this chain can prevent the accident and the resulting injury.

An Unsafe Situation Mark's alarm clock didn't go off this morning. As a result, he overslept and has to rush to get ready for school.

An Unsafe Habit Mark often leaves his books on the stairs.

An Unsafe Action Mark hurries down the stairs without watching where he's going.

The Accident Mark trips over his books and falls down the stairs.

The Consequences Mark lands on his wrist and sprains it. He's also late for school.

R

Preventing Fires

Common causes of household fires include burning candles and incense, smoking, kitchen fires, and faulty electrical wiring. To prevent fires in your home, follow these precautions:

- Keep matches, lighters, and candles away from children. Don't leave burning candles unattended.
- Make sure that smokers extinguish cigarettes completely, and that no one smokes in bed.
- Don't leave cooking food unattended. Clean stoves and ovens to prevent grease buildup, which can catch fire.
- Follow the operating instructions for using space heaters.

If a fire does occur, two lifesaving devices can help you escape without harm:

- **Fire extinguisher**, *a portable device for putting out small fires.* Keep an all-purpose fire extinguisher in your kitchen—one that is approved for flammable materials, flammable liquids, and electrical fires. Make sure that everyone in the house knows how to use it.

U

- **Smoke alarm**, *a device that produces a loud warning noise in the presence of smoke.* Having working smoke alarms in your home more than doubles your chances of surviving a house fire. Every home should have a smoke alarm on each floor, near the kitchen and bedrooms.

It's also imortant to plan an escape route ahead of time. Identify an escape path from every room of your home and a designated spot to meet up with your family after you get out.

AL

More About...

Injuries According to the National Center for Health Statistics, unintentional injuries were the leading cause of death for Americans under 35 in a recent year. Here are some more facts about unintentional injuries.

- In a recent year, unintentional injuries ranked fifth as the most common cause of death. In comparison, homicide ranked eleventh, and suicide ranked fifteenth.

- In the same year, motor vehicle deaths accounted for over 43,000 deaths, firearms accounted for about 30,000 deaths, poisoning accounted for about 29,000 deaths, and falls accounted for about 18,000 deaths.

■ **Figure 26.5** Test your smoke alarms once a month, and change the batteries twice a year. *How do smoke alarms protect your safety?*

CHAPTER 26

LESSON 2

When you are escaping from a fire, stay close to the ground so that you can crawl under the smoke. If your clothes catch fire, stop, drop, and roll to put out the flames.

Staying Safe with Electricity

Because wiring problems are a common source of house fires, knowing about electrical safety can help prevent electrical fires as well as electric shock. Here are some safety tips to follow:

- Avoid overloading your electrical system.
- Inspect electrical cords regularly. If you find any worn or exposed wiring, unplug the appliance *immediately* and don't use it anymore.
- Make sure extension cords are properly rated for their intended use and have polarized (three-prong) plugs.
- Do not run electrical cords under rugs or behind baseboards. Don't let furniture sit on cords, and don't attach cords to walls using nails or staples.
- Avoid using an electrical appliance near water, and *never* reach into water to retrieve a dropped appliance without first unplugging it.
- In homes with small children, cover unused outlets with safety caps.

Preventing Falls

Falls are responsible for about half of all accidental deaths in the home. To reduce the risk of injury from falls, take precautions in these areas of the home:

- **Stairs.** Keep stairways well lit, in good repair, and free of clutter. Staircases should have sturdy handrails, and all stair coverings should be securely fastened down. Never put small rugs at the foot of a staircase.

G̶Online

Visit **glencoe.com** and complete the Student Web Activity on safety at home.

AL Active Learning
Preparedness Questionnaire
Have pairs of students design a questionnaire about fire preparedness in the home. Questions might include: Are there smoke alarms in your home? How many? Does your home have a fire extinguisher? Then have student pairs use their questionnaire to take a survey of three or four homes in their neighborhood. Lead a class discussion on the results of all the surveys. **OL**

Caption Answer

Figure 26.5 A smoke alarm warns you of a fire in the home.

C Critical Thinking
Identifying Problems and Solutions Describe a situation in which a teen loves to lie in a bathtub while listening to a radio. For ease of changing stations, the teen plugs in the radio and places it on the edge of the tub. Ask students to identify the problem in this situation and describe how another setup could solve this problem. (The problem is that the electrical appliance is too near the bath water. The solution might be to place the radio far enough away from the tub that it could not fall into the water.) **BL**

Academic Integration

Math **Finding Percentages** The Real World Connection feature asks students to find percentages of the total number of unintentional injuries, given the numbers for specific causes of nonfatal unintentional injuries. To find what percentage the part is of the whole, students should divide the part by the whole. For example, to find the percentage of the total that resulted from falls, divide the number of falls (462,000) by the total number of unintentional injuries (2,700,000). The result is 0.1711. To convert that to a percent, multiply by 100. The answer is about 17 percent.

LESSON 2

U Universal Access

Preventing Falls Poster Explain that because falls are responsible for about half of all accidental deaths in the home, preventing this type of unintentional injury could make a big difference. Divide the class into small groups, and ask each group to make a poster that incorporates many of the precautions for preventing falls in the home. Display the completed posters around the classroom and in the school's hallways. **EL**

AL Active Learning

Student-Led Learning Divide the class into five groups. Assign each group one of the tips to prevent poisonings. Have each group develop the steps to take to safeguard their home. Have each group present their steps in front of the class. **OL**

HS Health Skills Practice

Practicing Healthful Behaviors After students have read the steps for preventing poisonings in the home, bring in several common household products so students can examine the labels. These might include over-the-counter medications, cleaning products, and fertilizers or other garden chemicals. Read aloud some of the warnings on the labels, and ask students where each product should be kept in the home to prevent poisonings. **BL**

Have students visit **glencoe.com** and complete the Student Web Activity on safety at home.

- **Bathrooms.** Put nonskid mats or strips in the tub or shower. Keep a night-light in the bathroom.
- **Windows.** If there are small children in the home, install window guards on the upper floors. However, make sure the windows can be opened completely in case of a fire.
- **Kitchens.** Keep the floor clean, and mop up spills promptly. Use a step stool to get things down from high places.
- **Living areas.** Keep the floor clear of clutter. Use nonskid rugs or place nonskid mats under rugs. Keep phone and electrical cords out of the flow of traffic.

U

Preventing Poisonings

Many common household items can be harmful or even fatal if swallowed. **Figure 26.6** shows some poisonous products that might be found in different parts of the home. To prevent poisonings, follow these tips:

HS

- **Store products safely.** Store all medications and other hazardous substances in childproof containers, and keep them out of the reach of children. Put locks or safety latches on cabinets where dangerous chemicals are stored. Discard medicines that are past their expiration date. Don't store household chemicals near pet food or water dishes, and clean up spills promptly.

AL

Figure 26.6   **Common Household Poisons**

Room	Poisons that might be found there
Bathroom	• Medications of any kind • Mouthwash • Hair spray • Toilet bowl cleaner • Astringents (such as rubbing alcohol) • Antiseptics
Bedroom	• Mothballs and crystals • Perfumes and colognes • Nail polish remover and nail glue remover
Kitchen	• Cleaning products • Rust removers • Drain cleaners • Furniture polish or floor wax • Metal polishes
Living room	• Lead paint (especially if chipped or peeling) • Poisonous houseplants
Garage or shed	• Pesticides • Fertilizer • Pool cleaners

Teens Want to Know

I Love to Cook—How Can I Prevent Cooking Fires? The leading cause of home fires in the United States is cooking, and cooking fires are the leading cause of fire injuries. Here are a few tips to prevent fires in the kitchen:

- Don't leave cooking food unattended, even for a short period. A cooking fire can start in seconds.

- Keep towels, curtains, and pot holders away from flames and burners.

- When cooking, always wear short, tight-fitting sleeves.

- Clean grease from cooking surfaces regularly. If grease builds up, it can catch fire.

Never try to put out a grease fire with water. Instead, use a fire extinguisher or cover the pan with a lid.

- **Pay attention to labels.** Unless directed by a doctor, never take more of a drug than the label recommends. Check with your doctor if you are taking two or more drugs. Follow instructions for using household chemicals. Mixing chemicals can result in dangerous fumes, explosions, home fires, and burns. Also, fuel-burning appliances, such as barbecue grills or kerosene lamps, must be properly vented to prevent carbon monoxide poisoning.

Using Computers Safely

Using a computer for a long period of time can lead to eyestrain and sore muscles. It can also cause injuries to the wrists, hands, or arms. To reduce these problems

- adjust your position from time to time.
- stretch your hands, arms, and body.
- stand up and walk around for a few minutes every hour.
- sit in a "neutral body position," a comfortable posture in which your joints are naturally aligned.
- Blink your eyes to moisten them and reduce eyestrain.

Handling Firearms Safely

Nearly half the households in the United States contain one or more guns. Gun accidents result in an estimated 650 deaths and 15,000 injuries per year. Most gunshot injuries in the home occur when a child finds a loaded gun. Children need to know that guns are dangerous and can kill people. Instruct them never to touch a gun and to leave the area and tell an adult if they find one.

Adults should also take precautions with firearms. When handling a gun, always assume that it is loaded. Never point a gun at anyone. Add a trigger lock, and keep your finger off the trigger except when firing. Store guns unloaded and in a locked cabinet, lock ammunition away separately, and keep the keys where children can't find or get to them.

Guarding Against Intruders

Accidents aren't the only threat to the safety of your home. There is also the risk that an intruder could break into your home. To keep intruders out, follow these guidelines:

- Keep your doors and windows locked. Deadbolt locks are the most secure kind. If doors or windows are damaged, repair them promptly. Don't hide a spare key outside the house. Instead, give a key to a neighbor you trust.
- Use a peephole to identify people who come to the door. Don't open the door to a stranger. Never tell people that you're home alone.

■ **Figure 26.7** Setting up your computer workstation correctly will reduce eyestrain, fatigue, headaches, and injury. *What other precautions can you take when working on your home computer?*

 **READING CHECK**

Describe What are three ways that you can stay safe at home?

R Reading Strategy

Reinforcing Concepts Have students read the section on "Using Computers Safely." Emphasize that using a computer for a long time can lead to problems. **Ask Students:** *What is the best body position when using the computer?* ("a neutral body position," in which the joints are naturally aligned.) **OL**

W Writing Support

Narrative Writing Ask students to write a dialogue about a situation in which two teens find a gun in a house. One teen wants to go outside and shoot at a target. The other teen uses refusal skills to resist the first teen's pressure. Ask students to end the dialogue with an agreement to take the safest action in this situation. **OL**

✓ READING CHECK

Answer Answers will vary but should include any three tips related to lesson content.

Cooperative Learning

Brochure for Childproofing a Home
When there are young children in a home, the home should be childproofed, such as keeping matches out of reach, placing covers on electrical outlets, storing hazardous materials properly, using secure caps on medicines, and securely locking away firearms. Divide the class into small groups, and ask each group to research what steps should to be taken to childproof a home. Resources might include both library materials and relevant Web sites. Ask groups to prepare a brochure, with information and illustrations that could be used by a parent to childproof a home.

735

Real World CONNECTION

Answers to Activity

1. 17 percent
2. 77 percent
3. Sample answer: Don't leave cooking food unattended. Avoid overloading your electrical system. Keep the kitchen floor clean, and mop up spills promptly.

Main Idea

Keeping Your Community Safe It's possible to work with others to protect safety at school, at work, and in communities. **Ask Students:** *Have you ever worked with friends or family to keep your community or school safe?* (Answers will vary.)

R Reading Strategy

Compare Have students read "Safety at School" on page 737 and "Keeping Your Community Safe." Ask students how the actions listed to make schools safer are similar to those that make communities safer? Have a class discussion and make a list on the board comparing the similarities and differences. **BL** **EL**

Real World CONNECTION

Accidents and Unintentional Injuries

The graph below compares the top five causes of nonfatal unintentional injuries to Americans between the ages of 15 and 19. Study the graph, then answer the questions that follow.

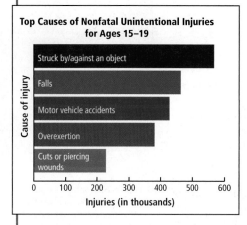

Top Causes of Nonfatal Unintentional Injuries for Ages 15–19

Activity Mathematics

Assume the total number of nonfatal unintentional injuries for this age group was 2.7 million.

1. What percentage of these injuries resulted from falls?
2. What percentage of all injuries do the five causes listed here account for?
3. **Writing** Identify at least three steps you could take to reduce your risk of accidents and unintentional injuries.

Concept Numbers and Operations: Percents A percent can be used to express the relationship between two numbers (A and B). To calcuate what percent of B is represented by A, use this formula: $(A \div B) \times 100$. For example, $(2 \div 8) \times 100 = 25$. Therefore, 2 is 25 percent of 8.

- Make sure your answering machine does not tell callers you are away from home.
- If you come home and see something suspicious, such as an unfamiliar car parked in your driveway or a window that's been forced open, don't go inside. Instead, call the police from a neighbor's house.

Keeping Your Community Safe

Main Idea You can work with others to protect your safety at school, at work, and in your community.

You have a right to be safe everywhere you go—at school, at work, and in your community. Many communities are taking the following steps to make neighborhoods safer:

- **Increased police presence.** Putting more police officers on the streets can reduce crime by as much as 15 percent.

R

Promoting School Wellness

Ensuring School Security A safe school environment is one of the components of a successful school health program. If students and staff do not feel safe in the school, then progress in education becomes difficult. Let students know that the school administration has taken steps to ensure the safety of students on many levels, beginning with security measures to make sure no violence can occur at the school to threaten students. Perhaps list some school programs and policies that work together to prevent violence, including any zero-tolerance policies, anti-bullying programs, and peer mediation programs. Encourage interested students to investigate what other schools in the area are doing to ensure school security.

- **Neighborhood Watch programs.** Through these programs, citizens watch for suspicious activity and report it to the police.
- **After-school programs.** These programs give students a place to go during after-school hours, when many crimes are committed. Keeping students at school or at a community center makes them less likely to commit crimes and less likely to become victims.
- **Improved lighting in public areas.** Better lighting can discourage crime by making it harder to commit crimes under cover of darkness.

Safety at School

Violence in schools can include fights between students, bullying, gang activity, and the presence of weapons. Other problems that can make school an unsafe environment include vandalism and alcohol and drug use. Eliminating these problems takes a joint effort by school staff, students, and parents.

- **School staff** can develop security procedures, such as hiring security guards, working cooperatively with the police, or using metal detectors to keep weapons out. Schools can also put disciplinary policies in place to deal with offenders. Some schools have adopted "zero-tolerance" policies, which means that a student can be expelled or **suspended** for a single offense.
- **Students** can develop peer mediation programs to help settle conflicts. They can report crimes or other suspicious activities to school staff. They can also clean up graffiti, lead anti-violence groups, and get others involved in community service.
- **Parents** can play a role by being aware of the conditions at the school. They can become involved in school affairs by joining parent-teacher groups, chaperoning field trips, and helping out in the classroom.

Academic Vocabulary

suspend *(verb):* to bar temporarily

Safety on the Job

Millions of teens in the United States hold full-time or part-time jobs. Part-time or summer jobs offer a way to earn extra cash, build responsibility, and learn useful skills. However, work also has its risks. Each year, about 70,000 teen workers suffer injuries or illnesses serious enough to send them to a hospital emergency room.

 READING CHECK

Cause and Effect List three problems that can make school less safe. Identify three strategies for dealing with these problems.

 Home and Community

Neighborhood Watch Programs
Neighborhood watch programs are private organizations that provide security for local communities. Although they are not sponsored by local governments, these volunteer organizations commonly work in cooperation with the police, serving as extra eyes and ears in looking out for crime. Ask students to investigate whether there are neighborhood watch programs in action in their community. Have them find out what functions local programs carry out and how they can participate. Students should write down what they find out and read it aloud to the class.

U Universal Access

School Security Lead a discussion on security measures in the school. Review school policies about weapons, fights, and vandalism, including the consequences for violating those policies. Ask a school administrator to make a brief presentation and answer students' questions about security measures. **OL**

Academic Vocabulary

Suspend Read the definition of the word aloud. Then have students compare being suspended with being expelled from school. Ask for one similarity and one difference between the meanings of the two words. (A similarity is being barred from school. A difference is that being suspended is temporary, while being expelled is permanent.)

AL Active Learning

Computer Workstations After students have examined **Figure 26.7**, encourage interested students to assess the computer workstations in the school to see if they are set up correctly to reduce eyestrain, fatigue, headaches, and pain or injuries. For example, students should examine the position of monitors, light sources, and chairs. Ask students to prepare a report about what they find. **AL**

3 ASSESS/
CLOSE

Progress Monitoring

Reteaching
Call on students to state a safety tip related to preventing fires. When students can think of no more tips about preventing fires, use the same process for tips about staying safe with electricity, preventing falls, preventing poisonings, handling firearms safely, using computers safely, and guarding against intruders.

Enrichment
Have each student write a paragraph on how to prevent poisonings in the home. Make sure that students describe what prevention measures both adults and young children can take.

Go Online

Have students visit **glencoe.com** and complete the Interactive Study Guide for this lesson.

■ **Figure 26.8** The law places restrictions on the types of work that teens can do. *Why might it be unsafe for teens to do certain jobs?*

The federal government has enacted laws to protect the health of young workers. First, all employers must meet standards set by the **Occupational Safety and Health Administration (OSHA)**. OSHA is *the agency within the federal government that is responsible for promoting safe and healthful conditions in the workplace.* Other laws place limits on the kinds of jobs that teens can do. For example, workers under 18 years old are not allowed to drive forklifts, work as miners or loggers, operate certain types of power-driven equipment, or work with explosives or radioactive materials.

Teen employees and their employers can take additional steps to prevent work-related injuries. Young workers can be aware of the risks of their jobs, follow safe work practices, and refuse to work in unsafe conditions. Employers can provide adequate training and supervision.

LESSON 2 **ASSESSMENT**

After You Read

Reviewing Facts and Vocabulary

1. Define *unintentional injuries*.
2. Identify two important pieces of fire safety equipment.
3. What are two steps you can take to prevent poisonings in your home?

Thinking Critically

4. **Synthesize.** Seventeen-year-old Claude finds his father's shotgun on the kitchen table. It looks like his dad was interrupted in the middle of cleaning it. What should Claude do?
5. **Analyze.** What factors may make teens especially vulnerable to being injured on the job?

Applying Health Skills

6. **Practicing Healthful Behaviors.** Think of a specific job that a teen might have. Develop a list of strategies for preventing injuries on that job.

Writing Critically

7. **Narrative.** Write a short story about an accident involving a teen. Your story should clearly show each of the steps in the accident chain and how all of them work together to result in the accident.

Go Online

Visit **glencoe.com** and complete the Interactive Study Guide for this lesson.

LESSON 2 ASSESSMENT ANSWERS

1. Injuries resulting from an unexpected event
2. Fire extinguishers and smoke alarms
3. Store products safely, and pay attention to labels.
4. Sample answer: He should treat the gun as if it's loaded. If there are young children in the home, he might lock the trigger and lock the gun away.
5. Sample answer: Teens lack the experience and training of older workers, and teens may lack the judgment to avoid unsafe behaviors.
6. Answers will vary but should identify a common job that teens hold, such as in a restaurant or grocery store, and include a list of strategies for preventing injuries on that job.
7. Stories will vary but should reflect a clear understanding of the accident chain.

Outdoor Safety

Real Life Issues

Safety at Risk. Janelle and her class are enjoying a whitewater-rafting trip. Toward the end of their lunch break, her friend Daria says, "Hey, a few of us are going for a quick swim before it's time to take off again. Want to join us?" Janelle is nervous. She knows that even in clear water, it's hard to tell how deep a river really is—and this river is full of rocks and breakers. Still, she's not sure how to say no.

Writing *Write a dialogue in which Janelle responds to Daria's invitation in a way that protects her safety.*

Outdoor Recreation

Main Idea Planning ahead can protect you from injury during outdoor activities such as camping, hiking, and winter sports.

The most important general rule for all outdoor activities is to plan ahead. Here are some specific ways to do just that:

- **Know your limits.** Stick with tasks that match your level of ability. Brush up on necessary skills ahead of time.

- **Bring supplies.** Take plenty of safe drinking water with you. Never drink the water from lakes, rivers, or streams. Plan simple meals and bring what you need to store the food safely. Don't forget first-aid supplies and any medications you normally take.

- **Plan for the weather.** Check the local weather forecast and plan for expected conditions. See Chapter 12 for tips on hot-weather and cold-weather activities.

- **Wear appropriate clothing.** Choose clothes that are right for the weather and will protect you from poisonous plants and insects. Dress in layers.

- **Tell people your plans.** Let your family know where you're going and when you'll be back. If possible, carry a cell phone for emergencies. A sports whistle can also be useful as a way to signal for help.

BIG Idea *Common sense and caution can minimize the risk of accidental injuries during outdoor activities.*

Before You Read

Create a Cluster Chart. In the center of a sheet of paper, write "Outdoor Activities" and circle it. Surround it with circles labeled "Camping and Hiking," "Winter Sports," "Swimming and Diving," and "Boating." As you read, add information about staying safe during each type of activity.

New Vocabulary
▶ personal flotation device (PFD) (p. 742)

Review Vocabulary
▶ frostbite (Ch.12, L.4)
▶ hypothermia (Ch.12, L.4)

Outdoor Safety

1 FOCUS

GUIDE TO READING

BIG Idea Students will learn that common sense and caution can minimize the risk of accidental injuries during outdoor activities. **Ask Students:** *What common-sense precaution do you think would prevent most swimming injuries?* (Answers will vary but most may include only swimming in designated areas with a lifeguard present.)

Before You Read
Cluster Chart
Students' word webs will vary.

Main Idea

Outdoor Recreation Planning ahead can protect a person from injury during outdoor activities. **Ask Students:** *Suppose you are in charge of planning for a younger brother or sister's camping trip with a scout group. What plans would be most important for you to put into action?* (Answers will vary but may include finding a good sleeping bag or packing the right clothes.)

Real Life Issues

After students have read the scenario, divide the class into pairs, and ask each pair to write a dialogue between Janelle and Doria. After students finish writing, ask volunteers to role-play their dialogues for the class. Discuss which role-played strategy would best protect Janelle's safety.

Teacher to Teacher

Timothy Johnson • Coweta High School, Coweta, OK

Safety Foremost I tell my students about Dick and Rick Hoyt who are a father-and-son team that compete together in marathon races and triathlons. For the past 25 years or more, Dick has pushed his son Rick across the country. Rick was born a nonvocal quadriplegic with cerebral palsy. I ask students to brainstorm and discuss the emergency preparedness and planning that would need to be done to compete on such a high level with such great challenges.

❷ TEACH

R Reading Strategy

Ways to Plan Ahead Call on volunteers to read aloud each of the ways to plan ahead for outdoor recreation—know your limits, bring supplies, plan for the weather, wear appropriate clothing, and tell people your plans. For each way, encourage students to tell about instances when they either avoided problems by adhering to the guideline or encountered problems because they didn't plan ahead. **BL**

AL Active Learning

Cartoon Camping Divide the class into small groups, and ask each group to create a cartoon strip that illustrates one of the guidelines for staying safe while camping and hiking. Tell groups that their cartoons can be either humorous or serious. Display the completed comic strips on the classroom walls. **OL EL**

W Writing Support

Expository Writing Explain to students that when campers register at the park's campground, they are often given a pamphlet that contains park rules they must follow. Many of these rules were developed to ensure the safety of campers. Ask students to write a list of rules a campground could give to campers. Students might want to research campground rules using online resources. **AL**

Caption Answer

Figure 26.9 Answers will vary but should include food, safe drinking water, first aid supplies, medications, and appropriate clothing, as well as a tent and a sleeping bag.

■ **Figure 26.9** Packing the right supplies will help guarantee that outdoor activities are safe as well as fun. *What supplies would you bring on a camping trip?*

Camping and Hiking

There's nothing like a day out on the trails or a night sleeping under the stars. Just make sure you steer clear of bears, poison ivy, and sprained ankles! To enjoy your stay in the woods and reduce your risk of injury, follow these tips:

- **Camp with a group.** Having at least one other person with you means one person can go get help if the other is ill or injured.
- **Stick to well-marked trails.** In case you do get lost, bring a map and a compass, and know how to use them.
- **Be cautious around wildlife.** Don't feed wild animals. Avoid keeping food in or near sleeping areas, where wild animals may come looking for it.
- **Take care with fires.** Before starting a campfire, make sure it's **legal**. Keep fires at least 10 feet away from the tent. Put your fire out completely before going to bed.
- **Respect the environment.** If there aren't any trash bins at your campsite, pack your waste with you when you go.

Academic Vocabulary

legal *(adjective):* permitted by law

🗹 READING CHECK

Predict Give two examples of problems that might occur while engaging in outdoor recreation.

Winter Sports

When you take part in cold-weather activities, wear warm, layered clothing to protect you from frostbite (skin and tissue damage) and hypothermia (dangerously low body temperature). To avoid sunburn, you should also apply sunscreen to all exposed skin. The sunscreen should have an SPF of at least 15. Make sure you have a buddy with you to help out in an emergency.

More About...

Safety While Camping The feeding of wild animals in parks by campers and other visitors causes real problems beyond the immediate danger of getting too close to these animals. One problem is when people feed animals, the animals become dependent on human-given food, and when people are not around to provide food, the animals suffer. A more pressing problem, however, occurs when animals are drawn to campsites and other areas where people gather. If the animals are used to being fed or finding food trash, they naturally keep coming to the source of food. As a result, feeding wild animals or leaving food trash available for animals can cause danger for future visitors to a park.

Tips for specific winter activities include the following:

- **Sledding.** Make sure your equipment is in good condition. Choose safe spots to sled in: gently sloped hills with plenty of space and a level area to come to a stop at the bottom. Don't sled on or near frozen lakes, because the ice may not be solid.
- **Ice skating.** Skate only in designated areas. Never skate where you don't know the thickness of the ice. Wear skates that fit comfortably and support your ankles.
- **Skiing, snowboarding, and snowmobiling.** Wear an approved, properly fitting ski helmet. Make sure that your other equipment, such as your snowmobile, boots, and bindings, are in good condition. Stick to marked trails that are appropriate for your level of ability. Remember to look both ways and uphill before crossing or merging onto a trail. When heading downhill, give the people ahead of you the right of way, since they may not be able to see you coming from behind. If you need to stop, get to the side of the trail, out of the path of others.

Water Safety

(Main Idea) Following safety precautions can prevent drowning and other water-related injuries.

Swimming, boating, and other water sports are great ways to beat the summer heat. However, it's important not to lose sight of water safety. Every year, nearly 3,000 people die from drowning. Although most drowning incidents involve young children, people of all age groups need to pay attention to water safety guidelines.

Swimming and Diving

The most important rule for safety in the water is to know how to swim. Know your limits as a swimmer. If you're just learning, don't try to keep up with skilled swimmers. Instead, stick to shallow areas where your feet can touch the bottom. If you are a strong swimmer, keep an eye on friends who aren't as skilled as you are. No matter how good a swimmer you are, never swim alone. Even experienced swimmers can suffer a muscle cramp or other medical emergency.

Here are additional rules for safe swimming and diving:

- Swim only in designated areas where a lifeguard is present. Obey "No Swimming" and "No Diving" signs.
- Dive only into water that you know is deep enough. Diving into shallow water could result in permanent spinal cord damage or death.

■ **Figure 26.10** Proper clothing and equipment are two of the keys to outdoor winter safety. *What kind of clothing should you choose for cold-weather activities?*

C Critical Thinking

Snowmobile Accident Describe the following scenario: Two teens are riding a snowmobile through the woods on a cold, snowy day. They are deep in the woods when they have an accident. The snowmobile is too damaged to use, and one of the teens is too injured to walk. They begin to worry that no one will find them. Ask: How could the teens have planned ahead for this possibility? (Answers will vary but might include having packed extra clothing, taken a cell phone with them, and told someone where they were going and when they would be back.) **OL**

(Main Idea)

Water Safety Following safety precautions can prevent drowning and other water-related injuries.
Ask Students: *What kind of safety precautions do you take when swimming or boating?* (Answers will vary but may include wearing a personal flotation device.)

Caption Answer

Figure 26.10 Answers will vary but should include a winter coat and various layers of warm clothing.

Writing Strategy

Rules of the Beach Many students have spent time at a public beach. Most public beaches post rules explaining what people can and cannot do. Ask students to use what they've learned from this lesson to write a list of rules for visitors to a public beach. Encourage students to go online and find out what rules are like in state parks or at other state beaches.

LESSON 3

 **Health Skills Practice**

Refusal Skills Divide the class into small groups, and ask each group to choose one of the rules for swimming and diving safely. Have groups create a role-play in which one teen or a group of teens pressures another teen to swim or dive in an unsafe situation. The role-play should show the teen using refusal skills to decline participation in the activity. Have each group perform its role-play for the class. **OL**

READING CHECK

Answer Swim only in designated areas where there's a lifeguard present, and dive only into water that you know is deep enough.

AL Active Learning

Boating Laws Ask interested students to investigate the boating laws in their area. Have them find the answer to questions such as: *Does a boat need a license to be used on area waters? Does the driver need a license? What other laws are there about boats used on area lakes and rivers?* Have students write a report and discuss with the class what they find. **AL**

R Reading Strategy

Analyzing a Graphic Have students examine the figure about drowning prevention. Call students' attention to the H.E.L.P. posture.

Ask Students: *If someone fell into cold water wearing a PFD, why would he or she want to assume the H.E.L.P. position?* (To retain as much body heat as possible) **BL**

- When swimming, always enter the water feet first. Check for hidden rocks and other hazards.
- Avoid swimming near piers and reefs. These areas are subject to rip currents that can drag you into open water.
- If you get caught in a current, swim with the current until it releases you, then swim back to the shore.
- Pay attention to the weather. When it's hot, drink plenty of fluids and reapply sunscreen frequently. If you start to shiver, it's time to get out of the water.
- Be prepared for emergencies. Knowing first aid can help you save a life.

 HS

Boating

Every year, more people die in boating accidents than in airplane crashes or train wrecks. Following a few common-sense guidelines can help you stay safe while boating: **AL**

- Make sure the person handling the boat is experienced. Never get into a boat with an operator who has been using alcohol or other drugs.
- Always wear a **personal flotation device (PFD)**, better known as a *life jacket,* when you go out in a boat. PFDs come in a wide variety of types and styles for boaters of different ages and levels of swimming ability. Inflatable toys or "water wings" are *not* a substitute for an approved PFD.
- Plan ahead and check weather reports. If a storm is predicted, do not go out onto the water. If you are already on the boat, head back to shore immediately.
- Make sure someone on land knows where you are and when you expect to be back.

When canoeing or kayaking, be prepared to fall into the water. Because the water is likely to be cold, dress in layers and choose synthetic fabrics that will wick moisture away from your body. **Figure 26.11** shows some survival techniques you can use if you fall into deep water. Know your limits when canoeing or kayaking, and don't attempt rivers or rapids that are beyond your abilities. Make sure you know how to handle a boat properly and recognize river hazards before heading out on the water.

The same safety rules that apply to boating also apply to personal watercraft. According to the U.S. Coast Guard, 60 percent of all accidents involving personal watercraft occur because of a lack of experience and speeding. Some states have additional laws governing the use of personal watercraft devices. For example, there may be an age limit for operating one or a test you have to pass before you can use one.

READING CHECK

Classify List two safety tips you should follow when swimming and two tips for safe boating.

742 **Chapter 26** Safety and Injury Prevention

Myths & Reality

Drowning Truths

Myth: Drowning takes a long time to occur.

Fact: Children are most at risk for drowning, and a child can lose consciousness under water in 20 seconds or less.

Myth: Drowning is very noisy, and listening to a child in a pool is enough supervision.

Fact: Drowning often occurs with little noise or as a silent event. For example, a child can lose his or her balance in relatively shallow water and slip under water without a sound.

Figure 26.11 **Preventing Drowning**

R

If you fall into cold water while wearing a PFD, assume one of these positions. If you are not wearing a PFD, tread water gently while keeping your head out of the water.

A. The Heat Escape Lessening Posture (H.E.L.P.) involves drawing your knees up and holding your arms tight across your chest, elbows bent. Keep your head out of the water to avoid losing body heat.

B. If you are with a group of people, huddle in a circle with your chests pressed together to hold in body heat. Small children should be sandwiched between adults or larger people.

LESSON 3 ASSESSMENT

After You Read

Reviewing Facts and Vocabulary

1. Identify three strategies for preventing accidental injuries while hiking or camping.

2. List three general safety guidelines for participating in winter sports.

3. What is the main safety rule for diving?

Thinking Critically

4. **Analyze.** You and your friend Jake are skiing. Jake suggests trying the advanced slope, even though you're both beginners. What are the possible consequences of going along with this idea?

5. **Synthesize.** You and your family are taking a boat out on the lake for the afternoon. What supplies and safety equipment should you bring with you?

Applying Health Skills

6. **Decision Making.** Some friends invite you to go on a canoe ride. You've never canoed before and don't know how to handle the boat. On a sheet of paper, outline a response to this situation, using the six steps of the decision-making process.

Writing Critically

7. **Personal.** Write a journal entry about a day spent doing some kind of outdoor activity. You may describe an activity you have actually done or a fictitious one. In your journal, discuss the steps you took to protect your health and safety while outdoors.

 Go Online

Visit glencoe.com and complete the Interactive Study Guide for this lesson.

3 ASSESS/ CLOSE

Assessment Resources

📁 *FAST FILE* **ACTIVITIES**
Lesson 3 Quiz

 ExamView
Assessment Suite CD-ROM

Visit glencoe.com for:
Online Quizzes
Online Learning Center

Progress Monitoring

Reteaching
Call on students to describe a problem or injury that can occur as a result of an outdoor activity. Then call on a volunteer to explain how paying attention to a particular safety guideline might have prevented that problem or injury.

Enrichment
Have students research the different types of personal flotation devices, the benefits of each type, and for what conditions each type is made. Ask students to make a presentation to the class about what they learn.

 Go Online

Have students visit glencoe.com and complete the Interactive Study Guide for this lesson.

LESSON 3 ASSESSMENT ANSWERS

1. Sample answer: Take plenty of safe water with you. Plan for the weather. Wear appropriate clothing.
2. Wear warm clothing, apply sunscreen, bring a friend along.
3. Dive only into water that you know is deep enough.
4. Answers will vary, but students should recognize the possibility of suffering a serious injury.
5. Sample answer: An approved PFD for each person, drinking water, sunscreen, sunglasses, snacks, and a cell phone.
6. Answers will vary, but should reflect an understanding of the decision-making process and recognition that canoeing may be above his or her level of ability.
7. Journal entries will vary, but should reflect an understanding of safety in outdoor activities.

Safety on the Road

① FOCUS

📖 GUIDE TO READING

BIG Idea Students will learn that drivers, pedestrians, and others on the road need to follow rules to stay safe.
Ask Students: *Are there different rules for bicycles on the road than for cars on the road?* (No, a bicycle is required to obey the same traffic laws as cars.)

Before You Read

Organize Information
The students' tables will vary.

Main Idea

Auto Safety The two keys to driving safely are paying attention to what you're doing and following the rules of the road. **Ask Students:** *Why is it important for a person to always pay attention while behind the wheel?* (Answers will vary. Students might suggest that something unexpected might happen, and only if the driver is paying attention can an accident be avoided.)

Real Life Issues

Have students write their dialogues. Then ask volunteers to share their dialogues with the class. Discuss why the father might think that Shang is not able to handle driving at night.

📖 GUIDE TO READING

BIG Idea *Drivers, pedestrians, and others on the road need to follow rules to stay safe.*

Before You Read
Organize Information. Draw a chart with three columns. In the first column, list facts you already know about traffic safety. In the second, list questions about this topic you would like to have answered. As you read, fill in the third column with the answers.

Facts	Questions	Answers

New Vocabulary

▶ vehicular safety (p. 744)
▶ graduated licensing (p. 745)
▶ road rage (p. 746)
▶ defensive driving (p. 746)

Safety on the Road

Real Life Issues

Limits on Driving. Shang was excited when he passed his driver's test. The first thing he did was to ask his dad if he could borrow the car that night to take a friend to a movie. Shang was surprised and disappointed when his dad said, "I don't think that's a good idea. You just got your license, and driving at night is a lot trickier. You should wait until you've been driving for a while."

Writing *Write a dialogue in which Shang and his dad use good communication and conflict resolution skills to reach an acceptable solution.*

Auto Safety

Main Idea Paying attention and following the rules of the road are the keys to safe driving.

Motor vehicle crashes are the leading cause of death for people between the ages of 15 and 20. Young drivers are more than twice as likely to be involved in a crash as the rest of the population. This is why **vehicular safety**—*obeying the rules of the road and exercising common sense and good judgment while driving*—is such an important issue for teens.

The most important rule of driving safety is: Pay attention. According to the National Highway Traffic Safety Administration (NHTSA), at least 25 percent of car crashes happen when a driver is distracted. The driver may be talking on a cell phone, drowsy, or lost in thought. Reduce distractions when you drive by positioning the seat and mirrors and fastening your safety belt before starting the engine. Adjust the radio and temperature controls before moving.

Myths & Reality

Safety Belts

Myth: By not fastening the safety belt, a passenger has a good chance of surviving an accident by being thrown clear of the car.

Fact: By not wearing a safety belt, a passenger might be thrown from the car in an accident. That would normally not be helpful, though. There is a 25 percent greater chance of being killed in an accident if you are thrown from the car.

Myth: You do not need to wear a safety belt if you're driving only a short distance from home.

Fact: About 75 percent of accidents that cause death happen within 25 miles of a person's home.

Here are some examples of things you need to pay attention to when you're in the driver's seat:

- **Other drivers.** Be aware of the cars around you and how they're moving. Make sure other drivers can see you by switching on your headlights at night and in bad weather.
- **Road conditions.** Reduce your speed if the road is icy or wet, if heavy snow or rain is limiting your vision, if a lane narrows, if there are sharp curves ahead, or if there is construction or heavy traffic.
- **Your physical state.** Never drive when you're tired. Drowsiness can impair your reaction time and your judgment. If you feel tired, try to wake yourself up by stopping for a snack or a bit of exercise. If you're still drowsy, pull over at the nearest safe, well-lit area and call home.
- **Your emotional state.** Being angry or upset can affect your driving. Ask someone else to drive, or if you're alone, pull over to a safe spot until you calm down.

Passengers riding with teen drivers are responsible for reducing the risk of accidents, too. Avoid doing anything that might distract the driver's attention from the road. Passengers must also take responsibility for their own safety. They should avoid getting into a vehicle with an impaired driver. If you're with a driver who has used alcohol or other drugs, try taking the keys away from the individual. You could also call a parent or other trusted adult to pick you up.

Teen Drivers

AL Young drivers may be more likely to get into an accident because they lack the experience and skills needed to drive safely. They are more likely to underestimate the hazards of the road. They may also take more risks such as speeding, running red lights, making illegal turns, or driving after using alcohol or drugs.

U To help protect young drivers and others on the road, most states have graduated driver's licensing programs. **Graduated licensing** is *a system that gradually increases driving privileges over time.* Many programs have three stages: learner, provisional, and full driver's license. Each stage has a different set of driving restrictions. For example, a driver with a first- or second-stage license may not be allowed to drive at night or have teen passengers. In order to move up to the next level, drivers need to maintain a clean record, with no crashes or traffic violations.

G⦿ Online

Go to **glencoe.com** and complete the Student Web Activity on the dangers of driving while tired.

■ **Figure 26.12** Getting lessons from an experienced driver will help you improve your driving skills. *Why might young or inexperienced drivers be more likely to get into accidents?*

② **TEACH**

G⦿ Online

Remind students to go to **glencoe.com** and complete the Student Web Activity on the dangers of driving while tired.

AL Active Learning

Driving Research Ask students to investigate the licensing system in their state. Have them find out if a graduated licensing system has been put in place, and, if so, what are the stages and the restrictions associated with each stage. To obtain this information, students might use an online search engine or make a call to the state's department of motor vehicles. Ask students to report to the class what they find. **AL**

U Universal Access

A Graduated System Students may have difficulty understanding the use of the word *graduated* in this context, having likely heard the word in the context of a person who has graduated from high school or college. Explain that here the word means "divided into grades or intervals." In this case, the grades are the three stages of the system: learner, provisional, and full. **EL**

Caption Answer

Figure 26.12 They lack the experience and skills.

 **Writing**

Narrative Writing After students have read about road rage, ask them to write a short story with a teen driver as the main character. Explain that the teen is driving through the city alone one evening when another driver becomes enraged for one reason or another. Ask students to write a realistic story about how the teen safely handles the incident and arrives home without injury. OL

✓ **READING CHECK**

Answer Pay attention to the road when driving, and get away from someone who threatens you.

C **Critical Thinking**

Discussing Defensive Driving Ask students to read the definition of defensive driving. Then ask students how many of them defensively drive their car. For those who don't, ask them why they do not and encourage that they do. OL

 **HEALTH NEWS**

After students have watched the video, *Safer Driving Through Technology,* ask them to write a paragraph about feeling safer in a vehicle with the blind spot protection system. Remind students to use examples in their paragraphs. Then, ask volunteers to read their paragraphs aloud. Lead a discussion on whether the development of new technology will make driving safer in the future.

746

Figure 26.13 **Driving Do's and Don'ts**

Do:	Don't:
• Maintain a safe speed—not too fast, not too slow.	• Drive after using alcohol or any other depressant.
• Maintain a safe distance from other cars. Follow the three-second rule; when the car in front of you passes an object, you should pass it at least three seconds later.	• Drive while drowsy.
	• Use a cell phone while driving.
	• Be distracted by adjusting the radio or other controls.
• Signal all turns.	• Eat food while driving.
• Obey traffic signals.	• Drive with someone who has been drinking alcohol or using illegal drugs.
• Let other drivers merge safely.	• Use your horn inappropriately. It's meant to be a warning signal; save it for that.
• Wear your safety belt, and make sure your passengers wear theirs.	

R

✓ **READING CHECK**

Identify Problems and Solutions Name two actions you can take to stay safe while driving.

VIDEO **BusinessWeek**

HEALTH NEWS

Safer Driving Through Technology

Analyze. Go to glencoe.com and watch the video *Safer Driving Through Technology.* When driving, would you feel safer in a vehicle with the blind spot protection system? Briefly explain your answer. Remember to use examples to support your points.

Avoiding Road Rage

You're driving along when another driver suddenly swerves into your lane without signaling, forcing you to slam on your brakes. Some drivers respond to this type of situation with **road rage**. This means *responding to a driving incident with violence.* Examples of road rage behaviors can include

- honking, shouting, gesturing, or flashing lights.
- chasing or tailgating another vehicle.
- cutting off another car or forcing it off the road.
- deliberately hitting or bumping another car.
- threatening or physically attacking another driver.

If you see these kinds of behaviors, stay a safe distance away. If you're threatened, lock your doors and drive to the nearest police station. Never try to retaliate, or the conflict could turn deadly.

W

Being a Responsible Driver

Unfortunately, you can't always trust other drivers to drive safely. To protect yourself, you need to drive defensively. **Defensive driving** means *being aware of potential hazards on the road and taking action to avoid them.*

When you drive defensively, you stay alert and take responsibility for your behavior. You also watch out for potential dangers. A car that is weaving, crossing the center line, making wide turns, or braking without warning may have an impaired driver. If you spot such a vehicle, keep your distance, or pull over and notify the police. **Figure 26.13** lists other ways to protect yourself while driving.

C

 **More About...**

Graduated Licensing Systems of graduated licensing were first put in effect in New Zealand, Australia, and Canada. In 1996, Florida became the first U.S. state to adopt graduated licensing. Many states have adopted some form of graduated licensing since then. Restrictions vary among the states. Common restrictions include not being allowed to drive at night and not being allowed to have more than one passenger at any time during the day. Graduated licensing targets young people—not all beginning drivers—because young people are more likely to get into crashes. Studies have shown that a reduction in vehicle crashes of 10 to 30 percent in states that have adopted graduated licensing.

Sharing the Road

Main Idea Everyone on the road shares a responsibility to follow traffic laws.

You share the road with other motorists, pedestrians, cyclists, and people on skates, scooters, or small motor vehicles. When you're driving, watch for other vehicles and pedestrians. When you're on foot, on a bike, or skating, be aware of vehicles and follow the rules of the road.

Pedestrian Safety

CA Always use the sidewalk. If there is no sidewalk, walk on the left side of the road, facing oncoming traffic. This will make it easier for cars to see you. It also makes it easier for you to see them, and get out of the way if a driver comes too close. Before you cross a street, look left, then right, then left again. Cross only at marked crosswalks, or at a corner. Make sure the cars have seen you and stopped before you step into the street.

Bicycle Safety

Riding a bike is a great way to travel around and get exercise at the same time. Here are tips for safe cycling:

- Always wear a safety-approved helmet that fits properly.
- Follow the rules of the road, and obey traffic laws.
- Signal turns about half a block before reaching the intersection. Extend your left arm straight out to the side to signal a left turn. Bend your left arm upward at the elbow to signal a right turn.
- Ride single file, and keep to the far right side of the road. Watch out for obstacles such as opening car doors, sewer gratings, soft shoulders, and cars pulling into traffic.
- Do not tailgate motor vehicles or ride closely behind a moving vehicle.
- Look left, right, and left again before riding into the stream of traffic.
- Wear bright colors in the daytime and reflective clothing at night. Place reflectors on the front and rear of your bike, on both wheels, and on both pedals.

■ **Figure 26.14** Cyclists ride with the flow of traffic and obey the same traffic signs and signals as cars. *What are some safety measures you can take when riding a bike?*

Lesson 4   Safety on the Road   **747**

Main Idea

Sharing the Road Motorists, pedestrians, cyclists, and others on the road all share a responsibility to follow traffic laws. **Ask Students:** *When you ride your bike, do you stop at the stop sign?* (Answers will vary. Encourage students to always stop at stop signs.)

CA Cultural Awareness

The Right Side of the Road Read aloud the Pedestrian Safety content. Emphasize that pedestrians should walk on the sidewalk but if there is no sidewalk, to walk facing oncoming traffic. In the U.S. we would walk on the left side of road. **Ask Students:** *Would this guideline be the same for most roads in the world?* (Walking facing traffic would be the same, but in some countries like England, drivers drive on the left side of the road so pedestrians would walk on the right side of the road.) **OL**

R Reading Strategy

Analyzing a Chart Direct students' attention to the chart in **Figure 26.13** of Driving Do's and Don'ts. Ask a student to read aloud the first Do guideline. **Ask Students:** *Does maintaining a safe speed, not too fast and not too slow, mean always going the same speed?* (No. It means going the speed limit or below, depending on the conditions of the road.) Continue with the same process until students have discussed all the Do's and Don'ts on the chart. For each, ask students to tell of their experiences on the road. **BL**

Writing Strategy

Magazine Article After students have read about being a responsible driver and examined the Do's and Don'ts of driving, ask students to write a magazine article that describes a teen driving home from a high school football game on a Friday night. Tell students that they should use the information they've learned about defensive driving and the risks that teen drivers take to describe hazards the teen encounters during the drive and how the teen makes it home safely.

LESSON 4

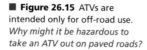 AL Active Learning

Skating Safety Poster Divide the class into small groups, and ask each group to create a poster that informs and illustrates important guidelines about skating safety. Illustrations can be photos from magazines or the Web as well as artwork created by students. Mount the posters in the classroom and in the school's hallways. OL

W Writing Strategy

Summarizing After students have read the Small Motor Vehicle Safety section, have them summarize in paragraph form, the safety rules for operating an ATV. OL

R Reading Strategy

Organizing Information After students have read about skating safely, help them organize the information by writing the title *Small Motor Vehicle Safety* on the board. Then ask students to use the information they've read to make a bulleted list of safety guidelines. Make the first bullet below the title, and write *Wear the proper equipment.* Call on volunteers to identify more guidelines. The completed bulleted list should have at least nine guidelines. BL

Caption Answer

Figure 26.15 Sample answer: An ATV may be unable to keep up with traffic, and an ATV might not be able to withstand a collision with a car.

Skating Safety

To protect yourself while skating, wear the proper equipment, including: helmet, knee and elbow pads, wrist guards, and gloves. If you're a beginner, avoid skating in high traffic areas. Watch out for pedestrians, cyclists, and others on the road. Avoid skating in the street, and cross streets safely when you come to them. If you start to lose your balance, crouch down so that you won't have as far to fall. Try to keep your body loose and roll, rather than absorbing the force of the fall with your arms, which can cause wrist injuries. AL

Small Motor Vehicle Safety

Small motor vehicles include motorcycles, mopeds, and all-terrain vehicles. Motorcycles and mopeds are motor vehicles, just like cars, and are subject to the same traffic laws. Motorcyclists must have a special license in addition to their driver's license. W

According to the NHTSA, motorcyclists and passengers are 32 times more likely to die in a crash than automobile drivers and passengers. Head injuries cause the most deaths in motorcycle accidents. In 20 states, all motorcyclists and passengers must wear protective helmets. In another 27 states, motorcyclists and passengers under the age of 18 are required to wear a helmet. R

Helmets should meet the standards set by the U.S. Department of Transportation (DOT). Wearing sturdy clothing that covers the arms and legs also provides some protection. Passengers should avoid riding with a motorcyclist who is impaired by drug or alcohol use.

■ **Figure 26.15** ATVs are intended only for off-road use. *Why might it be hazardous to take an ATV out on paved roads?*

More About...

Bicycle Helmets About 75 percent of bicycle accidents involve head injuries, and a head injury can mean permanent disability or even death. For that reason, wearing a bicycle helmet is critical for safe riding. When buying a helmet, you should try it on to make sure the fit is secure. Explain to students that a good helmet should fit snugly on the head, without tilting forward, backward, or sideways. You should also look inside the helmet to see if it is approved by one of two safety organizations, The Consumer Product Safety Commission (CPSC) or the Snell Memorial Foundation.

Another type of small vehicle is the all-terrain vehicle (ATV). ATVs have either three or four wheels. These off-road vehicles are used for recreation, as well as for work on farms and ranches. It's important to take safety precautions when operating ATVs. About 46 percent of all injuries and deaths from ATV use occur among children and teens under age 16.

The Consumer Product Safety Commission (CPSC) wants to ban ATVs with three wheels. The CPSC is also proposing other rules for safe ATV use. Those proposals include licensing ATV users, restricting people under age 16 from using ATVs, and requiring all ATV users to complete safety classes. To operate ATVs safely, keep these guidelines in mind:

- Only one person should ride on an ATV at a time.
- Avoid using attachments that will reduce the stability and braking of the ATV.
- Wear appropriate gear when riding an ATV. In addition to a DOT-approved helmet, you should wear eye protection, a long-sleeved shirt, long pants, gloves, and boots that cover your ankles.
- Avoid taking an ATV out on paved roads.
- Avoid ATV drivers who have been using alcohol or drugs.

✓ READING CHECK

Classify Identify two safety rules that apply to pedestrians, cyclists, and skaters.

LESSON 4 ASSESSMENT

After You Read

Reviewing Facts and Vocabulary

1. What is the most important rule of driving safety?
2. Identify three behaviors associated with road rage.
3. What piece of safety equipment is required for both cycling and in-line skating?

Thinking Critically

4. **Evaluate.** According to an old saying, "It's better to be alive than right." How could this saying be applied to vehicular safety?
5. **Evaluate.** What are some of the risks associated with operating motorcycles, mopeds, and ATVs?

Applying Health Skills

6. **Advocacy.** Work with a small group to produce a safety guide that educates teens and others on how to stay safe while operating a motorcycle, moped, or ATV. Produce your guide as a video, public service announcement, brochure, or comic book.

Writing Critically

7. **Expository.** List three risks you might face while driving, skating, or riding a bicycle. Then write a paragraph explaining how your behavior can increase or reduce these risks.

Go Online

Visit **glencoe.com** and complete the Interactive Study Guide for this lesson.

---

❸ ASSESS/ CLOSE

Assessment Resources

 FAST FILE **ACTIVITIES**
Lesson 4 Quiz

 ExamView
Assessment Suite CD-ROM

Visit glencoe.com for:
Online Quizzes
Online Learning Center

Progress Monitoring

Reteaching

Ask students to state the two keys to safe driving. Then call on volunteers to describe how violating these key concepts can result in injuries for drivers, pedestrians, school-bus riders, bicyclists, skaters, motorcyclists, and ATV operators.

Enrichment

Ask students to research laws in their area about the use of motorcycles and all-terrain vehicles. Have students find out if drivers need special licenses to operate those vehicles and what restrictions apply.

LESSON 4 ASSESSMENT ANSWERS

1. Pay attention to what you're doing.
2. Sample answer: Chasing another vehicle, tailgating, and forcing a car off the road
3. Helmet
4. Sample answer: Even if you're right and another driver is wrong, it's better to yield than to force your way in and risk an accident.
5. Sample answer: Risks may include head injuries and/or death.
6. Group products will vary, though each should reflect an understanding of how to stay safe on the road.
7. Risks and paragraphs will vary, though students should demonstrate an understanding of how behaviors increase or reduce risks on the road.

Go Online

Have students visit **glencoe.com** and complete the Interactive Study Guide for this lesson.

Cruise Control

Focus

Motivator

Ask students, "Is driving and talking on a cell phone becoming more prevalent? Do most people you see use a hands-free set?"

TEACH

Cell Phones Explain that several states are considering laws that require drivers to use hands-free sets when talking on a cell phone and others are considering a complete ban on the use of cell phones while driving. Ask students to research the impact of cell phones and other electronic devices on driver distractions and motor vehicle safety. Have students explore enacted and pending state laws on the topic.

About Traffic Violations Have students review the article. Initiate conversation about tattletale bumper stickers. Ask students, "Have you seen these types of stickers? How would you feel if your parents or a court of law mandated that you display one on your car if you received a ticket? Do you think that it would motivate you to improve your driving?" Brainstorm a list of good driving habits. Include techniques that help relax in tense driving situations.

750

Cruise Control

New teen driving restrictions put parents in the rear window.

How's My Driving?
Tell-My-Mom.com
1-866-2-TELLMOM

Anne Rekerdres likes to call it "the everlasting punishment." When the 17-year-old North Dallas senior came home with a speeding ticket, her dad, Randy, slapped the back bumper of her beloved car with a sticker that read: "How's my driving? 1-866-2-TELLMOM." "It was humiliating," says Anne. Still, there was nothing she could do. Randy recalls, "I told her, 'If the sticker comes off, there go your keys.'"

Tattletale bumper stickers, which publicize where to call to notify parents about bad driving, are a trend that won't end soon. Besides the Web site on which Anne's dad bought hers, two other services—the San Diego–based Dad's Eyes (877-DADS-EYES) and 800-4-MYTEEN of Arlington, Texas—also allow strangers to report on teen driving. The stickers have even become popular in Texas's municipal court system, where several judges regularly sentence speeding teens to six months with the embarrassing banners.

Do the stickers actually make teens drive more safely? Stephanie Collins, 16, from Green Bay, Wisconsin, thinks so. "I always think about the sticker when I'm driving. When other drivers do something stupid, sometimes I feel like I want to cut them off, but then I remember the sticker is there, and I stay calm."

Anne's dad agrees. "As long as she perceives she can be reported," says Randy, "it works." His attitude doesn't make Anne happy, but she's learning to accept her punishment.

Amanda Holmes, 16, from Mesquite, Texas, offers this advice to other teens who might be thinking about driving carelessly: "I wouldn't recommend speeding if this sticker is the punishment. They make your car stand out because they are bright orange like the one I have." ■

TIME to THINK... | About Traffic Violations

The sticker described in the article is one way to deter teens from speeding or breaking other traffic laws. With a group, think up other ways that might also be effective. Devise public service ads promoting one of your ideas. Include catchy headlines and create pictures that will make the ads dramatic.

Teens Want to Know

Q: I'll be getting my driver's license soon. My parents are willing to put me on their auto insurance policy, but I have to pay the premium. What can I do to help keep the cost of my insurance low?

A: The most important thing you can do is to keep a clean driving record. Even a single fender-bender can drive your insurance premium sky-high. Here are a few other tips:

- Keep your grades up. With a "B" average or above, you may be able to save 25%.

- Drive a slower, used car with lots of safety features.

- If you have a credit card, maintain a good credit history.

To download quizzes and eFlashcards to your PDA, go to **glencoe.com** and click on the Study to Go icon.

LESSON 1

Personal Safety and Protection

Key Concepts

▶ Personal safety precautions can help you avoid becoming a victim of crime.

▶ Self-defense strategies include being able to spot dangerous situations and knowing how to evade or fight off an attacker.

▶ Internet safety strategies include keeping your identity private and not responding to inappropriate messages.

Vocabulary
▶ personal safety (p. 726)
▶ self-defense (p. 727)
▶ cyberbullying (p. 729)

LESSON 2

Safety at Home and in Your Community

Key Concepts

▶ The accident chain includes an unsafe situation, an unsafe habit, and an unsafe action.

▶ Home safety hazards include fires, electric shock, falls, poisonings, firearms, and intruders.

▶ Neighborhood Watch programs, after-school programs, and improved lighting in public areas can reduce crime.

Vocabulary
▶ unintentional injuries (p. 731)
▶ accident chain (p. 731)
▶ fire extinguisher (p. 732)
▶ smoke alarm (p. 732)
▶ carbon monoxide (p. 735)
▶ peer mediation (p. 737)
▶ OSHA (p. 738)

LESSON 3

Outdoor Safety

Key Concepts

▶ It's important to plan ahead for all kinds of outdoor activities.

▶ To prevent drowning and other water-related injuries, know how to swim and know your limits as a swimmer.

Vocabulary
▶ frostbite (p. 740)
▶ hypothermia (p. 740)
▶ personal flotation device (PFD) (p. 742)

LESSON 4

Safety on the Road

Key Concepts

▶ To drive safely, pay attention and follow traffic laws.

▶ Graduated licensing programs help young drivers develop the experience and skills they need to drive safely.

▶ Motorists, pedestrians, cyclists, and others can share the road safely by watching out for each other and obeying traffic laws.

Vocabulary
▶ vehicular safety (p. 744)
▶ graduated licensing (p. 745)
▶ road rage (p. 746)
▶ defensive driving (p. 746)

Chapter 26 Review **751**

 Go Online

Students can visit **glencoe.com** to

• review content online with the Online Student Edition.

• test their knowledge of chapter content with Online Quizzes.

• access Interactive Health Tutor for more practice with vocabulary.

Assessment Resources

📁 **FAST FILE ACTIVITIES**
Chapter 26 Test

💿 *ExamView*
Assessment Suite CD-ROM

Visit glencoe.com **for:**
Audio Chapter Summaries
Online Quizzes

 Tell students to visit **glencoe.com** where they can download quizzes and eFlashcards.

Study Tips

Taking Notes Tell students that taking notes is one of the most effective ways of absorbing material presented in class, and taking notes well will become more and more important in higher grades and in college. Emphasize that every student should always have a notebook and a pencil or pen at hand to make notes of what's being presented by the teacher, by other students, or by some kind of media. Explain that a note taker should not try to write down everything. Rather, the note taker should listen for and record facts, connections, and main ideas. This task becomes easier with practice.

Assessment

Chapter 26 Assessment Answers

LESSON 1

Vocabulary Review

1. personal safety
2. self-defense
3. cyberbullying

Understanding Key Concepts

4. c
5. b

Thinking Critically

6. Sample answer: They will know where to reach you in an emergency. If you are not home at the expected time, they will know something is wrong and will come looking for you.
7. Sample answer: People may not want to get involved if they think a crime is being committed, but if they think there is a fire, they will believe they might also be in danger.
8. Cyberbullies try to hurt their victims, while sexual predators try to build up trust so they can lure their victims into a face-to-face meeting.

LESSON 2

Vocabulary Review

9. unintentional injury
10. accident chain
11. fire extinguisher
12. smoke alarm
13. the Occupational Safety and Health Organization (OSHA)

Understanding Key Concepts

14. b
15. d
16. d

LESSON 1

Vocabulary Review

Correct the sentences below by replacing the italicized term with the correct vocabulary term.

1. Recognizing and avoiding dangerous situations is a part of *everyday precautions.*
2. Learning how to size up a situation, figure out what to do, and catch your attacker off-guard are examples of *martial arts.*
3. Cruel or hurtful online contact is called *harassment.*

Understanding Key Concepts

After reading the question or statement, select the correct answer.

4. To protect yourself from an attack while walking on the street, you should *not*
   a. stick to brightly lit, well-traveled streets.
   b. walk briskly and confidently.
   c. openly display expensive items.
   d. know where you can seek help.
5. If you think you are being followed in a public place, you should
   a. pretend you aren't aware of the stalker.
   b. go into a business that's open.
   c. challenge your attacker.
   d. avoid making a scene.

Thinking Critically

After reading the question or statement, write a short answer using complete sentences.

6. **Analyze.** How does letting your family know your plans protect your personal safety when you go out?
7. **Make Inferences.** Why might a person trying to escape from an attacker be more likely to get a response by shouting "fire" instead of "help"?
8. **Compare and Contrast.** How do the tactics used by cyberbullies differ from those used by Internet predators?

LESSON 2

Vocabulary Review

Use the vocabulary terms listed on page 751 to complete the following statements.

9. The kinds of accidents that pose a real danger are the ones that result in a(n) ________.
10. The ________ is a sequence of events that leads to an unintentional injury.
11. A(n) ________ is a portable device for putting out small fires.
12. A(n) ________ is a device that produces a loud warning noise in the presence of smoke.
13. The agency within the federal government that is responsible for promoting safe and healthful conditions in the workplace is called ________.

Understanding Key Concepts

After reading the question or statement, select the correct answer.

14. How often should smoke alarms be tested to make sure they are working?
    a. Every week
    b. Every month
    c. Twice a year
    d. Once a year
15. What is responsible for approximately half of all accidental deaths in the home?
    a. Poisonings
    b. Fire
    c. Electrical shock
    d. Falls

Health eSpotlight VIDEO Wrap-Up

Staying Safe Have students reread the Health eSpotlight questions at the beginning of the chapter (page 725) and look at their original answers. **Ask Students:** *What do you now know about injury prevention that you didn't know before watching the video and reading the chapter?* Call on volunteers to describe what they have learned and how they would change their responses.

16. Which of the following steps can students take to improve the safety of their schools?
    a. Hire security guards.
    b. Put metal detectors at school entrances.
    c. Adopt zero-tolerance policies for offenses.
    d. Develop peer mediation programs.

Thinking Critically

After reading the question or statement, write a short answer using complete sentences.

17. **Identify.** What are the five steps in the accident chain?

18. **Explain.** How does following rules for electrical safety help prevent home fires?

19. **Analyze.** Why is it dangerous to mix household chemicals, such as cleaning fluids?

LESSON 3

Vocabulary Review

Use the vocabulary terms listed on page 751 to complete the following statement.

20. Wearing warm, layered clothing will protect you from _____, or a dangerously low body temperature.

21. Another name for a(n) _____ is a life jacket.

22. Damage to the skin and tissue caused by the cold is _____.

Understanding Key Concepts

After reading the question or statement, select the correct answer.

23. When skiing, snowboarding, or snowmobiling, you should give the right of way to
    a. the people ahead of you.
    b. the people coming from behind you.
    c. the people to your left.
    d. the people to your right.

24. The only safe place to swim is
    a. in a swimming pool.
    b. in a lake or river.
    c. in a designated area with a lifeguard present.
    d. near piers and reefs.

25. Which of the following water safety rules applies *only* to boating?
    a. Know how to swim.
    b. Don't go out alone.
    c. Pay attention to the weather.
    d. Always wear a life jacket.

Thinking Critically

After reading the question or statement, write a short answer using complete sentences.

26. **Explain.** Why should you avoid keeping food in or near sleeping areas while camping?

27. **Evaluate.** What is the advantage of having a buddy with you for all types of outdoor activity?

28. **Apply.** What should you do if you get caught in a current while swimming?

LESSON 4

Vocabulary Review

Correct the sentences below by replacing the italicized term with the correct vocabulary term.

29. *Traffic law* is a system that gradually increases driving privileges over time.

30. Responding to a driving incident with violence is called *highway anger*.

31. *Responsiveness* means being aware of potential hazards on the road and taking action to avoid them.

Chapter 26   Assessment   **753**

Thinking Critically

17. An unsafe situation, an unsafe habit, an unsafe action, an accident, and consequences of the accident
18. Following the rules prevents wiring problems, which are a common cause of house fires.
19. The combination could result in toxic fumes, explosions, fires, or burns.

LESSON 3

Vocabulary Review

20. hypothermia
21. personal flotation device (PFD)
22. frostbite

Understanding Key Concepts

23. a
24. c
25. d

Thinking Critically

26. Wild animals may come looking for it.
27. Someone will be there to help in an emergency.
28. Swim with the current while gradually trying to work your way back to the shore.

LESSON 4

Vocabulary Review

29. Graduated licensing
30. road rage
31. Defensive driving

Create and customize tests in minutes with this convenient digital platform.

- Create differentiated tests quickly and easily.
- All questions correlated to National/State Standards.
- Enhance tests with Document Based Questions (DBQ) and add your own photos or graphics.
- Build tests in both English and Spanish.
- Generate progress reports.

To order, go to **glencoe.com** and search for ISBN 0-07-888173-0.

Understanding Key Concepts

32. a

33. b

34. d

Thinking Critically

35. They lack the experience and skills needed to drive safely. They may underestimate the hazards of the road or take risks.

36. It enables young drivers to build up their skills gradually and work their way up to trickier driving situations.

37. Crouch down so you won't have as far to fall. Try to keep your body loose and roll rather than absorbing the force of the fall with your arms.

Understanding Key Concepts

After reading the question or statement, select the correct answer.

32. The National Highway Traffic Safety Administration (NHTSA) estimates that at least 25 percent of car crashes happen when a driver
   a. is not paying attention.
   b. is not wearing a safety belt.
   c. is angry or upset.
   d. is on wet or icy roads.

33. The proper place to ride a bicycle is
   a. on the left side of the road, facing oncoming traffic.
   b. on the far right side of the road.
   c. as close to the middle of the road as possible.
   d. on the sidewalk.

34. All-terrain vehicles (ATVs) should be ridden only
   a. on paved roads.
   b. by licensed drivers.
   c. for recreation.
   d. by one person at a time.

Thinking Critically

After reading the question or statement, write a short answer using complete sentences.

35. **Analyze.** What factors make teen drivers more likely to be involved in accidents?

36. **Evaluate.** What are the advantages of graduated licensing?

37. **Apply.** What should you do if you start to lose your balance while on a skateboard?

Project-Based ASSESSMENT

Preventing Poisonings

Background
Households contain a surprising number of toxic substances. Cleaners, paints, insecticides, medicines, and even some houseplants can be poisonous. Many home poisonings involve small children. A tiny amount of a toxic substance can be deadly. Moreover, small children can't always tell you what they have taken. Treatment often depends on the type of the poison. The good news is that most poisonings can be prevented.

Task
Create a poison prevention flyer.

Audience
Families in your area

Purpose
Provide families with information to prevent household poisonings.

Procedure

1 Review the poison prevention information presented in this chapter.

2 Conduct research to find additional information on poison prevention.

3 Compile a list of steps people can take to prevent household poisonings.

4 Add emergency measures that can be taken if someone is poisoned.

5 Find the 24-hour toll-free number for the Centers for Disease Control and Prevention's poison control hotline.

6 Keep the poison control kit in your home, or offer the kit to a family with small children.

Project-Based ASSESSMENT

Step 1 Brainstorm Before students research, have them brainstorm or recall information from the chapter on how to prevent poisonings.

Step 2 Research Students should go online or visit the library to find resources on what steps to take if someone is poisoned. Students should make a list.

Step 3 Make a Kit Have students gather materials to make their poison control kit. The kit should contain a small poster showing the different kinds of poisonous substances found at home.

Visit **glencoe.com** for Project-Based Assessment Rubrics.

Math Practice

Interpret Graphs. The bar graph below shows the percentage of total hospitalized injuries based on a sample size of 650,000 people. Use the graph to answer Questions 1–3.

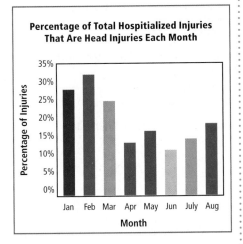

Percentage of Total Hospitialized Injuries That Are Head Injuries Each Month

Percentage of Injuries (y-axis: 0% to 35%)

Month (x-axis: Jan, Feb, Mar, Apr, May, Jun, July, Aug)

1. If 32% of the sample size were injured in February, how many people were injured?
   A. 175,000   C. 324,000
   B. 208,000   D. 475,000

2. Which month had the fewest number of injuries?
   A. January
   B. April
   C. June
   D. August

3. Approximately how many injuries occurred during the month with the fewest injuries?
   A. 117,000   C. 71,500
   B. 91,000   D. 65,000

Go Online

For more test practice, visit glencoe.com and complete the Online Quizzes for Chapter 26.

Reading/Writing Practice

Understand and Apply. Read the passage below, and then answer the questions.

> A fire broke out Thursday night in the home of the Levin family in Deep Valley. Mr. and Mrs. Levin and their two children, Sam and Jamie, escaped unhurt.
>
> "Our smoke detector saved our lives," reported Debbie Levin. "It woke us all up out of a sound sleep. Dave and I went to check on the kids, but they were already on their way out—crawling under the smoke just the way we taught them."
>
> "It's really worth the effort to make a fire safety plan and have drills with your kids," added Dave Levin.
>
> The Levins escaped to the home of their neighbors, the Johnsons, and called the fire department. Firefighters were able to extinguish the blaze before it caused significant damage.

1. Which of the following sentences would best complete the third paragraph?
   A. The fire was caused by bad wiring.
   B. We have a fire extinguisher on hand.
   C. The Johnsons let us use their phone to call the fire department.
   D. Our kids knew exactly what to do in this situation.

2. What is the purpose of this passage?
   A. To urge people to buy fire extinguishers
   B. To report a neighborhood fire
   C. To explain how smoke detectors work
   D. To generate sympathy for the Levins

3. Write a conclusion for this article that describes how the fire in the Levin home started. Include advice on how readers can protect themselves from fires in their own homes.

National Education Standards

Math: Number and Operations, Data Analysis
Language Arts: NCTE 1, NCTE 3, NCTE 4

Standardized Test Practice

Standardized Test Practice Answers

Math Practice
1. B
2. C
3. C

Reading/Writing Practice
1. D
2. A
3. Conclusions will vary. In describing how the fire started, students might cite any of the fire hazards discussed in Lesson 2. For that fire hazard, students should describe a preventative measure.

National Education Standards

Math: Number and Operations, Data Analysis

Language Arts: NCTE 1, NCTE 3, NCTE 4

For the complete Math and Language Arts standards, visit glencoe.com.

Go Online

Online Study Tools
For more test practice, visit glencoe.com and complete the Online Quizzes for Chapter 26.

Test-Taking Tip

Your Own Ideas Explain to students that some questions based on a reading passage may ask them to respond to the passage by writing ideas of their own. The final question in the Standardized Test Practice is an example. To respond to this question, students should read the passage at least twice, looking for information that would help them answer the question and bring to mind their own knowledge of the main subject of the passage. Finally, they should use both information gleaned from the passage and their own thoughts to write an answer to the question.

Chapter 27 pages 756–789	Standards		Features
	National	State/Local	
	1.12.5, 7.12.1, 7.12.2, 8.12.4		**Hands-On HEALTH** • First-Aid Station *(Practicing Healthful Behaviors)*, page 784
Lesson 1 **Providing First Aid** pages 758–763 BIG Idea *Knowing how to perform first aid can save a life in an emergency.*	1.12.5, 3.12.3, 7.12.1, 7.12.2, 8.12.1, 8.12.4		**TEENS Making a Difference** • Becoming a First Responder, page 761
Lesson 2 **CPR and First Aid for Shock and Choking** pages 764–770 BIG Idea *Medical emergencies that are life threatening include loss of breathing, shock, and choking.*	1.12.5, 3.12.3, 7.12.1, 7.12.2, 8.12.1		**Health Skills Activity** • Calling Emergency Services *(Communication Skills)*, page 766 ⏱ Out of Time
Lesson 3 **Responding to Other Common Emergencies** pages 771–777 BIG Idea *You can use first aid to deal with common emergencies such as muscle and bone injuries, impaired consciousness, animal bites, nosebleeds, and poisoning.*	1.12.5, 3.12.3, 7.12.1, 7.12.2, 8.12.1		
Lesson 4 **Emergency Preparedness** pages 778–783 BIG Idea *Planning ahead and knowing what to expect can help a person survive severe weather and natural disasters.*	1.12.5, 3.12.3, 6.12.4, 7.12.1, 7.12.2, 8.12.1		**Real World CONNECTION** • Sheltering in Place, page 783 ⏱ Out of Time

(Each lesson marked **30 Min**)

Key to Ability Levels

Teaching Strategies and activities have been coded for ability level and appropriateness.

AL Activities for students working above grade level   **BL** Activities for students working below grade level

OL Activities for students working on grade level   **EL** Activities for English Learners

756A

Glencoe Exclusive!
TeacherWorks *Plus*
All-In-One Planner and Resource Center

Resources	Lesson Assessment	Technology
Student Activity Workbook `TEACH` *FAST FILE* RESOURCES Vocabulary Practice `TEACH` Health Labs `EXTEND`	Chapter 27 Review Chapter 27 Assessment Standardized Test Practice ⊙ *ExamView® Assessment Suite* CD-ROM	**Teaching Tools:** ⊙ *TeacherWorks*™ Plus DVD ⊙ *StudentWorks*™ Plus DVD ⊙ *ExamView® Assessment Suite* CD-ROM 🕹 Transparency ⊙ Fitness DVD ⊙ PowerPoint® DVD ⊙ Health eSpotlight Video Series DVD
FAST FILE RESOURCES Reading Strategies Activity `TEACH` Reteaching Activity `REVIEW` Enrichment Activity `EXTEND` Health Skills Practice `TEACH`	Lesson 1 Assessment, page 763 📁 Lesson 1 Quiz *Fast File* ⊙ *ExamView® Assessment Suite* CD-ROM	
FAST FILE RESOURCES Reading Strategies Activity `TEACH` Reteaching Activity `REVIEW` Enrichment Activity `EXTEND` Health Skills Practice `TEACH`	Lesson 2 Assessment, page 770 📁 Lesson 2 Quiz *Fast File* ⊙ *ExamView® Assessment Suite* CD-ROM	**Web-Based Resources:** **Go Online** glencoe.com • Health Podcast Activities • Audio Chapter Summaries (English/Spanish) • Interactive Health Tutor • Health Skills Activities • Vocabulary PuzzleMaker • Parent Letters (English/Spanish) • Lesson Plans • Health Inventories • Online Quizzes • Study-to-Go • Unit Web Projects • Student Web Activities • Fitness Zone Activities
FAST FILE RESOURCES Reading Strategies Activity `TEACH` Reteaching Activity `REVIEW` Enrichment Activity `EXTEND` Health Skills Practice `TEACH`	Lesson 3 Assessment, page 777 📁 Lesson 3 Quiz *Fast File* ⊙ *ExamView® Assessment Suite* CD-ROM	
FAST FILE RESOURCES Reading Strategies Activity `TEACH` Reteaching Activity `REVIEW` Enrichment Activity `EXTEND` Health Skills Practice `TEACH`	Lesson 4 Assessment, page 783 📁 Lesson 4 Quiz *Fast File* ⊙ *ExamView® Assessment Suite* CD-ROM	

StudentWorks *Plus*

This is the student's backpack solution.

Includes:
- complete Interactive Student Edition
- full audio of English text and Spanish chapter summaries
- allows students to record assignments and track grades.
- links to online activities and additional student resources
- access to all student worksheets and workbooks

FOLDABLES®
Study Organizer

Dinah Zike Foldables®
Chapter Activity
Refer to the *Dinah Zike Reading and Study Skills for Glencoe Health*. Have students make a three-tab book Foldable to record what they learn about responding to an emergency. As they read about the three "Cs" in Lesson 1, direct them to record notes under the appropriate tab.

Key to Symbols

  Transparencies   `REVIEW` activities to review or reinforce content

 CD-ROM   `TEACH` activities to teach basic concepts

glencoe.com   `EXTEND` activities to extend or enrich lesson content

 Print Resources

First Aid and Emergencies

Chapter Overview

Chapter 27 describes how to perform first-aid procedures for common medical emergencies. Preparing for severe weather and natural disasters are also discussed.

Lesson 1

Immediately responding to an emergency with the appropriate first-aid treatment can mean the difference between life and death.

Lesson 2

The most urgent medical emergencies are those in which the victim is unresponsive or has stopped breathing.

Lesson 3

The most common medical emergencies, such as muscle and bone injuries, impaired consciousness, animal bites, nosebleeds, and poisoning, are treated with standard first-aid procedures.

Lesson 4

Paying attention to weather warnings, following safety guidelines, and knowing what to expect are the best defenses against severe storms and natural disasters.

▶ **Activating Prior Knowledge**

After students have written their paragraphs, invite them to share with the class their reasons for taking a first-aid class. Poll the class to find out if any students have taken a first-aid class. Ask those students to explain why they took the class and whether or not they have used their first-aid skills.

Lesson 1

Providing First Aid

BIG Idea *Knowing how to perform first aid can save a life in an emergency.*

Lesson 2

CPR and First Aid for Shock and Choking

BIG Idea *Medical emergencies that are life threatening include loss of breathing, shock, and choking.*

Lesson 3

Responding to Other Common Emergencies

BIG Idea *You can use first aid to deal with common emergencies such as muscle and bone injuries, impaired consciousness, animal bites, nosebleeds, and poisoning.*

Lesson 4

Emergency Preparedness

BIG Idea *Planning ahead and knowing what to expect can help you survive severe weather and natural disasters.*

Activating Prior Knowledge

Using Visuals Look at the picture on this page. What skills is this teen learning? How could these skills help protect the teen's health and the health of others? Write a paragraph explaining why this teen decided to take this class.

756

Universal Access

Differentiated Learning Glencoe provides teacher support and student materials for all learners in the health classroom.

- Chapter Summaries in English and Spanish are available online at **glencoe.com**.

- *Fast Files* and related worksheets support reluctant readers.

- Universal Access strategies throughout the Teacher Wraparound Edition and *Fast Files* help you present materials for gifted students, at-risk students, physically impaired students, and those with behavior disorders or learning disabilities.

Chapter Launchers

Health in Action

Discuss the **BIG** Ideas

Before beginning this chapter, think about how you would answer these questions:

▶ When was the last time you or someone who was with you suffered an injury?

▶ How did you respond to the injury when it happened?

Watch the *Health* eSpotlight Video Series

Be Prepared

Knowing first aid can help save lives. Have you ever had to use first aid on yourself or a friend to treat an injury?

Assess Your Health

Go Online

Visit **glencoe.com** and complete the Health Inventory for Chapter 27.

Chapter 27   First Aid and Emergencies   **757**

CHAPTER 27

Chapter Launchers

Health in Action

Discuss the **BIG** Ideas

Assign this activity before students read the chapter. Explain that the purpose of the questions is to help students assess their current knowledge of first aid and emergencies.

Health eSpotlight
Video Series

    Be Prepared

Before Viewing the Video

Ask Students: *Have you ever been in a situation where someone, or maybe you, required first aid?* (Students' answers will vary.) After students have watched the video, ask if anyone is interested in learning CPR.

Go Online

Have students go to **glencoe.com** and take the Health Inventory for Chapter 27.

Chapter Skills

Reading Skills

- Reviewing Facts and Vocabulary, pp. 763, 770, 777, 783
- Reading/Writing Practice, p. 789

Vocabulary

- New Vocabulary, pp. 758, 764, 771, 778
- Reviewing Facts and Vocabulary, pp. 763, 770, 777, 783

BIG Idea

Knowing how to perform first aid can save a life in an emergency.

Health Skills

- Health Skills Activity, p. 766
- Applying Health Skills, pp. 763, 770, 777, 783

Writing Skills

- Real World Connection, p. 783
- Writing Critically, pp. 763, 770, 777, 783
- Reading/Writing Practice, p. 789

757

LESSON 1

Providing First Aid

1 FOCUS

GUIDE TO READING

BIG Idea Knowing how to perform first aid can save a life in an emergency. **Ask Students:** *Have you ever known someone who has needed first aid?* (Answers will vary.)

Before You Read

Comparison Chart Students' charts should include information from this lesson.

Main Idea

First Steps in an Emergency
Check, call, and *care* are the three steps for responding to an emergency. **Ask Students:** *Why should a rescuer check the scene of an emergency before caring for injured victims?* (To protect the rescuer from getting injured when entering the scene)

Real Life Issues ··············

Before students begin writing, discuss what Eva should do. **Ask Students:** *What might have happened to the woman if Eva had not stopped?* (Accept any logical responses.) After students complete this lesson, have them review the conclusion they wrote for the scenario and make changes to it based on what they learned.

758

LESSON 1

GUIDE TO READING

BIG Idea *Knowing how to perform first aid can save a life in an emergency.*

Before You Read

Create a Comparison Chart. Divide a sheet of paper into three columns. Label the columns "First Steps," "Bleeding," and "Burns." As you read, fill in information about each topic.

First Steps	Bleeding	Burns

New Vocabulary

▸ first aid (p. 758)
▸ Good Samaritan laws (p. 759)
▸ universal precautions (p. 759)

Providing First Aid

Real Life Issues ··············

Helping Out a Stranger. Eva was driving in her neighborhood when she saw someone lying by the side of the road. She pulled over and got out of her car. The person was a woman wearing a bicycle helmet. An overturned bike was lying nearby. Cautiously, Eva touched her shoulder. "Hey, are you okay?" she asked. "Can you move?" The woman responded with a muffled groan.

Writing *Write a conclusion to this story that shows how Eva responded to this emergency and what effect her actions had on herself and on the stranger she helped.*

First Steps in an Emergency

Main Idea The three steps for responding to an emergency are *check, call,* and *care.*

If you ever find yourself in an emergency—like a car crash, a hurricane, or even a terrorist attack—would you know what to do? In a situation like this, knowing first aid could save someone's life. **First aid** is *the immediate, temporary care given to an ill or injured person until professional medical care can be provided.* In the seconds and minutes right after an emergency strikes, first aid can mean the difference between life and death. By learning and using proper first-aid procedures, you can help prevent victims from suffering further injury and reduce the number of victims who die.

Recognizing an emergency is the first step in responding to it. The next step is to check the scene to make sure it's safe for you to respond. Look out for hazards such as downed electrical lines or oncoming traffic that might put your own life at risk if you approach. Remember, you can't help the other person if you become injured yourself. Once you've determined that the scene is safe, you can follow the three Cs of emergency care.

◢ Promoting School Wellness

First Aid at School Make students aware of the health services provided for students at your school. Describe to students the role of the school nurse. The school nurse will most likely provide emergency care for illnesses and injuries, as well as monitor student vaccination records and track student absences. Find out if anyone in your school, besides the school nurse, is a certified first-responder to a medical emergency. Let students know that a certified first-responder is anyone who has completed 40 to 60 hours of training in providing care for medical emergencies. Inform students of these staff members and encourage them to notify one of these staff members in an emergency.

The three Cs include these steps:

- **Check** the victim. A victim who is unconscious or has a life-threatening condition (for example, someone who is not breathing) needs immediate care. Only move the victim if he or she is in direct physical danger or if you must move the victim in order to provide lifesaving care.

- **Call** 911 or your local emergency number. If the victim is in need of immediate care, get someone else at the scene to call 911 while you provide first aid. If no one else is present, make the call yourself. Emergency operators may be able to talk you through the steps of helping the victim. Stay on the line until help arrives.

- **Care** for the victim. If possible, get the victim's permission before giving first aid. If the victim refuses help, respect this decision. However, if the victim can't speak to give permission, don't hesitate to provide care. Most states have **Good Samaritan laws**—*statutes that protect rescuers from being sued for giving emergency care.*

Universal Precautions

One risk of giving first aid is that blood and other body fluids can carry pathogens, including the viruses that cause AIDS and hepatitis B. Health care workers follow **universal precautions**—*steps taken to prevent the spread of disease through blood and other body fluids when providing first aid or health care.* These steps require people who provide first aid or medical care to treat all body fluids as if they could carry disease. Universal precautions include

- wearing sterile gloves whenever you could come into contact with someone's blood or body fluids.
- washing hands immediately after providing first aid.
- using a mouthpiece, if one is available, when providing rescue breathing (see Lesson 2).

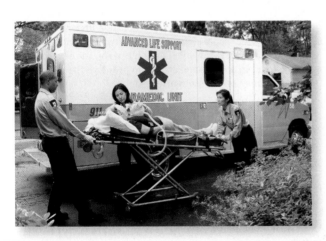

■ **Figure 27.1** Although first aid can help keep a victim alive, it is still important to call emergency services and get the victim professional medical care. *What is the number for emergency services in your area?*

Lesson 1 Providing First Aid **759**

READING CHECK

Identify What are the three Cs of emergency care?

② TEACH

R Reading Strategy

Sequencing Work with students to make a flowchart that shows the steps in responding to an emergency. Students should include "checking the scene" as the first step after recognizing that an emergency has occurred. Students can augment their flowcharts with drawings or explanatory phrases to clarify meaning. Encourage students to add to their flowcharts relevant information from the lessons that follow. **BL** **EL**

READING CHECK

Answer Check the scene and the victim, call 911, and provide care until medical help arrives.

C Critical Thinking

Inferring Have students describe three universal precautions taken by health care workers to prevent the spread of disease. Then ask students to explain how these universal precautions work to prevent the spread of disease. Students may say that sterile gloves and the rescue-breathing mouthpiece act as barriers to keep germs away from the rescuer. Washing with soap and water kills germs. **OL**

Caption Answer

Figure 27.1 Although most areas use 911 for emergency services, some do not. Check your local telephone directory.

Cooperative Learning

Enacting the Emergency Response
Direct groups of four to write the script for a short skit that describes an emergency situation and the appropriate emergency response. Before students perform their skits for the class, review their scripts for the correct use of the three "Cs" of emergency care, as well as universal precautions. If you wish, have groups perform their skits at the end of the chapter after they have added relevant first-aid procedures they will learn in subsequent lessons.

First Aid for Bleeding Treatment for bleeding depends on the kind of injury and how severe it is. **Ask Students:** *What makes some wounds more severe than others?* (Sample answer: More severe wounds are deeper and bleed more heavily.)

U Universal Access

Cooperative Learning Pair English language learners with English proficient students and have them create information cards for each type of open wound. Information cards should include the type of wound, an illustration, and simple words to describe the wound. Students can later add to these cards the appropriate first-aid treatments for each wound. **EL** **BL**

HS Health Skills Practice

Practicing Healthful Behaviors Supply student pairs with gauze pads, gauze strips, protective gloves, and access to soap and water. Direct students to take turns administering first aid to an imaginary open wound on the lower arm of their partner. Students should wash the wound with soap and running water, elevate the arm, cover the wound with sterile gauze and apply pressure. After students become proficient, have them treat the wound as if it will not stop bleeding. Make sure they continue placing gauze pads on the wound without removing the one below until the bleeding stops. **OL**

Academic Vocabulary

Minor Explan that the word *minor* is based on the Latin *minuere,* meaning smaller or inferior. Show students pictures of various injuries and have them classify them as either minor or serious.

760

Academic Vocabulary

minor *(adjective):* not serious or involving risk to life

First Aid for Bleeding

Main Idea The steps for treating bleeding depend on the type of injury and how severe it is.

Minor injuries that cause bleeding, such as small cuts and scrapes, can usually be treated at home. Severe bleeding, however, can be a life-threatening emergency. The appropriate first aid for bleeding depends on what type of wound you are dealing with and how severe the bleeding is.

Types of Open Wounds

Open wounds are injuries in which the skin is broken. Types of open wounds include the following:

- **Abrasions,** also known as scrapes. These occur when the skin is scraped against a hard surface, bursting the tiny blood vessels in the outer layer of skin. The chief danger with this type of wound is that dirt and bacteria can penetrate the skin. It's important to clean the wound well to prevent infection and speed healing.

- **Lacerations.** These are cuts caused by a sharp object slicing through layers of skin. Minor lacerations can be treated at home, but medical care is needed for deep cuts, cuts that won't stop bleeding, and cuts on the face and neck. These wounds may require stitches. A tetanus booster may also be needed.

- **Punctures.** A puncture wound is a small but deep hole caused by a sharp and narrow object (such as a nail) that pierces the skin. Puncture wounds do not usually cause heavy bleeding, but they do carry a high risk of infection, including tetanus infection. If a puncture wound is deep, dirty, or in the foot, see a doctor. The victim may need a tetanus shot or booster.

- **Avulsions.** An avulsion occurs when skin or tissue is partly or completely torn away. Such wounds usually require stitches. If a body part, such as a finger, is partly or completely separated from the body, seek emergency medical care right away. If possible, wrap the severed body part in a cold, moist towel to preserve the tissue; doctors may be able to reattach it.

U

Controlling Bleeding

When treating an open wound on someone other than yourself, wear clean protective gloves. If medical help is needed, call 911 before taking any other steps. Next, wash the wound thoroughly with mild soap and running water to remove dirt and debris.

HS

👥 Home and Community

Emergency Telephone Numbers Give student index cards and telephone directories. Have them find the emergency telephone numbers for the emergency organizations in the area, such as the police or sheriff's department, the fire department, ambulance or emergency medical service, and the poison control center, as well as the family doctor, dentist, and counselor. Have students record these emergency contacts on their index cards and post the cards near a telephone at home. Also encourage students to program these telephone numbers into their cell phones.

Follow these steps to control the bleeding:

- If possible, raise the wounded body part above the level of the heart.
- Cover the wound with sterile gauze or a clean cloth.
- Press the palm of your hand firmly against the gauze. Apply steady pressure to the wound for five minutes or until help arrives. Do not stop to check the wound; you may interrupt the clotting of the blood.
- If blood soaks through the gauze, add another gauze pad on top of the first and continue to apply pressure.
- Once the bleeding slows or stops, **secure** the pad firmly in place with a bandage, strips of gauze, or other material. The pad should be snug, but not so tight that you can't feel the victim's pulse.
- If you can't stop the bleeding after five minutes, or if the wound starts bleeding again, call for medical help (if you have not done so already). Continue to apply pressure to the wound until help arrives.

Academic Vocabulary

secure *(verb):* to make firm or to fasten

TEENS — Making a Difference

Becoming a First Responder

Timothy E., from Texas, learned about first aid at a young age. "When I was 6 or 7 years old, my older brother was hit by a drunk driver. His legs were broken and he was unconscious. I held him in my lap and kept his head elevated until help came."

The experience later motivated Timothy to attend Teen CERT (Community Emergency Response Team) and become trained as a first responder. He learned how to protect himself and others in emergency situations. He also received special training in assisting physically and mentally challenged students.

Timothy is glad that he's trained to be a first responder. "I don't think about how big the responsibility is. I want to do what I can for my family, school, and community."

"I want to do what I can."

Activity Write your answers to the following questions in your personal health journal.

1. What motivated Timothy to become a first responder?
2. What skills did he gain by attending Teen CERT?
3. What training would you need to respond to the kinds of emergencies that could occur in your town or school?

Academic Integration

Science Blood contains several specialized cells and proteins that work together to form the clots that stop wounds from bleeding. Platelets, which form in the bone marrow, are tiny oval-shaped cells that collect at breaks in capillaries (the smallest blood vessels) to block the flow of blood. Set up several microscopes with prepared slides of red blood cells, platelets, and bone marrow. Have students compare and contrast the size and shape of red blood cells and platelets. Encourage them to make inferences about the size and shape of platelets and how they work to form blood clots.

W Writing Support

Writing a Rap Have student groups write a rap that describes the steps in controlling bleeding. Raps should also explain what to do if the wound does not stop bleeding and when to call for emergency medical help. Have students perform their rap for the class and have the class rate the raps. Arrange for the three best raps to be performed for physical education classes or students in middle school or elementary school. **OL**

TEENS Making a Difference

Answers to Activity Questions

1. He was motivated because his older brother was hit by a drunk driver.
2. He became trained as a first responder and learned how to protect himself and others in emergency situations. He also received special training in assisting physically and mentally challenged students.
3. Answers will vary.

Academic Vocabulary

Secure After reviewing the meaning of *secure* as it is used here, begin a list of actions in which an object is secured. (For example, locking the door, tying shoelaces, and taping a box closed.) Discuss what happens if something is not secure.

Main Idea

First Aid for Burns Minor burns receive different first-aid treatment than severe burns. **Ask Students:** *How is a severe burn treated differently than a minor burn?* (Severe burns require immediate medical care. A large burn should not be immersed in cold water; the victim could go into shock. The burned area should be covered with a clean, moist cloth, but burned clothing should not be removed.)

✔ **READING CHECK**

Answer Blood from a damaged blood vessel spilling into a body cavity

AL Active Learning

Burn Prevention Many young children are burned because they do not know which objects are hot and which are not. Their skin is also more sensitive to heat than adult skin. Have students work in small groups to develop a brochure that gives tips for preventing burns. Suggest that they target this brochure to teens who babysit or to new parents. **OL**

R Reading Strategy

Classifying Have students look at the photographs of burns in **Figure 27.2**. Ask them to explain how burns are classified. (Burns are classified by the amount of tissue that is burned.) Lead a discussion on how each type of burn differs by asking such questions as what layers of skin are involved and what the skin looks like. Emphasize the characteristics of burns that indicate increasing severity, such as the appearance of blisters or charred skin. Then have students match the types of burns with the appropriate first-aid treatment described in the text. **OL**

✔ **READING CHECK**
Explain What is internal bleeding?

Certain types of injuries can cause internal bleeding—blood from a damaged blood vessel entering one of the body's cavities. Internal bleeding is difficult to detect. However, bleeding from the eyes, nose, mouth, or ears may be a sign that internal bleeding is occurring. Internal bleeding requires emergency care, so call for help right away. While waiting for help to arrive, you can take steps to prevent the victim from going into shock (see Lesson 2).

First Aid for Burns

Main Idea Treatment for burns depends on the severity of the burn.

Burns can occur in a variety of ways. Burns caused by heat are the most common type. They may occur as a result of exposure to flame, touching a hot object such as a stove, scalding with hot water or steam, or overexposure to the sun. Burns can also result from exposure to electricity and to certain chemicals, such as bleach. Electrical and chemical burns require special first-aid procedures. **AL**

Figure 27.2 **Types of Burns**

Burns are classified according to the amount of damage they cause.

First-degree burns involve only the outer layer of skin. This outermost layer is called the epidermis. In a first-degree burn, the skin becomes red, and the burned area may become swollen and painful. First-degree burns are considered minor burns unless they involve a major joint or cover large areas of the hands, feet, face, groin, or buttocks.

Second-degree burns involve the epidermis and the underlying layers of skin (the dermis). The skin becomes very red and develops blisters. There is severe pain and swelling. A second-degree burn no larger than 2 to 3 inches in diameter can be treated as a minor burn. Larger burns, or burns that affect the hands, feet, face, groin, buttocks, or a major joint, require professional medical care.

Third-degree burns, the most serious kind, involve all layers of the skin and may penetrate the underlying tissues. The skin may be charred black or may appear white and dry. It may also be possible to see muscle and even bone. These burns can destroy nerve endings, so victims may not experience pain. Third-degree burns require immediate medical attention.

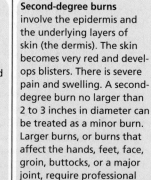

R

Myths & Reality

Treating Wounds and Burns

Myth: Applying hydrogen peroxide to a wound will prevent infection and promote healing.

Fact: Hydrogen peroxide kills everything, including the body's immune cells, and can actually delay healing.

Myth: Putting butter on a burn will help it heal.

Fact: Butter may actually seal in the heat and make a burn feel worse. Butter can also trap germs in the burned skin, increasing the likelihood of infection.

Figure 27.2 shows how to distinguish the different types of burns. First-degree burns and small second-degree burns are considered minor and can be treated with these steps:

1. Cool the burned area by holding it under cold, running water for at least five minutes. If this isn't possible, immerse the burned area in cool water or wrap it in cold, wet cloths. Do not use ice, which may cause frostbite and further damage the skin.
2. Cover the burn loosely with a sterile gauze bandage.
3. The victim may take an over-the-counter pain reliever. Make sure the victim isn't allergic to the medication.
4. Minor burns usually heal without further treatment, though the skin may be discolored. If signs of infection develop—including increased pain, redness, fever, swelling, or oozing—seek medical help.

Some second-degree burns and all third-degree burns require immediate medical care. Call 911 and provide first aid until help arrives. Cover the burned area with a clean, moist cloth, but do not remove burned clothing unless it is still smoldering. Do not immerse a large burned area in cold water; the victim could go into shock. Be prepared to give first aid for shock or loss of circulation (see Lesson 2).

 READING CHECK

Classify Which kind of burn always requires professional medical care?

 **LESSON 1**

 READING CHECK

Answer Third-degree burns

3 ASSESS/ CLOSE

Assessment Resources

📁 *FAST FILE* **ACTIVITIES**
Lesson 1 Quiz

💿 *ExamView*
Assessment Suite CD-ROM

Visit glencoe.com for:
Online Quizzes
Online Learning Center

Progress Monitoring

Reteaching
Have pairs of students make a chart that organizes types of open wounds and burns and the appropriate first-aid treatment for each. Students should include a brief description of each type of wound and burn.

Enrichment
Have students develop a First Steps in an Emergency poster for display in their school. Students' posters should include the three steps: check, call, care.

LESSON 1 📖 **ASSESSMENT**

After You Read

Reviewing Facts and Vocabulary
1. What are the three first steps for responding to an emergency?
2. Identify the four types of open wounds.
3. Describe the procedure for treating a minor burn.

Thinking Critically
4. **Synthesize.** Suppose that you are looking after your seven-year-old neighbor. The boy steps on a tack and gets a puncture wound in his foot. How would you respond?
5. **Evaluate.** Which types of open wounds are most likely to require professional medical care? Why?

Applying Health Skills
6. **Advocacy.** Write a persuasive flyer designed to encourage other teens to learn first aid. Your flyer should explain the value of knowing first aid and the situations in which it can be useful.

Writing Critically
7. **Narrative.** Write a short story in which a teen responds to a medical emergency and provides appropriate first aid.

 Go Online

Visit **glencoe.com** and complete the Interactive Study Guide for this lesson.

LESSON 1 ASSESSMENT ANSWERS

1. Check, call, care
2. Abrasions, lacerations, punctures, and avulsions
3. Cool the burn with cold water, cover it with a sterile bandage, and give an over-the-counter pain reliever.
4. Wash the wound with soap and water, then call a doctor. The victim might need a tetanus shot.

5. Puncture wounds because of the risk of infection, and deep lacerations and avulsions because stitches are usually required
6. Flyers will vary.
7. Short stories will vary.

Go Online

Have students visit **glencoe.com** and complete the Interactive Study Guide for this lesson.

LESSON 2

CPR and First Aid for Shock and Choking

① FOCUS

GUIDE TO READING

BIG Idea Students will learn the first-aid responses to loss of breathing, shock, and choking. **Ask Students:** *How can you tell if a person is choking?* (The person cannot breathe and is not coughing, and might be clutching his or her throat.)

Before You Read

Organize Information
Students should list, in order, the steps of the first-aid procedures for CPR, shock, and choking as described in the lesson.

Main Idea

The Chain of Survival A sequence of specific actions could save the life of a person experiencing a medical emergency. **Ask Students:** *When you check the victim of a medical emergency and find that he or she is unresponsive, what do you think you should do?* (Answers will vary but might include calling 911.)

Real Life Issues ....

Discuss the importance of taking a CPR class. **Ask Students:** *When would it be useful to know how to perform CPR and other first-aid procedures?*

764

GUIDE TO READING

BIG Idea *Medical emergencies that are life threatening include loss of breathing, shock, and choking.*

Before You Read

Organize Information. Make a three-column chart. Label the columns "CPR," "First Aid for Shock," and "First Aid for Choking." As you read, fill in the appropriate columns with the steps in each first-aid procedure.

CPR	Shock	Choking

New Vocabulary

▶ chain of survival (p. 764)
▶ defibrillator (p. 765)
▶ cardiopulmonary resuscitation (CPR) (p. 765)
▶ rescue breathing (p. 767)
▶ shock (p. 770)

CPR and First Aid for Shock and Choking

Real Life Issues ....

Learning CPR. When Ally saw the poster advertising CPR classes at the local Y, she felt torn. She knows CPR is useful to learn and could save someone's life in an emergency. The trouble is, her schedule is already busy. Between homework, sports, and looking after her little brother on weekends, she doesn't see how she could squeeze in one more class. Is learning CPR important enough to take the place of another activity?

Writing *Write a paragraph explaining how Ally might make time for the CPR class.*

The Chain of Survival

Main Idea In a medical emergency, a victim's life depends on a specific series of actions called the *chain of survival.*

The most urgent medical emergencies are often those in which the victim is unresponsive, or unable to speak or react to his or her surroundings. This condition can result from a heart attack, a stroke, or cardiac arrest. In this type of emergency, you need to act quickly, because the first few minutes after a medical crisis are usually the most critical. The key is to know what to do, remain calm, and take action.

An unresponsive victim is in immediate danger. Her or his best hope lies in the **chain of survival**, *a sequence of actions that maximize the victim's chances of survival.*

Skills for the 21st Century

First Aid and Social Responsibility
Once a person has learned first aid, he or she has a responsibility to respond to any victim of a medical emergency. Impress upon your students that first aid is a life skill that all socially responsible people should learn. Make available first-aid class list-

ings throughout the school year. Organize first-aid classes to be held after school or at other times convenient to students. Consider rewards of extra credit or a "free test" to those students who take classes to become certified in first aid.

The links in the chain of survival include the following:

- **A call to emergency medical services.** This first step is important for all victims. The 911 operator will ask you questions about the victim's condition and instruct you on what to do next. If the victim's heart has stopped, you will be instructed to move on to the next link in the chain of survival.

- **CPR,** or cardiopulmonary resuscitation. CPR gives the victim a chance to survive until medical help arrives.

- **Defibrillation.** A **defibrillator** is *a device that delivers an electric shock to the heart to restore its normal rhythm.* An increasing number of public places now provide automated external defibrillators (AEDs).

- **Advanced care.** Paramedics and other trained medical personnel can provide the care needed to keep the victim alive on the way to the hospital.

CPR

Main Idea CPR can save the life of a person whose heartbeat or breathing has stopped.

The second link in the chain of survival is to perform CPR on the victim. CPR, or **cardiopulmonary resuscitation**, is *a first-aid procedure that combines rescue breathing and chest compressions to supply oxygen to the body until normal body functions can resume.* It takes training from a certified professional to learn how to perform CPR correctly. However, if no trained person is present, it's better to have CPR done by an untrained person than to wait for paramedics to arrive. Giving CPR as soon as possible is a crucial link in the chain of survival. In some parts of the country, 911 dispatchers are taught how to talk an untrained person through the steps of CPR.

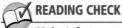

Figure 27.3 The increased availability of AEDs has improved the survival rate for victims of cardiac arrest. *What is the next step after defibrillation in the chain of survival?*

READING CHECK

Make Inferences
What is the purpose of the chain of survival?

Go Online

Go to **glencoe.com** and complete the Student Web Activity on the chain of survival and treatment of common medical emergencies.

Caption Answer

Figure 27.3 Advanced care

READING CHECK

Answer To maximize the victim's chance of survival

Main Idea

CPR CPR can save the life of a person whose heartbeat or breathing has stopped. **Ask Students:** *What should you always do before performing CPR on adult?* (Check to see if the adult is conscious and breathing.)

AL Active Learning

Demonstration Invite a certified CPR trainer to the class to give a demonstration on CPR. Ask the trainer to bring along training mannequins so that students can practice the technique after the demonstration. Also have the trainer emphasize the importance of knowing CPR and encourage students to enroll in a first-aid class. Ask the trainer to share a listing of upcoming classes. The trainer should also explain that CPR should not be performed on a person with a heartbeat because it will make the heart beat irregularly. **OL**

C Critical Thinking

Inferring Have students read the paragraph about CPR. Ask students to infer what happens when the chest is compressed during CPR. (Blood is forced out of the heart and into the vessels.) Then ask them what happens when the pressure on the chest is released. (Blood flows back into the heart.) **AL**

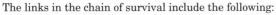

ELL Support

Interpreting *Chain of Survival* **As with many English words, the word** *chain* **has many different meanings. The most common is "a series of joined metal rings." Other meanings include businesses under one ownership, a series of geographical formations, and a sequence of related events or facts.**

Beginning Have students diagram the chain of survival as a chain with links representing each step. Students can use diagrams to illustrate each step.

Intermediate Have students use short phrases to describe each step.

Advanced Have students write a sentence that describes each step.

765

Health Skills Activity

Communication Skills: Calling Emergency Services

NHES Standard 4 Students will demonstrate the ability to use interpersonal communication skills to enhance health and avoid or reduce health risks.

Objectives

- Analyze strategies for responding to a medical emergency.
- Demonstrate interpersonal communication skills to call for emergency medical help.

Teaching Strategies

- Invite the class to suggest questions that the 911 dispatcher would ask Kenji about the victim. List these questions on the board.
- Review the steps in the chain of survival. Relate these steps to the scenario and encourage students to incorporate them into their dialogues.

Assessment

Using a rubric, student work should provide comprehensive evidence of the following criteria to achieve the highest score:

√ Demonstrates an accurate interpretation of first-aid responses

√ Creates a dialogue with clear and concise questions and answers

Health Skills Activity

Communication Skills

Calling Emergency Services

Kenji is at the mall when he sees another shopper suddenly clutch his chest and collapse. Kenji checks the victim and realizes that he has lost consciousness. Grabbing his cell phone, he dials 911 as a crowd gathers. The 911 dispatcher asks, "What is your emergency?" and "Where are you calling from?" Kenji struggles to stay calm as he answers the questions. He knows that the victim's life depends on it.

Writing Write a dialogue in which Kenji responds to the 911 dispatcher's questions. Follow these guidelines:

1. Listen carefully to the questions.
2. Respond clearly and concisely, providing only the requested information.
3. Follow the dispatcher's instructions, or repeat them exactly to other rescuers. Confirm that other rescuers are following the instructions.
4. Stay on the line until instructed to hang up.

CPR for Adults

Before performing CPR on an adult, check to see if the person is conscious. Tap the victim on the shoulder while shouting, "Are you okay?" If the victim doesn't respond, start the chain of survival by calling 911. Then begin performing the steps for CPR shown in **Figure 27.4**.

CPR for Infants and Children

If the victim is an infant or a young child (under eight years old), the cycle of CPR is still 30 chest compressions for every two rescue breaths. However, the procedure is different in several ways:

- Check to see if the child is breathing *before* calling 911. If the child is not breathing, give five cycles of CPR—about two minutes' worth—before making the call.
- When performing rescue breathing on a baby, place your mouth over the baby's nose and mouth at the same time—not the mouth only, as for an adult.
- Do not use a face mask designed for adult CPR when performing CPR on an infant.

> **READING CHECK**
>
> *Compare and Contrast* List three ways in which CPR for infants differs from CPR for adults.

Teens Want to Know

Can I Get an Infection from the Victim When Performing Rescue Breaths? There is always the possibility of getting an infection while giving rescue breaths, especially if the victim has a respiratory virus such as the cold or flu. The American Red Cross has made a pocket mask available to use as a barrier for rescue breaths. Getting a blood-borne infection is more unusual, unless the victim is bleeding from the mouth. If this is the case, do not give rescue breaths without a protective barrier such as the pocket mask. People certified in CPR often carry a kit with clean gloves, gauze, hand sanitizer, and a pocket mask to protect their own health when giving first aid.

Figure 27.4   Adult CPR

The basic cycle of CPR for adults alternates two rescue breaths with 30 chest compressions.

Check to see if the victim is breathing. Look, listen, and feel for normal breathing for five to ten seconds. Signs of normal breathing include

▶ seeing the person's chest rise and fall.

▶ hearing breathing sounds, including wheezing, gurgling, or snoring.

▶ feeling air moving out of the person's mouth or nose.

W

If you cannot detect signs of breathing, begin **rescue breathing**, or *breathing for a person who is not breathing on his or her own.* Follow these steps:

1. Tilt the victim's chin upward to open the airway. Then, pinch the victim's nose shut with your thumb and forefinger.

2. If you have a sterile breathing mask available, place it securely over the victim's mouth and nose. Then take a breath and place your mouth over the opening in the mask. If you do not have a mask, take a breath and place your mouth over the victim's mouth, forming a tight seal.

3. Exhale for one second and watch to see if the victim's chest rises.

4. Remove your mouth from the person's mouth and take another breath. Allow the victim's chest to fall, and feel the air escape. Then give the victim a second breath.

U

After giving two rescue breaths, begin chest compressions. To position your hands correctly, follow these steps:

1. Use your fingers to find the end of the victim's sternum (breastbone), where the ribs come together.

2. Place two fingers over the end of the sternum.

3. Place the heel of your other hand against the sternum, directly above your fingers (on the side closest to the victim's face).

4. Place your other hand on top of the one you just put in position. Interlock the fingers of your hands and raise your fingers so they do not touch the person's chest.

HS

Perform chest compressions using the following procedure:

1. Straighten your arms, lock your elbows, and line your shoulders up so they are directly above your hands.

2. Press downward on the person's chest, forcing the breastbone down by 1.5 to 2 inches (3.8 to 5 cm).

3. Begin compressions at a steady pace. You can maintain a rhythm by counting, "One and two and three and . . ." Press down each time you say a number.

4. After performing 30 compressions, give two more rescue breaths.

5. Repeat the cycle of 30 compressions and two breaths until the victim breathes, coughs, or moves, or until professional rescuers arrive to take over.

Lesson 2   CPR and First Aid for Shock and Choking   **767**

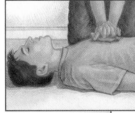

W **Writing Support**

Checklist Direct students to write a checklist summarizing the steps listed in **Figure 27.4** for rescue breathing. Remind students to include what to do before beginning rescue breathing. **OL**

U **Universal Access**

Modeling Use a skeleton model or a poster of one to demonstrate how to correctly position the hands for CPR. Point out the location of the sternum on the model and encourage students to locate the end of their own sternum. Place your two fingers over the end of the sternum on the model to show students how to place their hands properly. Point out the ribs and caution students to avoid pushing on them. Then invite students to practice positioning their hands correctly on the model. **BL**

HS **Health Skills Practice**

Practicing Healthful Behaviors Demonstrate how to self-administer abdominal thrusts by pressing your fist into your upper abdomen and giving yourself quick, upward and inward thrusts. Do not use any force behind these thrusts while demonstrating. Then demonstrate how to use the back of a chair or a countertop to move your abdomen upward and inward. Then encourage students to try this maneuver themselves. Strongly caution students not to use any force behind the thrusts. **OL**

Reading Strategy

Using Visuals Infographics, or illustrations combined with captions that organize information, are useful tools to summarize concepts. However, some students might skip over infographics while reading because the information is separated from the main body of the text. As students read, direct them to pay careful attention to the information in the infographics on these pages. Have them create their own flowcharts to sequence the steps and procedures in performing CPR.

R Reading Strategy

Using Visuals Have students examine **Figure 27.5** and compare the position of the hands and fingers in CPR for an infant and a child. Ask students to describe the position of the hands when performing CPR on an infant. (The fingers are placed just below the nipples.) Then have students describe how the hands are positioned for CPR on a child. (The heel of one hand or two is used depending on the size of the child.) **BL**

Academic Vocabulary

Survival Illustrate the meaning of this term by drawing a time line for a living thing that begins with birth. Explain that *survival* does not describe the beginning of life, but its continuation. Draw the line longer and explain that the survival of the living thing continues as long as the living thing is alive. Its survival ends with death. Then ask students to explain how first aid is important for survival.

Main Idea

Other Emergencies Choking and shock are life-threatening medical emergencies that require medical attention. **Ask Students:** *Why is CPR not required to treat a person who is choking or a victim in shock?* (Rescue breathing will not help a choking person because the airway is blocked. CPR will not help a victim in shock because the heart is still beating.)

768

Figure 27.5 | **Infant and Child CPR**

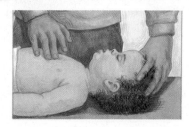

R

▶ This image shows how to position your fingers to perform chest compressions on an infant.

▶ This image shows how to position your hands for chest compressions on a child between one and eight years old.

- To perform chest compressions on an infant, position your fingers on the baby's sternum. Press the sternum down about one-third to one-half the depth of the baby's chest.

- To perform chest compressions on a child between one and eight years old, you can either use the heel of one hand or use both hands as in adult CPR. Position your hands about two finger widths above the end of the sternum, and press the sternum down about one-third to one-half the depth of the child's chest.

Figure 27.5 illustrates how to position your hands when performing CPR on an infant or a child.

Other Emergencies

Main Idea Choking and shock are life-threatening medical emergencies that require immediate attention.

Academic Vocabulary

survival *(noun):* the continuation of life or existence

The chain of **survival** does not apply to every medical emergency. If a person is choking, for example, rescue breathing will not help because the airway is blocked. Knowing the specific first-aid procedures for choking and shock can save lives in a medical emergency.

First Aid for Choking

Choking occurs when an object, such as a piece of food, becomes stuck in a person's windpipe, cutting off the flow of air. Clutching the throat is the universal sign for choking. Other signs of choking include an inability to speak, difficulty breathing, an inability to cough forcefully, turning blue in the face or lips, and loss of consciousness.

More About...

Infant CPR The chain of survival is slightly different for infants and children under the age of 8 who are not breathing. If the child is not breathing, about 2 minutes of CPR is performed before calling for emergency medical help. CPR is given immediately because a child's heart is probably still beating even though the child has stopped breathing. By beginning CPR before calling for medical help, the child will most likely start breathing again before the heart stops beating.

U If you see these signs in an adult, help the person immediately by performing abdominal thrusts. If someone else is nearby, ask that person to call 911 while you help the victim. For a choking infant, perform back blows and chest thrusts to dislodge the object. **Figure 27.6** illustrates these procedures.

If the choking victim is unconscious, lower the person to the floor and try to clear the airway. Reach into the mouth and sweep the object out with one finger. Be careful not to push the obstruction deeper into the throat. If the obstruction cannot be dislodged, begin performing CPR. The chest compressions may dislodge the object.

If you begin to choke when you're alone, you can perform abdominal thrusts on yourself by covering your fist with the other hand and pushing upward and inward. Another method is to bend over and position your abdomen over a rigid structure, such as a countertop or the back of a chair. Press against it to thrust your abdomen upward and inward.

 READING CHECK

Explain How can you help a choking adult?

Figure 27.6 Treatment for Choking

AL Use abdominal thrusts on a choking adult. For an infant, alternate back blows with chest thrusts. *Why do you think different methods are used for adults and infants?*

If an adult is choking:

1. Stand behind the victim and wrap your arms around his or her waist. (For a pregnant or obese victim, wrap your arms around the rib cage.)
2. Make a fist with one hand and grasp it with your other hand.
3. Pull your hands into the abdomen with a quick, upward thrust.
4. Repeat the abdominal thrusts until the object is dislodged.

If an infant is choking:

1. Sit down and hold the baby facedown over your forearm, which should be resting on your thigh.
2. With the heel of your hand, give the infant five gentle but firm blows between the shoulder blades.
3. If this doesn't dislodge the object, turn the infant faceup, with the head lower than the body. Perform five chest compressions as you would when performing infant CPR.
4. If the baby still isn't breathing, have someone call emergency services immediately while you repeat the back blows and chest thrusts. If breathing doesn't resume, begin infant CPR.

Lesson 2   CPR and First Aid for Shock and Choking   **769**

Universal Access

Charades Divide the class into small groups, mixing English language learners with English proficient students. Have students play a game of charades in which one student in a group acts out a sign of choking or a symptom of shock. The rest of the group members must guess which medical emergency is being acted out. Before students play the game, instruct them to write the signs of choking and symptoms of shock on slips of paper for the actors to use. Encourage English language learners to write these signs and symptoms in simple terms with the help of English fluent students. **EL**

AL Active Learning

Making a Comic Strip Have students make a comic strip about a person who is either choking or going into shock. Students should clearly describe the signs of choking or the symptoms of shock. They should also illustrate the correct first-aid techniques for the emergency they choose to feature. Encourage students to be both creative and instructional. Display the comic strips in the lunch room or hallways. **OL**

Caption Answer

Figure 27.6 Infants are smaller than adults and require a gentler means of clearing the airway.

 **READING CHECK**

Answer Perform abdominal thrusts and call 911

Writing Strategy

Descriptive Writing Have students write a scenario in which they describe a victim of a medical emergency who has gone into shock. Students should tell what the emergency is and give a detailed description of the symptoms of shock experienced by the victim. Also tell students to describe the first-aid steps the rescuer takes, including the three "Cs," the chain of survival, and treatment for shock.

③ ASSESS/ CLOSE

Assessment Resources

📁 **FAST FILE ACTIVITIES**
Lesson 2 Quiz

💿 *ExamView Assessment Suite* CD-ROM

Visit glencoe.com for:
Online Quizzes
Online Learning Center

Progress Monitoring

Reteaching
Have students write a sentence using each vocabulary term.

Enrichment
Have students produce a video that shows how to perform CPR and the proper first-aid procedures for treating shock and choking.

Go Online

Have students visit glencoe.com and complete the Interactive Study Guide for this lesson.

■ **Figure 27.7** A person suffering from shock should lie down with the legs elevated, unless the person has an injury to the head, neck, legs, or spine. *What purpose might raising the victim's legs serve?*

First Aid for Shock

Shock is *a life-threatening condition in which the heart is not delivering an adequate supply of blood to the body.* Symptoms of shock include

- cold, clammy skin, which may appear pale or grayish.
- weak, rapid pulse and altered breathing.
- dull, staring eyes, which may have dilated pupils.
- faintness, weakness, confusion, or loss of consciousness.

If someone displays these symptoms, call 911 right away. Get the victim to lie down and raise his legs about 12 inches if he is conscious and doesn't have an injury to the head, neck, legs, or spine. If the victim has any wounds or other injuries, give first aid for these while you wait for help. Some shock victims become anxious or agitated, so try to keep the person calm. Monitor the victim's breathing, and be prepared to start CPR immediately if breathing stops. Loosen the victim's clothing and try to keep him warm and comfortable. Don't give the victim anything to eat or drink. If the victim vomits, drools, or starts bleeding from the mouth, roll him into the recovery position (see Lesson 3).

LESSON 2 ASSESSMENT

After You Read

Reviewing Facts and Vocabulary
1. Identify the steps in the chain of survival.
2. What is the basic cycle of CPR?
3. What is the universal sign for choking?

Thinking Critically
4. **Evaluate.** Why is calling emergency services the first step in the chain of survival?
5. **Analyze.** Explain how the strategy for responding to choking differs depending on whether the victim is an adult or an infant.

Applying Health Skills
6. **Accessing Information.** Use community or Internet resources to find out where and when CPR classes are offered in your area. If possible, arrange to take one of these classes.

Writing Critically
7. **Creative.** Write a jingle that uses rhyme and rhythm to help people remember the steps for a first-aid procedure discussed in this lesson.

Go Online

Visit glencoe.com and complete the Interactive Study Guide for this lesson.

LESSON 2 ASSESSMENT ANSWERS

1. Call emergency medical services (911), CPR, defibrillation, and advanced care
2. Two rescue breaths followed by 30 chest compressions
3. Clutching the throat
4. Sample answer: The sooner this call is made, the sooner help will arrive. Without emergency medical services, the unconscious victim may not survive.
5. Abdominal thrusts are used for adults. A combination of back blows and chest thrusts should be used for infants.
6. Times and locations of CPR classes will vary.
7. Jingles will vary.

Responding to Other Common Emergencies

Real Life Issues

Feeling Faint. Kim has been looking forward to the school dance all month. She's so excited on the day of the dance that she forgets to eat lunch. At the dance, she is having a great time out on the hot, crowded dance floor. Then she starts to feel dizzy, and the next thing she knows, she's lying outside on the ground. Looking up, she sees a teacher and a couple of her friends. "You fainted," the teacher explains. "You need to lie still for a while." Kim is embarrassed. She wants to reassure the teacher that she's fine and go back to the dance.

Writing *Write a dialogue between Kim and the teacher. Show how the two of them deal with Kim's situation in a way that protects her health.*

Muscle, Joint, and Bone Injuries

Main Idea Muscle and joint injuries can be minor or severe, but bone injuries are always medical emergencies.

As you learned in Chapter 12, sports and other physical activities can cause injuries to your muscles, joints, and bones. These kinds of injuries can occur in other situations as well. For example, you could sprain your ankle by tripping over a branch on the sidewalk, break your arm in a car crash, or dislocate your shoulder falling from a ladder.

You can take safety precautions to help avoid injuries such as these. However, you still need to be prepared in case accidents happen. That's why you should know the proper first-aid procedures for treating injuries such as strains, sprains, fractures, and dislocations.

GUIDE TO READING

BIG Idea *You can use first aid to deal with common emergencies such as muscle and bone injuries, impaired consciousness, animal bites, nosebleeds, and poisoning.*

Before You Read

Make a T-Chart. On one side of the chart, list common medical emergencies. On the other side, list strategies to deal with each type of emergency.

Emergencies	Strategies

New Vocabulary

▶ fracture (p. 772)
▶ dislocation (p. 772)
▶ unconsciousness (p. 773)
▶ concussion (p. 774)
▶ poison (p. 775)
▶ poison control center (p. 775)
▶ venom (p. 776)

Review Vocabulary

▶ strain (Ch.12, L.4)
▶ sprain (Ch.12, L.4)

Responding to Other Common Emergencies

① FOCUS

GUIDE TO READING

BIG Idea Students will learn the first-aid procedures to treat some common medical emergencies. **Ask Students:** *How have you treated a muscle injury?* (Answers will vary but may include icing or resting it.)

Before You Read
T-Chart Students' T-charts will vary.

Main Idea

Muscle, Joint, and Bone Injuries Unlike injuries to muscles and joints, bone injuries usually require immediate advanced medical care. **Ask Students:** *Why do bone injuries always require advanced medical care?* (A doctor must set the injured bone in the correct position so it will heal properly.)

Real Life Issues

Before students begin writing the dialogue, talk about why Kim fainted (lack of food) and what she needs (juice and food). **Ask Students:** *What do you think Kim should do before returning to the dance floor?* (Drink some juice or eat some food and rest until she no longer feels lightheaded or dizzy.)

Teacher to Teacher

Marsha Morton • Campbell County High School, Jacksboro, TN

First Aid and Emergencies When teaching first aid, CPR, and safety, present the students with real-life scenarios and hold a discussion. Explain different situations, such as car wrecks, choking victims, fires, water safety, and CPR rescue breaths. Ask students what they would do in the different situations. For example, ask, "If you come upon a wreck, would you move the injured victim?" Continue your questions by adding new elements to the scenario. For example, "Would you move the victim if the car was on fire?" Be sure to include questions that will bring out the correct response from students.

② TEACH

AL Active Learning

Demonstration Have small groups plan and organize a demonstration in which they show how to treat a minor strain or sprain using the P.R.I.C.E. procedure. Demonstrations should include an introduction that tells what students will be demonstrating and examples of cases in which the P.R.I.C.E. procedure would be used. After screening the demonstrations, arrange to have students give them to peers in physical education classes. **OL**

R Reading Strategy

Sequencing Have students create a flowchart in which they sequence the first-aid procedure for treating a fracture or dislocation. Whenever there is an optional procedure based on the injury, such as washing an open wound, suggest that students create a fork in the flowchart. **BL**

Number Game Have students form circles in groups of 6–8. Have groups number off from 1 so each is assigned a number.

- Leader (number 1) in each group begins a pattern (i.e., stomp, stomp, clap, clap, snap, snap).
- Students in each group perform the same pattern in unison.
- Leader calls out a number and an action (number 2, snap).
- Number 2 snaps a pattern, then calls another number and an action.
- Continue through the group, changing patterns on the second round each time.

Muscle and Joint Injuries

Two common and fairly minor injuries are strains and sprains. A strain is a tear in a muscle, while a sprain is an injury to the ligaments around a joint. These injuries produce similar symptoms, including pain, stiffness, swelling, difficulty moving the affected body part, and discoloration or bruising of the surrounding skin. Strains and sprains vary in severity. Severe strains and sprains will require medical care. Call 911 for emergency medical help if

- the victim is unable to move the affected muscle or joint.
- the pain is severe.
- the injury is bleeding.
- the joint appears deformed.
- you hear a popping sound coming from the joint.

You can treat minor strains and sprains with the P.R.I.C.E. procedure, which includes these steps:

- **Protect** the affected area by wrapping it in a bandage or splint.
- **Rest** the injured body part for at least a day.
- **Ice** the area to reduce swelling and pain. Wrap ice cubes in a cloth or towel and hold it against the affected area for 10 to 15 minutes at a time, three times a day.
- **Compress** the affected area by wrapping it firmly, but not too tightly, in a bandage.
- **Elevate** the injured body part above the level of the heart, if possible.

AL

You can gradually begin to use the affected body part again as the pain and swelling subside. If the swelling lasts more than two days, see a doctor.

Fractures and Dislocations

Injuries to bones include fractures and dislocations. A **fracture** is *a break in a bone;* a **dislocation** is *a separation of a bone from its normal position in a joint.* Symptoms for fractures and dislocations include severe pain, swelling, bruising, and inability to move the affected body part. The limb or joint may be visibly misshapen, discolored, or out of place.

Fractures and dislocations are emergencies that require immediate medical care. The first-aid procedures for both conditions are the same:

1. Call 911 or your local emergency medical service.
2. Do your best to keep the victim still and calm.
3. If the skin is broken, rinse it carefully to prevent infection, taking care not to disturb the bone. Cover the wound with a sterile dressing, if available.

R

FITNESS ZONE

A lot of people like the saying, "No pain, no gain," but my coach says that feeling pain during exercise means something is wrong. Coach says that if you feel pain, you should stop exercising right away. Listen to your body. It knows the difference between real pain and the mild discomfort of a muscle working. For more fitness tips, visit the Online Fitness Zone at **glencoe.com**.

Health Literacy

Stimulating the Healing of Fractures
When fractured bones heal, a complex of proteins and cells forms a matrix that joins together the bone fragments. Researchers have found that bone growth is stimulated by proteins located in the matrix. Many of these proteins have been genetically produced. One of these proteins, called recombinant human bone morphogenic protein 7 (rhBMP7) has been shown to stimulate bone repair. This protein is particularly useful in inducing bones to heal that will not heal on their own.

4. If necessary, apply a splint. A splint will immobilize the injured body part to prevent further injury. Attach any kind of rigid support—such as a board or stick—to the injured body part with strips of cloth, immobilizing the area extending above and below the injured bone.

5. Apply an ice pack to reduce pain and swelling.

6. If the injury does not affect the head, neck, legs, or spine, have the victim lie down and raise his or her legs about 12 inches to prevent shock.

Unconsciousness

Main Idea A victim who loses consciousness for any amount of time requires medical care.

Unconsciousness is *the condition of not being alert or aware of your surroundings*. Victims who are unconscious are not able to respond to simple commands. They also cannot cough or clear their throats, putting them at risk of choking. Nearly any major injury or illness can cause unconsciousness. Alcohol and drug abuse can also cause a person to lose consciousness.

CA If you encounter someone who has lost consciousness, call 911, check the victim's breathing, and be prepared to perform CPR if necessary. If the victim is breathing and does not seem to have an injury to the spine, lay the victim down on his or her side. Bend the top leg so that the hip and knee joints form right angles. Gently tilt the victim's head back to open the airway. This position, known as the recovery position, will help the victim breathe. Keep the victim warm until help arrives.

■ **Figure 27.8** The recovery position is the safest position for an unconscious person because the airway is protected. *Why is it important to keep the airway open?*

Main Idea

Unconsciousness A victim who loses consciousness requires medical care. **Ask Students:** *What should you do if you find someone unconscious?* (Call for medical help. Check the victim to see if he or she is breathing and perform CPR if necessary.)

✓ READING CHECK

Compare and Contrast Name one way in which fractures and dislocations are similar and one way in which they are different.

✓ READING CHECK

Answer Both injuries cause similar symptoms and require similar treatment. A fracture is a break in a bone, while a dislocation is a separation of a bone from the joint.

CA Cultural Awareness

Caring for a Victim of a Medical Emergency Remind students to always consider another person's beliefs, needs, and concerns when responding to a medical emergency. Emphasize to students that they should always ask a victim's permission before providing first aid. If the person is unconscious, students should ask the victim's companions for permission. If the victim or the victim's companions do not give permission, students should respect that decision and offer to call for emergency medical help. **OL**

Caption Answer

Figure 27.8 Unconscious people can choke because they cannot cough or clear their throat.

English Language Coach

Prefixes and Suffixes Prefixes and suffixes are word parts that when added to a base word change its meaning or usage. Prefixes go before the base word, suffixes go after. For example, *conscious* is an adjective that means "being aware of one's self." By adding the prefix *un-*, which means "not," *conscious* becomes *unconscious*, meaning "lacking awareness." *Unconscious* is also an adjective. However, when adding the suffix –*ness*, which means "state or condition," the base word *conscious* becomes the noun *consciousness*, changing the way the word is used in sentences.

Main Idea

Other Common Emergencies
Animal bites, nosebleeds, and poisonings are medical emergencies with specific first-aid treatments.
Ask Students: *How have you treated a nosebleed?* (Answers will vary but may include pinching the nostrils shut and leaning forward.)

Academic Vocabulary

Seek After reading to students the definition of *seek*, have a volunteer explain how to play the game Hide 'n' Seek. Reinforce that the person seeking is going in search of those who are hiding. Explain that in a similar way, a person seeking emergency medical care is going in search of professional medical help.

READING CHECK

Answer Call 911, and move the person into the recovery position if the person vomits and head and neck injuries are not obvious.

HS Health Skills Practice

Advocacy According to the American Veterinary Medical Association (AVMA), between 500,000 and 800,000 people require medical treatment each year for dog bites. Have students do research at AVMA on how to prevent dog bites. Have them write a letter to the editor of a newspaper that describes measures dog owners and the parents of young children can take to prevent a child from being bitten. **OL**

READING CHECK

Explain What can you do to help someone who is unconscious, has fainted, or has a concussion?

Academic Vocabulary

seek *(verb):* to go in search of

Fainting

Fainting is a temporary loss of consciousness that occurs when not enough blood is flowing to the brain. If you see someone faint, try to catch the person to stop him or her from falling. Lay the victim on the floor or ground and elevate the legs. Loosen any tight clothing around the victim's neck. If the person vomits, quickly roll him or her into the recovery position. If the victim does not regain consciousness within a couple of minutes, call 911. If the victim regains consciousness, keep the person lying still for at least 10 to 15 minutes.

A single episode of fainting may not be serious, but it is a warning that medical attention is needed. Victims of fainting should see a doctor as soon as possible if they have never fainted before or they are fainting frequently.

Concussion

A **concussion** is *a jarring injury to the brain that can cause unconsciousness.* Anyone who loses consciousness or experiences memory loss or confusion because of a head injury might have a concussion. Call 911 for all cases of suspected concussion. If the victim is conscious, have him or her lie down. Use first aid to treat any bleeding while you wait for help to arrive. If the victim is unconscious, avoid moving him or her if there is reason to suspect a head or neck injury. Otherwise, you can place the victim in the recovery position.

Other Common Emergencies

Main Idea It's important to learn first-aid procedures for emergencies such as animal bites, nosebleeds, and poisoning.

Other common medical emergencies include animal bites, nosebleeds, and poisoning. Learning proper first-aid procedures will help you stay calm and respond appropriately in the event of an emergency.

Animal Bites

Animal bites can transmit serious diseases such as rabies, a viral infection that can be deadly if not treated immediately. Once a person develops symptoms of rabies, the disease cannot be cured. However, a vaccine can prevent the disease if it is given within two days of exposure to the virus. Anyone who is bitten by an unknown or wild animal should **seek** emergency medical care immediately.

In general, animal bites should be treated like any other open wound. If you're providing first aid to a bite victim, wash your hands thoroughly and put on protective gloves.

HS

774 **Chapter 27** First Aid and Emergencies

More About...

Seizures and Unconsciousness Seizures are sudden changes in behavior caused by uncontrolled electrical activity in the brain. Symptoms for seizures include uncontrolled twitching and unconsciousness. Seizures have many causes including high fever, brain tumors, and epilepsy. Although seizures are frightening to witness, they are not life-threatening. Stay calm. Protect the person from harm. Do not try to hold the tongue or hold the person down. When the seizure is over, place the person in the recovery position. If the seizure lasts more than five minutes, call for emergency help.

Then wash the bite area thoroughly with mild soap and water. Apply pressure as needed to stop any bleeding. Apply antibiotic ointment and a sterile dressing. If the wound swells, apply ice wrapped in a towel for ten minutes. A tetanus booster shot may be required for any bite that has broken the skin. If the bite develops signs of infection (such as redness, pain, or swelling), seek emergency medical care.

Nosebleeds

Nosebleeds can occur after an injury to the nose or when very dry air causes the lining of the nose to become irritated. An occasional nosebleed isn't a cause for concern. If your nose starts bleeding, sit down and squeeze the soft part of the nose between your thumb and finger, holding the nostrils closed, for five to ten minutes. Breathe through your mouth and lean forward to avoid swallowing the blood. An ice pack or cold compress applied to the bridge of the nose may also help. If the bleeding doesn't stop after 20 minutes, seek emergency medical help.

Poisoning

A **poison** is *any substance that causes injury, illness, or death when it enters the body.* The substance can be a solid, liquid, or gas. Almost 2.5 million cases of poisoning occur in the United States each year, resulting in nearly 1,000 deaths. **Figure 27.10** on page 776 shows some ways poisons can enter the body.

The first step in any case of suspected poisoning is to call a **poison control center**, *a round-the-clock service that provides emergency medical advice on how to treat victims of poisoning.* You can reach the National Poison Control Hotline at 1-800-222-1222. Keep this number near your phone, and dial it at once in any case of suspected poisoning. Even if you aren't sure the victim has been poisoned, call right away, rather than wait for symptoms to develop. Some poisons require quick action to minimize damage or prevent death. When you call, be prepared to provide

- your name, location, and telephone number.
- the victim's condition, age, and weight.
- the name of the poison, when it was taken, and the amount of poison that was involved. If you do not have this information, tell as much as you know.

The poison control expert will provide you with step-by-step instructions on how to treat the victim. Do not give the victim any medication unless the expert tells you to do so.

■ **Figure 27.9** Pinching the nostrils closed will stop almost all nosebleeds. *What factors can trigger a nosebleed?*

Lesson 3 Responding to Other Common Emergencies **775**

C Critical Thinking

Evaluating The cold, dry air of winter coupled with indoor heating make conditions especially conducive for nosebleeds. Allergies, colds, or other upper respiratory infections and the medications used to relieve their symptoms also increase the incidence of nosebleeds in winter. Ask students to describe the advantage of a furnace system with a built-in humidifier. Students may say that humidifiers add water to the air, making it less dry, which helps the lining of the nose remain moist. **AL**

HS Health Skills Practice

Communicating Have students work in mixed ability groups, with English language learners mixed with English fluent students. Give each group a clean, empty bottle of a poisonous substance. Then instruct groups to write a dialogue they would have with experts at a poison control center if the child they were babysitting drank some of the substance. Remind students to describe the characteristics of the child they are babysitting. Have groups role-play their dialogue for the class. Invite the class to give constructive criticism about the communication between the babysitter and the poison control center. **EL OL**

Caption Answer

Figure 27.9 An injury to the nose or very dry air

ELL Support

First Aid for Poisoning Display clean, empty containers of poisonous substances such as household cleaners and lawn care products.

Beginning Paraphrase the first-aid instructions on the containers. Help students write the phone number for the poison control center on a card.

Intermediate Read the first-aid instructions. Have students write the instructions in their own words as simple phrases on the poison control phone card.

Advanced Have students compare the first-aid instructions on the containers with those in the lesson. Have them write these instructions as sentences on the poison control card.

R Reading Strategy

Analyzing a Table Have students study the table in **Figure 27.10**. Ask them to explain how poisons enter the body. (By swallowing and breathing in, and through the eyes and skin) Then have students explain what should be done in all cases of poisoning. (Call the poison control center.) Finally, ask students to describe how to treat each method of poisoning. (Swallowing: response depends on what is swallowed; inhalation: get victim to fresh air immediately; eyes: flush eyes with water; skin: remove clothing and rinse skin) BL EL

AL Active Learning

Treating Snakebites Explain that treating snakebites is much easier if the species of snake causing the bite is known. Provide students with several field guides, photographs, or even live specimens of snakes indigenous to your area. Have students learn to identify which snakes are harmless and which are poisonous. Students can summarize what they have learned by creating a brochure or information card that identifies poisonous snakes and describes appropriate first-aid procedures. OL

U Universal Access

Making Connections Give students pictures that depict each step of the "3Cs" and the chain of survival. Also give them an insect bite scenario. Have students place the pictures in order to show the complete emergency response. Have intermediate and advanced English language learners write a phrase or sentence for each picture that describes the step in the response. EL

Figure 27.10 **Forms of Poisoning**

Poisons can enter the body in several ways.

How Poison Enters the Body	Examples	What Action to Take
Swallowing	Household cleaners, medicines	Call poison control and follow instructions. You may be instructed to give the victim a small amount of milk or water or to induce vomiting. Do not take these actions unless instructed to do so.
Inhalation	Carbon monoxide from heating fixtures, fumes from certain solvents, fumes produced by mixing cleaning products together	Get the victim to fresh air right away. Then call poison control. Be prepared to perform rescue breathing if necessary.
Through the eyes	Any strong chemical that enters the eye	Flush the eye with fresh water for 15 to 20 minutes. Call poison control.
Through the skin	Caustic chemicals such as drain cleaner or rust remover; certain pesticides	Remove clothing the poison has touched. Rinse skin with running water for 15 to 20 minutes. Call poison control.

READING CHECK

Identify List one thing you can do in the event of a snakebite.

Snakebite. Certain types of snakes can inject **venom**, *a poisonous secretion,* into the victim's body. In the United States, poisonous snakes include rattlesnakes, copperheads, water moccasins (also known as cottonmouths), coral snakes, and cobras. You should treat any snakebite seriously unless you are absolutely sure of the species. Follow these steps:

- Call 911 for medical help and follow the dispatcher's instructions.
- Try to keep the victim from moving. Keep the affected body part below chest level to reduce the flow of venom to the heart.
- Remove rings and other constricting items, since the affected area may swell up.
- Try using a snakebite suction kit, if one is available in your first-aid kit.
- Do *not* apply a tourniquet, use cold compresses, cut into the bitten area with a blade, suck the venom out by mouth, or give the victim any medications without being advised to do so by a doctor or 911 dispatcher.

Insect and Spider Bites or Stings. The stings of insects such as bees, hornets, and wasps, as well as the bites of certain spiders, are painful but usually not dangerous. If someone allergic to the venom of these insects or spiders has been stung or bitten, call 911. For other cases, follow these steps:

- Remove the stinger by scraping it off with a firm, straight-edged object such as a credit card. Do not use tweezers, since they may squeeze the stinger and release more venom.

776 Chapter 27 First Aid and Emergencies

Myths & Reality

Treating Snakebites

Myth: Apply a tourniquet on the limb between the heart and the bite to prevent the venom from flowing through the body.

Fact: The tourniquet can cut off blood flow to the limb, which can result in the loss of the limb.

Myth: Cut away the skin from around the bite site to remove the venom from the body.

Fact: Cutting the skin around the bite may actually cause the venom to diffuse through the tissue more quickly.

- Wash the site thoroughly with mild soap and water to help prevent infection.
- Apply ice (wrapped in a cloth) to the site for ten minutes to reduce pain and swelling. Alternate ten minutes on, ten minutes off.
- Antihistamines and anti-itch creams may help reduce itching.
- If the victim shows signs of severe reaction, such as weakness, difficulty breathing, or swelling of the face, call 911 immediately.

Poisonous Plants. Most people are allergic to poison ivy, poison oak, and poison sumac. Exposure to these plants will cause itching, swelling, redness, burning, and blisters at the site of contact. If you brush up against one of these plants, do not rub your skin, because that will spread the plant oils that cause an allergic reaction. Washing the area immediately with soap and water may prevent a reaction. Take care to wash any clothing or other objects that have touched the plant as well. If an allergic reaction develops, an over-the-counter cream or oral antihistamine may ease the itching.

■ **Figure 27.11** Exposure to poison ivy, poison oak, and poison sumac can cause itching, swelling, and blisters. *What should you do if you accidentally brush against one of these plants?*

 **READING CHECK**

Answer Call 911 for medical help.

③ ASSESS/ CLOSE

Assessment Resources

📁 **FAST FILE ACTIVITIES**
Lesson 3 Quiz

💿 *ExamView Assessment Suite* CD-ROM

Visit glencoe.com **for:**
Online Quizzes
Online Learning Center

Progress Monitoring

Reteaching
Have students make an outline of Lesson 3 in which they include the first-aid procedures for each medical emergency.

Enrichment
Have students plan and organize a first-aid relay race for the class. The relay race can be composed of different stations at which a "victim" of a medical emergency described in this lesson is waiting to be treated. The team that gets through each station the quickest and has correctly treated each "victim" is the winner.

G⊙ Online

Have students visit **glencoe.com** and complete the Interactive Study Guide for this lesson.

LESSON 3 📖 ASSESSMENT

After You Read

Reviewing Facts and Vocabulary
1. What are the symptoms of a fracture or dislocation?
2. Why is the recovery position the safest position for an unconscious person?
3. What is the first step in any case of suspected poisoning?

Thinking Critically
4. **Evaluate.** Why should you always seek professional medical care for fractures and dislocations?
5. **Analyze.** List the items you would need to treat a bee sting in a victim who is not allergic to the venom.

Applying Health Skills
6. **Practicing Healthful Behaviors.** Make a poster illustrating the steps of the P.R.I.C.E. procedure.

Writing Critically
7. **Narrative.** Write a newspaper-style article about a child or teen who is bitten by a wild animal. The article should describe the steps the victim and his or her parents take to treat the wound and prevent rabies and other diseases.

G⊙ Online

Visit **glencoe.com** and complete the Interactive Study Guide for this lesson.

LESSON 3 ASSESSMENT ANSWERS

1. Severe pain, swelling, bruising, and inability to move the affected body part
2. It protects the airway.
3. Call a poison control center.
4. Without medical treatment, the injury may not heal properly.
5. Sample list: credit card, water, mild soap, ice, cloth, anti-itch cream, antihistamines
6. Posters should include all the steps of the P.R.I.C.E. procedure.
7. Articles will vary.

LESSON **4**

Emergency Preparedness

① FOCUS

GUIDE TO READING

BIG Idea Students will learn how to prepare for severe weather and natural disasters. **Ask Students:** *How have you prepared for severe storms?* (Answers will vary but may include seeking shelter.)

Before You Read

Organize Information
Web diagrams should include information that reflects the discussion in the lesson.

Main Idea

Storm Safety It is important to pay attention to weather warnings and follow safety guidelines during a severe storm. **Ask Students:** *What happened in a severe storm that you have experienced?* (Answers will vary but will include descriptions of severe storms.)

Real Life Issues ⋯⋯⋯⋯

Discuss reasons why it is not safe to play outside during a blizzard. Then discuss fun indoor activities that Dean could do with his younger siblings. **Ask Students:** *What could happen to the children if they went ahead and played outside in the blizzard?*

LESSON **4**

GUIDE TO READING

BIG Idea *Planning ahead and knowing what to expect can help you survive severe weather and natural disasters.*

Before You Read

Organize Information.
Write "Weather Emergencies & Natural Disasters" in a circle. Surround this circle with the following terms: "Thunderstorms," "Hurricanes," "Tornadoes," "Blizzards," "Floods," "Earthquakes," and "Wildfires." As you read, add information about each type of emergency.

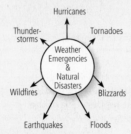

New Vocabulary

▶ hurricane (p. 779)
▶ tornado (p. 779)
▶ blizzard (p. 780)
▶ flash floods (p. 781)
▶ earthquake (p. 781)
▶ emergency survival kit (p. 782)

Emergency Preparedness

Real Life Issues ⋯⋯⋯⋯⋯⋯⋯⋯⋯

Safe in a Storm. Dean is at home looking after his younger brother and sister when it begins to snow heavily. Turning on the radio, he hears that it is a blizzard and everyone is advised to stay indoors. However, Dean's younger brother and sister want to go out and play in the snow. Dean doesn't want to spoil their fun, but he knows he's responsible for keeping them safe.

Writing *Write a dialogue between Dean and his siblings in which he explains the need to stay indoors during the snowstorm and proposes an alternative activity for them to enjoy.*

Storm Safety

Main Idea It is important to pay attention to weather warnings and follow safety guidelines during a severe storm.

When a severe storm or any other type of harsh or dangerous weather condition may occur, the National Weather Service will issue a severe weather alert. A *watch* indicates that severe weather is possible during the next few hours. A *warning* means that severe weather has already been observed or is expected soon. Watches and warnings go out over radio, television, and the Internet to let the public know about the dangers and take steps to protect themselves.

Severe Thunderstorms

Thunderstorms typically produce heavy rain and are accompanied by lightning, strong winds, and sometimes hail or tornadoes. If a thunderstorm is forecast, or if you see signs

---

✦ Promoting School Wellness

Disaster Preparedness All schools have some kind of response plan for severe weather or natural disasters. Inform your students about your school's response plan. Explain, for example, the criteria administrators use to cancel classes and the plan for severe storms while school is in session. Have students develop ways to inform other students about the school's severe weather response plan. Choose the most effective presentations and give students time and materials to implement them.

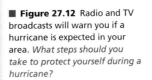
■ **Figure 27.12** Radio and TV broadcasts will warn you if a hurricane is expected in your area. *What steps should you take to protect yourself during a hurricane?*

that one is approaching, get indoors as soon as you can. The lightning produced by thunderstorms can result in electrocution. If you are in a car and cannot reach secure shelter, stay in the car and avoid touching anything made of metal. If you are on open water, return to shore. If you are in a forest, seek shelter under shorter trees. If you are trapped in an open area, try to get into a low-lying spot such as a valley or ravine; however, be on the alert for flash floods.

If you see lightning or hear thunder, use the 30/30 rule for lightning safety. Get or stay indoors if you hear thunder within 30 seconds of seeing lightning, and stay there for 30 minutes after hearing the last peal of thunder. Avoid bathing or showering since plumbing and bathroom fixtures can conduct electricity. Unplug all electrical appliances. Avoid using a corded telephone, except in an emergency. Cordless and cellular phones are safe to use.

Hurricanes

A **hurricane** is *a powerful storm that generally forms in tropical areas, producing winds of at least 74 miles per hour, heavy rains, and sometimes tornadoes.* In the United States, hurricanes strike mainly along the eastern and southern coasts. Hurricanes cause **major** flooding, and flying debris can injure or kill people and cause property damage. High winds can topple trees, power lines, and even buildings. The deadliest part of a hurricane is the storm surge, a massive wave that sweeps in from the ocean, occasionally advancing up to hundreds of miles inland.

If a hurricane is predicted in your area, take steps to secure your property. Listen to radio or TV reports for information on the progress of the storm. Follow their instructions, and be prepared to evacuate if ordered to do so by local authorities.

Tornadoes

Hurricanes and severe thunderstorms can produce a **tornado**—*a whirling, funnel-shaped windstorm that causes destruction as it advances along the ground in a narrow path.*

Academic Vocabulary

major *(adjective):* notable in effect or scope

② TEACH

W Writing Support

Descriptive Writing Have students write a description of how to stay safe during a severe storm. Students can choose a severe thunderstorm, hurricane, tornado, or blizzard. Direct students to include in their descriptions a detailed account of how to prepare for the storm. **OL**

C Critical Thinking

Applying Concepts Explain that safety guidelines suggest that a person avoid using a corded telephone during a thunderstorm, but cordless or cellular phones are safe to use. Ask students to explain why cellular phones and cordless phones are safe to use during a thunderstorm. (Cell phones and cordless phones do not have a physical connection with the electrical system in the house.) **AL**

Caption Answer

Figure 27.12 Secure your property. Listen to radio or TV reports for information on the progress of the storm and be prepared to evacuate.

Academic Vocabulary

Major Explain that the word *major* has many different meanings based on its usage and place in a sentence, but all definitions are from the Latin word *major*, which means "great" or "large." Point out that while minor is an antonym of major, the meanings in this chapter are not exactly opposite. Have students write a sentence that conveys the meaning of major as it is used here.

Cooperative Learning

Watch vs. Warning Have student groups of mixed learning levels develop a public service announcement that describes the differences between a weather watch and a weather warning. Groups can choose to write the script for a radio or TV spot, or design a billboard or bumper sticker. Encourage groups to create announcements that are informative, yet fun. Arrange for the announcements to be broadcast or displayed.

CHAPTER 27

LESSON 4

U Universal Access

Classifying Storms Write on the board the name of each type of severe storm discussed in the lesson. Next to each, draw a symbol to represent the storm. If you wish, find meteorological symbols used by the National Weather Service or local television news programs. Use simple one- or two-word descriptions to differentiate each type of storm. Differentiate between hurricanes and tornadoes, for example, by describing hurricanes as developing over ocean water and tornadoes as developing over land. For more advanced English language learners, have students say, then write, a descriptive sentence for each storm. **EL** **BL**

AL Active Learning

Guest Speaker Invite a local weather forecaster to the class to describe the types of severe storms that typically occur in your area. Suggest that the speaker bring weather maps and radar pictures that show the storms and how they travel. Ask the speaker to explain how these storms form and how weather forecasters predict them to issue watches and warnings. Finally, have the speaker describe safety measures people can take when these storms are imminent. **OL**

READING CHECK

Answer A watch means that a storm is possible; a warning means that the storm is on its way.

Tornadoes are most common east of the Rocky Mountains. The whirling winds of a tornado can reach speeds of 300 miles per hour and can leave a trail of damage a mile wide.

Although tornadoes can strike without warning, there are danger signs you can look for, such as

- darkened or greenish looking skies.
- a hailstorm that produces large hailstones.
- a large, dark, low-lying cloud that may be rotating.
- a loud roar like that of a freight train.

If you see any of these signs, or if you see a tornado cloud, take shelter immediately. Safe places to go include the lowest level in a house or other building, or the center of an interior room, such as a bathroom or closet. You should be as far away as possible from windows, doors, and outer walls. To protect yourself, crouch down as close to the floor as possible and use your arms and hands to shield your head. If possible, cover yourself with a mattress or blankets to protect yourself from falling debris.

If you are in a car or a mobile home when a tornado strikes, leave the vehicle and get into a secure shelter as quickly as possible. Never try to outrun a tornado in your car. If you are caught out in the open, lie flat in a ditch or other low-lying area and cover your head with your hands.

Winter Storms

Severe winter storms can block roads, knock down power lines, and cause floods. One type of hazardous winter storm is a **blizzard**, *a snowstorm with winds that reach 35 miles an hour or more.* To protect yourself during a winter storm, follow these guidelines:

- Stay indoors. It's the safest place to be.
- If you must go outdoors, wear layers of loose-fitting, lightweight clothing. Choose an outermost layer that will repel wind and water. Wear a hat, a scarf to protect your mouth and neck, and mittens or gloves. Wear insulated, water-resistant boots to keep your feet warm and dry.
- Whenever you are outside in a winter storm, watch out for signs of frostbite and hypothermia. (See Chapter 12.)
- Avoid driving during a severe winter storm unless it is absolutely necessary. If you must go out, use main roads.
- If you are caught in a blizzard while driving, pull off the road and turn on your emergency flashers. Stay in the car until help arrives or the storm ends. Turn on the engine and run the heater for about ten minutes each hour to help you stay warm. Roll down a window slightly to avoid carbon monoxide poisoning.

READING CHECK

Compare and Contrast What is the difference between a storm watch and a storm warning?

Myths & Reality

Tornadoes

Myth: You can outrun a tornado in a car.

Fact: Although tornadoes typically travel around 30 mph, they can go faster than 250 mph. Tornadoes are unpredictable and can change their direction in an instant. They are also capable of picking up a car and moving it through the air.

Myth: Open the windows before a tornado hits to equalize the pressure and prevent the windows from blowing out.

Fact: Opening the windows allows the strong winds and rain to get inside and make a mess of everything. Instead, seek shelter immediately.

Natural Disasters

Main Idea Know what to expect during natural disasters.

All natural disasters, from floods to earthquakes to wildfires, have one thing in common: knowing what to expect is your best defense.

Floods

Some floods develop slowly as heavy rain raises the level of rivers and lakes. **Flash floods**, however, are *floods in which a dangerous volume of water builds up in a short time*. Listen to radio and TV broadcasts for instructions if a flood is expected. If ordered to evacuate, secure your home and move essential items to an upper floor. Shut off utilities and disconnect electrical appliances. Don't walk through moving water or drive into a flooded area. If floodwaters surround your car, leave the car and flee to higher ground.

After a flood, return home only when authorities tell you it is safe to do so. Clean and disinfect everything in your home that got wet. Floods can contaminate the water supply, so drink bottled water until authorities tell you the water is safe to drink.

Earthquakes

An **earthquake** is *a series of vibrations in the earth caused by a sudden movement of the earth's crust*. Eathquakes are most common in western states. In the event of an earthquake, take the following precautions.

- **If you are indoors:** Drop to the ground. Take cover under a sturdy table or desk and hold on until the shaking stops. If there is no nearby table, crouch in a corner and cover your head with your arms.
- **If you are outdoors:** Stay clear of buildings, trees, streetlights, and power lines.
- **If you are in a car:** Stop the car and stay inside. Avoid stopping near or under trees, buildings, freeway overpasses, and power lines.

■ **Figure 27.13** Floods are one of the most common natural disasters in the United States. *Why should you avoid drinking tap water after a flood?*

Explore **glencoe.com** and complete the Student Web Activity on how to prepare for a natural disaster.

 READING CHECK

Explain What is the best defense against all natural disasters?

Main Idea

Natural Disasters The best way to prepare for a natural disaster, such as a flood, earthquake, or wildfire, is to know what to expect. **Ask Students:** *How would you prepare for a flood?* (Answers will vary but may include moving items to a higher location and evacuating.)

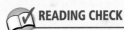 **Health Skills Practice**

Advocacy Explain that some people refuse to leave their homes when public officials order an evacuation. Have students write a letter of advocacy that would convince a person to evacuate when weather conditions warrant it. To prepare for writing, begin a discussion on why people might stay. Then discuss what could happen to people who stay as opposed to people who leave. **OL**

Caption Answer

Figure 27.13 Floods can contaminate the water supply.

READING CHECK

Answer Know what to expect.

Academic Integration

Science Explain that earthquakes are caused when sections of the earth's crust slide over, under, or past each other. Students can model this movement with thin pieces of Styrofoam floating on water in a large container. The water represents earth's mantle, molten magma or liquid rock on which earth's crust floats. The pieces of Styrofoam represent sections of earth's crust. Earthquakes frequently occur in subduction zones, areas in which one section of earth's crust slides under another. Have students model this movement and make inferences about how and why earthquakes are so damaging.

■ **Figure 27.14** An emergency survival kit can help you wait out a disaster at home or travel with you if you must evacuate your area. *Why might you need each of the items shown here?*

 READING CHECK

Classify Which two items would you need in your emergency survival kit if you had to evacuate your home?

After an earthquake, be prepared for aftershocks—smaller tremors that occur after the main quake. Use caution when opening overhead cabinets, and be aware that utilities such as gas, power, and sewer lines may be damaged.

Wildfires

Wildfires are most likely to occur in especially dry regions. People who live in areas where wildfires are common can create a "safety zone" around their homes that is free of most vegetation and other flammable materials. If you spot a wildfire, call 911 to report it, then evacuate before the fire reaches your home. Before you leave, shut off gas and oil supplies at their source and clear away any flammable materials near the house. Close all doors and windows, but don't lock the house since firefighters may need to get inside.

Being Prepared for Emergencies

Main Idea Emergency supplies can help you survive.

In an emergency, you may need to evacuate your home in a hurry, or "shelter in place"—stay in a secure location in your home until the crisis has passed. In either case, you'll need supplies to get you through the disaster. An **emergency survival kit** is *a set of items you will need in an emergency situation.* These items may include **AL**

- a three-day supply of food and water for your family. Choose shelf-stable, ready-to-eat foods. Store at least 3 gallons of water per person (1 gallon per person per day).
- a battery-powered radio or television (with extra batteries).
- a change of clothing for each family member.
- sleeping bags or bedrolls for each family member.
- first-aid supplies, including any necessary medications.
- duct tape and plastic sheeting, in case you need to seal off the windows in your home.
- copies of important documents, such as passports and birth certificates (if you need to leave your home).
- money (if you need to leave your home).

Keep a list of phone numbers for each member of your family so that you can reach one another if you are separated. Identify an out-of-town contact person to call if you can't get through to one another. Choose a meeting place for family members to go if you have to evacuate your area.

👫 Home and Community

ICE Cards Explain that ICE stands for <u>I</u>n <u>C</u>ase of <u>E</u>mergency. Have students make an ICE card to place in their wallet with their driver's license. Explain that this card should contain information about whom emergency responders should contact in an emergency. Point out that this contact person (or persons) should know the student's health history and be able to take responsibility for the student. Students should also include on their ICE card relevant medical history such as current medications, allergies, and other medical conditions.

Real World CONNECTION

Sheltering in Place

During certain disasters, including terrorist attacks, people in the area may need to "shelter in place" until it's safe to go outside. Select a small, interior room with as few windows as possible for your shelter in place. A room at or above ground level is best, and it should contain a landline phone, since cell phone systems can be overwhelmed in an emergency.

Follow these steps when taking shelter:

▶ Close and lock all windows and exterior doors. Also close window shades or blinds if there is a risk of explosions.

▶ Turn off all fans and heating and air-conditioning systems. Close fireplace dampers.

▶ Gather all family members and pets in your safe room. Bring your emergency survival kit with you. You should also have a plastic bucket with a tight lid to use for personal waste, along with soap, toilet paper, and disinfectant.

▶ Use duct tape and plastic sheeting to seal off the room you are in, including all vents and cracks around the door.

▶ Keep listening to your radio or television until you hear that it is safe to leave.

Activity

Role-play a scene involving a family sheltering in place. Show the steps the family takes to stay safe during the crisis.

Real World CONNECTION

Answers to Activity

Role-plays will vary. Scenes should describe how the family keeps itself safe and occupied.

③ ASSESS/ CLOSE

Assessment Resources

📁 **FAST FILE ACTIVITIES**
Lesson 4 Quiz
💿 *ExamView*
Assessment Suite CD-ROM

Visit glencoe.com for:
Online Quizzes
Online Learning Center

Progress Monitoring

Reteaching
Have students write a paragraph in which they use each of the vocabulary terms from the lesson. The meaning of each term should be given within the context of the paragraph.

Enrichment
Arrange for students to make a presentation to elementary school students about how to prepare for a severe storm or natural disaster and what to do when one occurs.

LESSON 4 📖 ASSESSMENT

After You Read

Reviewing Facts and Vocabulary

1. Explain the 30/30 rule for lightning safety.

2. Identify two warning signs of an approaching tornado.

3. What should you do if you are in a car during an earthquake?

Thinking Critically

4. **Synthesize.** Suppose you hear on the radio that a tornado watch has been issued for your area. How would you respond?

5. **Evaluate.** What are some of the possible consequences of not having an emergency survival kit?

Applying Health Skills

6. **Goal Setting.** Develop an emergency plan for your family. Make a list of the items you will gather for your emergency kit and the steps you will take in case of an emergency. Then set a deadline for completing your emergency preparedness goal.

Writing Critically

7. **Expository.** Choose one of the emergencies discussed in this lesson. Write an informational handout for families about what steps to take in this emergency.

G͘ Online

Visit **glencoe.com** and complete the Interactive Study Guide for this lesson.

Lesson 4   Emergency Preparedness   **783**

LESSON 4 ASSESSMENT ANSWERS

1. Get inside if thunder sounds within 30 seconds of lightning; stay inside for 30 minutes after the last thunderclap.

2. *Any two:* Darkened or greenish-looking skies; large hailstones; a dark, low-lying rotating cloud; a loud roar like that of a freight train

3. Stop the car and stay inside.

4. Sample answer: Stay close to home or another secure building with a basement or storm cellar. Continue listening to radio reports and go inside if a warning is issued.

5. Sample answer: Running out of food and water; leaving behind or losing important documents

6. Emergency plans will vary.

7. Handouts will vary.

G͘ Online

Have students visit **glencoe.com** and complete the Interactive Study Guide for this lesson.

First-Aid Station

NHES Standard 7 Students will demonstrate the ability to practice health-enhancing behaviors and avoid or reduce health risks.

Teaching Objectives

- Develop injury-management strategies for personal, family, and community health
- Describe how to respond to an imaginary emergency situation

Teaching Strategies

- Divide class into four groups. Assign one of the following to each group: muscle; joint; bone injuries; unconsciousness; animal bites.
- Have students brainstorm creative ways to present their demonstration.
- Review with students how to respond to the medical emergencies listed above.

Assessment

Using a rubric, student work should provide comprehensive evidence of the following criteria to achieve the highest score:

✓ Identifies first-aid steps for common emergencies.

✓ Lists first-aid steps in correct sequence.

✓ Explains what action to take after first aid has been provided.

Hands-On HEALTH

Activity **First-Aid Station**

In this activity you will set up a first-aid learning station. You will develop a creative presentation demonstrating how to respond to a common emergency.

What You'll Need

- pen or pencil
- notebook paper
- poster board and markers
- props (optional)

What You'll Do

Step 1

Working in small groups, select a common emergency discussed in this chapter. Identify how to recognize the emergency, appropriate steps to take, and what to do after first aid has been provided.

Step 2

Decide on a creative way to present your material at a learning station. Ideas might include a poster, a board game, a quiz show, a puzzle, a news story, or demonstrations with props such as bandages.

Step 3

Set up your learning station and give your presentation to the class.

Apply and Conclude

Write a brief essay discussing the importance of learning first-aid procedures for common emergencies.

Checklist: Practicing Healthful Behaviors

✓ Identify how to recognize a common emergency.

✓ List appropriate first-aid steps for responding to this emergency.

✓ Explain what action to take after first aid has been provided.

Home and Community

Bringing First-Aid Education to the Community Invite a representative from the Red Cross to review each group's first-aid station and demonstration. After groups have made any recommended changes, arrange for groups to present their demonstrations to a community group identified by the class. The community group might be a senior center, a Boys and Girls Club, or a Boy Scout or Girl Scout troop. Alternatively, have students provide Red Cross certified first-aid information at a community event.

To download quizzes and eFlashcards to your PDA, go to glencoe.com and click on the Study to Go icon.

LESSON 1

Providing First Aid

Key Concepts

▶ When responding to an emergency, remember three steps: check, call, and care.
▶ Take universal precautions when providing first aid.
▶ Major burns require professional medical care.

Vocabulary

▶ first aid (p. 758)
▶ Good Samaritan laws (p. 759)
▶ universal precautions (p. 759)

LESSON 2

CPR and First Aid for Shock and Choking

Key Concepts

▶ CPR combines rescue breathing and chest compressions.
▶ In cases of choking, abdominal thrusts can be used to dislodge the object blocking the windpipe.
▶ Treatment for shock involves elevating the legs and trying to keep the victim warm and calm.

Vocabulary

▶ chain of survival (p. 764)
▶ defibrillator (p. 765)
▶ CPR (p. 765)
▶ rescue breathing (p. 767)
▶ shock (p. 770)

LESSON 3

Responding to Other Common Emergencies

Key Concepts

▶ Use the P.R.I.C.E. procedure to treat minor sprains and strains.
▶ Fractures and dislocations are medical emergencies that require professional care.
▶ Animal bites that break the skin require medical attention.
▶ In all cases of suspected poisoning, call a poison control center for emergency assistance.

Vocabulary

▶ fracture (p. 772)
▶ dislocation (p. 772)
▶ unconsciousness (p. 773)
▶ concussion (p. 774)
▶ poison (p. 775)
▶ poison control center (p. 775)
▶ venom (p. 776)

LESSON 4

Emergency Preparedness

Key Concepts

▶ It is important to pay attention to weather warnings.
▶ During severe storms, stay indoors and follow guidelines for protecting yourself and your home.
▶ To protect yourself during an earthquake, stay close to the ground, protect your head, and avoid objects that might fall.

Vocabulary

▶ hurricane (p. 779)
▶ tornado (p. 779)
▶ blizzard (p. 780)
▶ flash floods (p. 781)
▶ earthquake (p. 781)
▶ emergency survival kit (p. 782)

Chapter 27   Review   **785**

 G̶ Online

Students can visit **glencoe.com** to

- review content online with the Online Student Edition.
- test their knowledge of chapter content with Online Quizzes.
- access Interactive Health Tutor for more practice with vocabulary.

Assessment Resources

📁 *FAST FILE* **ACTIVITIES**
Chapter 27 Test

 ExamView Assessment Suite CD-ROM

Visit glencoe.com for:
Audio Chapter Summaries
Online Quizzes

 Tell students to visit **glencoe.com** where they can download quizzes and eFlashcards.

Study Tips

Making an Outline Suggest to students that they make an outline for the chapter as they read it, being sure to include all the vocabulary terms and main ideas for each lesson. Point out that outlines should contain parallel information, or the same kind of information for each topic. Outlines should include details, but be readable so that the relevant information is clear and easy to find.

Assessment

Chapter 27 Assessment Answers

LESSON 1

Vocabulary Review

1. first aid
2. Good Samaritan laws
3. universal precautions

Understanding Key Concepts

4. d
5. c
6. b

Thinking Critically

7. Contracting a disease transmitted through the blood
8. Wash the wound with soap and water, cover with sterile gauze, raise the wounded area above the level of the heart, apply pressure until the bleeding stops, and secure the pad in place with a bandage.
9. If it is a first-degree burn or a small second-degree burn that does not affect the hands, feet, face, groin, buttocks, or a major joint, it can be treated at home.

LESSON 2

Vocabulary Review

10. defibrillator
11. Cardiopulmonary resuscitation (or CPR)
12. Shock

Understanding Key Concepts

13. a
14. c
15. d

LESSON 1

Vocabulary Review

Use the vocabulary terms listed on page 785 to complete the following statements.

1. During an emergency, _____ can mean the difference between life and death.

2. Statutes that protect rescuers from being sued for giving emergency care are called _____.

3. You can protect yourself from disease by following _____.

Understanding Key Concepts

After reading the question or statement, select the correct answer.

4. Universal precautions require you to wear sterile gloves whenever you
   a. encounter an emergency.
   b. treat a burn.
   c. perform rescue breathing.
   d. come into contact with someone's blood.

5. What kind of wound may not cause heavy bleeding, but carries a high infection risk?
   a. Abrasions
   b. Lacerations
   c. Punctures
   d. Avulsions

6. When treating a minor burn, you should *not*
   a. cool the burned area with running water.
   b. apply ice to the burned area.
   c. cover the burn with a sterile gauze bandage.
   d. give the victim pain relievers.

Thinking Critically

After reading the question or statement, write a short answer using complete sentences.

7. **Predict.** What are the possible consequences of treating a wound without following universal precautions?

---

8. **Summarize.** Describe the procedure for treating an open wound.

9. **Evaluate.** How can you tell if a burn is minor enough to be treated at home?

LESSON 2

Vocabulary Review

Correct the sentences below by replacing the italicized term with the correct vocabulary term.

10. A *shock machine* is a device that delivers an electric shock to the heart to restore its normal rhythm.

11. *First aid* is a lifesaving procedure that can replace a patient's normal heartbeat and breathing when these body functions have stopped.

12. *Fainting* is a life-threatening condition in which the heart is not delivering an adequate supply of blood to the body.

Understanding Key Concepts

After reading the question or statement, select the correct answer.

13. Before beginning rescue breathing, you should check to see
    a. whether the victim is breathing.
    b. whether the victim has a pulse.
    c. whether there is something in the victim's mouth.
    d. whether the victim has any open wounds.

14. A person who clutches his or her throat is most likely experiencing
    a. a heart attack.
    b. a stroke.
    c. choking.
    d. shock.

Health eSpotlight *Wrap-Up*

Be Prepared Have students reread the Health eSpotlight question at the beginning of the chapter (page 757) and look at their original answer. **Ask Students:** *What do you know now about being prepared for emergency situations that you didn't know before reading the chapter and watching the video?* Call on volunteers to describe what they have learned and how they would change their response.

15. You should wrap your arms around the rib cage, rather than the abdomen, when assisting a choking victim who is
    a. an infant.
    b. seated.
    c. unconscious.
    d. pregnant.

Thinking Critically

After reading the question or statement, write a short answer using complete sentences.

16. **Cause and Effect.** What is the likely consequence of keeping automated external defibrillators in public places?

17. **Describe.** What is the correct position in which to place your hands for performing chest compressions?

18. **Identify.** List three symptoms of shock.

LESSON 3

Vocabulary Review

Choose the correct term in the sentences below.

19. A *fracture / dislocation* is a separation of a bone from its normal position in a joint.

20. Fainting is a form of temporary *concussion / unconsciousness.*

21. *Poison / Venom* is a harmful substance secreted by some types of snakes, spiders, and insects.

Understanding Key Concepts

After reading the question or statement, select the correct answer.

22. You should always seek professional medical care for
    a. strains.
    b. sprains.
    c. fractures.
    d. animal bites.

23. When treating a nosebleed, you should *not*
    a. squeeze your nostrils shut.
    b. breathe through your mouth.
    c. try to swallow the blood.
    d. apply a cold compress to the nose.

24. The first step in any case of suspected poisoning is to
    a. find out what poison has been taken.
    b. call a poison control center.
    c. induce vomiting.
    d. see if the victim develops symptoms.

Thinking Critically

After reading the question or statement, write a short answer using complete sentences.

25. **Explain.** How can you tell if someone is unconscious?

26. **Describe.** When should you suspect that a victim has a concussion?

27. **Evaluate.** Under what circumstances are insect bites and stings medical emergencies?

LESSON 4

Vocabulary Review

Choose the correct term in the sentences below.

28. A *hurricane / tornado* is a powerful storm that generally forms in tropical areas, producing strong winds and heavy rains.

29. In a *blizzard / hurricane,* falling and blowing snow reduces visibility to less than a quarter mile, making it very easy to lose your way.

30. You should stay indoors and take cover under a sturdy table or desk during a(n) *earthquake / flash flood.*

Chapter 27   Assessment   **787**

Thinking Critically

16. More victims of cardiac arrest will receive early defibrillation and will survive.

17. Place the heel of one hand two finger-widths from the bottom of the victim's sternum, place the other hand above it, and interlock your fingers.

18. *Any three:* clammy skin; paleness or grayness; weak, rapid pulse; slow, shallow breathing; hyperventilation; dull, staring eyes; dilated pupils; faintness; weakness; confusion; loss of consciousness; extreme anxiety or agitation

LESSON 3

Vocabulary Review

19. dislocation
20. unconsciousness
21. Venom

Understanding Key Concepts

22. c
23. c
24. b

Thinking Critically

25. Unconscious people cannot follow simple commands. They also cannot cough or clear their throats.
26. When a head injury causes unconsciousness or symptoms such as confusion or memory loss
27. When the victim is allergic to the venom

LESSON 4

Vocabulary Review

28. hurricane
29. blizzard
30. earthquake

ExamView®
Assessment Suite

Create and customize tests in minutes with this convenient digital platform.

- Create differentiated tests quickly and easily.
- All questions correlated to National/State Standards.
- Enhance tests with Document Based Questions (DBQ) and add your own photos or graphics.
- Build tests in both English and Spanish.
- Generate progress reports.

To order, go to **glencoe.com** and search for ISBN 0-07-888173-0.

Assessment

Understanding Key Concepts

31. b
32. b
33. a

Thinking Critically

34. Both kinds of storms produce strong winds. However, hurricanes also produce heavy rains, while tornadoes produce faster, spinning winds that form a funnel shape.

35. Call 911 to report the fire, then evacuate the area. Shut off utilities before leaving, clear away flammable materials, close doors, cover windows, but leave the doors unlocked.

36. Floodwaters may be contaminated.

Understanding Key Concepts

After reading the question or statement, select the correct answer.

31. You should *not* stay in your car if you are out on the road during
   a. a severe thunderstorm that includes hail and sleet.
   b. a tornado.
   c. an earthquake.
   d. a wildfire.

32. If you are caught in a blizzard while driving, you should
   a. keep driving at a slow speed.
   b. pull off the road and turn on your emergency flashers.
   c. leave your car and attempt to find your way on foot.
   d. have the heater turned on the entire time and keep the windows tightly closed.

33. Earthquakes are most common in
   a. western states.
   b. eastern states.
   c. summer.
   d. winter.

Thinking Critically

After reading the question or statement, write a short answer using complete sentences.

34. **Compare and Contrast.** How are hurricanes and tornadoes alike? How are they different?

35. **Describe.** How should you respond to a wildfire?

36. **Explain.** Why is it necessary to clean and disinfect items that have been through a flood?

Project-Based ASSESSMENT

Administering First Aid

Background
First aid is the immediate care given to someone who is injured or ill. First aid is provided until professional medical care can be reached. Proper first-aid procedures can help reduce further injury or even prevent death.

Task
Create a video that effectively demonstrates proper first-aid procedures.

Audience
Fellow students and adults in the community

Purpose
Show the steps in first-aid procedures for specific injuries and medical conditions.

Procedure

1 Choose several of the first-aid procedures discussed in the chapter to demonstrate in the video. Review the steps that are required in the procedures.

2 Write a script to accompany each first-aid procedure that you will demonstrate.

3 Make a storyboard of your video, in which you show what will happen in each scene of the video.

4 Work on special features that will appear in the video, such as props and titles.

5 Revise your storyboard, as necessary, and finalize the script.

6 Assign roles in the video to the members of your group, and rehearse the scenes.

7 Tape your video, and present it to the class.

Project-Based ASSESSMENT

Step 1 Choose Students can work in groups of three or more. They should choose a few of the first-aid procedures covered in the chapter to demonstrate in the video.

Step 2 Write Tell students to first write their scripts before filming. There should be a script for each procedure featured in the video. Students should also make a storyboard to show what happens in each scene.

Step 3 Evaluate After students have taped their video, consider showing some of the videos to middle school or elementary school students. First aid demonstrations should clearly show complete and accurate procedures.

Visit **glencoe.com** for Project-Based Assessment rubrics.

Math Practice

Solve Word Problems. Use the passage below to answer Questions 1–3.

> While hiking, Antonio and his younger brother saw that a young woman had collapsed on the hiking trail. The woman was unconscious, not breathing, and had no heartbeat.
>
> "Here, take my cell phone," he told his brother. "Go back to the beginning of the trail entrance and call 911. Tell them that I'm starting CPR."
>
> As his brother ran for help, Antonio began to do the chest compressions for CPR. After every 15 chest compressions, he gave two rescue breaths. He repeated these two steps—four continuous cycles of compressions and breaths every minute—until the paramedics arrived to take over.

1. Imagine that x represents the total number of chest compressions Antonio had to do until the paramedics arrived. Which expression below represents how many total minutes Antonio had to perform CPR on the woman?
   - **A.** $x(4 \times 15)$
   - **B.** $4x/15$
   - **C.** $15x/4$
   - **D.** $x/(4 \times 15)$

2. If Antonio performed CPR steadily as described, how much time has passed in three cycles of compressions and breaths?
   - **A.** 45 seconds
   - **B.** 1 minute
   - **C.** 3 minutes
   - **D.** 3 minutes 45 seconds

3. How many total chest compressions did Antonio have to perform if the paramedics took 15 minutes to arrive?

G⊙ Online

For more test practice, visit glencoe.com and complete the Online Quizzes for Chapter 27.

Reading/Writing Practice

Understand and Apply. Read the passage below, and then answer the questions.

> BROWNWOOD, TEXAS—At South Elementary today, a tornado touched down, injuring a teacher. Tyrone Rasco, a third-grade teacher who was standing outside the building, suffered minor injuries from the storm.
>
> Thirty children under the supervision of Ann Katz, a physical education teacher, were outside on a playground adjacent to the building. Because the playground was next to the building, Mrs. Katz rushed the children into the building as soon as she heard the tornado alarm. The kids hurried to hallways in the center of the building before the tornado hit. The storm broke the school's front door and most of its windows.
>
> "We are thankful that no students were injured in the storm," said Principal Jennifer Rodriguez.

1. What is the purpose of this article?
   - **A.** To describe the damage that a tornado caused at a school
   - **B.** To report about Mrs. Katz's actions
   - **C.** To explain why people should stay inside during tornadoes
   - **D.** To promote tornado warning systems

2. Which word or phrase has the same meaning as the words *adjacent to* in the second paragraph?
   - **A.** next to
   - **B.** nearby
   - **C.** far from
   - **D.** underneath

3. Write an article about how to stay safe during a tornado.

National Education Standards
Math: Algebra, Problem Solving
Language Arts: NCTE 1, NCTE 3, NCTE 4

Standardized Test Practice Answers

Math Practice
1. D
2. A
3. 900 chest compressions

Reading/Writing Practice
1. A
2. B
3. Answers will vary, but should include descriptive details answering who, what, and where. The new article should also focus on an aspect different from the one described in the article here.

National Education Standards

Math: Algebra, Problem Solving

Language Arts: NCTE 1, NCTE 3, NCTE 4

For the complete Math and Language Arts standards, visit glencoe.com.

G⊙ Online

Online Study Tools
For more test practice, visit glencoe.com and complete the Online Quizzes for Chapter 27.

Test-Taking Tip

Reading Directions Remind students of the importance of reading the directions carefully before each part of an exam. Suggest that they circle important words and phrases in the directions, such as *similar, different, only one,* or *best*. Explain that misreading the directions can cause them to answer questions incorrectly. As a practice, give students different forms of directions for the same kind of activity such as true/false questions. Point out how their answers would be different for the same question with different directions.

Chapter 28 pages 790–817	Standards		Features
	National	**State/Local**	
	1.12.3, 1.12.5, 1.12.6, 2.12.4, 2.12.10, 7.12.1, 7.12.2, 8.12.4		**TIME** HEALTH • What You Can Do, page 812
30 Min **Lesson 1** **Community and Public Health** pages 792–799 **BIG Idea** *Many people and organizations work together to promote individual and public health.*	1.12.6, 2.12.4, 2.12.10, 3.12.3, 3.12.4, 3.12.5, 7.12.1, 8.12.1		*Real World* **CONNECTION** • Evaluating Health Care Services, page 797 Out of Time
30 Min **Lesson 2** **Air Quality and Health** pages 800–805 **BIG Idea** *Both outdoor and indoor air quality can affect health.*	1.12.3, 2.12.10, 7.12.1, 7.12.2, 8.12.4		VIDEO BusinessWeek HEALTH NEWS • Fluorescent Light Bulbs, page 803
30 Min **Lesson 3** **Protecting Land and Water** pages 806–811 **BIG Idea** *Human actions can either damage or protect land and water.*	1.12.3, 2.12.10, 7.12.1, 7.12.2, 8.12.4		*Health Skills* **Activity** • Promoting Recycling (*Advocacy*), page 811 Out of Time

Key to Ability Levels

Teaching Strategies and activities have been coded for ability level and appropriateness.

AL Activities for students working above grade level

OL Activities for students working on grade level

BL Activities for students working below grade level

EL Activities for English Learners

Chapter 28 Planning Guide

Glencoe Exclusive!
TeacherWorks™ Plus
All-In-One Planner and Resource Center

Resources	Lesson Assessment	Technology
Student Activity Workbook TEACH *FAST FILE* RESOURCES Vocabulary Practice TEACH Health Labs EXTEND	Chapter 28 Review Chapter 28 Assessment Standardized Test Practice ExamView® Assessment Suite CD-ROM	**Teaching Tools:** TeacherWorks™ Plus DVD StudentWorks™ Plus DVD ExamView® Assessment Suite CD-ROM Transparency Fitness DVD PowerPoint® DVD Health eSpotlight Video Series DVD
FAST FILE RESOURCES Reading Strategies Activity TEACH Reteaching Activity REVIEW Enrichment Activity EXTEND Health Skills Practice TEACH	Lesson 1 Assessment, page 799 Lesson 1 Quiz *Fast File* ExamView® Assessment Suite CD-ROM	**Web-Based Resources:** Go Online glencoe.com • Health Podcast Activities • Audio Chapter Summaries (English/Spanish) • Interactive Health Tutor
FAST FILE RESOURCES Reading Strategies Activity TEACH Reteaching Activity REVIEW Enrichment Activity EXTEND Health Skills Practice TEACH	Lesson 2 Assessment, page 805 Lesson 2 Quiz *Fast File* ExamView® Assessment Suite CD-ROM	• Health Skills Activities • Vocabulary PuzzleMaker • Parent Letters (English/Spanish) • Lesson Plans • Health Inventories
FAST FILE RESOURCES Reading Strategies Activity TEACH Reteaching Activity REVIEW Enrichment Activity EXTEND Health Skills Practice TEACH	Lesson 3 Assessment, page 811 Lesson 3 Quiz *Fast File* ExamView® Assessment Suite CD-ROM	• Online Quizzes • Study-to-Go • Unit Web Projects • Student Web Activities • Fitness Zone Activities

StudentWorks Plus

This is the student's backpack solution.

Includes:
- complete Interactive Student Edition
- full audio of English text and Spanish chapter summaries
- allows students to record assignments and track grades.
- links to online activities and additional student resources
- access to all student worksheets and workbooks

Dinah Zike Foldables®
FOLDABLES® Study Organizer

Chapter Activity
Refer to the *Dinah Zike Reading and Study Skills for Glencoe Health*. Ask students to make a three-pocket Foldable to record and organize notes about community and public health, air quality and health, and protecting land and water. Encourage students to use their completed Foldable to review chapter content.

Key to Symbols

 Transparencies
 CD-ROM
 glencoe.com
 Print Resources

REVIEW activities to review or reinforce content
TEACH activities to teach basic concepts
EXTEND activities to extend or enrich lesson content

Community and Environmental Health

Chapter Overview

Chapter 28 focuses on the health care system, public health, the impact of air quality on health, and ways that human actions influence the environment.

Lesson 1

The health care system includes all the ways that people receive and pay for medical care.

Lesson 2

Both outdoor and indoor air pollution can put people's health at risk. Outdoor air pollution also contributes to the greenhouse effect and global warming.

Lesson 3

Many human actions, such as improper disposal of wastes, can pollute both land and water. Other human actions, such as energy conservation, can help protect the environment.

▶ **Activating Prior Knowledge**

Ask students to write a short paragraph about why they think protecting the environment is important. After students finish writing, ask a few volunteers to read their paragraphs to the class.

CHAPTER 28 **Community and Environmental Health**

Lesson 1
Community and Public Health

BIG Idea *Many people and organizations work together to promote individual and public health.*

Lesson 2
Air Quality and Health

BIG Idea *Both outdoor and indoor air quality can affect your health.*

Lesson 3
Protecting Land and Water

BIG Idea *Human actions can either damage or protect land and water.*

Activating Prior Knowledge

Using Visuals Look at the picture on this page. How are these teens contributing to community and environmental health? Why do you think it is important to protect the environment? Write a paragraph explaining your thoughts.

790

Universal Access

Differentiated Learning Glencoe provides teacher support and student materials for all learners in the health classroom.

- Chapter Summaries in English and Spanish are available online at glencoe.com.

- *Fast Files* and related worksheets support reluctant readers.

- Universal Access strategies throughout the Teacher Wraparound Edition and *Fast Files* help you present materials for gifted students, at-risk students, physically impaired students, and those with behavior disorders or learning disabilities.

Chapter Launchers

Health in Action

Discuss the **BIG** Ideas

Before beginning this chapter, think about how you would answer these questions:

▶ Why is community and public health important?

▶ How do your surroundings affect your personal health?

▶ How can your actions affect your environment?

Watch the *Health* eSpotlight Video Series

Taking Care of Everyone

It's important to get regular health screenings. When else do you use the health care system?

Assess Your Health

G꣣ Online

Visit **glencoe.com** and complete the Health Inventory for Chapter 28.

Chapter Launchers

Health in Action

Discuss the **BIG** Ideas

Assign this activity before students read the chapter. Explain that the questions will help them focus on the big idea in each lesson. If students save their responses to the questions, they can review them at the end of the chapter to see how much they have learned.

Health eSpotlight
Video Series

 Taking Care of Everyone

Before Viewing the Video

Ask Students: *What are some community events that support environmental issues?* (a farmer's market or community cleanup project)

G꣣ Online

Have students go to **glencoe.com** and take the Health Inventory for Chapter 28.

Chapter Skills

Reading Skills
- Reviewing Facts and Vocabulary, pp. 799, 805, 811
- Reading/Writing Practice, p. 817

Vocabulary
- New Vocabulary, pp. 792, 800, 806
- Reviewing Facts and Vocabulary, pp. 799, 805, 811

BIG Idea

People and organizations work together to promote individual and public health, including reducing air pollution.

Health Skills
- Health Skills Activity, p. 810
- Applying Health Skills, pp. 799, 805, 811

Writing Skills
- Real World Connection, p. 797
- Writing Critically, pp. 799, 805, 811
- Reading/Writing Practice, p. 817

Community and Public Health

1 FOCUS

GUIDE TO READING

BIG Idea Individual and public health is fostered by the work of people and organizations. **Ask Students:** *Who are some of the people you visit and what are some of the places you go to receive health care?* (Sample answers: I visit my family doctor at a clinic and my dentist at his practice.)

Before You Read

Cluster Chart Students' cluster charts may vary. Important details might include a definition of the health care system, examples of health care providers and facilities.

Main Idea

The Health Care System All the ways that people receive and pay for medical care make up the health care system. **Ask Students:** *What are examples of health care professionals that make up the health care system?* (Sample answers: Doctors, dentists, nurses, pharmacists)

Real Life Issues

Have students read the scenario. **Ask Students:** *How would you finish the following statement? "A good family doctor should be…"*

LESSON 1

GUIDE TO READING

BIG Idea *Many people and organizations work together to promote individual and public health.*

Before You Read

Create a Cluster Chart. Write "Health Care System" and circle it. Surround it with circles labeled "Health Care Professionals," "Health Care Facilities," "Health Insurance," and "Health Agencies." As you read, add details for each topic.

New Vocabulary

▶ health care system (p. 792)
▶ primary care physician (p. 792)
▶ specialists (p. 792)
▶ medical history (p. 794)
▶ health insurance (p. 795)
▶ public health (p. 796)

Review Vocabulary

▶ health fraud (Ch.2, L.4)

Community and Public Health

Real Life Issues ....

Choosing a New Doctor. Caleb's family is moving to a new town, so they need to choose a new family doctor. Their health insurer's Web site offers a "physician search" feature that looks for doctors within a given area. However, Caleb wants more from his new doctor than a convenient location. He wants someone who is easy to talk to, like his previous doctor. He isn't sure how he can find a new doctor he'll be comfortable with.

Writing *Brainstorm a list of questions Caleb could ask to help him choose a new doctor. Then write a dialogue between Caleb and a doctor he's considering.*

The Health Care System

Main Idea The health care system includes all the ways you receive and pay for medical care.

All the health care professionals you see on a regular basis—your doctor, your dentist, the pharmacist at your local drugstore—are part of the nation's health care system. A **health care system** includes *all the medical care available to a nation's people, the way they receive care, and the way they pay for it.* You use the health care system when you

- go for a checkup with a **primary care physician**, *a medical doctor who provides physical checkups and general care.*
- see the school nurse about an injury.
- have your teeth examined by a dentist.
- consult **specialists**, *medical doctors who focus on particular kinds of patients or on particular medical conditions.*

Teens Want to Know

When Should I Go to an Emergency Room? You should go to an emergency room for any of the following potentially life-threatening problems.

- Severe cuts, animal bites, or any bleeding that does not stop
- Head or neck injuries with loss of consciousness or vomiting
- Fainting or difficulty waking

- Severe burns, sudden severe pain, or poisoning
- Difficulty breathing, shortness of breath, or uncontrollable choking
- Signs of shock (pale, clammy skin and weak, rapid pulse)
- Severe headache with vomiting, stiff neck
- Coughing up or vomiting blood, or severe or persistent vomiting

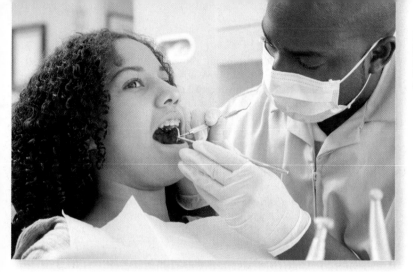

■ **Figure 28.1** Your dentist is just one of the people who may provide health care to you. *Who are other members of your health care "team"?*

Examples of specialists include allergists (who treat allergies and asthma), dermatologists (who treat skin problems), gynecologists (who care for the female reproductive system), and pediatricians (who treat children).

Types of Health Care Facilities

AL You can receive health care in a variety of settings. For instance, if you become ill or injured at school, you might see the school nurse. If you need a checkup, you might visit a doctor's office or a clinic. A clinic is a community health facility where patients can receive *outpatient care,* which means being treated and returning home the same day.

Hospitals provide both outpatient care and *inpatient care,* which involves an overnight stay. Most hospitals have an emergency room where they handle urgent injuries or illnesses. Problems that are not life threatening may be treated at a facility called an urgent care center. Unlike ordinary doctor's offices, urgent care centers are typically open evenings and weekends and will see patients without an appointment.

Other types of health care facilities deal with specific problems or situations. Here are some examples:

• Birthing centers deliver babies in a homelike setting staffed by nurse-midwives.

• Drug treatment centers help people recover from drug and alcohol abuse.

• Assisted-living facilities provide care for people who need some help with everyday activities but do not need extended medical care.

• Hospices provide care for people who are terminally ill.

❷ TEACH

C Critical Thinking

Analyzing Read the definition of *health care system.* Then ask students to define the term *system.* (A group of parts that work together as a whole) Ask students why health care is referred to as a system. (Because health care is provided by many different people and facilities and paid for by different insurance plans, all working together) **OL**

Caption Answer

Figure 28.1 Sample answer: Family doctor, allergist, dentist, pharmacist

AL Active Learning

Making Pamphlets Have groups of students identify several different types of health care facilities in or near their community and make a pamphlet about the services they provide. Pamphlets should also list the addresses and phone numbers of the facilities. Arrange for students to display their pamphlets in public places in the community. **OL**

English Language Coach

Using Word Parts to Understand New Terms On the board, write the following words and word parts, including their definitions: ped- ("child"), *physic* ("medicine"), *obstetric* ("relating to childbirth"), *-iatric* ("relating to medical treatment"), and *-ician* ("practitioner of"). Ask students to combine the words and parts to form terms that refer to different types of doctors. As students say the terms, write them on the board and ask other students to provide literal definitions. (Possible terms include: *pediatrician,* "practitioner of medical treatment for children;" *physician,* "practitioner of medicine;" and *obstetrician,* "practitioner of childbirth.")

FITNESS ZONE

Exercise Buddy Have students pair with different buddies for each part of this activity:

- Have buddies shake hands and perform one exercise with that buddy for 10 reps.
- Call out "Find a new partner," give a high-5, select a new exercise and do 10 reps.
- Have students find the first partners, perform a complete exercise set that includes a handshake and two additional exercises, 10 reps each.

FITNESS ZONE

When I made the lacrosse team, I had to get a physical to show that I was healthy enough to play. I've had the same doctor since I was a kid, so he knew all about my medical history. He gave me a checkup, signed the permission form, and said he'd try to make it to one of my games. It's nice to have a doctor who really cares about you. For more fitness tips, visit the Online Fitness Zone at **glencoe.com**.

U Universal Access

Building on Prior Knowledge Most students are likely to be familiar with medical history forms from their visits with doctors. Obtain a medical history form from a doctor's office and make copies for students. Go through the form, line by line, explaining how the information requested on the form relates to the items in a medical history that are listed on this page. **BL** **EL**

HS Health Skills Practice

Communication Skills Guide students in listing information they would typically need to communicate to a doctor during a routine visit (e.g., symptoms, length of illness, current medicines, allergies to medications). Then ask students to develop a list of questions they might ask if they were visiting the doctor for flu symptoms (e.g., When should I start feeling better? When can I do my normal activities?) **EL**

You and Your Health Care

A doctor shouldn't just be someone you call when you're sick or injured. Ideally, you should have an ongoing relationship with your health care provider to keep track of your health. Seeing a primary care physician regularly allows you to build up a relationship of trust.

Your relationship with your health care provider is a partnership. Your doctor can treat problems and make recommendations for your health, but you need to take an active role in promoting your own wellness. You should be aware of your **medical history**—*complete and comprehensive information about your immunizations and any health problems you have had to date.* Also, make sure your doctor knows your medical history, including **U**

- any health conditions you have now.
- major physical or psychological problems you've had in the past.
- all medicines you are taking.
- any allergies you have to food or medication.
- any health problems that run in your family.
- your lifestyle and habits (for example, diet and exercise).

Your doctor should keep a record of your medical treatment on file. It will include information about health conditions, medications, and results of lab tests. A current trend in health care is to store these records in electronic form. This makes it easier for doctors to share information with each other and check for such problems as drug interactions. Whenever you have a doctor's appointment, note the reasons for your visit and list any questions you'd like to ask. During the visit, feel free to ask questions about the doctor's diagnosis or anything else you don't understand. Ask the doctor to write down any instructions so you won't forget them. If you have to fill a prescription at the pharmacy, you can also ask the pharmacist any questions you have about your medication. **HS**

■ **Figure 28.2** Your pharmacist can be a good source of information about both prescription and over-the-counter medicines. *What kinds of questions might you ask a pharmacist?*

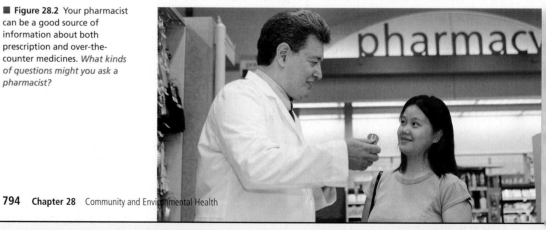

Health Literacy

Donate Life According to the U.S. Department of Health and Human Services, each organ and tissue donor saves or improves the lives of as many as 50 people. People of all ages and medical histories are considered potential donors. The donor's medical condition at the time of death will determine what organs and tissue can be donated. The United Network for Organ Sharing (UNOS) maintains computerized data on potential recipients and donors. Point out to students that in most states, there is a spot on the back of driver's licenses to indicate a desire to be an organ donor. However, it is important for them to talk to their families as they will be consulted before donation can take place.

Paying Health Care Costs

Modern health care can be very expensive. Most people need some kind of health insurance to help pay their medical bills. **Health insurance** includes *private and government programs that pay for part or all of a person's medical costs.* People typically pay for health insurance with a monthly fee, known as a *premium.* There are two main forms of health insurance:

- **Fee-for-service.** Under these plans, the patient must pay for all medical expenses up to a certain minimum amount, known as the *deductible.* After the deductible is reached, the insurance company will cover a percentage of the patient's costs. The portion that the patient must still pay for is called *coinsurance.* In many cases, the patient must pay medical bills up front and then send a form to the insurance company to be reimbursed. One advantage of fee-for-service plans is that patients typically can go to any doctor they choose.

- **Managed care.** These plans hold down costs by limiting patients' choices and encouraging preventive care. Some plans, such as health maintenance organizations (HMOs), require patients to choose their doctors from a limited pool of physicians. Managed care plans may not cover certain types of medical care, such as mental health care. However, they require less paperwork than fee-for-service plans. Rather than paying medical costs up front and applying for reimbursement, the patient typically pays a small fixed fee, known as a *copayment,* for each visit. Also, *out-of-pocket expenses*—the portion of medical costs paid by the patient—tend to be lower with managed care plans.

Most Americans receive insurance through their jobs (or through a family member's job). This is called group insurance. The employer may pay for part of the employee's premiums. People who cannot get insurance at work may buy individual policies. These vary widely in cost and in the benefits they offer, but in general, they cost more than group policies. People who cannot afford insurance at all may be covered under a federal government plan called Medicaid. All Americans over age 65 can receive coverage through a separate government program called Medicare.

Before selling a health policy to an individual, insurers generally require a medical exam to assess the person's level of health risk. People who are at a higher risk of developing health problems will be charged higher rates for insurance. A current **trend** is for group health plans to follow this practice as well. This reduces the risk that a plan will end up with more high-risk employees in its pool than it can afford.

READING CHECK

Explain What costs must patients pay out of pocket with a fee-for-service plan? With a managed care plan?

Academic Vocabulary

trend *(noun):* a line of general direction or movement

READING CHECK

Answer With a fee-for-service plan, patients must pay premiums, a deductible, and coinsurance. With a managed-care plan, they must pay premiums and copayments.

R Reading Strategy

Using Tables Work with students to make a table comparing types of health insurance plans so they can see their similarities and differences. Columns in the table might include *Type of Insurance, Types of Payments, Pros,* and *Cons.* There should be rows for fee-for-service and managed-care plans. **BL**

U Universal Access

Using Examples Use the example below to help students understand the difference between a *copayment* and *coinsurance.* Explain that, with managed care, patients pay the same amount, say $25, every time they visit the doctor. This is a copayment. With fee-for-service, patients pay a certain percentage, say 20 percent, of the cost of each doctor visit. The percentage they pay is the coinsurance. For example, if a doctor visit costs $160 and the coinsurance is 20 percent, the patient would pay 20 percent of $160, or $32, for that particular doctor visit. **EL**

Academic Vocabulary

Trend Have students read the definition of *trend.* Then draw a set of axes on the board, and label the x-axis "Time" and the y-axis "Cost of Insurance." Call on a volunteer to draw a line that shows a rising trend in the cost of insurance.

Writing Strategy

Personal Writing Have students write a sentence or short paragraph about their own health in response to each of the bulleted items on this page. Encourage them to ask a parent or guardian or call their doctor's office for any information they do not know or are unsure of. Advise students to keep their writing private, and remind them to proofread their responses and correct any errors. Suggest that they keep their responses in a safe place and take them to doctor visits and refer to them when filling out medical forms.

Main Idea

Public Health Services Promoting public health is the responsibility of many different agencies at all levels of government. **Ask Students:** *What are examples of health problems that might affect an entire population?* (Sample answers: Epidemics of contagious diseases such as flu; health problems due to air pollution or contaminated food)

C Critical Thinking

Inferring Explain that certain diseases and conditions are reportable, which means that doctors must report cases of the diseases to a local or state health department or to a federal agency. Reportable diseases include HIV/AIDS, cholera, gonorrhea, hepatitis, measles, and tuberculosis, to name just a few. Ask students to infer why diseases such as these are reportable. (Sample answer: Because they are serious, contagious diseases that could involve the health of many people, not just the individuals who have them) **OL**

AL Active Learning

Interviewing Have students interview personnel at their city or county health department to learn how the agency promotes teen health. For example, does it have any programs or services specifically for teens? Ask students to summarize the information they gather in a brief written report and read the report to the class. **OL**

Caption Answer

Figure 28.3 State and local health departments and national organizations such as the American Red Cross.

796

Public Health Services

Main Idea Agencies at all levels of government promote public health.

Your physician and other health care professionals help you take care of your personal health. However, you are also part of a community, and some health issues affect your community as a whole. To help deal with these issues, various agencies exist to promote public health. **Public health** includes *all efforts to monitor, protect, and promote the health of the population as a whole.* Public health agencies operate on all levels—local, state, national, and even worldwide. They work to make communities healthier by

- researching health problems.
- providing health services.
- educating the public.
- developing and enforcing policies that promote health.

C

Local Health Agencies

Local health departments are government agencies that operate at the city, county, or state level. They promote public health in various ways, including

- investigating threats to public health, such as outbreaks of disease.
- helping to plan responses to public health emergencies.
- enforcing local health regulations.
- providing information about health issues.

AL

■ **Figure 28.3** Nonprofit organizations such as AmeriCares promote community health in various ways. *What other groups contribute to public health?*

Skills for the *21st* Century

Self-Management Skills Explain to students that personal responsibility is an important self-management skill for maximizing the quality of one's health care. Share with students that responsible patients should

- keep their medical history up to date and make sure their doctor is aware of any changes.

- know their risk factors for serious conditions and diseases.

- learn about any conditions or diseases that they already have or are at high risk for.

- get a second opinion for any diagnosis or treatment plan about which they are uncomfortable or uncertain.

- evaluate their doctor and change if they are dissatisfied with their quality of care.

Real World CONNECTION

Evaluating Health Care Services

Some communities offer a wide variety of health care options. People who live in these communities can choose from several different primary care physicians, dentists, and medical specialists. They may be able to receive care at a local hospital, an urgent care center, or a walk-in clinic. In other communities, there may be only a single doctor to provide care for an entire area. How accessible are the health care services in your community?

Activity Reading / Writing

Consult the listings under "Physicians" in a local phone directory. Choose a physician listed near your home, and visit or call that physician's office. Find out the answers to the following questions:

- When is the practice open?
- How much does an office visit cost? Which types of insurance are accepted?
- How soon can one get an appointment for a checkup? For a medical problem?
- Is the practice accepting new patients?

Write a brief report that evaluates this health care provider in terms of accessibility and cost.

National Health Agencies

Nonprofit agencies, such as the American Red Cross and the American Heart Association, work at the national level, but they may also have local chapters. These groups focus on specific health problems or goals. They may provide health services or help educate the public about specific health issues. They may also fund research into new treatments to fight disease.

Several departments of the U.S. government also promote public health at the national level.

- The **Environmental Protection Agency (EPA)** protects the country's land, air, and water. A major part of its job is enforcing environmental laws. The EPA also works to research issues related to the health of the environment and to educate the public about these issues.

W
- The **Occupational Safety and Health Administration (OSHA)** is part of the U.S. Department of Labor. It works to prevent injuries and other health problems in the workplace. OSHA sets safety standards for workplaces and helps train and educate workers.

- The **U.S. Department of Agriculture (USDA)** has several offices that promote public health. For example, the **Food Safety and Inspection Service** ensures the safety of meat, poultry, and eggs. The **Food and Nutrition Service** provides food to needy families.

Lesson 1   Community and Public Health   **797**

Real World CONNECTION

Answers to Activity Questions

If students live in an urban area, you may want them to note the number of listings of just primary care physicians. If students live in a rural area, you may want them to note the number of listings of physicians within a wider geographic range.

In addition to calling the physician they select, students should go to the physician's office, if possible. They can see how crowded the waiting room is and how long patients have to wait. They should tell office personnel that they are working on a report for school and will need only a few minutes of their time.

Report

Each student's report should evaluate the chosen physician on the basis of both accessibility and cost. Evaluations should be supported by facts gathered from the physician's office.

W Writing Support

Expository Writing Ask students to research how OSHA tries to protect teen workers and have them write a newspaper article about it. Suggest that students read a few newspaper articles before they start writing to get a feel for the appropriate writing style. They should be sure to write a catchy headline. Encourage students to submit their articles to their school or hometown newspaper. **OL**

Cooperative Learning

Creating a Table Assign each of four small groups of students one of the following objectives of public health agencies: researching health problems, providing health services, educating the public, and developing and enforcing policies that promote health. Have students identify at least one public health agency that focuses on the assigned objective (for example, NIH for researching health problems). Tell them to find details and specific examples that illustrate how the agency addresses the objective. Then have groups pool their information and create a table with the following columns: *Name of Agency, Objectives of Agency, How Agency Meets Objectives,* and *Examples of Agency Work.* Give students a chance to present their tables to the class.

Cultural Awareness

Minority Health Agencies
Point out the Indian Health Service in **Figure 28.4**. Tell students that the CDC also has an agency that deals with health issues in ethnic populations, called the Office of Minority Health. Ask students why there are health agencies for ethnic minorities. (Sample answer: They might be at higher risk for certain health problems; they might have less access to health information because of language differences.)
EL

HS Health Skills Practice

Accessing Information Refer students to the lists of health agencies on this page and the next. Then have them access information in the lists to answer questions about the agencies, such as: *Which agency protects the public from health fraud?* (Federal Trade Commission) *What is the role of the Administration for Children and Families?* (aiding low-income families) **BL EL OL**

Caption Answer

Figure 28.4 The FDA ensures the safety of foods and cosmetics and the safety and effectiveness of medicines.

 **READING CHECK**

Answer Federal Trade Commission

Figure 28.4 **Health and Human Services Agencies**

The agencies in HHS oversee more than 300 health-related programs. *How does the FDA contribute to public health?* **CA**

National Institutes of Health (NIH)	Conducts and funds medical research
Food and Drug Administration (FDA)	Ensures the safety of foods and cosmetics and the safety and effectiveness of medicines
Centers for Disease Control and Prevention (CDC)	Works to track, prevent, and control outbreaks of disease
Indian Health Services (IHS)	Provides health care to Native Americans
Health Resources and Services Administration (HRSA)	Provides access to health care for low-income and uninsured people
Substance Abuse and Mental Health Services Administration (SAMHSA)	Funds programs to prevent and treat substance abuse and mental disorders
Agency for Healthcare Research and Quality (AHRQ)	Supports research on the health care system
Centers for Medicare and Medicaid Services (CMS)	Administers federal health insurance programs for elderly and low-income Americans
Administration for Children and Families (ACF)	Oversees programs to aid low-income families
Administration on Aging (AoA)	Provides services and support for older Americans

- The **Federal Trade Commission (FTC)** enforces consumer protection and antitrust laws. It prosecutes cases of *health fraud,* the sale of worthless products or services that claim to improve people's health or appearance. The FTC also educates consumers about how to choose health products and services wisely.

READING CHECK

Identify Which U.S. government agency works to fight health fraud?

- The **Department of Health and Human Services (HHS)** includes ten agencies that promote public health in various ways. **Figure 28.4** shows the agencies that are part of HHS.

Global Health Organizations

Many countries don't have the same access to health care that the United States and other developed nations do. In addition, disasters such as war, drought, flooding, or economic collapse can harm the public health of a nation. Government agencies and private organizations from around the world work to help countries in such crises. **HS**

 Home and Community

Learning About a Local Health Agency Have students find and contact the local chapter of a national nonprofit health organization, such as the American Red Cross, American Cancer Society, or American Heart Association. Students should learn what the agency does to promote public health and how people in the community can contribute to the efforts. Ask students to share what they learn by preparing a factsheet on the agency, including contact information.

- The **World Health Organization (WHO)** is the health agency of the United Nations. Its goals include improving health care systems and fighting diseases such as AIDS and malaria.
- The **United Nations Children's Fund (UNICEF)** promotes children's health and well-being through immunization, disaster relief, and education.
- The **International Committee of the Red Cross** aids victims of war and other forms of violence. The organization also works to promote and strengthen humanitarian laws.
- The **U.S. Agency for International Development (USAID)** provides aid to foreign countries to promote health, economic growth, and democratic reforms.
- The **Peace Corps,** a U.S. government agency, sends volunteers to developing nations to promote such goals as health, education, and economic development.
- **Cooperative for Assistance and Relief Everywhere (CARE)** fights global poverty. Its work includes promoting education, improving sanitation, and fighting HIV/AIDS.

LESSON 1 ASSESSMENT

After You Read

Reviewing Facts and Vocabulary

1. What is the difference between a primary care physician and a specialist?
2. List three types of health care facilities.
3. Identify two organizations that work to promote global health.

Thinking Critically

4. **Synthesize.** Why is it important for your doctor to know your medical history?
5. **Compare and Contrast.** Compare the advantages of fee-for-service insurance and managed care.

Applying Health Skills

6. **Accessing Information.** Use reliable print and online resources to learn more about one of the public health agencies listed in this lesson. Write a report explaining how the agency promotes public health and prevents disease.

Writing Critically

7. **Expository.** Write a newspaper-style article advising other teens about how they can take an active role in their own health care. Include tips on how to get the most out of a visit to the doctor.

G⊘ Online

Visit glencoe.com and complete the Interactive Study Guide for this lesson.

LESSON 1 ASSESSMENT ANSWERS

1. A primary care physician provides physical checkups and general care. A specialist focuses on a particular kind of patient or medical condition.
2. *Any three:* Private practices, group practices, clinics, hospitals, urgent care centers, birthing centers, drug treatment centers, assisted living facilities, hospices
3. *Any two:* WHO, UNICEF, International Red Cross, USAID, Peace Corps, CARE
4. To correctly diagnose and manage new medical problems; to give health advice
5. Fee-for-service insurance plans let you choose any doctor. Managed care plans require less paperwork and costs are less.
6. Reports will vary.
7. Articles will vary. Students should include tips about visiting the doctor and other specific examples from the lesson.

❸ ASSESS/ CLOSE

Assessment Resources

📁 *FAST FILE* **ACTIVITIES**
Lesson 1 Quiz

 ExamView Assessment Suite CD-ROM

Visit glencoe.com **for:**
Online Quizzes
Online Learning Center

Progress Monitoring

Reteaching

Have students work in pairs to develop four lists: *Types of Health Care Providers, Types of Health Care Facilities, Types of Health Insurance,* and *Examples of Public Health Agencies.* Have them give examples of the items listed.

Enrichment

Have students research medical specialists not mentioned in the lesson and create a table listing the different types of specialists and the kinds of conditions they treat.

Have students visit glencoe.com and complete the Interactive Study Guide for this lesson.

799

Air Quality and Health

1 FOCUS

GUIDE TO READING

BIG Idea Outside and inside air pollutants can have a negative impact on health.
Ask Students: *What substances might pollute indoor air?* (Sample answers: Fumes from cleaning products, cigarette smoke, dust, mold)

Before You Read

Comparison Chart
Students' charts should have three columns. Make sure students have defined all three types of pollution and, for each type, listed causes, effects, and solutions.

Main Idea

Understanding Air Pollution
Pollutants in both indoor and outdoor air may be harmful to human health and to the environment. **Ask Students:** *What health problems does air pollution cause?* (Sample answers: asthma, cancer)

Real Life Issues

Before students write their paragraphs, brainstorm ways to reduce energy use. **Ask Students:** *What are some ways people can use less energy?* (Sample answers: Using fans instead of air conditioners; turning off electric devices such as computers when not in use) Have volunteers read letters to the class.

800

GUIDE TO READING

BIG Idea *Both outdoor and indoor air quality can affect your health.*

Before You Read

Create a Comparison Chart. Make a three-column chart. Label the columns "Outdoor Air Pollution," "Indoor Air Pollution," and "Noise Pollution." As you read, use the chart to define each term, list causes and effects, and identify solutions.

Outdoor Air Pollution	Indoor Air Pollution	Noise Pollution

New Vocabulary

▶ air pollution (p. 800)
▶ smog (p. 801)
▶ Air Quality Index (AQI) (p. 801)
▶ greenhouse effect (p. 801)
▶ global warming (p. 802)
▶ noise pollution (p. 804)
▶ decibel (p. 804)

Air Quality and Health

Real Life Issues

Saving Energy. Rachel has always been in the habit of turning on the television as soon as she comes home from school. Even if she's not watching it, she likes having it on in the background. Lately, though, she's started to wonder just how much electricity she's wasting by doing this—and how much air pollution she might be causing. This makes her think about what other habits she might have that waste energy and what she could do to cut back.

Writing *Evaluate your own energy usage. How might you reduce the amount of energy you use? Write your thoughts in a paragraph.*

Understanding Air Pollution

Main Idea Indoor and outdoor air pollutants can harm human health and damage the natural environment.

You normally can't see it, but air is all around you. The quality of the air you breathe has a significant impact on your health. **Air pollution**, *the contamination of the earth's atmosphere by harmful substances*, poses serious health concerns. In fact, numerous studies have linked it to a wide variety of health problems, including lung disease, cardiovascular disease, and cancer.

Air Quality

In the United States, the Environmental Protection Agency (EPA) sets air quality standards to prevent and correct problems related to environmental air pollution.

Promoting School Wellness

Reducing School Bus Idling Diesel school buses give off hazardous air pollutants when they are idling. The pollutants can enter schools through windows and vents and pollute outdoor loading and unloading zones. Several states have enacted laws requiring school bus drivers to reduce the amount of time they let their buses idle. If your state has an idle-reduction law, make sure that bus drivers in your school or district are in compliance. School personnel can spot-check loading and unloading zones and, if necessary, remind drivers to reduce idling. If your state does not have an idle-reduction law, support the adoption of an idle-reduction program by your school or district. The EPA's National Idle-Reduction Campaign can help. It provides sample policies, materials to publicize programs, and useful tips. If possible, get students involved in the effort.

The EPA has placed limits on the levels of six pollutants that harm human health and the environment.

- **Ozone (O_3)** forms at ground level when certain other pollutants react chemically in the presence of sunlight. Ground-level ozone is a major **component** of **smog**, *a brownish haze that sometimes forms in urban areas*. Ozone irritates the lungs and makes breathing difficult. It can worsen respiratory problems such as asthma, bronchitis, and emphysema.

- **Particulate matter (PM)** is a general term for small particles found in the air, such as dust, soil, soot, smoke, mold, and droplets of liquid. PM can cause breathing difficulties, certain lung diseases, and even heart attacks.

- **Carbon monoxide (CO)** is a colorless, odorless gas that forms when carbon in fuel is not burned completely. Outdoor sources of CO include automobile exhaust and industrial processes. CO harms the body by preventing oxygen from reaching body tissues. At high enough levels, CO can be deadly.

- **Sulfur dioxide (SO_2)** comes chiefly from power plants, especially those that burn coal. In addition to harming respiratory health, SO_2 can combine with water to form acid rain, which is harmful to plants and animals.

- **Nitrogen oxides (NO_x)** are highly reactive gases that form when fuel is burned at high temperatures, as in motor vehicles and power plants. NO_x contributes to the formation of ground-level ozone, acid rain, PM, and a wide variety of toxic chemicals.

- **Lead** is a metal found naturally in the environment as well as in manufactured products. Exposure to lead can damage the kidneys, liver, brain, and nerves and can cause cardiovascular disease and anemia.

To track the levels of pollutants in the air, the EPA has created the **Air Quality Index (AQI)**, *an index for reporting daily air quality*. The AQI, shown in **Figure 28.5** on page 802, informs the public about local air quality and whether pollution levels pose health risks.

Greenhouse Gases

Air pollutants can also contribute to global climate change. The **greenhouse effect** is *the trapping of heat by gases in the earth's atmosphere*. These gases allow sunlight to enter our atmosphere but block radiation from escaping to outer space—much like the glass roof of a greenhouse. The chief greenhouse gas produced by human activity is carbon dioxide (CO_2). The burning of fossil fuels in power plants and motor vehicles is the chief source of CO_2 buildup.

Academic Vocabulary

component (noun): a constituent part or ingredient

Go Online

Go to **glencoe.com** and complete the Student Web Activity on climate change and what people and governments can do to help solve the problem.

❷ TEACH

C Critical Thinking

Explaining Point out that ozone forms when other pollutants, such as nitrogen oxides, undergo chemical reactions in the presence of sunlight. Explain that the reactions occur faster at higher temperatures. Ask students to explain why ozone is a greater problem in summer than winter. (Temperatures are higher in summer, so more ozone forms.) **OL**

HS Health Skills Practice

Accessing Information Ask a different student each day to go online and find the AQI for their community (or the nearest community for which the AQI is available). The student should report the AQI and any air quality health warnings to the class. **OL**

Academic Vocabulary

Component Point out that *ingredient* is a synonym for the word *component*. Ask students to name typical ingredients in a common food, such as salad or pizza, and to explain how the ingredients are related to the whole.

Go Online

Assign students to complete the Student Web Activity on climate change at **glencoe.com**. Have them report on what can be done to improve air quality and reduce global warming.

Reading Strategy

Identifying Cause and Effect Ask students to divide a sheet of paper into two columns. In the first column, have them write *air pollution* and below that a list of specific air pollutants, such as ozone. In the second column, have students list health problems caused by air pollution in general and by each specific air pollutant they listed. Students' charts should show, for example, that ozone causes lung irritation, difficulty breathing, and worsening of asthma, bronchitis, and emphysema. Suggest that students save their charts and use them as study guides.

Caption Answer

Figure 28.5 You can use the AQI to help you avoid unhealthy exposure to air pollution.

AL Active Learning

Demonstrating Concepts Show students a picture of a greenhouse and ask a small group to make a model greenhouse with materials such as plastic wrap, craft sticks, and glue. Place their model in an open outdoor location. Then provide the students with two thermometers and ask them to measure the temperature of the air both inside and outside the model greenhouse. Challenge other students to explain how the model represents the greenhouse effect. For example, what does the plastic wrap represent? (greenhouse gases) **BL EL**

READING CHECK

Answer Human actions, particularly the burning of fossil fuels, raise the level of carbon dioxide in the atmosphere. Carbon dioxide is a greenhouse gas that traps heat in the atmosphere and contributes to global warming.

W Writing Support

Narrative Writing Ask interested students to research "sick building syndrome." Then have the students write a fictional account to convey what they learn. For example, they might describe a day in the life of a person who works in a sick building. In their narratives, students should reveal information about the type of building that causes the syndrome, symptoms of the syndrome, and how the syndrome is treated or prevented. Make copies of the narratives for the rest of the class to read. **OL AL**

802

Figure 28.5 **Air Quality Index (AQI)**

The EPA created this index to inform the public about daily air quality. *How can you use the AQI in your community to help protect your health?*

Range	Air Quality	Color Code
0 to 50	**Good:** There is little or no health risk.	Green
51 to 100	**Moderate:** Some pollutants may pose a moderate health concern for a very small number of people.	Yellow
101 to 150	**Unhealthy for Sensitive Groups:** Members of sensitive groups, such as people with lung disease, may experience health effects.	Orange
151 to 200	**Unhealthy:** Everyone may begin to experience health effects.	Red
201 to 300	**Very Unhealthy:** Everyone may experience more serious health effects.	Purple
301 to 500	**Hazardous:** Emergency conditions. The entire population is at risk.	Maroon

READING CHECK

Cause and Effect
How do human actions contribute to global warming?

The greenhouse effect is actually normal and necessary to support life on this planet. In the past 200 years, however, the concentration of greenhouse gases trapped in the earth's atmosphere has risen, resulting in **global warming**. This is *an overall increase in the earth's temperature.* Since 1900, the earth's average surface temperature has risen by 1.2 to 1.4 degrees F. If levels of greenhouse gases continue to rise, average temperatures could increase anywhere from 2.5 to 10.4 degrees F by the end of the twenty-first century.

The exact effects of global warming are hard to predict. Already, though, glaciers are beginning to melt, causing sea levels to rise. Global weather patterns could also shift. Areas might receive much less or much more rainfall than they do now. Plants and animals that cannot adapt to the new conditions could become extinct. The world's food supply could also be at risk if crop-growing areas are struck by drought.

AL

Indoor Air Pollution

Research has found that in many cases, the air inside buildings contains more pollutants than the outdoor air, even in the biggest cities. Common sources of indoor air pollution include household chemicals, such as cleaning fluids and pesticides, and chemicals used in building and furnishing materials. Lack of ventilation makes the problem worse by trapping air pollutants inside.

W

Myths & Reality

Energy-Saving Myths

Myth: Leaving lights and computers on uses less energy than turning them off and on.

Fact: Although some devices use a little extra energy when turned on and off, it is usually much less than the energy used by keeping them on when they are not needed.

Myth: Electric heating is more efficient than gas or oil heating.

Fact: Although electric furnaces use energy more efficiently than gas or oil furnaces, making electricity in a power plant from gas or oil is less efficient than burning gas or oil in a home furnace.

Specific problems with indoor air quality include

- **carbon monoxide,** produced by fuel-burning equipment, such as stoves, furnaces, and fireplaces.
- **asbestos,** a mineral fiber. In the past, asbestos was often used as a fire retardant in insulation and building materials. Cutting or sanding these materials can release particles of asbestos into the air. Inhaling these particles can lead to lung cancer and other forms of lung damage.
- **radon,** an odorless, radioactive gas produced during the natural breakdown of the element uranium in soil and rocks. It can enter homes through dirt floors, cracks in concrete floors and walls, or floor drains. Exposure to high levels of radon can cause lung cancer.

Reducing Air Pollution

Main Idea Your choices can fight air pollution.

 You can make choices to help reduce air pollution. Since power plants and home heating systems are sources of air pollution, reducing your use of energy is a good place to start. Here are some tips for saving energy:

- Switch off lights whenever you leave a room. Consider replacing regular incandescent lightbulbs with compact fluorescent bulbs, which use less energy and last longer.
- Turn off radios, computers, televisions, and other such appliances when they are not in use.
- In the winter, wear extra layers of clothing to stay warm so you can keep the thermostat at around 68 degrees F. Turn the thermostat down even lower at night. In the summer, set the thermostat at around 78 degrees F to keep the air conditioning from coming on too often. Instead, use a fan to cool rooms.
- Insulate your home to reduce your need for heating and cooling. Seal leaks around doors, windows, and electrical sockets to prevent heated or cooled air from escaping.
- Wash clothes in warm or cold water rather than hot water.
- When cooking, don't preheat the oven longer than necessary. Try cooking small amounts of food in a toaster oven or microwave rather than a full-size oven.

Cars are another major source of air pollution. Whenever you can, try walking, riding a bicycle, using public transportation, or carpooling to save gas. Another way to conserve gasoline is to reduce the use of motorized equipment, such as power mowers, chain saws, and leaf blowers. When possible, use hand tools to get the job done.

Fluorescent Light Bulbs

Analyze. Go to glencoe.com and watch the video *Fluorescent Light Bulbs.* With a partner, discuss the pros and cons of switching to fluorescent light bulbs (CFLs). Decide whether you think CFLs are an effective energy-saving alternative, and be ready to share your ideas with the class.

✔ READING CHECK

Identify List three actions you and your family can take to reduce air pollution.

Lesson 2   Air Quality and Health   **803**

Academic Integration

Science Tell students that the Arctic is warming up at twice the rate of other parts of the earth, causing the melting of Arctic Sea ice. Since the 1970s, an area of Arctic ice bigger than California and Texas combined has melted. Explain that Arctic ice reflects sunlight back into space and reduces the amount of heat the earth absorbs. Call on students to explain why the melting of Arctic ice causes the earth to become even warmer. (With less ice, the earth absorbs more heat.) Ask students to create drawings or graphic organizers that show how the effects of global warming in the Arctic feed back to increase global warming.

Main Idea

Reducing Air Pollution People can help reduce both indoor and outdoor air pollution by making choices to use less energy. **Ask Students:** *What are some ways people can use less energy?* (Sample answers: Walking instead of driving, turning down the heat)

After students have watched the video, ***Fluorescent Light Bulbs,*** have them choose a partner and discuss the pros and cons of using compact fluorescent light bulbs (CFLs). Partners should try to decide whether using CFLs is an effective way to save energy. Give partners a chance to share their ideas with the class.

ⓤ Universal Access

Using Diagrams Students may not see the connection between energy use and air pollution. Create a simple diagram on the board to show how the two are related. The diagram should show that energy comes from power plants, which give off pollutants into the air. Based on the diagram, ask students to explain what happens when people use more energy. (Power plants produce more energy and give off more pollutants into the air.) **EL** **BL**

✔ READING CHECK

Answer Students may identify any three of the strategies on this page.

R Reading Strategy

Using Concept Maps Work with students to create a concept map to organize the information in the text under the heading *Managing Indoor Air Pollution.* The concept map should show that there are three basic strategies for managing indoor air pollution: finding and eliminating pollutants, increasing ventilation, and using air cleaners. **BL**

Main Idea

Noise Pollution Loud sounds can damage your hearing. **Ask Students:** *What are some loud sounds teens might be exposed to?* (Sample answers: Lawn mowers, sirens, motorcycles, rock concerts)

C Critical Thinking

Computing Use examples to show students how to interpret the decibel scale. Explain that the intensity of a sound of 20 decibels is ten times greater than the intensity of a sound of 10 decibels; and the intensity of a sound of 30 decibels is 10 × 10, or 100, times greater than the intensity of a sound of 10 decibels. Ask students to compute how much more intense a sound of 40 decibels is than a sound of 10 decibels. (10 × 10 × 10, or 1,000, times more intense) **OL** **AL**

READING CHECK

Answer Harmful, unwanted sound loud enough to damage hearing

■ **Figure 28.6** Riding mass transit is one way to reduce the air pollution associated with car use. *What are other transportation options that help reduce air pollution?*

READING CHECK

Define What is *noise pollution?*

Managing Indoor Air Pollution

To improve indoor air quality, you can identify sources of pollution and get rid of them. Home test kits and detectors can help you measure the levels of radon and carbon monoxide in your home. Depending on what you find, you may be able to eliminate the pollution sources yourself, or you may need the help of a professional.

If you can't get rid of all the sources completely, you may be able to reduce the pollutant levels in the air by increasing the ventilation in your home. Opening windows and turning on window or attic fans can help remove pollutants that build up in the short term. A long-term, more expensive solution is to modify your home's ventilation system. You can also try using air cleaners to filter out particle pollution. However, these devices cannot eliminate most gaseous pollutants. **R**

Noise Pollution

Main Idea Exposure to loud noises can harm your health.

Traffic, loud music, construction equipment, and power tools are all sources of **noise pollution**. This is *harmful, unwanted sound loud enough to damage hearing.* To better understand what types of noise levels can harm your hearing, take a look at **Figure 28.7**. This graph shows the decibel levels of some common sounds. A **decibel** is *a unit that measures the intensity of sound.* A level of 0 decibels represents the lowest level of sound the human ear can detect. Noise levels of 130 decibels or higher can cause pain.

If you are exposed to loud noise, you may experience a temporary hearing loss, which may be accompanied by ringing in the ears. In most cases, you will recover your normal hearing shortly after the noise stops. However, repeated exposure to noise at levels around 90 decibels or higher can lead to permanent hearing loss. **C**

If you are going someplace where you are likely to be exposed to loud noise, wear earplugs or earmuffs. You can also avoid contributing to noise pollution by keeping the volume down on stereos and TV sets. Use manual tools instead of power tools, and avoid using your car horn unnecessarily.

Teens Want to Know

How Can I Protect My Hearing from Noise? Whenever you are exposed to noises at or above 90 decibels for more than an hour or two, you should wear either earplugs or earmuffs. Earplugs are better at blocking low-pitched noises, and earmuffs are better at blocking high-pitched noises. Properly fitting earplugs and earmuffs provide a complete seal between the hearing protector and ear. If they do not fit properly and the seal is incomplete, they will not be as effective. Pre-molded earplugs are less likely to form a complete seal than expandable or moldable earplugs, and earmuffs may not form a complete seal on people who wear glasses or have long hair. Wearing earplugs and earmuffs together provides better protection than either alone and is recommended for noise above 105 decibels.

Figure 28.7 Decibel Levels of Common Sounds

A decibel is not a fixed unit of sound. Instead, each 10-decibel increase roughly doubles the loudness of a sound.

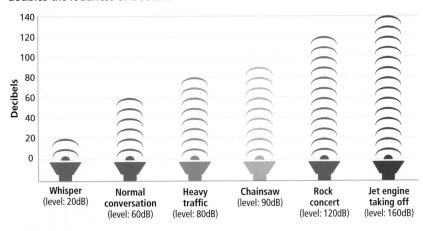

| Whisper (level: 20dB) | Normal conversation (level: 60dB) | Heavy traffic (level: 80dB) | Chainsaw (level: 90dB) | Rock concert (level: 120dB) | Jet engine taking off (level: 160dB) |

LESSON 2 ASSESSMENT

After You Read

Reviewing Facts and Vocabulary

1. Name the six outdoor air pollutants for which the EPA sets limits.

2. How is radon harmful to human health?

3. What might result from repeated exposure to sounds of 90 decibels or louder?

Thinking Critically

4. **Evaluate.** How might your health be affected if the EPA stopped regulating common air pollutants?

5. **Analyze.** Explain the connection between the greenhouse effect and global warming.

Applying Health Skills

6. **Decision Making.** The morning news has reported an AQI of 145. Paul, who has asthma, was planning to go in-line skating with his friends. Use the decision-making process to determine what you would do in Paul's place.

Writing Critically

7. **Persuasive.** Write a script for a public service announcement urging teens and others to take steps to reduce air pollution. List specific steps in your announcement and show how each is tied to the goal of reducing air pollution.

Go Online

Visit **glencoe.com** and complete the Interactive Study Guide for this lesson.

3 ASSESS/ CLOSE

Assessment Resources

📁 *FAST FILE* ACTIVITIES
Lesson 2 Quiz

💿 *ExamView Assessment Suite* CD-ROM

Visit glencoe.com for:
Online Quizzes
Online Learning Center

Progress Monitoring

Reteaching

Play a quiz game by reading the definitions of the lesson vocabulary and asking students to identify the words. Continue until all the students have had a chance to identify at least one word.

Enrichment

Have students write a concise paragraph explaining why a greenhouse is a good model for the trapping of heat by the atmosphere. Have volunteers read their paragraphs aloud.

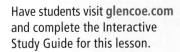

Have students visit **glencoe.com** and complete the Interactive Study Guide for this lesson.

LESSON 2 ASSESSMENT ANSWERS

1. Ozone, particulate matter, carbon monoxide, sulfur dioxide, nitrogen oxides, lead

2. Exposure to high levels of radon can cause lung cancer.

3. Permanent hearing loss

4. Levels of common air pollutants might rise, increasing the risk for health problems such as lung disease.

5. The greenhouse effect is the trapping of heat by gases in the atmosphere. This causes an overall increase in the earth's temperature, which is called global warming.

6. Students should apply the six steps of the decision-making process. (Sample answer: If I were Paul, I would not go skating because the air quality might harm my health.)

7. Scripts should be persuasive and reflect knowledge of ways to reduce air pollution.

Protecting Land and Water

1 FOCUS

GUIDE TO READING

BIG Idea The earth's land and water can be either harmed or protected by human actions. **Ask Students:** *What are some human actions that can harm the earth's land or water?* (Sample answers: Clearing forests and leaving the soil bare so it erodes away; dumping chemicals into streams)

Before You Read

Word Web Students' word webs for a healthy environment might include such characteristics as clean air and clean water.

Main Idea

Waste Disposal Land and water can be protected by properly disposing of wastes. **Ask Students:** *What happens to items that you throw in the trash?* (They go to a landfill or are burned.)

Real Life Issues ••••••••••••

Divide the class into small groups to brainstorm waste-reduction strategies. **Ask Students:** *How can changing buying habits reduce waste?* (Sample answer: Buying one large item instead of several smaller ones reduces packaging materials to be recycled.)

GUIDE TO READING

BIG Idea *Human actions can either damage or protect land and water.*

Before You Read

Create a Word Web. Write "Healthy Environment" in the center of a sheet of paper. Around it, jot down characteristics of a healthy environment. As you read, add more notes to your word web.

Healthy Environment

New Vocabulary

▸ biodegradable (p. 806)
▸ landfill (p. 807)
▸ hazardous wastes (p. 807)
▸ deforestation (p. 808)
▸ urban sprawl (p. 809)
▸ wastewater (p. 809)
▸ conservation (p. 810)
▸ precycling (p. 810)
▸ recycling (p. 810)

Protecting Land and Water

Real Life Issues •••••••••••••••••••••

Wondering About Waste. Carlos has started to notice just how much trash his family throws out every day. A lot of it seems to be packaging, such as empty juice boxes and snack wrappers. He wonders whether changing some of their buying habits could make a big dent in the amount of waste they create. However, he's not sure how to convince his family that it's worth the effort.

Writing *Brainstorm a list of strategies to reduce waste. Then write a dialogue in which Carlos persuades his family to try some of these ideas.*

Waste Disposal

Main Idea Wastes need to be disposed of safely.

Getting rid of the waste we produce is a big problem for our society. If wastes aren't properly contained or destroyed, they can pollute the land and water we rely on to live. This can harm human health by making water supplies unsafe to drink or contributing to the spread of pathogens.

Many types of waste are **biodegradable**, or *able to be broken down by microorganisms in the environment.* Biodegradable wastes will not break down if they are disposed of in ways that do not expose them to the environment. Many other wastes are not biodegradable and need to be disposed of in ways that will do the least possible damage to the environment.

Solid Waste

Municipal solid waste (MSW) is another term for trash or garbage. There are two ways to dispose of MSW:

More About...

Disposing of Household Hazardous Waste In addition to disposing of household hazardous waste at hazardous waste collection sites, you can safely dispose of some types of hazardous waste in other ways. For example, you can

• return empty printer cartridges to the manufacturer or an office supply store for recycling.

• take used engine oil and oil filters to a service station, old tires to a tire dealer, and spent car batteries to an auto parts store to be recycled.

Many people take partly used cans of latex paint to hazardous waste collection sites, but this is not necessary and wastes money, because latex paint is not hazardous. To dispose of latex paint, let it dry in the can and then place the can in the trash.

- **Landfills.** A **landfill** is *a specially engineered area where waste can be buried safely.* Modern landfills have a variety of safeguards in place to prevent wastes from damaging the nearby land and water. For example, they must be located away from sensitive natural areas and operated in ways that control odors and pests. They also must use special liners to prevent leakage that could contaminate groundwater.

AL

- **Incineration.** Burning wastes in specially designed incinerators reduces the volume of trash that otherwise would go into landfills. Waste incinerators use "scrubbers" and filters on their smokestacks to reduce air pollution. Some incinerators use the energy from burning waste to produce electricity, reducing the need for fuel.

■ **Figure 28.8** Some MSW is burned in specially designed incinerators. *What is another way to dispose of solid waste?*

Hazardous Wastes

Hazardous wastes are *waste materials with properties that make them dangerous to human health or the environment.* Wastes may be considered hazardous because they are corrosive, chemically unstable, highly flammable, or toxic. Most hazardous wastes must be treated to make them less harmful before being discarded at special disposal sites. Types of hazardous waste include

- **industrial wastes.** These include solvents used for cleaning and degreasing as well as sludge and wastewater from certain industries, such as oil refining.

- **household wastes.** Products such as pesticides, paints, cleaning fluids, and batteries may be hazardous when discarded. Some household wastes are banned from landfills and must be disposed of at special collection sites.

- **radioactive wastes.** Sources such as nuclear power plants produce wastes that emit radiation. Exposure to radiation can increase the risk of cancer. It can also cause mutations, harmful changes in the body's DNA, which may be passed on to offspring. Extremely high levels of radiation can cause burns and radiation sickness.

 **READING CHECK**

Explain What properties make certain wastes hazardous?

Lesson 3   Protecting Land and Water   **807**

Cooperative Learning

Tracking Biodegradable Waste Have a group of students investigate what happens to biodegradable waste, such as kitchen scraps and yard waste, when it is thrown in the trash. Have another group of students investigate what happens to the same waste when it is composted. The first group should find out how long it takes the waste to break down inside a plastic bag in a landfill (possibly hundreds of years). The other group should find out how long it takes the waste to break down in a compost pile (less than one year). Ask the groups to compare their findings and discuss the benefits of composting biodegradable waste.

② TEACH

AL Active Learning

Debating Have students learn more about the pros and cons of landfilling vs. incineration. For example, incineration produces energy but releases greenhouse gases, whereas landfills release fewer greenhouse gases but may cause water pollution. Ask students to decide which method of solid waste disposal they think is better for the environment. Then have any students who take opposing views debate the issue. **AL**

Caption Answer

Figure 28.8 Put it in landfills

HS Health Skills Practice

Practicing Healthful Behaviors Have students assume that they have cleaned their basement or garage and found a number of items they must dispose of, including an old mercury thermometer, a can of used motor oil, a stack of newspapers, an old car battery, and several glass bottles. Have students describe the proper way to dispose of these items. (The newspapers and glass bottles should be recycled. The thermometer, can of oil, and car battery should be disposed of at a hazardous waste collection site.) **OL**

READING CHECK

Answer Wastes are hazardous if they are corrosive, chemically unstable, highly flammable, or toxic.

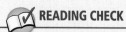

Main Idea

Problems of Development
The environment can be harmed by urban development. **Ask Students:** *What is urban development?* (Sample answer: The building of new neighborhoods, streets, and other structures on previously undeveloped land)

READING CHECK

Answer Trees absorb carbon dioxide, which is the chief greenhouse gas. With fewer trees, there is more carbon dioxide in the atmosphere. This contributes to the greenhouse effect, which causes global warning.

R Reading Strategy

Finding Topic Sentences Have students find the topic sentence in the paragraph on disappearing forests. Suggest that they first determine the topic of the paragraph by asking themselves: "What is this paragraph about?" Then they should look for the sentence that is a general statement of what the paragraph is about. **BL**

Caption Answer

Figure 28.9 Extinction of some species, greater risk for soil erosion and flooding, hotter and drier local climates, increased global warming

Because of these risks, such wastes must be isolated in secure storage sites until the radioactive materials decay, or cease to be radioactive.

- **mercury.** This naturally occurring substance is highly toxic to humans and other animals. It is found in some medical and dental wastes and in certain parts of cars.

Problems of Development

Main Idea Urban development impacts the environment.

Throughout human history, the number of people on the planet has been growing at a faster and faster rate. As the world population grows, so does our use of resources. Wilderness areas give way to new urban developments, with drastic impacts on the environment.

Disappearing Forests

READING CHECK

Cause and Effect How does deforestation contribute to global warming?

In many parts of the world, forests are being cleared away to make room for new developments. Timber from these forests is also used for fuel and manufacturing. **Deforestation**, or *destruction of forests*, causes a variety of problems.

- It destroys the habitats of plant and animal species.
- The loss of trees puts these areas at risk for soil erosion and flooding.
- It alters the local climate, making it hotter and drier.
- It contributes to global warming because trees absorb carbon dioxide, a greenhouse gas, from the atmosphere.

R

■ **Figure 28.9** Forests play a vital role in the environment, providing oxygen, homes for a variety of living organisms, and natural beauty. *What are some of the consequences of destroying forests?*

808 Chapter 28 Community and Environmental Health

Home and Community

Evaluating Community Runoff Point out that runoff is the major source of water pollution in the United States and that it is increasing with urban sprawl. Suggest that students research the problem of runoff in their own or another community. They should try to answer such questions as: Where is runoff the worst? Where does runoff come from? What areas does runoff flow over? What pollutants might the runoff be picking up? Ask volunteers to share their research findings with the class. Work with students to identify strategies—such as planting grass or trees on bare soil—that might reduce the amount of runoff and the pollutants it contains.

Urban Sprawl

The spreading of city development (houses, shopping centers, businesses, and schools) onto undeveloped land is called **urban sprawl**. Sprawl contributes to several environmental problems. For example, paved areas do not filter rainwater the way soil does. As a result, runoff can carry pollutants into the water supply. Sprawl also destroys wildlife habitats and reduces air quality.

To combat these problems, some city planners have embraced a concept called *smart growth*. It involves planning communities in ways that use fewer resources and create less pollution. For example, planners may incorporate *mixed-use development*. In this type of development, businesses, homes, and schools are located close together, making it easier for people to walk from place to place instead of driving. Smart growth also involves building more compactly, which preserves open land and provides more **transit** choices.

Academic Vocabulary

transit *(noun):* local transportation

Water: A Limited Resource

Main Idea Pollution threatens our limited water supply.

Less than 1 percent of the earth's water is in a form humans can use. This limited supply makes water a precious resource. The EPA is responsible for protecting the water supply in the United States. It sets standards for the quality of drinking water and seeks to protect the health of oceans, rivers, and other water systems.

Sources of Water Pollution

Rivers, lakes, and aquifers (bodies of groundwater) provide much of our water supply. Pollutants can enter the supply in several different ways:

- **Runoff.** When rainwater or melting snow flows across the ground and into the water supply, it can pick up pesticides, fertilizers, salt, and other wastes.
- **Wastewater,** *used water from homes, communities, farms, and businesses.* Wastewater can contain pollutants, such as human wastes, metals, and pathogens. The EPA requires that wastewater be treated to remove pollutants before it is released back into the environment.
- **Sediment.** Runoff can carry soil and other sediments into the water supply. This can clog lakes and rivers.
- **Oil.** Spills from oil tankers and offshore drilling rigs can pollute the water. Oil poured down drains or onto the ground can also enter the water supply.

 **READING CHECK**

Identify Name four sources of water pollution.

Main Idea

Water: A Limited Resource The earth's water supply is limited and threatened by pollution. **Ask Students:** *If water covers about 70 percent of the earth's surface, why is water for human use limited?* (Most of the earth's water is salty, and humans cannot use salt water for drinking or most other purposes.)

Academic Vocabulary

Transit Explain that mass transit systems use just one or a few vehicles to transport many people, who might otherwise individually drive vehicles and create more pollution. Ask students to identify mass transit systems, such as buses or subways, that are available in their own or a nearby community.

U Universal Access

Using Visuals Have students use an online image search engine to find pictures of the four ways pollutants can enter the water supply (runoff, wastewater, sediment, and oil). If students have access to a printer, you can ask them to print some of the pictures and use them to create a bulletin board display. **EL**

READING CHECK

Answer Runoff, wastewater, sediment, oil

Teacher to Teacher

Theresa Despino • Alexandria Sr. High School, Alexandria, LA

Protecting Land and Water To increase awareness of our responsibility to keep our environment clean, spend a class period picking up trash and sorting it for recycling. Make arrangements with the school custodians to pick up the trash for a designated time. Provide trash bags and latex gloves and have students collect all the trash. After the collection is complete, divide trash into different types (paper, plastic, cans, etc.) and sort for recycling. Having the actual hands-on experience of picking up trash helps them become more aware of their responsibility to keep the school and their environment clean.

Advocacy: Promoting Recycling

NHES Standard 8 Students will demonstrate the ability to advocate for personal, family, and community health.

Objectives

* Identify the benefits of recycling.
* Apply the skill of advocacy to help promote recycling.

Teaching Strategies

* Have students name recycling options NOT offered in their community.
* Have the class brainstorm reasons that some people do not recycle and ways to convince people to recycle.

Assessment

Using a rubric, student work should provide comprehensive evidence of the following criteria to achieve the highest score:

√ Clear statement of the benefits of recycling
√ Persuasive use of arguments for why people should recycle
√ Encouragement of others to make healthful choices
√ Presentation of convincing reasons for starting a curbside recycling program

Water Scarcity

Not only is the world's supply of water limited, but this supply is also unevenly distributed. An estimated 500 million people around the world have trouble getting the water they need to live. As the world population continues to grow, the demand for water increases. Disputes over water resources could lead to major conflicts between nations.

Protecting the Environment

Main Idea Conservation helps protect the environment.

People can help protect the environment by practicing **conservation**. This means *avoiding waste through careful management of natural resources,* such as energy, water, and materials. In Lesson 2, you learned about ways to conserve energy. You can also conserve water and land by reducing your water use and minimizing pollution:

* Repair leaky faucets, and never leave water running unnecessarily.
* Wait until you have a full load before doing laundry or running the dishwasher.
* Consider installing low-flow showerheads, faucet aerators, and low-flush toilets.
* Avoid overwatering your lawn and garden. Consider landscaping with plants that require less water.
* Try reducing your use of household chemicals or looking for versions that are less hazardous.
* Check with local authorities to find out how to discard hazardous wastes such as oil, paint, and batteries safely.

You also can reduce the amount of waste you produce by practicing the three Rs:

* **Reduce.** Source reduction, or **precycling**, means *reducing waste before it is generated.* For example, you can choose reusable products (such as cloth napkins) and products with less packaging.
* **Reuse.** Next to precycling, the most efficient way to reduce waste is to reuse items. If you have an item that you no longer need, you can sell it, give it to a friend, or donate it to a charity instead of throwing it away. You can also repair broken items instead of buying new ones.
* **Recycle. Recycling** is *the processing of waste materials so that they can be used again.* Recycling conserves materials and energy and reduces the need for new landfills and incinerators.

✓ **READING CHECK**

List What are three steps you can take to help conserve natural resources?

Go Online

Go to glencoe.com and complete the Student Web Activity on the benefits of recycling.

Skills for the **21st** Century

Life and Learning Skills Have students imagine that they live in a community that does not have a recycling program and they plan to give a speech about starting a recycling program at their next city council meeting. Ask students to prepare a brief but effective speech in which they argue that funding a community recycling program is a socially responsible action for the city council to take. Students should use clear, persuasive communication and present arguments backed with accurate facts and convincing reasons. Give students a chance to present their speeches to the class.

Health Skills Activity

Advocacy

Promoting Recycling

Kathy's family has just moved to a new town. In her old neighborhood, her family could leave recyclables at the curb to be picked up, but her new town doesn't offer this service. There is a local drop-off center, but not many people seem to use it. Most people put all their recyclables—newspapers, cans, bottles, and so on—in the regular garbage.

Kathy wonders what she can do to encourage more of her neighbors to recycle and maybe even get a curbside recycling program started. She decides to write a letter to the editor of her local paper.

Writing Write Kathy's letter. In it, discuss the benefits of recycling and encourage people to use the drop-off center for recyclables. The letter should also urge city leaders to start a curbside recycling program.

LESSON **3** ASSESSMENT

After You Read

Reviewing Facts and Vocabulary

1. Name four types of hazardous wastes.
2. How can wastewater harm the environment?
3. What is the difference between *reuse* and *recycle*?

Thinking Critically

4. **Analyze.** What rights do individuals and groups have when it comes to the environment?
5. **Explain.** How does population growth contribute to environmental problems?

Applying Health Skills

6. **Advocacy.** Create a comic book for elementary school students about a superhero who fights pollution. The comic should contain a strong message encouraging young people to reduce land and water pollution.

Writing Critically

7. **Descriptive.** Write a description of a real or imaginary town that is built according to the principles of smart growth.

Go Online

Visit **glencoe.com** and complete the Interactive Study Guide for this lesson.

---

3 ASSESS/CLOSE

Assessment Resources

📁 ***FAST FILE*** **ACTIVITIES**
Lesson 3 Quiz

💿 *ExamView*
Assessment Suite CD-ROM

Visit glencoe.com for:
Online Quizzes
Online Learning Center

Progress Monitoring

Reteaching

Ask students to write a paragraph or two using all the lesson vocabulary terms. Then have them exchange paragraphs with a partner and read each other's paragraphs. Students should reread the text definitions of any terms that either partner thinks were used incorrectly.

Enrichment

Have students learn more about the disposal of hazardous wastes. For example, what precautions are taken to protect the wastes from contaminating the water supply? Ask students to share the information in a PowerPoint presentation or oral report.

Go Online

Have students visit **glencoe.com** and complete the Interactive Study Guide for this lesson.

LESSON **3** ASSESSMENT ANSWERS

1. Industrial wastes, household wastes, radioactive wastes, mercury
2. Wastewater can contain pollutants, such as human wastes, and it can also be a source of excess heat that may harm fish and wildlife.
3. *Reuse* means repairing, selling, or donating unwanted items so they can be used again. *Recycling* means processing waste materials to be used in some other way.
4. Sample answer: Everyone has the right to live in a clean, safe environment.
5. Population growth may lead to greater use of resources, creation of more wastes and pollution, increased deforestation, and urban sprawl.
6. Comics will vary but should show that students know how to reduce pollution.
7. Descriptions will vary, but the towns should reflect principles of smart growth.

What You Can Do

Focus

Motivator
Write "Think globally, act locally" on the board. Ask students, "What do you think this phrase means? How would you 'live' this phrase?"

Teach

Recycling Program Ask students to assess your school's lunch waste. Direct students to collect data on such things as:

- Does the cafeteria use disposable products? What are they? How much is thrown away?

- Are recycling bins accessible?

- Do students who bring their lunches use reusable containers?

Then ask, "How might you get a school waste program started?" If your school already has such a program, ask students, "How might you improve the school's lunch waste program?" Have students create a step-by-step plan to either improve or implement a lunch waste program and submit it to school administrators.

Exploring Divide students into two groups: scientists who argue global warming is a real phenomenon and scientists who argue that global warming is too complex for current computer models to predict accurately. Ask students to research global warming and present a position paper that clearly articulates the assigned perspective. Position papers should include information such as greenhouse gas emissions; whether greenhouse gases are responsible for a rise in global temperatures; how global warming would affect the earth's sea levels, weather patterns, and desertification; alternative theories; etc.

TIME HEALTH
SCIENCE & TECHNOLOGY

What You Can Do

People in the United States produce an average of 20,000 pounds of carbon dioxide (CO_2) a year. Decreasing that number would make us healthier (by making the atmosphere cleaner and slowing down global warming) and wealthier (by lowering bills for electricity, heating fuels, and gas). To reduce the amount of CO_2 in the air, follow these tips from Environmental Defense and the World Wildlife Fund.

1. Get It Just Right
Don't overheat or overcool rooms. Set the thermostat lower in winter and higher in summer.
Average annual CO_2 reduction: approximately 500 pounds for each 2°F adjustment

2. Pitch In
Reduce waste and promote energy-efficient measures at your school. Help set up community recycling programs.
Average CO_2 reduction: 4 pounds for every pound of office paper recycled

3. Get Smart on Wash Day
Wash laundry in warm or cold water, not hot.

Average annual CO_2 reduction: as much as 500 pounds for two loads a week

4. Home Improvement
Plant trees next to your house, and paint your house a light color if you live in a warm climate or a dark color in a cold climate.
Average annual CO_2 reduction: approximately 5,000 pounds

5. Don't Bag It
Buy minimally packaged goods and reusable products. Recycle.
Average annual CO_2 reduction: 1,000 pounds for 25 percent less garbage ■

TIME to THINK... About CO_2

One problem associated with CO_2 buildup is that it can increase global warming. With your class, create a flow chart showing how CO_2 contributes to global warming. Do any of your daily activities make you part of the flow chart?

Home and Community

Making a Difference Review the five tips from the Environmental Defense and the World Wildlife Fund. Write each of the headings on the board. Have students expand the list of actions under each that can be taken to reduce the amount of CO_2 in the air. Have each student identify an item from the list that they can accomplish on their own and write a report on how they could make a difference in their school, home, or community. Encourage them to take action and report their progress to the class.

To download quizzes and eFlashcards to your PDA, go to **glencoe.com** and click on the Study to Go icon.

LESSON 1

Community and Public Health

Key Concepts

▸ Types of health care providers include primary care physicians, school nurses, dentists, and specialists.

▸ You may receive health care in settings such as doctor's offices, clinics, hospitals, and urgent care centers.

▸ It is important to develop an ongoing relationship with a primary care physician.

▸ The two main forms of health insurance are fee-for-service and managed care.

▸ Agencies at all levels of government promote public health.

Vocabulary

▸ health care system (p. 792)
▸ primary care physician (p. 792)
▸ specialists (p. 792)
▸ medical history (p. 794)
▸ health insurance (p. 795)
▸ public health (p. 796)
▸ health fraud (p. 798)

LESSON 2

Air Quality and Health

Key Concepts

▸ The Environmental Protection Agency (EPA) places limits on the levels of six air pollutants: ozone, particulate matter, carbon monoxide, sulfur dioxide, nitrogen oxides, and lead.

▸ Greenhouse gases such as carbon dioxide contribute to global warming, which can dramatically alter the earth's climate.

▸ Examples of indoor air pollutants include carbon monoxide, asbestos, and radon.

▸ You can help reduce air pollution by using less energy in your home and reducing car use.

▸ Exposure to loud noises can damage your hearing.

Vocabulary

▸ air pollution (p. 800)
▸ smog (p. 801)
▸ Air Quality Index (AQI) (p. 801)
▸ greenhouse effect (p. 801)
▸ global warming (p. 802)
▸ noise pollution (p. 804)
▸ decibel (p. 804)

LESSON 3

Protecting Land and Water

Key Concepts

▸ Solid waste can be disposed of in landfills or incinerators.

▸ Hazardous wastes require special treatment for safe disposal.

▸ The impacts of population growth on the environment include deforestation and urban sprawl.

▸ Water pollution from runoff, wastewater, sediment, and oil threaten the earth's limited water supply.

▸ People can reduce environmental problems by conserving resources, reducing waste, and reusing or recycling materials.

Vocabulary

▸ biodegradable (p. 806)
▸ landfill (p. 807)
▸ hazardous wastes (p. 807)
▸ deforestation (p. 808)
▸ urban sprawl (p. 809)
▸ wastewater (p. 809)
▸ conservation (p. 810)
▸ precycling (p. 810)
▸ recycling (p. 810)

Chapter 28 Review **813**

Go Online

Students can visit **glencoe.com** to

• review content online with the Online Student Edition.

• test their knowledge of chapter content with Online Quizzes.

• access Interactive Health Tutor for more practice with vocabulary.

Assessment Resources

 FAST FILE ACTIVITIES
Chapter 28 Test

 ExamView Assessment Suite CD-ROM

Visit glencoe.com for:
Audio Chapter Summaries
Online Quizzes

Tell students to visit **glencoe.com** where they can download quizzes and eFlashcards.

Study Tips

Studying for Comprehension Students may think that they have mastered new material when they can answer objective questions without thinking too much. Advise students to check their comprehension by writing—and then trying to answer in their own words—open-ended questions about the material. Suggest that they write questions that begin with *How* or *Why*. These generally require more thought than questions that begin with *What* or *When*. If students cannot answer the questions in their own words, then they probably do not really understand the material. If they are unsure whether their answers make sense, they can get feedback from a classmate.

Assessment

Chapter 28
Assessment Answers

LESSON 1

Vocabulary Review

1. health care system
2. health insurance
3. Public health

Understanding Key Concepts

4. d
5. c
6. a
7. d

Thinking Critically

8. It is easier to talk about your health problems with a doctor whom you know and trust, and a doctor who sees you regularly will know your medical history.
9. Health conditions, major past problems, medicines, allergies, family health problems, and lifestyle and habits
10. Group insurance generally costs less, and employers may pay part or all of the premiums.
11. Health care refers to the medical care individuals receive from health care professionals. Public health refers to the health of the population as a whole.
12. The FTC combats health fraud by prosecuting cases of health fraud and educating consumers about how to choose health products and services wisely.

LESSON 2

Vocabulary Review

13. air pollution
14. The greenhouse effect
15. Air quality index
16. noise pollution

LESSON 1

Vocabulary Review

Use the vocabulary terms listed on page 813 to complete the following statements.

1. All the health care professionals you see are part of the nation's _____.
2. The two main forms of _____ are fee-for-service and managed care.
3. _____ includes all efforts to monitor, protect, and promote the health of the population as a whole.

Understanding Key Concepts

After reading the question or statement, select the correct answer.

4. You would likely see a specialist for
   a. an annual checkup.
   b. a flu shot.
   c. a minor injury.
   d. a condition that does not respond to normal treatment.

5. How are urgent care centers different from ordinary doctor's offices?
   a. They handle only medical emergencies.
   b. They can provide inpatient care.
   c. They see patients without appointments.
   d. They have several doctors working in the same place.

6. The regular monthly fee you pay for most health insurance plans is called a
   a. premium.
   b. deductible.
   c. copayment.
   d. coinsurance.

7. Which of the following is not a duty of local health departments?
   a. Investigating threats to public health
   b. Enforcing local health regulations
   c. Educating the public about health issues
   d. Funding research for new treatments

Thinking Critically

After reading the question or statement, write a short answer using complete sentences.

8. **Evaluate.** What are the benefits of seeing a primary care physician on a regular basis?

9. **Describe.** What does your medical history include?

10. **Evaluate.** What are the advantages of receiving group insurance through your employer over buying an individual policy?

11. **Explain.** What is the distinction between *health care* and *public health?*

12. **Explain.** What role does the Federal Trade Commission play in promoting public health?

LESSON 2

Vocabulary Review

Choose the correct term in the sentences below.

13. Particulate matter, carbon monoxide, and sulfur dioxide are all components of *air pollution / smog.*

14. *The greenhouse effect / Global warming* is natural and is necessary to support life on earth.

15. The EPA created the *Air Quality Index / decibels* to track the levels of pollutants in the air.

16. Traffic, loud music, construction equipment, and power tools such as lawn mowers can all be sources of *air pollution / noise pollution.*

Health eSpotlight *Wrap-Up*

Taking Care of Everyone Have students reread the Health eSpotlight questions at the beginning of the chapter on page 791 and look at their original answers. **Ask Students:** *Now that you have read the chapter and watched the video, how would you respond differently to what kinds of community events support environmental issues?* Call on volunteers to describe how their responses would change.

Understanding Key Concepts

After reading the question or statement, select the correct answer.

17. The pollutant that makes up the largest component of urban smog is
   a. ozone.
   b. carbon monoxide.
   c. sulfur dioxide.
   d. nitrogen oxides.

18. An AQI of 76 falls into the "moderate" range. This means that the quality of the air poses
   a. little or no health risk for anyone.
   b. a moderate concern for a very small number of people.
   c. a threat to members of sensitive groups, such as those with lung disease.
   d. a serious threat to everyone.

19. Which of the following is *not* a common indoor air pollutant?
   a. Asbestos
   b. Carbon monoxide
   c. Ozone
   d. Radon

20. Which of the following noises is loud enough to cause hearing damage?
   a. Whispered conversation
   b. Normal conversation
   c. Heavy traffic
   d. Rock concert

Thinking Critically

After reading the question or statement, write a short answer using complete sentences.

21. **Analyze.** How does reducing your use of energy combat global warming?

22. **Evaluate.** Suppose your school has old asbestos insulation in its walls. Is it a good idea to cut into the walls and remove it? Why or why not?

23. **Identify.** Give two examples of specific steps you can take to reduce air pollution.

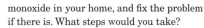

24. **Synthesize.** Suppose your family wants to find out whether there is an unsafe level of carbon monoxide in your home, and fix the problem if there is. What steps would you take?

LESSON 3

Vocabulary Review

Correct the sentences below by replacing the italicized term with the correct vocabulary term.

25. Many types of waste are *recyclable,* or able to be broken down by microorganisms in the environment.

26. Waste materials with properties that make them dangerous to human health or the environment are known as *municipal solid waste.*

27. Soil erosion, flooding, and an increase in global warming are all problems associated with *urban sprawl.*

Understanding Key Concepts

After reading the question or statement, select the correct answer.

28. Which of the following is an example of smart growth?
   a. Zoning regulations that require homes and businesses to be in separate parts of a city or town
   b. Buying farmland to build new housing developments and shopping malls
   c. Buildings that have shops on the bottom level and apartments on the upper levels
   d. Widening streets to make more room for parking

Chapter 28   Assessment   **815**

Assessment

Understanding Key Concepts

17. a
18. b
19. c
20. d

Thinking Critically

21. Electric power plants are major sources of the greenhouse gas carbon dioxide. Reducing energy use reduces the need for power and the amount of carbon dioxide generated.

22. It is not a good idea, because cutting into building materials that contain asbestos can release asbestos particles into the air. The best way to deal with asbestos is to contain it.

23. Students should identify any two of the energy-saving tips listed on page 803.

24. Measure the level of carbon monoxide with a CO detector. If the level is too high, have furnaces and other fuel-burning appliances checked to make sure they are not producing too much CO. If that doesn't solve the problem, increase ventilation.

LESSON 3

Vocabulary Review

25. biodegradable
26. hazardous waste
27. deforestation

ExamView® Assessment Suite

Create and customize tests in minutes with this convenient digital platform.

- Create differentiated tests quickly and easily.
- All questions correlated to National/State Standards.
- Enhance tests with Document Based Questions (DBQ) and add your own photos or graphics.
- Build tests in both English and Spanish.
- Generate progress reports.

To order, go to **glencoe.com** and search for ISBN 0-07-888173-0.

Assessment

Understanding Key Concepts

28. c
29. d
30. d
31. a

Thinking Critically

32. Radiation from these wastes is harmful to human health. Therefore, they need to be contained in a secure site until they decay and cease to be radioactive, and this takes a long time.

33. Polluted runoff, loss of wildlife habitat, and reduction in air quality

34. Less than 1 percent of the earth's water is in a form that humans can use, and this water is unevenly distributed around the globe.

35. Precycling is the most effective strategy for reducing waste because it keeps waste from being created in the first place. Reuse is the second most effective strategy because it turns waste into useful items without the need for reprocessing. Recycling is the least effective strategy because recycled items must be reprocessed before they can be used again, and this requires energy and produces pollution.

29. Which of the following is *not* a problem associated with deforestation?
    a. Loss of habitat for plants and animals
    b. Increased soil erosion
    c. Changes in the local climate
    d. Destruction of old farms and ranches

30. The best way to dispose of used motor oil is to
    a. dump it down a storm drain.
    b. pour it out onto the ground.
    c. put it out with your regular trash.
    d. take it to a service station for recycling.

31. Which of the following is an example of precycling?
    a. Using cloth shopping bags
    b. Giving your old computer to a friend
    c. Repairing your broken radio instead of throwing it out and buying another
    d. Returning empty bottles to the manufacturer to be sterilized and refilled

Thinking Critically

After reading the question or statement, write a short answer using complete sentences.

32. **Explain.** Why do radioactive wastes need to be isolated in secure storage sites for a long time?

33. **Identify.** List three problems associated with urban sprawl.

34. **Analyze.** If 70 percent of the earth's surface is covered with water, why do 500 million people around the world have trouble getting the water they need?

35. **Evaluate.** Rank the strategies of precycling, reuse, and recycling in terms of their effectiveness in reducing waste. Give reasons for your answer.

Project-Based ASSESSMENT

Promoting Precycling

Background
Precycling is a strategy for reducing waste before it is generated. It is an effective and important way to conserve natural resources, but it is not as widely understood or as widely promoted as recycling.

Task
Create a poster that promotes one specific method of precycling.

Audience
Students in your school

Purpose
Show one strategy for precycling, and show the benefits of precycling.

Procedure

1 Review the concept of precycling (covered in Lesson 3 of this chapter). Conduct further research to explore the benefits of precycling. Investigate effective strategies for precycling that could be practiced by students.

2 Brainstorm specific ways that the students at your school could practice precycling.

3 Select one of these precycling strategies to be the focus of your poster.

4 Design and create your poster.

5 Submit your poster to your teacher. Exceptional posters will be displayed in your school.

Project-Based ASSESSMENT

Step 1 Research Allow time for students to research specific examples of precycling methods, including local success stories and programs that advocate precycling.

Step 2 Identify Have students brainstorm ways that students in your school could apply precycling strategies in a schoolwide program. After brainstorming a list of ideas, ask students to identify one effective strategy for their posters.

Step 3 Create Provide options for creating posters. Encourage creativity in their choice of materials. You might ask students to bring a variety of materials from home to include in their posters, such as found objects, recycled art supplies, and other recycled products.

Visit **glencoe.com** for Project-Based Assessment rubrics.

Math Practice

Calculating Costs. Read the paragraph below, and then answer the questions.

> Two families have medical insurance policies through different employers. The Lopez family pays $250 a month, and the insurance company will pay 85 percent of the cost of hospital stays. Family members pay $20 for each doctor visit. This insurance plan does not cover any vision costs. The Perez family's plan costs $410 a month, and hospital stays are completely covered. Family members pay $15 for each doctor visit. This plan pays the entire cost of an eye exam and $100 toward a pair of glasses or contact lenses.

1. Pedro Lopez had a hospital stay that cost $4,000. Before that, he had three doctor's appointments, each of which cost $93. Which function describes what Pedro has to pay? (Hint: C is Pedro's cost, H is the cost of the hospital stay, and D is the cost of each doctor visit.)
   A. $C = H + D$
   B. $C = H + 3D$
   C. $C = 0.15H + 20D$
   D. $C = 0.15H + 3D$

2. Melissa Perez has an eye exam and finds out she needs glasses. The glasses cost $395, and the exam is $95. How much does she have to pay?
   A. $295
   B. $300
   C. $395
   D. $490

3. In one year, both families had the following medical expenses: a hospital stay that cost $12,000, 14 trips to the doctor, four eye exams at $100 each, and two pairs of glasses at $300 each. Which policy would be the best to have under these circumstances? Why?

Go Online

For more test practice, visit glencoe.com and complete the Online Quizzes for Chapter 28.

Reading/Writing Practice

Understand and Apply. Read the passage below, and then answer the questions.

> Did you know that Americans throw away more than 245 million tons of trash each year? Much of that garbage ends up in landfills. Before these landfills fill up, we need to come up with new ways to get rid of our garbage. One way to do it is recycling.
>
> Some people worry that recycling costs too much, but it actually saves money because it uses less energy than manufacturing new items. Others say that people are too lazy to separate trash and wash out cans and bottles. This is not true.
>
> The best thing about recycling is that it is something everyone can do to help our planet. No matter what our age or our economic or education level, we can all take part. Earth is where we all are living and so we should care.

1. Which sentence should be added at the end of paragraph 2 to support the topic?
   A. It's hard to peel the labels off jars.
   B. It's better to precycle instead.
   C. Across the country, recycling rates have risen steadily over the years.
   D. My school started a recycling program.

2. What is the most effective way to rewrite the last sentence?
   A. We should all care about where we live.
   B. Why don't people care about recycling?
   C. Earth is our home, and we should keep it safe and healthy.
   D. Our planet is beautiful from space.

3. Write a persuasive paragraph urging sports arenas to recycle bottles and cans.

National Education Standards
Math: Algebra, Problem Solving
Language Arts: NCTE 1, NCTE 3, NCTE 4

Standardized Test Practice Answers

Math Practice
1. D
2. A
3. The Perez family's policy would be better under these circumstances because the Perez family paid a smaller total than the Lopez family for the same medical expenses. The Lopez family paid $3,000 in premiums, $1,800 for the hospital, $280 for doctor visits, and $1,000 for vision, for a total of $6,080. The Perez family paid $4,920 in premiums, nothing for the hospital, $210 for doctor visits, and $400 for vision, for a total of $5,530.

Reading/Writing Practice
1. C
2. C
3. Paragraphs will vary but should include a clear statement of the message and relevant facts and convincing arguments to support it.

National Education Standards

Math: Algebra, Problem Solving

Language Arts: NCTE 1, NCTE 3, NCTE 4

For the complete Math and Language Arts standards, visit glencoe.com.

Test-Taking Tip

Understanding Directions Tell students that they should carefully read the directions before they start working on each section of a test. It is also a good idea to circle key words in the directions, such as *compare*, *contrast*, *similar*, and *different*. If they do not understand the directions, they should ask the test administrator to clarify them. Remind students that they should always indicate their answers on a test exactly as the directions state.

Go Online

Online Study Tools
For more test practice, visit glencoe.com and complete the Online Quizzes for Chapter 28.

Safety and Environmental Health

Is Graduated Driver Licensing Good for Teens?

Being able to drive on their own is very important to most younger teen drivers. Some young teens think that special age restrictions on their driving are unfair and unnecessary. Most parents feel otherwise.

Parents' Views Having teens who can drive on their own may be important to parents because it means that they no longer have to drive their children to and from school, work, practices, and social activities. However, most parents worry about the safety of their teens when they are behind the wheel. The majority of parents of teen drivers favor restrictions that make teen driving safer. A recent survey found that 97 percent of parents favor some type of graduated driver licensing.

Effective Programs Graduated licensing programs have been adopted in most states, but the programs differ in how many requirements they include. The most effective programs have all of following requirements:

- A minimum age of 15½ to obtain a learner permit
- A waiting period of at least three months after obtaining a learner permit before applying for a license
- A minimum of 30 hours of supervised driving to apply for a license
- A minimum age of 16 to apply for a license
- A restriction on nighttime driving until age 17
- A restriction on carrying passengers until at least age 17

818

Is Graduated Driver's Licensing Good for Teens?

*T*een drivers are much more likely to get into accidents than older drivers, who have more experience. A recent study found that among teens ages 16 to 19, there were 148 crashes for every 1,000 teen drivers. This rate was much higher than the rate for any other age group.

To protect young drivers, most states now have graduated licensing programs. These programs put various restrictions on young drivers, which gradually decrease as these drivers gain experience. Read on to find out what two teens have to say about graduated licensing programs.

More About...

Net Cost of Graduated Driver Licensing Programs Some people have argued against graduated driver licensing programs because of the costs involved. They point out that states may need to spend thousands of dollars each year to administer and enforce the programs. However, this view does not take into account the money saved by reducing teen car crashes. A single car crash, even without a fatality, may involve hundreds of thousands of dollars in medical, property, and other costs. A recent analysis of data from Oregon found that the annual cost to the state of a graduated licensing program was about $150,000, but the estimated money saved due to the reduction in teen car crashes was almost $11 million.

Drawbacks of Graduated Licensing

With graduated licensing, newly licensed teen drivers cannot engage in certain types of driving. For instance, they may not be allowed to drive at night or with more than one passenger. These restrictions apply to all young drivers, not just the problem drivers. As a result, teens may have trouble getting to school, work, and after-school activities.

> " My state's graduated license program says that I can't drive after dark unless I have an adult with me. I don't think it's fair that they're assuming I'll be a bad driver just because I'm a young person."
>
> —Nancy B., age 17

Benefits of Graduated Licensing

Graduated licensing gives teens a chance to gain experience driving in safer situations. They can improve their driving skills with adult supervision. They can also practice driving in the daytime and without passengers to distract them. Graduated licensing has been found to reduce the rate of accidents by 10 to 30 percent.

> " Learning to drive is kind of like learning to swim. You don't want to jump into the deep end until you've had some practice. I like the idea that with my provisional license, I can gradually become more comfortable with the toughest kinds of driving, instead of being thrown into the deep end."
>
> —Ali S., age 16

Teaching Strategies

- **Brainstorming** After students read about the benefits and drawbacks of graduated driver licensing, lead the class in brainstorming other pros and cons. Record them on the board.

- **Debating** Ask students to write a paragraph expressing their own thoughts and feelings about graduated driver licensing. This will help them formulate their position on the issue. Call on several volunteers to state and explain their position. Generate an impromptu debate by encouraging students to argue against opposing positions.

Activity Beyond the Classroom

1. **Research** graduated licensing requirements in your state. Do teens go directly from a learners' permit to full driving privileges, or is there an intermediate stage? If there is a special license for beginners, what restrictions does it impose?

2. **Discuss** these graduated licensing requirements with other teens and with adults. How do they feel about this issue? What arguments do they make for and against the program?

3. **Summarize** your findings in a newspaper article. Discuss the attitudes teens and adults have toward graduated licensing. In the last paragraph, draw your own conclusions about whether the benefits of graduated licensing outweigh the drawbacks.

Go Online

For more information about graduated licensing, go to **glencoe.com**.

Unit 9   Real-World Health   **819**

Activity Beyond the Classroom

Writing

1. Students should list any restrictions on intermediate driver licenses in their state. They can find the information online by searching for their state's Bureau of Motor Vehicles or they can pick up written materials at the closest Bureau of Motor Vehicles office.

2. Suggest that students list any new arguments, pro or con, that they hear when discussing graduated licensing with other teens and adults. Give students a chance to share and discuss the arguments.

Glossary / Glosario

Pronunciation Key

The following key will help you sound out words in the glossary.

a	back (BAK)	yoo	pure (PYOOR)
ay	day (DAY)	yew	few (FYEW)
ah	father (FAH thur)	uh	comma (CAH muh)
ow	flower (FLOW ur)	u (+ cons.)	rub (RUB)
ar	car (CAR)	ur	number (NUM bur)
e	less (LES)	sh	shelf (SHELF)
ee	leaf (LEEF)	ch	nature (NAY chur)
ih	trip (TRIHP)	g	gift (GIHFT)
i (i + cons. + e)	idea (i DEE uh)	j	gem (JEM)
oh	go (GOH)	ing	sing (SING)
aw	soft (SAWFT)	zh	vision (VIH zhun)
or	orbit (OR buht)	k	came (KAYM)
oy	coin (COYN)	s	cent (SENT)
oo	foot (FOOT)	z	zone (ZOHN)
ew	food (FEWD)		

Como usar el glosario en español:

1. Busca el término en inglés que desees encontrar.

2. El término en español, junto con la definición, se encuentran en la columna de la derecha.

Content vocabulary are words that relate to health content. They are boldface and highlighted in yellow in your text. Words below that have an asterisk (*) are academic vocabulary. They help you understand your school subjects and are blue bold-faced in your text.

English / A / Español

Abstinence A deliberate decision to avoid high-risk behaviors, including sexual activity and the use of tobacco, alcohol, and other drugs. (Ch. 1, 19)

Abstinencia Decisión deliberada de evitar conductas de alto riesgo, como la actividad sexual, el consumo de tabaco, alcohol y otras drogas.

Abuse The physical, mental, emotional, or sexual mistreatment of one person by another. (Ch. 9, 178)

Abuso Maltrato físico, mental, emocional o sexual que una persona le provoca a otra.

Accident chain A sequence of events that leads to an unintentional injury. (Ch. 26, 731)

Cadena de accidentes Serie de sucesos que generan una lesión no intencional.

Acquired Immune Deficiency Syndrome (AIDS) The final stage of the HIV infection. (Ch. 24, 661)

Síndrome de Inmunodeficiencia Adquirida (SIDA) Etapa final de la infección por VIH.

Action plan A multi-step strategy to identify and achieve your goals. (Ch. 2, 44)

Plan de acción Estrategia de varios pasos para identificar y lograr metas.

Active listening Paying close attention to what someone is saying and communicating. (Ch. 6, 154)

Escucha activa Escuchar atentamente lo que alguien dice o comunica.

Addiction A physiological or psychological dependence on a drug. (Ch. 22, 595)

Adicción Dependencia fisiológica o psicológica a una droga.

Addictive drug A substance that causes physiological or psychological dependence. (Ch. 20, 543)

Droga adictiva Sustancia que causa dependencia fisiológica o psicológica.

Additive interaction Occurs when medicines work together in a positive way. (Ch. 19, 528)

Interacción aditiva Situación en la cual los medicamentos interactúan de una manera positiva.

Adjust* To bring to a more satsfactory state. (Ch 22, 614)

Adolescence The period between childhood and adulthood. (Ch. 18, 496)

Adoption The legal process of taking a child of other parents as one's own. (Ch. 18, 505)

Adrenal glands Glands that help the body deal with stress and respond to emergencies. (Ch. 16, 444)

Advertising A written or spoken media message designed to interest consumers in purchasing a product or service. (Ch. 2, 46)

Advocacy Taking action to influence others to address a health-related concern or to support a health-related belief. (Ch. 2, 39)

Aerobic exercise All rhythmic activities that use large muscle groups for an extended period of time. (Ch. 12, 327)

Affect* To produce an effect upon. (Ch. 1, 19)

Affirmation Positive feedback that helps others feel appreciated and supported. (Ch. 7, 170)

Aggressive Overly forceful, pushy, or hostile. (Ch. 6, 152)

Air pollution The contamination of the earth's atmosphere by harmful substances. (Ch. 28, 800)

Air Quality Index (AQI) An index for reporting daily air quality. (Ch. 28, 801)

Alcohol abuse The excessive use of alcohol. (Ch. 21, 575)

Alcohol poisoning A severe and potentially fatal physical reaction to an alcoholic overdose. (Ch. 21, 570)

Alcoholic An addict who is dependent on alcohol. (Ch. 21, 581)

Alcoholism A disease in which a person has a physical or psychological dependence on drinks that contain alcohol. (Ch. 21, 575)

Alienation Feeling isolated and separated from everyone else. (Ch. 5, 122)

Allergy A specific reaction of the immune system to a foreign and frequently harmless substance. (Ch. 25, 702)

Americans with Disabilities Act (ADA) A law prohibiting discrimination against people with physical or mental disabilities in the workplace, transportation, public accommodation, and telecommunications. (Ch. 25, 713)

Amniocentesis A procedure in which a syringe is inserted through a pregnant female's abdominal wall to remove a sample of the amniotic fluid surrounding the developing fetus. (Ch. 17, 481)

Anabolic-androgenic steroids Synthetic substances that are similar to male sex hormones. (Ch. 22, 601)

Ajustar Traer a un estado más satisfactorio.

Adolescencia Etapa entre la infancia y la edad adulta.

Adopción Proceso legal para tener como hijo a un niño de otros padres.

Glándulas suprarrenales Glándulas que ayudan al cuerpo a lidiar con el estrés y a reaccionar ante emergencias.

Publicidad Mensaje oral o escrito en los medios de comunicación, diseñado para incentivar a los consumidores a adquirir un producto o servicio.

Defensa Tomar medidas para influir en otras personas, con el propósito de abordar preocupaciones o apoyar creencias en relación con la salud.

Ejercicio aeróbico Toda actividad rítmica que use los grupos musculares grandes por un periodo prolongado.

Afectar Producir un efecto en algo o en alguien.

Afirmación Retroalimentación positiva que ayuda a que otras personas se sientan apreciadas y respaldadas.

Agresivo Excesivamente enérgico, insistente u hostil.

Contaminación atmosférica Contaminación de la atmósfera de la Tierra producto de sustancias peligrosas.

Índice de calidad del aire Indicador para informar sobre la calidad diaria del aire.

Abuso de alcohol Consumo excesivo de alcohol.

Intoxicación alcohólica Reacción física grave y potencialmente fatal a una sobredosis de alcohol.

Alcohólico Persona adicta al alcohol.

Alcoholismo Enfermedad en que la persona es adicta física o psicológicamente a las bebidas alcohólicas.

Alienación Sentirse solo y aislado de todo el mundo.

Alergia Reacción específica del sistema inmunológico a una sustancia extraña que usualmente es inofensiva.

Ley para Estadounidenses Discapacitados (ADA) Ley que prohíbe la discriminación de personas con discapacidades físicas o mentales en los lugares de trabajo, transporte, lugares públicos y telecomunicaciones.

Amniocentesis Procedimiento en el cual se inserta una jeringa a través de la pared abdominal de una embarazada hasta llegar al líquido amniótico que rodea al embrión en desarrollo.

Esteroides anabolizantes-androgénicos Sustancias sintéticas semejantes a las hormonas masculinas.

Anaerobic exercise Intense short bursts of activity in which the muscles work so hard that they produce energy without using oxygen. (Ch. 12, 328)

Angina pectoris Chest pain that results when the heart does not get enough oxygen. (Ch. 25, 690)

Anorexia nervosa An eating disorder in which an irrational fear of weight gain leads people to starve themselves. (Ch. 11, 300)

Antagonistic interaction Occurs when the effect of one medicine is canceled or reduced when taken with another medicine. (Ch. 19, 529)

Antibiotics A class of chemical agents that destroy disease-causing microorganisms while leaving the patient unharmed. (Ch. 24, 664)

Antibody A protein that acts against a specific antigen. (Ch. 23, 641)

Anticipate* To expect. (Ch. 4, 94)

Antigens Substances that are capable of triggering an immune response. (Ch. 23, 640)

Anxiety The condition of feeling uneasy or worried about what may happen. (Ch. 5, 114)

Anxiety disorder A condition in which real or imagined fears are difficult to control. (Ch. 5, 119)

Apathy A lack of strong feeling, interest, or concern. (Ch. 5, 116)

Appendicitis The inflammation of the appendix. (Ch. 15, 427)

Appetite The psychological desire for food. (Ch. 10, 255)

Approach* A particular manner of taking steps. (Ch. 2, 52)

Appropriate* Proper or fitting. (Ch. 1, 8)

Arrhythmias Irregular heartbeats. (Ch. 25, 690)

Arteries Blood vessels that carry oxygenated blood away from the heart. (Ch. 15, 411)

Arteriosclerosis A disease characterized by the accumulation of plaque on artery walls. (Ch. 25, 689)

Arthritis A group of more than 100 different diseases that causes pain and loss of movement in the joints. (Ch. 25, 707)

Aspect* A feature or phase of something. (Ch. 8, 202)

Assault An unlawful physical attack or threat of attack. (Ch. 9, 233)

Assertive Expressing your views clearly and respectfully. (Ch. 6, 153)

Asthma An inflammatory condition in which the trachea, the bronchi, and bronchioles become narrowed, causing difficulty breathing. (Ch. 15, 420)

Ejercicio anaeróbico Periodos cortos de actividad física intensiva, en los cuales los músculos trabajan tan arduamente que producen energía sin usar oxígeno.

Angina de pecho Dolor en el pecho causado porque el corazón no está recibiendo suficiente oxígeno.

Anorexia nerviosa Trastorno de la alimentación en la cual el miedo irracional a aumentar de peso provoca que las personas sigan una dieta de hambre.

Interacción antagónica Situación en la cual el efecto de un medicamento se elimina o reduce al interactuar con otro.

Antibióticos Tipo de agentes químicos que destruye los microorganismos que provocan enfermedades sin dañar al paciente.

Anticuerpo Proteína que ataca antígenos específicos.

Anticipar Esperar.

Antígenos Sustancias capaces de provocar una respuesta inmune.

Ansiedad Estado en el cual una persona se siente abrumada o preocupada acerca de lo que le pueda pasar.

Trastorno de ansiedad Estado en el cual el miedo, ya sea real o imaginario, es difícil de controlar.

Apatía Falta de sentimientos intensos, interés o preocupación.

Apendicitis Inflamación del apéndice.

Apetito Deseo psicológico de comer.

Acceso Una manera particular de tomar medidas.

Apropiado Apropiado o quedando bien.

Arritmia Palpitaciones irregulares del corazón.

Arterias Los vasas sanguineos que llevan sangre oxigenarado desde el corazón.

Ateroesclerosis Una enfermedad caracterizada por la acumulación de la placa en las parede de la arteria.

Artritis Grupo de más de 100 enfermedades que causan dolor y pérdida de movimiento en las articulaciones.

Aspecto Caracteristica o fase de algo.

Asalto Ataque o amenaza de ataque físico ilegal.

Asertivo Persona que expresa sus puntos de vista clara y respetuosamente.

Asma Condición inflamatoria en que la tráquea, los bronquios y los bronquiolos se estrechan provocando dificultad para respirar.

Asymptomatic People who are infected show no symptoms or the infections produce mild symptoms that disappear. (Ch. 24, 659)

Atherosclerosis A disease characterized by the accumulation of plaque on artery walls. (Ch. 25, 689)

Attribute* A quality or characteristic. (Ch. 8, 193)

Auditory ossicles Three small bones linked together that connect the eardrum to the inner ear. (Ch. 13, 371)

Authority* The right to make decisions and give commands. (Ch. 7, 168)

Autoimmune disease A condition in which the immune system mistakenly attacks itself, targeting the cells, tissues, and organs of a person's own body. (Ch. 25, 705)

Autonomy The confidence that a person can control his or her own body, impulses, and environment. (Ch. 17, 485)

Asintomático Persona infectada que no presenta síntomas o infecciones que producen síntomas leves que desaparecen.

Ateroesclerosis Enfermedad caracterizada por la acumulación de depósitos en las paredes de las arterias.

Atributo Cualidad o característica.

Osículos auditivas Tres huesas pequeños conectados juntos que unen el tímpano con el oido interno.

Autoridad Derecho para tomar decisiones y dar órdenes.

Enfermedad autoinmune Condición en la cual el sistema inmune se ataca a sí mismo por error, afectando las células, los tejidos y los órganos del cuerpo de una persona.

Autonomía Capacidad que tiene una persona para controlar su propio cuerpo, impulsos y medio ambiente.

English — B — Español

Bacteria Single-celled microorganisms. (Ch. 23, 629)

Behavior therapy A treatment process that focuses on changing unwanted behavior through rewards and reinforcement. (Ch. 5, 128)

Benign Noncancerous. (Ch. 25, 696)

Bile A yellow-green, bitter fluid important in the breakdown and absorption of fats. (Ch. 15, 424)

Binge drinking Drinking five or more alcoholic drinks at one sitting. (Ch. 21, 570)

Binge eating disorder An eating disorder in which people overeat compulsively. (Ch. 11, 301)

Biodegradable Able to be broken down by microorganisms in the environment. (Ch. 28, 806)

Biopsy The removal of a small piece of tissue for examination. (Ch. 25, 700)

Blended family A married couple and their children from previous marriages. (Ch. 7, 167)

Blizzard A snowstorm with winds that reach 35 miles an hour or more. (Ch. 27, 780)

Blood alcohol concentration (BAC) The amount of alcohol in a person's blood expressed as a percentage. (Ch. 21, 578)

Blood pressure A measure of the amount of force that the blood places on the walls of blood vessels, particularly large arteries, as it is pumped through the body. (Ch. 15, 413)

Bacteria Microorganismos compuestos de una sola célula.

Terapia del comportamiento Terapia que se enfoca en cambiar las conductas no deseadas a través de recompensas y refuerzos.

Benigno No canceroso.

Bilis Líquido amargo de color amarillo verdoso que es importante para la descomposición y absorción de las grasas.

Borrachera Consumo de cinco o más bebidas alcohólicas consecutivas.

Trastorno de atracones compulsivos Trastorno de la alimentación caracterizada por comer demasiado y de manera compulsiva.

Biodegradable Algo que los microorganismos del medio ambiente pueden descomponer.

Biopsia La extirpación diagnóstica de una pequeña muestra de tejido.

Familia mixta Pareja casada y sus hijos de matrimonios anteriores.

Ventisca Tormenta de nieve con vientos que superan las 35 millas por hora.

Concentración de alcohol en la sangre Cantidad de alcohol en la sangre de una persona expresada como porcentaje.

Presión arterial Medida de la presión que ejerce la sangre sobre las paredes de los vasos sanguíneos, especialmente en las arterias grandes, a medida que es bombeada por el cuerpo.

Glossary / Glosario

Body image The way you see your body. (Ch. 11, 297)

Body language Nonverbal communication through gestures, facial expressions, behaviors, and posture. (Ch. 6, 155)

Body mass index (BMI) A measure of body weight relative to height. (Ch. 11, 291)

Brain stem A three-inch-long stalk of nerve cells and fibers that connects the spinal cord to the rest of the brain. (Ch. 14, 396)

Bronchi The main airways that reach into each lung. (Ch. 15, 417)

Bulimia nervosa An eating disorder that involves cycles of overeating and purging, or attempts to rid the body of food. (Ch. 11, 301)

Bullying Deliberately harming or threatening another person who cannot easily defend himself or herself. (Ch. 6, 150)

Imagen corporal Forma en que uno ve su propio cuerpo.

Lenguaje corporal Comunicación no verbal a través de gestos, expresiones faciales, comportamientos y postura.

Índice de masa corporal (IMC) Medida de peso corporal en relación con la estatura.

Vástago cerebral Ramificación de neuronas y fibras de tres pulgadas de largo que conecta la médula espinal con el resto del cerebro.

Bronquios Vías aéreas principales que llegan a los pulmones.

Bulimia nerviosa Trastorno de la alimentación que implica ciclos en que la persona come en exceso y purga o intenta eliminar la comida del cuerpo.

Matonaje Daño o amenazas deliberadas hacia una persona que no se puede defender fácilmente.

English	C	Español

Calorie A unit of heat used to measure the energy your body uses and the energy it receives from food. (Ch. 10, 254)

Cancer Uncontrollable growth of abnormal cells. (Ch. 25, 695)

Capillaries Small vessels that carry blood from arterioles to small vessels called venules, which empty into veins. (Ch. 15, 412)

Carbohydrates Starches and sugars found in foods which provide your body's main source of energy. (Ch. 10, 259)

Carbon monoxide A colorless, odorless, and poisonous gas. (Ch. 20, 544)

Carcinogen A cancer-causing substance. (Ch. 20, 543)

Cardiac muscles A type of striated muscle that forms the wall of the heart. (Ch. 14, 388)

Cardiopulmonary resuscitation (CPR) A first-aid procedure that combines rescue breathing and chest compressions to supply oxygen to the body until normal body functions can resume. (Ch. 27, 765)

Cardiorespiratory endurance The ability of your heart, lungs, and blood vessels to send fuel and oxygen to your tissues during long periods of moderate to vigorous activity. (Ch. 12, 324)

Cardiovascular disease A disease that affects the heart or blood vessels. (Ch. 25, 688)

Cartilage A strong, flexible connective tissue. (Ch. 14, 383)

Caloría Unidad de calor que mide la energía que usa el cuerpo y la energía que la comida proporciona al cuerpo.

Cáncer Crecimiento incontrolable de células anormales.

Capilares Vasos sanguíneos delicados que transportan sangre desde las arteriolas hasta vasos pequeños conocidos como vénulas, las cuales terminan en las venas.

Carbohidratos Almidones y azúcares que se encuentran en los alimentos, los cuales proporcionan al cuerpo la fuente principal de energía.

Monóxido de carbono Gas incoloro, inodoro y venenoso.

Cancerígeno Sustancia que produce cáncer.

Músculo cardiaco Tipo de músculo estriado que forma las paredes del corazón.

Resucitación cardiopulmonar (RCP) Procedimiento de primeros auxilios que combina la respiración artificial con compresiones en el pecho a fin de proporcionar oxígeno hasta que las funciones vitales puedan reanudarse.

Resistencia cardiorrespiratoria Capacidad que tienen el corazón, los pulmones y los vasos sanguíneos de enviar energía y oxígeno a los tejidos durante largos periodos de tiempo con actividad moderada a enérgica.

Enfermedad cardiovascular Enfermedad que afecta el corazón o los vasos sanguíneos.

Cartílago Tejido conjuntivo fuerte y flexible.

Cerebellum The second largest part of the brain. (Ch. 14, 395)

Cerebral palsy A group of neurological disorders that are the result of damage to the brain before, during, or just after birth or in early childhood. (Ch. 14, 399)

Cerebrum The largest and most complex part of the brain. (Ch. 14, 394)

Cervix The opening to the uterus. (Ch. 16, 454)

Chain of survival A sequence of actions that maximize the victim's chances of survival. (Ch. 27, 764)

Character The distinctive qualities that describe how a person thinks, feels, and behaves. (Ch. 3, 73)

Child abuse Domestic abuse directed at a child. (Ch. 7, 179)

Cholesterol A waxy, fatlike substance. (Ch. 10, 262)

Chromosomes Threadlike structures found within the nucleus of a cell that carry the codes for inherited traits. (Ch. 17, 478)

Chronic disease An ongoing condition or illness. (Ch. 1, 10)

Chronic stress Stress associated with long-term problems that are beyond a person's control. (Ch. 4, 97)

Chronic villi sampling (CVS) A procedure in which a small piece of membrane is removed from the chorion, a layer of tissue that develops into the placenta. (Ch. 17, 482)

Circumstances* An event that influences another event. (Ch. 7, 175)

Cirrhosis Scarring of the liver tissue. (Ch. 23, 635)

Citizenship The way you conduct yourself as a member of the community. (Ch. 6, 144)

Clique A small circle of friends, usually with similar backgrounds or tastes, who exclude people viewed as outsiders. (Ch. 8, 195)

Closure Acceptance of a loss. (Ch. 4, 103)

Cluster suicides A series of suicides occurring within a short period of time and involving several people in the same school or community. (Ch. 5, 123)

Cognition The ability to reason and think out abstract solutions. (Ch. 18, 498)

Cognitive therapy A treatment method designed to identify and correct distorted thinking patterns that can lead to feelings and behaviors that may be troublesome, self-defeating, or self-destructive. (Ch. 5, 129)

Commitment A promise or a pledge. (Ch. 18, 504)

Communicable disease A disease that is spread from one living organism to another or through the environment. (Ch. 23, 628)

Cerebelo La segunda parte más grande del cerebro.

Parálisis cerebral Grupo de trastornos neurológicos que son el resultado de daños al cerebro antes, durante o inmediatamente después del nacimiento o durante la niñez temprana.

Corteza cerebral La parte más grande y compleja del cerebro.

Cuello del útero La entrada del útero.

Cadena de supervivencia Secuencia de acciones que tiene como objetivo maximizar las posibilidades de supervivencia de una víctima.

Carácter Características distintivas que describen cómo una persona piensa, siente y actúa.

Maltrato infantil Abuso doméstico dirigido hacia los niños.

Colesterol Sustancia cerosa de apariencia grasa.

Cromosomas Estructuras parecidas a hilos que se encuentran dentro del núcleo de una célula y que tienen los códigos de los rasgos heredados.

Enfermedad crónica Afección o enfermedad permanente.

Estrés crónico Estrés relacionado con problemas de largo plazo y fuera del control de una persona.

Biopsia de vellosidades coriónicas Procedimiento en el cual se saca una pequeña muestra de membrana del corion, una capa de tejido que se desarrolla en la placenta.

Circunstancia Acontecimiento que influye en otro acontecimiento.

Cirrosis Lesiones en el tejido del hígado.

Ciudadanía Manera de comportarse como miembro de la comunidad.

Pandilla Grupo pequeño de amigos, generalmente con gustos y experiencias similares, que excluyen a otras personas consideradas ajenas a ellos.

Resignación Aceptación de una pérdida.

Serie de suicidios Varios suicidios que ocurren en un periodo de tiempo corto y que involucran a personas de un mismo colegio o comunidad.

Cognición Capacidad de razonar y generar soluciones abstractas.

Terapia cognoscitiva Terapia diseñada para identificar y corregir patrones de pensamiento distorsionados, los cuales pueden generar sentimientos y comportamientos problemáticos, contraproducentes o autodestructivos.

Compromiso Una promesa.

Enfermedad contagiosa Enfermedad que se quede transmitir de un ser vivo a otro o a través del medio ambiente.

Community* A population of individuals in a common location. (Ch. 23, 648)

Comparison shopping Judging the benefits of different products by comparing several factors, such as quality, features, and cost. (Ch. 2, 47)

Competence Having enough skills to do something. (Ch. 3, 68)

Component* A constituent part or ingredient. (Ch. 28, 801)

Compromise A problem-solving method in which each participant gives up something to reach a solution that satisfies everyone. (Ch. 6, 146)

Computer* A device that can store, retrieve, and process data. (Ch. 6, 147)

Concussion A jarring injury to the brain that can cause unconsciousness. (Ch. 27, 774)

Conduct disorder* Patterns of behavior in which the rights of others or basic social rules are violated. (Ch. 5, 121)

Confidentiality Respecting the privacy of both parties and keeping details secret. (Ch. 9, 227)

Confine* To keep within limits. (Ch. 24, 671)

Conflict Any disagreement, struggle, or fight. (Ch. 9, 220)

Conflict resolution The process of ending a conflict through cooperation and problem solving. (Ch. 2, 36)

Conservation Avoiding waste through careful management of natural resources. (Ch. 28, 810)

Consistent* Free from variation or contradiction. (Ch. 1, 25)

Constructive* Promoting improvement or development. (Ch. 5, 129)

Constructive criticism Nonhostile comments that point out problems and encourage improvement. (Ch. 3, 76)

Consumer advocates People or groups whose sole purpose is to take on regional, national, and even international consumer issues. (Ch. 2, 51)

Contact* Union or junction of surfaces. (Ch. 23, 630)

Contract To draw together. (Ch. 15, 409)

Contradict* To imply the opposite of. (Ch. 6, 155)

Cool-down Low-level activity that prepares your body to return to a resting state. (Ch. 12, 335)

Cooperation Working together for the good of all. (Ch. 6, 146)

Coping Dealing successfully with difficult changes in your life. (Ch. 4, 103)

Cornea A transparent tissue that bends and focuses light before it enters the lens. (Ch. 13, 368)

Comunidad Población de personas que viven en el mismo lugar.

Compras informadas Evaluar los beneficios de diferentes productos comparando diversos factores, como calidad, características y precio.

Competencia Capacidad suficiente para realizar algo.

Componente Parete o ingrediente constitutivo.

Acuerdo Método para resolver problemas en que cada participante debe sacrificar algo para llegar a una solución satisfactoria para todos.

Computadora Recuperar datos.

Conmoción cerebral Lesión violenta en el cerebro que puede conducir a la pérdida de conocimiento.

Trastorno de conducta Patrón de comportamiento en el cual se infringen los derechos de los demás o las reglas sociales básicas.

Confidencialidad Respetar la vida privada de ambas partes y mantener en secreto los detalles.

Confinar Encerrar en un lugar.

Conflicto Cualquier desacuerdo, pelea o enojo.

Resolución de conflictos Proceso de resolver un conflicto a través de métodos de cooperación y solución de problemas.

Conservación Evitar el desperdicio de recursos a través de un manejo correcto de los recursos naturales.

Coherente Sin variaciones ni contradicciones.

Constructivo Que promeuve mejoras o progresos.

Crítica constructiva Comentarios no hostiles que señalan los problemas y fomentan su mejoramiento.

Defensores del consumidor Gente o grupos cuyo único propósito es confrontar los problemas regionales, nacionales y hasta internacionales del consumidor.

Contacto Unión o conexión de superficies.

Contraer Reducirse, disminuir.

Contradecir Decir o hacer lo contrario.

Enfriamiento Actividad liviana que prepara al cuerpo para volver a un estado de descanso.

Cooperación Trabajar juntos para el beneficio de todos.

Capacidad de lidiar Encargarse exitosamente de los cambios difíciles de la vida.

Córnea Tejido transparente que refracta y enfoca la luz antes de pasar al cristalino.

Crisis center A facility that offers advice and support to people dealing with personal emergencies. (Ch. 7, 182)

Cross-contamination The spreading of pathogens from one food to another. (Ch. 10, 279)

Crucial* Important or essential. (Ch. 03, 76)

Culture The collective beliefs, customs, and behaviors of a group. (Ch. 1, 13)

Cumulative risks Related risks that increase in effect with each added risk. (Ch. 1, 18)

Custody The legal right to make decisions affecting children and the responsibility for their care. (Ch. 7, 174)

Cyberbullying Cruel or hurtful online contact. (Ch. 26, 729)

Cycle of violence Pattern of repeating violent or abusive behaviors from one generation to the next. (Ch. 7, 180)

Cystitis An inflammation of the bladder. (Ch. 15, 432)

Centro para crisis Plantel que maneja emergencias y envía a un individuo que necesita ayuda a especialistas.

Contaminación cruzada Transmisión de agentes patógenos de una comida a otra.

Crucial Importante o esencial.

Cultura Las creencias, costumbres y comportamientos colectivos de un grupo de personas.

Riesgos acumulativos Riesgos relacionados que aumentan en efecto con cada nuevo peligro.

Custodia Derecho legal de tomar decisiones que afecten a los niños y la responsabilidad de cuidarlos.

Matonaje cibernético Contacto cruel o dañino que se produce en línea.

Ciclo de violencia Patrón de comportamiento violento o abusivo que se repite de una generación a la siguiente.

Cistitis Inflamación de la vejiga.

English	**D**	Español

Date rape One person in a dating relationship forces the other person to take part in sexual intercourse. (Ch. 9, 238)

Decibel A unit that measures the intensity of sound. (Ch. 28, 804)

Decision-making skills Steps that enable you to make a healthful decision. (Ch. 2, 41)

Defense mechanisms Mental processes that protect individuals from strong or stressful emotions and situations. (Ch. 3, 81)

Defensive driving Being aware of potential hazards on the road and taking action to avoid them. (Ch. 26, 746)

Defibrillator A device that delivers an electric shock to the heart to restore its normal rhythm. (Ch. 27, 765)

Deforestation Destruction of forests. (Ch. 28, 808)

Deoxyribonucleic acid (DNA) The chemical unit that makes up chromosomes. (Ch. 17, 479)

Depressant A drug that slows the central nervous system. (Ch. 21, 567)

Depression Prolonged feeling of helplessness, hopelessness, and sadness. (Ch. 5, 115)

Dermis The thicker layer of skin beneath the epidermis that is made up of connective tissue and contains blood vessels and nerves. (Ch. 13, 356)

Designer drug A synthetic drug that is made to imitate the effects of hallucinogens and other drugs. (Ch. 22, 605)

Violación durante una cita (violación por un conocido, violación a escondidas) Una persona que se encuentra en una cita obliga a la otra a participar en una actividad sexual.

Decibelios (Decibeles) Medida que se usa para expresar la intensidad del sonido.

Habilidades para tomar decisiones Pasos necesarios para tomar una decisión correcta.

Mecanismos de defensa Procesos mentales que protegen a los individuos de emociones y situaciones intensas o estresantes.

Conducción a la defensiva Estar consciente de posibles peligros en la carretera y tomar medidas para evitarlos.

Máquina de desfibrilación Un aparato que proporciona choques eléctricos al corazón para recuperar su ritmo normal.

Deforestación Destrucción de los bosques.

Ácido desoxirribonucleico (ADN) Unidad química que compone los cromosomas.

Depresor Sustancia que tiende a disminuir el funcionamiento (actividad) del sistema nervioso central.

Depresión Sentimiento prolongado de soledad, desesperación y tristeza.

Dermis La capa más gruesa de la piel que se encuentra debajo de la epidermis que está compuesta de tejidos conectivos y contiene vasos sanguíneos y nervios.

Droga de diseño Sustancias sintéticas que tratan de imitar los efectos de los alucinógenos y otras drogas peligrosas.

Developmental tasks Events that need to happen in order for a person to continue growing toward becoming a healthy, mature adult. (Ch. 17, 484)

Devote* To give time or effort to an activity. (Ch. 12, 321)

Diabetes A chronic disease that affects the way cells convert sugar into energy. (Ch. 25, 705)

Diaphragm A muscle that separates the chest from the abdominal cavity. (Ch. 15, 417)

Dietary Guidelines for Americans A set of recommendation about smart eating and physical activity for all Americans. (Ch. 10, 266)

Dietary Supplements Products that supply one or more nutrients as a supplement to, not as a substitute for, healthful foods. (Ch. 11, 304)

Disability Any physical or mental impairment that limits normal activities, including seeing, hearing, walking, or sleeping. (Ch. 25, 709)

Dislocation A separation of a bone from its normal position in a joint. (Ch. 27, 772)

Display* To make evident. (Ch. 5, 123)

Divorce A legal end to a marriage contract. (Ch. 7, 175)

Domestic* Relating to the household or family. (Ch. 7, 180)

Domestic violence Act of violence involving family members. (Ch. 7, 178)

Drug therapy The use of certain medications to treat or reduce the symptoms of a mental disorder. (Ch. 5, 129)

Drug watches Organized community efforts by neighborhood residents to patrol, monitor, report, and otherwise stop drug deals and drug abuse. (Ch. 22, 613)

Drug-free school zone Areas within 1,000 feet of schools and designated by signs, within which people caught selling drugs receive especially severe penalties. (Ch. 22, 613)

Drugs Substances other than food that change the structure, function of the body, or mind. (Ch. 19, 524)

Tareas requeridas para el desarrollo Sucesos necesarios para que una persona continúe creciendo y se convierta en un adulto saludable y maduro.

Dedicar Destinar tiempo o esfuerzo a una actividad.

Diabetes Una enfermedad crónica que afecta el modo en que las células del cuerpo convierten los alimentos en energía.

Diafragma El músculo que separa la cavidad toráxico de la cavidad abdominal.

Guías alimentarías para estadounidenses Conjunto de recomendaciones acerca de alimentarse inteligentemente y de la actividad física para todos los estadounidenses.

Suplementos alimentarios Productos que suministran uno o más nutrientes en forma de suplementos, no de sustitutos, a los alimentos saludables.

Discapacidad Cualquier impedimento físico o mental que limita el desarrollo de actividades normales tales como ver, oír, caminar o dormir.

Dislocación Separación del hueso de su posición normal en una articulación.

Exponer Hacer evidente.

Divorcio Fin legal de un contrato de matrimonio.

Doméstico Relativo al hogar o a la familia.

Violencia doméstica (intrafamiliar) Acto de violencia que incluya a los miembros de una familia.

Terapia farmacológica Uso de ciertos medicamentos para tratar o reducir los síntomas de una enfermedad mental.

Vigilantes de la droga Un grupo de personas de un vecindario organizadas para supervisar, controlar, denunciar o directamente frenar el abuso y la venta de drogas.

Zona de escuela libre de drogas Un área que comprende 1,000 pies alrededor de una escuela y se encuentra señalizada, en la cual las personas que son atrapadas vendiendo drogas son gravemente penalizadas o castigadas.

Drogas Sustancias distintas de los alimentos, que cambian la estructura o el funcionamiento del cuerpo o la mente de las personas.

English | E | Español

Earthquake A series of vibrations in the earth caused by sudden movements of the earth's crust. (Ch. 27, 781)

Eating disorders Extreme, harmful eating behaviors that can cause serious illness or even death. (Ch. 11, 300)

Terremoto Serie de vibraciones en la tierra provocada por movimientos repentinos de la superficie de la tierra.

Trastorno Alimentario Un comportamiento que se caracteriza por comer en forma extrema y dañina lo que causa que la persona se pueda enfermar o morir.

Eggs Female gametes. (Ch. 16, 452)

EIA (Enzyme immunoassay) The first test to be run to detect HIV antibodies. (Ch. 24, 677)

Elder abuse The abuse or neglect of older family members. (Ch. 7, 179)

Embryo A cluster of cells that develops between the third and eighth week of pregnancy. (Ch. 17, 470)

Emergency survival kit A set of items you will need in an emergency. (Ch. 27, 782)

Emerging infection Communicable diseases whose occurrence in humans has increased within the past two decades or threatens to increase in the near future. (Ch. 23, 645)

Emotional abuse A pattern of attacking another person's emotional development and sense of worth. (Ch. 9, 237)

Emotional maturity The state at which the mental and emotional capabilities of an individual are fully developed. (Ch. 18, 502)

Emotions Signals that tell your mind and body how to react. (Ch. 3, 78)

Empathy The ability to imagine and understand how someone else feels. (Ch. 3, 80)

Emphysema A disease that progressively destroys the walls of the alveoli. (Ch. 15, 421)

Empty-nest syndrome The feelings of sadness or loneliness that accompany children's leaving home and entering adulthood. (Ch. 18, 510)

Encounter* To experience. (Ch. 26, 728)

Endocrine glands Ductless or tubeless organs or groups of cells that secrete hormones directly into the bloodstream. (Ch. 16, 442)

Environment The sum of your surroundings. (Ch. 1, 12)

Environmental tobacco smoke (ETS) Air that has been contaminated by tobacco smoke. (Ch. 20, 553)

Epidemic An occurrence of a disease in which many people in the same place at the same time are affected. (Ch. 24, 663)

Epidermis The outer, thinner layer of the skin that is composed of living and dead cells. (Ch. 13, 356)

Epilepsy A disorder of the nervous system that is characterized by recurrent seizures—sudden episodes of uncontrolled electric activity in the brain. (Ch. 14, 399)

Escalate Become more serious. (Ch. 9, 221)

Estimate* To determine roughly the size or extent of. (Ch. 24, 674)

Ethanol The type of alcohol in alcoholic beverages. (Ch. 21, 566)

Óvulos Gametos femeninos.

EIA (Enzimo inmunoanálisis) Primera prueba realizada para detectar los anticuerpos del VIH.

Abuso de mayores El abuso o la negligencia de miembras ancianos de la familia.

Embrión Grupo de células que se desarrolla entre la tercera y la octava semana del embarazo.

Botiquín de emergencia Conjunto de elementos necesarios para una situación de emergencia.

Infección emergente Una enfermedad infecciosa cuya incidencia en humanos ha aumentado durante las últimas dos décadas o que amenaza con aumentar en el futuro cercano.

Abuso emocional Patrón de ataque al desarrollo emocional y al sentido de estima de otra persona.

Madurez emocional Un estado en el cual las capacidades mentales y emocionales de una persona se encuentran totalmente desarrolladas.

Emociones Señales que le comunican a la mente y al cuerpo cómo actuar.

Empatía La habilidad para imaginar y entender cómo siente otra persona.

Enfisema Una enfermedad que destruye progresivamente las paredes de los alvéolos.

Síndrome del nido vacío Sentimiento de tristeza y soledad que ocurre cuando los hijos, quienes ya se convirtieron en adultos, se van de la casa de sus padres.

Encuentro Expriencias.

Glándulas endocrinas Órganos o grupos de células sin conductos o tubos que secretan hormonas directamente al torrente sanguíneo.

Medio ambiente Todo lo que nos rodea.

Ambiente con humo de cigarro Aire que ha sido contaminado por el humo de cigarrillos.

Epidemia Una situación en la cual mucha gente contrae una enfermedad al mismo tiempo y en el mismo lugar.

Epidermis La capa más fina y externa de la piel la cual se encuentra compuesta de células vivas y muertas.

Epilepsia Trastorno del sistema nervioso caracterizado por convulsiones continuas—repentinos episodios de actividad eléctrica incontrolable en el cerebro.

Escalada Situación que se hace más grave.

Estimar Determinar aproximadamente el tamaño o la extension de algo.

Etanol Tipo de alcohol que se encuentra en las bebidas alcohólicas.

Euphoria A feeling of intense well-being or elation. (Ch. 22, 605)

Euforia Sentimiento de un intenso bienestar o alegría.

Eventually* At an unspecified later time. (Ch. 17, 471)

Eventual Sin especificar un rato más después.

Exclude* To prevent or restrict the entrance of. (Ch. 8, 195)

Excluir Para prevenir o restringir la entrada de.

Exercise Purposeful physical activity that is planned, structured, and repetitive, and that improves or maintains physical fitness. (Ch. 12, 319)

Ejercicio Actividad física dirigida que es planeada, estructurada y repetitiva y que tiene como objetivo el mantenimiento o el mejoramiento del estado físico de una persona.

Expand* To open up. (Ch. 15, 417)

Expandir Ampliar.

Exposure* The condition of being unprotected. (Ch. 12, 340)

Exposición Falta de protección.

Extended family A family that includes additional relatives beyond parents and children. (Ch. 7, 167)

Familia extendida Familia que incluye a otros parientes, distintos a padres e hijos.

Extensor The muscle that opens a joint. (Ch. 14, 388)

Extensor Músculo que abre una articulación.

| **English** | **F** | **Español** |

Factor* An element that contributes to a particular result. (Ch. 1, 13)

Factor Elemento que contribuye a un resultado en particular.

Fad diet Weight-loss plans that tend to be popular for only a short time. (Ch. 11, 298)

Dietas de moda Planes para perder peso que son populares por poco tiempo.

Fallopian tubes A pair of tubes with fingerlike projections that draw in the ovum. (Ch. 16, 453)

Trompas de falopio Un par de conductos con terminaciones en forma de dedos que atrae el ovario.

Family therapy Helping the family function in more positive and constructive ways by exploring the patterns in communication and providing support and education. (Ch. 5, 129)

Terapia familiar Ayudar a que la familia funcione de maneras más constructivas y positivas mediante la exploración de los patrones de comunicación y en proporcionar apoyo y educación.

Fermentation The chemical action of yeast on sugars. (Ch. 21, 566)

Fermentación Reacción química de la levadura en los azúcares.

Fertilization The union of a male sperm cell and a female egg. (Ch. 17, 470)

Fertilización La unión del espermatozoide y el óvulo.

Fetal alcohol syndrome A group of alcohol-related birth defects that includes both physical and mental problems. (Ch. 17, 474)

Síndrome de alcoholismo fetal Un grupo de defectos de nacimiento causados por el alcohol y que incluyen problemas físicos y mentales.

Fetus Group of developing cells after about the eighth week of pregnancy. (Ch. 17, 470)

Feto Grupo de células en desarrollo después de las ocho semanas de embarazo.

Fiber A tough, complex, carbohydrate that the body cannot digest. (Ch. 10, 259)

Fibra Un carbohidrato complejo y duro que el cuerpo no puede digerir.

Fire extinguisher A portable device for putting out small fires. (Ch. 26, 732)

Extintor de incendios Aparato portátil para apagar fuego.

First aid The immediate, temporary care given to an ill or injured person until professional care can be provided. (Ch. 27, 758)

Primeros auxilios La atención inmediata y temporal que se le proporciona a una persona hasta que se le puede otorgar atención profesional.

Flash floods Floods in which a dangerous volume of water builds up in a short time. (Ch. 27, 781)

Inundaciones rápidas Inundaciones en las cuales se acumula un volumen peligroso de agua en poco tiempo.

Flexibility The ability to move your body parts through their full range of motion. (Ch. 12, 325)

Flexibilidad La capacidad de mover una parte del cuerpo fácilmente y en muchas direcciones.

Flexor The muscle that closes a joint. (Ch. 14, 388)

Músculo flexor Músculo que abre una articulación.

Food additives Substances added to a food to produce a desired effect. (Ch. 10, 275)

Aditivos alimentarios Sustancias que son adicionadas a los alimentos en forma intencional para generar un efecto deseado.

Food allergy A condition in which the body's immune system reacts to substances in some foods. (Ch. 10, 281)

Alergia alimentaria Una condición en la cuál el sistema inmunológico del cuerpo reacciona a sustancias contenidas en algunos alimentos.

Foodborne illness Food poisoning. (Ch. 10, 278)

Enfermedad producida por alimentos Intoxicación alimentaria.

Food intolerance A negative reaction to food that does not involve the immune system. (Ch. 10, 281)

Intolerancia alimentaria Reacción negativa a los alimentos (o un elemento particular del alimento) en la cual no participa el sistema inmunológico.

Foster care The temporary placement of children in the homes of adults who are not related to them. (Ch. 7, 167)

Cuidados temporales Colocación provisoria de niños en hogares de adultos que no son sus parientes.

Fracture A break in a bone. (Ch. 27, 772)

Fractura Ruptura de un hueso.

Friendship A significant relationship between two people that is based on trust, caring, and consideration. (Ch. 6, 143)

Amistad Una relación importante entre dos personas que está basada en solidaridad, confianza y consideración.

Frostbite Damage to the skin and tissues caused by extreme cold. (Ch. 12, 339)

Congelamiento Daño a la piel y a los tejidos provocados por frío extremo.

English G Español

Gastric juices Secretions from the stomach lining that contain hydrochloric acid and pepsin, an enzyme that digests protein. (Ch. 15, 424)

Jugos gástricos La secreciones que provienen del revestimiento del estómago y que contienen ácido clorhídrico y pepsina, una enzima que digiere la proteína.

Gene therapy The process of inserting normal genes into human cells to correct genetic disorders. (Ch. 17, 482)

Terapia genética Un proceso que consiste en introducir genes normales en las células humanas para corregir trastornos genéticos.

Genes The basic units of heredity. (Ch. 17, 479)

Genes Unidades básicas de la herencia.

Genetic disorders Disorders caused partly or completely by a defect in genes. (Ch. 17, 481)

Trastorno genético Trastorno causado parcial o completamente por defectos en los genes.

Giardia A microorganism that infects the digestive system. (Ch. 23, 647)

Giardia Microorganismo que infecta el sistema digestivo.

Global warming An overall increase in the earth's temperature. (Ch. 28, 802)

Calentamiento global Aumento general de la temperatura de la Tierra.

Goals Those things you aim for that take planning and work. (Ch. 2, 42)

Meta Las cosas de que te esfuerzas que necesita planificación y trabajo.

Good Samaritan laws Statutes that protect rescuers from being sued for giving emergency care. (Ch. 27, 759)

Leyes del Buen Samaritano Estatutos que protegen a los rescatistas de ser demandados por otorgar atención de urgencia.

Graduated licensing A system that gradually increases driving privileges over time. (Ch. 26, 745)

Licencia graduada Sistema que gradualmente aumenta los privilegios de conducción en el transcurso del tiempo.

Greenhouse effect The trapping of heat by gases in the earth's atmosphere. (Ch. 28, 801)

Efecto invernadero Calor atrapado por gases en la atmósfera de la Tierra.

Group therapy Treating a group of people who have similar problems and who meet regularly with a trained counselor. (Ch. 5, 129)

Terapia de grupo Tratamiento de un grupo de personas que tienen problemas similares.

Glossary / Glosario

Hair follicles Sacs or cavities that surround the roots of hairs. (Ch. 13, 360)

Halitosis Bad breath. (Ch. 13, 365)

Hallucinogens Drugs that alter moods, thoughts, and sense perceptions including vision, hearing, smell, and touch. (Ch. 22, 605)

Harassment Persistently annoying others. (Ch. 8, 199)

Hazardous wastes Waste materials with properties that make them dangerous to human health or the environment. (Ch. 28, 807)

Hazing Making others perform certain tasks in order to join the group. (Ch. 6, 150)

Health The combination of physical, mental/emotional, and social well-being. (Ch. 1, 6)

Health consumer Someone who purchases or uses health products or services. (Ch. 2, 46)

Health disparities Differences in health outcomes among groups. (Ch. 1, 23)

Health education Providing accurate health information and health skills teaching to help people make healthy decisions. (Ch. 1, 22)

Health fraud The sale of worthless products or services that claim to prevent diseases or cure other health problems. (Ch. 2, 52)

Health insurance Private and government programs that pay for part or all of a person's medical costs. (Ch. 28, 795)

Health literacy A person's capacity to learn about and understand basic health information and services and to use these resources to promote one's health and wellness. (Ch. 1, 25)

Health skills Specific tools and strategies to maintain, protect, and improve all aspects of your health. (Ch. 2, 34)

Health care system All the medical care available to a nation's people, the way they receive care, and the way they pay for it. (Ch. 28, 792)

Healthy People A nationwide health promotion and disease prevention plan designed to serve as a guide for improving the health of all people in the United States. (Ch. 1, 22)

Heat exhaustion A form of physical stress on the body caused by overheating. (Ch. 12, 340)

Heatstroke A dangerous condition in which the body loses its ability to cool itself through perspiration. (Ch. 12, 340)

Folículos pilosos Sacos o cavidades que rodean las raíces de los pelos.

Halitosis Mal aliento.

Alucinógenos Drogas que alteran el estado de ánimo, el pensamiento y la percepción, lo que incluye vista, oído, olfato y tacto.

Acoso Molestar continuamente a otra persona.

Desechos peligrosos Materiales de desecho que se caracterizan por ser peligrosos para la salud humana o el medio ambiente.

Acoso personal Forzando otras a complir ciertas tareas para formar parte del grupo.

Salud Combinación de bienestar físico, mental-emocional y social.

Consumidor de salud Cualquier persona que adquiere o consume productos o servicios de salud.

Desigualdades de salud Diferencias de los resultados de salud entre distintos grupos.

Educación en salud Proveer a las personas información adecuada y enseñar destrezas de salud para que puedan tomar decisiones saludables.

Fraude de salud Venta de productos o servicios inútiles que supuestamente sirven para prevenir enfermedades o mejorar otros problemas de la salud.

Seguro de salud Programas privados y gubernamentales que financian total o parcialmente los costos médicos de una persona.

Educación en salud Capacidad que tiene una persona para aprender y comprender información básica de salud y los servicios relacionados, y usar esos conocimientos para mejorar su propia salud y bienestar.

Destrezas de salud Herramientas y estrategias específicas que ayudan a mantener, proteger y mejorar todos los aspectos de la salud.

Sistema de atención de salud Toda atención médica disponible para los habitantes de un país, la forma en que la reciben y el sistema de pago.

Healthy People Plan de promoción de la salud y prevención de enfermedades diseñado para que sirva como guía en el mejoramiento de la salud de todos los habitantes de Estados Unidos.

Agotamiento debido al calor Forma de estrés físico provocado por el sobrecalentamiento del cuerpo.

Insolación Estado peligroso en el cual el cuerpo pierde su capacidad de enfriarse mediante la transpiración.

Hemodialysis A technique in which an artificial kidney machine removes waste products from the blood. (Ch. 15, 433)

Hemodiálisis Técnica en la cual una máquina de diálisis limpia los desechos de la sangre.

Hemoglobin The oxygen-carrying protein in blood. (Ch. 15, 410)

Hemoglobina Proteína que lleva el oxígeno en la sangre.

Herbal supplements Dietary supplements containing plant extracts. (Ch. 11, 308)

Suplementos herbales Suplementos alimentarios que contienen extractos vegetales.

Heredity All the traits that were biologically passed on to you from your parents. (Ch. 1, 11)

Herencia Todo rasgo biológicamente transmitido de padres a hijos.

Hernia Occurs when an organ or tissue protrudes through an area of weak muscle. (Ch. 14, 390)

Hernia Cuando un órgano o tejido sobresale en un área de músculos débiles.

Hierarchy of Needs A ranked list of those needs essential to human growth and development, presented in ascending order, starting with basic needs and building toward the need for reaching your highest potential. (Ch. 3, 70)

Jerarquización de necesidades Lista priorizada de aquellas necesidades esenciales para el desarrollo óptimo del ser humano, presentada en orden ascendente, comenzando con las necesidades básicas y ascendiendo hacia la necesidad de alcanzar los potenciales máximos.

Histamines Chemicals that can stimulate mucus and fluid production. (Ch. 25, 703)

Estaminas Sustancias químicas que pueden estimular la producción de mucosidades y líquidos corporales.

HIV (Human Immunodeficiency Virus) The virus that causes Acquired Immune Deficiency Syndrome (AIDS). (Ch. 24, 669)

VIH (Virus de la Inmunodeficiencia Humana) Virus que provoca el Síndrome de Inmunodeficiencia Adquirida (SIDA).

Homicide The willful killing of one human being by another. (Ch. 9, 233)

Homicidio Cuando una persona mata intencionalmente a otra.

Hormones Chemicals produced by your glands that regulate the activities of different body cells. (Ch. 3, 78)

Hormonas Produciónes químicas secretadas por las glándulas que regulan las actividades de diferentes células corporales.

Hostility The intentional use of unfriendly or offensive behavior. (Ch. 3, 79)

Hostilidad Comportamiento intencional que es antipático, desagradable u ofensivo.

Hunger The natural physical drive to eat, prompted by the body's need for food. (Ch. 10, 255)

Hambre Impulso físico natural de comer, provocado por la necesidad del cuerpo de obtener alimento.

Hurricane A powerful storm that generally forms in tropical areas, producing winds of at least 74 miles per hour, heavy rains, and sometimes tornadoes. (Ch. 27, 779)

Huracán Una tormenta muy fuerte que se origina en áreas tropicales y que se caracteriza por vientos de al menos 74 millas por hora, fuertes lluvias, inundaciones y, algunas veces, tornados.

Hypertension High blood pressure. (Ch. 25, 689)

Hipertensión Presión arterial alta.

Hypothermia Dangerously low body temperature. (Ch. 12, 340)

Hipotermia Descenso peligroso de la temperatura corporal.

English — I — Español

"I" message A statement that focuses on your feelings rather than on someone else's behavior. (Ch. 6, 154)

Mensaje por primera persona Una declaracion enfocada en sus propias sensaciones mas bien que en el comportamiento de alguien mas.

Illegal drugs Chemical substances that people of any age may not lawfully manufacture, possess, buy, or sell. (Ch. 22, 592)

Drogas ilegales Sustancias químicas que ninguna persona, cualquiera sea su edad, puede legalmente producir, poseer, comprar o vender.

Illicit drug use The use or sale of any substance that is illegal or otherwise not permitted. (Ch. 22, 592)

Uso ilegal de drogas El uso o venta de cualquier sustancia que es ilegal o no permitida.

Glossary / Glosario

Immune system A network of cells, tissues, organs, and chemicals that fight off pathogens. (Ch. 23, 639)

Immunity The state of being protected against a particular disease. (Ch. 23, 640)

Implantation The process by which the zygote attaches to the uterine wall. (Ch. 17, 470)

Infatuation Exaggerated feelings of passion. (Ch. 8, 206)

Infection A condition that occurs when pathogens in the body multiply and damage body cells. (Ch. 23, 628)

Inflammatory response A reaction to tissue damage caused by injury or infection. (Ch. 23, 639)

Inhalants Substances whose fumes are sniffed or inhaled to give a mind-altering effect. (Ch. 22, 601)

Insecure* Not confident or sure. (Ch. 9, 230)

Instance* To mention as a case or example. (Ch. 12, 334)

Integrity A firm observance of core ethical values. (Ch. 3, 74)

Intense* Existing in an extreme degree. (Ch. 22, 600)

Intermediate* Being at the middle place or stage. (Ch. 16, 444)

Interpersonal communication The exchange of thoughts, feelings, and beliefs between two or more people. (Ch. 2, 35)

Interpersonal conflict Conflicts between people or groups of people. (Ch. 9, 220)

Intimacy Closeness between two people that develops over time. (Ch. 8, 206)

Intoxication The state in which the body is poisoned by alcohol or another substance and the person's physical and mental control is significantly reduced. (Ch. 21, 567)

Involve* To require as a necessary accompaniment (Ch. 15, 423)

Isolation* The act of being withdrawn or separated. (Ch. 21, 575)

Sistema de defensas (inmunológico) Una combinación de células, tejidos, órganos y sustancias químicas que combaten a los agentes patógenos.

Inmunidad Estado de protección contra una enfermedad en particular.

Implantación El proceso en que el cigoto se adhiere a la pared uterina.

Encaprichamiento Sentimientos exagerados de pasión.

Infección Una condición que ocurre cuando agentes patógenos entran al cuerpo, se multiplican y dañan las células.

Respuesta inflamatoria Reacción al daño de tejidos causada por una lesión o infección.

Inhalantes Sustancias cuyos gases se aspiran o inhalan para alcanzar un estado que altera la mente.

Inseguro Que no tiene confianza o seguridad.

Caso Para mencionar como un caso o ejemplo.

Integridad Adherencia firme a los valores éticos fundamentales.

Intenso Que existe en grado extremo.

Intermedio Que está en medio de un lugar o de una etapa.

Comunicación interpersonal Intercambio de pensamientos, sentimientos y creencias entre dos o más personas.

Conflicto interpersonal Desacuerdo entre personas o grupos de personas.

Intimidad Cercanía entre dos personas que se desarrolla en el transcurso del tiempo.

Intoxicación Estado en el cual el cuerpo se encuentra envenenado por el alcohol u otra sustancia, y el control físico y mental de la persona se encuentra reducido significativamente.

Implicar Que incluye algo.

Aislamiento Acción de retirar o separar.

English	J	Español

Jaundice A yellowing of the skin and eyes. (Ch. 23, 635)

Ictericia Estado en el cual la piel y los ojos se ponen de color amarillo.

English	L	Español

Labyrinth The inner ear. (Ch. 13, 371)

Landfill A specially engineered area where waste can by buried safely. (Ch. 28. 807)

Laberinto Oído interno.

Vertedero Área diseñada especialmente para enterrar los desechos en forma segura.

Legal* Permitted by law. (Ch. 26, 740)

Leukoplakia Thickened, white, leathery-looking spots on the inside of the mouth that can develop into oral cancer. (Ch. 20, 544)

Lifestyle factors The personal habits or behaviors related to the way a person lives. (Ch. 1, 20)

Ligament A band of fibrous, slightly elastic connective tissue that attaches one bone to another. (Ch. 14, 383)

Link* A connecting element or factor. (Ch. 25, 697)

Long-term goal A goal that you plan to reach over an extended period. (Ch. 2, 43)

Lymph The clear fluid that fills the spaces around body cells. (Ch. 15, 412)

Lymphocyte Specialized white blood cell that coordinates and performs many of the functions of specific immunity. (Ch. 23, 640)

Legal Permitido por la ley.

Leucoplaquia Granos con apariencia de piel blanca dura y espesa que se encuentran dentro de la boca y que pueden llegar a producir un cáncer oral.

Factores del estilo de vida Hábitos o conductas personales relativos a la forma de vivir de las personas.

Ligamento Tejido conjuntivo fibroso y levemente elástico que une dos huesos.

Enlace Elemento o factor de conexión.

Meta a largo plazo Meta que planeas alcanzar en un periodo prolongado.

Linfa Líquido transparente que llena los espacios entre las células del cuerpo.

Linfocito Glóbulo blanco especializado que coordina y realiza muchas de las funciones de inmunidad específica.

English — M — Español

Mainstream smoke The smoke exhaled from the lungs of a smoker. (Ch. 20, 553)

Malignant Cancerous. (Ch. 25, 696)

Malocclusion A misalignment of the upper and lower teeth. (Ch. 13, 365)

Malpractice Failure by a health professional to meet accepted standards. (Ch. 2, 52)

Manipulation An indirect, dishonest way to control or influence others. (Ch. 8, 200)

Marijuana A plant whose leaves, buds, and flowers are usually smoked for their intoxicating effects. (Ch. 22, 599)

Mastication The process of chewing. (Ch. 15, 423)

Media Various methods for communicating information. (Ch. 1, 14)

Mediation Bringing in a neutral third party to help others resolve their conflicts peacefully. (Ch. 9, 226)

Medical history Complete and comprehensive information about your immunizations and any health problems you have had to date (Ch. 28, 794)

Medicines Drugs that are used to treat or prevent diseases or other conditions. (Ch. 19, 524)

Megadoses Very large amount. (Ch. 11, 308)

Melanin A pigment that gives the skin, hair, and iris of the eyes their color. (Ch. 13, 356)

Melanoma The most serious form of skin cancer. (Ch. 13, 360)

Menstruation The shedding of the uterine lining. (Ch. 16, 454)

Humo directo Humo exhalado por los pulmones de un fumador.

Maligno Canceroso.

Oclusión defectuosa Alineación defectuosa de los dientes superiores e inferiores.

Mala práctica médica (mala praxis) Condición en la que un profesional de la salud no cumple con los estándares aceptados.

Manipulación Controlar o influenciar a otros de manera indirecta y deshonesta.

Marihuana Una planta cuyas hojas, brotes y flores son generalmente fumados por su efecto intoxicante.

Masticación Proceso de masticar.

Medios de comunicación Diversos métodos para comunicar información.

Mediación Proceso en el cual una tercera parte neutra ayuda a otros a resolver sus conflictos pacíficamente.

Historial médico Información completa acerca de las vacunas recibidas y los problemas de salud que una persona ha teido hasta la fecha.

Medicamentos Fármacos para tratar o prevenir una enfermedad u otro problema de salud.

Megadosises Gran cantidad.

Melanina Pigmento que da el color a la piel, el cabello y el iris del ojo.

Melanoma El cáncer de la piel más grave de todos.

Menstruación El eliminación del revestimiento del útero.

Mental* Of or relating to the mind. (Ch. 3, 67)

Mental Relativo a la mente.

Mental disorder An illness of the mind that can affect the thoughts, feelings, and behaviors of a person, preventing him or her from leading a happy, healthful, and productive life. (Ch. 5, 118)

Trastorno mental Enfermedad mental que puede afectar la manera de pensar, los sentimientos y el comportamiento de una persona, y que le impide tener una vida feliz, saludable y productiva.

Mental retardation A below-average intellectual ability present from birth or early childhood and associated with difficulties in learning and social adaptation. (Ch. 25, 712)

Retardo mental Capacidad intelectual inferior al promedio que se presenta desde el nacimiento o la niñez temprana y que se relaciona con dificultades de aprendizaje y adaptación social.

Mental/emotional health The ability to accept yourself and others, express and manage emotions, and deal with the demands and challenges you meet in your life. (Ch. 3, 66)

Salud mental-emocional Habilidad para aceptarse a sí mismo y a otras personas, expresar, manejar las emociones y hacer frente a las exigencias y desafíos de la vida.

Metabolism The processes by which the body breaks down substances and gets energy from food. (Ch. 11, 290)

Metabolismo Proceso mediante el cual el cuerpo procesa las sustancias y obtiene energía de los alimentos.

Metastasis The spread of cancer from the point where it originated to other parts of the body. (Ch. 25, 696)

Metástasis Extensión del cáncer desde el punto de origen a otras partes del cuerpo.

Minerals Elements found in food that are used by the body. (Ch. 10, 262)

Minerales Elementos que se encuentran en los alimentos y son utilizados por el cuerpo.

Minor* Not serious or involving risk to life. (Ch. 27, 760)

Menor Que no es grave ni representa riesgo vital.

Misinterpret* To understand wrongly. (Ch. 9, 221)

Malinterpretar Entender equivocadamente.

Monitor* To watch or keep track of. (Ch. 15, 431)

Controlar Vigilar o comprobar.

Mood disorders Illness that involves mood extremes that interfere with everyday living. (Ch. 5, 120)

Trastornos del ánimo Enfermedad que involucran estados de ánimo extremos, los cuales interfieren con la vida diaria.

Mourning The act of showing sorrow or grief. (Ch. 4, 104)

Luto Acto de mostrar pena o dolor.

Mucous membrane The lining of various body cavities, including the nose, ears, and mouth. (Ch. 23, 634)

Membrana mucosa Revestimiento de diferentes cavidades corporales que incluyen la nariz, los oídos y la boca.

Muscle cramps Sudden and sometimes painful contractions of the muscles. (Ch. 12, 341)

Calambres musculares Contracciones repentinas y, algunas veces, dolorosas de los músculos.

Muscular endurance The ability of your muscles to perform physical tasks over a period without tiring. (Ch. 12, 325)

Resistencia muscular Capacidad de los músculos para hacer actividades físicas durante un periodo de tiempo sin fatigarse.

Muscular strength The amount of force your muscles can exert. (Ch. 12, 324)

Fuerza muscular Fuerza que puedan ejercer los músculos.

MyPyramid An interactive guide to healthful eating and active living. (Ch. 10, 267)

MyPyramid Guía interactiva para alimentarse sanamente y llevar una vida activa.

English **Español**

Neglect The failure to provide for a child's basic needs. (Ch. 7, 179)

Abandono No satisfacer las necesidades básicas de un niño.

Negotiation The use of communication and, in many cases, compromise to settle a disagreement. (Ch. 9, 225)

Negociación Uso de la comunicación y, frecuentemente, el compromiso para resolver un desacuerdo.

Nephrons The functional units of the kidneys. (Ch. 15, 430)

Nefronas Unidades funcionales de los riñones.

Neurons Nerve cells. (Ch. 14, 393)

Neutralize* To counteract the effect of. (Ch. 19, 525)

Nicotine The addictive drug found in tobacco. (Ch. 20, 543)

Nicotine substitute A product that delivers small amounts of nicotine into the user's system while he or she is trying to give up the tobacco habit. (Ch. 20, 551)

Nicotine withdrawal The process that occurs in the body when nicotine, an addictive drug, is no longer used. (Ch. 20, 551)

Noise pollution Harmful, unwanted sound loud enough to damage hearing. (Ch. 28, 804)

Noncommunicable disease A disease that is not transmitted by another person, a vector, or the environment. (Ch. 25, 688)

Nuclear family Two parents and one or more children living in the same space. (Ch. 7, 167)

Nutrient-dense A high ratio of nutrients to calories. (Ch. 10, 269)

Nutrients Substances in food that you body needs to grow, to repair itself, and to supply you with energy. (Ch. 10, 254)

Nutrition The process by which your body takes in and uses food. (Ch. 10, 254)

Neuronas Células nerviosas.

Neutralizar Contrarrestar el efecto de algo.

Nicotina Droga adictiva que se encuentra en el tabaco.

Sustituto de la nicotina Producto que libera pequeñas cantidades de nicotina en el cuerpo de una persona que está tratando de dejar de fumar.

Reacción al retiro de la nicotina Proceso que ocurre en el cuerpo cuando la nicotina, una droga adictiva, deja de ser consumida.

Contaminación acústica Nivel de ruido perjudicial y no deseado que es lo suficientemente alto como para dañar la audición de las personas.

Enfermedad no contagiosa Enfermedad que no se transmite entre las personas o por un vector, y que tampoco proviene del medio ambiente.

Familia nuclear Ambos padres y uno o más hijos que viven en el mismo espacio.

Rico en nutrientes Que tiene una relación alta de nutrientes a calorías.

Nutrientes Sustancias presentes en los alimentos que el cuerpo necesita para crecer, regenerarse y producir energía.

Nutrición Proceso mediante el cual el cuerpo absorbe y usa los alimentos.

English	O	Español

Obese Having an excess of body fat. (Ch. 11, 292)

Occupational Safety and Health Administration (OSHA) The agency within the federal government that is responsible for promoting safe and healthful conditions in the workplace. (Ch. 26, 738)

Opiates Drugs like those derived from the opium plant that are obtainable only by prescription and are used to relieve pain. (Ch. 22, 609)

Ossification The process by which bone is formed, renewed, and repaired. (Ch. 14, 383)

Osteoarthritis A disease of the joints in which cartilage breaks down. (Ch. 25, 707)

Osteoporosis A condition in which the bones become fragile and break easily. (Ch. 10, 264)

Ovaries The female sex glands that store the ova, eggs, and produce female sex hormones. (Ch. 16, 452)

Over the counter (OTC) Medicines you can buy without a prescription. (Ch. 19, 531)

Obeso Que tiene exceso de grasa corporal.

Administración de Seguridad y Salud Ocupacional (OSHA) Agencia del gobierno federal que es responsable de promover condiciones de trabajo seguras y saludables.

Opiáceos Drogas, como aquellas derivadas del opio, que sólo se obtienen con prescripción médica y se utilizan para aliviar el dolor.

Osificación Proceso mediante el cual el hueso se forma, renueva y repara.

Osteoartritis Enfermedad de las articulaciones en la cual el cartílago se deteriora.

Osteoporosis Enfermedad en la cual los huesos se vuelven frágiles y se rompen con facilidad.

Ovarios Glándulas sexuales femeninas que contienen los óvulos y producen hormonas sexuales.

Medicamentos de venta libre (OTC) Medicamentos que se pueden comprar sin prescripción médica.

Glossary / Glosario

Overdose A strong, sometimes fatal reaction to taking a large amount of a drug. (Ch. 22, 593)

Overexertion Overworking the body. (Ch. 12, 340)

Overload Exercising at a level that's beyond your regular daily activities. (Ch. 12, 333)

Overweight Heavier than the standard weight range for your height. (Ch. 11, 291)

Ovulation The process of releasing a mature ovum into the fallopian tube each month. (Ch. 16, 452)

Sobredosis Reacción fuerte, y algunas veces fatal, al consumir una droga en grandes cantidades.

Esfuerzo excesivo Cuando el cuerpo trabaja demasiado.

Sobrecarga Ejercitarse a un nivel que sobrepasa las actividades diarias normales.

Sobrepeso Peso superior al rango normal según la estatura.

Ovulacion El proceso de saltar un ovario maduro cada mes en las trompas de falopio.

English		Español

Pancreas A gland that serves both the digestive and endocrine systems. (Ch. 16, 443)

Pandemic A global outbreak of an infectious disease. (Ch. 23, 648)

Paranoia An irrational suspiciousness or distrust of others. (Ch. 22, 600)

Parathyroid glands Produce a hormone that regulates the body's balance of calcium and phosphorus. (Ch. 16, 443)

Partner* One associated with another. (Ch. 9, 238)

Passive Unwilling or unable to express thoughts and feelings in a direct or firm manner. (Ch. 6, 152)

Pasteurization Treating a substance with heat to kill or slow the growth of pathogens. (Ch. 10, 279)

Pathogen A microorganism that causes disease. (Ch. 15, 412)

Peer mediation Processes in which specially trained students help other students resolve conflicts peacefully. (Ch. 9, 228)

Peer pressure The influence that people your age may have on you. (Ch. 8, 198)

Peers People of the same age who share similar interests. (Ch. 1, 13)

Penis A tube-shaped organ that extends from the trunk of the body just above the testes. (Ch. 16, 447)

Peptic ulcer A sore in the lining of the digestive tract. (Ch. 15, 427)

Percent* One part in a hundred. (Ch. 5, 119)

Perception The act of becoming aware through the senses. (Ch. 4, 92)

Performance enhancers Substitutes that boost athletic ability. (Ch. 11, 307)

Peridontium The area immediately around the tooth. (Ch. 13, 363)

Period* The completion of a cycle. (Ch. 12, 327)

Páncreas Glándula utilizada tanto por el sistema digestivo como el endocrino.

Pandemia Brote global de una enfermedad infecciosa.

Paranoia Sospecha o desconfianza irracionales hacia otras personas.

Glándulas paratiroides Glándulas que producen una hormona que regula el equilibrio de calcio y fósforo en el cuerpo.

Socio Persona asociada con otra.

Pasivo Persona que no está dispuesto o no es capaz de expresar sus pensamientos y sentimientos.

Pasteurización Tratamiento de una sustancia con calor para matar organismos patógenos o para hacer más lento su desarrollo.

Patógeno Microorganismo que causa enfermedades.

Mediación de los pares Proceso en el cual estudiantes especialmente entrenados ayudan a otros a resolver sus conflictos pacíficamente.

Presión de los pares La influencia que gente de tu misma edad puede tener en ti.

Pares Personas cuya edad e intereses son similares a los tuyos.

Pene Órgano con forma de tubo que se extiende desde el tronco del cuerpo, justo arriba de los testículos.

Úlcera péptica Herida en el revestimiento del tracto digestivo.

Porcentaje Una parte de cada cien.

Percepción Acto de tomar conciencia de algo a través de los sentidos.

Potenciadores del rendimiento Sustitutos que mejoran las capacidades atléticas.

Periodontio Área que rodea los dientes.

Periodo Ciclo de tiempo.

Periodontal disease An inflammation of the periodontal structures. (Ch. 13, 365)

Peristalsis A series of involuntary muscle contractions that move food through the digestive tract. (Ch. 15, 424)

Personal flotation device Life jacket. (Ch. 26, 742)

Personal identity Your sense of yourself as a unique individual. (Ch. 3, 72)

Personal safety The steps you take to prevent yourself from becoming the victim of crime. (Ch. 26, 726)

Personality A complex set of characteristics that make you unique. (Ch. 3, 73)

Phagocyte White blood cells that attack invading pathogens. (Ch. 23, 640)

Physical abuse A pattern of intentionally causing bodily harm or injury to another person. (Ch. 9, 237)

Physical activity Any form of movement that causes your body to use energy. (Ch. 12, 318)

Physical fitness The ability to carry out daily tasks easily and have enough reserve energy to respond to unexpected demands. (Ch. 12, 319)

Physical maturity The state at which the physical body and all its organs are fully developed. (Ch. 18, 502)

Physiological dependence A condition in which the user has a chemical need for the drug. (Ch. 21, 572)

Pituitary gland Regulates and controls the activities of all other endocrine systems. (Ch. 16, 443)

Plaque A combination of bacteria and other particles, such as small bits of food, which adheres to the outside of a tooth. (Ch. 13, 364)

Plasma The fluid in which other parts of the blood are suspended. (Ch. 15, 410)

Platelets Types of cells in the blood that cause blood clots to form. (Ch. 15, 410)

Platonic friendship A friendship with a member of the opposite gender in which there is affection but the two people are not considered a couple. (Ch. 8, 194)

Pneumonia An infection of the lungs in which the air sacs fill with pus and other liquids. (Ch. 23, 634)

Poison Any substance—solid, liquid, or gas—that causes injury, illness, or death when it enters the body. (Ch. 27, 775)

Poison control center A round-the-clock service that provides emergency medical advice on how to treat poisoning victims. (Ch. 27, 775)

Portion* A part set off from the whole. (Ch. 13, 368)

Pose* To put or set forth. (Ch. 11, 298)

Enfermedad periodontal Inflamación de la estructura de soporte dental.

Movimientos peristálticos Serie de contracciones musculares involuntarias que mueven la comida a través del tracto digestivo.

Dispositivo de flotación personal Chaqueta salvavidas.

Identidad personal Sentirse como un individuo único.

Seguridad personal Medidas que se toman para evitar ser víctima de un delito.

Personalidad Conjunto complejo de características que hacen que una persona sea única.

Fagocito Glóbulo blanco que combate la invasión de patógenos.

Abuso físico Patrón intencionalmente de causar daño o lesión corporal a otra persona.

Actividad física Cualquier forma de movimiento que provoque que el cuerpo consuma energía.

Buena condición física Capacidad de realizar fácilmente las tareas diarias y tener suficiente energía para responder a exigencias inesperadas.

Madurez física Estado en el cual el cuerpo y todos sus órganos se encuentran totalmente desarrollados.

Dependencia fisiológica Enfermedad en la cual el usuario tiene una necesidad física de consumir una droga.

Glándula pituitaria Glándula que regula o controla las actividades de todas las glándulas endocrinas.

Placa Combinación de bacterias y otras partículas, tales como pequeños trozos de alimentos, que se adhieren a la parte externa de los dientes.

Plasma Líquido en el cual están suspendidos los componentes de la sangre.

Plaquetas Tipos de células sanguíneas que provocan la formación de coágulos.

Amistad platónica Amistad con una persona del sexo opuesto en la cual hay sentimientos mutuos de afecto, pero que no se consideran una pareja.

Neumonía Infección de los pulmones en la cual los alvéolos se llenan de pus y otros líquidos.

Veneno Cualquier sustancia, sea sólida, líquida o gaseosa, que al entrar en el cuerpo causa una herida, una enfermedad o la muerte.

Centro para el control de envenenamientos Servicio que funciona las 24 horas del día para dar consejos médicos de emergencia sobre el tratamiento de víctimas de intoxicaciones.

Porción Parte separada de un todo.

Plantear Exponer o presentar.

Glossary / Glosario

Precycling Reducing waste before it is generated. (Ch. 28, 810)

Prejudice An unfair opinion or judgment of a particular group of people. (Ch. 6, 150)

Prenatal care Steps that a pregnant female can take to provide for her own health and the health of her baby. (Ch. 17, 473)

Prescription medicines Medicines that cannot be used without the written approval of a licensed physician or nurse practitioner. (Ch. 19, 531)

Prevention Taking steps to keep something from happening or getting worse. (Ch. 1, 18)

Primary care physician A medical doctor who provides physical check-ups and general care. (Ch. 28, 792)

Priorities The goals, tasks, values, and activities that you judge to be more important than others. (Ch. 8, 205)

Process* A series of actions geared toward an end result. (Ch. 8, 206)

Profound deafness Hearing loss so severe that a person affected cannot benefit from mechanical amplification such as a hearing aid. (Ch. 25, 710)

Progression Gradually increasing the demands on your body. (Ch. 12, 333)

Promote* To contribute to the growth of. (Ch. 2, 38)

Proteins Nutrients the body uses to build and maintain its cells and tissues. (Ch. 10, 260)

Psychoactive drugs Chemicals that affect the central nervous system and alter activity in the brain. (Ch. 22, 603)

Psychological* Directed toward the mind. (Ch. 10, 255)

Psychological dependence A condition in which a person believes that a drug is needed in order to feel good or to function normally. (Ch. 21, 572)

Psychosomatic response A physical reaction, which results from stress rather than from an injury or illness. (Ch. 4, 95)

Psychotherapy An ongoing dialogue between a patient and a mental health professional. (Ch. 5, 128)

Puberty The time when a person begins to develop certain traits of adults of his or her gender. (Ch. 18, 496)

Public health All efforts to monitor, protect, and promote the health of the population as a whole. (Ch. 28, 796)

Pulp The tissue that contains the blood vessels and nerves of a tooth. (Ch. 13, 364)

Reciclaje previo Reducir la basura antes de generarla.

Prejuicio Opinión o juicio injusto acerca de un grupo específico de personas.

Cuidado prenatal Todas las medidas que una mujer embarazada puede tomar para cuidar su propia salud y la de su bebé.

Medicamentos con prescripción Medicamentos que no se pueden utilizar sin la aprobación escrita de un médico o enfermera profesionales.

Prevención Tomar medidas para evitar que algo ocurra o empeore.

Médico de atención primaria Médico que realiza chequeos físicos y se encarga del cuidado general de los pacientes.

Prioridades Metas, tareas, valores y actividades que se consideran más importantes que otras.

Proceso Serie de acciones para obtener un resultado final.

Sordera profunda Pérdida de la audición tan grave que no se beneficia con la amplificación mecánica (por ejemplo, los audífonos).

Progresión Aumento gradual de las exigencias corporales.

Promover Contribuir al crecimiento de algo.

Proteínas Nutrientes que el cuerpo utiliza para generar y mantener las células y los tejidos.

Drogas psicoactivas Sustancias químicas que afectan el sistema nervioso central y alteran la actividad del cerebro.

Psicológico Relativo a la mente.

Dependencia psicológica Enfermedad en la cual una persona cree que una droga es necesaria para sentirse bien o para funcionar normalmente.

Respuesta psicosomática Reacción física producida por el estrés en lugar de corresponder a una lesión o una enfermedad.

Psicoterapia Diálogo continúo entre un paciente y un profesional de la salud mental.

Pubertad Periodo en el cual una persona comienza a desarrollar ciertos rasgos de adultez que son característicos de su sexo.

Salud pública Todo esfuerzo para supervisar, proteger y promover la salud de la población como una unidad.

Pulpa Tejido que contiene los vasos sanguíneos y los nervios de un diente.

English	R	Español

Random violence Violence committed for no particular reason. (Ch. 9, 233)

Range* The distance between possible extremes. (Ch. 11, 292)

Rape Any form of sexual intercourse that takes place against a person's will. (Ch. 9, 234)

Rapid test Used in situations where the infected person might not come back to learn the results to the test. A blood sample is collected and analyzed immediately. (Ch. 24, 677)

Reaction* A response to a stimulus or influence. (Ch. 10, 264)

Recovery The process of learning to live an alcohol-free life. (Ch. 21, 583)

Recycling The processing of waste materials so that they can be used again. (Ch. 28, 810)

Refusal skills Communication strategies that can help you say no when you are urged to take part in behaviors that are unsafe or unhealthful, or that go against your values. (Ch. 2, 36)

Regulate* To fix the time, amount, degree, or rate of. (Ch. 25, 690)

Rehabilitation Process of medical and psychological treatment for physiological or psychological dependence on a drug or alcohol. (Ch. 22, 614)

Relationship A bond or connection you have with other people. (Ch. 6, 142)

Relaxation response A state of calm. (Ch. 4, 99)

Remission A period of time when symptoms disappear. (Ch. 25, 701)

Remove* To get rid of. (Ch. 13, 358)

Require* To demand as necessary. (Ch. 5, 115)

Rescue breathing Breathing for a person who is not breathing on his or her own. (Ch. 27, 767)

Resilient The ability to adapt effectively and recover from disappointment, difficulty, or crisis. (Ch. 3, 67)

Resolve* To deal with successfully. (Ch. 4, 104)

Resource* A source of supply or support. (Ch. 3, 82)

Respiratory tract The passageway that makes breathing possible. (Ch. 23, 633)

Respond* To react in response. (Ch. 25, 705)

Resting heart rate The number of times your heart beats per minute when you are not active. (Ch. 12, 336)

Retina The inner layer of the eye wall. (Ch. 13, 368)

Violencia aleatoria Violencia infringida sin una razón en especial.

Rango Distancia entre posibles extremos.

Violación Cualquier tipo de acto sexual que ocurre contra la voluntad de una persona.

Prueba rápida Prueba que se realiza cuando la persona infectada podría no regresar para conocer los resultados. Se toma y analiza una muestra de sangre en forma inmediata.

Reacción Respuesta a un estimulo o influencia.

Recuperación Proceso de aprender a vivir sin consumir alcohol.

Reciclaje Proceso en el cual los desechos se pueden utilizar nuevamente.

Destrezas de negación Estrategias de comunicación que ayudan a decir no cuando te presionan a participar en actividades peligrosas, no saludables o que van en contra de tus valores.

Regular Organizar el tiempo, la cantidad, el grado o el rtimo de algo.

Rehabilitación Proceso de tratamiento médico y psicológico para la dependencia fisiológica o psicológica de una droga o del alcohol.

Relación Lazo que una persona tiene con los demás.

Respuesta de relajación Estado de calma.

Remisión Periodo en el cual desaparecen los síntomas.

Eliminar Deshacerse de algo o de alguien.

Requerir Solicitar como necesario.

Respiración de rescate Respiración artificial para una persona que no está respirando por sí misma.

Resiliencia Capacidad de adaptarse eficazmente y recuperarse después de una decepción, dificultad o crisis.

Resolver Manejar algo con éxito.

Recurso Fuente de suministro o apoyo.

Tracto respiratorio Vías que hacen posible la respiración.

Reaccionar Actuar en respuesta a algo o alguien.

Ritmo cardiaco en reposo Número de latidos por minuto que se producen cuando la persona se encuentra en estado pasivo.

Retina Capa interna de la pared ocular.

Glossary / Glosario

Rheumatoid arthritis A disease characterized by the debilitating destruction of the joints due to inflammation. (Ch. 25, 708)

Risk behaviors Actions that can potentially threaten your health or the health of others. (Ch. 1, 16)

Road rage Responding to a driving incident with violence. (Ch. 26, 746)

Role The parts you play in your relationships. (Ch. 6, 144)

Role model Someone whose success or behavior serves as an example for you. (Ch. 3, 73)

Artritis reumatoide Enfermedad caracterizada por la destrucción debilitadora de las articulaciones debido a la inflamación.

Comportamiento riesgoso Acciones que pueden poner en peligro tu salud o la de otras personas.

Agresividad al volante Reaccionar de manera violenta a un incidente de conducción.

Función Papel que desempeña una persona en una relación.

Modelo de conducta Alguien cuyo éxito o comportamiento sirve de ejemplo para otros.

English — S — Español

Sclera The white part of the eye. (Ch. 13, 367)

Scoliosis A lateral, or side-to-side, curvature of the spine. (Ch. 14, 384)

Scrotum An external skin sac, which holds the testes. (Ch. 16, 447)

Sebaceous glands Structures within the skin that produce an oily secretion called sebum. (Ch. 13, 358)

Secure* To make fast or seal. (Ch. 27, 760)

Sedentary Involving little physical activity. (Ch. 12, 321)

Seek* To go in search of. (Ch. 27, 774)

Self-actualization To strive to become the best you can be. (Ch. 3, 70)

Self-control A person's ability to use responsibility to override emotions. (Ch. 8, 207)

Self-defense Any strategy for protecting yourself from harm. (Ch. 26, 727)

Self-directed Able to make correct decisions about behavior when adults are not present to enforce rules. (Ch. 18, 506)

Self-esteem How much you value, respect, and feel confident about yourself. (Ch. 3, 68)

Semen A thick fluid containing sperm and other secretions from the male reproductive system. (Ch. 16, 447)

Separation A decision by two married people to live apart from each other. (Ch. 7, 174)

Sexual abuse A pattern of sexual contact that is forced upon a person against his or her will. (Ch. 9, 237)

Sexual assault Any intentional sexual attack against another person. (Ch. 9, 234)

Sexual violence Any form of unwelcome sexual contact directed at an individual. (Ch. 9, 234)

Sexually transmitted diseases (STDs) Infectious diseases spread from person to person through sexual contact. (Ch. 8, 208)

Esclerótica Parte blanca del ojo.

Escoliosis Desviación lateral, o de lado a lado, de la columna.

Escroto Saco de piel externa que sostiene los testículos.

Glándulas sebáceas Estructuras dentro de la piel que producen una secreción aceitosa llamada sebo.

Asegurar Dejar firme y seguro.

Sedentarismo Poca actividad física.

Buscar Hacer algo para encontrar a alguien o algo.

Realización personal Esfuerzo para lograr lo mejor de uno mismo.

Dominio de sí mismo Capacidad de una persona para controlar sus emociones por medio de la responsabilidad.

Defensa propia Cualquier estrategia para protegerse de un daño.

Auto-dirigido Capaz de tomar decisiones correctas acerca de su comportamiento en la ausencia de adultos que impongan las reglas.

Autoestima Valor, respeto y sentimiento de confianza que uno tiene de sí mismo.

Semen Líquido espeso que contiene los espermatozoides y otras secreciones del aparato reproductor masculino.

Separación Cuando una pareja casada decide vivir aparte uno del otro.

Abuso sexual Patrón de contacto sexual realizado a la fuerza o contra la voluntad de una persona.

Agresión sexual Cualquier ataque sexual intencional en contra de otra persona.

Violencia sexual Cualquier forma de contacto sexual no deseado dirigido a una persona.

Enfermedades de transmisión sexual (ETS) Enfermedades que se transmiten a través del contacto sexual entre dos personas.

Sexually transmitted infections (STIs) Infections spread from person to person through sexual contact. (Ch. 24, 658)

Shock A life-threatening condition in which the heart is not delivering an adequate supply of blood to the body. (Ch. 27, 770)

Short-term goal A goal that you can reach in a short period of time. (Ch. 2, 43)

Siblings Brothers or sisters. (Ch. 7, 167)

Side effects Reactions to medicine other than the one intended. (Ch. 19, 528)

Sidestream smoke The smoke from the burning end of a cigarette, pipe, or cigar. (Ch. 20, 553)

Significant* Having meaning. (Ch. 18, 497)

Skeletal muscles Muscles attached to bone that cause body movements. (Ch. 14, 388)

Smog A brownish haze that sometimes forms in urban areas. (Ch. 28, 801)

Smoke alarm A device that produces a loud warning noise in the presence of smoke. (Ch. 26, 732)

Smooth muscles Muscles that act on the lining of the body's passageways and hollow internal organs. (Ch. 14, 388)

Sobriety Living without alcohol. (Ch. 21, 583)

Specialists Medical doctors who focus on particular kinds of patients or particular medical conditions. (Ch. 28, 792)

Specificity Choosing the right types of activities to improve a given element of fitness. (Ch. 12, 333)

Sperm Male gametes. (Ch. 18, 446)

Spiritual health A deep-seated sense of meaning and purpose in life. (Ch. 1, 8)

Spirituality A deep-seated sense of meaning and purpose in life. (Ch. 1, 8)

Spousal abuse Domestic violence or any other form of abuse directed at a spouse. (Ch. 7, 178)

Sprains Injuries to the ligaments around a joint. (Ch. 12, 342)

Stages of grief A variety of reactions that may surface as an individual makes sense of how a loss affects him or her. (Ch. 4, 103)

Stalking Repeatedly following, harassing, or threatening an individual. (Ch. 9, 237)

Stereotype Exaggerated or oversimplified beliefs about people who belong to a certain group. (Ch. 6, 150)

Sterility The inability to reproduce. (Ch. 16, 450)

Stigma A mark of shame or disapproval that results in an individual being shunned or rejected by others. (Ch. 5, 118)

Infecciones de transmisión sexual Infecciones que se transmiten a través del contacto sexual entre dos personas.

Shock Enfermedad que puede ser fatal en la cual el corazón no envía suficiente sangre al cuerpo.

Meta a corto plazo Meta que se puede lograr en un periodo breve.

Hermanos Hermanos o hermanas.

Efectos secundarios Reacciones inesperadas a un medicamento.

Humo indirecto Humo que proviene de una colilla de cigarrillo, pipa o cigarro.

Significativo Que es importante.

Músculos del esqueleto Músculos unidos a los huesos y que producen el movimiento del cuerpo.

Smog Bruma de color café que se forma algunas veces en las áreas urbanas.

Alarma de humo Dispositivo que emite un sonido de advertencia que se activa en presencia del humo.

Músculos lisos Músculos que actúan sobre el revestimiento de los conductos y órganos internos.

Sobriedad Vivir sin consumir alcohol.

Especialistas Médicos que se dedican a un tipo particular de pacientes o condiciones medicas particulares.

Especificidad Elegir el tipo correcto de actividades que mejoren un elemento específico del bienestar físico.

Espermatozoides Gametos masculinos.

Salud espiritual Un sentido profundo de significado y proposito en vida.

Espiritualidad Sentido profundamente asentado del significado y propósito de la vida.

Abuso conyugal Violencia doméstica o cualquier forma de abuso dirigida hacia el esposo o la esposa.

Esguince Daño a los ligamentos que rodean una articulación.

Etapas del duelo Variedad de reacciones que pueden aparecer a medida que una persona entiende cómo le afecta una pérdida.

Acecho Seguimiento, acoso o amenaza repetidos que una persona hace a otra.

Estereotipos Creencias exageradas o demasiado simplificadas acerca de las personas que pertenecen a un grupo específico.

Esterilidad Incapacidad de reproducirse.

Estigma Señal de vergüenza o desaprobación que da como resultado el rechazo de una persona por parte de los demás.

Glossary / Glosario

Stimulant A drug that increases the action of the central nervous system, the heart, and other organs. (Ch. 20, 543)

Strains Overstretching and tearing a muscle. (Ch. 12, 341)

Stress The reaction of the body and mind to everyday challenges and demands. (Ch. 2, 38)

Stress management The use of healthy ways to reduce and manage stress in your life. (Ch. 2, 38)

Stress management skills Skills that help you reduce and manage your stress. (Ch. 2, 38)

Stressor Anything that causes stress. (Ch. 4, 93)

Stroke An acute injury in which blood flow to the brain is interrupted. (Ch. 25, 692)

Substance abuse Any unnecessary or improper use of chemical substances for non-medical purposes. (Ch. 22, 592)

Suicide The act of intentionally taking one's own life. (Ch. 5, 122)

Survival* The continuation of life or existence. (Ch. 27, 768)

Suspend* To bar temporarily. (Ch. 26, 737)

Synergistic effect* The interaction of two or more medicines that results in a greater effect than when the medicines are taken alone. (Ch. 19, 528)

Estimulante Droga que acelera el funcionamiento del sistema nervioso central, el corazón y otros órganos.

Distensión muscular Estirar en exceso y rasgar un músculo.

Estrés Reacción del cuerpo y la mente a las exigencias y desafíos de la vida diaria.

Manejo del estrés Utilización de formas saludables para reducir y manejar el estrés en tu vida.

Habilidades del manejo del estrés Habilidades que le ayudan a reducir y manejar el estrés.

Estresante Cualquier cosa que produce estrés.

Accidente cerebrovascular Lesión aguda que interrumpe el flujo de sangre al cerebro.

Abuso de sustancias Cualquier uso inapropiado o excesivo de sustancias químicas con propósitos no médicos.

Suicidio Acto de quitarse la vida intencionalmente.

Supervivencia Continuación de la vida o de la existencia.

Suspender Prohibir temporalmente.

Efecto sinérgico Interacción entre dos o más medicamentos que produce un efecto más fuerte que si se toman por separado.

English	T	Español

Tar A thick, sticky, dark fluid produced when tobacco burns. (Ch. 21, 543)

Technique* A method of accomplishing a desired aim. (Ch. 4, 99)

Technology Radio, television, and the Internet. (Ch. 1, 14)

Tendon A fibrous cord that attaches muscle to the bone. (Ch. 14, 383)

Tendonitis The inflammation of a tendon. (Ch. 14, 389)

Testes Two small glands that secrete testosterone and produce sperm. (Ch. 16, 447)

Testosterone The male sex hormone. (Ch. 16, 446)

Thyroid gland Produces hormones that regulate metabolism, body heat, and bone growth. (Ch. 16, 443)

Tinnitus A condition in which a ringing, buzzing, whistling, roaring, hissing, or other sound is heard in the ear in the absence of external sound. (Ch. 13, 373)

Tolerance The ability to accept others' differences. (Ch. 6, 150)

Alquitrán Líquido espeso, pegajoso y oscuro que se forma al quemarse el tabaco.

Técnica Método para lograr el propósito deseado.

Tecnología Radio, televisión e Internet.

Tendón Tejido fibroso que une los músculos a los huesos.

Tendinitis Inflamación de un tendón.

Testículos Par de pequeñas glándulas que secretan testosterona y producen espermatozoides.

Testosterona Hormona sexual masculina.

Tiroides Glándula que produce las hormonas que regulan el metabolismo, el calor del cuerpo y el crecimiento de los huesos.

Tinnitus Enfermedad en la cual se oye un timbre, zumbido, silbido, siseo, rugido u otro sonido en ausencia de ruidos externos.

Tolerancia Capacidad para aceptar las diferencias de los demás.

Tornado A whirling, funnel-shaped windstorm that extends from a storm to the ground and advances along the ground. (Ch. 27, 779)

Toxin A substance that kills cells or interferes with their functions. (Ch. 23, 629)

Trachea The windpipe. (Ch. 15, 417)

Transit* Conveyance of persons or things from one place to. (Ch. 28, 809)

Transitions Critical changes that occur in all stages of life. (Ch. 18, 508)

Transmit* To send from one person or place to another. (Ch. 24, 660)

Traumatic event Any event that has a stressful impact sufficient to overwhelm your normal coping strategies. (Ch. 4, 105)

Trend* A line of general direction or movement. (Ch. 28, 795)

Trigger* To initiate or set off. (Ch. 11, 305)

Tuberculosis A contagious bacterial infection that usually affects the lungs. (Ch. 15, 421)

Tumor An abnormal mass of tissue that has no natural role in the body. (Ch. 25, 695)

Tornado Tormenta de viento en forma de embudo giratorio que se extiende desde una tormenta hasta el suelo y avanza por la tierra.

Toxina Sustancia que mata células o que interfiere con su funcionamiento.

Tráquea Vía respiratoria principal.

Tránsito Desplazamiento de personas o cosas de un lugar a otra.

Transiciones Cambios críticos que ocurren en todas las etapas de la vida.

Transmitir Trasladar desde una persona o lugar a otro.

Suceso traumático Todo suceso que tiene un efecto estresante suficiente como para sobrepasar las estrategias normales para lidiar con un hecho.

Tendencia Linea general de dirección o movimiento.

Desencadenar Comenzar o iniciar algo.

Tuberculosis Infección bacteriana contagiosa que comúnmente afecta los pulmones.

Tumor Masa de tejido anormal que no cumple ninguna función natural en el cuerpo.

| English | U | Español |

Unconditional love Love without limitation or quantification. (Ch. 18, 506)

Unconsciousness The condition of not being alert or aware of your surroundings. (Ch. 27, 773)

Underweight Below the standard weight range for your height. (Ch. 11, 293)

Unintentional injury An injury resulting from an unexpected event. (Ch. 26, 731)

Universal precautions Steps taken to prevent the spread of disease through blood and other body fluids when providing first aid or health care. (Ch. 27, 759)

Urban sprawl The spreading of city development (houses, shopping centers, businesses, and schools) onto undeveloped land. (Ch. 28, 809)

Ureters Tubes that connect the kidneys to the bladder. (Ch. 15, 430)

Urethra The tube that leads from the bladder to the outside of the body. (Ch. 15, 431)

Urethritis The inflammation of the urethra. (Ch. 15, 432)

Uterus The hollow, muscular, pear-shaped organ that nourishes and protects a feterilized ovum until birth. (Ch. 16, 452)

Amor incondicional Amor sin límite ni cuantificación.

Inconciencia Condición en la cual una persona no está alerta o consciente de lo que lo rodea.

Bajo peso Peso inferior al rango normal según la estatura.

Lesión no intencional Lesión resultante de un suceso inesperado.

Precauciones universales Medidas que se toman para evitar el contagio de enfermedades a través de la sangre y otros fluidos corporales cuando se proporcionan primeros auxilios o atención médica.

Expansión urbana Crecimiento del desarrollo de una ciudad (casas, centros comerciales, negocios y escuelas) hacia zonas no desarrolladas.

Uréter Cada uno de los dos canales que conectan los riñones y la vejiga.

Uretra Canal que nace en la vejiga y se extiende hacia el exterior del cuerpo.

Uretritis Inflamación de la uretra.

Útero El órgano baso, muscular, en forma de pera que alimenta y protege el ovario hasta nacimiento.

Glossary / Glosario

English	Español
Vaccine A preparation of dead or weakened pathogens that are introduced into the body to stimulate and immune response. (Ch. 23, 641)	**Vacuna** Preparación de agentes patógenos muertos o debilitados que se introducen en el cuerpo para estimular el sistema inmune.
Vagina A muscular, elastic passageway that extends from the uterus to the outside of the body. (Ch. 16, 454)	**Vagina** Conducto muscular y elástico que va desde el útero hasta la parte externa del cuerpo de una mujer.
Valid* Well-grounded or justifiable. (Ch. 2, 48)	**Válido** Correctamente fundamentado o justificable.
Values The ideas, beliefs, and attitudes about what is important, that help guide the way you live. (Ch. 2, 41)	**Valores** Ideas, creencias y actitudes sobre lo que es importante que guíen la vida de una persona.
Vector An organism that carries and transmits pathogens to humans or other animals. (Ch. 23, 630)	**Vector** Organismo que lleva y transmite agentes patógenos a personas y otros animales.
Vegetarian A person who eats mostly, or only, plant-based foods. (Ch. 11, 304)	**Vegetariano** Persona que come principal o exclusivamente alimentos que provienen de las plantas.
Vehicular safety Obeying the rules of the road and exercising common sense and good judgment while driving. (Ch. 26, 744)	**Seguridad vehicular** Usar el sentido común, un buen criterio y obedecer las reglas de tránsito mientras se conduce.
Venom A poisonous secretion. (Ch. 27, 776)	**Veneno** Secreción venenosa.
Verbal abuse The use of words to mistreat or injure another person. (Ch. 9, 237)	**Abuso verbal** El uso de palabras para maltratar o dañar a otras personas.
Violence The threatened or actual use of physical force or power to harm another person and to damage property. (Ch. 9, 229)	**Violencia** Amenaza o uso de la fuerza física o el poder para maltratar a una persona o dañar una propiedad.
Virus A piece of genetic material surrounded by a protein coat. (Ch. 23, 629)	**Virus** Partícula de material genético rodeada de una capa proteica.
Visualize* To form a mental image of. (Ch. 10, 270)	**Visualizar** Formarse una imagen mental.
Vitamins Compounds found in food that help regulate many body processes. (Ch. 10, 262)	**Vitaminas** Compuestos que se encuentran en los alimentos y que ayudan a regular muchos procesos corporales.
Volume* The degree of loudness. (Ch. 25, 711)	**Volumen** Intensidad del sonido.

English	Español
Warm-up Gentle cardiovascular activity that prepares the muscles for work. (Ch. 12, 334)	**Precalentamiento** Actividad cardiovascular liviana que prepara los músculos para el ejercicio.
Warranty A company's or a store's written agreement to repair a product or refund your money if the product does not function properly. (Ch. 2, 48)	**Garantía** Acuerdo escrito en el cual una empresa o tienda se compromete a reparar un producto o a devolver el dinero si el producto no funciona correctamente.
Wastewater Used water from homes, communities, farms, and businesses. (Ch. 28, 809)	**Aguas residuales** Agua ya utilizada que proviene de casas, comunidades, granjas e industrias.
Weight cycling A repeated pattern of losing and regaining body weight. (Ch. 11, 298)	**Ciclo de peso** Patrón repetido de subir y bajar de peso.
Wellness An overall sense of well-being or total health. (Ch. 1, 9)	**Bienestar** Sensación general de gozar de buena salud.
Western blot Used to both detect HIV antibodies and to confirm the results of earlier EIA tests. (Ch. 24, 677)	**Western blot** Prueba utilizada tanto para detectar anticuerpos de VIH como para confirmar el resultado de pruebas EIA anteriores.
Workout The part of an exercise session when you are exercising at your highest peak. (Ch. 12, 335)	**Entrenamiento** Parte de un programa de actividad física en la que los ejercicios se realizan en el nivel más alto de rendimiento.

Index

Page numbers in italics refer to pictures or features.

A

Abortion, spontaneous, 554
Abrasions, 760
Absorption
  in digestive system, 422
  in small intestine, 425
Abstinence
  committing to, 210
  and consequences of sexual activity, 208–209
  definition of, 19
  for female reproductive health, 455
  from high-risk behaviors, 19
  for male reproductive health, 449
  in peer relationships, 206–210
  for prevention of STDs, 664–667
  recommitting to, 210
  from sexual activity, 206–207
Abuse, 236–241. *See also* Alcohol abuse; Drug abuse
  acquaintance rape, 238–239
  child, 179
  date rape, 238–239
  definition of, 178, 236
  effects of, 180
  elder, 179
  forms of, 237–238
  overcoming, 240–241
  protecting yourself from, 238
  in relationships, 236–238
  spousal, 178–179
Abusers, help for, 241
Acceptance
  in positive friendships, 194
  as stage of grief, 103
Accessing information, 14, 37, 48
  to evaluate supplements, 309
  as health skill, 37
  from Internet, 14
  recognizing reliable resources, *117*
Accident chain, 731
Accidents. *See* Unintentional injuries
Acetaminophen, 526
Achievement, need for, 70
Acid. *See* LSD
Acid reflux, 426
Acne, 359
Acquaintance rape, 238–239
Acquired Immunodeficiency syndrome (AIDS), 661. *See also* HIV/AIDS
Acromegaly, 463
ACTH (adrenocorticotropic hormone), 444
Action plans
  definition of, 44
  for reaching goals, 44–45
Active immunity, 641, 642
Active listening, 35, 154–155
ADA (Americans with Disabilities Act), 713
Addiction
  to alcohol, 582
  cycle of, 594
  to drugs, 594, 605, 609, 613
  from medicine misuse, 533

  of newborns, 596
  to nicotine, 546, 550, 551
  to opiates, 609
  to pain relievers, 526
  professional help for, 127, 594, 614
  support groups for, 613
  Addictive drugs, 543
  ethanol, 566
  illegal. *See* Illegal drugs
  and medicine misuse, 533
  nicotine, 543, 551
  pain relievers, 526
Additive interactions (medicines), 528
Additives, food, 275
Adenoids, 413
ADH (antidiuretic hormone), 430, 444
Adipose tissue, 262
Adjustment disorder, 115
Adolescence, 496–501
  accomplishments in, 499–501
  definition of, 496
  overscheduling for, 136–137
  puberty, 496–499
Adoption, 505
Adoptive families, 167, 174
Adrenal cortex, 444
Adrenal glands, *95, 443,* 444
Adrenal medulla, 444
Adrenaline, *95,* 444
Adrenocorticotropic hormone (ACTH), 444
Adulthood, 502–503, 508–511
  late, 503, 510–511
  maturity for, 502–503
  middle, 503, 508–510
  young, 503
Adults
  choking first aid for, 768–769
  CPR for, 766, *767*
Advertising
  of alcohol, 588
  and alcohol use, 573
  definition of, 46
  and food choices, 256
  health fraud in, 52–53
  hidden messages/techniques used in, 46, *47*
Advocacy
  consumer advocates, 51
  definition of, 39
  for diabetes prevention, 708
  as health skill, 39
  for people with disabilities, 712
  for recycling, 811
  staying tobacco-free, 552
AEDs (automated external defibrillators), 765
Aerobic exercise, 327, 328, 419
Affection, setting limits for expressing, 207
Affirmation, 170
After-school programs, 737
Afterbirth, 477
Age
  and cardiovascular disease, 693
  and nutrition needs, 303
Aggression
  as communication style, 152
  as response to peer pressure, 204
  and violence in media, 231

Agoraphobia, 134
Agreement, in peer mediation, 228
AIDS (acquired Immunodeficiency syndrome), 669. *See also* HIV/AIDS
AIDS-opportunistic illnesses, 671, 672, 678
Air pollution, 800–804
  indoor, 802–803
  reducing, 803–804
  and respiratory health, 419
Air quality, 800–801
Air Quality Index (AQI), 801, *802*
Airborne transmission of disease, 631
Al-Anon, 583
Alarm, as stress response, 94, *95*
Alateen, 583
Alcohol
  advertising of, 588
  dependence on, 575, 576
  as depressant, 607
  drug interactions with, 568
  use of. *See* Alcohol use
Alcohol abuse, 566
  and alcoholism, 580–582
  binge drinking, 569
  definition of, 575
  and driving, 578–579
  effects on family, 176, 582
  as first stage of alcoholism, 582
  societal effects of, 582
  and suicide, 122, 123, 594
  support groups for, *182*
  treatment for, 582–583
Alcohol poisoning, 569, 570
Alcohol use
  and abusive relationships, 238
  avoiding, 576–577
  and crime, 576, 594
  as CVD risk factor, *693*
  and date rape, 239
  dependence on, 572
  and engagement in high-risk behaviors, 208
  factors influencing, 572–573
  health risks of, 566–571, 573–575
  illegal, 573–574
  long-term effects of, 569–570
  during pregnancy, 474, 580
  and risk of STDs, 666
  short-term effects of, 567, *568*
  stress caused by, 99
  underage, 584
  and violent crimes, 230
Alcoholics, 581
Alcoholics Anonymous, 583, 584
Alcoholism, 575, 580–582
  recovery from, *582*
  treatment for, 582–583
Alcopops, 581
Alienation, 122
All-terrain vehicle (ATV) safety, 748–749
Allergens, 702
Allergies, 702–703
  to antibiotics, 526
  food, 281, 305
  medicines for, 527
  and white blood cells, 410
Allergists, 721
Alternatives, suggesting, 203

Index

C

D

EIA test, 677
Einstein, Albert, 63
EKGs (electrocardiograms), *691*
Elder abuse, 179
Electrical safety, 733
Electrocardiograms (EKGs), *691*
Elimination, in digestive system, 422
Embryo, 470
   development of, *472*
   growth of, 471
Emergency care
   animal bites, 774–775
   chain of survival in, 764–765
   first steps in, 758–759. *See also* First aid
   muscle/joint/bone injuries, 771–773
   nosebleeds, 775
   poisoning, 775–777
   unconsciousness, 773–774
   universal precautions, 759
Emergency preparedness, 778–783
   American Red Cross, 722
   natural disasters, 781–782
   storm safety, 778–780
Emergency survival kits, 782
Emerging infections, 645–648
Emerson, Ralph Waldo, 139, 353
Emotional abuse, 237
Emotional independence, 500
Emotional maturity, 502, 504
Emotional release, as stage of grief, 103
Emotional support groups, 77
Emotions. *See also* Mental and emotional health
   during adolescence, 499
   definition of, 78
   depression and changes in, 116
   envy, 196
   families' ways of expressing, 172
   in friendships, 196
   jealousy, 196
   managing, 80–83
   of rape or abuse survivors, 240
   as reason for eating, 256
   understanding, 78–79
Empathy
   definition of, 80
   as listening skill, 155
   with people considering suicide, 124
   in positive friendships, 194
   to support grieving, 104
Emphysema, 421, *555*
Employment opportunities
   and alcohol abuse, 575
   and arrests, 574
   and gang membership, 232
   and piercings/tattoos, 359
Empty-nest syndrome, 510
Encephalitis, *636*
Endocrine glands, 442, *443*
Endocrine system, 442–445
   problems of, 463
   and secondary sex characteristics, 497
   in stress response, 94
Endometriosis, 456
Endometrium, *453*, 454
Endurance
   cardiorespiratory, 324, 325, 328
   muscular, 325–330
Energy
   calories as measure of, 254
   from carbohydrates, 259–260

   from fats, 261–262
   nutrients providing, 258
   from proteins, 260
   redirecting. *See* Channeling energy
Energy balance, 290
Energy drinks, 307, 606
Environment
   culture, 13
   definition of, 12
   and food choices, 256
   and human growth and development, 475
   influence on health, 12–13
   inherited traits affected by, 478
   physical, 12
   social, 13
Environmental health
   air quality, 800–804
   conservation, 810
   noise pollution, 804–805
   recycling, *811*
   sun exposure, 258–259
   and urban development, 808–809
   waste disposal, 806–808
   water, 809–810
Environmental Protection Agency (EPA), 797, 800–801, 809
Environmental tobacco smoke (ETS), 553–555
Envy, 196, 221
Enzymes, 424
EPA. *See* Environmental Protection Agency
Ephedra, 308
Epidemics
   definition of, 648
   polio, 654
   STDs as, 663
Epidermis, 356, *357*
Epididymis, *449*
Epiglottis, 418, 423
Epilepsy, 399
Epinephrine, 444, 527
Equipment, protective. *See* Protective equipment
Erections, 447
Escalating conflict, 221
Esophagus, 424
Essential amino acids, 260
Estrogen, 444
Ethanol, 566
Ethical values, core, 73, 74
Ethnic diversity, appreciation of, 499
ETS. *See* Environmental tobacco smoke
Euphoria, 605
Eustachian tube, 371
Evaluating health information and services, 48
Excretion, 429–430, 471
Excretory system, 429–433, *546*
Exercise. *See also* Physical activity
   aerobic, 327, 328
   anaerobic, 328
   benefits of, *456*, 694
   for bone strength, 384
   definition of, 319
   with friends, *146*
   isokinetic, 329
   isometric, 329
   isotonic, 329
   making time for, 322
   principles of, 335
Expectations, realistic, 69, 149

Experimental drugs, 530
Expiration dates (on food labels), 277
Extended families, 167, 506
Extensors, 388
External auditory canal, 371
External respiration, 416
Eye contact, 203
Eyes, 367–371
   damage from UV rays, 341
   parts of, 367–368
   problems with, *370*
   vision, 369
   vision impairment, 709, 710
   vision screenings, 486

F

Fad diets, 298–299
Fainting, emergency care for, 774
Fairness
   as good character trait, 74
   in positive friendships, 194
   and relationship strength, 147
Fallopian tubes, 453, 454
Falls, prevention of, 733–734
Families, 166–171. *See also* Parenthood
   and alcohol use, 572
   blended, 184
   coping with changes in, 173–177
   and drug use, 593, 595
   health behaviors in parenting and child development, 506–507
   help for problems in, 178–183
   as influence on food choices, 256
   interactions in, 168
   kinds of, 166–168
   living arrangements of children, 168
   negative effects of sexual activity on, 209
   relationships with, 143
   sources of support for, 181–183
   strengthening, 172–177
   violence in, 178–180
   and your health, 169–171
Family counselors, 248
Family therapy, 129
FAS. *See* Fetal alcohol syndrome
Fasting, 299
Fat-soluble vitamins, 261, *263*
Fatigue, as stress response, 94, *95*
Fats, 261–262
   and calorie content of foods, 291
   as cancer risk factor, 698
   digestion of, 424
   limiting, 269
Fatty acids, 261
FDA. *See* Food and Drug Administration
Fear, 79
Fear management, 81–82
Feces, 430
Federal Trade Commission (FTC), 798
Fee-for-service health insurance, 795
Feedback, offering, 156–157
Feelings. *See* Emotions
Female reproductive system, 452–457
   breast self-exam, 455
   maintaining health of, 455
   menstruation, 454
   organs of, 452–454
   problems with, 456

Index

710 Age Fotostock/SuperStock; 710 Tim Fuller Photography; 710 Richard Hutchings/Corbis; 712 John Birdsall/AgeFotoStock; 713 Photodisc/Superstock; 714 Rick Gomez/Masterfile; 716 ThinkStock/SuperStock; 717 LWA-JDC/Corbis; 718 Galvezo/Zefa/Corbis; 720 Image Source Pink/Jupiterimages; 720 Michael Newman/PhotoEdit; 720 Masterfile; 722–723 Tony Freeman/PhotoEdit; 724–725 Ed-Imaging; 726 Tim Fuller Photography; 728 Michele D. Bridwell/Photo Edit; 729 Getty Images/Rubberball Product; 730 Masterfile Royalty Free; 731 AFP/Getty Images; 733 Tim Fuller Photography; 738 Jupiter/Purestock; 739 Mike Langford/AA World travel; 740 Tim Fuller Photography; 741 Mike Watson Images/SuperStock; 744 Tim Fuller Photography; 745 Masterfile Royalty Free; 747 Ed-Imaging; 748 Mike Powell/Digital Vision/Getty; 750 Brent Humphreys; 752 AFP/Getty Images; 753 Mike Langford/AA World travel; 754 Tim Fuller Photography; 756–757 Ed-Imaging; 758 Michael Newman/PhotoEdit; 759 Masterfile Royalty Free; 762 A.D.A.M., Inc.; 762 A.D.A.M., Inc.; 762 David Young-Wolff/Photo Edit; 764 Dennis McDonald/

PhotoEdit; 765 Tim Fuller Photography; 766 Tim Fuller Photography; 770 Tim Fuller Photography; 771 Masterfile Royalty Free; 773 Tim Fuller Photography; 775 Tim Fuller Photography; 777 Glencoe Stock; 777 Glencoe Stock; 777 Glencoe Stock; 778 ThinkStock/SuperStock; 779 Rick Fischer/Masterfile; 781 Mitch Wojnarowicz/Amsterdam; 782 Tim Fuller Photography; 784 image100/Corbis; 786 Michael Newman/PhotoEdit; 787 Dennis McDonald/PhotoEdit; 787 Masterfile Royalty Free; 788 ThinkStock/SuperStock; 790–791 Ed-Imaging; 792 Tim Fuller Photography; 793 Lucidio Studio/Corbis; 794 Tim Fuller Photography; 796 Michael Newman/PhotoEdit; 800 Comstock/SuperStock; 804 BlendImages/Alamy; 806 Tim Fuller Photography; 807 Robert Brenner/PhotoEdit; 808 Alan&Sandy Carey/Zefa/Corbis; 811 Tim Fuller Photography; 812 Gary Buss/Getty Images; 814 Tim Fuller Photography; 815 Comstock/SuperStock; 816 Tim Fuller Photography; 818 LWA/Dann Tardiff/BlendImages; 819 Corbis/Jupiterimages; 819 Photonica/Getty Images.

Scope & Sequence

Content Strands	Chapter 1 Understanding Health and Wellness	Chapter 2 Taking Charge of Your Health	Chapter 3 Achieving Mental and Emotional Health
Personal Health	• Being responsible for your own health (1-1) • Understanding the health triangle (1-1) • Staying mentally and emotionally healthy (1-1) • The importance of spiritual health (1-1) • Maintaining a balance of wellness (1-1) • Understanding influences (1-2) • Understanding lifestyle factors (1-3) • Becoming health-literate (1-4)	• Building health skills to stay healthy throughout life (2-1) • Learning conflict resolution (2-1) • Accessing information to benefit well-being (2-1) • Setting goals for health (2-2)	• Maintaining mental and emotional health (3-1) • Controlling self-esteem (3-1) • Being aware of personal identity (3-2) • Expressing good character (3-2) • Understanding and dealing with emotions (3-3)
Consumer and Community Health	• Impact of community on spiritual health (1-1) • Maintaining social health (1-1) • How social environment influences your health (1-2) • Role of culture in your environment (1-2) • Encountering the media (1-2) • Promoting the health of others (1-2) • The importance of health education (1-4)	• Using advocacy to share information with others (2-1) • Making informed buying decisions (2-3) • Protecting against health fraud (2-4)	• Demonstrating good citizenship (3-2) • Volunteering in the community (3-2)
Injury Prevention and Safety	• Understanding the health continuum (1-1) • Recognizing valid health information (1-2) • Identifying health risks (1-3) • Consequences of risk behaviors (1-3) • Reducing risks (1-3) • Developing programs to promote health and prevent disease (1-4)	• Evaluating products (2-3)	• Importance of safety to good mental health (3-1)
Alcohol, Tobacco, and Other Drugs	• Avoiding high risk behaviors (1-2)	• Using refusal skills to avoid unsafe or unhealthful behaviors (2-1)	• Avoiding high-risk behavior (3-2)
Nutrition and Physical Activity	• Taking actions to stay healthy (1-1) • Participating in health promoting activities (1-3)	• Importance of long-term and short-term goals (2-2)	• Importance of mental/emotional health on physical health and nutrition (3-1) • Taking healthful risks (3-2)
Environmental Health	• The influence of environment on health (1-2)		• Advocating for a safe and healthy environment (3-2)
Family Living	• The influence of heredity on health (1-2) • Learning from parents' example (1-2)	• Using communication skills to build relationships with others (2-1) • How decision-making affects values (2-2)	• Effects of mental/emotional health on relationships (3-1) • Developing self-esteem (3-1) • Defining identity through family (3-2) • Forming meaningful relationships (3-2)
Growth and Development	• Lifelong commitment to wellness (1-1)	• Importance of responsible decision-making and goal-setting (2-2)	• Adapting to changes in life (3-1) • Using Maslow's Hierarchy of needs (3-1) • Evaluating personal development (3-1) • Forming identity in the teen years (3-2) • Effects of hormones during puberty (3-3)
Communicable and Non-communicable Disease	• Chronic disorders and the health continuum (1-1)		• Understanding how promoting mental/emotional health helps prevent disease (3-1)

Chapter 4
Managing Stress and Coping with Loss

- The role of perception in stress (4-1)
- Understanding the causes of stress (4-1)
- The body's stress response (4-1)
- Physical symptoms of stress (4-1)
- The additive effects of chronic stress (4-2)
- Dealing with individual stressors (4-2)
- Experiencing loss and grief (4-3)

- The influence of cultural background on grieving (4-3)

- Strategies for avoiding and limiting stress (4-2)
- Achieving a relaxation response (4-2)
- Getting adequate rest (4-2)

- The role of dangerous substances in increasing stress (4-2)

- Redirecting energy in stress prevention (4-2)
- Getting regular physical activity to aid in relaxation (4-2)

- Identifying potential stressors (4-1)

- Seeking support from family (4-2)
- Showing empathy in grieving (4-3)
- Managing shock and grief (4-3)

- Stress as an asthma trigger (4-1)

Chapter 5
Mental and Emotional Problems

- Normalcy of experiencing many emotions (5-1)
- Understanding anxiety (5-1)
- Recognizing the signs of depression (5-1)
- Learning about mental and emotional disorders (5-2)
- Getting help for a mental health problem (5-4)

- Helping a suicidal friend (5-3)
- Getting help in the community (5-4)
- Types of mental health professionals (5-4)

- Using stress management techniques (5-1)
- Preventing suicide (5-3)
- Treating mental health problems (5-4)

- Substance abuse and anxiety (5-1)

- Eating disorders (5-2)

- Environmental factors for depression (5-1)
- Understanding anxiety disorders (5-2)

- Talking to parents about problems (5-4)

- Types of mental disorders (5-2)

Chapter 6
Skills for Healthy Relationships

- Building healthy relationships (6-1)
- Balancing the different roles in life (6-1)
- Recognizing the qualities of healthy relationships (6-1)
- Learning effective communication skills (6-1)
- Having self-respect as a foundation for healthy relationships (6-2)

- The impact of a strong community on personal health (6-1)
- Reinforcing ties to the community (6-1)
- Showing respect through common courtesy (6-2)
- Demonstrating tolerance and valuing diversity (6-2)
- Appreciation in relationships (6-3)

- Understanding bullying and hazing (6-2)

- Harmful behaviors (6-2)

- Playing different roles in relationships (6-1)

- The importance of relationships with family (6-1)
- The impact of family relationships on the health triangle (6-1)

- Helping to build social skills and values (6-1)
- Developing traits that strengthen relationships (6-1)
- Searching for personal identity and developing a value system (6-2)

Chapter 7
Family Relationships

- Influence of family relationships on health (7-1)
- Boosting self-esteem (7-1)
- Learning values to develop character (7-1)
- Talking about feelings (7-2)
- Making an effort to support family members (7-2)
- Benefits of individual counseling (7-3)

- Healthy families as the foundation for a healthy society (7-1)
- Contributing to social development (7-1)
- Abusive situations and victims (7-3)
- Dealing with family problems (7-3)
- Seeking help from community services (7-3)

- Family as a protective factor (7-1)
- Setting rules and limits on behavior (7-1)
- Stopping domestic violence (7-3)

- Facing substance abuse in families (7-2)

- Providing for physical needs (7-1)

- Providing a safe environment for expression of emotions (7-1)
- Domestic violence situations (7-3)

- The evolving definition of family (7-1)
- Meeting mental and emotional needs (7-1)
- Instilling values (7-1)
- Sharing culture and traditions (7-1)
- The importance of family counseling (7-3)

- Gaining health skills as we grow (7-1)
- Learning important social skills from family (7-1)
- Coping with change in circumstances (7-2)

- Promoting mental/emotional health in preventing disease (7-1)

Content Strands	Chapter 8 Peer Relationships	Chapter 9 Resolving Conflicts and Preventing Violence	Chapter 10 Nutrition for Health
Personal Health	• Building healthy friendships (8-1) • Avoiding unhealthy friendships (8-1) • Responding to peer pressure (8-2) • Practicing assertive communication (8-2) • Establishing healthful dating expectations (8-3) • Choosing abstinence (8-3) • Effects of a sexual relationship on mental/emotional health (8-3)	• Strengthening health by learning to manage conflicts (9-1) • Adjusting attitude and behavior (9-1) • Compromising to resolve conflicts (9-2) • Understanding sexual violence and responding to a sexual attack (9-3) • Protecting yourself from abusive relationships (9-4) • Overcoming abuse through counseling (9-4)	• How food affects your health and quality of life (10-1) • Learning about nutrition (10-1) • How the body uses nutrients (10-2) • Choosing healthier fats (10-2) • Using the MyPyramid guidelines (10-3) • Planning your meals and snacks (10-3)
Consumer and Community Health	• Role of positive peer pressure in the community (8-2)	• Understanding interpersonal conflicts (9-1) • Principles of effective mediation (9-2) • Using peer mediation (9-2) • Effects of exposure to violence in the media (9-3) • Forms of hate crimes (9-3) • Forms of abuse in relationships (9-4)	• Role of advertising on food choice (10-1) • Analyzing the ingredient list (10-4) • Evaluating nutritional claims (10-4) • Understanding organic food labels (10-4)
Injury Prevention and Safety	• Guidelines for online friendships (8-1) • Learning assertive refusal skills (8-2) • Setting limits on relationships (8-3) • Practicing abstinence (8-3)	• Understanding the causes of violence (9-3) • Availability of weapons and violence (9-3) • Avoiding sexual violence (9-3) • Understanding date rape and acquaintance rape (9-4) • Evaluating gang violence (9-3)	• Avoiding foodborne illnesses (10-4) • Common symptoms of foodborne illnesses (10-4) • Recognizing food allergies (10-4)
Alcohol, Tobacco, and Other Drugs	• Resisting negative peer pressure (8-2) • Practicing abstinence (8-3) • Avoiding places with high-risk behaviors (8-3)	• The role of alcohol in violent crime (9-3) • The role of alcohol and drugs in date rape (9-4)	
Nutrition and Physical Activity	• Using positive peer pressure to do physical activities (8-2)		• Understanding nutrients (10-1) • Eating a variety of healthful foods (10-1) • Types of carbohydrates (10-2) • Importance of fiber (10-2) • Role of proteins (10-2) • Understanding fats (10-2) • Balancing food and physical activity (10-3) • Features of the food label (10-4)
Environmental Health	• Using positive peer pressure (8-2) • Choosing safe dating locations (8-3) • Avoiding being isolated on dates (8-3)	• Recognizing escalating situations (9-1)	• Environmental influences on food choices (10-1)
Family Living	• Making dating decisions (8-3) • Setting limits on dating relationships (8-3) • Discussing risk situations (8-3) • Effects of teen sexual activity on family relationships (8-3)	• Power struggles between teens and parents (9-1) • Risk factors for children from poor families (9-3) • The importance of strong ties to family (9-4)	• Family influence on food choices (10-1)
Growth and Development	• Changing friendships (8-1)	• Conflicting attitudes between friends (9-1)	• Importance of nutrients in growth and development (10-1) • Getting a proper balance of nutrients in the teen years (10-1)
Communicable and Non-communicable Disease	• Consequences of sexual activity (8-3)		• Lowering risks for threatening conditions as you age (10-1) • Reducing risk of osteoporosis (10-2)

Chapter 11 Managing Weight and Eating Behaviors	Chapter 12 Physical Activity and Fitness	Chapter 13 Personal Health Care
• Understanding metabolism (11-1) • Measuring BMI (11-1) • Benefits of regular physical activity (11-1) • Evaluating your body image (11-2) • Understanding obesity (11-1) • Understanding anorexia nervosa (11-2) • Understanding bulimia nervosa (11-2)	• Leading a physically active life (12-1) • Improving personal fitness (12-1) • Promoting mental and emotional health through activity (12-1) • The importance of five elements of fitness in personal health (12-2) • Identifying specific fitness goals (12-3) • Wearing layers to stay warm (12-4)	• The main functions of skin (13-1) • The main parts of a tooth (13-2) • The parts of the eye (13-3) • Understanding vision (13-3) • The main sections of the ear (13-3) • Understanding hearing and balance (13-3)
• Influences on body image (11-2) • Cultural reasons for vegetarianism (11-3)	• Making new friends through physical activity (12-1) • Making sure helmets are approved by Snell or ANSI (12-4)	• Using sunscreen (13-1)
• Seeking help for an eating disorder (11-2) • Avoiding performance enhancers (11-3) • Concerns about dietary supplements (11-3)	• Risks of being sedentary (12-1) • Preventing injury by stretching (12-2) • The importance of warm-ups and cool-downs (12-3) • Preventing major and minor injuries (12-4)	• Protecting skin from UV rays (13-1) • Function of nails (13-1) • Keeping teeth and mouth healthy (13-2) • Wearing protective gear (13-3) • Preventing hearing loss (13-3)
• Substance abuse and family stress (11-2)	• Avoiding alcohol and other drugs for total fitness (12-3)	• Avoiding tobacco to keep teeth healthy (13-2)
• The importance of calories in maintaining weight (11-1) • Eating a well-balanced diet every day (11-1) • Losing weight healthfully (11-1) • Gaining weight healthfully (11-1) • Recognizing and avoiding fad diets (11-2) • Role of dietary supplements (11-3) • Preventing dehydration (11-3)	• Achieving fitness goals through exercise (12-1) • Improving the five elements of fitness (12-2) • Evaluating cardiorespiratory fitness (12-2) • Measuring flexibility with the sit-and-reach test (12-2) • Using the F.I.T.T. formula to plan work-outs (12-3)	• Reducing amount of sweet snacks and drinks (13-2) • Getting adequate vitamin A (13-3)
	• Avoiding exercise in extreme weather (12-4)	• Being aware of sun exposure (13-1)
• Help with accepting yourself (11-2) • Hereditary nature of eating disorders (11-2) • Family's role in recovery (11-2)	• Learning skills to improve relationships (12-1)	• Positive effects of good hygiene (13-1)
• Factors that affect nutritional needs (11-3)	• Increasing demands on your body (12-3) • Improving fitness over time (12-3)	• Common skin problems (13-1) • Potential hair problems (13-1) • Common tooth and mouth problems (13-2) • Categories of hearing loss (13-3)
• Health risks of being overweight (11-1) • Health conditions triggered by foods (11-3)	• Lowering risk of cardiovascular disease and type 2 diabetes (12-2) • Protecting yourself from skin cancer (12-4)	• Risks of hepatitis B, hepatitis C, and HIV through body piercing and tattooing (13-1) • Identifying early stages of melanoma (13-1)

Scope & Sequence

Content Strands	Chapter 14 Skeletal, Muscular, and Nervous Systems	Chapter 15 Cardiovascular, Respiratory, and Digestive Systems	Chapter 16 Endocrine and Reproductive Health
Personal Health	• How the skeletal system works (14-1) • Components of the skeletal system (14-1) • Understanding the muscular system (14-2) • Understanding muscular problems (14-2) • Importance of the nervous system (14-3)	• How the circulatory system works (15-1) • Types of blood vessels (15-1) • How the lymphatic system works (15-1) • Understanding blood pressure (15-1) • How the respiratory system works (15-2) • The parts of the digestive system (15-3) • How the excretory system works (15-4) • The parts of the urinary system (15-4)	• The functions of the endocrine system (16-1) • The function of the male reproductive system (16-2) • The role of the female reproductive system and its parts (16-3)
Consumer and Community Health	• Getting scoliosis screenings (14-1)	• Treating pneumonia with antibiotics (15-2)	• Testicular self-exam (16-2) • Breast self-exam (16-3)
Injury Prevention and Safety	• Caring for the skeletal system (14-1) • Types of fractures (14-1) • Wearing appropriate clothes (14-2) • Using proper equipment (14-2) • Warming up and stretching properly (14-2) • Caring for the nervous system (14-3)	• The role of respiratory structures in disease prevention (15-2) • Preventing infection with regular hand washing (15-2)	• The role of the adrenal glands in stress control (16-1) • Wearing equipment to protect the reproductive organs (16-2)
Alcohol, Tobacco, and Other Drugs	• Effects of drug and alcohol on the nervous system (14-3)	• Maintaining circulatory health (15-1) • Maintaining respiratory health (15-2)	• Drug use and risk of sterility (16-2)
Nutrition and Physical Activity	• Keeping muscles strong and healthy (14-2) • Getting regular exercise (14-2) • Eating high-protein foods (14-2)	• Maintaining circulatory health (15-1) • Maintaining digestive health (15-3) • Keeping the excretory system healthy (15-4)	• Balanced diet for healthy endocrine system (16-2)
Environmental Health		• Limiting exposure to environmental pollutants (15-2)	
Family Living		• Role of heredity in cardiovascular problems (15-1)	• Advocating for self-exams for early detection (16-2)
Growth and Development	• Understanding ossification (14-1)	• Congenital heart defects (15-1) • The development of varicose veins (15-1)	• How hormones control growth (16-1) • Maturation of the male reproductive system (16-2) • Maturation of the female reproductive system (16-3)
Communicable and Non-communicable Disease	• Understanding osteoporosis (14-1) • Understanding muscular dystrophy (14-2) • Diseases of the nervous system (14-3)	• Problems of the cardiovascular system (15-1) • Problems of the lymphatic system (15-1) • Respiratory disorders (15-2) • Functional problems of the digestive system (15-3)	• Problems of the male reproductive system (16-2) • Problems of the female reproductive system (16-3)

Chapter 17 The Beginning of the Life Cycle	Chapter 18 The Life Cycle Continues	Chapter 19 Medicines and Drugs
• Understanding inherited traits (17-2) • Influence of DNA on inherited traits (17-2) • Role of the zygote (17-2) • Dominant and recessive genes (17-2) • Determining gender (17-2)	• Understanding changes of adolescence (18-1) • Building a personal value system (18-1) • Identifying vocational goals (18-1) • Gaining control over behavior (18-1) • Difference between physical maturity and adulthood (18-2) • Health concerns in middle adulthood (18-3) • Moving into late adulthood (18-3)	• Using medicines to restore health (19-1)
• The process of childbirth (17-1) • Genetically engineering drugs (17-2)	• Social changes during adolescence (18-1) • Social transitioning in middle adulthood (18-3) • Public health policies and programs (18-3)	• Using vaccines to prevent or protect against diseases (19-1) • Role of antibodies in fighting pathogens (19-1)
• Importance of prenatal care (17-1) • Using caution with cleaning products while pregnant (17-1) • Testing for genetic disorders before birth (17-2) • Getting health screenings during childhood (17-3)		• Minimizing risk by following FDA regulations (19-2) • FDA label requirements for OTC and prescription medicines (19-2)
• Avoiding alcohol while pregnant (17-1) • Giving birth to a healthy baby (17-1) • Getting doctor approval of over-the-counter medicine (17-1)	• Choosing abstinence from tobacco, alcohol, and drugs (18-1)	• Negative effects of medicines when misused (19-1) • Addictive properties of certain pain relievers (19-1) • Dangers of mixing medicines or other drugs (19-2)
• Nourishment during pregnancy (17-1) • Staying fit while pregnant (17-1) • Smoking as a risk for low birth weight (17-1)	• Maintaining lifelong healthful habits (18-3)	• Chemical properties of herbal supplements (19-2)
• Being aware of hazards in the environment (17-1) • Effect of the environment on inherited traits (17-1)		• Managing allergic reactions with medicine (19-1)
• Birthing process (17-1)	• Building a successful marriage (18-2) • Parenting demands (18-2) • Challenges of teen parenting (18-2)	
• Stages between conception and birth (17-1) • How traits are inherited (17-2) • Genetics and fetal development (17-2) • The four stages of childhood (17-3) • Social development in late childhood (17-3)	• Role of hormones in adolescence (18-1) • Three major stages of adulthood (18-2) • Changes during middle adulthood (18-3) • Mental/emotional transitions in middle adulthood (18-3)	• Avoiding medicine misuse (19-2) • Understanding medicine labels (19-2)
• Fetal Alcohol Syndrome (17-1) • Genetic disorders (17-2) • Testing for PKU (17-2) • Genetic counseling (17-2) • Screening for scoliosis (17-3)	• Risk of cancer in middle adulthood (18-3) • Risk of heart disease in middle adulthood (18-3) • Conditions that result from aging (18-3)	• Using medicines to prevent or treat chronic ailments (19-1)

Scope & Sequence

Content Strands	Chapter 20 Tobacco	Chapter 21 Alcohol	Chapter 22 Illegal Drugs
Personal Health	• Reading and understanding warning labels (20-1) • Physiological and psychological dependance on nicotine (20-1) • Preparing a quit day (20-2)	• Varying intoxicating effects of alcohol (21-1) • Physical and mental effects of alcohol (21-1) • Benefits of living alcohol-free (21-2) • Understanding Blood Alcohol Concentration (BAC) (21-3)	• Perceptions of drug use (22-1) • Effects of illegal drug use on total health (22-1) • Other consequences of drug use (22-1) • Choosing a drug-free life (22-3)
Consumer and Community Health	• The cost of tobacco use (20-1) • Factors contributing to reduced use of tobacco (20-2) • Creating a smoke-free society (20-3)	• Alcohol advertising (21-1) • Media messages about alcohol (21-2) • Means of advertising (21-2) • Alcoholism's effects on society (21-3) • Resources and programs for alcoholics and their families (21-3)	• The influence of peer pressure on drug use (22-1) • Relating teen depression and suicide to drug abuse (22-1) • Harming society with drug abuse (22-1) • Types of drug treatment centers (22-4)
Injury Prevention and Safety	• Health risks of tobacco use (20-1) • Understanding tobacco products (20-1) • Choosing a tobacco-free lifestyle (20-2) • Strategies for avoiding tobacco (20-2) • The effects of tobacco smoke on nonsmokers (20-3)	• Risks of binge drinking (21-1) • Symptoms of alcohol poisoning (21-1) • Linking alcohol to fatalities (21-2) • Breaking the law (21-2) • Drinking's effect on violent behavior (21-2) • Drinking and driving (21-3)	• Effect of drugs on risky behaviors (22-1) • Avoiding situations where there are drugs (22-1) • Using refusal statements (22-4)
Alcohol, Tobacco, and Other Drugs	• How nicotine works (20-1) • The poisonous components of tobacco smoke (20-1) • Types of tobacco products (20-1) • Components of second-hand smoke (20-3)	• Health risks of alcohol use (21-1) • Alcohol's effects on other medicines (21-1) • Choosing to live alcohol-free (21-2) • Impact of alcohol abuse (21-3) • Symptoms of alcoholism (21-3) • Treating alcoholism (21-3)	• Understanding substance abuse (22-1) • Dangers of inhalants (22-2) • Damaging effects of psychoactive drugs (22-3) • Different types of stimulants (22-3) • The effects of depressants (22-3)
Nutrition and Physical Activity	• Replacing tobacco use with healthy behaviors (20-2)	• Food slows alcohol passage into bloodstream (21-1)	• Choosing healthy alternatives to drug use (22-4)
Environmental Health	• Motivations for tobacco use (20-2) • Enforcing no-smoking policies (20-2) • Reducing effects of second-hand smoke (20-3)	• Banning alcohol in schools (21-2) • Alcohol-free settings (21-2) • Environmental factors for alcoholism (21-3)	• Choosing friends who will help you remain drug-free (22-4) • Enforcing drug-free school zones (22-4)
Family Living	• Influence of family values on tobacco use (20-2)	• Influence on alcohol use (21-2) • Losing trust of friends and family (21-2) • Alcohol abuse in families (21-2)	• Help in resisting drug use (22-1) • Effect of substance abuse on families (22-1)
Growth and Development	• Short term and long term damage caused by smoking (20-1) • Effect of tobacco smoke on asthma development (20-3) • Health risks to unborn children and infants (20-3)	• Effect of alcohol on brain development (21-1) • Age of drinker and dependency (21-2) • Fetal Alcohol Syndrome (21-3)	• Using drugs while pregnant (22-1) • Fetal death resulting from heroin use (22-3)
Communicable and Non-communicable Disease	• Linking smoking to disease (20-1) • Signs of leukoplakia (20-1) • Health problems associated with smoking (20-1)	• Alcohol and increasing risk of contracting STDs (21-2)	• Increased risk of contracting diseases (22-1) • Side effects of steroid use (22-2) • Drugs putting teens at risk for STDs (22-3) • Increased exposure to HIV/AIDS (22-3)

Chapter 23 Communicable Diseases	Chapter 24 Sexually Transmitted Diseases and HIV/AIDS	Chapter 25 Noncommunicable Diseases and Disabilities
• Understanding communicable diseases (23-1) • Protecting yourself by hand washing (23-1) • Knowing the body's natural defenses (23-3) • Understanding the role of the immune system (23-3)	• Committing to abstinence (24-2) • Avoiding high-risk behavior (24-2) • Responsibly reporting infection (24-2) • Practicing refusal skills to avoid high-risk behavior (24-4)	• Understanding noncommunicable diseases (25-1) • Knowing the risk factors for cardiovascular disease (25-1) • Recognizing the risk factors for cancer (25-2) • Practicing healthful behavior to reduce risk for cancer (25-2)
• How diseases are spread (23-1) • Understanding immunity (23-3) • Developing active immunity (23-3) • Role of vaccination in society (23-3) • Tracking reportable diseases (23-3) • The importance of immunization (23-3)	• Risks for contracting STDs (24-1) • FDA approval of HPV vaccine (24-2) • Controlling the STD epidemic (24-2) • HIV/AIDS statistics (24-3) • How HIV/AIDS is transmitted (24-3) • Treating HIV/AIDS (24-4)	• Exposure to carcinogens (25-2) • Advertising for allergy medicine (25-3) • The rise in incidence of type 2 diabetes (25-3) • Accommodating people with physical and mental challenges (25-4) • The passing of the Americans with Disabilities Act (25-4)
• Understanding the causes of communicable diseases (23-1) • Taking steps to prevent transmission (23-1) • Preventing respiratory disease (23-2) • Strategies to aid the immune system in protecting the body (23-3)	• Importance of early diagnosis and treatment (24-1) • Using vaccines to prevent HPV (24-1) • Preventing STDs through abstinence (24-2) • Identifying high-risk behavior (24-2) • Preventing the spread of HIV/AIDS (24-4)	• Recognizing diseases of the heart and their warning signs (25-1) • Detecting and treating cancer (25-2) • Diagnosing allergens (25-3) • Strategies to reduce risk of arthritis (25-3)
• Abstain from smoking to prevent respiratory infections (23-2)	• Transmitting HIV via needle sharing (24-3)	• Taking medication properly (25-3)
• Preventing the spread of disease (23-3)		• Making unhealthful food choices (25-1) • Committing to regular exercise and weight control (25-1) • Debilitating effects of arthritis (25-3) • Symptoms of rheumatoid arthritis (25-3) • Dealing with physical disabilities (25-4)
• Airborne transmission of germs (23-1) • How salmonella and E. coli are spread (23-4) • Understanding recreational water illnesses (23-4)	• Knowing about the behaviors of those around you (24-4)	• The causes of allergies (25-3) • Common triggers of asthma (25-3)
	• Transmitting HIV/AIDS from mother to child (24-3)	
• Developing passive immunity (23-3)	• Practicing abstinence to avoid STDs (24-1) • Abstinence as protection against HIV protection (24-3)	• Benign and malignant tumors (25-2) • Learning to manage asthma (25-3)
• How viruses work (23-1) • Types of bacteria (23-1) • Identifying pneumonia (23-2) • Emerging infections (23-4)	• Symptoms and treatment for common STDs (24-2) • Understanding the transmission of HIV/AIDS (24-3) • Diagnosing HIV/AIDS (24-4)	• Types of cardiovascular disease (25-1) • Different forms of cancer and their characteristics (25-2) • Type 1 and Type 2 diabetes (25-3)

Content Strands	Chapter 26 Safety and Injury Prevention	Chapter 27 First Aid and Emergencies	Chapter 28 Community and Environmental Health
Personal Health	• Protecting personal safety (26-1) • Learning self-defense (26-1) • Recognizing Internet hazards (26-1) • Wearing a Personal Flotation Device, PFD (26-3) • Driving responsibly and following the rules of the road (26-4)	• Learning and using proper first aid procedures (27-1) • Protecting yourself during a severe storm (27-4)	• Using the health care system (28-1) • Seeing a physician regularly (28-1) • Being aware of your medical history (28-1) • Improving indoor air quality (28-2) • Conserving to protect the environment (28-3)
Consumer and Community Health	• Safety tips on electricity (26-2) • Making neighborhoods safer (26-2) • Setting laws to protect workers (26-2) • Road safety (26-4) • Protecting young drivers with graduated license programs (26-4) • Noticing pedestrians (26-4)	• Contacting a poison control center (27-3) • What to expect during a natural disaster (27-4) • National services for weather emergencies and natural disasters (27-4)	• Receiving health care in a variety of settings (28-1) • Paying for health insurance (28-1) • Promoting public health (28-1) • National Health Agencies' role in providing health services and education (28-1) • Effects of global warming (28-2)
Injury Prevention and Safety	• Following safety tips to prevent injury (26-1) • Taking precautions online (26-1) • Breaking the accident chain (26-2) • Planning a fire escape route (26-2) • Reducing risk of injury due to falls (26-2) • Taking precautions to prevent poisoning (26-2) • Keeping guns out of reach of children (26-2) • Important rules for outdoor activity (26-3) • Following water safety precautions (26-3) • Paying attention while driving (26-4)	• Steps for responding to an emergency (27-1) • Universal precautions for first aid (27-1) • Identifying the types of open wounds (27-1) • Treatment for burns (27-1) • Performing CPR (27-2) • Recognizing the universal sign for choking (27-1) • Delivering first aid to a shock victim (27-2) • Responding to unconscious victims (27-3) • Maintaining an emergency survival kit (27-4)	• Importance of Occupational Safety and Health Administration (28-1) • Common sources of indoor air pollution (28-2) • Improving indoor air quality (28-2) • Identifying hazardous waste (28-3)
Alcohol, Tobacco, and Other Drugs	• Avoiding riding with drivers who have been using alcohol or other drugs (26-4)		• Cigarette smoke as a source of air pollution (28-2)
Nutrition and Physical Activity	• Taking self-defense classes (26-1) • Tips for camping and hiking (26-3) • Participating in winter activities (26-3) • Staying safe while swimming and diving (26-3) • Bike riding safety (26-4)	• Drinking bottled water in case of contaminated water supply (27-4)	• Knowing your lifestyle and habits (28-1)
Environmental Health	• Taking safety precautions at home (26-2) • Reducing risk of falls (26-2) • Storing guns safely (26-2) • Making school a safer place (26-2) • Respecting the environment (26-3) • Preparing for winter sports (26-3)	• Exposure to poisonous plants (27-3) • Paying attention to weather warnings (27-4) • Recognizing a hurricane or tornado (27-4)	• Role of the Environmental Protection Agency (EPA) (28-1) • Understanding air pollution (28-2) • Causes and effects of global warming (28-2) • Common sources of indoor air pollution (28-2)
Family Living	• Preventing fires in the household (26-2) • Taking precautions with firearms (26-2)	• Securing the home in case of evacuation (27-4)	• Knowing if health problems run in your family (28-1) • Role of the Food and Nutrition Service (28-1)
Growth and Development	• Influence of emotional state on driving (26-4) • Protecting self from road rage (26-4)	• Learning CPR for adults and infants (27-2)	• Learning CPR for adults, children, and infants (28-2) • How to help an adult, child, or infant who is choking (28-2)
Communicable and Non-communicable Disease	• Techniques for preventing chronic injury due to computer use (26-2)	• Risks of giving first aid when there is blood present (27-1)	• Relationship between air pollution and chronic respiratory disorders (28-2)